SUFFOLK

Stour

STOUR RESERVE

HARWICH

Colne

ARDLEIGH
RES.

COLCHESTER

Holland Brook

HAMFORD
WATER

THE
NAZE

Roman

THE HYTHE

FRIDAY
WOOD

ABBERTON
RES.

FINGRINGHOE WICK

HOLLAND HAVEN

Colne

CLACTON-ON-SEA

MERSEA
ISLAND

OLD HALL

COLNE POINT

TOLLESBURY
WICK

BRIDGE
PLEX

BRADWELL

BRADWELL BIRD
OBSERVATORY

N

Blackwater

DENGIE
PENINSULA

AM FERRERS

BURNHAM-ON-CROUCH

Crouch

Roach

FOULNESS

HEND-ON-SEA

WAKERING

EE ISLAND

SHOEBURY

*Here be
Dragons.*

ND

15-99.

THE BIRDS OF
ESSEX

Simon Wood

CHRISTOPHER HELM
LONDON

To Mel, Ollie and Amy

Published 2007 by Christopher Helm, an imprint of A&C Black Publishers Ltd.,
38 Soho Square, London W1D 3HB

www.acblack.com

ISBN 978-0-7136-6939-8

A CIP catalogue record for this book is available from the British Library

This book is produced using paper that is made from wood grown in managed sustainable forests. It is natural, renewable and recyclable. The logging and manufacturing processes conform to the environmental regulations of the country of origin.

Commissioning Editor: Nigel Redman

Project Editor: Jim Martin

Design: Wordstop Ltd, Chennai, India.

Printed in China by Leo Paper Products

10 9 8 7 6 5 4 3 2 1

Publication of the colour plates in this book has been aided by financial assistance from *Essex & Suffolk Water*

This book was produced on behalf of *The Essex Birdwatching Society*

CONTENTS

FOREWORD

For many people, watching birds is simply a pleasure. Others, however, choose to document their observations and, when appropriate, to publish them or make them available to organisations such as the Essex Birdwatching Society. In this county, we have been fortunate to have a long line of ornithologists and all-round naturalists who have been motivated to do just that and in consequence there is a wealth of published data on the birds of Essex.

The author of this book and his support team have researched a vast number of publications in order to identify, and whenever possible to interpret, trends in our constantly changing bird population and to relate these to changes nationally and even further afield. The result is by far the most detailed of the five Essex avifaunas published to date, a truly valuable benchmark at a time when there are many real concerns about the future of the wildlife of this planet that we are privileged to live on.

Not only do books such as this serve as a tribute to the many thousands of observers, both amateur and professional, who have contributed to our ever growing knowledge of the natural world, they also highlight the benefits of a collective effort and act as a stimulus to identify areas where we need to know even more about our environment and the way we are affecting it. That, surely, is what makes it all worthwhile.

Simon Cox
President of the Essex Birdwatching Society

ACKNOWLEDGEMENTS

"If I see further, it is because I stand on the shoulders of giants" — Isaac Newton

Never being one to stand on ceremony, I would like to say my "and finally" first. Without the support, encouragement and considerable personal sacrifices that have been made by my wife, Mel, there is simply no way that this major undertaking would ever have been finished. I simply cannot thank her enough. At times, progress was difficult but she was always there to restore my morale and enthusiasm for the project. For that, and for our two wonderful children, Ollie (born August 2000) and Amy (born February 2004), I am eternally grateful; they all make me realise that there is more to life than books and birds!

A very big thank you must also go to Nick Green for his considerable help, encouragement, enthusiasm and his faith in my ability to finally complete the task at hand. He assisted greatly with background work and research, including many hours spent at numerous museums, data analysis, drafting several of the species' texts, and proof reading. He also wrote several of the introductory chapters. Nick gained a goddaughter, Amy, in the process!

Steve Grimwade did a marvellous job as Art Editor, organising the photographers and artists, designing the dust cover and redesigning the County map.

Graham Ekins not only provided very useful ringing summaries for each species but also assisted with countless queries over the years.

Greg Bond, the late Mike Dennis and Geoff Gibbs, who were part of the original Avifauna Working Group that met regularly from late 1998 to May 2001, also gave freely their considerable and varied knowledge of the County's birds and drafted some of the initial species' accounts. Others who assisted with these drafts were: the late Ken Barrett; David Blurton; Paul Charlton; Simon Cox; Jeremy Dagley; Adrian Dally; John Emberson; John Fitzpatrick; Andy Goodey; Steve Grimwade; Derek Gruar; John Hart; Neil Harvey; Clive Ireland; Roy Ledgerton; Colin MacKenzie-Grieve; Andy Malley; Margaret Mitchell; Alf Mullins; Russell Neave; the late Jean Patterson; Graham Smith; Jim Smith; Les Steward; Andrew Thompson; John Thorogood; Chris Tyas; David Wimpress; Derek Wood.

Chris Gibson, David Corke and Mike Daniels put together fascinating chapters on very different aspects of the Essex avifauna, whilst many artists (Alan Harris – who also provided the illustrations for the front cover – Richard Allen, George Brown, Simon Patient, Sam Shippey and Gary Wright) and photographers (Steve Arlow, J. K. Clayden of the Saffron Walden Museum, Chris Gomersall, Andy Hay of the RSPB, Adrian Kettle, Reston Kilgour, Steve Lindsell, Ian Lycett, John Skinner of the Southend Museum, Dave Stewart of Birding Images, Alan Tate and Rob Wilson) all gave their work free of charge. All images and drawings are copyright © of the artist/photographer. Chris Mason also gave freely of his many research papers. Simon Cox kindly provided the Foreword to the book in his capacity as President of the EBS; this is fitting since he was the author of the last Essex Avifauna in 1984.

Proof readers spent many hours combing the text for errors and contradictions and also provided useful constructive comments. These included Steve Arlow, Greg Bond, Simon Cox, Mike Dent, Andy Goodey, Roy Ledgerton, Margaret Mitchell, Daryl Rhymes, and Howard Vaughan. Howard, in his role as current Senior EBS County Recorder, also responded promptly to many questions and gave free access to the Society's database.

I thank all those people who dug out their old note books to check on the details of historic records or provided answers to numerous questions: the late Ken Barrett; Bradwell Bird Observatory; Simon Cox; the late Mike Dennis; East London Birders Forum; Peter Evans; Graham Ekins; John Fitzpatrick; Neil Harvey; the late Stan Hudgell; Southend Ornithological Group; Les Steward; Phil Vines; John Wright.

My thanks must also go to the EBS's County Recorders who comprehensively documented the raw bird data over the years and made this project possible. EBS Recorders (with years in office in brackets) include the late Geoff Pyman (1949–58), Robert Hudson (1957–61), the late Mr and Mrs Weston (1961–72), Richard Hull (1972–73), John Thorogood (1972–79), John Howard (1979–87), John Miller (1987–93), the late Mike Dennis (1987–2001), Les Steward (1994–99), Howard Vaughan (2001-present), Bob Flindall (2001-present), Peter O'Toole (2001–02), Roy Ledgerton (2003-present) and Paul Levey (2003-present). Of course, none of this would have been possible without the large number of observers who have sent in records over the decades, and it is hoped that this book will inspire both existing and up-and-coming birders to provide the data that will become ever more important in protecting our avifauna in the future.

Rare and unusual records were assessed by the EBS Records Committee from 1949–91 and thereafter by the Identification Panel, which consisted of Steve Arlow (from 2004), Greg Bond (from 1992–2006), Simon Cox (to 2006), Graham Ekins (to 2006), the late Stan Hudgell (to 2003), Adrian Kettle (from 2001), Jim Smith, Phil Vines (to 2006) and John Wright (1990–91). Mike Dent, Chairman of the EBS Records Committee (2001–04), is sincerely thanked for chasing various records and details.

The Essex Atlas Working Group consisted of Geoff Gibbs (Chairman), the late Mike Dennis (Senior Editor), the late Maurice Adcock, John Clarke, Martin Henry, Roy Ledgerton, Margaret Mitchell and the late Jean Patterson. Many field workers assisted in the collection of data from 1988–92 to produce breeding maps, graphs, etc.

Data were supplied by the Wetland Bird Survey (WeBS), a joint scheme of the British Trust for Ornithology (BTO), The Wildfowl & Wetlands Trust (WWT), Royal Society for the Protection of Birds (RSPB) and Joint Nature Conservation Committee (JNCC), the latter on behalf of the Countryside Council for Wales, Department of the Environment Northern Ireland, English Nature and Scottish Natural Heritage. Colette Hall of the WWT is thanked for providing all Essex data, including north Stour and all the Lea Valley and Metropolitan Essex, 1961–2000 for wildfowl and waders; Howard Vaughan collated and supplied data for the years 2001–2004. These data are critical for the calculation of the five-year, average peak counts and setting up the respective tables.

The BTO kindly supplied all Essex ringing recovery data for the period 1979–2002. The BTO ringing scheme is funded by a partnership of the BTO, JNCC, Duchas the Heritage Service – National Parks and the Wildlife (Ireland) and the ringers themselves. The BTO also supplied local CBC data and David Noble and Andrew Joys are thanked for their time in providing this. The BTO's website pages www.bto.org.uk/birdtrends2004/index.htm and www.bto.org.uk/birdfacts/index.htm have both been used extensively. The website is an excellent source of data and is thoroughly recommended.

The Game Conservancy and MAFF Fisheries Statistics Division are thanked for providing data without charge.

The late Mike Rogers, Secretary of the BBRC, is thanked for responding to numerous queries, whilst BBRC Chairman Colin Bradshaw is also thanked for an early peek at the BBRC Report 2004. Steve Piotrowski gave us much useful advice following the successful production of his *The Birds of Suffolk* (Piotrowski 2003).

Various librarians at the Zoology Library, Tring, Herts, are sincerely thanked for fielding e-mails regarding various research topics and promptly posting photocopies of key references where necessary. Ian Dawson, Senior Librarian at the RSPB, is also thanked for his extensive help fielding numerous questions. Tim Melling, Secretary of the BOURC, also gave prompt answers to many questions. The many visits to museums and collections always met with the enthusiastic assistance of the curators for which I am most grateful (see Museums chapter).

Special thanks are due to Linda Hewitt, Librarian of the LNHS, for assistance at Imperial College, South Kensington, London, where the LNHS library is kept and for ensuring that EBS's collection of *London Bird Reports* was complete for the period 1949–2000.

There would not have been any colour plates in this book without the help of Miranda Davis of Essex & Suffolk Water, who organised the magnificent sum of £3,000 in sponsorship. Many others also sponsored species' write-ups, to all of whom I am most grateful. Anthony Harbott, EBS Treasurer, did a marvellous job as ever, holding on to the purse-strings. Colin Mackenzie-Grieve, the then EBS's solicitor, provided invaluable advice and support when the terms of the contract were negotiated with A&C Black. Gerry Johnson also supplied Nick and me with copious reams of free paper!

Just two months before the script was completed, my PC suffered a catastrophic Windows crash and, although only one day's work was lost, I must pass a very big thank you to Martin Meddle who got the PC up and running again, despite the complexity of the failure.

Nigel Redman, Marianne Taylor and Jim Martin at A&C Black/Christopher Helm and copy editor Tim Harris must be thanked for their patience and skill at various stages of the book. I would like to thank Jim and Tim in particular for turning over 400,000 words, hundreds of tables and artwork into the excellent publication you see before you.

Whilst every attempt has been made to iron out any errors or discrepancies, in a publication of this size some may slip through the net. I would of course be pleased to receive notification of any errors, care of the publishers.

Finally, I would like to say a very personal thank you to those who provided help and advice during the long evolution of this project but who are sadly no longer with us: Ken Barrett, Mike Dennis, Stan Hudgell, Chris McClure, Jean Patterson and Geoff Pyman.

Simon Wood, Maldon, September 2006

THE COUNTY OF ESSEX

— a brief introduction

INTRODUCTION

In the Dark Ages, Essex was a kingdom, the kingdom of the Saxons that (some of the time) had boundaries that would be familiar to today's geographers and naturalists. Thus, the rivers Lea and Stort in the west, Thames to the south, Stour to the north, and the North Sea to the east bound the county.

In 1873 when Watson divided the counties of the British Isles into vice-counties of approximately equal size for botanical recording purposes, the boundaries of Essex administered by Essex County Council were pretty much the same as those administered by the King of Essex 1,200 years earlier. Watson split Essex into northern and southern vice-counties (18 and 19 in his national system) and these two vice-counties have formed the basis of almost all Essex biological recording ever since. Except for Essex losing the parishes of Heydon and Great and Little Chishill in the extreme northwest to Cambridgeshire in 1895 and some minor revisions to the boundary along the Lea Valley (Harris 2002), there have been no other changes to the physical area defined as Essex for recording purposes in this book. Large areas of Essex are now London boroughs and considered Metropolitan. For the purpose of this book and to keep in line with other publications, Metropolitan Essex is that part of Essex that falls within 32.2km (20 miles) of St Paul's Cathedral.

Around 70 environmental organisations are active in Essex, the principal two being the Essex Wildlife Trust and the RSPB. The former has some 16,000 members and 3,000 corporate members and manages over 3,000ha on 92 nature reserves, including Abberton, Hanningfield, Colne Point and Thorndon CP. The RSPB is Europe's largest independent conservation organisation and manages four reserves in Essex, including the extremely important Old Hall and Rainham Marshes.

GEOLOGY

"Essex is NOT flat and uninteresting; Essex is slightly undulating and uninteresting." – Anon

It is sometimes said that the geology of Essex does not play a major part in determining the distribution and abundance of birds in Essex; it could, however, be argued most strongly that the reverse is true. It is the county's geological history and consequent landforms which have produced a rather flat land with slow-flowing rivers reaching the sea in saltmarsh and mudflat-edged estuaries that make Essex famous for its flocks of coastal birds.

Deep below the surface of Essex are Silurian and Devonian rocks dating from a time when the ancestors of humans and birds were the same primitive fish. The rocks nearer the surface in Essex are fairly young in geological terms, the oldest being the chalks of the Grays area and extreme northwest which were laid down less than 100 million years ago when early birds and dinosaurs were dominant and Essex was beneath the same large crystal-clear sea that covered much of Europe. Above the chalk is a layer of pebble and gravel deposits. These include the Oldhaven Beds, which contain a large number of fossils, including what appears to be the bones of the earliest Essex (sea?) bird. Over these are the pebbles and gravels of the London Clay that make up the surface of the greater part of the county.

WEATHER AND CLIMATE

Long-term weather records show that Essex has a low rainfall of around 500–600mm per year, although the majority falls in the summer months. Compared to the rest of the east coast, Essex has warmer, sunny summers and winters that are not quite so cold. This probably has considerable significance for food availability in coastal habitats. In estuarine localities, where nutrients are available in abundance, the biological productivity is linked to temperature. Thus, the Essex mudflats should be especially rich feeding grounds with high productivity starting earlier in the spring and later in the autumn than in colder regions.

Weather patterns appear to be getting less predictable with a greater frequency of extreme weather. Thus, recent years have seen periods of drought and hot weather interspersed with high rainfall. Although they have become fewer in recent years, prolonged periods of frosts can have significant impacts on local populations of species such as Grey Herons, Kingfishers and Wrens.

The long-term sea level rise associated, in part at least, with global warming is having two contradictory effects on the areas of saltmarsh and mudflats. Sea level rises flood or erode existing habitats and these are not replaced where efficient seawalls are maintained. However, the huge cost of seawall maintenance, and the lower perceived value of agricultural land defended by these walls, is leading to a policy of 'managed retreat': breaches in seawalls are left and new saltmarsh and mudflats allowed to develop in areas previously protected from the sea.

Very densely populated regions, such as Metropolitan Essex, maintain high night-time temperatures, due primarily to heat escaping from houses. This can raise temperatures by 6º C compared to the neighbouring countryside and be vitally important for the survival of roosting, small birds.

HYDROLOGY

Most of Essex consists of drainage basins that are wholly within the county. The southern boundary is the tidal Thames, in effect an inlet of the sea as far as Essex is concerned. To the east is the North Sea. Draining into these marine surroundings are the Colne, Blackwater, Crouch, Roach and Roding. These rivers and their tributaries are entirely within Essex and drain most of the county. The flatlands of Tendring, Dengie, Foulness, Southend and the Thames marshes are drained by smaller river, brook and dyke systems, also within Essex.

The Lea and Stort form the western boundary and drain the western strip of the county, with the Stour in the north. The extreme northwest chalk is the only area drained by a river that flows out of the county, the Cam.

The drainage of almost all Essex farmland, combined with the deepening and straightening of many stretches of river, has led to rapid run-off of rainwater. This, combined with high abstraction rates from aquifers beneath the chalk, has meant that many farm ditches and headwaters are dry for much of the time. The lower reaches of the main rivers are prevented from drying up by the substantial input of large quantities of treated sewage. The northern outfall sewer is the largest tributary of the Thames and on most days around 50% of the water in the lower reaches of most Essex rivers is derived from sewage.

GEOGRAPHICAL CHANGES

When the tundra habitats, which covered Essex in the most recent Ice Age, gave way to those associated with the present climatic phase there would have been three major habitat types covering the county: broad-leaved wildwood; broad rivers with wide marshy or fenland floodplains; estuaries and coasts bounded by saltmarsh and mudflats. The conversion, over a period of about 3,000 years, of the 'natural' Essex into what we see today is the history of farming and the development of the urban population. Before this process began there was no immensely long period of stability, since climatic changes at the end of the Ice Age caused a succession of changes in the structure of the wildwood. From around 800–1800AD, there was probably a relatively stable mix of habitats but from the 1830s, and particularly from the mid-1900s, the changes to the Essex countryside were much faster than in any other period.

The creation of open farmland and heathland, leaving the remaining woods isolated from each other, has been achieved over several millennia. Seawalls, which mark an abrupt transition from saltmarsh to dry land, are perhaps 300 years old at most. Practically all freshwater habitats have also been deliberately created since the 19th century, whilst 95% of all urban habitat and road networks appeared during the 20th century.

Changing climate and habitat will affect the species occurring across the county. The original wildwood may have held an avifauna similar to the remnants still present in Bialowieza, Poland. The change to traditional farming would have allowed what were originally steppe species such as Skylark, Stone Curlew, Grey Partridge and Yellowhammer to increase; the modern agricultural revolution has hit these species hard.

THE HABITATS OF ESSEX

Despite our modern technology, it is surprisingly difficult to find reasonable estimates of the proportion of Essex covered by different habitats. The table shows the split between the major types; where these differ from published estimates, this is because the percentages are of the land area of the geographical county of Essex and not the administrative one.

Farmed Land and Hedges

The statistics on agricultural uses are, not surprisingly, more accurate than for other habitat types, although estimates given in the table for linear habitats are much less accurate. Today, the huge expanses of cereal land have little ornithological interest and what there is continues to decline as industrial farming methods progress towards making much of the countryside a monoculture. The widespread increase in autumn sowing has made most land unsuitable for stubble-feeding passerines in winter and has also been associated with the huge loss of Skylarks. Lapwings, which were also fairly common, have now all but disappeared and the small Stone Curlew population in the northwest has also succumbed.

Habitat Type	% of land area of Essex
Farmed land and hedges	60-62%
Urban (buildings, town roads & gardens)	25-30%
Woodlands (inc. wood/pasture forests)	7-8%
Interurban roads, railways, verges, airports	2-4%
Still or flowing water	about 1%
Total area APPROX 4,000km^2	100%
Intertidal habitats at low tide, about 400km^2	an additional 10%

The percentage of the land area of the geographical county of Essex occupied by each major habitat type

Oil-seed Rape makes up about 50% of non-cereal arable crops and these are also of little ornithological interest although the Woodpigeon has successfully exploited the rich winter feeding it provides.

Set-aside land has proved to be an interesting, if expensive, addition to the Essex farming scene that in some circumstances can have an interest far greater than normal crop fields, although many areas designated as set-aside are merely planted up with crops such as Oil-seed Rape that are not destined for human consumption. Rotational set-aside can provide a welcome increase in food diversity on farm fields, as can permanent set-aside, managed with gamebirds in mind; Pheasant and Partridge shooting is still an important rural business in some areas. Nearer the coast, specially subsidised winter crops are provided to attract Brent Geese away from commercial crops where they may do considerable damage.

Land use	Area (km^2)	% of Essex
Cereals	1,340	33
Other arable crops	470	12
Set aside	380	9
Grass	350	9
Coastal grazing marsh	65	1.9
Hedges	30?	less than 1.0
Orchards	12	less than 0.5
Cereal margins	10?	less than 0.5
Ditches	4?	less than 0.5

Farmed land in Essex

The intensively fertilised grasslands, composed of very low diversity grass and herb communities, provide grazing and silage or hay crops for Sheep and Cattle and continue to be important feeding grounds for Rooks. The extremely low insect numbers in these grasslands probably has a lot to do with today's low bird numbers; even those insects associated with Cattle dung have been significantly reduced by the widespread use of worming drugs.

Unlike the intensive modern grasslands, the coastal grazing marshes are of huge interest and importance to birds. These ancient pastures, derived from saltmarshes now protected by seawalls, have suffered significant losses due to deep drainage and conversion to arable. The remaining 6,500ha are mostly protected under ESA or similar grant schemes. The main landowners are conservation bodies and the MoD, although there are still some large private landowners. These marshes provide the principal or only breeding sites for, amongst others, Shelduck, Garganey, Shoveler, Gadwall, Snipe, Redshank and Yellow Wagtail. In the winter, Brent Geese, Lapwing and Golden Plovers roost in huge numbers.

Although a tiny part of Essex is given over to commercial fruit production, around 65ha is old orchard that is listed in the Essex BAP as requiring conservation; such habitat is important for owls, woodpeckers, Spotted Flycatchers and Bullfinches.

The length of hedgerows in Essex could be established from aerial photographs but this has never been done; the figure of 17,237km of old hedges is an extrapolation from a single farm study. The importance of this habitat is immense for nesting sites, feeding and as a 'corridor' between habitats. The substantial loss of hedgerows has been a significant factor in the decline of many farmland species and is isolating many remaining small populations.

Around 500km of seawalls protect Essex farmland and produce a sharp transition from one habitat to the next. Many seawalls provide good nesting sites for such species as Skylarks, Meadow Pipits, Yellow Wagtails and Corn Buntings, which have declined inland. However, overzealous mowing and herbicide treatment are almost certainly adversely affecting populations even here.

Drainage ditches on arable land, when unaccompanied by hedges, still provide important habitats as they have their own microclimate, long vegetation and good insect populations, and they provide good cover for partridges and ground-nesting passerines. Like seawalls, however, even these are suffering at the hands of modern agriculture.

Cereal field margins, where a wildlife strip is left unsown with cereals or a wide conservation headland is sown but left largely unsprayed, are an increasing and important feature of many Essex farms. Until recently, the main incentive was to improve gamebird chick survival. Now, however, grant aid and legal restrictions on pesticide use close to hedges have seen increasing areas given over to these habitats, which have great potential for restoring some of the bird diversity lost in intensively farmed areas.

Urban Habitats

There has been a massive increase in the proportion of Essex that is covered with housing, a trend that looks set to continue apace into the future. The ratio of gardens to buildings and roads decreases in Metropolitan Essex as one nears the City; in the most urban areas it is the Feral Pigeon that becomes the dominant, if not always welcome, member of the avifauna.

There are probably around one million private gardens in Essex (including Metropolitan Essex) and together with public gardens, graveyards and burial grounds they probably cover 8–15% of Essex. The great increase in feeding garden birds and providing nest boxes has allowed species such as the Blue Tit, the nation's top garden bird, to breed at densities in gardens well above the level in more natural habitats, despite the high mortality rate caused by domestic Cats.

Robins, Chaffinches, Greenfinches and canopy-feeding insect eaters seem to be doing well in gardens. On the other hand, four once very common species, Blackbird, Dunnock, House Sparrow and Starling, whilst still featuring in the national top ten of garden birds, have entered the BTO Amber List because of notable declines. Conversely, the Collared Dove has, in just a few decades after its arrival in Britain, become a near-ubiquitous garden bird.

With the exception of Feral Pigeons, nearly all birds that breed mainly in or on buildings have decreased in recent years. Thus, House Martins, Swifts, Swallows, House Sparrows and Starlings have all declined, although only in the case of the Swift is the cause likely to be entirely attributable to the loss of breeding sites.

Woodland, Forest and Parks

Wooded habitats have by far the greatest variety of bird species associated with them. This is largely because of their complex vertical structure, which provides birds with many different ways to feed and breed, both of which will also alter with the season and the availability of seeds and insect prey. A typical Essex wood will hold 40–55 species in summer or winter.

Large areas of ancient woodland that were historically wood/pasture and/or hunting forests remain, with the most important examples being in Epping and Hatfield Forests. All the woods or woodland blocks of significantly more than 100ha remaining in Essex fall into this category. Because these woods contain mature or senescent trees, they are the most important habitats for larger hole-nesting species. Of the woodpeckers, for example, the Green Woodpecker, which often feeds from ants' nests in woodland pasture, is particularly associated with large woodland blocks. Older, more mature woodlands are also favoured by some of our rarest breeding woodland birds such as Lesser Spotted Woodpeckers and Hawfinches.

Medium-sized blocks of woodland of ancient origin remain, although the Forestry Commission converted many to conifers, a trend that is now being reversed (thus holding out the hope of reversing the decline of the Tree Pipit in some areas). Almost all Essex woods fall in this category and dramatic improvements in the avifauna should follow the removal of conifers and a reversion to broad-leaved woodland with wide rides and clearings.

Small to medium-sized (under 50ha) blocks of ancient woodland, often with a past history of coppicing, occur across the county. The reintroduction of coppicing improves the shrub layer and encourages woodland warblers, and—if bird boxes are provided—breeding densities among tits may reach unnaturally high densities. Grazing of the scrub layer by Muntjac and other deer, however, present a significant threat to the future health of all woodland plant communities and hence the plants and animals that rely on them. Likewise, Grey Squirrels appear to be a significant nest predator in woodlands. The increasing isolation of these smaller woodland blocks due to the loss of natural 'corridors' such as hedges threatens the survival of isolated populations of birds.

In uncoppiced woodland with little in the way of scrub, the main birding community will be in the canopy and favour species such as Woodpigeons, Jays and Rooks. In virtually all privately owned Essex woods and many Forestry Commission ones, large numbers of Pheasants are released and represent the greatest avian biomass.

Heaths and Commons

Two hundred years ago heathland was one of the major inland habitats in Essex, the 1778 Chapman and André map identifying heathland on all the gravel and sandy soils. A surprisingly high proportion of these areas survive, although they now exist as public access woodlands with little heathland and virtually no Heather heath remaining. Birds that specialised in heathland have therefore disappeared from Essex. Nightjar and Red-backed Shrike have gone, whilst Stonechats now survive in small numbers in non-heathland habitat. Today, Skylarks and Meadow Pipits are the typical species in the small remaining areas.

There are optimistic Essex BAP plans to restore existing heathlands, and some conservation work has already begun, in addition to work in progress at Tiptree Heath. Unfortunately, English Heritage have so far failed to designate Mill Green Common, once one of the most important heathlands in the county, as an SSSI.

If the lost heathland birds return to Essex, it is more likely to be in open habitats created within large, deconifered, woodlands than on conservation-managed heaths.

Roads and Verges

Few areas of Essex are more than 1km from a metalled road or about 5km from a major road. Most of the substantial increases in the road network in recent decades have been in town roads serving new developments but it is the new motorways, dual carriageways and bypasses that have had the most significant effects on the Essex avifauna.

For Magpies, Crows and Rooks the roads provide a new and important feeding habitat where they scavenge road-kills; Magpies have been particularly successful in exploiting this opportunity. Buzzards may also be learning to scavenge such areas, which may be aiding their recolonisation of the county.

Road-kills include large numbers of relatively common birds, although the proportion of the population killed in this way and its overall effect has not been researched. Mortality appears to be highest on smaller rural roads where hedgerow birds suffer most; most birds can react to speeds of less than 40km per hour. Roads, especially the larger trunk roads, provide large, wide and relatively undisturbed verges that are important for voles and hence Kestrels. Unfortunately, Barn Owls have suffered severe mortality; their low level hunting technique puts them directly in collision with vehicles.

Inland Wetlands and Waters

Rivers and streams

Essex rivers are the only natural freshwater habitat in the county, although they have been substantially altered by man. Thus, most have lost their natural tendency to flood except briefly at times of highest water flow. There are around 560km of permanently flowing Essex rivers of which about 16% are of the highest (least polluted) water quality. Most Kingfishers nest in riverbanks created where the river flow cuts a natural bank into which they can burrow.

Ponds, pits and reservoirs

All the bodies of still water in Essex are artificial and the great majority are less than 100 years old. These fall into three categories, which in order of size and importance to birds are: large reservoirs constructed by water companies or state bodies; gravel pits and farm reservoirs; lakes and ponds.

Reservoirs

It is no error that all of the larger reservoirs are designated as SSSIs despite being such new and artificial habitats. They are the second most important bird habitat in Essex and include Abberton, the county's only site of international significance that is not found on the coast. All these sites hold large numbers of wildfowl and, periodically, waders during the autumn and winter. They are particularly attractive to huge flocks of moulting birds such as Coot, Pochard and Tufted Duck.

The interest of Abberton and Hanningfield is greater not just because they are the largest reservoirs but because they are relatively close to the sea and attract large numbers of coastal birds, some of which are particularly rare elsewhere inland. Abberton

has the largest inland breeding colony of Cormorants in Britain, whilst there is another substantial colony at Walthamstow, near to the county's largest heronry.

Gravel-pits and farm reservoirs

Worked-out gravel-pits have created a large number of medium-sized freshwater bodies, most of which are in the Lea Valley and eastern Essex. In all there are said to be 1,000 of these and they provide important nesting habitat for grebes, ducks and warblers as well as wintering areas for many other ducks. Those in the Lea Valley have a significant wintering Bittern population, most Cetti's Warblers are found in this type of habitat and Hobbies have also increased as dragonflies have become more widespread. Whilst still a relatively new addition to the breeding avifauna, Little Ringed Plovers may nest around gravel-pits. Farm reservoirs continue to be constructed and provide similar habitat to gravel-pits. The fauna of both types of freshwater ultimately rests on their management; many are used for both coarse and fly fishing and tend to have limited bird communities.

Lakes and ponds

Many ornamental lakes were created during the 19th century, whereas many farm and village ponds are probably of considerable age and originally used for Cattle watering. The latter usually hold very small populations of Moorhens and Mallards, although larger ones in, for example, Hatfield Forest and Epping Forest, hold a greater variety of species. Garden ponds have become a very important habitat for amphibians and aquatic insects but their value to birds is limited except perhaps for bathing and drinking by garden birds. The loss of ancient farm ponds as part of the general industrialisation of agriculture has probably reduced insect biodiversity and hence food for farmland birds.

Coastal borrow dykes and reed beds

Borrow dykes were dug inside the seawalls to provide the material to build the walls. Most are filled with mildly saline water and are often choked with reed beds, which are an important habitat for Reed Warblers, Reed Buntings and Bearded Tits. Where the borrow dykes dry out, Avocets breed on the resulting salt-rich mud, and sandpipers and Snipe feed there.

Coasts and Estuaries – Intertidal Habitats

Ornithologically, the habitats between the seawalls and the low water mark are by far the most important in Essex. With the exception of Abberton, all the county's internationally important sites are coastal.

It is difficult to estimate the size of these habitats. "The coastal zone around Essex constitutes the largest habitat type within the county … ", so begins the section on coastal habitats in the Essex Wildlife Trust's *Essex Wildlife 2000* (Anon. 1996). The claim is true only if one considers natural habitats; farmland and the built environment cover larger areas; Wheat alone exceeds the area of coastal mudflats by a factor of about three, even when low tide exposes the maximum area of mud.

Almost all of the intertidal habitats are designated as SSSIs and NNRs, thus identifying the most important Essex habitats. These areas cover over 31,000ha. Of course, this includes some coastal grazing marshes and other land habitats but it does not include Buxey and Gunfleet Sands, which are offshore island mudflats. It therefore seems that Essex intertidal habitat covers around 35,000ha at low tide, although this varies significantly between spring and neap tides.

Mudflats

Some 90–95% of Essex intertidal habitats are mudflats, hugely productive habitats whose food chain begins with single-celled algae or bacteria decaying the organic matter washed down the estuaries and ending with the huge numbers of wildfowl and waders that feed on the countless millions of worms, molluscs and crustaceans either in or on the mud. Relatively small areas of the mudflats are covered in eelgrass where significant parts of the biological productivity is in the form of rooted flowering plants (*Zostera*) and multicellular algae (*Enteromorpha*).

Almost 500,000 wildfowl and waders annually visit the Essex mudflats, many of them in nationally and internationally important numbers and representing up to 10% of all the waders and wildfowl occurring in Britain.

The eelgrass beds feature in the Essex BAP. No accurate figures exist for the area covered by the various *Zostera* species but the bed off Foulness covers over 300ha and is the largest expanse of Dwarf Eelgrass in Europe. With the nearby bed off Two Tree Island, they provide autumn feeding for a significant proportion of the British population of Dark-bellied Brent Geese.

Salt marsh

Salt marshes cover about 2,000ha, the largest expanse covering most of the length of the Dengie coast and the rest in more sheltered estuaries and inlets like Hamford Water. The largest numbers of birds to use this habitat are the mudflat feeding waders and wildfowl that move onto the salt marshes to roost at high tide. Few species breed on the salt marshes: Redshanks, Black-headed Gulls and a few pairs of terns and larger gulls. The seeds of salt-loving plants are an important food source during the winter for several species of passerines, particularly the much-declined Twite, whilst Rock Pipits feed on invertebrates in the marshes.

Cliffs

Essex has no rocky cliffs and only three cliffs of any kind. These are at Cudmore Grove CP, Jaques Bay on the Stour and at The Naze. All are important geological sites but, apart from Sand Martins nesting at Cudmore Grove and The Naze, have little avian interest.

Shingle spits and banks

Until recently, the Maplin Bank, off Foulness, was an important artificial seabird breeding site. Constructed in connection with the proposed Maplin Airport, the site was free from humans and predators and was quickly colonised by terns and gulls. The colony grew to an impressive size until high tides effectively destroyed it as a breeding site. Elsewhere, natural shingle spits, such as those at Colne Point, suffer from disturbance and predation, although Little Terns, Oystercatchers and Ringed Plovers continue to breed; the largest population of the last are now found within the seawall rather than in its traditional habitat.

Sandy beaches

The principal beaches are in the northeast between Colne Point and The Naze; little breeds on them because of disturbance by holidaymakers and only Sanderlings occur in any numbers during the winter.

The Sea

The North Sea used to be one of the richest fishing grounds in British waters; large numbers of local boats used to catch huge numbers of Herrings and Sprats. However, with the near-extinction of the Herring and low Sprat numbers, the fishing industry virtually collapsed. Although the Sprat is once again numerous, there is little sign of a recovery in Herring numbers.

The presence of birds in Essex coastal waters is largely dependent on the presence of food. Locally, the arrival of the Sprat shoals from late December is one of the main attractions to seabirds. Their arrival often augurs the appearance of larger numbers of divers and fish-eating wildfowl, together with gulls, including Kittiwakes. Counts of more than 3,000 Red-throated Divers off Suffolk in recent years have been attributed to the presence of huge Sprat shoals in the Sole Bay area. The presence of auks in Essex waters appears to depend mainly on weather conditions rather than food, whilst large Common Scoter flocks, when they occur, gather over the best and most accessible mollusc beds.

Protected Areas

The Essex Wildlife Trust is the largest of its kind in Britain. Other major bodies in Essex are the RSPB, which currently manages around 1,000ha, the National Trust, English Heritage and various local authorities. In total these organisations manage perhaps 5,000ha. Until it acquired Rainham in 2000, the RSPB had a remarkably low profile in Essex. Rainham's purchase, however, has been a major boost to conservation in the area and signals a proactive future for the RSPB in the county. Much of the undeveloped coastline is now in the hands of conservation organisations with more likely to come into their control in future.

Across Essex there are 86 SSSIs, 36 Local Nature Reserves, seven National Nature Reserves, 11 Special Protection Areas/Ramsar wetland sites and two Special Areas of Conservation (Epping Forest and the Essex estuaries) that afford legal protection of varying degrees to the sites that they cover.

THE FUTURE

Essex has since early times seen pressure for land from two very different sources: urban development and sea encroachment. With plans to build one million homes in southeast England over the next 20 years, there will be intense pressure on the existing Metropolitan green belt. Large areas of farmland are likely to disappear under concrete but, given the current barren nature of most farmland for birds, might development actually benefit birds if planned correctly? Pressures to expand Stansted Airport and the development 'necessary' to accommodate the 2012 Olympics are both likely to have significant impacts on the environment. From the sea will come the problem of ever increasing sea levels; managed retreats will mitigate against some of the losses but to be really effective this would have to be on a scale that would be politically impossible. Recent events in New Orleans, USA, have taught us that it is simply not possible to hold back Mother Nature. In the next 50 years some fundamental and far-reaching decisions will have to be made about how best to deal with an intractable problem.

On the positive side, politicians and the public in general are increasingly aware of our countryside and there has been a change in attitude in recent years that is slowly bearing fruit. At the front of this, in Essex at least, are the EWT and RSPB, who through their contact with the public are educating young and old alike. The children are the future and it is they whom we must encourage to cherish and nurture their natural heritage.

David Corke and Simon Wood

FOSSIL BIRDS IN ESSEX

Birds are ancient creatures, and their history can be traced to very primitive forms that existed around 180 million years ago. Before that, only the lack of fossils prevents us from confirming their presence even further into the remote past. The feathers that cover their bodies today may have developed from scales as found on snakes and lizards. Indeed, birds have scaly legs and retain other reptilian features such as the ring of plates (sclerotic plates) which surround the eye. Perhaps it was the need to move more freely amongst vegetation that caused the adaptation of a body covering that would at first help jumping from branch to branch, then gliding from tree to tree, and eventually to achieve powered flight and the manoeuvrability enjoyed by modern birds.

Approaching 200 million years of avian evolution is a period so vast that its length is difficult to comprehend. After all, just 1 million years is 1,000 millennia. Now, only six years into a new one, we may be soberly reminded that the previous millennium started before the Norman Conquest and much of recorded British history occurred during this period. Then just contemplate the antiquity of Essex birds. Even devoid of any fossils approaching the age of, say, *Archaeopteryx*, the Essex fossil avifauna nevertheless dates back 55 million years.

Most of the bird remains found in Britain have been obtained from the London Clay, a marine deposit of the Lower Eocene that underlies much of our county and is traceable west to Wiltshire and Dorset and east well into the Baltic.

In Essex, not only can we claim to have many excellent birding localities, but in Walton-on-the-Naze we have one of the world's most important sites for finding the fossils of prehistoric birds. In David Attenborough's book *The Life of Birds* (1998) he mentioned Walton (page 23) and the astonishing evidence provided by that place (primarily based on data obtained by reference to my collection) of the extraordinary pace of bird evolution. What is more, the fossils found at Walton are magnificent because, unlike so many bird fossils in museum collections, The Naze has produced numerous multi-element skeletal examples. With such informative material it is possible to gain reasonable appreciation of how the birds may have appeared in life. Problems arise when attempts are made to relate fossils to modern species, and this is where science is often found wanting. Not infrequently, based on the flimsiest of evidence, the character of an isolated bone is seized upon to describe the whole animal and to liken it to some supposed modern counterpart.

With the understanding acquired from the study of The Naze birds, it soon becomes clear that many have no living relatives, being simply ancient representatives of a once successful community that contained numerous forms, most of which were destined to become extinct during the long period since London Clay times. Some doubtlessly have modern descendants but have been so changed in their structure since the Eocene period that whatever similarities we find in their skeletons to modern species, it is rarely possible to place them in contemporary taxonomic groups. To give some impression of this ancient avian population, in the accompanying table an attempt has been made to demonstrate the great diversity of these London Clay birds. Although I have had to resort to using recent bird classifications, this is solely to give some basic idea of the birds' appearance in relation to types familiar to us today.

In the 30 years I have been assembling my avian fossil collection I have been ever burdened with the nagging question as to why so many birds clearly and collectively experienced such an untimely end. Something really disastrous must have been the cause and its effect was not just confined to the Walton area. The seam from which the fossils emerge can be traced far and wide under Essex. Sites near Bishop's Stortford, South Ockendon and Walthamstow have all produced avian relics from the same silty strata. Also, there are other vertebrate animals to be found, commonly in the form of sharks' teeth and the bones of teleost fishes. When we travel further east across the North Sea to Denmark, here again deposits of low London Clay age contain bird fossils; likewise, into the Baltic. Even across the Atlantic a similar story emerges. What is particularly remarkable is that in both America and Europe some of the birds appear to be of exactly the same species, even those from as far as Wyoming!

So what did occur 55 million years ago? Until fairly recently, to talk of a possibly extra-terrestrial dimension would have attracted no little derision. Now the subject of comets and asteroid collisions with Earth is a frequent news topic. There is little doubt that an impact in the Yucatan Peninsula of Mexico 65 million years ago (the so-called KT Boundary) had much to do with the final extinction of the dinosaurs. The new thinking sends teams of scientists searching for signs of past celestial visitations, craters or mineral remains having strange, unearthly chemical compositions. What then is the evidence for considering the London Clay birds may have such a story to tell? Perhaps the secret to what actually occurred in the Lower Eocene lies not essentially with the fossils but is more likely to be confirmed from some interesting non-organic particles recovered by the writer from The Naze in 1978.

Group (see cautionary note in text)	See notes	Earliest Record	Likeness			Possible relatives elsewhere, Eocene and earlier
			A	B	C	
Paleognath/lithornithid	1	Paleocene	40			
Diving bird - petrel/duck		UC	1	3		UC
Petrel	2	LE (Naze)	2	1		
Pseudodontorn	3	LE (Naze)	1			
Tropicbird		LE (Naze)		1		
Ibis mosaic		LE (Naze)		4		Europe (ME)
Screamer		LE (Naze)	7	5		North America (LE)
Swan		LE (Naze)		1		
Duck		LE (Naze)	8	1		
Hawk		LE (Naze)		1	1	Europe (UE)
Accipitrine/coraciiform mosaic		LE (Naze)		3		
Falcon/caracara		LE (Naze)		1		
Osprey		LE (Naze)		1		
Fowl/gamebird		LE (Naze)	6	4		
Megapode		LE (Naze)		2		Europe (UE)
Rail		UP		2		UP
Finfoot/mesite		LE (Naze)		3		
Bustard		LE (Naze)		4	3	
Gruiform/charadriiform		LE (Naze)		7		North America (LE)
Buttonquail		LE (Naze)	1	3		
Messelornithid	4	Palaeocene?	1			Europe (UP); North America (LE)
Rail/wader		LE (Naze)		7		
Pratincole/plover		LE (Naze)	1			
Oystercatcher		LE (Naze)		2		
Jacana		LE (Naze)		5		
Thick-knee		LE (Naze)		2		
Gull		LE (Naze)		1		
Tern		LE (Naze)	3			
Auk		LE (Naze)		1		
Dove		LE (Naze)	5	4	2	
Pigeon/sandgrouse		LE (Naze)		?		
Parrot		LE (Naze)	9	4		
Phorusrhacid	5	LE (Naze)	5	2		
Touraco, also Cuckoo-roller	6, 7	LE (Naze)	4	10		Europe (LE)
Hoatzin etc mosaic	8	LE		3		North America (LE)
Cuckoo		LE (Naze)		1		
Cuckoo/owl mosaic	9	LE (Naze)	17	4		North America (LE)
Owl		MP	4	9		North America (MP)
Nightjar		LE (Naze)		2		North America? (LE)
Potoo/frogmouth etc		LE (Naze)		2		
Oilbird		LE		2		North America (LE)
Caprimulgiform		LE		5	8	North America (LE)
Swift		LE (Naze)			1	
Crested Swift	10	LE	20	8		North America (LE)
Early swift		LE (Naze)	2			
Trogon	11	LE (Naze)	4	18	2	
Mousebird		LE (Naze)		4	4	
Coly mosaic		LE			?	North America (LE)
Coraciiform		LE		20	5	North America (LE)
Kingfisher		LE (Naze)		2		
Roller		LE (Naze)		2		
Tody		LE (Naze)		2		
Motmot		LE (Naze)		10	4	
Hoopoe		LE (Naze)	14	1		Europe (ME)
Hoopoe mosaic sister group?		LE (Naze)	8			
Wood-hoopoe mosaic	12	LE (Naze)	14	1		North America (LE)
Perching bird mosaic	13	LE	30	35		North America (LE); Australia? (LE)
Passerine/coly etc mosaic		LE (Naze)	?			

LEGEND

UC = Upper Cretaceous
MP = Middle Paleocene
UP = Upper Paleocene
LE = Lower Eocene
ME = Middle Eocene
UE = Upper Eocene

Likeness

A   Similar
B   Some similarity
C   Vague similarity

Notes

1. Once a successful group now entirely extinct; thought to be connected to the ratites, particularly tinamous. However, the skeleton displays many confusing features which led the Victorian anatomist, Sir Richard Owen, working on remains from the Isle of Sheppey, Kent, to consider it related to the vultures. Hence he chose the now misleading name *Lithornis vulturinus*.
2. Represented by specimens similar to living petrels, but there are also remarkable mosaics where the bird's lower leg resembles that of diving ducks and the beak is more like that of a coot.
3. Members of this extinct group were among the largest seabirds ever known. They are distinguished by the possession of bony tooth-like projections on the jaws. The Naze individual may have had a wingspan of 3–4m.
4. A form of wading bird apparently widespread in the mid-Eocene, with many beautifully preserved fossils found in the Messel quarry near Darmstadt, Germany. The Naze specimens are likely forerunners of this group.
5. The Naze birds are convincing members of this group which, in more recent times, reached great size. Later phorusrhacids were of truly fearsome appearance and stood up to 3m in height; it is hardly surprising that they are sometimes called 'terror birds'. The ones we have in the London Clay were no giants, about rooster size and some much smaller; nevertheless, their anatomy is quite distinctive. Seriemas have been suggested as living relatives but recent thinking would associate them better with touracos. Whatever, the Essex London Clay types were fully volant, but later phorusrhacids were flightless.
6–8. Touracos and the Hoatzin are regarded as primitive birds, the latter especially so with the wings of its fledglings bearing claws. Taxonomists have particular problems in ascribing them to order; should they be classed with the cuckoos or with the galliforms? Naze fossils may hold answers to these questions and additionally throw light on the relationships of the Courol, supposedly an aberrant roller.

9. A common Naze fossil; there is a near-identical form of the same age from the US. Its original description was based on a fossil from Wyoming. It is thought to be an ancestral piciform near to the puffbirds, but close scrutiny of the numerous Naze specimens shows that it has no connection with woodpecker-like birds and appears to show affinities with the cuckoos and owls.
10. Many treeswift-like birds have been found in Naze deposits and in western North America (probably the same species). They also appear in the low London Clay in Denmark (where it is known as the Mo Clay).
11. Trogons (or trogon-like birds at least, given their distinctive heterodactyl toe arrangement with first and second toes reversed) are not uncommon at The Naze.
12. Wood-hoopoe-like is the safer description of these birds, which have very similar forms from the US.
13. It has been proposed on rather flimsy evidence (two ends of a bone from Australia) that passerines arose in the southern hemisphere. The Naze collection includes many that provide solid data on early passerine evolution. True, their forerunners seem to have a strange foot anatomy, with the first and fourth toes reversed as in parrots, cuckoos and woodpeckers, but major changes in the world's vegetation may have created the need for a remodelled grasp. Other parts of the skeleton show remarkable similarity to living songbirds, especially in the structure of the shoulder girdle and wings.

These tiny, but exquisitely shaped glassy objects, about 120 in number, emerged from a pocket dug from Walton foreshore when I was searching for bird bones. I regard these particles as probably the most important and telling finds I have ever discovered. Their identity fits well with the description of tektites (see the particularly informative article about them in *Encyclopaedia Britannica* for added insight). Tektites are now viewed as part of a mass of ejected material thrown out when some form of space rock impacted Earth's surface and, since such a collision would generate heat of unimaginable intensity, earthrock would either be completely vaporised or suffer meltdown over a wide area. Just a moderate-sized asteroid travelling at, say, 18 miles per second striking Earth would cause destruction to the environment of massive proportions, probably affecting the atmosphere of the entire planet.

I know that some will still be sceptical over such a scenario. Other explanations will be offered as to why so many millions upon millions of birds perished in such a short interval of time. But these explanations need to confront a simple home truth of which I can claim to have some understanding. This comes from my need to acquire so-called 'comparative material' ... modern bird carcasses to give me a basic appreciation of varied avian anatomy. So I have trudged the Essex countryside and foreshores in search of specimens. Only at times of extreme weather will one encounter corpses in any number and even these will soon attract the attention of the hungry. Otherwise, predators and scavengers will soon sense the existence of an occasional injured bird and will quickly home in on a meal whatever its state, wholesome or otherwise. So under normal circumstances those that are unwell or suffer demise do not stay around long and, unless one can compete with the efficiency of Foxes, Rats and Crows, all that will be found is feathers and perhaps the odd bone. Thus, in my view it was reasonable to believe that if animal remains occur in great numbers, something extraordinary must have occurred.

Given the way scientific knowledge is now developing on the cause of past great extinctions, I was drawn to conclude that these London Clay times may have experienced yet another event of this nature which apparently annihilated in particular the avian population over a wide area and in this case took out prey, predator and scavenger alike. Ultimately, supported by the existence of the tektites, it became my favoured view that indeed there had to be an extra-terrestrial explanation. In 1994, my attempts to gain publicity for my theory, without the crucial evidence of a 'bolide' crash site in northwest Europe, fell largely on deaf ears. Then in 2001 considerable excitement occurred in scientific circles when Britain's first impact crater (it was named Silverpit) was discovered in the North Sea, 130km from the Yorkshire coast and no great distance from The Naze. The age of the impact that created the crater has been calculated to within a time frame embracing the age of the low London Clay of Walton. It is an important story, particularly so because here we have the unique opportunity to link a crater with excellent evidence of the catastrophic destruction wrought by the impact in our own back yard.

Those who travel far for their birds will undoubtedly see in the accompanying table names that would apply to a more exotic avifauna, species not usually met with in the British Isles. Even though many will have only speculative relationships to fossil types, I think it preferable to add the proviso "-like" to the names given. For instance, in respect of the Motmot record, The Naze fossils are only applied to this variety because no other coraciiform bird skeleton approximates more closely to the detail of the ancient remains and indeed it is referred just simply because it is a poor best. The similarity applies to many types I have detailed. Some may be true ancestors of living birds, but far more likely are types that, due to a unique set of circumstances, we have the opportunity to visualise their form. Birds long gone that, at some time in the remote past, succumbed to the forces of extinction, unsuccessful participants in what Darwin famously described as 'the struggle for life'.

A few birds have been recovered from later deposits of the London Clay. These, except for two associated bones found in a clay pit at Brentwood, are of solitary incomplete items. A foreshore exposure along the River Crouch near Burnham has produced several specimens. These have been described in scientific literature, but their assignments have been disputed. The deep quarry at High Ongar produced a partial leg bone that was identified as a rail-like bird, although this subsequently proved erroneous. I have obtained a solitary leg bone associated with other relics accumulated in and under the extensive remains of a fossil log eroding out of the strata exposed on the Clacton foreshore. Remarkably, this was immediately comparable with specimens from The Naze. Although probably not a close relative of those found at Walton, it was obviously another example of a mousebird-like form.

Many types of birds must have come and gone during the great length of time subsequent to the London Clay period. In Essex, there are a few patches of a sandy nature that date to the upper Eocene. These occur on high ground, but few fossils are known from them and certainly no birds. Then there are a number of records dating to the Ice Ages or warmer intervening stages, but their age is to be counted more in thousands than millions of years. These relics were almost exclusively obtained from the Brickearth deposits and sometimes found with a wide mammalian fauna. Assiduous collecting by several wealthy Victorian gentlemen was responsible for most of these discoveries, the majority of which were left to the Natural History Museum. These avian remains are mostly of waterbirds and have been reliably identified. From Walthamstow have come Greylag Goose, Mallard, Tufted Duck and White-tailed Eagle; from Grays, Cormorant, Whooper and Mute Swans, Greylag and Red-breasted Geese. From the extensive Ilford Brickearths, Whooper and Mute Swans, White-fronted and Greylag Geese, Mallard and a "large extinct species of crane". Some items may well have been the vestiges of meals consumed by prehistoric man.

The interesting foreshore exposures at East Mersea have also produced the remains of Whooper Swan along with Garganey, Smew, Sandwich Tern, Song Thrush, Fieldfare and Redwing; these all came from the 300,000-year-old Hoxnian 'elephant bone bed'. Some of the mammals that have been found include Straight-tusked Elephant, Narrow-nosed Rhinoceros and Giant Deer. Among other finds it is certainly worth recording that this site has produced the richest collection of amphibians and reptiles found in Britain that lived within the last two million years (Urquhart 2000).

Michael Daniels

ARCHAEOLOGICAL REMAINS AND PLACE NAMES

Although there are plentiful Iron Age and Bronze Age sites in Essex, many of the archaeological excavations have involved sites of predominantly Roman antiquity, although as a result of these digs much medieval evidence has also been unearthed. Colchester, initially as Camulodunum and later as Colonia Victricensis, was a very important Roman town whilst many other settlements nearby have evidence of Roman influence. In Colchester, digs during the period 1971–85 did not yield large numbers of wild birds, despite its proximity to the coast (Luff 1993). In all, 28 species were identified. Whether the Crane was breeding on the surrounding marshes or was simply a winter visitor or passage migrant is not known, although the former is likely. Corncrakes and Great Grey Shrikes are also notable; is it possible that the latter bred at this time? Sparrowhawks have also been found at Great Holts Farm, Boreham, together with thrushes, and perhaps point to the use of the former for hunting. Earlier digs in Colchester identified Grey Heron, Whooper and perhaps Bewick's Swans. There is virtually no other archaeological evidence of birds from anywhere else in Essex.

Place names may also hint at the former ranges of now extinct species, although some care has to be taken in interpreting these as for example the word "hawk" may seem to have an obvious origin but may mean an angular bend in a field boundary (from the Old English [OE], haca). Also, place names may simply derive from a person's name, for example Richard Hawk or John Raven.

Purleigh comes from the OE *pur* meaning Bittern or Snipe. Ramsden Bellhouse and Crays, Ramsey and Ramsey Marsh Island all come from the OE name for Raven, *Hræfn*, although in the case of Ramsey there may be a connection with Wild Garlic (OE, *hramsa*). The local Oystercatcher name, Sea-pie, gave its name to Pyefleet and Pye Sands. Rawreth derives its name from the OE *hraga*, rid or "heron stream", although Herongate, near Brentwood, actually comes from the OE *hyrne* meaning "nook or corner" despite the tradition that there was once a heronry nearby. Cranbrook comes from *cranebroc* which meant "crane or heron brook", although Cranham, another locality linked to the presence of Cranes prior to the medieval period, actually comes from *craohv* meaning either "Crawe's ridge and farm" or "crow-ridge and farm". Some of our coastal localities clearly have long associations for man with large numbers of birds, Foulness or *fugal-næss* (OE), meaning "wild-bird's ness," being an obvious example. Finally, the origin of Bustard Green near Lindsell, which was named as such in 1777, remains obscure; was it a person's name or more intriguingly was it named after the Great Bustard, which might have survived in the northwest of Essex into the 1700s?

Simon Wood

Species	Roman	Medieval	Post Medieval
Swan sp.	X		
Wigeon	X	X	
Teal	X	X	X
Tufted Duck	X	X	
Grey Partridge	X		
Pheasant	X	X	
Sparrowhawk	X		
Buzzard	X		
Corncrake	X		
Crane	X		
Golden Plover	X		
Golden or Grey Plover	X		
Lapwing	X		
Dunlin	X		
Snipe	X		
Woodcock	X	X	X
Bar-tailed Godwit	X	X	
Black-tailed Godwit	X	X	
Curlew	X		
Whimbrel	X		
Stock Dove or Rock Dove	X		
Mistle Thrush	X		
Redwing	X	X	
Great Grey Shrike	X		
Jackdaw	X		
Rook	X		
Crow	X		
Raven	X	X	

Occurrence of birds at Colchester

WETLAND BIRD SURVEY IN ESSEX

Once a month, throughout the winter, the wetland birds of Essex are counted as part of a massive, coordinated effort throughout Britain and western Europe. Hardy bands of volunteer counters scour the coastline and major inland waters for wildfowl, waders and other waterbirds, to contribute to a detailed picture of this international avian resource. These data contribute to one of the most definitive sources of information on the health of some of our key wildlife habitats, and provide a highly effective tool in the conservation of wetland habitats in the face of innumerable human pressures.

Why is so much voluntary effort put into this one aspect of our bird life? Because the UK is motorway, service station and destination rolled into one for these highly mobile wetland birds. Many of them breed in Arctic regions and move south along the western seaboard of Europe for the winter. Inevitably they pass through Britain and, while they are here, they must maintain their energy levels to allow onward migration or simply survival in hard weather. Britain benefits from the warming influence of the North Atlantic Drift, such that its wetland habitats are less prone to freezing than our latitude might otherwise suggest. So, many wetland birds terminate their migration here, or descend upon us when severe weather forces them to abandon feeding grounds elsewhere on the Continent.

Site Name	National Rank	Mean peak waterfowl count	No. of species of at least national importance	No. of species of international importance
Thames	4	159,778	21	11
Blackwater	11	90,716	16	6
Hamford Water	21	49,966	13	5
Stour	24	48,052	14	5
Dengie	29	39,456	8	4
Colne	33	35,150	10	0
Abberton	36	32,261	9	0
Crouch/Roach	48	23,192	4	1
Hanningfield	80	11,070	5	0
Lea Valley GPs	90	7,719	8	2
Met. Essex	~		5	0

Notes:
1. National ranking based on mean peak waterfowl numbers (Pollitt et al. 2003)
2. Waterfowl excludes gulls and non-native wildfowl
3. Rank is only given for principal sites as defined by the WeBS report i.e. sites supporting at least 10,000 waterfowl and/or at least one species in internationally important numbers

Table 1: Summary of the importance of Essex WeBS count sites.

The wetlands of Britain are therefore of an importance to wetland birds that is almost impossible to overstate—refuelling on migration, sustenance over the winter and as refuges in severe weather. Essex is critical to this. Although Manningtree to London is only some 100km as the Brent Goose flies, following the twists and turns of our heavily-indented coastline it is more like 650km in length—one of the longest coastlines of any English county—encompassing vast areas of intertidal mud. Essex also has a huge human population, which places demands on the environment for, amongst other things, water and building aggregates. These demands have led to the construction of new wetlands—reservoirs and gravel-pits—which have assumed an ever-increasing role in supporting wetland bird populations.

To the untutored eye, our wetlands can be bleak. Estuaries in particular are full of mud, at least when the tide is out: nasty, empty, smelly, worthless places, ripe for development. Or so the thinking seems to go. Nothing could be further from the truth: the twice-daily tides bring in food that sustains a biological productivity exceeding that of the most intensive arable system in the world. The worms, snails and other invertebrates, and the surface veneer of green algae and (locally) eelgrass, are the resources that support the birds. To destroy the habitat that provides the food, or disrupt the ability of birds to use that food, is to strike at the very integrity of international conservation efforts. In order to make the case for conservation, though, hard data are required about the importance of an area, at a range of scales. It is this information which is provided by the efforts of the counters. Counting birds in the teeth of an icy wind may not be the most attractive prospect, but all those of us who do it can take heart from the fact that through our efforts in the past we have made a difference, and this will continue to be the case—the pressures on our wetlands will never go away.

History of wetland bird surveys

Systematic counting of wetland birds began nationally in 1947. Since then it has grown into a formal scheme—the Wetland Birds Survey (WeBS)—covering all major wetlands, with the objectives of:

Site Name	MS	DB	SU	WN	GA	T	PT	SV	PO	TU	GN
Thames		I	N	N	N	I		N			
Blackwater		I	N	N		N	N				N
Hamford Water		I	N	N		N					
Stour			N	N				N			N
Dengie			N								
Colne			N	N							
Abberton	N					I		N	I	N	N
Crouch/Roach		I									
Hanningfield			N					N		N	
Lea Valley						I		I	N	N	
Met. Essex						N		N		N	

Standard species codes:	MS	Mute Swan	GA	Gadwall	PO	Pochard
	DB	Dark-bellied Brent Goose	T	Teal	TU	Tufted Duck
	SU	Shelduck	PT	Pintail	GN	Goldeneye
	WN	Wigeon	SV	Shoveler	SY	Smew
Table Entries	N	National Importance	I	International Importance		

Table 1a: Wildfowl species (for which thresholds have been set) based on WeBS data for 2000/01-2003/04

- obtaining population estimates for wildfowl and waders in the UK outside the breeding season;
- monitoring trends in abundance of these populations;
- identifying adverse trends at particular sites; and
- providing a sound basis for the protection of sites and populations.

Further details of WeBS, its history, survey methodology, interpretation and uses of the data can be found on the British Trust for Ornithology website (www.bto.org) and in publications, including Prater (1981), Gilbert *et al.* (1998), Musgrove *et al.* (2003) and the annual WeBS reports.

Site Name	OC	AV	RP	GP	GV	KN	SS	DN	BW	BA	CU	RK	TT
Thames	I	I	I	N	I	I		N	I	I	I	N	N
Blackwater	N	N	N	I	I		I		I			I	
Hamford Water	N	I	N	I	I				N	N		I	
Stour		I			I	I		N		I		I	N
Dengie					I	I		N		I			
Colne	N	N	N	N				N	N			N	
Crouch/Roach				N						N			

Standard species codes:					
OC	Oystercatcher	KN	Knot	CU	Curlew
AV	Avocet	SS	Sanderling	RK	Redshank
RP	Ringed Plover	DN	Dunlin	TT	Turnstone
GP	GoldenPlover	BW	Black-tailed Godwit		
GV	Grey Plover	BA	Bar-tailed Godwit		
Table Entries	N	National Importance	I	International Importance	

Table 1b: Wader species (for which thresholds have been set) based on WeBS data for 2000/01-2003/04

The wetlands of Essex

All major Essex wetland sites and several smaller ones are routinely counted under the WeBS scheme. Below are presented details of each of those sites, and where appropriate a few examples of the conservation cases that have benefited from the availability of WeBS data. The details refer primarily to the past 25 years - for an earlier period (1969-75), Blindell (1977) and Prater (1972, 1981) present comprehensive summaries.

The important wetlands of Essex can be viewed in many ways. At one extreme, they can be seen as individual sites, some exceptionally important, others less so. Table 1 presents the basic information about the individual sites. Clearly, they fall into two groups - coastal and inland. Or do they? It is well known that birds using the major reservoirs also fly to the estuaries for certain of their needs - witness the regular flights of Cormorants from Abberton to feed on the Blackwater Estuary, or movements south from Hanningfield to the inner Thames. It would not be impossible to construct a case for all Essex wetlands to be treated as a unit ecologically. But the linkages are certainly the strongest between estuaries. As I write this in Dovercourt, I can look up and see vast flocks of Knots passing overhead from feeding areas on the Stour to high water roosts by Hamford Water. Similar movements take place the length and breadth of the Essex coast (Glover 1979).

To really assert the position of the Essex coast as a wetland of outstanding international importance for waterbirds, we should treat it as a whole, along with adjacent Suffolk and Kent estuaries. We have a concept of the Greater Thames, which encompasses the area from Harwich to the Thanet Coast. And in ecological terms, there would be a strong case to add in the south Suffolk estuaries (Stour, Orwell and Deben) to complete the picture. Imagine the site: all the estuaries on Table 1, plus Abberton (in view of its very close proximity to the coast), plus the Orwell, Deben, Medway and Swale Estuaries. It is not valid to simply add up the site totals, but at a conservative estimate this Greatest Thames Estuary must support in excess of 600,000 wintering waterbirds (excluding gulls)! Truly one of Europe's premier wetlands.

A similar cumulative approach can be taken with the inland sites. The Lea Valley GPs complex, together with Walthamstow, KGV and Girling are all within one river valley system; these too are believed to have significant interchange of birds with other wetland systems in and around the capital, especially the Thames, west of London, and the Hertfordshire Colne. The linkage and movements between these water bodies is

Site Name	RH	LG	GG	CA	CO
Thames		N		N	
Blackwater		N		N	
Hamford Water		N			
Stour			N	N	
Dengie	N			N	
Colne				N	
Abberton			N	N	N
Crouch/Roach		N			
Hanningfield				N	N
Lea Valley		N	N	N	N
Met SX		N			N

Standard species codes:				
	RH	Red-throated Diver	CA	Cormorant
	LG	Little Grebe	CO	Coot
	GG	Great Crested Grebe		
Table Entries	N	National Importance		

Table 1c: Other waterfowl species for which thresholds have been set based on data for 2002/01-2003/04 and excluding gulls

currently the subject of a research review, the London Waterfowl Strategy, which is likely to affirm the position of the peri-London waters as an inland waterbird site of considerable eminence in an international context.

Site Name	ET	H	JE	CG	MN	GY	RY	WA	MH	JS	WK	WM	DR	GK	GE	OD	CS	MU	LU	YM	CN	AF	BJ	KF
Thames	X	X	X			X	X		X	X				X	X		X	X	X	X	X			X
Blackwater	X						X				X	X	X	X	X							X		X
Hamford Water														X								X		X
Stour	X			X					X															
Colne	X														X									
Abberton			X	X					X							X								
Crouch/Roach	X													X										
Hanningfield		X				X																	X	
Lea Valley		X		X		X	X	X											X					X

Standard species codes:

ET	Little Egret	MH	Moorhen	CS	Common Sandpiper
H	Grey Heron	JS	Jack Snipe	MU	Mediterranean Gull
JE	Greylag Goose (naturalised)	WK	Woodcock	LU	Little Gull
CG	Canada Goose	WM	Whimbrel	YM	Yellow-legged Gull
MN	Mandarin	DR	Spotted Redshank	CN	Common Tern
GY	Garganey	GK	Greenshank	AF	Little Tern
RY	Ruddy Duck	GE	Green Sandpiper	BJ	Black Tern
WA	Water Rail	OD	Wood Sandpiper	KF	Kingfisher

Table Entries   X   Occurs in significant numbers

Table 1d: Waterfowl species for which no thresholds have been set, including scarce species for which insufficient data exist to set a national threshold, and introduced species

The bigger picture may be impressive, but of course it is the more local level to which most of us as counters relate. The following sections will focus at this level, but it is important always to be aware of the wider context.

Essex coastal habitats

Each estuary is individual. It has its own character and wildlife. However, it is possible to identify a range of typical estuarine features and generic threats on the Essex coast, which are detailed below to avoid repetition later. An estuary is a mosaic of habitats, each element of which supports key wildlife features (Gibson 2003). Working landward, these habitats include:

Subtidal channels

Permanently filled with water, the channels are the most marine element of an estuary. The salinity of the water fluctuates with the tidal cycle - more-or-less fully saline at high tide, but less so at low water, especially in those (rather few) estuaries which have a significant fluvial freshwater input. Animal life consists of those species (e.g. some shellfish and worms) that can tolerate the varying salinity, and the more mobile invertebrates and fish that move in when conditions are suitable. Such creatures are food for waterbirds, although in deeper waters they are accessible only to diving birds, including Cormorants, grebes and some ducks. More importantly, perhaps, the subtidal areas act as nursery grounds for the invertebrates, which populate the intertidal flats. Plant life is restricted in the channels to a few seaweeds (largely green species) and, locally, eelgrass; both are important food resources for grazing wildfowl, but their distribution is limited to shallow waters in Essex as the muddy (turbid) water restricts light penetration to a few tens of centimetres.

Intertidal flats

The most extensive habitats within most estuaries are the mud and sand flats, covered by twice-daily tides. Each tide brings in a supply of nutrients, which underpins an incredibly high rate of biological productivity. Worms, snails and other invertebrates constitute a massive food resource, which together with the relatively frost-free climate, is the reason why the Essex coast is of such importance to waterbirds. The invertebrate life again has to withstand a fluctuating environment, with alternate inundation by seawater and exposure to the air; many species retreat into burrows at low tide, hence the preponderance of probing waders and filter-feeding wildfowl in this habitat. As in the shallow subtidal channels, green algae and eelgrass complete the range of foods, which support estuarine bird populations.

A key determinant of the precise nature of the animal communities is the nature of the sediment. Typically, more sheltered intertidal areas have muddier sediments, while more exposed flats have sandier sediments; this affects the range of invertebrate life, and hence the distribution of birds. Outer-estuarine sand flats are characterised by Bar-tailed Godwits, Knots and Sanderlings, whereas inner-estuarine muds more typically support Black-tailed Godwits, Redshanks and Dunlins; however, there is considerable overlap between these groups.

Saltmarshes

Tides bring not only nutrients into an estuary, but also sediment. In suitably sheltered positions, the sediment load is deposited, causing the flats to grow vertically, until the point where a range of higher plants can colonise. Thus are formed our saltmarshes, a habitat for which Essex is of particular importance. Our estuaries support more saltmarsh than any other British county, more than 10% of the national resource.

It is actually an oversimplification to treat saltmarshes as a single habitat: it is more a series of interrelated habitats, each occupying a particular position on the shore gradient. All saltmarsh is washed by saline water at some time: the lower marshes by every tide, but the upper marshes by only the highest tides of the year. Annual plants such as glassworts, succulent species that are grazed by wildfowl and produce abundant seeds, which are an especially important autumn food resource for Teal, dominate the lower marshes. The higher marshes may be of great importance as high-tide roosts for waders, breeding sites for Redshank and Black-headed Gulls, and the source of seeds, which sustain wintering flocks of passerines, most notably Twite.

Sand dunes, shingle and shell banks

More minor in extent, but no less important, are the localised deposits of sand, shell and shingle. Blown or thrown by storms into banks, they constitute a series of skeletal, stressed habitats, characterised by a diverse range of scarce plants and invertebrates. From the bird perspective, they are of key importance for ground-nesting species, such as Ringed Plover, Oystercatcher and Little Tern, and provide safe high-water refuges for roosting waders.

| | Area (hectares) | | | Area lost and percentage | | | |
| | 1973 | 1988 | 1997/98 | 1973-1997/98 | | 1988-1997/98 | |
				Ha	%	Ha	%
Stour	264	148	107	157	59	41	28
Hamford Water	876	765	621	255	29	144	19
Colne	792	744	695	97	12	49	7
Blackwater	880	739	684	196	22	55	7
Dengie	474	437	410	64	14	27	6
Crouch	467	347	308	159	34	39	11
Thames (Essex)	366	197	181	185	51	16	8
TOTAL	4119	3377	3006	1113	27	371	11

Table 2: Saltmarsh losses 1973-1997/98
The extent in hectares of saltmarshes in 1973 compared with that in 1988 (Burd 1992) and 1997/98 (Cooper *et al.* 2000), taken from aerial photographs and including small areas lost to land claim in addition to erosion

Seawalls and borrow dykes

Since at least early medieval times, and possibly as far back as the Romans, humans have set about modifying the Essex coast to make it less susceptible to sea flooding. In particular, seawalls have been built, amounting to some 500km in length, initially to facilitate the use of low-lying coastal land for grazing. This undoubtedly resulted in massive losses to the wildlife of the Essex coast, but in retrospect, it has left us with a series of habitats which are now of considerable significance.

Even the seawall itself is important, at least for rare and scarce plants and insects; likewise, the borrow dyke, the ditch created by the excavation of clay to construct the wall. The water in the borrow dyke is brackish, a mixture of freshwater draining off the land, and saltwater seeping through the wall. It supports a unique range of plants and lagoon invertebrates, and substantial breeding populations of the smaller reed bed birds and wildfowl. For wintering waterfowl, the majority of coastal Moorhens, Coots, Tufted Ducks and Little Grebes are to be found in the borrow dykes.

Grazing marsh

The former saltmarsh, which was removed from tidal influence by the rapid construction of a seawall, reverted to coastal grazing marsh, traditionally grazed by cattle in the summer and sheep throughout the year. Those areas that have remained in this state are of considerable wildlife value for plants, insects and birds. Wildfowl (e.g. Shelducks, Pochards and Shovelers) and waders (e.g. Redshanks, Lapwings and Avocets) breed in grazing marsh; in winter, grazing marshes are the haunt of raptors, such as Hen Harriers and Short-eared Owls. Also in winter, wildfowl, especially Brent Geese and Wigeons, graze the sward where the surface of the marsh is not too uneven.

Arable land

Sadly, much of the former grazing marsh has now been drained, levelled and ploughed for arable cultivation. But some birds are nothing if not adaptable: coastal arable fields have become important as high-tide wader roosts, and autumn-sown cereals and Oil-seed Rape are some of the key food resources, especially from December onwards, for Brent Geese—the epitome of our winter coastline. Although it is generally assumed that goose grazing and farming interests are in direct conflict, recent indications are that this might not always be the case. At least one Essex farmer believes that goose grazing benefits his autumn-sown Linseed: grazed, it grows several stems where otherwise there would be one, each shorter and easier to harvest and together producing a greater yield than ungrazed (J. Threadgold pers. comm.).

Threats to the Essex coast

Situated as we are in the densely populated southeast, it will come as no surprise that all of these coastal habitats are under threat. A selection of the major concerns (and some solutions) is given below: for more details see for example Gibson (2003), Davidson *et al.* (1991) and Doody *et al.* (1993).

Land claim

Nationally, one of the greatest threats to estuarine wildlife and habitats is land claim. This is what its proponents usually refer to as reclamation: to reclaim implies to take land back from the sea. This is not the case: most land claim involves taking it from the sea for the first time; the use of the term reclamation is an attempt to give a veneer of respectability to what is always a disastrous activity in ecological terms. All our estuaries have suffered from historical land claim—witness the long stretches of seawall—but nowadays, examples of active land claim are thankfully rather few.

Agricultural, urban and industrial development

Following land claim, whether historical or recent, land use changes compound the impacts upon wildlife. Throughout Essex, some 65% of grazing marsh has been lost over the past 100 years, most of it converted to arable cultivation. This practice of agricultural intensification has now largely ceased—the prime areas for conversion have already been done, and there are now significant incentives through the designation of the Essex Coast Environmentally Sensitive Area for landowners to maintain or revert to traditional marshland management practices. However, this is practical only if stock are available: the recent crises in farming have led to a shortfall in supply of suitable grazing stock.

Remote marshes are also, by their very nature, seen as an ideal place to locate 'undesirable' industry, such as oil refineries and power stations—they are after all not in anybody's back yard. Consequently, significant areas of coastal habitat have disappeared under this sort of development, and on Thames-side the rate of grazing marsh loss is thus elevated to around 80%.

One subset of industrial development, ports and related industries, must of course be located by the sea: the expansion of the major ports, especially at Harwich and on the Thames, have required significant land claim. Furthermore, ongoing maintenance and improvement of those ports requires intervention in coastal processes. In particular, channel dredging may be required, leading to continued impacts on sediment supply, and so on habitats, invertebrates and birds.

The Essex Coast also has large urban developments, some of which are located on low-lying, former estuarine land (e.g. Canvey and Jaywick). Given the flooding risks associated with these areas, there is now fortunately considerable resistance to further expansion of built-up areas in such places, but what is already there provides considerable headaches in respect of sea defence.

Sea defence

For centuries, the people of Essex have fought a hard battle against encroachment by the sea. On occasions, the most recent being the Great Flood of 1953, the sea has won spectacularly, with tragic effect. Sea defence works represent human attempts to conquer this threat, although really it is only delaying the inevitable. On the more vulnerable stretches of the coast, the 'traditional' response to a sea defence issue has been to throw concrete at it—but this simply exacerbates the problem. Waves bouncing off hard walls lead to a double dose of foreshore erosion.

Since the 1980s though, there has been an increasing trend, promoted by English Nature, towards using nature's own sea defences—working with nature rather than against it is not only more environmentally sustainable, but also, generally, economically advantageous. It can also be equally, if not more, effective. 'Hard' sea defences—the engineer's solution—interrupt the natural dynamism of the coastline; replacing or supplementing them with 'soft' defences—sand, gravel and saltmarsh—works with that dynamism.

Sea level rise

Currently, much attention is being paid to sea defence, in all its guises, because the Essex coast is experiencing high rates of sea level rise. This has two components: globally, sea levels are rising at some 30cm per century, thermal expansion of the water as the world warms up due to climate change. On top of this, Essex is sinking, the result of a tilting of the British Isles following the retreat of the last Ice Age. The rate of settlement is also around 30cm a century, so in Essex the rate of sea level rise relative to the land is about 60cm per century, or 6mm every year. This means that sea defences, both natural and artificial, are under ever-increasing wave attack. Moreover, it means that intertidal habitats which are of key importance to waterbirds are being squeezed year on year, between rising seas and a largely inflexible sea defence line.

Undoubtedly mudflats are losing out, but the most obvious manifestation of coastal squeeze is a high rate of erosion of our saltmarshes. Reports from the former Nature Conservancy Council (Burd 1992) and the Environment Agency (Cooper *et al.* 2000) demonstrate this alarmingly (Table 2). The message is clear: fundamental changes to our saltmarsh resource can take place within as little as 25 years: the net loss of saltmarsh in Essex amounts to some 40ha every year. This information helped drive English Nature's Campaign for a Living Coast, which in turn encouraged a rethink of policy and practice, such that consideration of sustainable solutions is now part of each and every coastal defence project nationally.

In respect of the eroding marshes, the only real sustainable solution is to allow nature to do as it would naturally—to breach sea defences and allow saltmarshes to reform up the slope. This approach, termed managed realignment, is contentious, but necessary if our estuaries are to be maintained in favourable condition for the birds and other wildlife. A few, largely experimental, areas have already been treated in this way (e.g. at Northey Island, Tollesbury and Abbotts Hall), and it is likely to become a much more frequent feature of the Essex coast as pressures grow to achieve environmental sustainability and reduce the escalating costs of sea defence.

One thing we are not likely to see in the future, thankfully, is a repeat of the ideas that originated in the 1980s of using domestic refuse to bolster the sea defences. This tried to kill two birds with one stone (too much rubbish to get rid of and deteriorating sea defences); unfortunately, it runs the risk of killing rather more birds than that. When the sea breaks through, as it almost inevitably will, the pollution of the adjacent intertidal land could have serious consequences; to try and prevent this from happening places an extreme practical and financial burden on future coastal managers, and restricts the options for working with natural coastal dynamism.

Pollution

Rivers and estuaries have long been seen as waste disposal units, the thinking being that the sea will dilute harmful pollutants to an acceptable level. With changes in the amounts and types of pollutants, however, that is not now (if it ever was) the case, and legislation (especially from the EU) is requiring the cleaning up of deliberate discharges.

Somewhat contentious though is the requirement to clean up sewage discharges: from a human health point of view this is certainly desirable, but it is well known that estuaries thrive on organic inputs. Cockles grow fat on sewage, and to remove that source of nutrient input could be argued as leading to a reduction in the carrying capacity of an estuary for waterbirds.

Other pollutants include, or at least have included until recently, tributyl tin (TBT) used as an antifouling agent on boats; it is incredibly toxic to invertebrate life, and its ban and replacement by supposedly less-toxic alternatives is to be welcomed. There still remains, though, the ever-present threat of oil spillage, and the chronic input of fertilisers and other agrochemicals that may be having impacts on the estuaries at sub-lethal concentrations.

Disturbance

There are numerous activities, which can and do cause disturbance in estuaries, from dog walking and birdwatching, to wildfowling, water sports, low-flying aircraft and military uses. Disturbance may be either direct or indirect. Direct disturbance of birds is a complex issue (see, for example, Davidson & Rothwell 1993) as it is influenced by a range of factors, including the nature of the disturbance, its duration, timing and extent, the topography of the estuary, the availability of refuges from disturbance and the species of birds affected.

And its actual impact on birds is equally contentious, although it is reasonable to assume that any activity, which reduces feeding time or efficiency or increases energy expenditure, is likely to have some effect. Birds are most vulnerable at times of their greatest energy requirement—on migration or during severe weather conditions.

Indirect disturbance occurs when the activity reduces the availability of resources, for example through erosion of marshes. Of key concern is disturbance to mudflat sediments: as a legacy of past pollution, mud often contains trapped pollutants such as heavy metals which become biologically active only when liberated through sediment disturbance. An important difference between direct and indirect disturbance is that direct disturbance can occur only when the activity is temporally coincident with the presence of birds; indirect disturbance may have effects separated in time and space from the cause.

There are statutory means through which some disturbing activities may be controlled (for example, hard-weather suspensions of wildfowling), and it may be that additional statutory provisions will be needed to extend this to all such activities—even birdwatching! But the most effective way is to get all users talking and agreeing on acceptable partitioning of the estuary's resources (perhaps through zonation, whether spatial or temporal). This is the aim of Estuary Management Plans: to achieve a balance with an underlying principle of sustainable use and development. Estuary-wide plans have now been drawn up for most Essex estuaries and, crucially, several are now being actively implemented.

Unsustainable exploitation

People have since time immemorial exploited the abundant resources of estuaries. Fish, shellfish, crustaceans, wild-fowl and samphire have been, and still are, taken directly for food, while Lugworms and other invertebrates are used as fishing bait. Ensuring that exploitation of such resources is sustainable – such that wise use today does not limit the ability to use the same resource in the future – is a key aim of Estuary Management Plans. Less tangibly, perhaps, solitude or wilderness is another resource which must be looked after in the same way.

Another resource of critical importance in the southeast, the driest and increasingly drought-prone part of the country, is the freshwater that flows into our estuaries. There is increasing pressure for agricultural abstraction of that water before it is 'lost' to the sea. However, any birdwatcher knows that one of the best places to see birds on an estuary is around a freshwater inflow – it is used for both drinking and bathing. In the mid-1990s, agricultural demands on this water reached such a peak that the Environment Agency commissioned a study to ascertain the wildlife importance of freshwater inflows into estuaries (Ravenscroft & Beardall 2003). As we might expect, the study indicated that densities of many waterfowl species are significantly higher around freshwater inflows than on open mudflats; as a result, an embargo was placed upon the issue of further abstraction licences from near-estuarine watercourses.

However, what is not yet clear is exactly why these areas are so important – it could be due simply to the presence of freshwater; it may be that spring water emerging at a constant 8°C helps keep the mudflats ice-free during freezing weather; or perhaps the birds are taking advantage of the creek topography to roost in relative shelter. Such questions need answering before a comprehensive strategy for sustainable freshwater use can be devised.

Vegetation change

Most of the above-mentioned issues and threats relate to human impacts on the coast. There are also a number of more natural threats to estuaries and their bird life, exemplified by the dieback of eelgrass in the 1930s. This was due to a wasting disease, which decimated the eelgrass stocks, and brought the birds which fed upon it (notably Brent Geese) to the brink of extinction. There were also other impacts, perhaps less immediately apparent: eelgrass dieback in the Stour is known to have coincided with a rapid and dramatic erosion of the foreshore mud, and presumably changes to the invertebrate, and hence bird, populations. A stable or accreting estuary was flipped into an unstable configuration through the loss of the binding vegetation layer; the situation persists to this day, with strong ebb tides carrying away more sediment than the weaker flood tide deposits.

The other major vegetation change relates to Common Cord-grass, a fertile hybrid between the native Small Cord-grass and the introduced Smooth Cord-grass, which did not exist before the end of the 19th century. This vigorous hybrid is capable of invading natural saltmarsh and also downshore onto the upper mudflats. Here it impinges on the important pre-roost feeding areas for waders, and has been implicated in nationwide declines in Dunlin numbers reported until recent years. Furthermore, in many places Common Cord-grass is now in a state of dieback, for unknown reasons, but this, as with eelgrass, is likely to further destabilise estuarine systems, which are already suffering as a result of sea level rise.

Essex coastal sites in detail

Stour Estuary

The Stour Estuary, forming the boundary between Essex and Suffolk, is a long, linear estuary with predominantly natural banks formed by rising ground: that is, unlike most other Essex estuaries, it is a drowned river valley, rather than a coastal plain estuary. Its current linear configuration is not natural, however. Historically, it was much more typically digitate in form, with fingers of estuary radiating from its mouth; all these have now been cut off by sea-walls, the last being in the mid-19th century when Ray Creek was blocked by linking the 'island' of Parkeston to the mainland when the railway arrived.

By virtue of its topography, the Stour exhibits little in the way of grazing marsh. The only significant area is Cattawade Marshes (now an RSPB reserve), inland of the A137 Manningtree to Ipswich road. Much of the tidal influence on this former saltmarsh was lost when a surge barrage was constructed just downstream of the road. Further inland still, this grassland-dominated valley becomes the Dedham Vale; and above Judas Gap, the River Stour is entirely non-tidal. A significant feature of the shore of the estuary is its transition to woodland in a few places, notably Copperas Wood. This transition is unique in Essex and supports a range of important plant species, such as Marsh Mallow at its only Essex site.

Much of the Stour Estuary is essentially rural, with development concentrated at its head—at Manningtree, Mistley, with its small port, and Brantham—and mouth, Harwich Haven. The latter is the common mouth of the Stour and Orwell and hosts the major ports of Felixstowe and Harwich International (Parkeston Quay). Between Harwich International Port and Harwich town lies Bathside Bay, currently the subject of a proposal to construct a major container port. This development would result in the total loss of some 70ha of feeding habitat.

Of particular concern in the Stour Estuary is the loss of saltmarsh to erosion: Table 2 indicates that the situation here is worse than any of the other estuaries studied. It is likely that this is a phenomenon related to the increasing sandiness of the outer estuary, increased wave and/or tidal energy leading to both marsh erosion and winnowing out of finer sediments. Why should the Stour have suffered more than elsewhere? Undoubtedly there are lots of factors, but it is not unreasonable to suggest that dredging activity to service the ports, more intensive in the Stour than any of the other estuaries, is one cause.

WeBS Core Counts have taken place on the Stour, including much of the surrounding farmland, since the mid-1960s, although solid data exist only since 1972. Currently, a count team of 18 operates from August to April inclusive, counting the site in ten sections. At high water, waders are concentrated into a large number of roosts, typically four on saltmarsh, two on shingle banks and 6–10 on adjacent arable land. In addition, there are considerable wildfowl loafing areas in Seafield, Holbrook, Jacques and Copperas (Deep Fleet) Bays. In view of the relatively narrow nature of the estuary, and the ease with which all the main roosts can be viewed, it is considered that the site is adequately covered by WeBS Core Counts. Some interchange of birds occurs with both the Orwell Estuary and Hamford Water; this can be very significant on occasions when flocks of roosting birds, such as on the gravel embankment at the eastern end of Copperas Bay, are disturbed, especially on very high tides.

Typical mean peak count totals lie in the range of 35,000 to 50,000 (excluding gulls). In common with most other estuaries in the southeast, bird numbers were increasing until recently, despite the numerous pressures upon the site. However, the most recent signs have been less optimistic: 7 of the 8 species for which the Stour (together with the Orwell) is designated as a Special Protection Area (SPA) are now the subject of alerts in view of their decline over a range of timescales.

Black-tailed Godwit is an especially important species on the Stour, recent mean peaks representing between 2% and 3% of the biogeographic population. Five-year mean winter peaks increased from 642 (1970/71–1974/75) to 2166 (1995/96–1999/00), perhaps as a result of climatic amelioration on their Icelandic breeding grounds (Cranswick *et al.* 1999), although they have dropped back a little recently (2,008 in 2000/01–2004/05). There are other indications that all may not be well—the feeding distribution within the estuary is undergoing a marked change. From the 1990s, Black-tailed Godwits progressively declined in the outer bays of the Stour, such that the greatest concentrations are now to be found towards the head of the estuary. It is believed that this trend may be related to changes in sediment size distribution, with sloppy silts being eroded from the outer estuary. Several factors may have combined to this effect, notably sea level rise, historical eelgrass dieback and dredging.

Two other species also deserve a special mention. Mute Swans, concentrated at the Mistley dock and maltings, ranked amongst the nationally important species until the late 1980s. Herds of several hundred were found regularly, especially around the discharge points for maltings waste, until new pollution controls were installed. Once the food supply ceased, the flock declined and those that remained started to lose condition: a remnant group now subsists largely on bread and other food provided by local people. Over a similar time period, numbers of Canada Geese have risen dramatically: the 2000/01–2004/05 mean peak was some 772 birds. Although they are counted as part of the WeBS scheme, as a non-native species they do not contribute to the overall figures of estuarine importance. Most Canada Geese are to be found around the head of the estuary and Cattawade Marshes, where there is a substantial breeding population, with birds also commuting to Alton Water, Suffolk, and especially sugar beet fields in that vicinity. Increases in this species are taking place throughout Britain, although in many places the increase is subject to some check through egg pricking and the culling of adults. There has been little in the way of a coordinated attempt to control the size of the Stour group, especially as reports of agricultural damage from their grazing activities are infrequent; hence, the increase goes on.

WeBS counts, both Core and Low Tide, have proved of immense value in addressing the issues relating to dredging of the estuary. Given the long-term concerns about the instability of the Stour Estuary, it is not surprising that when, in 1997, the Harwich Haven Authority (HHA) lodged an application to further deepen the approach channel, involving the removal of some 18 million cubic metres of sea bed, all the conservation bodies became closely involved in the development of the project.

Commendably, HHA took full account of their environmental responsibilities. They investigated in detail the likely impacts of the scheme, and proposed a series of measures to counter the adverse effects. The main ecological impacts were identified as a loss of intertidal land as a result of small changes to the tidal range of the estuary, and accelerated erosion of the intertidal area as a result of an increased maintenance-dredging requirement. Measures to offset these impacts included:

- the creation of a new area (Trimley, adjacent to the Orwell Estuary) of intertidal habitat to replace immediate losses;
- the development of an innovative scheme of sediment recycling, returning maintenance dredgings of silt to the estuaries rather than disposal in offshore dumping grounds;
- use of much of the capital dredgings beneficially, including in sustainable sea defences; and
- implementation of a comprehensive monitoring programme.

After complex negotiations between all parties over many months, the scheme was finally given approval in October 1998, with capital dredging continuing to spring 2000.

Novel techniques such as the targeted return of dredged sediment to the estuary are of particular interest, and potentially the experiences here will lead to an enhanced ability to manage working estuaries in a sustainable way. Prior to the most recent scheme, large amounts of dredged sand and gravel had been reintroduced into the Stour, primarily for sea defence purposes as in the construction of the defensive bank west of Parkeston. This has had knock-on benefits, including the provision of breeding sites for Little Terns and other ground nesters. Equally importantly, this bank has been adopted as a secure high tide wader roost. Following the 1999 dredge, the recycling of finer material (silt) has commenced, both by direct channel placement and by allowing overspill from the dredging process. The intention is to try and counteract the additional erosion attributable to the dredge. And it is likely that continued innovation will take place: there are plans to place silt directly onto the now badly-eroded Deep Fleet saltings, with a view to sustaining and restoring this area as one of the key wader roosts in the estuary. Although this is seen as novel work, the idea is certainly not new: such proposals were amongst the key recommendations to come out of the Maplin study (Boorman & Ranwell 1977), in relation to the thankfully aborted airport proposal.

The role of WeBS data in a case such as this cannot be over-estimated. It was this information which led to the classification of the Stour & Orwell Estuaries as an SPA in the first place: without this designation and the force of European law, there would have been many fewer requirements for investigation, mitigation and monitoring upon HHA. It was one of the key sets of data which resulted in the acceptance by HHA that the identified impacts on habitats were significant in terms of the birds using the estuary. Also commissioned Low Tide Counts are being used to monitor the (hopefully) lack of impacts of the dredge and success of mitigation.

One outcome of the involvement of HHA in the Stour Estuary, and the development of the ports through dredging and land claim, is that the Stour is now one of the best studied of any estuary systems in Britain, if not the world. As well as work commissioned by HHA, the RSPB have carried out important research, for example the characterisation of mudflats using satellite imagery. Also, Dr Jenny Gill of the University of East Anglia has undertaken a considerable programme of research on Black-tailed Godwits, and Professor Chris Mason from the University of Essex has carried out research into, amongst other things, the effects of sub-lethal concentrations of environmental contaminants upon saltmarsh stability. There is hardly an element of its ecology, morphology and coastal processes that has not been measured, monitored and modelled, and a synthesis of all these investigations should provide a robust background for future estuary management and sustainable development.

These examples are just a summary of the many activities affecting the Stour. It is a very active site, and one with a clear need for the coordination provided by an Estuary Management Plan, in this case a joint plan with the Orwell Estuary, implemented under the watchful eyes of the Suffolk Coast and Heaths Project. As part of that implementation, studies have been carried out into, for example, moorings provision and use, bait digging, wildfowling and other disturbance.

Hamford Water

Although usually treated as such, Hamford Water—between Dovercourt and Walton-on-the-Naze, and often referred to as the Walton Backwaters—is not actually an estuary. That is, it has no river running into it and freshwater input is entirely from relatively minor sources. The reason it is there at all stems from its geology: the underlying rock, London Clay, is formed into a shallow depression which, as sea levels have risen since the last Ice Age, has become filled with marine sediments. The result is an embayment, filled with an estuary-like complex of mudflats and saltmarshes, with fringing, protective beaches of sand and gravel on their outer edges. The geology is readily visible to the south at The Naze, where London Clay forms the basal deposits of the eroding cliff, overlain by more recent, fossil-rich Red Crag.

For many people, Hamford Water is the most unspoilt part of the Essex coast—our nearest thing to wilderness. The major modern intrusions are Titchmarsh Marina at Walton, and intensive agriculture, which has resulted in the conversion of most former grazing marshes to arable (the most significant exception being on the private Horsey Island). On the northern shore, Bramble Island (actually not an island, but equally inaccessible for security reasons) holds a chemical works (formerly an explosives factory); whilst such a development poses pollution risks, it does leave an extensive area of rough grassland and reed bed free from disturbance. It is thus of major importance to raptors and owls and supports an important population of Fisher's Estuarine Moth (almost unique in Britain to the Walton Backwaters) and its food-plant, Hog's Fennel.

Hamford Water demonstrates clearly the dynamic nature of coastal sites over historical times. While there are numerous examples of land claim for agriculture, which remain to this day, there are also large areas that were claimed in the past but where the walls have been breached and the sea has reclaimed the land. Garnham's Island is a good example, the old seawalls still projecting above the surrounding saltmarshes and creeks, and providing a largely supra-tidal breeding refuge for Black-headed Gulls.

WeBS Core Counts have taken place in Hamford Water every year since 1950, from September to March. Unlike at many other sites August is not counted; while this may miss some significant autumn passage, recreational pressures, especially from sailing and general beach users, would make it impractical. A team of 13, including some who count from the warden's boat, count eight sections—this is the only practical way of counting the remote areas in the interior of the site. Even so, it is believed that duck are under-counted, as they are apt to hide away in the complex maze of creeks and pools in the vast areas of salt marsh. Optional species such as gulls are included in the counts.

The roosts are largely on sand and shingle banks, both natural and man-made, in the outer estuary and saltmarsh further into the site. There are also two roosts on grazing marsh and, on exceptionally high tides only, two on arable land. The movement of birds between estuaries is also apparent on the highest tides with, sometimes, large numbers of waders moving from the Stour to the beach roosts in the northern part of Hamford Water.

Total mean peak counts rose from around 30,000 in the early 1980s to 60,000 in the mid-1990s, although the count organiser feels that a significant part of that was due to an improved level of coverage of the site. There have, however, been some changes in species numbers and proportions. To take Dark-bellied Brent Goose as an example, numbers have fluctuated, although as a proportion of the total count, they have fallen from 25% to under 10% over 20 years. This must be seen in the context of progressively rising numbers nationwide until the late 1980s, followed by indications of a tailing off towards the current world total of around 250,000 birds. At Hamford Water, the suspicion must be that the declining proportion is due to more of other species being counted—as an obvious, flocking species, it would seem likely that Brent Goose numbers have always been counted fully, and so with improved count coverage, few if any 'new' Brents were counted. However, local counters have reported a decline in the number that remain in the area over the winter; this is attributed to the repeated harassment by farmers protecting their autumn-sown crops.

In common with most other sites, Grey Plovers have shown a strong and largely sustained increase (five-year peak mean rising from 729 to 2,665 between 1970 and 2004), presumably reflecting a global population increase. Likewise, Avocets and Black-tailed Godwits have both increased from very low levels in the 1980s, although latterly the increases seem to have slowed, stopped or even, in the case of godwits, reversed. For both species, this may be a result of population redistribution within Essex. As numbers have stabilised or fallen at Hamford Water, so new or increased wintering groups have become established on estuaries to the south. Avocets, which from the early-1980s were a renowned winter feature of Hamford Water (almost exclusively so in the Essex context), especially to the south of Horsey Island, are now an increasing winter feature of the Colne and Thames in particular. A wonderful legacy of their colonisation, however, has been the establishment of a small but increasing breeding population in suitable areas around Hamford Water.

An important species to watch is Teal. Although there is no clear evidence of decline as yet, counters suggest that it may be coming under pressure as a result of the apparent smothering of some of the beds of Samphire by Common Cord-grass. In certain areas, the spread of *Spartina* into the muddy basins occupied by Samphire has almost eradicated the preferred food for Teals during the autumn: *Salicornia* seeds.

One species that has occasionally appeared in the nationally important list for Hamford Water is Sanderling. It is the characteristic wader of open coast and sandy shores, such as are found along much of the sea frontage of the site: at West End Beach, Middle Beach, Irlam's Beach, Pewit Island and Stone Point. They are not, however, well sampled by WeBS Core Counts, being typically widely dispersed on all manner of open sandy coastlines, including the traditional seaside beaches at Dovercourt and Walton.

Low Tide Counts have been undertaken over two winters—1992/93 and 1997/98—although the area covered has been limited only to the major accessible mud- and sandflats, just 13% of the site area. As a result, few conclusions can be drawn from these partial data. It is fortunate, therefore, that at least in development control terms, there has been little need for detailed site usage information. The importance of the site is fully appreciated and valued by local people and planners alike, giving considerable assurance about its future protection. Furthermore, Tendring District Council employs a warden, equipped with boat, with contributions to the costs coming from a wide range of interested parties. One of the key roles of the warden is to control disturbance, especially during the summer months, by for example, ensuring the speed limit byelaws are adhered to. Unfortunately, though, some repeated sources of disturbance, including overflying by light aircraft and military helicopter training, are outside his control.

The relationship between wildfowling and conservation is often assumed to be at best uneasy. However, the aims of both interest groups are not dissimilar, and in Essex the interaction can be fruitful. This is especially the case in Hamford Water, where the three wildfowling clubs work closely with the 'official' conservationists in many ways. This is a shining example, which conservationists and wildfowlers would do well to emulate in other parts of the country. Wildfowlers constitute an effective wardening presence, both during and outside the shooting season: the Little Terns that breed on Stone Point have benefited from protection schemes organised by the clubs. They organise litter clearance and habitat management events; carry out and organise surveys, including WeBS; attempt to manage the increasing problem of feral geese; and generally keep a watchful eye over the site, which provides their sport. And what is more, they have proved willing to demonstrate their commitment to the site with hard cash. Most notably, the Little Oakley and District Wildfowlers' Association have now purchased a substantial part of the site to ensure its protection. In recognition, most of these areas are now included in the Hamford Water National Nature Reserve, the clubs being classed as 'approved bodies' by English Nature.

Hamford Water differs from all other Essex estuaries in one important way: its shape. It is 'short and fat' rather than 'long and thin', and were it not for the presence of protective sandbanks, beaches and islands, the marshes would long since have been eroded away by the North Sea. It is accepted by the Environment Agency that maintenance of these frontline defences is paramount in protection of the marshes and the surrounding arable land. Hence, considerable investment has been made in bolstering the walls at Foulton Hall and Horsey Island, supplemented by feeding of the beaches and foreshores with sand and gravel. Such 'soft' defences are, it is accepted, going to move and erode. That is how they work: in moving, they are absorbing wave energy. They will have to be topped up periodically, but they are a lot cheaper than concrete walls. And they provide an ecological niche, which concrete does not: Little Terns, Ringed Plovers and Oystercatchers soon move in during the breeding season, and large flocks of waders may roost there in the winter. The year 1999 saw a considerable amount of feeding activity on the beaches of Hamford Water; this was related to the availability of sediment from the Harwich Haven capital dredging programme. Stone Point beach, which over the past few years had been eroded almost to oblivion, was restored in a big way, giving a new lease of life to the saltmarshes behind. It may sound drastic, even unnatural, but it is returning the system to something more like its past, before maintenance dredging of the Haven Ports approach channel robbed Essex of its share of the fruits of coastal erosion in Suffolk.

Colne Estuary

The Colne Estuary forms the northernmost section of the vast continuous expanse of estuarine habitat which extends down to the North Kent coast. The main channel funnels inland to Colchester, and there are numerous side channels (e.g. Roman River, Alresford Creek and Flag Creek) which radiate from it. The largest expanses of intertidal flats are located off Mersea Island, where the relatively exposed conditions ensure they are generally rather sandy in nature. This exposure is also reflected in the sand and gravel beach deposits along the outer reaches of the Colne Estuary, especially at East Mersea and Colne Point. The latter is a particularly magnificent feature, a mobile gravel spit formed by the westward drift of sea-borne sediment. At a length of some 4km, it is small in comparison with, say, Orfordness in Suffolk, but it is large enough to support areas of the internationally rare vegetated shingle habitat, as well as a range of ground-nesting seabirds and specialist invertebrates.

The most extensive saltmarshes are in the southern part of the site, protected by virtue of being owned by the Ministry of Defence which operates a live-firing range at Fingringhoe. The safety zone of the range also encompasses the whole of Langenhoe Marsh, the largest remaining grazing marsh by the Colne (and indeed one of the largest in the county), albeit at present a largely ungrazed grazing marsh. The MoD is very conscious of the key role it plays in maintaining biodiversity, and recent habitat management works at the Fingringhoe Ranges demonstrate they are taking their responsibilities seriously. Most importantly, through the installation of simple water control features, the water levels on the marsh have been raised significantly, benefitting both wintering and breeding waterbirds.

Other significant areas of grazing marsh are found at Howlands Marsh, St Osyth, Brightlingsea Marsh and Cudmore Grove, East Mersea. As with Langenhoe, low water levels have been a great concern at these sites, especially during recent drought summers: at each site, the managers have invested considerably in water management structures to improve the ability of the site to be managed for nature conservation. An especially fruitful relationship has been established at Brightlingsea between English Nature and Alresford Sand and Ballast: water, which has to be pumped from the gravel-workings, is fed, via a silt settlement pond, into the grazing marsh, providing an assured supply even in the summer months.

Sand and gravel operations have a long history on the rising land around the Colne. As pits have become worked out, some have been restored to agriculture (often with landfill as an intermediate stage), but many have reverted to nature, leaving a complex of mostly small pools amid an ever-encroaching blanket of trees and scrub. These sites therefore make relatively little contribution to the overall wetland interest of the Colne Estuary. At one site, Fingringhoe Wick, former gravel-pits are managed specifically for nature conservation. Recent years have seen the completion of major restoration works, part-funded by the Heritage Lottery Fund, which aim to rejuvenate the wetland habitats whilst retaining the diversity of scrub age structure for birds such as Nightingale (Forsyth 2005).

Grazing marsh extends right up the Colne to Colchester, with further large expanses at Wivenhoe and Rowhedge. These marshes have generally received a degree of agricultural improvement, and thus do not support the diversity of more pristine sites. A large area at the Hythe has been enwalled and used for the disposal of river channel dredgings. The silt lagoons formed in this way have been an important wader breeding and feeding site, especially renowned for some of the scarcer species such as Green Sandpiper, Little Ringed Plover and Little Stint. However, the lagoons are now almost full, and anyway there is no further input of silt following the closure of Colchester Port. Unless the lagoons are supported by conservation management efforts, their value for wetland birds may prove to be only a transient feature.

WeBS Core Counts are carried out from September to April inclusive. Around eight counters count the estuary in six sectors; gulls are included. There are two major roosts on saltmarshes, two on sand/shingle banks, and a variable number on other habitats, including arable land, according to disturbance and tidal height. The majority of the estuary is considered to be covered adequately, although it has not always proved possible to organise regular access onto Langenhoe Marsh. It may well be that some count figures represent a significant underestimate for those species, especially ducks, which use the MoD land in large numbers.

In most winters almost 50% the total count is made up of just two species, Lapwing and Dunlin. A slight decline in Dunlin during the 1990s was more than compensated by an apparent increase in Lapwing numbers. However, it has to be stressed that Lapwing numbers are very much dependent upon the severity of winter weather, and so may not be a good indicator of habitat condition; likewise, as a large proportion may remain almost permanently associated with the arable hinterland, variation in numbers may relate to the completeness of survey of agricultural fields.

Three species that typically occupy the estuarine channels, Cormorants, Great Crested Grebes and Goldeneyes, all appear to have declined, albeit from relatively low numbers. This could again perhaps be an artefact of observer coverage. A noted decline in Mute Swans, which goes back to the 1980s, is certainly real, however. As on the Stour Estuary, it is the result of a decline in supplementary food availability, in this case due to a progressive reduction in the shipping of grain, soya and other foodstuffs through the Colne Ports. Herds of Mute Swans are still a feature of the Rowhedge area in particular, though in much smaller numbers: these are largely sustained by deliberate feeding.

One notable increase in recent years has been in Avocet numbers. Whereas until the early 1990s, Avocets were only sporadic visitors to the Colne in very small numbers, often feeding in shallow scrapes such as at Fingringhoe Wick, nowadays a group of several hundred is an annual winter feature, especially on the expansive mudflats around the mouth of Alresford Creek. A similar pattern to that at Hamford Water seems to be taking place: increasing winter flocks as a prelude to the establishment of breeding: in 1999, Avocets bred for the first time within the MoD ranges.

The Colne was included in the Low Tide Count programme for 1994/95. The results again indicate the overwhelming abundance of both Dunlin and Lapwing: the mean density of each during 1994/95 was almost five times higher than for any other species. In fact, the densities of Lapwing (average 12.3 birds per hectare; maximum 118.2 birds/ha; more than 90% of the area supporting the species) were higher than for any of the other nine UK estuaries counted that winter.

With the closure of the Colne ports, one significant concern about the future of the estuary relates to the repackaging of former port areas as hotspots for leisure and recreation, and as ideal sites for waterfront housing development. The Colne Barrier at Wivenhoe may also have an impact in this respect. Although it is a surge barrier, designed to be closed only on the highest tides (and so not affecting the estuarine hydrodynamics for most of the time), it significantly reduces the flood risk upstream, and so low-lying areas of wildlife significance may become vulnerable to development pressures. There are now even suggestions that a barrage may be constructed across the river at the Hythe, so to 'improve' the look of the area by retaining water in the channel permanently or, from another viewpoint, to erase the last vestiges of its maritime heritage, which was so dominated by the tidal cycle. The lessons of Cardiff Bay have clearly not yet been learned.

The Colne is already an important estuary for water-based leisure activities. Ensuring the compatibility of these with each other and with wildlife is a complex task. To some extent, environmental sustainability is achieved through the leisure activities occurring predominantly during the summer, when the wintering birds are not there to be disturbed. Further controls on the potentially more damaging, noisy activities such as jet-skiing and water-skiing have been introduced by restricting them to defined areas, as at Brightlingsea and in Pyefleet Channel, north of Mersea Island. It is by reconciling such potentially competing activities in a non-confrontational way that the Colne Estuary Project is trying to secure the future of the Colne for wildlife and people.

The loss of saltmarsh to erosion is a significant concern in the Colne, as it is with all Essex estuaries, even though at less than 12% loss between 1973 and 1998 the Colne has fared better than most. Part of the problem lies in the reduction in sediment supply through interruption to longshore drift. In order to reach the Colne, sediment eroded from the Suffolk coast must get past the Harwich dredged channel and then run the gauntlet of the numerous groynes from Dovercourt to Clacton. Little wonder then that Colne Point, built by the longshore drift of gravel, is showing signs that all is not well—the beach ridge is narrowing and lowering, and is now breached in places. The only way of addressing this, by bypassing the groyned frontage and feeding the beach at St Osyth, thankfully has now been started as part of a package of Environment Agency sea defence improvements.

Blackwater Estuary

Almost 6,000 hectares in extent, the Blackwater Estuary is second in size in Essex only to the Thames. It forms an integral part of the Mid-Essex Coast SPA, contiguous in the north with the Colne and in the south with Dengie. As well as vast areas of intertidal mud, the estuary contains more than 1,000 hectares of saltmarsh, the largest area in Essex and the fifth largest in Great Britain.

The Blackwater can be considered in two major sections. The northern area, between West Mersea and Tollesbury, is a complex of relatively small channels within large tracts of saltmarsh and even larger areas of grazing marsh, which is protected by considerable lengths of vulnerable seawall. Much of this northern section is under the ownership and management of voluntary conservation bodies, including RSPB at Old Hall Marshes, EWT at Tollesbury Wick and Abbotts Hall, and the National Trust at Ray Island and Copt Hall. Ray Island is noted as one of the very few sites on the Essex coast where the natural transition from saltmarsh to coastal grassland and scrub is not truncated by a seawall. Old Hall Marshes is the largest area of grazing marsh in Essex. The older marshes, covered in millions of anthills, are dissected by a complex of ditches and dykes, which also support a substantial area of reed bed. Further inland, the marshes have been improved (in agricultural terms), i.e. levelled and reseeded. However, they are still of great importance as feeding sites for species such as Golden Plover and Brent Goose. Another feature, especially of Tollesbury Wick, is the abundance of deposited shells. The remains of Cockles, Periwinkles, the alien Slipper Limpet and other shellfish that are so abundant in the intertidal and subtidal areas have been washed into banks, and these have become of key importance for ground-nesting birds, roosting waders and a range of scarce plants and insects.

The southern part of the Blackwater Estuary is wider, more open and consists predominantly of mudflats. Saltmarshes are largely restricted to a narrow band on the upper intertidal, with larger areas associated with some of the smaller creeks and the two islands of Osea and Northey. An important adjunct habitat to the estuary is the non-tidal open water at Heybridge GP; although subject to recreational disturbance, the pits immediately inside the seawall provide habitat for good numbers of dabbling and diving ducks.

Much of the Blackwater is very rural in character, its hinterland typically being devoted to arable cultivation. The main towns are West Mersea at its mouth and Maldon at the head of the estuary, with smaller settlements on the south shore at Maylandsea and St Lawrence and in the north at Tollesbury. All are important holiday destinations, complete with caravan sites, moorings and marinas, and lots of yachts, but the primary recreational season falls outside the time when most wintering birds are present. Maldon, in particular, has a long and venerable maritime history, with wharfage facilities on the waterfront; nowadays, mainly recreational shipping, including the traditional Essex barges and fishing smacks, use these. In full sail down the estuary, these boats provide one of the two characteristic and definitive sights of the Blackwater; the other, of course, is the twin square hulks of Bradwell Nuclear Power Station near the estuary mouth.

Gibbs (1993) gave a fully detailed account of the wildfowl and waders, both wintering and breeding, of the Blackwater Estuary. Two teams of counters operate in the Blackwater Estuary, one on the north shore and one on the south, totalling 22 counters in 12 sections for Core Counts. Almost all months are counted, apart from June and sometimes July; terns are counted, but not gulls. Coverage of the site has improved in recent years, with the addition of Lawling and Mayland Creeks into the count sectors, although Northey Island remains a significant concern: precise timing is necessary to ensure access across the causeway, and many roosting waders on the outer walls are hidden from the counters. However, waterfowl are generally easier, especially on big tides.

The width of the estuary means that long distances are involved, which may lead to undercounting of some roosts; in addition, the north shore team in particular has a problem with glare on sunny days. Counters have also raised concerns that Brent Goose numbers may be undercounted, especially when they are feeding on arable land which is not adjacent to the lengths of seawall walked. The number of wader roosts is variable according to tidal heights and the type of crops grown in the coastal fields; typically, there are around 20 roosts on saltmarsh, four on shell banks, and six on arable land.

In common with most other estuaries, the total number of waterbirds using the Blackwater has increased in recent years: mean peak counts rose from 39,844 in the mid-1980s to 90,716 by the beginning of the 2000s. An increase of this magnitude is not likely to be wholly real—the improvement in count coverage must be partially responsible. Dunlins, Brent Geese and Lapwings are the most significant in number, together totalling some 60% of the birds counted. Dunlin numbers have increased markedly, from a mean peak of 12,513 (1970/71–1974/75) to 21,452 (2000/01–2004/05), although their proportion of the total count stayed almost constant at one-third. This suggests to me that, as Dunlin are widely distributed across the whole site, their apparent increase is more to do with better coverage than an actual increase in number. In contrast, and to some extent counter to the national picture of increase, Brent Geese numbers since the 1980s have been relatively constant at around 7,000–8,000 birds, representing around 3% of the total world population of the dark-bellied race. As the world population has grown, so has the British wintering population. However, core sites such as the Blackwater have not reflected the increase (the implication being perhaps that they are full, at carrying capacity); the growth has been accommodated by exploitation of new sites, especially on the south coast of England.

The deeper water channels within the estuary are important as roosting and loafing sites for waterfowl, especially Shelducks and Brent Geese, and as feeding areas for the more strictly aquatic species, particularly Goldeneyes, Great Crested Grebes and Cormorants. Numbers of such birds may be especially high when inland waters are frozen. Abberton lies only 5km from the Blackwater, and there is regular interchange between the two sites: much of the food for the breeding colony of Cormorants at Abberton is provided by the estuary, where numbers have increased in line with the breeding population. Although not present in nationally important numbers, the Blackwater also supports good numbers of Eiders, Little Grebes and Slavonian Grebes. The most recent five-year mean peak of 12 Slavonian Grebes, usually along the north shore from Tollesbury to Goldhanger, exceeds the 1% criterion but is below the accepted minimum threshold of 50 for national importance.

Low Tide Counts in the Blackwater Estuary present particular problems due to the extent of the mudflats and the number of volunteers needed. Nevertheless, at least partial coverage was achieved on three occasions during the 1990s: 1991/92 for the then National Rivers Authority (complete); 1994/95 for WeBS; and 1997/98 in the northern part of the estuary for the RSPB. As is often the case, there are considerable discrepancies for certain species between Core Counts and Low Tide Counts. Golden Plovers and Lapwings both figure more prominently at low tide; it is suggested (Gibbs 1993) that at high water the surplus is feeding inland, and thus not counted. Usually the birds on the mudflats are simply roosting, although feeding flocks have been noted following heavy overnight frosts which limit food availability inland. It is also suggested (Mason & Macdonald 1999) that estuarine feeding may be an increasing phenomenon, as global warming raises the winter growth rate of cereals, rendering the fields unsuitable for foraging. Dunlins, too, are present in greater numbers at low tide. For example, in 1991/92 the peak Low Tide Count of over 40,260 was in January, and the peak Core Count of 20,900 in February. A likely explanation of this is that high tide roosts are missed, and perhaps large congregations under-counted.

The Blackwater Estuary is a site of considerable recreational activity, both onshore and on the water. The intensity of use grew during the latter part of the 20th century, with the inevitable result that many proposals were lodged to increase the provision of facilities for visitors. Fortunately, Maldon District Council has very strong planning policies, which aim to restrict the spread of such development, both spatially (onto the undeveloped coast) and temporally (into the winter months). But the existence of policies doesn't prevent new proposals coming forward, and WeBS counts have played a key role in defending the estuary against inappropriate recreational developments. Furthermore, given the importance of the Blackwater as demonstrated by WeBS, the council has made byelaws, which, amongst other things, impose speed limits for craft using parts of the estuary. This has the effect of controlling some of the noisier and potentially disturbing and erosive activities such as jet-skiing.

Maldon District Council was also at the forefront of the national initiative promoted by English Nature for the production of Estuary Management Plans. A comprehensive plan was published in 1996, jointly with Colchester Borough Council, and importantly this is now being actively implemented by the Blackwater Project. As a result, the future of the estuary and its wildlife now seems largely assured.

Since the 1980s the Blackwater Estuary has developed into almost an outdoor laboratory to investigate novel methods of coastal management, a test-bed for new techniques of 'soft' engineering to replace or supplement more traditional sea defences. First it was the installation of brushwood groynes and polders to try and regenerate eroding saltings, then the recharging of foreshores with dredged sand and gravel to protect vulnerable localities. In 1991, the opportunity arose on Northey Island to establish the first experimental managed realignment of a seawall, the purpose being to allow natural migration of saltmarsh as a counterbalance to the erosive trend in the open estuary. The experiment, a partnership between the National Trust, Environment Agency and English Nature, proved successful: within three years, saltmarsh had regenerated. This success was sufficient to justify establishing a larger trial of some 24ha on land at Tollesbury; there, the seawall was breached in 1995, and now around half of the site has developed saltmarsh. Still more recently, further examples of managed realignment have come on stream, notably an area of 'operational realignment' at Orplands, on the south shore, where the Environment Agency considered it uneconomic to maintain a stretch of wall, and at Abbotts Hall, the largest realignment to date in the UK. The net effect of these schemes has been to counteract some of the recent losses of saltmarsh to erosion, to the benefit of both wildlife and sustainable sea defence. It is a model of what will have to happen on a larger scale if the estuaries and their wildlife are to have a long-term future.

Dengie Flats

The Dengie peninsula is the epitome of the windswept, desolate Essex coast. Inland, it is flat and largely arable; offshore, it is flatter still, the mudflats (3km wide at low tide) and sea merging imperceptibly with the sky. Apart from Bradwell Power Station, St Peter's Chapel and a Marconi radar installation, the most significant feature of relief is the seawall itself.

Dengie Flats are pretty much exposed to the North Sea, their only protection being an offshore sandbank, Buxey Sands. These sands dry out at low tide, but because of their position their importance for birds is essentially unknown. They are known, however, to support Cockle stocks, so it would be surprising if these were not exploited. The limited shelter provided by Buxey is sufficient to ensure that the inshore Dengie Flats have a muddy component, which is absent on the coarse-grained Buxey.

Fringing the 15km Dengie coastline is a more-or-less continuous stretch of saltmarsh, extending up to 1,500m out from the wall. It was these saltmarshes which provided the first documented evidence of significant saltmarsh erosion in Essex (Greensmith & Tucker 1965); recognition of this phenomenon led to the evolution of policy and practice in relation to sustainable shoreline management. Along the seaward edge of some of the saltmarsh there are substantial accumulations of shells, mostly Cockles, reflecting the abundance of Cockles in the adjacent intertidal zone. The shell banks are extremely dynamic, shaped by storm events; this helps to maintain them in a relatively unvegetated condition, and this in turn benefits both roosting waders and nesting terns. However, the mobility also creates problems: shellbanks rolling back onto the saltmarsh contribute to saltmarsh erosion and have been blamed for the loss of one of only two Essex populations of the Sea-heath, a scarce saltmarsh plant.

As well as continual loss of saltmarsh to sea level rise and shellbank rollover, Dengie also demonstrates well the impacts of rare events. During a very cold spell in the late 1980s, the mudflats froze; the incoming tide swept the ice onshore, pushed by strong easterly winds, and the resulting ice floes left the surface of the marsh looking as though it had been ploughed. It is a highly dynamic part of the Essex coast, and as such is considered to be key site for the study of saltmarsh geomorphology. A corollary of this dynamism is that sea defence is an ever-present concern, and Dengie has been the site for several experiments to investigate low-cost methods of securing those defences, bearing in mind the extremely high cost of 'traditional' hard concrete structures. During the 1980s, a stretch of wall in the south at Deal Hall was rebuilt using domestic refuse; several large brushwood polders were constructed to promote sedimentation; and two lines of old Thames lighters were sunk offshore to act as wavebreaks. Of these, only the last solution is really viable. Domestic refuse leaves the risk of pollution, and brushwood polders seem ill-suited to the rigours of an Essex winter.

Inland of the seawall, the prospect is almost unbroken, intensive arable cultivation—some of the most productive arable land in the country. Because of this and the potential resource implications, the Dengie coastline was one of the few parts of the undeveloped Essex coast which was omitted from the boundary of the Essex Coast Environmentally Sensitive Area. Thus, there has been no financial incentive for farmers to restore more traditional, less intensive management practices. In just a couple of small areas, notably at Sandbeach Meadows, grassland has survived the plough: it has been retained and managed in such a way as to attract grazing Brent Geese, so taking pressure off nearby arable fields. Wouldn't it be wonderful if wider areas of this remote peninsula could be restored to their former glories, days when the duck decoys (of which at least one survives more-or-less intact) were full? Although nowadays we might hope that the decoy would be put to a conservation use, for ringing and tagging birds to understand more of their movements. In this, it would be following something of a tradition at Dengie: Bradwell Bird Observatory does the same for migrant passerines, and logs seabird movements, while Britain's (if not the world's) largest moth trap is operated nearby at Curry Farm. This trap has added considerably to our knowledge of moth migration and dispersal, and several new species to the British moth list. Not bad for an oasis in an arable desert!

For WeBS purposes, Dengie is divided into two count sectors. North Dengie is counted in five sections by a team of four, and South Dengie is counted by the Crouch team. Counts in both sectors date back to the 1950s. When possible, counts are made in every month of the year: the disturbance problems affecting summer counts elsewhere are not such an issue here. Of the optional species, terns are counted but gulls are not. As most roost sites are on the saltmarsh edge and shellbanks, there are problems in making accurate counts because of the distances involved, except on high spring tides when the roosting birds are pushed nearer the seawall or on to the adjacent arable land.

Given the contiguity of estuarine habitat with the Blackwater to the north and Foulness to the south, it is not surprising that there appears to be considerable interchange of birds between these sites. Many waders move out of the Blackwater to roost in the northern sector of Dengie, and conversely others, especially Oystercatchers, move from feeding locations on Dengie to roost on the massive shell banks at Foulness Point, particularly on the higher tides. Likewise, the large flock of Brent Geese usually associated with Foulness may be located on the south Dengie or indeed the Crouch, perhaps in response to disturbance.

Although Dengie is not nationally important for any wildfowl species other than Brent Geese, dabbling ducks, Shelducks and Eiders are counted in significant numbers. However, counters have reported a decrease in most of these species over the past 20 years. The most significant and sustained increase over that period relates, in common with most other sites, to Grey Plovers, with the five-year mean peak now around 4,500 birds.

As WeBS reports list only the most significant counts on a national scale, the observations of long-term counters are a valuable source of information on the changing fortunes of less frequent species. At this site, Black-tailed Godwits, Spotted Redshanks and Green Sandpipers have all been identified as showing an increasing trend, albeit in small numbers. One species that has come into the nationally important category in recent times is Red-throated Diver. The latest five-year mean peak of 96 birds probably only scratches the surface of the true population size, representing simply the numbers which are close enough to be seen from land. Certainly anecdotal evidence suggested that waters in the Dengie/Buxey area may regularly support several hundred divers—but actually counting them was a different matter, at least until the advent of a major offshore windfarm proposal. Environmental assessment work for this revealed the outer Thames area to support an estimated 7,500 birds, some 150% of the previously assumed UK wintering population!

Low Tide Counts have taken place twice, in 1992/93 (the February count memorably coinciding with a tidal surge) and 1993/94. The vast extent of intertidal habitat creates problems for the counters operating from the seawall or saltmarsh edge, but their opinion is that these counts are more accurate than the Core Counts. It is an inescapable fact that in a site such as Dengie, with few good vantage points and lots of distant birds, both when feeding and at roost, counts cannot be as precise as on some of the more contained sites. It speaks volumes about the quality and commitment of the counters that they are able to produce the figures they do.

Given the Dengie's remote nature, it is perhaps not surprising that there has been little need to use WeBS data to defend it against development. It is simply too far away from anywhere to attract the attention of developers, and it is fully protected by conservation legislation. Of course this is not to undermine the value of WeBS counts here: they were needed to justify the designations; as complete coverage of major sites as possible is necessary to see the wider national and international picture; and who knows when some unexpected proposal may come out of the woodwork? This almost occurred during the late-1980s when Dengie was selected as the location for a mechanical Lugworm harvester, as used in the Netherlands. The vessel arrived unannounced and commenced operation; only very rapid action by the authorities prevented wider damage, and eventually the operator was persuaded to leave the site.

This example represented almost a hybrid between two existing activities—hydraulic dredging for Cockles, which takes place sporadically on the outer edges of Dengie Flats and more frequently on Buxey Sands, and hand digging for Lugworms and other bait species. Bait digging is a traditional activity, which has been interpreted by the courts as a common law right, ancillary to fishing, provided it is not for commercial purposes. At times, the number of bait diggers working the Dengie Flats has been excessive, especially given their reluctance to backfill their holes. As the flats are a National Nature Reserve, the then Nature Conservancy Council was able to address the problem through a licensing system: the diggers were required to form a local bait digging association to whom the licence was granted, and they were given the role of policing their interests against interlopers. As a means of tackling the perennial problem of conflicts between bait diggers and birds/birdwatchers, it appears to have been remarkably successful.

As agricultural support mechanisms evolve and sea defence costs escalate, it is possible that the arable hinterland of Dengie may begin to reclaim some of its lost marshland glory. One feature of particular relevance is the underlying soil. This is derived from Wallasea Series clays, in which the soil structure is supported by residual salinity. Over time, following drainage, the salt is washed out, the soil structure collapses, land drains are blocked and agriculture becomes less viable - a process known as saline deflocculation. At present, soil structure is maintained by the addition of gypsum, but it is possible to foresee a time when such intervention ceases to make economic or agricultural sense. We may yet see the rebirth of the Dengie marshes.

Crouch and Roach Estuaries

WeBS report the estuaries of the Rivers Crouch and Roach as a single site, albeit counted by two separate teams; the Crouch team also counts south Dengie. The estuaries share a common mouth, north of Foulness Island, and are similar in character—long, thin and muddy, each occupying relatively narrow valleys in the underlying clays. The Crouch in particular penetrates a considerable distance inland: the tidal limit lies some 25km from the sea near Wickford, although the majority of the waterbirds are to be found downstream of South Woodham Ferrers and Hullbridge. The latter two settlements, together with Burnham-on-Crouch and several other areas, are important centres for water-borne recreation, especially sailing. There are few other forms of development, apart from one minor port at the western end of Wallasea Island, largely importing timber.

From Wallasea seawards, the channels become rather braided, forming a complex series of small creeks surrounding several large islands. Wallasea Island itself is almost exclusively arable, apart from an area planned for managed realignment in 2006, the Government's compensatory measures for permitting developments on the Orwell and Medway in the 1980s and 1990s, respectively. The other islands, Foulness (including New England and Havengore), Potton and Rushley are owned and operated as testing sites and their buffer lands by agencies of the MoD. Although testing involves the production of very big bangs, the birds appear fully habituated to the noise, and the history of military ownership must be seen as the primary reason why this area remains relatively undeveloped. However, it has not prevented large tracts of former grazing marsh being ploughed and converted to intensive arable cultivation, although some significant areas have survived, notably the former Atomic Weapons Research Establishment at Foulness.

Upstream on the Crouch, large tracts of grazing marsh remain, including the EWT reserve at Blue House Farm. Another significant area is Marsh Farm Country Park, which constitutes an important local resource, especially so in view of its close proximity to the expanding new town of South Woodham Ferrers.

Almost the whole of the intertidal zone in the two estuaries is delimited by a seawall. In just a couple of localities, Woodham Fenn and parts of Paglesham Lagoon, there are small examples of the now rare transition of higher saltmarsh to coastal grassland dominated by Sea Couch. Although well sheltered from the rigours of the open sea, the Crouch still demonstrates the highly dynamic nature of coastal habitats. There are three significant areas of secondary saltmarsh, formed as a result of breaching of the seawalls around the end of the 19th century: Bridgemarsh Island, Brandy Hole and North Fambridge Marsh. These are examples of 'unmanaged realignment': reclamation in its truest sense. Wildfowling clubs have an important presence in these areas; their involvement in and sustainable exploitation of them has helped ensure the continued survival of these marshes to date. As well as its importance in supporting wintering wildfowl, Bridgemarsh Island is also renowned for its breeding colony of Black-headed Gulls, of the order of 250 pairs, which nest on the old, isolated seawalls, although with increasingly poor success rates as sea levels rise.

WeBS Core Counts are carried out by two teams, one of 12 people on the Crouch and another small and poorly supported team of three on the Roach. Indeed the Roach has always been the ugly sister: WeBS counts started only as recently as 1976 (compared with the 1950s for the Crouch) and it has not proved possible to count it every year. And within the year, the Crouch is counted if at all possible in every month, while the Roach is counted only from September to March. In terms of designation, parts of the Crouch have been an SSSI since 1955, but it was extended to include the Roach only in 1996.

The Crouch and Roach WeBS site has shown a gradual reduction in total waterbird numbers since the 1980s, mean peaks falling from around 26,000 to 23,000. In part this seems to be due to a decline since 1990 in Brent Geese, perhaps as a result of intensive scaring from arable land; additional declines in dabbling ducks and certain waders may be related to the high rate of saltmarsh erosion (Table 2). The lack of width in the estuaries tends to magnify the effects of coastal squeeze. Over similar timescales, Golden Plovers and Black-tailed Godwits have increased to levels of national importance; these may be a result of better coverage.

Low Tide Counts took place on the Crouch and Roach in 1991/92 and 1995/96. For the latter, the Crouch team drafted extra counters in to assist, while the Roach team wished they had the luxury of others to ask. Dark-bellied Brent Geese, the only species for which the site is of international importance, were distributed throughout the area, although with notable intertidal concentrations around Wallasea Island and west of Bridgemarsh Island. Typically, only around 40% of the Core Count total was recorded at low tide, as presumably the remainder of the population was feeding inland; those noted within the estuary were generally preening and bathing rather than feeding. Wigeons were distributed primarily along the north shore, as were Teals, which were also concentrated at the head of the Roach, where the largest numbers of Mallards were to be found. The upper Roach also appears to be favoured by Black-tailed Godwits, Redshanks and Curlews. Dunlins proved to be the most abundant species on the Low Tide Counts, with an average of some 5,000 birds; these were widely distributed throughout the site. Their mean density of 4.5 birds per hectare of mudflat is on the high side in relation to other estuaries; this may be related to both the relatively small area of intertidal within the site, and the immediate proximity of vast areas of intertidal (Foulness and Dengie) which could help sustain the Crouch/Roach birds if their food becomes limiting.

Perhaps the most significant opportunities for the estuaries arise from changes to agricultural practices. The Essex Wildlife Trust is leading the way at Blue House Farm, showing how a working farm can be integrated with the needs of nature conservation. At Marsh Farm, Essex County Council is doing something similar, although with a slightly different emphasis, on informal recreation as much as wildlife. The real challenge is to extend such considerations beyond the bounds of nature reserves and public land. Parts of Wallasea are now being reclaimed from intensive agriculture: given current agricultural support mechanisms and the spiralling cost of maintaining seawalls, perhaps this may be a continuing process. And what of the MoD areas, which have been allowed to become arable deserts: could they have their biodiversity restored? Again this is not beyond the bounds of possibility, as there is repeated speculation about the future of the establishment at Foulness. Given the presence of an unparalleled inter-tidal testing range at Maplin Sands, their complete withdrawal is most unlikely, but rationalisation of the estate is a real possibility. Of course, military withdrawal is a double-edged sword: it provides an opportunity for conservation organisations to get in there to shape the area for wildlife, but it also runs the risk of developers getting their piece of the action. The Memorandum of Understanding between MoD and English Nature is vital in this respect: on land designated as SSSI, conservation is specified as the primary objective after military requirements, and there are consultation mechanisms put in place relating to the disposal of such land by the MoD.

Thames Estuary

Superlatives feature in any description of the Thames, England's longest and—for many—greatest river. At its mouth is one of the largest estuaries in the country. At the head of the estuary, is one of the world's great cities, home and workplace to millions of people. For long stretches, there is wall-to-wall port and dockside development, served by a constant stream of seaborne transport; in other places, the estuary frontage is devoted to pleasure, to the recreation and entertainment of those living in the metropolis; and still elsewhere, there are oases of green and tranquillity. It is an estuary of contrasts, of almost overwhelming human pressures, but still the wildlife is there: it is the fourth most important estuary for wetland birds in the country.

The Thames Estuary forms the boundary between Essex and Kent. For WeBS purposes, the Thames includes the Kentish shore as far east as the Isle of Grain; the Medway and Swale Estuaries, while clearly with a close geographical relationship, and presumably at least a degree of ecological linkage, are counted separately. On the Essex side, the whole of the north shore together with the broad sweep of Maplin Sands is treated as a part of the site. Although the flats fronting Southend-on-Sea and those off Foulness are different SSSIs, there is evidently a considerable degree of interchange with birds passing both ways off Shoeburyness to roost either at Foulness Point or in the Leigh-on-Sea/Canvey area (Rudge 1970).

A river with such a wealth of history as the Thames comes with a legacy: historical land claim; a severely modified set of coastal processes; and pollution and contamination of the river and its banks. While much of the modern pollution has now been cleared up and the river brought back to a reasonable state of health, this has not been without its wildlife casualties: during the 1960s and 1970s the upper reaches of the Thames became especially suitable for large flocks of Pintail, feeding on Tubifex worms. These are tolerant of deoxygenation, one result of organic pollution; as the pollution status has improved, so Tubifex declined, followed by the Pintail, coinciding with a northward shift in the Essex population.

In order to maintain the shipping channels the Port of London Authority operate a regular silt-dredging programme. As well as the effects where the river is dredged, this activity also has great implications for the places where the dredgings are deposited. There are essentially two options, to dispose at sea or on land. Sea disposal is expensive, wasteful of a key coastal resource (at least when the dredgings are not polluted), and uncertain—the dredgers may not be able to cope with the sometimes severe weather conditions and sea states in the outer estuary. Land disposal is cheaper and easier, if a suitable site can be found, and it can create important wildlife habitat, albeit temporary. Witness the importance of the silt lagoons at Rainham and Tilbury and the fly-ash lagoons at West Thurrock, for feeding and roosting birds, at least while the lagoons were in operation. Once full, though, they can rapidly lose their value, and the birds have to find new sites. The fact that they can do so is testament to the birds' adaptability. However, finding new sites that are suitable for disposal is becoming just about impossible nowadays since almost every bit of the estuary is either developed or of existing conservation interest. A recent public inquiry decision not to allow the extension of silt dumping onto the important Kent site of Barksore Marshes is most welcome.

Looking at the habitats of the Thames Estuary, it is a general trend that they are more extensive in the outer estuary, and less extensive, used by fewer birds, but closer to a lot more people and thus of considerable importance for that alone, in the inner estuary. The intertidal flats are sandy in the outer estuary, but muddy in the inner estuary, especially west of Canvey Island, reflecting differences in the wave energy climate. The largest area, Foulness and Maplin Sands, covering some 10,000 hectares and constituting the largest continuous area of tidal flats in Britain, is very much at the sandier end of the spectrum and characterised by huge densities of Cockles. Fortunately, its ownership and use by the MoD as a test firing range, one of the longest in Europe, keeps non-military disturbance and exploitation to a minimum: the only Cockle stocks to be harvested are on the very outer reaches of the sands, where they are taken by suction dredgers. Restrictions on disturbance, from walkers, to sailors, to over-flying light aircraft more than compensate, in terms of the effects on birds, for the effects of disturbance from weapons testing.

Of course, things could have been very different if the proposal to build the third London airport on Maplin Sands during the 1970s had come to fruition. Although environmental considerations played a part in the rejection of this proposal, economics were perhaps the key factor. The cost of extensive land claim, together with the significant risks of bird-strike, saved Maplin Sands. However, the story may not be over: even during the 1990s, proposals were made to claim an area even further offshore, with a monorail link to terminal facilities near Tilbury. More recently, Cliffe Marshes in north Kent were proposed as a new airport site. Crackpot ideas perhaps, but ones that require time, money and information to fight.

Although they took up a considerable slice of the conservation resources of their time, the original Maplin proposals have left us with an important legacy. We have a mass of data on all topics ecological, covering the whole of the Essex coast (see, for example, Blindell 1977 and Boorman & Ranwell 1977). Those reports were crucial in establishing the key importance of the estuaries of the area, and helped set the foundation for conservation of the Essex coast. In return for the proposed loss of Maplin, five National Nature Reserves were established, from Hamford Water in the north to Leigh-on-Sea in the south, compensation in the form of added security for other areas—the sort of 'compromise' (i.e. net loss to conservation), which would not in itself be acceptable today. But as it turned out, Maplin was saved and we kept the NNRs! One other positive outcome of the scheme was an experimental gravel island that was constructed some 4km off Shoeburyness as a test of how the land claim for the airport would be carried out. Over the years, it has eroded, reshaped itself, developed sparse vegetation, and became, for a while, a seriously important breeding site for ground-nesting gulls and terns. Nowhere could they be more secure from disturbance and predation.

The other main area frequented by ground-nesters is Foulness Point, with its massive Cockleshell banks. Here they are more subject to predation, with everything from Crows to Foxes, Kestrels to Badgers implicated in the decline of Little Terns. No such problems for the roosting waders, though: Foulness Point holds probably the largest single roost in the county. It can be seen only by those with permission from the MoD, and the lack of disturbance must be a contributory factor in its importance.

Saltmarshes are found as relatively small, eroding fringes in the outer estuary, and as lower-salinity marsh dominated by Sea Club-rush in a few parts of the inner estuary, such as Stone Ness, West Thurrock. The largest saltmarshes are found around Canvey and Two Tree Islands, including the only significant sections of saltmarsh in Essex that are not designated as SSSIs, to the north and west of Canvey Island. The marshes at the eastern ends of both islands are especially important as high tide wader roosts; Old Leigh sea front is an excellent vantage point (if somewhat prone to midday glare) to see the birds in vast numbers pushed up by a rising tide. Just to the east of Two Tree Island, within Leigh NNR, there is the largest remaining eelgrass bed in Essex. This, with the remnant areas of eelgrass on Maplin Sands, helps support the second-largest wintering group of Dark-bellied Brent Geese in Britain, second only to the Wash.

The final semi-natural habitat, grazing marsh, has suffered the same fate as elsewhere in Essex—conversion to intensive arable cultivation. This is seen most noticeably on Hadleigh Marsh, below the castle, where Essex County Council managed to preserve a third of the former marsh area. The dull green bits in the country park are a haven for wildlife. One day, they could again provide a home for the long-extinct Dainty Damselfly, only ever known from this marsh, if talk of re-introduction is progressed. In contrast, bright green, fertilised cereals on the destroyed marsh have nothing apart from grazing Brent Geese when the eelgrass runs out ...

However, elsewhere in the Thames there have been additional losses of grazing marsh, of an even more permanent nature, for the development of the industries that are not welcomed close to habitation, such as oil refineries. A semi-continuous set of marshes remains between Canvey and Corringham, almost surrounding the vast landfill site at Pitsea. Large tracts of these marshes do not yet benefit from statutory conservation protection; in many cases, they are semi-improved (in agricultural terms) and suffer from very low water levels. All that looks set to change, however, as the RSPB and various landowners and authorities begin trying to create a green lung for the Thames Gateway, putting the sustainability into the office of the Deputy Prime Minister's Sustainable Communities Plan.

Working upriver, the final large area of grazing marsh on the Essex side is Rainham, Wennington and Aveley Marshes, which have links with the freshwater habitats along the Ingrebourne Valley. Rainham Marshes have had a long and complex history: the western end of the site was an MoD rifle range, been encroached upon by road improvements, proposed as a site for industrial development, a theme park and film studios. Likewise, the silt lagoons have had a chequered history. Important as both a feeding and roosting site for waterbirds, recent years have seen them becoming dry, overgrown and losing their value. But at last the site is safe under the wing of the RSPB, and the next few years will undoubtedly see Rainham start to live up to its potential.

Given the size of the Thames Estuary, it has to be counted by a number of separate teams, covering Foulness, the Leigh-on-Sea/Canvey area, Rainham Marshes, Pitsea, East Tilbury and the north Kent Coast. The details of each count, in terms of frequency etc., vary between the sectors. Combined data are presented in the WeBS reports for the whole estuary. It is accepted that the data presented by WeBS, impressive though they are, with a recent mean peak total of nearly 160,000 birds, may not give the full story. A large proportion of the birds is counted at the Foulness Point roost—there, access is difficult and the numbers so large that some inaccuracies must be introduced. Furthermore, in the inner Thames, roosts are prone to move in response to developments, disturbance and habitat changes. The Canvey Point roost is subject to disturbance from sailing, jet-skiing, dog walking etc., while until the RSPB moved in Rainham suffered disturbance from the activities of falconers, amongst others. Silt and ash lagoons have become much less favourable for roosting as they have become disused and colonised by vegetation, while disturbance associated with the construction of the QEII Bridge has been implicated in the relocation of some roosting groups. On top of all this, the presence of innumerable structures, such as jetties in the inner estuary, any of which can form a roost for not-inconsiderable numbers of Dunlins and Redshanks in particular, makes the task of compiling a comprehensive total almost impossible. The relatively recent recognition of Holehaven Creek, to the west of Canvey Island, as an important site has added considerably to the reported totals of Black-tailed Godwits in the Thames.

The appearance of Black-tailed Godwits in internationally important numbers is not, however, simply due to improved coverage: it is a genuine increase, and reflects the gradual southward relocation of the species in Essex over the past 20 years. Another significant change over a similar period is the rise to prominence of wintering Avocets; these feed predominantly on the Mucking Flats, but decamp to the Kent coast, especially at Cliffe, for roosting. Just five species of wader (Oystercatcher, Lapwing, Knot, Dunlin and Bar-tailed Godwit) typically make up around 70% of the waterbirds counted on the Thames, excluding gulls. Numbers of Oystercatcher and Dunlin have remained remarkably constant over the past 30 years, Lapwing have increased markedly to a current five-year mean peak of around 10,000, while Knot and Bar-tailed Godwits peaked during the late 1990s.

As these numbers are made up primarily of Foulness birds, changes in coverage are perhaps one reason for these observations. However, the Lapwing increase may be a further indication of a shift to estuarine feeding noted elsewhere (Mason & Macdonald 1999), and the massive increase in Knot (from under 10,000 in the 1970s, to 37,000 in the late 1990s, including a huge count of 54,592 in December 1997) surely cannot be anything other than genuine (Davidson & Wilson 1992). An increase on this scale, when the UK index has remained relatively constant, presumably relates to redistribution of the British wintering population, for reasons which are unknown.

In terms of the wildfowl, Dark-bellied Brent Goose is far and away the most numerous; the Thames Estuary is perhaps the archetypal locality for this bird, currently supporting about 5% of the world population. This percentage has fallen somewhat in recent years, presumably as birds have adopted arable feeding on other sites and as the south coast population has increased substantially. There is no clear indication that habitat quality has declined on the Thames: certainly, the eelgrass bed at Leigh-on-Sea appears to be in good heart, especially now that erosive swinging moorings have been relocated, although much less is known about the extent and abundance of eelgrass on the Maplin Sands. Most duck species are predominantly located in the inner Thames, where numbers are generally rising, apart from Teal. Counts of around 4,000 Teals 20 years ago at Rainham have dropped to 1,000 or so, although the most recent reports suggest a welcome increase is under way. Numbers of Pochards and Tufted Ducks are rather variable, according to the severity of winter weather: in extreme conditions when inland waters are frozen, counts can be exceptionally high, such as the 5,812 Pochards in January 1979.

Low Tide Counts on the Thames suffer from all the same problems of effective coverage as the Core Counts, with the added problem for Essex-based counters of viewing into the sun. The Thames was covered in both 1993/94 (Creekmouth to Tilbury only) and 1998/99, while specific low and through-tide counts were commissioned on the mudflats fronting Southend during the late 1980s; the latter were a response to a proposal to create an island marina, with hundreds of houses, around the pier. These data were of crucial importance in demonstrating the value of those flats: WeBS Core Counts could not do this as the immediate area lacks a significant roost—most birds move westwards to Canvey/Leigh-on-Sea. As a result, these counts were instrumental in securing the designation of the frontage as SSSI, and subsequently SPA and Local Nature Reserve. As with the Maplin airport proposal, waterbird counts supported the conservation case, but the primary cause of the demise of the proposals was economics. Similar counts were also commissioned more recently as part of the environmental assessment of a scheme to improve the Southend-on-Sea sea defences; this time, though, given the increased emphasis of nature conservation in development planning, it was the developers who had to pay for the additional work.

Further upriver, WeBS data supplemented with specific new counts were used to build the conservation case in respect of the London Gateway proposal, a new container port on the site of the former Shellhaven oil refinery. After a long public inquiry in 2003, the Secretary of State finally gave conditional approval to the scheme in 2005. But all the counting was not wasted effort: in order to satisfy the EU Habitats Directive, the likely damage to bird populations must be compensated for, so far as is possible, and to this end, major realignments are proposed on both sides of the river, designed to cater for at least the same number of the same species of birds that will be affected.

The nature and location of the Thames Estuary means there will always be human pressures upon it, of development, pollution, exploitation etc. There is thus a clear need to get all interested parties working towards a sustainable solution for the future of the estuary, but the complexity of the task makes it a more difficult proposition than for any other Essex estuary. However, the Thames Estuary Management Plan project was launched in 1999 and its implementation by the Thames Estuary Partnership is making excellent progress; given the continued support of all key parties, there is no reason why the Thames cannot become a model of sustainable estuarine development.

Inland Essex - the general picture

There are no significant natural wetlands in inland Essex: most of our rivers have been modified by engineering works or affected by intensive agriculture right to their margins, and natural ponds are restricted to pools within ancient woodland and perhaps an occasional glacial ice-melt pond such as Wormingford Mere. All the water bodies covered by WeBS are man-made, largely during the 20th century; they are either reservoirs (for domestic and agricultural water supply), gravel-pits or ornamental ponds. The reservoirs are broadly distributed across the county, reflecting the general demand for water, although, especially in the north, some of the domestic water supply is obtained from groundwater aquifers. Sand and gravel-pits are more clustered, given that the workable deposits are not evenly spread across Essex; they are focussed upon the valleys of the major rivers, and to a lesser extent on the eastern plateaux, along the line of prehistoric courses of the River Thames.

While the major reservoirs are very large, and can support important waterfowl populations in their own right, agricultural reservoirs, amenity ponds and gravel-pits are usually much smaller—they do individually support some waterfowl, especially ducks and feral geese, but it is only the major complexes of smaller sites (e.g. in the Lea Valley) which constitute a wetland resource of recognised importance. However, taken together, the smaller inland waters across the county (and indeed the country), which are not covered by WeBS counts are certainly of importance to waterfowl. To take just one example, Mallard is very typically a widely dispersed species, to be found almost anywhere there is water: as a result, no single site in Britain meets the 1% criterion for national importance.

There are a number of physical attributes of any artificial water body which influence its attractiveness to waterfowl (see, for example, Giles 1992). These include:

- Proximity to other wetland sites: sites that are close to other inland waters, or to the coast, are more able to sustain large numbers of waterfowl. For one thing, a site may be able to fulfil a part of the wintering bird requirements (e.g. feeding or roosting), the remainder being satisfied elsewhere; for another, if there is significant disturbance, the presence of alternative, perhaps less disturbed, locations nearby can be crucial.
- Size: bigger is not always better, but at least in a large site, the centre of the water body may provide refuge from disturbance around the banks. However, the middle of a large open water body, especially if it is deep, may be of little use for many species other than for roosting.
- Shape: an irregular shape provides a greater degree of edge, and usually a larger area of shallow water, in which feeding activity is likely to be concentrated. Irregular margins, with semi-enclosed bays are also important to provide shelter from severe weather emanating from different points of the compass.
- Depth: dabbling waterfowl feed primarily in shallow water, less than 50cm deep, while diving species may feed regularly at 4m or more depth. Water which is any deeper than this may not be without value of course—birds may roost safely on it, and fish or other food items may find refuge in the depths.
- Underwater profile: shallow slopes provide greater areas of valuable transition habitats, especially important where these promote the growth of structural vegetation (e.g. reed beds) or stands of important food plants, such as charophytes. Profile is also of key importance in those water bodies, especially water supply reservoirs, which experience significant drawdown at times of high demand. The shallower the slope, the longer that important shallow water habitats are maintained under a drawdown situation.

41

- Margins: the margins of these water bodies range from entirely vegetated and semi-natural, to concrete. For most birds, the more natural the better, although again even reservoirs with a concrete apron may be of great importance, at least for roosting birds. The vegetation growth around the water body is also of importance: trees may adversely affect a site by shading it, polluting the water each autumn with leaf fall, or interrupting the desirable flightlines of waterfowl; on the other hand, a tree fringe can be useful in reducing disturbance impacts.

Because many of the above also influence the attractiveness of a site for human uses, from sailing to angling, these factors also help determine the degree to which human disturbance pressures affect a site. But disturbance is not the only pressure wildlife on such sites have to contend with. Another key issue is water quality: most inland sites are fed by water derived from an agricultural landscape, and which is therefore eutrophic (over-fertile) as a result of pollution by fertiliser run-off. A degree of eutrophication is natural in lowland water bodies, and indeed desirable as the nutrient supports the food chains on which the waterfowl depend. There can be too much of a good thing though: a greater degree of eutrophication leads to the production of algal blooms, which can eliminate more desirable vegetation and substantially alter the ecology of the site, especially as a result of oxygen depletion when it dies and rots. Furthermore, algal blooms, especially in recent drought summers, have sometimes been caused by toxic blue-green algae, although their toxicity to wildlife is unproven. However, in similar circumstances, botulism may outbreak, and this does lead to bird deaths.

Water quality is also an issue in relation to the large, and expanding, populations of feral waterfowl, especially Canada and Greylag Geese. Their abundant manuring may lead to local eutrophication, while their paddling stirs up bottom sediments, making the waters turbid and relatively unproductive. Grazing by these birds can also lead to vegetation damage, including destruction of marginal reed fringes, and their aggressive nature reduces the value of a site to more desirable, native waterfowl.

Any artificial wetland site undergoes natural changes as it ages. Typically, water life is sparse in the very early stages, but this rapidly gives way to a high productivity, high biodiversity site, with communities dominated by the more dispersive species, including wildfowl. Over a period of decades, this initial flush subsides, and many of the early colonising species, particularly insects, may be lost. Bird numbers too often show a decline; this should always be borne in mind when trying to ascertain the cause of local declines: it may not be due to external factors, such as disturbance, but rather to a natural, successional change in the water body. In some situations it may be possible to introduce management practices to reintroduce early-successional elements. In the case of gravel-pits, which are usually worked sequentially, the excavation of new areas of water will achieve the same end.

Other problems occur at the other end of the intended life of both reservoirs and gravel-pits. At a reservoir, especially one with concrete margins and/or a substantial dam, maintenance costs spiral in later life, and it becomes increasingly uneconomic to maintain them. At some point, the reservoir operators will come to a decision that it must close, and discussions about decommissioning begin. To drain and perhaps develop an important site will obviously eliminate its wildlife value; to do so would be contrary to European legislation for SPA sites. But to whom would the responsibility for ongoing maintenance fall if closure and decommissioning were prevented by conservation legislation, or if alternative sites needed to be created? Such questions will have to be addressed seriously as the ageing reservoirs, especially around the London fringes, come to the end of their economic life. As far as gravel-pits are concerned, one problem lies in the after use required by the planning consent: generally, the restoration conditions are to agriculture, often with landfill as an intermediary, or to recreational uses. Conservation is rarely stated as an explicit requirement or priority.

Inland Essex sites

Abberton Reservoir

Abberton is the largest freshwater body in Essex, with a water area of some 500ha. It was created by the South Essex Water Company (now Essex and Suffolk Water) between 1935 and 1941 by damming Layer Brook near its junction with the Roman River (just south of Colchester) to provide a domestic water supply for north Essex. Much of the water stored in the reservoir is derived from surface water drainage in the Fens. Water is abstracted near Denver Sluice, piped to the headwaters of the Stour, then travels down the river channel to abstraction points in the lower reaches from where it is piped to Abberton.

The reservoir is in a very strategic location, situated just 5km from the Blackwater Estuary. There is considerable interchange of birds between the coast and Abberton, such that it would not be unreasonable to treat it as, in effect, a coastal site. Observational and other data have also demonstrated linkages with other inland sites—Ruddy Ducks are known to move between Abberton and Hanningfield; Great Crested Grebes to and from Ardleigh Reservoir and Alton Water; and the famous Abberton Cormorants have verified links with a range of other coastal and inland sites throughout northwest Europe.

Abberton falls into three sections, divided by two road causeways which provide admirable viewing stations. The largest and deepest eastern section contains the bulk of the water but lacks some of the diversity of waterfowl of the rest of the site, as its margins are entirely concrete. The wide open water areas do, however, attract large numbers of Coots and loafing wildfowl, and when the water level is low, usually in mid–late summer, areas of mud can be exposed. These provide feeding opportunities for waders, including typically estuarine species such as Black-tailed Godwits, and passage migrants more associated with inland waters, such as Green and Common Sandpipers. During droughts, mud and islands may persist for considerable periods, even allowing breeding (witness the famous occurrence of Gull-billed Tern in 1950). However, rafts provided for the purpose provide a more secure breeding site, attracting good numbers of Common Terns.

The central and western sections present an altogether different aspect. Their margins are semi-natural, with areas of reed swamp and stands of willow trees overhanging the water in places. There is thus potential for concealment for the more secretive species: most of the breeding waterfowl are to be found in these sections, including the thriving Cormorant colony in the trees. As the willows die under the guano onslaught, nesting locations are getting ever lower. The reservoir is set amidst an intensively arable area, in places extending right to the water's edge. Along parts of the margins, grassland swards have been retained, and these provide important grazing areas for geese (mostly feral) and Wigeon.

Abberton is the most important reservoir for wildfowl in the UK. Factors which contribute to this include its size, geographical position and lack of disturbance. Whilst it is possible to see most of the reservoir from the causeways, access to the banks is restricted to official counters and water company workers. In season, fishing is permitted from the causeways, but the disturbance this causes is very restricted in scale; no form of recreational activity is permitted on the water. Essex and Suffolk Water take their responsibilities for Abberton and its wildlife very seriously indeed.

Since 1990 a fruitful relationship has developed between the water company and EWT, which now runs a small reserve, viewing facilities and excellent visitor centre at the reservoir. This development followed from a history of cooperative ventures on the site, involving the Essex Birdwatching Society and Wildfowl & Wetlands Trust. A notable achievement was the establishment of a duck ringing station in 1949 by Major-General C.B. Wainwright; this was operated for many years by Roy King and others, and indeed continues sporadically to this day. The recoveries of birds at or ringed at Abberton have contributed immensely to our knowledge of wildfowl movements throughout the Western Palearctic. For a more comprehensive treatment of this and other aspects of Abberton, see Thompson (1996).

WeBS counts are carried out by a team of two or three, in all months apart from June and July. Counting of the largest section is facilitated by the fact that they are able to drive around the concrete apron of the reservoir. Gulls are not counted—at peak times it is considered there would simply not be enough daylight to complete the task! Coots make up a high proportion of the total waterfowl: Abberton is the most important site for the species in Britain, with a recent mean peak of around 8,000 birds being twice that of the second most important site, Rutland Water. There are suggestions of a recent decline from five-year mean peaks of 12,000, but numbers are prone to fluctuation with, for example, more than 15,000 birds (about 25% of the British winter population) being recorded occasionally.

Pochard and Tufted Duck are two of the more numerous duck species. Typically, the highest numbers of each occur during the moulting season (August–September); midwinter totals are usually around half the moulting numbers. Trends in the numbers of many duck species are difficult to interpret: while most increased to the 1990s, many of those have shown more recent declines, for reasons that are as yet unknown. One that we hope will decline is the Ruddy Duck. From the first record in 1971, to a 2000/01–2004/05 mean peak of 504, to a record single count of 678 in November 2003, the increase has been almost inexorable and gives rise to grave concerns to those who are interested in the future of the White-headed Duck. However, on the first day of the Government-sponsored cull, in January 2004, 99 birds out of a total of some 260 were shot, raising hopes of success.

Of more local concern perhaps are the growing numbers of feral ducks and geese that hang around the causeways, begging; clearly, the food benefits outweigh the risk of getting flattened by a car. Many are Mallards and domestic derivatives thereof; the remainder are largely Greylag and Canada Geese. Some steps have been taken, in the form of licensed egg pricking, to limit the size of the Canada Goose flock; this appears to be having some effect, a five-year mean peak of 976 between 1985/86 and 1989/90 subsequently fell to 660 between 2000/01 and 2003/04.

Given the level of protection afforded to Abberton and the positive attitude of the owners, routine WeBS data have rarely been needed to support conservation action on the site. They are, however, important as a monitor of the health of the system or, to adopt the jargon of the European designation, to assess whether the site has a favourable conservation status. Under the current regime, the major concern is about water quality; as the water derives from the agri-desert of the Fens, it is high in soluble nutrients. The reservoir is thus eutrophic, and this leads to considerable algal blooms most summers, including in at least some years toxic blue-green algae.

However, there is one threat on the horizon. Or is it an opportunity? To secure future supplies, Essex and Suffolk Water is proposing to raise the level of the eastern section by more than 3 metres. This will have the effect of producing large areas that are too deep for most waterfowl, except perhaps for loafers. This action will fundamentally change an internationally important site, but it should be possible to design and implement the scheme in such a way that the importance is not only safeguarded but enhanced.

Hanningfield Reservoir

Lying some five miles south of Chelmsford, Hanningfield is the most important wetland feature of central Essex. It is a public water supply storage reservoir, again owned and operated by Essex and Suffolk Water, the construction and filling of which was completed in 1957. When full, it has a water area of around 350ha, although in drought summers especially, when demand is high and input low, large areas of mud become exposed around the shallow margins. At peak levels, the average depth of the reservoir is about 8m, the deeper waters to be found near the dam. The reservoir is so large that an entire 1km grid square fits within its water area: when this square was selected at random for a national badger survey in the 1980s, not surprisingly it produced a negative result!

Hanningfield is second only amongst Essex inland waters to Abberton, in terms of both size and waterbird populations. However, it typically supports peak counts of just 25% of those at Abberton. Part of this difference is due to location: Hanningfield does not benefit from proximity to the coast, although there are well-documented interchanges with both the Crouch and Thames Estuaries. A second factor must be the greater degree of recreational use of Hanningfield: there is a thriving 'put and take' trout fishery, mostly done from boats, and until 1995 a windsurfing centre was rather unfortunately located within what had been in the past one of the more productive (especially for waders) sheltered bays. Windsurfing no longer takes place—the designated area was weed-prone and shallow, and indeed almost disappeared during drought summers. All recreational activities are strictly zoned, and general access is not permitted around the margins, so refuge areas are always available for birds. Visual access over most of the reservoir can be achieved satisfactorily from the road causeway in the southwest corner and the EWT nature trail on the southern shore.

A third relevant reason why Hanningfield attracts fewer wildfowl than Abberton may be the surrounding land use: there are small areas of grassland, especially around the eastern end, but commercial forestry plantations, in places comprising pure conifer stands, dominate the western fringes. These, of course, are not without their wildlife value—Hanningfield is one of the most reliable Essex locations for Crossbills, for instance—but they do give the water a rather enclosed feel, which may render the wooded margins unsuitable for many waterfowl. As the plantations have grown up, so the previously substantial breeding populations of Lapwing and Redshank have declined to extinction, but in the fullness of time, who knows—Ospreys perhaps?

The banks around much of the main part of the reservoir are protected by a concrete apron which, at least when water levels are high, restricts the feeding opportunities for waterbirds, especially those dependent upon shallow water. Where there are natural banks, small areas of reed and other marshland plants have colonised, providing breeding sites for a number of waterfowl species, most significantly Gadwall and Tufted Duck, the latter with 30–40 pairs. Much more extensive marshland habitats are to be found in the two sludge lagoons west of the main reservoir. These receive the chalk-rich sludge from the water treatment works, and the northernmost, now essentially full to the brim, has developed into one of the largest reed beds in Essex. The invasion of willow and other moisture-loving trees is proving to be something of a problem as the site becomes increasingly dry; one long-term solution may be to partially re-excavate the sludge for disposal or sale, thus rejuvenating the habitat and providing more space for disposal once the current receptor site—the southern lagoon—is full.

Within the main water body, there are two habitat features of note. Firstly, there is a small island about 100m off the southern shore. This provides a relatively safe breeding site for ducks and Black-headed Gulls, although the success of the latter during the 1970s, rising to over 200 pairs, was responsible for the displacement and decline in breeding success of several other wetland bird species. More recently, during drought summers, the island has been vulnerable to ground predators, especially Foxes; a deepened channel between it and the mainland helped to reduce the problem, and the fortunes of at least one species, Common Tern, have been much improved by the provision of a tern raft.

Secondly, especially along the western bank, there are extensive beds of aquatic macrophytes, particularly Fennel Pondweed. This is itself a food source for Coots and various ducks, and it harbours a considerable invertebrate and fish diversity and density, which in turn supports a wider range of waterfowl. It is a highly productive reservoir—indeed too productive in those years when excessive algal blooms develop. The reason for its eutrophic status lies in the sources of the water: most is derived from the Fens, with catchment transfer into the River Pant and abstraction at Langford on the Blackwater; a little is pumped from Sandon Brook. At times, treated wastewater has also been a significant input, on occasions up to 20% of the summer flow. It is likely that this may be the case again in the future, as the water company strives to make best use of the available water in our drought-prone corner of England. While treatment removes potential human health hazards, it does not necessarily reduce the high nitrate levels, so the water is something akin to a biological soup. I have heard it said that if scientists want examples of a fish disease to investigate, Hanningfield is one of the first places they look. Further details of the history and ecology of Hanningfield can be obtained from a series of excellent papers in *Essex Bird Reports*: Pyman (1956), Hudgell & Smith (1974) and Bond (1992).

WeBS counts have taken place on Hanningfield in every year since its inception in 1952. Counts are made in every month of the year by a team of six counters; although gulls are not counted routinely, they are subject to special counts every five years. It is considered that almost all species are covered accurately, with the possible exception of Ruddy Duck, Moorhens and other species that are found primarily around the reedy margins of the lagoons.

The water level in the reservoir has a clear influence upon the waterbirds. For example, waders such as Lapwings are counted in significant numbers only when there are large areas of undisturbed mud exposed. During long periods of drawdown, various plants colonise the mud, especially Red Goosefoot; these produce vast quantities of seed, which prove highly attractive to certain dabbling ducks, especially Teal and Pintail.

However, the largest regular numbers of birds consist of those species, which are dependent upon open water. In particular, Coots make up almost one-third of the total mean peak count: the latest WeBS figures indicate Hanningfield is the third most important site for Coots in Great Britain, with a five-year mean peak of more than 3,500, a figure which has remained consistent for the past 20 years. Pochard and Tufted Duck are also very numerous; Pochard peak during the midwinter period, but Tufted Duck peak during the late-summer moult, as they do on the London reservoirs.

As might be expected, given the increases at Abberton and the regular movement (demonstrated by ringing) between the two sites, Cormorants have also increased at Hanningfield, to the current average of around 350 birds. As the marginal plantations have grown up, so the site would appear to becoming suitable for the establishment of a breeding colony. Indeed, breeding has been attempted on several occasions. Not for nothing, though, have these attempts failed—prospecting pairs have generally been 'persuaded' not to continue their efforts in view of their conflicts with established fishing activities. Also mirroring events elsewhere in Essex, feral wildfowl are on the increase at Hanningfield: Greylag and Canada Geese numbers have both grown considerably since the 1960s, and Ruddy Duck have built up to a most recent five-year mean peak of 450. As at Abberton, Hanningfield is playing a key role in the culling programme for this species.

Two wintering species have undergone marked declines, for reasons that are unclear. Recent mean peaks for Great Crested Grebe and Little Grebe are considerably lower than typical counts from the early 1960s. Water quality and recreational disturbance may have played a part in these declines, but it is tempting to suggest that they are more related to natural cycles of abundance associated with the maturation of a newly-created water body.

Although WeBS counts indicate that, in recent years at least, waterfowl numbers supported by Hanningfield are relatively stable, this site does demonstrate the need to continue with regular monitoring. Recently, the importance of the site for birds was instrumental in blocking a planning application for a light aircraft landing strip near to the reservoir. And it is not too long ago that the water company was pressing to intensify its recreational activities ('Abberton is for birds, Hanningfield for people') by relaxing the limits of the disturbance-free zone. WeBS counts and the additional information held in the heads of the counters were a crucial part of the case for the defence.

Reservoir	Size (ha)	Date flooded	SSSI
Walthamstow Reservoirs	195	late 19th C	Yes
KGV	130	1912	Yes
Abberton	500	1940	Yes
Girling	135	1951	Yes
Hanningfield	350	1954	Yes
Ardleigh	55	1972	No
Leez	11	1967	No

Summary of Essex Reservoirs

Ardleigh Reservoir

Smaller and newer than either of the two previous sites, Ardleigh Reservoir has never attracted the number of wildfowl of its more venerable predecessors. It is again a public water supply site, operated jointly by Anglian Water Services and Tendring Hundred Water Services. The reservoir was formed in 1970 by damming a tributary of the Salary Brook, north of Colchester. It has a water area of only some 55ha, contained within a relatively narrow, partially wooded valley. Most of the water that is stored in the reservoir is in fact pumped from the Colne at East Mill, Colchester; it therefore suffers from problems of eutrophication.

The site has been fully counted throughout the year since 1990 by a team of two; recent five-year mean peak count totals have approached 1,500. Most of the native waterfowl on the site have relatively static numbers, apart from Pochards, which are almost absent between March and August, but rise to 80 or 90 birds during the winter. Canada Geese and Greylag Geese tend to leave the site during the late winter period, while Shelduck, which breed in small numbers, are present only from April to July.

Given the constrained size of Ardleigh Reservoir, and its use for sailing, windsurfing and fishing, it is unlikely ever to develop a very significant waterfowl population, even after it matures and despite its proximity to the coast. There are currently outline plans which may result in a slight increase in surface area. Whilst the effect on the wildlife of the reservoir are being considered, most conservation concern relates to possible effects of additional abstraction from a tributary of the internationally important Colne Estuary.

Coleman's Reservoir

Situated in the Blackwater valley just east of Witham, Coleman's Reservoir is a small site, with only some 4ha of open water, which in some respects is no different from dozens of other agricultural irrigation reservoirs in Essex. Its main differentiators are that is has a natural gravelly bottom (it is not lined with clay), it fills through groundwater seepage and it is counted as part of the WeBS scheme. If only more similar sites were counted, scattered as they are right across the county, then perhaps we would have a better idea of the distribution and true abundance of the more dispersed wildfowl, such as Mallard. Such sites make an unquantified, but probably significant, contribution to the conservation of our wetland birds, despite their lack of statutory designation. The situation of Coleman's Reservoir by the River Blackwater, a natural flyway, gives it a degree of strategic importance, representing a staging post for waterfowl moving between the coast and the Lea Valley.

The natural margins, albeit with dense tree and scrub cover on two sides, provide shelter and food, the latter supplemented by the farmer feeding the site, which attracts good numbers of Coots, Mallards and feral geese. Occasional groups of Teals and other ducks lead to recent peak mean counts of more than 1,200 birds. The site has been counted throughout the year since 1989 by a team of one or two.

Since there is good access to the site and it is close to Witham, there have been inevitable problems of vandalism, including damage to the hide. A rough shoot adjacent to the reservoir is the only other significant source of disturbance.

Connaught Water

Lying within Epping Forest, Connaught Water is an artificial lake of 3.5ha of open water, plus four islands. It was excavated in 1881 and enlarged in 1893; the gravel was used in the building of Rangers Road. Connaught Water was designed as an ornamental pond by William D'Oyley for the visit to the Forest of Queen Victoria in 1882. It is filled by surface and groundwater drainage off the Forest; although this is relatively clean, there are persistent problems of eutrophication, due to the build up of fertile silt and the activities of waterfowl. The water is a maximum of 1m deep, and the underlying silt layer is up to 1.2m deep in places.

It was used as a boating lake until the late 1970s, and subsequently heavily stocked with fish by anglers. Overstocking with Carp in particular, and the problems of silt, resulted in a drop in ecological quality of the lake; macrophytes were almost eradicated, Gadwalls and dragonflies went into decline, and amphibians ceased breeding. The Conservators have now removed the Carp, and the intention is to restore the ecology by planting vegetation and installing chestnut paling refuges for Tench and Roach. There still remains the issue of feral geese, especially Canada Geese; their droppings and the surplus bread fed to them by the public add to the eutrophication. Some steps have been taken to reduce the goose population by treating eggs with paraffin wax, although Connaught Water does attract a considerable accumulation from surrounding areas in the autumn.

The lake is covered for WeBS by a single counter throughout the year; recent five-year mean peaks have been around 340. Commendably, gulls are counted. Up to 40 Cormorants are frequent visitors, hence the need for fish refuges; these birds move freely to and from the Lea Valley reservoirs, as do Goosanders, occasionally counted in double figures.

Teal numbers are occasionally high for a site of this nature, but perhaps the most significant waterfowl population is not included in the totals by WeBS. Mandarin Ducks occurred from 2000/01 to 2003/04, with a mean peak of 75; these are birds that breed and forage for Beech mast in the Forest. Although not native, they do not appear to have any adverse ecological effects as they occupy a niche that is not filled in Europe. Numbers are low and vulnerable in their native Far Eastern breeding range, so the UK feral population can be considered of some conservation significance.

Lea Valley Gravel-pits and Reservoirs

The Lea Valley forms the southwestern boundary of Essex, including its Metropolitan section. As a tributary of the Thames, it links ecologically with the coast and forms a natural north–south flyway. During the 19th and 20th centuries, the valley has been much modified by the hand of Man, but despite heavy urbanisation these modifications have resulted in the creation of an internationally important wetland. Water storage reservoirs, especially closer to London, and more recently gravel-pits extending into rural Essex and Hertfordshire have provided habitat along the valley for breeding, migrant and wintering waterfowl alike.

For WeBS reporting purposes, four sites are recognised: Walthamstow, KGV, Girling and the Lea Valley GPs. This treatment undermines appreciation of the worth of the whole, and nor is it meaningful ecologically as there is considerable interchange of birds between sites, according to weather, patterns of disturbance etc. Nonetheless, for historical continuity and because of the complexity of combining WeBS data between sites, the division into separate WeBS sites is retained here. Whilst individual site figures have been used to justify SSSI designation for the major water bodies, these are insufficient and inappropriate for international designation: the numbers simply do not add up. In 2000, the Lea Valley SPA and Ramsar site was designated, encompassing most of the main waterfowl areas. For this the WeBS data have had to be recombined, with impressive results: the SPA is internationally important for wintering Gadwalls and Shovelers, and nationally important for Great Crested Grebes, Tufted Ducks, Pochards and Cormorants. In addition, Smew numbers exceed the 1% threshold (although below the accepted minimum figure of 50), and the SPA is designated also for supporting significant numbers of wintering Bitterns, with an average of around six birds (from a British total of about 100). Lea Valley data in the main Systematic List are presented as a single site.

Looking at each WeBS site in turn, working north out of London, the first site is Walthamstow. This constitutes a cluster of ten relatively small shallow-water storage basins with an open water area of some 150ha. Most were constructed during the latter half of the 19th century as drinking water storage and supply reservoirs for north London. Unlike many of the reservoirs surrounding and within London, several of the Walthamstow basins have natural, sloping earth banks and wooded islands. Two of the latter, in Reservoirs No. 1 and No. 5, are the location of the famous heronry, the largest in Essex and indeed one of the largest in the country, with in many recent years more than 100 pairs. Post-breeding concentrations of Grey Herons are greater here than at any other UK site, although this does not count as a nationally important species as WeBS has set no threshold for national importance.

The bankside vegetation forms a narrow strip of fenland; although better developed in the adjacent Walthamstow Marshes, around the water it provides breeding opportunities for one of the most diverse wetland bird communities of any of London's reservoirs, including a notable population of Tufted Ducks and Pochards. Tufted Ducks, in particular, also use Walthamstow and the nearby Chingford Reservoirs as a post-breeding refuge during their late-summer moult; peak numbers are generally during August. As expressed by annual indices, numbers of Tufted Ducks in Great Britain outside the breeding season are the most stable of any wildfowl species (Cranswick *et al.* 1999). Their stability is also demonstrated at the local level: the five-year mean peaks at Walthamstow since the 1970s remained between 950 and 1,000, just rising a little above that level very recently.

Numbers drop away a little during the midwinter period, as birds disperse to the diverse series of waterbodies on the periphery of London. Over recent years, at least, midwinter has become increasingly important for other species, including nationally important numbers of Shovelers and Cormorants. Rather less welcome perhaps, Walthamstow is among the top 12 sites in the country for Canada Geese, although the number have dropped by a half.

Only a little way to the north lie the Chingford Reservoirs: Girling and KGV. Although counted and treated individually by WeBS, only a road on a causeway separates them; their consideration as one SSSI seems eminently sensible. KGV is divided into two basins, which form the shallowest of London's larger reservoirs, with an open water area of some 200ha; Girling is a single lagoon of around 160ha. Both have concrete embankments, and therefore their main wildlife significance is as wintering and moulting refuges for waterbirds. As at Walthamstow, moulting Tufted Duck in summer are of national importance, with recent five-year mean peaks in excess of 700 in both KGV and Girling: how many of these are double-counted is a matter for conjecture, and depends on how tightly counts in the two WeBS sites are co-ordinated. Nevertheless, this series of reservoirs is clearly of major importance;

it forms one of the main moulting sites for Tufted Ducks in Britain, and interestingly one that would be missed if, as is the practice at certain other sites, WeBS counts during the summer months were omitted.

Tufted Duck and other species, such as Goosander (found especially on the concrete-lined Flood Relief Channel to the east of the reservoirs), Shoveler and Great Crested Grebe occasionally reach levels of national importance during winter months, but the only species to figure as nationally important in winter is Cormorant—the latest five-year mean peak for Girling is 163. Additional interest is provided by the increasing numbers of Black-necked Grebes, and at the other end of the numerical scale, vast gull roosts, the only major ones in the Lea Valley. Combined counts on the Chingford Reservoirs have totalled as many as 70,000 birds. All of the features of particular interest at these reservoirs are dependent upon the relative lack of disturbance to the sites, ample justification for the strict controls placed on access to the site by the owners, Thames Water. Sailing does take place over parts of the reservoirs, indeed there are proposals to intensify this activity to some extent—if permitted, it will only be on the basis that additional and sufficient wildfowl refuges are put in place.

Moving still further out of London, north of the M25 the Lea Valley has been subject to very considerable attentions from the gravel extraction companies. Thankfully, many pits have been retained as open water sites rather than being filled in and 'restored', and the valley is a near-continuous series of pits from Waltham Abbey all the way to Ware. There are several important adjunct sites, including Cornmill Meadows, marshland supporting a very diverse aquatic invertebrate fauna. Recent work by the Lea Valley Regional Park Authority (LVRPA) on this site has improved the ditch habitats and permitted more extensive seasonal flooding, attracting much improved numbers of waterbirds such as Snipe. Also of note is the former gunpowder factory site at Waltham Abbey. An Alder plantation dating to around 1700 was used to supply the high-quality charcoal needed for the process; the factory closed in the 1940s, and Grey Herons moved in from 1973. Since peak counts of 30 nests in 1983 and 36 in 1994, numbers have declined a little as a result of decontamination and other works on the site, but it remains one of the largest heronries in non-Metropolitan Essex.

The only part of the main gravel-pit complex to lie partly within Essex is Fisher's Green, famed for its often highly visible wintering Bitterns. The pits here span a period of over 40 years in operation from 1930 to the 1970s; numerous spits and islands give a very extensive shoreline. North Metropolitan Pit alone, for example, has a shoreline some 7.2km long. The majority of this SSSI, Turnford & Cheshunt Pits, is managed as a country park by LVRPA, with all the disturbance pressures that this brings. However, because water sports, shooting or other major disturbances are not permitted and angling is well managed, this site alone is of national importance for wintering Gadwalls and Shovelers.

There are a number of other pits, some in Essex, which are not protected as SSSIs: they are largely zoned for water sports and related leisure activities. However, they are not devoid of waterbirds, and may indeed make a positive contribution towards maintenance of the SPA bird populations. The key to successful conservation of the Lea Valley comes in the overview. Looking at the whole Lea Valley GPs WeBS area, the true value of this wetland complex becomes apparent: it is nationally important for six species—Great Crested Grebe; Cormorant, Gadwall; Tufted Duck and Coot—and of at least regional significance for Little Grebe, Smew, Moorhen and Kingfisher.

The SPA designation requires an effective overview to be taken of this complex wetland, including sites that are not so designated. The area is fortunate in coming under the remit of the LVRPA, which takes on a quasi-local authority role. As such it is responsible for ensuring the wildlife of the valley is supported and sustained within the context of the increasing demands for water sports, angling and other facilities. It has taken its responsibilities very seriously, as demonstrated by its development of habitats and visitor facilities at the Essex Filter Beds and Bow Creek, where the Lea meets the Thames. This is an example of strategic thinking since it lies directly opposite the Greenwich peninsula, with its own reed bed habitat creation as part of the Millennium Dome project, and is at the heart of Olympics-driven regeneration of east London.

The LVRPA has even gone to the extent of producing its own Biodiversity Action Plan. In common with all other BAPs, this is a visionary document, setting targets of how the countryside should be in 20 years' time, and proposing mechanisms for delivery of those targets. As always, a plan is only as good as its implementation, but if the Lea Valley BAP works, our wetland wildlife will be the richer for it.

POSTSCRIPT

Bird populations and all wildlife habitats are ever changing, for a huge number of reasons. The fact that I have been able to detail some of those changes in this chapter is a testament to the quality of survey information now at our fingertips. But, of course, it means that no sooner is the information written down than it is out of date, and nowhere is this truer than in the figures provided in support of the importance of each of these Essex wetlands. For the most recent information, the reader should always refer in addition to the current issues of the WeBS Report and the *Essex Bird Report*. Even more important is the need to ensure that available information continues to be as up to date as possible, so if anyone out there would like to do their bit, then your help will be welcomed. Pressures on our wetlands will never go away. The threat of developments may recede as conservation designations start to bite, but some—ironically the larger ones, most likely to be judged as in the national interest—will go ahead. And at the same time, the challenges of climate change (rising sea levels, increased storminess, more frequent summer droughts and, perversely, winter flooding) will continue to exert their influence. Future WeBS counters are almost certainly going to be counting many more Little Egrets, but how many of which other species? Only time will tell.

Acknowledgments

I am grateful to Maureen Gibson and Elliott Randerson for providing helpful comments on this chapter; Ian Black, Carl Borges, Jeremy Dagley, Graham Ekins, Robin Hamilton, Eric Steer, and Gordon Wyatt for background to some of the sites and cases; and Colette Hall at WeBS Secretariat for additional data to those published in the reports. I would like also to thank all those count organisers who took the time to respond to my questionnaire: Jeremy Alderton, Claire Cadman, the late Mike Dennis, John Fitzpatrick, Robert Gardiner, Geoff Gibbs, Alex Jeffries, Brian Knight, Russell Leavett, Julian Novorol, Colin Shields, Andrew Thompson, John Thorogood, Laurence Watts, Derek Wood, Ian Woodward. And I would like especially to pay tribute to the efforts of all counters, past and present, too many to mention personally, who have contributed so much to our knowledge of Essex wetlands and their birds; it is largely down to you that our coast, reservoirs and gravel-pits are still as good as they are. Finally, thanks must go to the many landowners who allow access to their land for the purposes of counting: it says much about the diplomacy of the counters themselves that access is rarely denied, in spite of landowners' initial suspicion of their motives!

Chris Gibson, English Nature, Colchester

ESSEX ORNITHOLOGY – A BRIEF HISTORY

There are few early references to ornithology in Essex and most are rather brief. The Old English poem "The Battle of Maldon" from 991AD referred to the Raven and Earn or Sea Eagle in 10th century Essex. Hollinshed (1586) described an influx of Short-eared Owls at Southminster, attracted by a plague of Short-tailed Voles, whilst Christopher Merrett in 1666 in *Pina Rerum Natularium Britannicarum* observed that the Hoopoe had occurred in Essex. John Ray (1628–1705) was arguably the finest naturalist that Essex ever produced but unfortunately he wrote little about the birds of his native county. However, he did publish *The Ornithology of Francis Willoughby* in 1678. In 1686, John Ray published the first volume of his great botanical work *Historia Plantarum,* the other two volumes following in 1687 and 1704.

There are 18th century wildfowling accounts, by Daniel Defoe (1724) for example, who described the infinite number of wildfowl to be found on Osea Island, whilst Thomas Pennant published his four volume *British Zoology* between 1761 and 1777, in which there were several references to Essex that Christy cited in his own work.

The Victorian bird collectors, who worked on the principle of "what's hit is history, what's missed is mystery", made a big impact. Many collectors were wealthy gentlemen, who developed a passion not only for shooting birds but also for purchasing specimens from dealers for their personal collections. Their legacy may still be found in museums around Essex and the country. Although there were no specific Essex ornithological journals, letters and papers were submitted by the county's ornithologists to *The Field, Zoologist* and *Ibis.*

The formation of the Essex Field Club

The Essex Field Club (EFC) held its inaugural meeting on 10th January 1880 and was the first organisation to make systematic records of all the county's wildlife, a role that it continues to fulfil to this day. One of the first four honorary members was Charles Darwin no less, whilst amongst its ordinary members were Professor Charles C. Babington, author of the first purely Suffolk avifauna *A Catalogue of the Birds of Suffolk* (1884–86) and Robert Miller Christy (Thompson 1930). Its publication, the *Essex Naturalist,* covers all fields of natural history, including ornithology, with Bird Notes in most volumes. The EFC set up a museum at Stratford, which opened to the public on 18th October 1900. It received many fine specimens and collections over the next century. Mr Passmore Edwards, after whom the museum was named, contributed significant sums of money for the erection of the building.

Robert Miller Christy's Avifauna

In 1890, Robert Miller Christy (1861–1928) published the county's first avifauna, *The Birds of Essex* (Christy), jointly with the EFC, having collated information over the previous 15 years. Christy was able to access letters and diaries of many contemporary naturalists and country gentlemen and summarised the activities of the principal Essex ornithologists of the 18th and 19th centuries. His sources and correspondents were extensive.

- Sir Robert Abdy, third baronet, of Albins, in Stapleford Abbots seems to have been a patron of Eleazar Albin, who edited *Natural History of Birds* (1731–38). Albin dedicated the first two volumes to Sir Robert.
- Reverend J.C. Atkinson (1814–1900) was born at Goldhanger and spent his first 24 years in Essex and became acquainted with many areas, but particularly the north Blackwater between Tollesbury and East Mersea; many of his ornithological notes may be found in the early volumes of the *Zoologist*. He wrote *British Birds Eggs and Nests Popularly Described* in 1861.
- Reverend J.C. Atkinson (1786?–1870?), the father of the above, also contributed notes to early volumes of the *Zoologist*. He was a curate at Goldhanger, Great and Little Wigborough, Peldon and elsewhere in Essex.
- G.H. Baxter of Hutton Park, Brentwood, had an interesting selection of mounted birds used as reference by Christy.
- Dr Charles Robert Bree, M.D. (1811–86) came to Essex in 1859 when he was elected physician to Essex and Colchester Hospital, a post he held for 22 years. He published the *History of the Birds of Europe, not observed in the British Isles* (1863) amongst several books that he wrote, which also included two that attacked the Darwinian theory of evolution. He put together a collection of skins that included a number of Essex specimens, including the bones of the Peldon Egyptian Vulture; some of his collection remains in the Colchester Natural History Museum.

- Joseph Clarke, F.S.A. (1802-95) was a naturalist and archaeologist and was closely associated with Saffron Walden and its Museum from its inception in 1834, when he was listed as a trustee of the Saffron Walden Natural History Society. He contributed many specimens, recorded rare birds in the neighbourhood between 1820 and 1845 and authored an abridged catalogue of the Museum's contents in 1845.

- Samuel Dale (1659?–1739) contributed notes and observations to *The History and Antiquities of Harwich and Dovercourt* (Taylor 1730), although his appendix to the work exceeded the main book in size! He provided a few general observations on birds around Harwich, although these were often vague.

- Reverend W.B. Daniel (1753?–1833) was a clergyman who "… indulged in sporting tastes to a degree which shocked even his tolerant age."! His *Rural Sports* (1801) contained a number of references to sport and natural history in Essex.

- Thomas Dix (1830–73) farmed for many years at Stanford Rivers Hall, near Romford, and knew Henry Doubleday well, although it appears he did not leave any observations of interest.

- Edward Doubleday (1811–49), the younger and only brother of Henry Doubleday, was primarily an entomologist, although in 1835 he published "A Catalogue of the Birds which have occurred in the Neighbourhood of Epping Forest" in the *Entomological Magazine* (3: 288–293).

- Henry Doubleday (1808–75) was also an entomologist but he contributed various articles to the *Entomologist* and *Zoologist* magazines, and many of his notes were used by Yarrell in his *History of British Birds* (1837–43). In 1836, he produced *A Nomenclature of British Birds*, which quickly ran through several editions. He was an excellent shot and collected and stuffed a number of birds from Epping Forest, which in time he presented to the British Museum. He is credited with adding Blue-headed Wagtail (3rd October 1834 at Walton-on-the-Naze) and Little Ringed Plover (about 1845 at Shoreham, Sussex) to the British List. His first contribution to science was probably "Notes on the Habits of the Hawfinch" in *Jardine's Magazine of Zoology* in 1837. He can probably be credited with introducing the method of sugaring to attract moths.

- James Lake English (1820–88) of Epping assisted and collected for Henry Doubleday and gained a reputation as a skilled preserver of birds and animals, although he was best known for his knowledge of fungi and lepidoptera.

- Edward Fitch, F.L.S., F.E.S., gave Christy great assistance and was President of the EFC from 1888–92 (Thompson 1930), Mayor of Maldon (where he farmed over 800ha) and very active in both natural and local natural history and archaeological societies. Glegg used Fitch's annotated copy of Christy's *Birds of Essex*.

- Jabez Gibson (1794–1838) was a key founder, financial supporter and Trustee of the Saffron Walden Museum.

- Johnathan Grubb (1808–?) of Sudbury made several contributions to Loudon's *Magazine of Natural History* and wrote a paper on "Birds of My Premises" published in the *Friends' Quarterly Examiner* of 1876, referenced by Christy.

- Reverend Walter Henry Hill of Southminster contributed a list of the birds in his area to Loudon's *Magazine of Natural History* (6: 452).

- George Palmer Hope (1845–1929) of Upminster Hall donated his collection of mainly Essex and Suffolk specimens to Chelmsford Museum in 1921; he was of great assistance to Christy.

- J.D. Hoy (1797–1839) was a "…first-rate shot, a skilled bird-stuffer and an ardent naturalist," although the Norfolk and Suffolk coasts were his main areas of "work". His collection, now in the Southend Museum, included several specimens shot around Stoke-by-Nayland, close to the Essex border.

- F. Kerry was based at Harwich and assisted Christy and Charles Babington in Suffolk with their books.

- William Doubleday King (1801–70), a cousin of the Epping Doubledays, was very active in the Sudbury area. He was a "…very clever bird-stuffer" and produced "A List of Birds found in the neighbourhood of Sudbury" in *Fulchers Sudbury Magazine* for the year 1838.

- Henry Laver, M.R.C.S., L.S.A., F.L.S., F.S.A. of Colchester gave Christy much valuable assistance. He was Mayor of Colchester and wrote *The Mammals, Fishes and Reptiles of Essex* (1898).

- Captain W. Vincent Legge, R.A., was stationed at Shoebury from 1865–66 and wrote three papers for the *Zoologist*: "Notes on the Nesting birds in the Flat Lands of Essex" (23: 9836), "Ornithological Notes from South-east Essex" (34: 89), and "Oological Notes from South-east Essex" (34: 599). He also authored *History of the Birds of Ceylon* (1880).

- Arthur Lister J.P., F.L.S. of Leytonstone aided Christy.

- Allan MacLean M.D. (1796–1869) of Colchester had an extensive knowledge of birds but apparently never published anything. He was an accomplished bird-stuffer and was apparently successful at netting birds with what he called "spider nets".
- Christopher Parsons (1807–82) resided at North Shoebury Hall Farm and kept natural history diaries, shot extensively on New England Island with his father and stuffed many specimens, which now reside in Southend Museum. He started but never finished a number of literary works in manuscript form including a "History of British Birds" that may still be referenced, together with his game books, in the Essex Records Office, Wharf Road, Chelmsford CM2 6YT. He wrote a number of articles for various natural history magazines, with his first in *Field Naturalist* in 1833 about Black-headed Gulls. He was an accomplished all-round naturalist who kept extensive records and correspondence, although he seems to have given up his natural history work after his second marriage in 1850.
- Colonel Champion Russell (1820–87) of Stubbers, North Ockendon, was a keen naturalist, enthusiastic wildfowler and friend of the "fishermen gunners". He was well known on the Blackwater where he had one of the biggest punt guns in the district. He wrote various letters to *The Times*, *The Field* and *Essex Chronicle* and other papers particularly on wildfowl. He advocated and successfully achieved a closed time for shooting all protected animals and was Chairman of the Court of Quarter Sessions appointed to look into the matter. Unfortunately, he left no notes or papers of ornithological interest.
- Reverend Revett Sheppard (?–1830?) of Wrabness was the joint author with Rev. William Whitear of the *Catalogue of Norfolk and Suffolk Birds* (1824–25) and made many observations around the Stour.
- Charles Smoothy of Old Riffhams, Danbury, donated his collection of stuffed birds to Chelmsford Museum and assisted Christy.
- Frederick Spalding of Colchester was curator of the Museum and provided Christy with information.
- Cornelius Walford (1803–1883) of Witham spent much time in Epping and Hainault Forests.

Christy investigated various bird collections within the county's museums, both private and public, including those of: Lord Braybrooke at Audley End; G.H. Baxter of Hutton; Dr Charles Bree of Colchester; Colchester Museum; G.P. Hope of Upminster (now in Chelmsford Museum); J. D. Hoy; W. D. King; Saffron Walden Museum; Charles Smoothy of Danbury (now in Chelmsford Museum); Sudbury Museum. He even re-catalogued the bird and animal collections in the Saffron Walden Museum in 1883. Christy also wrote a comprehensive chapter about wildfowl decoys and wildfowling in Essex, detailing the history and the locations of all the county's decoys. In 1903, he contributed to *The Victorian History of the County of Essex*, which updated his book of 13 years previous. He was EFC President from 1905–07.

Little systematic work had been done on ringing and migration but Christy did recognise that Light Ships (L.S.) and Light Houses (L.H.) could provide valuable information if collated systematically, work already begun by the British Association Migration Committee. He listed seven: Cork L.S., 8km south of Harwich River; Landguard Point L.H., entrance to Harwich River; Galloper L.S., 64km southeast of Orfordness; Kentish Knock L.S., 53km northeast of North Foreland, Kent; Swan Middle L.S., off Thames; Tongue L.S., off Thames; and Nore L.S., entrance to Thames.

William Edwin Glegg's Avifauna

William Edwin Glegg (1879–1952) was born in Edinburgh and moved to the London area in 1903, residing close to Epping Forest but never within the county's borders. He was an active and respected field ornithologist who tramped along many of the county's estuaries and wrote a number of papers for the EFC's *Essex Naturalist*. He authored the county's second avifauna, *A History of the Birds of Essex* (Glegg), which was published in 1929, 39 years after the first. Glegg contacted a large number of correspondents and his comprehensive literature review included London Natural History Society (LNHS) official ornithological records; there are 1,262 references in the Bibliography up to and including 1927.

Glegg adopted no hard-and-fast rule when admitting records but considered each case on its own merits i.e. he used his own judgement. What seems clear, however, is that if a specimen was not obtained the record was dismissed. In all, he admitted 273 species onto the Essex List. He rejected the records of the following species published in Christy: Baikal Teal, Great Shearwater, Black Stork, Great White Egret, Little Crake, Purple (Green-backed) Gallinule, Black-winged Stilt, Short-billed Dowitcher (Red-breasted Sandpiper), Roseate Tern, Passenger Pigeon, Snowy Owl, Eagle Owl, Gyr Falcon, Swallow-tailed Kite, Golden Eagle, Bluethroat, Savi's Warbler, Crested Tit, Chough and Parrot Crossbill. He also rejected Egyptian Goose (Tasker 1868), Wilson's Petrel (Christy 1903),

Buff-breasted Sandpiper (Westell 1903) and American Robin (Harting 1901). In addition, Glegg rejected records of the following subspecies: Black-bellied Dipper, Grey-headed Wagtail, Dark-breasted Barn Owl and Northern Long-tailed Tit (*British Birds* 5: 328).

Like Christy, Glegg visited museums: Chelmsford; Maldon; EFC Passmore Edwards Museum, Stratford; Saffron Walden; Southend; Booth Museum, Brighton, Sussex. Fewer museums now existed and many private collections had been dispersed, though Glegg detailed several correspondents who retained collections. These included P. M. Meeson who possessed the 1908 Spotted Eagle taken at Downham.

With respect to ringing and migration, Glegg accepted records from the following Light Ships (L.S.) and lighthouses (L.H.): Landguard L.H., 1.6km east of Harwich; Longsand L.S., 24km east-southeast of The Naze; Galloper L.S., 42km east-southeast of The Naze; Kentish Knock L.S., 43km east of Holliwell Point; Swin Middle L.S. 10km east of Holliwell Point; Mouse L.S., 11km east of Shoeburyness; Tongue L.S., 37km east of Shoeburyness; Nore L.S., 6km southeast of Shoeburyness. Dr Eagle Clarke observed migration on the Kentish Knock L.S. in 1903. The migration reports from 1906–14 produced by the British Ornithologists' Club were consulted. Glegg's research revealed 48 ringing recoveries involving Essex, including: a Dunlin from Germany; Black-headed Gulls from Holland (2), Denmark (2), Poland (1) and Sweden (1); three Common Gulls from Denmark.

Between the wars

The next 20 years (1929–49) saw more papers published in the EFC's *Essex Naturalist* including those by Glegg: "Various Notes on Birds" (1929); "The Lea Valley Reservoirs" (1934); "Heronries of Essex" (1934-35) and "Broad Features of the Ornithology of Essex" (1940). Ornithology in Essex benefited from the construction of various reservoirs, such as the 12 waters of Walthamstow between 1860 and 1900, KGV in 1912, Abberton in 1940, Girling in 1951, Hanningfield in 1954 and Ardleigh in the early 1970s. From 1936 onwards, the LNHS produced the annual *London Bird Report* (LBR), which summarised ornithological sightings for the area within "20 miles" of St Paul's Cathedral, including Metropolitan Essex. The whole Metropolitan area was comprehensively covered by the LNHS and culminated in the *Birds of the London Area Since 1900* (Homes 1964).

Formation of the Essex Birdwatching Society

In April 1949, Mr Albert Holman (1897–1980) wrote to the county press listing his garden birds in a letter (Pyman 1980); he can truly be said to be the Essex Birdwatching and Preservation Society's (EBWPS) founder. The publicity given to the letter resulted in many enquiries by letter and telephone suggesting that there was a great need for a County Ornithological Society. He therefore booked a room at the Headquarters of the Essex Farmers Union, 1 King Edward Avenue, Chelmsford, on 2nd July 1949 for a meeting of a group of 11 enthusiasts (Mrs Allen and Messrs Baker, Barton, Friedlein, Grant, Hooper, Holman, Makin, Pyman, Stott and Strutt) who decided to form the EBWPS. Consequently, another advertisement was placed in the *Essex Chronicle* and another meeting took place in Canons Restaurant in Duke Street, Chelmsford (Green 2000). The first Annual General Meeting was held on 1st March 1950 and an Interim Executive Committee was appointed; Albert Holman was elected the first chairman and Glegg its first President. Membership of the Society rose from around 80 at the end of 1949 to 220 by the end of 1950. The first bird report that summarised the status and distribution of the county's species covering 1949–50 was produced in mid–1950. Thereafter, an annual bird report was produced covering one calendar year.

The late Geoff Pyman MBE (1920–99) was one of the founder members of the Society and served on its Executive (1949–89; Chairman 1959–64) and Recording (1949–87; Chairman 1970–87) Committees, and also acted as Recorder (1949–58) and EBR Editor (1949–70). He has been described as "…one of the most able all-round naturalists ever to have lived in Essex" (Cox). In addition, he was elected the first General Secretary of the *British Birds* Rarities Committee (BBRC) in 1959 and was a committee member until 1970. Geoff also chaired the Essex Naturalists' Trust (ENT) formation committee in 1958, and when the ENT formed in 1959 he became Chairman. The ENT became the Essex Wildlife Trust in 1984. Geoff's obituary appeared in EBR 1998 (Green 2000).

In 1954, the RSPB, with the help of the EBWPS, produced a leaflet describing birdwatching in Essex (Pyman & Spencer 1954) to promote the EBWPS and LNHS. Also in 1954, the EBWPS helped set up Bradwell Bird Observatory, a site that has produced a wealth not only of ringing data but also more general observations, particularly on migration (Smith 2006). The EBR 1954 included the first ringing report from Romford Ringing Station based at the Sewage Farm there, the last report coming in 1962; a number of significant observations included records of large flocks of Tree Sparrows, among others. In 1957, the EBWPS produced its first biannual magazine, the *Bulletin*, under the editorship of the late Mike Freeman.

Coincidentally in 1954, Peterson, Mountfort & Hollom's *A Field Guide to the Birds of Britain and Europe* appeared and became very popular. The interest in ornithology and identification skills began to increase not only locally but also nationally.

Robert Hudson and Geoff Pymans' Avifauna

In 1968, 39 years after the publication of Glegg's avifauna (which in turn was published 39 years after Christy's), Robert Hudson and Geoff Pyman produced *A Guide to the Birds of Essex* (Hudson & Pyman) that comprehensively reviewed all Essex records and was to become a standard reference for 16 years. Examination of the Bibliography and species' texts show that the authors consulted available *EBRs* up to 1966 but included a number of 1967 records, LNHS LBRs up to at least 1964 and the EFC's *Essex Naturalist* to ensure that the coverage of Essex bird records was as complete as possible. A total of 297 species was admitted to the Essex list.

Hudson & Pyman rejected records of the following nine species accepted by Glegg, with the evidence considered unsatisfactory: Surf Scoter, Harlequin Duck, Goshawk, Sooty Tern, Bridled Tern, Hawk Owl (3), Richard's Pipit, all Marsh Warbler records and Icterine Warbler. Additionally, four Red-headed Bunting records were regarded as escapes. The Richard's Pipit (25th September 1903) and Icterine Warbler (22nd September 1903) records both came from the Kentish Knock Light Ship but, at 43km offshore, these were felt to be too distant to be considered Essex occurrences. They also rejected the 1912 Bradfield Northern Long-tailed Tit record, although accepted by Witherby *et al.* (1938–41). In addition, Hudson & Pyman reinstated the following species: Little Crake (1873) after Glegg's research (Glegg 1929); Black Stork (1881); Parrot Crossbill (1862) and the *guttata* subspecies of Barn Owl (1843 and 1864).

Survey work

The whole of the British Isles was surveyed during 1968–72, using the 10km grid system and confirmed, probable or possible breeding records were collated for each species. The results were published in *The Atlas of Breeding Birds of Britain and Ireland* (First National Atlas) by the BTO and the Irish Wildbird Conservancy. Whilst conducting this survey, members of the LNHS subdivided the study area into tetrads (2km x 2km squares) and the results were published in *The Atlas of Breeding Birds of the London Area* (First London Atlas).

The fieldwork for the Birds of Estuaries Enquiry (BoEE) took place during 1969–75. It was sponsored by the Nature Conservancy Council and organised by the BTO, RSPB and the Wildfowl Trust. The results were published in *Estuary Birds of Britain and Ireland* (Prater 1981). A third London airport was threatened at that time for Foulness Island and Maplin Sands but the survey helped highlight the extreme importance of this part of the Essex coast. An abridged version of the final report can be found in *EBR 1976* (Blindell 1977). Other ornithological surveys in conjunction with the Maplin Enquiry included a gull survey in the Foulness area and Thames Estuary and a study of the Brent Goose, both surveys funded by the Government.

Simon Cox's Avifauna

As interest in ornithology grew and the volume of data collected increased annually, the Society put in motion the production of a new avifauna. Dr Simon Cox took the reins and in 1984 *A New Guide to the Birds of Essex* (Cox) was published. The county's fourth avifauna again reviewed all records and reassessed the status of every species incorporating much data from recent surveys. Cox published two records that had been rejected by BBRC but were still regarded as genuine by the EBS Recording Committee: Great Snipe, two on the Crouch Estuary 17th August 1958, and Yellow-browed Warbler, one at The Naze on 16th March 1961. However, the EBS's policy now respects all BBRC decisions and these two records have been rejected.

The EBS's *Essex Bird Report* and Identification Panel

The EBS's annual bird report (*EBR*) has gone from strength to strength thanks to some very progressive Editors and sympathetic Recording and Executive Committees over the years. In 1953, the first black-and-white photograph appeared (Night Herons at Steeple and Foulness taken by the late Mrs P. V. Upton and the late V. G. Robson), whilst in 1964 the first histogram was included showing the seasonal distribution of Kestrel records. In 1965, the first vignette appeared, a scraper-board drawing of the Hanningfield Short-toed Lark by Richard Hull. In 1985, Categories D and E were included and in 1987, a colour photograph graced the cover for the first time, a Grey Plover at Bradwell by the late Bob Glover. In 1988, production became fully computerised using an Amstrad Word Processor, colour photographs became standard and the report was perfect-bound. The first digital image was used in 2001 and submission of records to the Recorders via the Internet began to catch on.

In 1990, Dr J. T. R. Sharrock, then Editor of *British Birds*, was persuaded to start an annual competition to judge county bird reports. With its imaginative and novel ideas on layouts and contents, the Society won the national competition five times against stiff opposition from 1992–95 and 1997. The success was undoubtedly due to the very high and demanding standards set by the EBR Editors, together with excellent cooperation from the Recording Committee and Editorial team. The highest standards have been maintained to the present. The BTO has since sponsored this competition and EBR 2000 came third equal for that year's competition.

With the publication of many good field guides, papers and reference material, increasing information through ringing, studies of migration, etc., Jim Smith proposed at the EBS Records Committee Meeting of 8th February 1990 that an Identification Panel should be set up with six highly respected Essex birdwatchers to review the submitted descriptions of the rarer county species. Dr Simon Cox, Graham Ekins, the late Stan Hudgell (1935–2003), Phil Vines and John Wright were duly elected to perform this onerous task. The Identification Panel currently (2005–06) consists of: Dave Acfield, Steve Arlow, Clive Atkins, David Bradnum, Andrew Thompson, Paul Wood and Adrian Kettle.

Into a new millennium

The BTO initiated fieldwork for a second national atlas from 1988–91, which culminated in *The New Atlas of Breeding Birds in Britain and Ireland* (Second National Atlas). At the same time, the LNHS updated its tetrad Atlas during 1988–92. The EBS decided to extend tetrad coverage to the whole of Essex during 1988–94 and this resulted in the late Mike Dennis's *Tetrad Atlas of the Breeding Birds of Essex* (Essex Atlas), published in 1996. Over 180 EBS members participated in the survey work covering the whole of the county.

In August 1997, Mike Dent initiated the East London Birders Forum (ELBF) encouraging local birders to meet, collate bird records and participate in various survey work (e.g. Mandarin and Woodcock). The first monthly meeting was in the Kings Inn, Chipping Ongar but this was eventually moved to The County Arms, Highams Park, where they are still held on the second Tuesday of each month. In 2000, Mike Dent and the ELBF set up a meeting with the Lea Valley Regional Park to discuss the possibility of organising a bird fair. Following the first successful Lea Valley Birdwatching Fair in February 2001 at Hayes Hill Farm, near Fishers Green, it has become an annual event and bigger and better each passing year, a very creditable achievement. The ELBF first produced an annual bird report in 2000 for their region and intend to do so in future years.

In 2004, Bradwell Bird Observatory celebrated its 50th birthday. Smith (2006) detailed its history at great length in his own inimitable style; what is clear is the debt owed in particular to Malcolm Chettleburgh for his decades of support for the Observatory. Thanks must also go to the band of stalwarts who continue to provide a wealth of data and cups of tea to this day.

The current avifauna and research

By 1998, it was realised that, because of the almost exponential increase in new data and information, another county avifauna was necessary just 14 years after the last. On a warm autumn day in 1997 Simon Wood met the late Chris McClure (1947–2000) on the Layer Breton causeway at Abberton. They discussed Wood's 1995 EBR paper *Rare Birds in Essex: an update* (Wood 1996). Chris suggested that a book or booklet expanding on the paper would have a market; anyone who knew Chris will know that he rarely missed a marketing opportunity! That winter, Simon completed a full and detailed analysis with a view to publication. In the summer of 1998, Mark Hawkes wrote a letter to the Editor of *Essex Birding* (92: 37), the EBS's biannual magazine, offering to initiate the new avifauna. However, Simon had already sown the seeds with the rarer species and so took the reins of the project and a Working Group was soon set up with Simon in the Senior Editor role. Details of the Working Group members and their responsibilities and achievements can be found in Acknowledgements.

Extensive research for this new avifauna directly or indirectly has caused the following changes to the ornithological record:

- New Essex records accepted by BOURC: 1826 American Bittern (Green 2002) in Saffron Walden Museum, the second British record.
- New Essex records accepted by BBRC: 1894 White's Thrush at Langley; 1970 Red-breasted Goose shot on Potton Island 30th December, held in Colchester Museum; 1989 Subalpine Warbler found as a roadside casualty at Lawford, near Manningtree, on 17th April, held in Colchester Museum.

- New Scottish record accepted by Scottish Ornithologists' Rarities Committee (SORC): White-billed Diver shot in Aberdeen in 1891 becomes the first for Scotland and 5th for Britain (Green 2005). The specimen is still in Chelmsford Museum although is not on display. The late Stan Hudgell first identified it.
- New Essex records accepted by the Identification Panel of the EBS Recording Committee: White-tailed Eagle, Wivenhoe, 16th or 17th December 1868 (Green 2004a), previously listed as eagle sp. in Glegg; various species found in museums (e.g. Little Auk, Honey-buzzard) and accordingly recorded in EBR 1999; Missing *London Bird Report* data (Green 2004b).
- New Suffolk record of Two-barred Crossbill at Dedham in July 1866 (Christy).
- Corrections to records: 1908 Spotted Eagle to include dates for both 10th and 13th–14th April (Green 2003). Glegg printed only 14th April and relegated Meeson's sighting on 10th April to a probable White-tailed Eagle, repeated by Hudson & Pyman and Cox.
- Deleted historic Essex records: after reviewing them with the late Geoff Pyman, Simon Wood proposed to BBRC that the records of two Great Reed Warblers at North Fambridge on 28th-29th August 1959 and male Collared Flycatcher there on 21st-23rd September 1957 be removed from the record, which was done. Also a probable White-tailed Eagle near Battlesbridge on 10th April 1908 was actually a Spotted Eagle (see above).

In addition, through its own reviews, BBRC has rejected the following historic Essex records since 1998:

- Baillon's Crake, one at Abberton on 13th June 1953.
- Laughing Gull, one at Abberton on 27th December 1957.

The following changes to the Essex List since Cox have been effected by recommendations of the BOURC; the brackets after the species' name indicate the year of the BOURC's decisions:

- Elevated from subspecies to species: Water Pipit (1986), American and Pacific Golden Plovers (1986), Mediterranean Shearwater (1991), Southern Grey Shrike (1996), Eastern and Western Bonelli's Warblers (1997), Green-winged Teal (2000), Common (Mealy) Redpoll (2000), Balearic (Mediterranean) Shearwater (2002), Hooded Crow (2002) and Yellow-legged Gull (2005).
- Elevated to Category C status: Snow Goose (2005).
- Elevated to subspecies level: Taiga and Tundra Bean Goose; Caspian Gull (2003).
- Relegated from Category A to D status: Baikal Teal (1993). In addition, the record of an Indigo Bunting at The Naze on 8th September 1973 still languishes in Category D after a recent BOURC review. Ruddy Shelduck is also included in Category D rather than A.
- Elevated to Category D status: Bar-headed Goose (1993), Muscovy Duck (1993), Falcated Duck (1993), Chukar (1993), Booted Eagle (2002).
- Relegated from Category D to E status: Bar-headed Goose (1998), Muscovy Duck (1998), Wood Duck (1998), Chukar (1998).
- Removed from Category E: Bobwhite (1991).
- Records still awaiting ratification at time of going to press: Least Tern at Colne Point from 29th June-1st July 1991. The identification has been accepted by BBRC and BOURC but it is now up to the BOURC's Taxonomic Sub-Committee (TSC) to determine subspecies or species' status.

Fraud

In all the research for this Avifauna, it is worth noting that that there has been little evidence of deliberate fraud in Essex. There were great opportunities in the Victorian era for collectors and dealers of stuffed birds to claim remarkable records for Britain e.g. the notorious Hastings Rarities affecting the collection of a number of rare birds shot allegedly in Sussex and Kent. Closer to home, Saffron Walden Museum houses a Bufflehead allegedly collected at Great Yarmouth, Norfolk, in winter 1830 but this record was considered unacceptable by the BOURC after detailed review (Knox 2001). Glegg listed three Chelmsford February records of Hawk Owl from 1913 from the collection of Sir Vauncey Harpur Crewe Bart. (1846–1925) of Calke Abbey in Nottinghamshire. Sir Vauncey appears to have been a hapless victim of unscrupulous taxidermists (Mairs 2004).

Nick Green

ESSEX MUSEUMS AND COLLECTIONS

Of all the authors of previous Essex avifauna books, only Christy and Glegg systematically visited and reviewed the key Essex museum collections to check specimens and to confirm their identification. Hudson & Pyman and Cox relied on their predecessors for the documentation of historic records.

All the present-day curators of Essex museums are sincerely thanked for their extensive cooperation and assistance during visits to the various collections and for further research into particular specimens. Special thanks must go to Sarah Kenyon, Jerry Bowdrey, John Skinner, Roger Payne and Tony Walentowicz.

Simon Wood, Nick Green, Russell Neave and Graham Ekins were able to visit most Essex museums together during the period 2000–02 to view all Essex specimens to confirm identification and, where necessary, research their history. Nick Green also visited the Queen Elizabeth Hunting Lodge, Epping (formerly the Epping Museum, organised by the Essex Field Club), and the Booth Museum of Natural History in Brighton, Sussex. Unfortunately, we were not able to visit the Essex Field Club's Passmore Edwards Museum, as this had to be moved in 2001 from Stratford to temporary accommodation where inspection of bird specimens was not possible. However, thanks to Mark Hanson, access was granted to their Accession Registers and any significant records are detailed below. In addition, correspondence regarding collections at various museums took place and the following are thanked for their assistance: David Lampard, Ipswich Museum, Ipswich; Dr Tony Irwin, Castle Museum, Norwich; Clem Fisher, Liverpool Museum; and Christine Taylor, Hampshire Museums Service.

A summary of the museums visited follows below, highlighting key Essex specimens and those of national significance. A detailed summary has never before appeared in an Essex avifauna.

Audley End House Collection
Audley End, Saffron Walden CB11 4JF. ✆ (01799) 822399
www.english-heritage.org.uk
Curator: Gareth Hughes
Richard Lord Braybrooke and Charles Lord Braybrooke compiled the collection of both foreign and native birds in the 19th century. Many of the specimens are exotics with few Essex specimens present or indeed documented.
Essex specimens
Bittern shot at Audley End in 1831 (Christy)

Chelmsford Museum
Oaklands Park, Moulsham Street, Chelmsford, CM2 9AQ. ✆ (01245) 615100
www.chelmsfordbv.gov.uk/museums/chfd.htm
Curator: Dr Tony Walentowicz
The Museum houses 19th and early 20th century collections from Dr Charles Smoothy of Old Riffhams, Danbury, Dr Salter of Tollesbury and George Hope from Upminster Hall. Interesting documentation includes the personal diary of P.M. Meeson, a rather notorious egg collector during the early 20th century, although the diary helped confirm the dates of the 1908 Spotted Eagle (Green 2003). There are also several 19th century specimens from Boulton's collection but these are all of doubtful origin: Black-winged Stilt from Woodbridge, Suffolk, in 1882; Spotted Sandpiper from Woodbridge, Suffolk; two Collared Pratincoles from Great Yarmouth, Norfolk, in November 1810.
Essex specimens
Baikal Teal immature male shot at Marsh House Decoy, Tillingham, on 1st January 1906 (Category D).
White-throated Needletail shot at Great Horkesley on 8th July 1846, first county and British record.
Rose-coloured Starling shot Maldon about 1870, second county record.
National specimens
Glossy Ibis. Two juveniles allegedly shot on the Orkney Islands in 1908; more likely two of ten shot from a flock of 19-20 at Sandwich in 1907.
White-billed Diver collected in Aberdeen 1891 (Hope's collection, previously identified as a Great Northern Diver) has been accepted by the Scottish Ornithological Rarities Committee and now constitutes Britain's fifth and Scotland's first record. The late Stan Hudgell first suspected that the identification of the diver was incorrect back on 24th September 1961! (Green 2005b).

Cream-coloured Courser immature male shot near Cheswick, Northumberland, 9th November 1846, tenth record for Britain (Hope's collection).

Great Snipe. Two shot Ramsholt Marshes, Suffolk, in 1882 and Woodbridge, Suffolk, in 1896 (not in Piotrowski 2003).

Pallas's Sandgrouse. Two shot at Barniston, North Yorkshire, 16th May 1888.

Of interest

Night Heron. One of a pair allegedly shot at Marazion, Cornwall, in 1875 – not in national statistics.

Egyptian Vulture allegedly shot in Jersey, Channel Isles, bought by Hope in 1873.

Pine Grosbeak allegedly shot in the New Forest in 1891 but there is no supporting documentation.

Further research

A case containing three eiders in Hope's collection contains undocumented specimens of an apparent male *borealis* Eider collected on the Orkney Islands on 10th June 1891 (a potential first British record if accepted by BOURC) and also a female King Eider shot 21st August 1888, again in the Orkney Islands.

Colchester Natural History Museum

High Street, Colchester CO1 1DN. ✆ (01206) 282927

www.colchestermuseums.org.uk

Curator: Jerry Bowdrey

A large collection of skins is stored and documented well.

Essex specimens

Red-breasted Goose shot on Ray Sands, Dengie coast, 6th January 1871, first county record.

Red-breasted Goose shot on Potton Island 29th December 1970, second county record.

Male Subalpine Warbler, a road casualty found on 17th April 1989 at Lawford, near Manningtree, the third county record.

Of interest

Chiloe Wigeon x Wigeon cross from the Point, Langenhoe, on 2nd October 1982.

Passenger Pigeon purchased from Sotherby's on 11th July 1968.

Indian Treepie. A female found dead at Braintree in February 1970.

Passmore Edwards Museum of the Essex Field Club

www.essexfieldclub.org.uk/

Many bird and other specimens have been donated and purchased since the formation of the Essex Field Club in 1880. At the time of writing (2006), the Museum is still in temporary accommodation and may not be visited.

Essex specimens

Red Kite. Christy donated two eggs from the last nest at Maldon in 1854.

Common Buzzard. Christy donated two eggs from the clutch at Purleigh in 1865.

Baillon's Crake caught by a dog at Dagenham Gulf on 3rd October 1874, the only county record.

Roller shot at Little Chesterford on 14th June 1865, first county record.

Nutcracker. One of three shot in the Colchester area, 1858-60.

Of interest

Swallow-tailed Kite shot at Mildenhall, Suffolk, by Mr. O.W. Travers between 1830 and 1840 (Glegg 1927, 1929).

Saffron Walden Museum

Museum Street, Saffron Walden CB10 1JL. ✆ (01799) 510333

www.uttlesford.gov.uk/museum/default.htm

Natural Sciences Curatorial Officer: Sarah Kenyon

A large collection mainly from the 19th century that is well documented and cross-referenced. The Museum opened on 12th May 1835 and the collection of British birds originated primarily from Joseph Clarke (specimens mainly from Yarmouth, Norfolk), Jabez Gibson, Stephen Salmon and Henry Doubleday.

Essex specimens

American Bittern shot spring 1826, first county and second national record (Green 2002).

Gull-billed Tern. One shot at Ashdon on 21st May 1901, first county record.

Woodchat Shrike. Two (pair) shot at Elmdon/Arkesden, 27th August 1880, first county record.

National specimens

Black-winged Stilt shot River Bure, Great Yarmouth, Norfolk, summer 1824.

Cream-coloured Courser shot Friston, near Saxmundham, Suffolk, 3rd October 1828, first Suffolk and fifth British record.

Of interest

Bufflehead allegedly collected at Great Yarmouth, Norfolk, but this specimen and record was considered unacceptable by the BOURC after a detailed review (Knox 2001).

Southend Museum: Central Museum

Victoria Avenue, Southend-on-Sea SS2 6EW. *C* (01702) 434449

http://southendmuseums.co.uk/

Curators: John Skinner and Roger Payne

The collection includes mainly 19th century specimens from the collections of local naturalist Christopher Parsons and Suffolk naturalist J.D. Hoy.

Essex specimens

Spotted Eagle shot at Leigh-on-Sea on 3rd November 1891, a spectacular specimen and second county record.

American Wigeon. A first-winter male shot on Foulness on 20th December 1962, first county record.

Temminck's Stint shot at Lower Fleet, New England Island, on 25th August 1835, first county record.

Lesser Yellowlegs shot at West Mersea on 8th August 1921, first county record.

Dartford Warbler shot on Shoebury Common, November 1837, first county record.

Further research

Within Christopher Parsons' collection, but unfortunately with no corroborating evidence found as yet in his documentation, are several potential first records for Britain: Kentish Plover, Short-billed Dowitcher and Spotted Sandpiper. Note all Parsons' documents are now held in the Essex Records Office, Wharf Road, Chelmsford CM2 6YT. The Short-billed Dowitcher is presumably listed as Brown Snipe.

Booth Museum of Natural History

194 Dyke Road, Brighton, East Sussex BN1 5AA. *C* (01273) 292777

www.boothmuseum.virtualmuseum.info/

Curator: Jeremy Adams

The large collection, mainly from the 19th century, is well documented and includes specimens from the notorious Hasting Rarities era that are clearly marked with red labels.

Essex specimens

Egyptian Vulture shot at Stanway Hall, Peldon, on 28th September 1868, the only county and second national record.

Pacific Golden Plover moulting adult shot 6th August 1882 at Shell Haven, first county and third national record.

National specimens

Cream-coloured Courser shot at Mawgan, Cornwall, in December 1884, the 22nd national record.

Of interest

Bridled Tern obtained in September 1875 on one of the lightships at the mouth of the Thames, but subsequently discredited.

Hawk Owl shot in 1913 in Chelmsford of dubious origin. From Sir Vauncey Harpur Crewe's collection.

Further research

There may be two White-billed Divers; one each in the two cases each containing three Great Northern Divers.

ESSEX ORNITHOLOGICAL HIGHLIGHTS

The following table highlights in chronological order significant ornithological events that have occurred in Essex. The left hand column gives the first year of occurrence; the one to its immediate right lists the species against the year of the first documented record and uses all listed references (some species have undated, earlier occurrences – see Systematic List). Every species on the Essex List is included. There is a considerable amount of information available around the 1810s–1840s, a time when there was a burgeoning interest in the natural world and hence the large number of species appearing for the first time. Further research using estate books, game books and similar old manuscripts may find some earlier references to those given.

A species or subspecies marked with an asterisk* and **emboldened** indicates that this is the first British record. A species or subspecies typed in *italics* constitutes the only Essex record. Those in [brackets] are clearly recognised subspecies and are not included in the cumulative Essex List total.

The right hand column includes important publications, exceptional weather events, details of influxes and the second and third and sometimes the last Essex records of rarer species (e.g. White-tailed Eagle, Dipper).

As at 31st December 2004, the Essex list stood at

Category A/B/C	- 384 species
Category D	- 8 species

YEAR	SPECIES	CUMULATIVE ESSEX LIST	POINTS OF INTEREST
c.991	White-tailed Eagle; Raven	2	Battle of Maldon
1059	Pheasant	3	First documented record of the species in Britain
1100s	Goshawk	4	
1247	Mute Swan	5	
1547	Bar-tailed Godwit	6	
1587	Short-eared Owl	7	Hollinshed's *Chronicles of England, Scotland and Wales*
1594	Grey Heron	8	Norden's *Description of Essex*
1600s	Grey Partridge; Cormorant; Hawfinch	11	
1662	Black-headed Gull	12	Fuller's *Worthies of England*
1667	Hoopoe	13	Merrett's *Pinax Rerum Naturalium Britannicarum*
1668	Lapwing	14	Charleton's *Onomasticon Zoicon*
1676	Song Thrush	15	
1700	Avocet	16	
1714	Wigeon; Teal; Mallard; Pintail	20	Steeple Wildfowl decoy records (1713–1727)
1730	Whooper Swan; Brent Goose; Shelduck; Pochard; Common Scoter; Osprey; Oystercatcher; Herring Gull	28	Taylor's *History and Antiquities of Harwich and Dovercourt*
1732	Chaffinch	29	
1735	Woodcock; Snipe; Blackbird	32	
1738	Hen Harrier; Greenshank; Sandwich Tern; Barn Owl; Nightjar; Goldcrest; Bearded Tit	39	Albin's *Natural History of Birds* (1731–1738)
1768	Red Kite; Nightingale	41	Morant's *History of Essex*
1777	Goldeneye; Quail; Red-legged Partridge; Red-throated Diver; Knot	46	Pennant's *British Zoology* (1768–1777)
1801	Storm Petrel	47	Lewin's *Birds of Great Britain* (1795–1801)
c.1805	Lesser Redpoll	48	

1808	House Sparrow	49	
1813	Great Northern Diver	50	
1815	Spoonbill	51	
1817	**Alpine Accentor***	52	
1818	Hobby; Turtle Dove; Cuckoo; Swift; Wryneck; Sand Martin; Swallow; House Martin; Tree Pipit; Redstart; Sedge Warbler; Whitethroat; Blackcap; Chiffchaff; Willow Warbler; Spotted Flycatcher; Red-backed Shrike	69	Rev. Whitear's *Observations on Summer Migrants at Wrabness* (1818–1830)
1819	Smew; Coot; Whimbrel; Common Sandpiper; Whinchat; Wheatear; Grasshopper Warbler; Reed Warbler; Lesser Whitethroat; Garden Warbler	79	
1820	Shag; Bittern; Great Skua; Little Tern; Yellow Wagtail; Twite	85	Joseph Clarke's notes (1820–45)
1821	Tufted Duck; Black-necked Grebe; Common Tern; Scops Owl; Wood Warbler	90	Graves' *British Ornithology* (1811–1821)
1822	Greylag Goose; Corncrake; Pied Flycatcher	93	Parson's game-books, draft manuscripts, etc. (1822–45)
1823	Leach's Petrel; Marsh Harrier; Peregrine; Little Bustard	97	
1824	Dunlin	98	Little Bustard 2nd
1825	Great Snipe	99	
1826	Red-breasted Merganser; *American Bittern*; Little Stint; Curlew Sandpiper; Curlew; Redshank; Turnstone; Crossbill	107	Sheppard & Whitears' *Catalogue of Norfolk and Suffolk Birds*
1827	Great Grey Shrike	108	
1828	Sanderling; Pomarine Skua	110	
1829	Velvet Scoter; Merlin; Black Tern; Long-eared Owl; Crested Tit	115	First modern White-tailed Eagle record
1830	Barnacle Goose; Scaup; Goosander; Gannet; Buzzard; Water Rail; Great Bustard; Dotterel; Lesser Spotted Woodpecker; Dipper; Golden Oriole; Snow Bunting	127	
1831	Grey Wagtail; Stonechat; Ring Ouzel; Redwing	131	Henry Doubleday's letters to T. C. Heysham (1831–46)
1832	Long-tailed Duck; Montagu's Harrier; Stone Curlew; Spotted Redshank; Green Sandpiper; Little Auk; Tawny Owl; Great Spotted Woodpecker; Woodlark; Starling; Linnet	142	
1833	Purple Sandpiper; Ruff; Tree Sparrow	145	
1834	Fulmar; Black-tailed Godwit; [**Blue-headed Wagtail***]; Fieldfare	148	
1835	Garganey; Shoveler; Little Bittern; Sparrowhawk; Temminck's Stint; Wood Sandpiper; Common Gull; Kittiwake; Rock Pipit; Waxwing; Treecreeper; Carrion Crow; Hooded Crow; Brambling; Mealy Redpoll	163	Dippers (2nd & 3rd); Crossbill influx; Yarrell's *History of British Birds 1st Ed.* Edward Doubleday's Catalogue of the birds of Epping Forest
1836	Canada Goose, Rough-legged Buzzard; [White Wagtail]	165	Great Snipe (2nd)
1837	Bewick's Swan; Gadwall; Red-necked Grebe; Honey Buzzard; Arctic Skua; Dartford Warbler	171	Little Bustard (3rd)

1838	Bean Goose; Little Grebe; Great Crested Grebe; Slavonian Grebe; Spotted Crake; Ringed Plover; Jack Snipe; Grey Phalarope; Lesser Black-backed Gull; Great Black-backed Gull; Stock Dove; Kingfisher; Green Woodpecker; Meadow Pipit; Robin; Nuthatch; Magpie; Rook; Goldfinch; Siskin; Bullfinch; Corn Bunting	193	William Doubleday King's List of the birds of Sudbury area
1839	Night Heron; Purple Heron	195	
1840	Black-throated Diver; Razorbill	197	
1841	Pink-footed Goose	198	
1842	White Stork; Grey Plover; Red-necked Phalarope; Long-tailed Skua; Puffin	203	
1843	[**Dark-breasted Barn Owl***] Woodpigeon	204	
1844	Red-crested Pochard	205	Crested Tit (2nd or 3rd and last)
1845	White-fronted Goose; Golden Plover; Little Gull	208	
1846	White-throated Needletail*; Two-barred Crossbill	210	
1847			Honey Buzzard only breeding record
1851			Morris' *History of British Birds* (1851–57)
1853			Great Snipe (3rd)
1854	Bee-eater; Long-tailed Tit; Cirl Bunting	213	
1855	Nutcracker	214	
1856	Rose-coloured Starling	215	
1857	Jackdaw	216	
1858	Cream-coloured Courser	217	
1860			Little Bittern (2nd); Rose-coloured Starling (2nd)
1861	Collared Pratincole; Guillemot; Parrot Crossbill	220	
1862	Sabine's Gull; Shorelark	222	Parrot Crossbill (2nd & last)
1863	Pallas's Sandgrouse (influx); Moorhen	224	
1864			[Dark-breasted Barn Owl (2nd)]
1865	Eider; LittleOwl; Roller; Skylark	228	
1866	Manx Shearwater; **Mediterranean Gull***	230	Little Bittern (3rd) Two-barred Crossbill (2nd & last)
1867	Arctic Tern	231	
1868	Egyptian Goose; *Egyptian Vulture (last British record)*	233	
1869	Black Guillemot	234	
1870			Rose-coloured Starling (3rd)
1871	Red-breasted Goose; Alpine Swift; Greenfinch	237	
1872	Glossy Ibis; Woodchat; Lapland Bunting	240	Nutcracker (2nd); Harting's *Handbook of British Birds*
1873	Red-footed Falcon; Little Crake	243	
1874	Baillon's Crake, Wren	244	
1875			Swallow over wintered
1876	Kentish Plover; Pied Wagtail	246	
1877	*Tengmalm's Owl*; Yellowhammer	*248*	
1878	Firecrest; Jay	250	

1879	Black Redstart	251	Great Bustard (2nd)
1880	Ferruginous Duck	252	2nd Night Heron; 2nd Woodchat Shrike: Essex Field Club formed
1881	Black Stork	253	Honey Buzzard influx
1883			Seebohm's *History of British Birds* (1883–85)
1884	Blue Tit	254	
1885	Glaucous Gull	255	Black Guillemot (2nd); Cirl Bunting (2nd)
1886	Rock Dove/Feral Pigeon	256	
1887	Iceland Gull	257	
1888	Crane; *Chough*	259	Pallas's Sandgrouse influx; Scops Owl (2nd and last) Cirl Bunting (3rd)
1890	Kestrel; Dunnock; Mistle Thrush; Marsh Tit; Coal Tit; Great Tit; Reed Bunting	266	**Christy published;** Great Bustard (3rd and last record); Raven last breeding records
1891	Spotted Eagle (1st and 2nd records)	267	Night Heron (3rd); Spotted Crake only confirmed breeding record; Baillon's Crake (2nd and last record)
1892	Little Bunting	268	
1894	*White's Thrush*	269	
1896	Pacific Golden Plover	270	Garganey first breeding record
1897			Red-footed Falcon (2nd)
1900			Nutcracker (3rd & 4th)
1901	Gull-billed Tern	271	Red-footed Falcon (3rd)
1908	Ortolan Bunting	272	Spotted Eagle (3rd and last record); Pallas's Sandgrouse influx
1910			Cirl Bunting nest found
1912	White-winged Black Tern; Willow Tit; [Northern Long-tailed Tit]	274	Glossy Ibis (2nd); Black Guillemot (3rd)
1913			Cirl Bunting last nest found
1916			Hard winter 1916–17 affected Goldcrest numbers
1920			Glossy Ibis (3rd)
1921	Lesser Yellowlegs	275	Gadwall first bred; Roller (2nd)
1923	Water Pipit	276	
1928			Black-necked Grebe influx; White-tailed Eagle (last record)
1929			**Glegg published**
1930			Alpine Swift (2nd)
1936	Bluethroat	277	LNHS published first London Bird Report
1938			Witherby's *Handbook of British Birds* (1938–41)
1939			Montagu's Harrier breeds
1940			Montagu's Harrier breeds
1944			Bittern only breeding record; Avocet first bred
1947	Mandarin; Little Ringed Plover; Black-winged Stilt	280	Blue-headed Wagtail nested
1948			Corncrake last breeding record; Black-winged Stilt (2nd); Dartford Warbler only breeding record
1949	Pectoral Sandpiper; Greater Yellowlegs	282	**Formation of Essex Birdwatching & Preservation Society (EBWPS);** White-winged Black Tern (2nd); [Dark-breasted Barn Owl (3rd)]; Black Redstart first bred

1950	Little Egret	283	EBWPS published first Essex Bird Report; Lesser Yellowlegs (2nd); Gull-billed Tern unsuccessfully bred (only British attempt); Wryneck last breeding record
1951	Tawny Pipit	284	Grey Wagtail first bred
1952			Leach's Petrel autumn influx; Woodchat Shrike (3rd)
1953			Extensive East Coast floods; Purple Heron (2nd)
1954	[Grey-headed Wagtail]		**RSPB published "Bird-Watching in Essex" leaflet (Pyman & Spencer 1954);** Peterson, Mountford & Holloms' *Field Guide to the birds of Britain and Europe;* Bradwell Bird Observatory inaugural year; Bee-eater (2nd); Hooded Crow last double-figure flock
1955			Bewick's Swan influx (200); Purple Heron (3rd); Alpine Swift (3rd); Tawny Pipit (2nd)
1956	Green-winged Teal; Marsh Sandpiper	286	Bewick's Swan influx (600+); Chaffinch influx (5,000+)
1957	**[Black Brant*];** Collared Dove; Aquatic Warbler; Yellow-browed Warbler	289	Garganey record breeding numbers; [Grey-headed Wagtail (2nd)]; Jay influx (600+); Ortolan Bunting (2nd)
1958	Ruddy Duck; Desert Wheatear	291	Collared Pratincole (2nd and last record); Wryneck influx (12+); Ortolan Bunting (3rd)
1959	Caspian Tern; Red-breasted Flycatcher	293	Formation of Essex Naturalists' Trust; White-winged Black Tern (3rd); Arctic Tern bred; Chaffinch influx (5,000+)
1960	*Black-winged Pratincole;* Pallas's Warbler	295	Arctic Tern bred (second and last occurrence); Collared Dove first breeding record; Bee-eater (3rd); Tawny Pipit (3rd);
1961	Melodious Warbler; Barred Warbler	297	Black-winged Stilt (3rd); Lesser Yellowlegs (3rd); Lesser Black-backed Gull first nested; Caspian Tern (2nd & 3rd); Blue-headed Wagtail nested; Blackbird November influx (20,000); Red-breasted Flycatcher (2nd); Tree Sparrow autumn passage (3,000); Lapland Bunting influx (70)
1962	[Greenland White-fronted Goose]; American Wigeon; Icterine Warbler	299	1962–63 severe winter
1963	**Snowy Owl**	300	Smew influx; Marsh Sandpiper (2nd); Skylark record influx (20,000+); Icterine Warbler (2nd)
1964	White-rumped Sandpiper	301	Montagu's Harrier bred; Melodious Warbler (2nd)
1965	Short-toed Lark; Great Reed Warbler	303	Little Crake (2nd); Red-breasted Flycatcher (3rd); Little Bunting (2nd)
1966	**Rustic Bunting**	304	Marsh Sandpiper (3rd); Aquatic Warbler (2nd)
1967	Solitary Sandpiper; Whiskered Tern	306	Foot & Mouth Disease outbreak; White-rumped Sandpiper (2nd)
1968	Richard's Pipit	307	**Hudson & Pyman published;** Roller (3rd); Nutcracker influx (16); Icterine Warbler (3rd); Tree Sparrow record winter flock (4,000)
1969	Sooty Shearwater; Red-rumped Swallow	309	Brambling record flock (1,000)
1970			Red-breasted Goose (2nd); Little Bittern (last record)
1971	Black Kite; Ring-necked Parakeet; Subalpine Warbler (1st & 2nd)	312	Melodious Warbler (3rd)
1972	Baird's Sandpiper	313	White-rumped Sandpiper (3rd); Mealy Redpoll summered after record winter influx with largest flock (27)
1973	*Western Sandpiper; Stilt Sandpiper;* Roseate Tern; Yellow-legged Gull	317	Little Crake (3rd); Richard's Pipit (2nd); [Grey-headed Wagtail (3rd)]; Aquatic Warbler (3rd); Great Grey Shrike influx (7)
1974	*Lesser Kestrel;* Laughing Gull	319	Rough-legged Buzzard record influx (20+); Solitary Sandpiper (2nd and last); Gull-billed Tern (3rd)
1975	Balearic Shearwater; Buff-breasted Sandpiper (1st & 2nd); *Asian Desert Warbler; Short-toed Treecreeper; Rose-breasted Grosbeak*	324	Red-breasted Goose (3rd); Roseate Tern (2nd); Red-rumped Swallow (2nd); [Northern Long-tailed Tit (2nd)]; Goldcrest influx

American Bittern *(J. K. Clayden for Saffron Walden Museum)*. 1826 – the second British record.

Greater Spotted Eagle *(John Skinner)*. The 1891 juvenile in Southend Museum.

Naumann's Thrush *(Reston Kilgour)*. Britain's only two records have occurred in Essex.

Southern Grey Shrike *(Rob Wilson)*. Holland-on-Sea, 1996.

Hume's Warbler *(Reston Kilgour)*. Fairlop CP, 2004. First Essex record.

Franklin's Gull *(Alan Tate)*. Creekmouth, 2000. First Essex record.

Cream-coloured Courser *(Ian Lycett)*. Hadleigh Marsh, 1984. Second and last record.

Red-throated Thrush *(Dave Stewart)*. The Naze, 1994. First British record.

The Naze *(Adrian Kettle)*. Arguably the most important site for migrants in Essex.

Willow Warbler *(Steve Lindsell)*. Common summer visitor, although declining in numbers.

Pheasant *(Steve Lindsell)*. A common resident, although under-recorded.

Grey Heron *(Steve Lindsell)*. Numbers in Metropolitan Essex have increased recently.

Tollesbury Managed Retreat *(Andrew Hay, RSPB)*. One of several along the Blackwater.

Abberton Reservoir *(Chris Gibson)*. The only site of international importance for wildfowl and waders in Essex not on the coast.

Pochard *(John Davis)*. Essex holds a significant proportion of the British breeding population.

Coal Tit *(Reston Kilgour)*. Conifer planting during the 20th century allowed the population to expand.

Shingle spit at Foulness *(Chris Gibson)*. A rare habitat in Essex.

Hanningfield Reservoir *(Reston Kilgour)*. Significant numbers of gulls bathe on the reservoir during the winter before moving off to roost.

Old Hall Marshes *(Chris Gomersall)*.　　　**Sedge Warbler** *(The late Bob Glover)*.

This important RSPB reserve is the home to many wetland species, including Sedge Warblers.

Secondary woodland *(Simon Wood)*. The Ridge, Danbury/Little Baddow, was open common 60 years ago.

Temminck's Stint *(Steve Arlow)*. A scarce but annual passage migrant.

Marsh Harrier *(Steve Lindsell)*. Has recently colonised Essex as a breeding species.

Barn Owl *(Steve Lindsell)*. Artificial nest boxes have helped save this species from decline.

Wren *(Steve Lindsell)*. A common and vocal resident.

Lapwing *(Steve Lindsell)*. Wintering numbers have increased almost nine-fold in recent years.

Ring-billed Gull *(Steve Arlow)*. 'Rossi,' who has returned to Westcliff every winter since 2000.

Rainham Marshes *(Chris Gibson)*. The most important site for wildfowl, waders and migrants along the inner Thames and just 13 miles from the City of London.

Farmland *(Chris Gibson)*. Oil-seed Rape accounts for 50% of the non-cereal arable crops.

Snow Bunting *(Steve Arlow)*. Favours the shingle banks of The Naze, Colne Point, Dengie and Foulness.

Wheatear *(Steve Lindsell)*. One of the most conspicuous passage migrants.

Dark-bellied Brent Goose *(Steve Lindsell)*. Up to 50% of the British population may occur in the county during the winter.

Kestrel *(Steve Lindsell)*. A common sight in the county.

Dunnock *(Steve Lindsell)*. Increased tree planting and landscaping should benefit the species.

Nightingale *(Steve Lindsell)*. 10% of the British population occurs within the county.

Turtle Dove *(Steve Lindsell)*. An individual ringed at Abberton in 1963 was recovered 4,422 km away in Mali, West Africa, a typical wintering area.

Woodland *(Chris Gibson)*. A typical Essex woodland will hold 40–55 species in summer or winter.

Saltings on Two Tree Island along the Thames Estuary *(Bob Glover)*.

Conifer Wood *(Chris Gibson)*. Many conifer woods are now being clear-felled.

Tiptree Heath *(Chris Gibson)*. One of the last remaining areas of heathland.

A brown field site near Grays *(Chris Gibson)*. Very important but undervalued wildlife refuges.

Gravel-pit *(Chris Gibson)*. A common habitat across Essex.

Grey Wagtail *(Steve Lindsell)*. Local resident, breeding in small numbers.

Firecrest *(Reston Kilgour)*. A very rare breeder but fairly common migrant.

Starling *(Steve Lindsell)*. A winter roost of up to 3,000,000 occurred at Wrabness during December 1988.

Red-necked Grebe *(Steve Lindsell)*. Has summered on five occasions, although no breeding has taken place.

Mediterranean Gull *(Steve Arlow)*. Breeding has occurred in every year since 1990. There are increasing numbers in autumn, particularly in the Southend-on-Sea area.

Purple Sandpiper and Sanderlings *(Steve Arlow)*. Two typical open-coast species.

Bittern *(Reston Kilgour)*. Only regularly recorded in the Lea Valley.

Greenfinch *(Reston Kilgour)*. An abundant species.

White-spotted Bluethroat *(Reston Kilgour)*. Gunners Park, March 2001.

Hatfield Forest *(Chris Gibson)*. A rare example of a surviving medieval Royal Forest.

Great Spotted Woodpecker *(Reston Kilgour)*.

Nuthatch *(Reston Kilgour)*.

The Nuthatch has benefited from the range expansion of the Great Spotted Woodpecker, the Nuthatch following once the woodpecker has carved out the nest holes.

Corn Bunting *(Steve Lindsell)*. Its distinctive jangling song is commonly heard along the Dengie coast.

The Lea Valley *(Chris Gibson)*. A substantial area of former gravel workings.

The Thames Estuary *(Chris Gibson)*. The fourth most important estuary in Britain for waders and wildfowl.

Redwing *(Reston Kilgour)*. Numbers vary considerably from year to year.

Swallow *(Reston Kilgour)*. Common summer visitor.

Dengie Coast *(Chris Gibson)*. Home of Bradwell Bird Observatory.

Little Ringed Plover *(Reston Kilgour)*. One of the earliest returning summer migrants.

House Sparrow *(Steve Lindsell)*. Still common but much reduced in numbers.

Year	Species	Page	Notes
1976	Sociable Plover; Citrine Wagtail; Cetti's Warbler; Serin; Arctic Redpoll	329	Dipper (10th and last record); Tree Sparrow record autumn passage (12,000+)
1977	*King Eider*; Wilson's Phalarope	331	BWP (1977–94); Black Kite (2nd); Sociable Plover (2nd); Baird's Sandpiper (2nd and last record); Buff-breasted Sandpiper (3rd); Roseate Tern (3rd-4th)
1978	Cory's Shearwater; Terek Sandpiper; Spotted Sandpiper	334	Balearic Shearwater (2nd); skua influx; [Northern Long-tailed Tit (3rd)]; Golden Oriole breeding attempt; Cirl Bunting (last record)
1979	Ring-necked Duck (1st–3rd); Long-billed Dowitcher; Ring-billed Gull; *Collared Flycatcher*; Black-headed Bunting	339	Hard weather in January/February; large wildfowl influx; Red-necked Grebe record influx (30+); Eider record influx (440+); Red-breasted Merganser record influx (364); Black Kite (3rd record)
1980			Balearic Shearwater (3rd); Slavonian Grebe record influx (50); Long-billed Dowitcher (2nd); Wilson's Phalarope (2nd); Red-rumped Swallow (3rd); Starling record flock (2,000,000)
1981	*Oriental Pratincole*; Savi's Warbler (1st & 2nd); Common Rosefinch	342	Cormorant first tree-nesting at Abberton; Barnacle Goose record influx (170+); record influx of auks; Kittiwake influx (10,000); Cetti's Warbler first bred; Chaffinch influx (5,000+); Greenfinch passage (10,000+)
1982	Red-throated Pipit; Penduline Tit	344	Goshawk, first modern record; Dotterel first national wintering record
1983	Marsh Warbler; Greenish Warbler	346	Seabird wreck in February; Black Stork (2nd); Long-billed Dowitcher (3rd); Spotted Sandpiper (2nd); Savi's Warbler (3rd & last); Jay October influx; Tree Sparrow autumn influx
1984	[*Common Gull of race* heinei]*; [Siberian Stonechat]		**Cox published**; Cream-coloured Courser (2nd and last record); Marsh Warbler (2nd); Great Reed Warbler (2nd)
1985	*Trumpeter Finch*	347	Green-winged Teal (2nd); Ring-billed Gull (2nd); Lapland Bunting record influx (120+)
1986	*Lesser White-fronted Goose*	348	Terek Sandpiper (2nd); Ring-billed Gull (3rd); [Siberian Stonechat] (2nd); Yellow-browed Warbler influx (8); Common Rosefinch (2nd); Blackheaded Bunting (2nd)
1987	Paddyfield Warbler; Dusky Warbler	350	Green-winged Teal (3rd); Hurricane wreck of Grey Phalaropes and Sabine's Gulls; Richard's Pipit (3rd); Desert Wheatear (2nd & last); Pallas's Warbler influx (4); Serin (2nd); Little Bunting (3rd)
1988	Broad-billed Sandpiper (1st–3rd); *Northern Mockingbird*; [*Bonelli's Warbler sp.*]; *Isabelline Shrike*	354	Red Kite influx (7–10); Wilson's Phalarope (3rd); Long-tailed Skua influx (9); Yellow-browed Warbler influx (11); Goldcrest influx; Serin (3rd)
1989	Blue-winged Teal; Black-eared Wheatear; Lesser Grey Shrike	357	Cory's Shearwater (2nd & 3rd); Leach's Petrel record influx (18); Black Stork (3rd); Great Snipe (last record); Spotted Sandpiper (3rd); Great Skua record influx (242); Common Rosefinch (3rd)
1990	Great Shearwater; **Naumann's Thrush***	359	Montagu's Harrier last bred; Little Auk influx (140); Lesser Grey Shrike (2nd & last); Arctic Redpoll (2nd); Crossbill influx (150+)
1991	*Bridled Tern*; [*Least Tern*]	360	February cold snap kills hundreds of coastal birds; Long-tailed Skua record influx (45); Puffin record influx (18); Little Auk influx (190); Arctic Redpoll (3rd); Crossbill influx (250)
1992	*Greater Sand Plover*; Olive-backed Pipit; *Pine Bunting*; *Baltimore Oriole*	364	HBW (1992-); Foulness Hailstorm caused 3,238 mortalities; Marsh Harrier first successful breeding since 1830; [Siberian Stonechat (3rd)]; Dusky Warbler (2nd)
1993	*Pallid Harrier*	365	Whiskered Tern (2nd); Red-throated Pipit (2nd to 4th)

1994	*Bonaparte's Gull; Hermit Thrush;* **Red-throated Thrush***; Southern Grey Shrike	369	Whiskered Tern (3rd); Citrine Wagtail (2nd and last); Olive-backed Pipit (2nd and last); Marsh Warbler (3rd); Yellow-browed (7) and Pallas's Warbler (8) influx
1995	Cattle Egret; [**Caspian Gull***]	370	Great Shearwater (2nd and last); Greater Yellowlegs (2nd and last); Little Auk record influx (460); Lesser and Mealy Redpoll influx
1996			**Essex Tetrad Atlas published**; Blue-winged Teal (2nd); Spoonbill record influx (18+); Southern Grey Shrike (2nd); Marsh Warbler first bred; Firecrest record influx (111); Arctic Redpoll influx (6)
1997	Canvasback; *Surf Scoter*	372	Short-toed Lark (2nd); Black-eared Wheatear (2nd); Naumann's Thrush (2nd); Penduline Tit (2nd); Crossbill record influx (880+)
1998			Leach's Petrel record influx (43); Cattle Egret (2nd); Peregrine first breeding record; Ring Ouzel record influx (196); Black-headed Bunting (3rd)
1999	*Forster's Tern*	373	Blue-winged Teal (3rd); Canvasback (2nd & 3rd); Laughing Gull (2nd); Short-toed Lark (3rd); Paddyfield Warbler (2nd); Dusky Warbler (3rd)
2000	*Franklin's Gull; Radde's Warbler*	375	Storm Petrel record influx (30); Little Egret first bred; Pacific Golden Plover (2nd); Honey Buzzard record influx (212) associated with other raptors
2001	*Pallid Swift*	376	Foot & Mouth Disease restrictions February to June; Black-necked Grebe first successful breeding; Sociable Plover (3rd); Long-tailed Skua influx (24)
2002	Great White Egret; *Yellow-breasted Bunting*	378	American Wigeon (2nd); Sooty Shearwater record influx (65+); Terek Sandpiper (3rd); Great Spotted Woodpecker coastal influx; Firecrest influx; Crossbill influx (500+)
2003	Lesser Scaup; *Blyth's Reed Warbler*	380	American Wigeon (3rd); Great White Egret (2nd); Red-rumped Swallow flock (3–4)
2004	*Squacco Heron; American Golden Plover; Arctic Warbler; Hume's Warbler*	384	Lesser Scaup (2nd); Mediterranean Gull record influx (peak 86); Redrumped Swallow influx (3); Great Reed Warbler (3rd); Greenish Warbler (2nd)

USING THIS BOOK

The Systematic List provides a summary of published information, since scientific records began, about species that have occurred in Essex and fall into the British Ornithologists' Union (BOU) categories defined (*Ibis* 147: 803–820) as follows:

Category A: Species that have been recorded in an apparently natural state at least once since 1st January 1950.

Category B: Species that were recorded in an apparently natural state at least once between 1st January 1800 and 31st December 1949, but have not been recorded subsequently.

Category C: Species that, although originally introduced by man, either deliberately or accidentally, have established breeding populations derived from introduced stock, that maintain themselves without necessary recourse to further introduction.

> (**C1**) Naturalised introduced species—species that have occurred only as a result of introduction, e.g. Egyptian Goose *Alopochen aegyptiaca*.
> (**C2**) Naturalised established species—species with established populations resulting from introduction by man, but which also occur in an apparently natural state, e.g. Greylag Goose *Anser anser*.
> (**C3**) Naturalised re-established species—species with populations successfully re-established by man in areas of former occurrence, e.g. Red Kite *Milvus milvus*.
> (**C4**) Naturalised feral species—domesticated species with populations established in the wild, e.g. Rock Dove *Columba livia*.
> (**C5**) Vagrant naturalised species—species from established naturalised populations abroad, e.g. possibly some Ruddy Shelducks *Tadorna ferruginea* occurring in Britain.
> (**C6**) Former naturalised species—species formerly placed in C1 whose naturalised populations are either no longer self-sustaining or are considered extinct, e.g. Lady Amherst's Pheasant *Chrysolophus amherstiae*.

Category D: Species that would otherwise appear in Categories A or B except there is reasonable doubt that they have ever occurred in the natural state.

Category E: Species that have been recorded as introductions, human–assisted transportees or escapees from captivity, and whose breeding populations (if any) are thought not to be self sustaining.

Species in Categories D and E form no part of the British List.

NOMENCLATURE AND DEFINITIONS

The scientific names and the sequence follow the latest taxonomic recommendations for British birds published by the BOU Records Committee up to the end of 2005. Familiar English names have been retained and where these differ from those recommended by the BOURC, the names are given in parentheses e.g. White-fronted Goose (Greater White-fronted Goose).

The accounts of species that have occurred in Essex in a wild state (Categories A, B and C) are detailed in the Systematic List. Species that have occurred, but are of uncertain wild status, follow the main Appendix 1 and appear under the heading of Category D species. Introduced species that have not become established and escapes from Category E are listed in Appendix 2. They follow the nomenclature and sequence listed by Clements (2000). Appendix 3 deals with unsubstantiated records and others of interest, details of which it was felt should be published for posterity lest they are lost from the record.

Subspecies

Distinctive and/or regularly reported subspecies are detailed separately.

Assessment of Essex records

Records prior to 1958 were published at the discretion of authors and editors. Since that time, they have come under the scrutiny of the Essex Birdwatching Society's Recording Committee. From 1991 the independent Identification Panel has assessed the records of all rarer species. Species designated nationally rare have been assessed by British Birds Rarities Committee (BBRC) and all BBRC decisions are adhered to. The status of national rarities is provided by the annual report in *British Birds* magazine and the figure for the number of occurrences is provided in the most recent report.

All accepted records up to the end of 2004 have been included. Any significant 2005 records are summarised on pp. 619–620.

THE SPECIES ACCOUNT LAYOUT

The first line under the species heading is a brief statement on status using the following definitions, which for consistency are based on those used in the recent Suffolk Avifauna (Piotrowski 2003):

Abundant:	occurs in large numbers in suitable weather and habitat
Common:	occurs regularly or is widely distributed in suitable habitat
Fairly common:	occurs in small numbers in suitable habitat and season
Locally common:	occurs in small numbers but restricted to specific habitats
Uncommon:	occurs annually in small numbers
Scarce:	one or two records each year or restricted to specific habitats
Rare:	occurs less than annually
Very rare:	6–25 records in the past 30 years
Accidental/Vagrant:	less than six records in the past 30 years

Population status of birds in the UK

Leading governmental and non-governmental conservation organisations in the UK have reviewed the population status of birds that are regularly found here. In all, 247 were assessed and each placed in one of three groups: Red List (40 species); Amber List (121 species); and Green List (the remainder).

Red List species are those that: are globally threatened according to IUCN criteria; whose populations and range have declined rapidly in recent years; or have declined historically and have not shown any recent recovery.

Amber List species are those that: have an unsatisfactory conservation status in Europe; have shown a moderate population decline; have declined historically but shown a substantial recent recovery; are rare breeders; or have internationally important or localised populations.

Green List species do not fall into categories Red and Amber.

Red and Amber List species are highlighted with the wording "Red List" and "Amber List" respectively next to the status summary at the start of each species' text. In addition, the five Essex Biodiversity Action Plan species are highlighted with the reference **BAP** next to the Red List text. For more information on birds of conservation concern see Gregory *et al.* (2002). More information on Essex BAPs can be found at www.essexbiodiversity.org.uk.

Ringing definitions

The term "re-trap" describes a record of a bird recaptured and released by the original ringer or his associates, at or near (within 5km) the locality where it was originally ringed or was last 'controlled'. A 'control' is a ringed bird caught again (whether by the original or other ringer) at a point more than 5km from the locality where it was first ringed. A 'recovery' is a bird found dead at another locality and not subsequently released, or caught accidentally (e.g. in fruit netting) or intentionally by non-ringers.

Boundaries

Watsonian vice-county boundaries are used except in the Lea Valley where the alterations to the course of the Lea over the years had meant a certain degree of fluidity and hence ambiguity in the boundary position over the years. Harris (2001) has been followed in that the boundary is now the Lea and Stort Navigations, although note that WeBS counts cover the whole Lea Valley (see below). A line drawn due north from Lower Hope Point, Kent, is taken to separate the Inner and Outer Thames regions. Historic records 32km or further from the nearest Essex coastline are not included in statistics, although they are referred to in the text.

Graphs and Tables

A principal aim of this book has been to present graphically as much data as possible so that trends may be quickly identified. Wherever possible, original data have been used to produce the graphs and tables. These have either come from the EBS archive and/or from the WWT and BTO. Unfortunately, the original Essex records prior to 1971 were 'disposed of' at some time in the past, which is a great loss. The effect of this has been that, unless the full data set was available in the *EBR* back to 1950, which was the case for most rarer species, then graphs have only been produced for the period 1971–2004. Additionally, the records for 1979 are missing and again, unless fully detailed in the 1979 *EBR*, it can be assumed that the graphs do not include data for 1979. A variety of graphs has been produced; further information on some of these is provided below.

WeBS data and five-year average peak count tables

Where sufficient data are available for certain wildfowl and wader species, summary five-year average of peak count tables are derived from the WeBS data provided by WWT. For a given period (e.g. September–November or December–March), the peak count for an estuary/all Essex is derived and added to a cumulative total for a five-year period for that location. The cumulative total for the five-year period is divided by the number of years of available data to obtain the five-year, average peak count for that five-year period and recorded in the published table. This methodology therefore summarises as much data as possible and has helped most to determine trends.

Where a five-year average peak count table is provided, there are two numbers in the top left of the table. These are firstly (e.g. GB 700), the qualifying level for a site to be of national importance, and secondly (e.g. IN 2,500), the qualifying level for the site to be of international importance (as given by the WWT). An asterisk (*) next to the figure indicates that where 1% of the British population is less than 50 birds, 50 is normally used as the minimum qualifying level. A plus sign (+) indicates that the population is too small for a meaningful figure to be obtained. A "p" or "w" signifies a passage or winter population. Occasionally, where no such designations are available for a species, the threshold count for inclusion in the 2000–01 WeBS report (Pollitt *et al.* 2003) is used as a guide for count significance. Introduced species are titled accordingly

The following conventions apply to the five-year average peak count table for a derived figure:-
- If a figure is in **bold**, it indicates that it is of international importance for that period
- If a figure is underlined, it indicates that it is of national importance for that period
- An * to the right of the figure indicates only 1–2 year's data were available
- An ^ to the right of the figure indicates only 3–4 year's data were available

Where sufficient EBS data are available, averages for 1950–60 have been shown; these are italicised and bracketed to show that they were not derived from co-ordinated counts but are nonetheless an important early source of information on wildfowl numbers.

The WeBS counts from the Stour Estuary include counts for the whole estuary, including the Suffolk shore, in order to include birds that feed in Essex but use Suffolk roosts at high tide when the counts are generally made. The Lea Valley WeBS grouping stretches from Middlesex Filter Beds in the south to Ware GPs, Hertfordshire, in the north with several water bodies wholly or partly in Middlesex or Hertfordshire. Metropolitan Essex Waters consist of about 45 named waters, including fishing lakes and park ponds that do not overlap with the Lea Valley or Thames-side sites and have been incorporated into WeBS counts since 2000 (Harris 2001).

The tables also identify the highest ever WeBS count and also the month that consistently records the highest average WeBS count in a particular period for the species in question.

In a few cases, WeBS counts are not representative of the numbers of an individual species present. 'Combined count' tables have therefore been produced, the figures for which are calculated in the same way as for WeBS count tables except that both WeBS and general EBS records are used.

Graphs of seasonal occurrence

These have been produced in one of two ways:

From WeBS data by simply summing the data for each month since counts were started. It should be borne in mind that WeBS counts from April to August inclusive are generally incomplete and that the figures presented are almost certainly underestimates.

By analysis of EBS records to produce cumulative monthly or weekly totals of individuals or counts over the period specified in the graph which is usually either 1950–2004 or 1971–2004.

The former is a relatively straightforward calculation; the latter involves a far more complicated process and the following points should be borne in mind when considering the graphs. To produce such graphs requires absolute data: the record states quite clearly the date(s) that it occurs and how many individuals are involved. This enables accurate graphs and tables to be produced. Unfortunately, a small, but nonetheless significant amount of original data were unusable as it was not specific, a typical example being, " 2–3 Wheatear were present throughout July and August". Such data have had to be ignored when producing the graphs and tables; it does not, however, have a significant effect on the overall results. **A plea, therefore, on behalf of the next avifauna author: please make your records date and number specific!**

Although there are several different types of seasonal graphs, they have all been produced using the same basic 'rules':

For weekly graphs, the peak count at each site in each period is used to produce the weekly totals. The analyst used their best judgement to arrive at this count. The peak weekly counts from each site are then summed and these are either used to produce weekly graphs of occurrence (or all the weekly totals are summed across the year to obtain the annual totals).

Monthly graphs of occurrence rely more upon a subjective assessment of all the records in that month given the longer time-period involved. This means taking into account the species' behaviour, localities involved, the time of year and weather, if known, at the time of the observations. Thus, both Shore Larks and Snow Buntings are known to cover large 'home' ranges and, at the mouth of the Blackwater, the same flocks clearly visit Bradwell, East Mersea and Colne Point over a relatively short space of time; analysis of past data have taken this into account and may have resulted in lower numbers than previously reported in the EBRs.

For some species, both the number of records and the number of individuals is shown as each may reveal different trends. Some graphs show the number of counts of a certain quantity (e.g. 100+) or the number of sites recording counts over a certain figure. Again this a relatively subjective assessment carried out as described above. The data used cover the whole period of the birds' stay not just its first arrival date, unless clearly specified to the contrary (e.g. Great Grey Shrikes). The horizontal axis on seasonal graphs will usually run from either (a) January to December or (b) July to June depending on whether or not the data being displayed refer principally to spring migrants and summer visitors (a) or autumn migrants and winter visitors (b). Weekly graphs use the standardised week numbers listed below. Note: week number 9 also incorporates 29th February.

Week	Week No.	Week	Week No.	Week	Week No.	Week	Week No.
01/01-07/01	1	02/04-08/04	14	02/07-08/07	27	01/10-07/10	40
08/01-14/01	2	09/04-15/04	15	09/07-15/07	28	08/10-14/10	41
15/01-21/01	3	16/04-22/04	16	16/07-22/07	29	15/10-21/10	42
22/01-28/01	4	23/04-29/04	17	23/07-29/07	30	22/10-28/10	43
29/01-04/02	5	30/04-06/05	18	30/07-05/08	31	29/10-04/11	44
05/02-11/02	6	07/05-13/05	19	06/08-12/08	32	05/11-11/11	45
12/02-18/02	7	14/05-20/05	20	13/08-19/08	33	12/11-18/11	46
19/02-25/02	8	21/05-27/05	21	20/08-26/08	34	19/11-25/11	47
26/02-04/03	9	28/05-03/06	22	27/08-02/09	35	26/11-02/12	48
05/03-11/03	10	04/06-10/06	23	03/09-09/09	36	03/12-09/12	49
12/03-18/03	11	11/06-17/06	24	10/09-16/09	37	10/12-16/12	50
19/03-25/03	12	18/06-24/06	25	17/09-23/09	38	17/12-23/12	51
26/03-01/04	13	25/06-01/07	26	24/09-30/09	39	24/12-31/12	52

Graphs of peak counts

These have been produced using the same methodology as for the seasonal graphs except that the resultant data are either presented annually (i.e. from January–December) or as a 'winter year' (i.e. July in one year to June in the next), depending on whether the species is predominantly a spring/summer or autumn/winter visitor.

CBC/BBS graphs

All data for the production of local breeding population trends were supplied by the BTO. The Index is based on data collected in several counties and is not specific to Essex. The other counties are Suffolk, Cambridgeshire, Hertfordshire, London, Bedfordshire and Kent. Indices are unsmoothed. BBS Values for 2001 are the means of 2000 and 2002 as no 2001 data were available due to FMD restrictions. Base Indices of 1 were set in 1981 for CBC data and 1994 for BBS data.

Atlas Summary tables

The tables provide a simple summary of the number of 10km squares or tetrads in which individual species bred (or probably bred) and possibly bred during the survey period in question. Data were obtained from the original survey maps and converted to numbers and percentages. There are 1,067 tetrads in Essex of which 200 are in Metropolitan Essex, whilst there are 57 10km squares; note that some of the tetrads/squares may overlap the county's boundary.

Ringing tables

The tables summarise ringing data provided by the BTO and show either the cumulative monthly totals of birds ringed in Essex and recovered at each locality or the month of ringing and origin of foreign-ringed birds recovered in Essex.

Abbreviations

The following abbreviations are used throughout the book:

Journals and organisations

BASC	British Association for Shooting and Conservation
BBO	Bradwell Bird Observatory
BBRC	British Birds Rarities Committee
BOC	British Ornithologists' Club
BOURC	British Ornithologists' Union Records Committee
BTO	British Trust for Ornithology
DEFRA	Department for Environment, Food and Rural Affairs
EBR	Essex Bird Report
EBS	Essex Birdwatching Society (was Essex Birdwatching and Preservation Society)
EFC	Essex Field Club
ELBF	East London Birders Forum
EN	English Nature (was Nature Conservancy Council)
EWT	Essex Wildlife Trust (was Essex Naturalists' Trust)
IUCN	International Union for the Conservation of Nature and Natural Resources
JNCC	Joint Nature Conservancy Council
LBR	London Bird Report
LNHS	London Natural History Society
MoD	Ministry of Defence
NHM	Natural History Museum
NRA	National Rivers Authority
RBBP	Rare Birds Breeding Panel
RSPB	Royal Society for the Protection of Birds
SOG	Southend Ornithological Group
WWRG	Wash Wader Ringing Group
WWT	Wildfowl and Wetland Trust (was Wildfowl Trust)

Surveys

BoEE	Birds of Estuaries Enquiry
BBS	Breeding Bird Survey
CBC	Common Birds Census
CES	Constant Effort Site
NeWS	Non-estuarine coastal Waterbirds Survey
WBS	Waterways Birds Survey
WeBS	Wetland Bird Survey
WiNGS	Winter Gull Roost Survey

Nature Reserves and conservation areas

ESA	Environmentally Sensitive Area
LNR	Local Nature Reserve
NNR	National Nature Reserve
SPA	Special Protection Area
SSSI	Site of Special Scientific Interest

Others

BAP	Biodiversity Action Plan
BCC	Birds of Conservation Concern
BSE	Bovine Spongiform Encephalopathy
CAP	Common Agricultural Policy
CP	Country Park
FMD	Foot and Mouth Disease
GC	Golf Course
GP	Gravel-pit
Old Hall	Old Hall Marshes RSPB Reserve
SF	Sewage farm
The Hythe	The Hythe at Colchester
The Naze	The Naze at Walton

Rivers and estuaries

The Stour, Colne, Blackwater, Crouch, Roach, Lea (or Lee), Roding and Thames (north shore only) may all be taken to refer to the respective river and estuary.

Reservoirs

In alphabetical order, Abberton, Ardleigh, Coleman's, Girling (William Girling on OS maps), Hanningfield, King George V (abbreviated to KGV), Leez and Walthamstow (includes Banbury and Lockwood) may all be assumed to refer to the respective reservoir. If there should be any possible confusion regarding the nearby habitation of the same name, then "village" or "town" will be stated e.g. Abberton, but Abberton village; Hanningfield, but West Hanningfield village; Walthamstow, but Walthamstow town.

Other site names

It became clear whilst compiling the species' accounts that several place names had been used for one site over the years. Thus the following name conventions have been used:

Belfairs Park	Includes Belfairs Wood, Hadleigh Wood and Hadleigh Great Wood.
Bradwell	Includes all records from Bradwell Bird Observatory (BBO) except those specifically referred to as The Dengie or named sites on The Dengie peninsula.
Chigborough Lakes	Includes the old name Great Totham GPs.
Colne Point	Includes the former site name of Leewick.
Dengie	The Dengie peninsula
East Mersea and Cudmore Grove CP	Both names are used, although the latter is a relatively recent name, so the name East Mersea will have included this Cudmore area previously.
Fingringhoe Wick and village	Both names are used; if the locality of the record is uncertain, just Fingringhoe is used.
Fishers Green	This includes the site formerly named Fishers Green GP.
Foulness	Includes Foulness Island and other islands in the area - New England, Potton, Havengore and Rushley—as well as Maplin Sands. Each individual site may also be mentioned within the text as are several sites on Foulness Island itself.
Hadleigh CP	Includes both the Downs and marshes, but note both are also referred to separately in the text, as is the town of Hadleigh.
Hainault Forest CP	Includes all records from Hainault Forest.
Lea Valley	The spelling Lee is equally valid.
Leigh-on-Sea and Two Tree Island	Unless there was evidence to point to the record coming from Leigh-on-Sea, Two Tree Island or Leigh NNR, the record has been listed as Leigh/Two Tree.
Pitsea & Wat Tyler CP	Records referred to as Pitsea may include Wat Tyler CP, unless there is a clear reference to the marshes or refuse tip, as the exact location of many of the records is impossible to pinpoint.
Rainham	Includes all parts of Rainham Marsh including those areas both inside and outside the RSPB reserve.
Saling	Great and Bardfield Saling and immediate surrounds
Southend Pier	Southend-on-Sea Pier.
Stour Reserve	Includes Stour and Copperas Wood RSPB

Mute Swan

Cygnus olor

Common resident and winter visitor

Amber List

The monotypic Mute Swan is patchily distributed across much of the Palearctic and is a popular ornamental species worldwide. In Britain and parts of Europe, the species has been tamed and partly, but not truly, domesticated for hundreds of years, perhaps from as early as 966AD in Britain. This semi-domestication probably saved the species from extinction in this country (Historical Atlas). In England during the 12th and 13th centuries, any wild swans became 'owned' by persons with freehold land, and strays were pronounced property of the Crown; this system continued into the 18th century. Swans became extremely valuable and

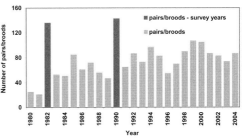

Annual number of pairs/broods of Mute Swans from 1980-2004

prized as a food but eventually fell out of favour as 'luxury' foods such as Turkey became more available and cheaper to rear. During the 20th century the Mute Swan has increased across Europe. The British population of 24,000–26,000 pairs is around 29% of the European population. Western populations are generally sedentary but eastern ones migrate to ice-free waters in winter.

Remains of either Mute or Whooper Swans have been found in the brick-earth deposits at Grays and Ilford (Michael Daniels pers. comm.).

Ticehurst (1957) set out in detail the species' early history in Britain, although little was relevant to Essex. However, between 1247 and 1251, Henry III issued many regulations for provisions to sheriffs in parts of the country that he was to visit; 22 Mute Swans had to be provided for the Feast of St Edward on 18th March by, amongst others, the Sheriff of Essex. In February 1776, a Mute Swan shot on Foulness had a gold ring fastened to its neck with the inscription 'Le Roi Dame', indicating that the bird was marked in Denmark (Moon 1926).

Christy described the Mute Swan as "common in a more or less domesticated state on ornamental waters", which suggested a rather restricted distribution across Essex. Apart from adding that the species did not have a very good claim to be on the British List he said nothing further. Glegg considered the Mute Swan "... a common resident, existing in a state of semi-domestication ... At the same time there are now Swans, which, although originated from domesticated stock, are truly wild birds, without ownership". Thus in the 40 years after 1890, Mute Swans appeared to have spread across Essex from their traditional 'domesticated' habitats and have continued to increase since, occupying a variety of habitats, both natural and man-made; the species is now considered truly wild.

The Mute Swan is "... one of those unfortunate species that receives only scant attention from most observers" (*EBR* 1980). Thus accurate monitoring of the population has only been made possible by thorough surveys in 1955, 1978, 1982 and 1990, together with one Essex and two national Atlas projects. The 1955 BTO survey recorded 103 breeding/territorial pairs from a total of 931 individuals (Campbell 1960). However, numbers subsequently declined, probably as a result of a run of severe winters in the late 1950s/early 1960s, lead-poisoning from discarded anglers' weights and perhaps also the increasing use of nylon fishing line, which swans either swallowed or became entangled in. River pollution and drainage associated with increasing boat traffic have also been cited as factors in the declines across some parts of Britain (Ogilvie 1981). The next national survey in 1978 covered Essex poorly, so that the figure of 75 pairs from 423 individuals (Ogilvie 1981) may have exaggerated the decline, which nationally was "between 8 and 15%". The average peak county wildfowl count during 1975/76–79/80 was around half of that during the 1950s, further evidence of a decline.

Atlas	Survey Area	% of 10km squares or tetrads in which	
		bred/probably bred	possibly bred or present
First National 10km	Essex	89.5	1.8
Second National 10km	Essex	82.5	8.8
First London Tetrad	Met. Essex	17.0	7.0
Second London Tetrad	Met. Essex	23.5	11.0
Essex Tetrad	Essex	18.0	6.2

Summary of results of Atlas surveys for Mute Swans

A comprehensive survey in 1982 located 136 breeding/territorial pairs from a total of 660 birds (Cox 1983). Thereafter, numbers continued to increase slowly, perhaps helped by the banning of lead weights in 1987, and 143 pairs were recorded during the most recent national survey in 1990 (Delaney *et al.* 1992). The Essex Atlas suggested a population of 150–170 pairs, with probable or confirmed breeding recorded in 18% of tetrads (some with multiple pairs) over the seven survey years. Breeding pairs were spread throughout Essex, except in the northwest where there is a lack of suitable habitat. Since the Essex Atlas survey, there has been a general but erratic increase.

Nationally the CBC/BBS (England) Index for the period 1975–2000 recorded a 67% increase, although BBS (England) data for 1994–2002 have suggested a 12% decline.

Swans require a long stretch of water from which to take off, and in the 1982 survey 79% of pairs were on gravel-pits, coastal borrow dykes and fleets, and reservoirs, with the number nesting on rivers having declined from 36% in 1955 to just 9%, though this trend may have reversed.

The most important breeding site has been Abberton, with up to 24 pairs (1992) annually, although there may be far fewer at times of low water levels. Over the last two decades other important breeding sites have been: Old Hall, 11 pairs, 1993; Chigborough Lakes, seven, 1986; Langenhoe, six, 1988; Hanningfield, six, 1994; and Bradwell, six, 1994. Many other sites have held up to five pairs.

Mute Swans become flightless for several weeks during their post-breeding season moult, at which time large gatherings occur. In Essex, Abberton has traditionally held the largest flocks with smaller gatherings at Hanningfield

GB 260 INT 2,400	1955- 1959	1969- 1964	1965- 1969	1970- 1974	1975- 1979	1980- 1984	1985- 1989	1990- 1994	1995- 1999	2000- 2004	Peak counts		Peak Month
WeBS totals	(760)	966	854	628	329	544	899	973	891	1,023	Oct 61	1,206	*Oct*
Stour	~	583	448	220	134^	190	250	176	179	184	Oct 61	720	Oct
Hamford Water	~	6	5	9	23	5	10	24	24	81	Sep 04	169	Oct
Colne	~	44^	179	118	~	~	224	169	57	22	Oct 86	348	Oct
Blackwater	~	80	104	138	48	64	71	45	68	55	Oct 69	260	Oct
Dengie	~	0	0	0	0	0	0	1	3	1	Oct 98	13	Oct
Crouch-Roach	~	~	2*	10*	4*	9	9^	13	26	35	Oct 98	61	Oct
Thames	~	36	64	48	55	88	45	63	58	44	Oct 96	183	Oct
Ardleigh	~	~	~	~	~	26^	20^	24	19	15	Sep 80	61	Sep
Abberton	(283)	220	126	76	187	292	498	576	496	353	Aug 90	635	Aug
Hanningfield	~	26	18	21^	20	8	16	48	122	74	Aug 96	160	Sep
Lea Valley	~	52	34	40	44	62	72	152	124	197	Oct 03	234	Oct
Met. Essex Waters	~	~	~	~	~	~	~	~	~	255	Aug 03	298	Oct

Five-year average of peak WeBS counts (Jul-Oct) of Mute Swans from 1955-2004

and Walthamstow. In the 1950s, when Mistley Maltings were still in operation, moult flocks of several hundred occurred on the Stour.

During winter, it was thought that the majority of Mute Swans moved on to tidal waters where they joined non-breeders, which may have been there all year (Cox). However, comprehensive counts over the last few years have located up to around 25% of the entire wintering population on the many small waters within Metropolitan Essex. Indeed up to half of the Essex wintering population appears to be present in the combined Lea Valley and Metropolitan areas; numbers here have increased in recent years, although this is likely to be in part due to improved observer coverage.

On the coast and estuaries, large gatherings used to occur around maltings or dock facilities where grain was regularly spilled. Large flocks occurred periodically at Mistley on the Stour, The Hythe, Wivenhoe and Brightlingsea on the Colne, Fullbridge, Maldon on the Chelmer and Silvertown on the inner Thames. These herds declined as the maltings and grain handling at the docks became more efficient, with less spillage. The highest ever recorded county total of 1,472 in October 1959 occurred when the Stour herd was at its peak: there were 950 in October 1958 and 1959, reckoned to be the second largest herd in Britain. It was allegedly formed in 1916 when a pair escaped from an ornamental collection at Mistley (Payn 1962). The decline at Abberton in the 1960s was attributed to the death of 50 swans during the wet summer of 1958, which in turn was due to a parasitic worm infestation and a shortage of natural food (Jennings *et al.* 1961). Overall numbers are steadily increasing.

Along the inner Thames, at the time when Mute Swans were declining elsewhere, numbers increased markedly from the 1968/69 winter following anti-pollution measures (Cox); numbers peaked at 420 in January and 616 in June 1973. Most gathered around the Silvertown grain wharf and in Bow Creek where they fed on the macrophyte *Potomogeton pectinatus* (Cox). Although it was possible that the swans had merely moved downriver (Harrison & Grant 1976), recruitment from Essex herds may also have taken place (Cox). The wharf closed in 1976 and numbers declined significantly.

Inland, away from Metropolitan Essex and the Lea Valley, the Mute Swan is relatively scarce in winter. At Abberton, three-figure counts between December and February are rare, although during the 1950s and early 1960s numbers were higher: of note were 313 on 30th December 1956 and 306 in December 1961. Since then, only once has a three-figure count been noted during winter, in 1988 when 397 were present in December. At Hanningfield, winter numbers are small.

GB 260 / INT 2,400	50/51-54/55	55/56-59/60	60/61-64/65	65/66-69/70	70/71-74/75	75/76-79/80	80/81-84/85	85/86-89/90	90/91-94/95	95/96-99/00	00/01-04/05	Peak counts		Peak Month
WeBS totals	~	(1,170)	993	904	639	457	494	849	667	632	927^	Dec 61	1,320	Dec
Stour	(552)	(802)	675	494	246	236	223	253	144	302	251^	Dec 60	812	Jan
Hamford Water	~	~	6	12	11	16	16	11^	25	27	69^	Feb 04	123	Nov
Colne	~	~	81	239	169	~	~	350	211	75	43^	Nov 87	618	Dec
Blackwater	~	~	170	153	144	74	80	58	73	131	101^	Nov 70	291	Feb
Dengie	~	~	2	1	0	2	2	3	5	1	2^	Nov 94	11	Feb
Crouch-Roach	~	~	4*	13*	11	8*	22	9	28	42	50^	Dec 03	69	Dec
Thames	~	~	85	87	80	113	101	87	77	43	62^	Jan 80	259	Jan
Ardleigh	~	~	~	~	~	85*	15^	14^	17	9	9^	Nov 76	85	Jan
Abberton	(290*)	(349)	113	23	37	31	32	128	103	110	45^	Nov 88	493	Nov
Hanningfield	~	(13)	9	7	7	9	3	10	25	42	43^	Nov 96	96	Nov
Lea Valley	~	~	31	38	39	45	65	87	142	98	196^	Nov 96	242	Nov
Met. Essex Waters	~	~	~	~	~	~	~	~	~	~	306^	Feb 02	290	Dec

Five-year average of peak WeBS counts (Nov-Mar) of Mute Swans from 1950/51-2003/04

Most Mute Swans are relatively sedentary, although it would appear that a proportion currently leave Essex after September when the moult flocks disperse. Ringing recoveries suggest that movements of up to 50km are quite common and there are a few involving Essex of movements of 50–100km within southeast England. From national data it can be assumed that a few travel further. There are now over 50 examples of British-ringed Mute Swans crossing the North Sea (Migration Atlas), including five from Essex: four to the Netherlands and one to France. There are fewer proven cases of immigration from the Continent with just two involving Essex: a Swedish bird from Ulesback, Kungsbackafjorden, 941km to the northeast, found off Clacton-on-Sea on 18th January 1982 after severe weather; and a Dutch bird found at Chigwell in 1987.

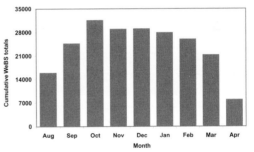

Three Abberton-ringed birds survived to over 15 years old, whilst another ringed as an adult at Abberton and usually present on Distillery Pond, Colchester, lived to at least 23 years old before being found dead near Ipswich, Suffolk, in November 1979. It was at one time the oldest known British-ringed Mute Swan.

Seasonal occurrence of Mute Swans from 1960-2004

The banning of lead weights and stricter pollution control have seen Mute Swan populations steadily increasing and these factors, together with the increase in large gravel-pits across Essex, suggest that the Mute Swan's foreseeable future is assured.

Sponsored by Alwynn Johnson

Bewick's Swan (Tundra Swan)

Cygnus columbianus

Locally common winter visitor and passage migrant

Amber List

The Bewick's Swan breeds on arctic tundra across the northern Russian Palearctic and North America. Two populations exist in Eurasia: one breeding west of the Urals winters in northwestern Europe and the other, east of the Lena Delta, winters mainly in the Far East. The western population is currently estimated at 18,000 birds and has been stable since the early 1980s, although marked fluctuations occur due to variable breeding success (European Atlas). The race *bewickii* occurs across Eurasia, whilst the nominate race *columbianus* occurs in North America, where it is known as  the Whistling Swan. Numbers have increased in Britain over the last few decades, corresponding to decreases in the Netherlands. The winter population peaked at over 8,000 in 1991/92, since when numbers have declined to a level close to that of the late 1970s (Pollitt *et al.* 2003). Around 75% of the British wintering population occurs on the Ouse Washes, Norfolk/Cambridgeshire.

The Bewick's Swan is the commoner of the two 'winter' swans to occur in Essex, although until the early 1950s it was the rarer. The species' early status may have been clouded by the fact that it was not recognised as distinct from the Whooper Swan until 1824. Christy described the species as "A not uncommon winter visitor to our coast, especially during long spells of severe weather, and occasionally met with inland". In all, he detailed some 6–7 occurrences, from the first shot near Sudbury in 1837. Glegg considered it the "… rarest of the swans which occur in Essex" and added just one record, five at Brightlingsea in 1890.

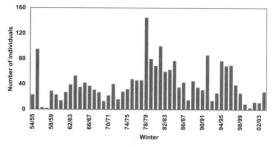

Annual peak counts of Bewick's Swans in the Abberton/Old Hall area from 1954/55-2003/04

Sporadic occurrences during the late 19th and early 20th centuries were typical of the situation across the rest of Britain and it was not until extremely severe conditions in the Netherlands during the winter of 1938/39 (Bircham 1989) that any sustained influx into Britain was noted. There were only two 20th century Essex records prior to 1953 (Hudson & Pyman). Since then, however, the species has been reported annually. Nationally, winter populations expanded rapidly in the latter half of the 20th century, particularly on the Ouse Washes and at Slimbridge WWT, Gloucestershire.

The only wintering herd that could be described as regular was centred on Abberton and Old Hall, with wanderers from there perhaps responsible for records on Mersea Island, Bradwell and the Crouch. The earliest reports were in early 1955 when 23 were present but, after a large national influx in early 1956, numbers at Abberton peaked at 95 in late February with 81 still present in early March. Numbers varied considerably from winter to winter with peaks of 145 (perhaps enticed by the provision of grain in the last years of the shooting regime) in the winter of 1978/79 and 100 in 1981/82. Numbers using Old Hall have declined to virtually nil in recent years, possibly due to cessation of the supplementary feeding (Paul Charlton pers. obs.). At Abberton, low water levels encouraged the largest gatherings; during the late 1990s and early 2000s water levels have been high and counts correspondingly low. However, numbers nationally have declined over the same period, relatively mild winters on the Continent perhaps accounting for the decrease, although increased mobility of birds between night-time roosts and feeding sites within the Ouse Washes has increased the difficulty in monitoring populations accurately.

Few other sites have been used with any regularity since 1950. However, short-staying herds have been reported occasionally from around the coast. Given that paired birds, particularly those with families, show a greater propensity to use known sites in successive years (Cranswick *et al.* 1999), it is perhaps not surprising that no new regular wintering areas have become established, particularly when a substantial area on the Ouse Washes provides excellent feeding and safe roosting. Immatures and individuals, on the other hand, tend to be more opportunistic and use a greater number of sites and it is perhaps these that stay for a few weeks in any given winter.

Numbers vary considerably from year to year, influenced not only by breeding success but also by weather and feeding conditions on wintering grounds. Many records involve flocks, sometimes quite large, moving through Essex, presumably to/from their main wintering areas in the Severn Valley and the Ouse Washes. Migration takes place principally between November and April, although most are resident between December and

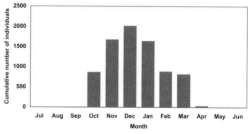

Seasonal occurrence of Bewick's Swans from 1971-2004

February. A herd of nine at Abberton on 30th September 1973 constituted the earliest autumn record, whilst one there on 10th May 1997 was the latest in spring; a 'pricked' bird was at Abberton until 30th June 1966. In 1974, large scale migration occurred particularly early, during late October, and included an unprecedented herd of 254 that paused briefly on the Stour before heading off north on 29th. Perhaps another 100 or so passed through Essex during the next few days of that month. The only other three-figure migrant flocks have been: 106 east over Leigh/Two Tree Island, 3rd March 1981; 100 in off the sea at Frinton-on-Sea, 15th December 1981; 175 in Hamford Water, 8th December 2002.

Ringing recoveries reveal that Bewick's Swans migrate from their Siberian breeding grounds through arctic Russia, the Baltic States and finally western Europe before settling at their chosen wintering site, individual birds being tracked at various sites in Germany, Holland, Norfolk, Essex and Gloucestershire. Many birds have been tagged with coloured neck-rings. One, blue 765P, was reported from Abberton in 1996 and again at Paglesham in 1997. Also in 1997, a flock of 19, which stayed in the Lea Valley throughout much of January, included one of Russian origin, again exhibiting a blue neck collar, 378P. It was one of 300 flightless adult swans marked by a Dutch research team in the Pechora Delta, Russia, in 1992 and was subsequently reported from the Netherlands and Germany in 1993, 1994 and 1995. The same bird was observed at High Bridge, Waltham Abbey and KGV during January and February 1997, and at Abberton in January 1998 when it was accompanied by its mate and a single cygnet.

Two of seven at KGV on 30th October 1988 were considered to show characteristics of the eastern form, somewhat doubtfully considered a subspecies, *jankowski* (*HBW*).

In the Fens there has been an increasing tendency for birds to supplement their 'natural' winter food sources by foraging for vegetable by-products on nearby farmland. Local cropping regimes and farming practices may largely preclude these opportunities within Essex.

Whooper Swan   *Cygnus cygnus*

Uncommon passage migrant and winter visitor   **Amber List**

The monotypic Whooper Swan breeds across the entire Palearctic in the northern taiga zone and winters in the coastal lowlands and wetlands of Europe and eastern Asia. The current British wintering population of some 5,600 individuals is found principally in Scotland and Ireland and, increasingly since the 1970s, at Welney WWT, Norfolk/Cambridgeshire.

Remains attributed to this species have been found in the Pleistocene brick-earths of Grays and Ilford (Glegg),

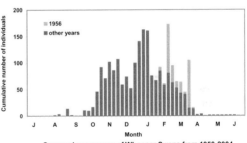

Seasonal occurrence of Whooper Swans from 1950-2004

whilst remains dating back some 300,000 years have been found at West Mersea (Urquhart 2000).

Early written records are likely to be clouded by the similarity of the two 'wild swans'. Christy considered the species "A not uncommon visitor ... during severe winters, when it is also sometimes met with inland". The first written reference came from Harwich in 1730 where "... in winter time [it] is often shot upon this coast" (Dale 1730). During the severe winter of 1837/38 many occurred, including one flock that settled on the Thames "... among a number of tame swans ... readily coming to feed on bread   ... that was thrown to them... they all disappeared after a sojourn of some weeks", whilst at Manningtree "... a number appear to have taken up abode, and it is expected will breed here". Several were also shot near Sudbury. In early 1879, flocks of 23 and 12 were on the Blackwater.

Glegg's description of the species was very similar, the largest flocks being 18 off Bradfield on the Stour in the winter of 1890/91 and 17 there on 22nd January 1924. What seems clear, from the evidence provided by Christy and Glegg, is that Whooper Swans, despite being far from common, were more regular visitors than Bewick's Swans during the 19th century (q.v.).

Hudson & Pyman observed that it was "... doubtful whether the Essex status of this swan has altered much over the last 70–80 years" and described it as "... generally a very scarce species in Essex..." a description that holds fairly well today. Since 1950, Whooper Swans have been recorded in every winter except 1951/52, although in some no more than a few individuals were reported. Numbers have remained remarkably constant over the last 40 years, the very slight increase noted recently probably due to a combination of increased observer coverage and birds moving to/from the much increased Norfolk population. When large herds do occur, they rarely stay for more than a day.

By far the largest influx occurred in early 1956, part of a substantial national influx. In Essex around 200 passed through in two distinct movements: almost half at the end of February/beginning of March and slightly fewer in early April. Only at Abberton did any linger, with birds present continuously from 24th February–21st March with a peak of 28 from 24th–26th February, and ten until 16th March. The other principal counts, mostly involving overflying birds were: 30 northwest over Manningtree, 22nd February; 22 at Fishers Green, 26th February; 19 south over KGV at 1610hrs, 1st April with 29 northeast two hours later; and a total of 28 over St Osyth, 1st April. In other years the largest herds reported have been 30 over Bocking on 3rd January 1951; 30 at Bradwell on 18th January 1960; and 28 at Bradwell on 5th February 1978. No single herd has numbered more than 30 individuals. It would seem that the Whooper Swan, at least

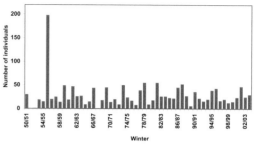

Annual totals of Whooper Swans from 1950/51-2003/04

in Essex, is not particularly affected by severe weather, as numbers in 1962/63 and 1978/79 were not significantly higher.

Single birds have summered twice, although the same individual may have been involved on each occasion. During May and June 1990, one was at North Fambridge, Foulness and Paglesham and one was present at North Fambridge from 10th May 1994 for over a month. It is possible that the bird(s) was/were either injured or had escaped from captivity, which was almost certainly the case of a very confiding individual at Hanningfield from 29th April–27th May 1962. Additionally, three were released on Horsey Island in 1999 and were largely resident in the Hamford Water area until the end of 2004 at least. These records aside, extreme dates have been 5th October at South Woodham Ferrers in 1993 and Abberton in 2003, and 19th April at Holland Haven in 1983. Numbers generally peak (the 1956 influx aside) between late November and January and decline during February.

Most records occur around the coast and whilst no one locality can claim to be a regular wintering site, Hamford Water, Dengie and Foulness are particularly favoured. Inland, Whooper Swans are fairly regular at Abberton and Hanningfield; otherwise, most inland records involve overflying flocks.

Whilst there have not been any ringing recoveries affecting Essex, observations of colour-ringed birds in Norfolk suggest that birds from the Icelandic population may occur. However, there have also been a small number of Finnish colour-ringed Whooper Swans in Norfolk, so it is possible individuals from this population may occur here, too.

Bean Goose   *Anser fabalis*

The Bean Goose is widely distributed across the northern Palearctic from north Norway to the east Siberian Khrebet peninsula, a wide range containing perhaps five subspecies, two of which occur in Europe, the Taiga Bean Goose *fabalis* and the Tundra Bean Goose *rossicus*, some authorities have suggested full species' status for these races (European Atlas).

Taiga Bean Goose   *A. f. fabalis*

Uncommon winter visitor   Amber List

The Taiga Bean Goose breeds in the taiga of Scandinavia, Russian Karelia and the Kola peninsula where it is typical of forest zones in areas of mire, ponds, lakes and small streams (European Atlas). The race winters in the Low Countries and central Europe. Small numbers winter in Britain, the nearest flock being in the Yare Valley, Norfolk, where numbers peaked at 485 in 1990/91 with a subsequent decline to 144 by 2002/03 (*Norfolk Bird Report* 2003).

Tundra Bean Goose   *A. f. rossicus*

Uncommon winter visitor

The Tundra Bean Goose breeds in the tundra belt from the Kanin peninsula east to the Khantanga River and Barents Sea coast (European Atlas) and winters mainly in the Low Countries, Belgium, Germany, Sweden and Denmark. Small numbers occur in Britain, usually following severe weather in eastern Europe, often arriving with influxes of the other grey geese.

It is only recently (*EBR* 1993) that racial identification in the field has been attempted, so the two races have been considered together here and all records should be considered as of indeterminate race, unless otherwise stated.

The close similarity of the grey geese probably clouded the early history of this group in Essex; indeed it was only in the last two decades of the 20th century that Bean and Pink-footed Geese were considered two separate species and not races of one (*Ibis* 122: 564–568).

Christy noted that the Bean Goose was an "… uncommon winter visitor, most often seen during severe weather". He detailed the observations of four observers, one of whom writing in 1838 considered the species not uncommon around Sudbury, whilst two others suggested that it was perhaps regular on the coast. Glegg felt that the Bean Goose was less common than the White-fronted Goose but more common than Pink-footed Goose. The species appears to have been quite numerous in Scotland and northern Britain at the end of the 19th century (Winter Atlas) but declined rapidly around the turn of the century (Thom 1986). There were just two further Essex records prior to 1950.

The next record was in 1958 when one was shot at Landermere on 20th December; in 1973 two were on Mersea Island from 8th and 11th January. Since then Bean Geese have been recorded in all but four winters.

The species' increasing incidence is probably due to greater observer coverage, although until the early 1990s the increase in the Yare Valley Taiga Bean Goose population may also have been a factor. Of the records ascribed to any race since 1993, 13 (involving 101 birds) were considered Tundra and ten (of 29 birds) Taiga Bean Geese with the former subspecies becoming the commoner of the two in recent years.

Increasingly, single birds have occurred, and whilst some may involve genuine wild birds, the species is known to be kept in captivity in small numbers and the likelihood of some being escapes should be borne in mind; several escapees are known to have occurred in Essex.

The substantial influx during early 1979 involved more than 100 individuals and was triggered by severe weather over the Low Countries, which displaced large numbers of Bean and Pink-footed Geese across the North Sea. Most were in the northeast, with up to 43 in the Hamford Water/Naze area from 23rd January–11th February. Elsewhere, there were up to 11 along the Colne and Blackwater with flocks of six and 11 (possibly the Colne/Blackwater birds) in the Great Wigborough/Abberton area, 19 on Foulness on 25th February and three on the Roach on 4th February.

Since this exceptional influx, annual totals have generally been higher and a further eight double-figure flocks have been recorded, two of them in another significant influx in late 2004: Dengie, 11, 11th February 1981; Horsey Island, ten, 1st January 1986; Old Hall, ten, 30th November 1993; Wrabness, 18, 12th and 22 (*rossicus*), 28th–29th December 1995 with 34 by mid-February 1996; Stour, 12 (*rossicus*), 17th January 1997; Holland Haven, 28, 14th December 1997; Abberton, 22 (*rossicus*), 1st January–4th March 2002 and 23 (*rossicus*), 23rd December 2004; Old Hall, 11 (*fabalis*), 7th January 2003; and 18 west over Skippers Island, 20th December 2004.

The majority of Bean Geese occur between December and February. Flocks of six at Abberton on 24th November 2002 and ten at Old Hall on 30th November 1993 were particularly early, whilst five on Foulness on 10th March 1984 were late.

Most records have come from the northeast, with the Stour and Hamford Water/Naze areas particularly favoured. However, Bean Geese have been reported from all around the coast, although just two records have come from the inner Thames: Mucking, one, 6th–7th February 1991 with presumably the same individual in the area on 18th; Rainham, three *fabalis*, 16th January 2000.

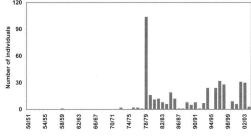

Annual totals of Bean Geese from 1950/51-2003/04

Most inland records (excluding presumed escapes) have come from the Abberton/Great Wigborough area with others coming from: Ardleigh, one; Hanningfield, two, including three (two *rossicus* and one *fabalis*), 16th–22nd December 2001; Fishers Green, one; Holyfield Marsh GPs, one; Nazeing GPs, one; and KGV, one record of six, 20th January 2001.

Sightings of neck-collared *fabalis* show a high degree of fidelity to the Yare Valley, Norfolk, as a wintering site. Very little information is available nationally on colour-marked *rossicus* (Migration Atlas).

Pink-footed Goose   *Anser brachyrhynchus*

Uncommon passage migrant and winter visitor   Amber List

The monotypic Pink-footed Goose breeds in Iceland, eastern Greenland, and western Svalbard on subarctic tundra and cliffs. It winters on lowland farmland in western Europe. The Greenland/Icelandic population winters mainly in Scotland and in northern and eastern England, whilst those from Svalbard move to the Low Countries (European Atlas).

Christy simply stated that the species was a "... winter visitor" and detailed just three records involving four birds, the first being one shot at Saffron Walden in 1841. Glegg noted that the Pink-footed Goose was an "... irregular winter visitor ... It seems to be the general idea that this Goose occurs more frequently than the Bean-Goose, but the limited number of records does not support this". Its early status is therefore unclear.

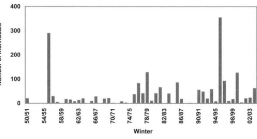

Annual totals of Pink-footed Geese
from 1950/51-2003/04

Since 1950/51, Pink-footed Geese have been recorded in all but three winters. However, despite the substantial increase in numbers wintering on the north Norfolk coast (Taylor *et al.* 1999), this has not been the case in Essex. There is a small, but apparently increasing feral population: individuals have occurred at Abberton since the early 1970s. It is therefore difficult to confirm the provenance of individuals or small flocks.

The largest influxes in 1955/56 and 1995/96 did not coincide with higher than average numbers of grey geese, although the 1978/79 influx did coincide with

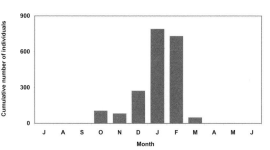

Seasonal occurrence of Pink-footed Geese
from 1950-2004

above average numbers of Bean Geese. The largest flocks have been: 221 northwest over Hamford Water, 27th February 1996; 200+ at Bradwell, February 1956; 103 west over Great Oakley, 22nd December 2004; 80–100 north over Hanningfield, 27th January 1986; 80 on Foulness, 16th January 2000; 75 over Hainault Forest CP, 28th January 1956; 65 at East Mersea, 29th January 1979; 60 at Bradwell, 3rd January 1977; 60 at St Lawrence, 11th January 1996; and 50 at Tollesbury, 25th January 1997. Most occur in January and February.

Records have come from all around the coast, although Hamford Water/The Naze, Dengie and Foulness are particularly favoured.

Inland, flocks of five or more, apart from those already mentioned, have come from: Sible Hedingham, ten, 1st February 2004; Abberton, 30 on 30th January with 11 still on 4th February 1979, seven on 4th and eight on 5th January 1981, 22 on 6th October 1991 (an unusually early arrival), nine on 3rd–23rd March 1996 with five still on 1st April and up to nine in January and February 1997; and Hanningfield, 15, 20th February 1956 and 29 west, 24th December 1956.

National ringing recoveries have shown that the large flocks in Norfolk are from the Icelandic population and most Essex records probably derive from there. Whilst it is possible that birds from Svalbard may be involved it is unlikely, as nationally there has been just a handful of ringing recoveries from this population (Migration Atlas).

(Greater) White-fronted Goose   *Anser albifrons*

The White-fronted Goose breeds across much of the open tundra of the northern hemisphere. Five subspecies are recognised of which two, the nominate *albifrons* and *flavirostris,* the Greenland White-fronted Goose, occur in Europe; a third subspecies *frontalis,* Pacific White-fronted Goose, may have occurred as a vagrant (*HBW*).

(Greater) White-fronted Goose

Locally common passage migrant and winter visitor

A. a. albifrons

Amber List

The nominate race White-fronted Goose breeds on the tundra of northern Russia and Siberia and winters in temperate Europe and Asia. The current British wintering population is in the order of 4,000–7,000 individuals, although overall the proportion of the Western Palearctic population occurring in Britain has fallen dramatically since the 1960s. Then, on occasions Slimbridge WWT, Gloucestershire, alone held 10% of the European population, compared with less than 1% in the whole country in most winters during the 1990s (Cranswick *et al.* 1997).

Whilst observed principally along the coast and estuaries, this subspecies is occurring increasingly inland, although escapes from captivity have in recent years clouded the pattern of occurrence and it may not be long before a self-sustaining feral population is founded. It has long been regarded as the commonest of the grey geese to visit Essex, although only in years of exceptional influxes are numbers likely to exceed those of the largely resident Greylag Goose population.

The remains of White-fronted Geese have been recovered from the brick-earth deposits at Ilford (Michael Daniels pers. comm.).

Christy described the White-fronted Goose as a "… not uncommon winter visitor". Most records referred to small numbers shot at coastal sites, although unusually one was obtained from the Marsh House decoy in 1889, the manner of its capture being described as "… remarkable, and probably quite unique …" for any goose, although he also mentions one caught "… in an ordinary rat-trap…" at the same location a few years earlier. The earliest documented records came from around Saffron Walden where the species was occasional in the first quarter of the 19th century, particularly after hard weather. Glegg considered that the White-fronted Goose was "… an irregular winter visitor, and probably the most numerous of the grey geese which visit Essex". There were 40 on the Thames around February 1923 but it was Glegg himself who observed the largest flock prior to 1950, about 150 on Corringham Marshes on 15th January 1928.

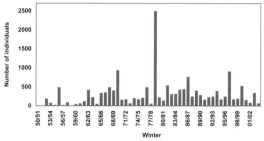

Annual totals of White-fronted Geese from 1950/51-2003/04

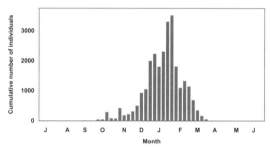

Seasonal occurrence of White-fronted Geese from 1950-2004

Numbers increased during the 1960s. Hudson & Pyman suggested that many records involved flocks moving to/from the north Kent, Swale, wintering population and that many groups of unidentified grey geese seen crossing the Thames were probably this species. Subsequently, flocks have been noted flying over the Thames with some regularity and flights from the Kent population can be seen from north of the Thames. Hudson & Pyman also suggested that high-flying skeins of grey geese, travelling east or west, usually between November and March, were almost certainly White-fronted Geese passing to/from the Severn Estuary region and records in recent years have tended to confirm this. Cox noted a general increase, although numbers since have remained relatively stable despite increased observer coverage.

Populations in northwest Europe increased dramatically (Madsen 1991) from 60,000 in the 1960s to as many as 600,000 in recent years (Scott & Rose 1996), although Mooij (1997) suggested that there is no strong evidence to indicate a significant increase in the Western Palearctic population as a whole and that redistribution from poorly counted regions of central and eastern Europe may be an important factor in this apparent growth.

Whilst numbers have increased since 1-950, annual totals vary markedly, primarily influenced by the severity of the weather over the Continent, although records of individual large flocks can significantly affect total numbers recorded in a particular winter. In general, between 50 and 500 have been recorded each winter over the last five decades. However, the effects of the extreme weather in early 1979 caused an influx that the *EBR* described as "… nothing short of spectacular …" as unprecedented numbers arrived from the Netherlands and, unlike the other grey geese, were reported from around almost all of the coast. Cox suggested that at least 1,500 were present at the end of January

1979 and that 2,000–3,000 may have passed through in total. The largest flocks were 400–500 at Abberton, 500 on the Crouch at Fambridge and 350–400 at East Mersea, all of which were greater than the previous largest flock recorded in Essex. However, the largest single flock to date was 593 in Hamford Water on 30th January 1997. Three-figure counts have occurred on a further 23 occasions since 1950, the largest being: 354 at Rainham, 16th January 2000; at least 350 in Hamford Water, 26th January 1977; and 300 briefly along the Blackwater, 21st January 1970. There have also been three counts of 200–299. Many records relate to very short-staying flocks or over-flying skeins.

Although regular, White-fronted Geese do not have any well-defined, traditional feeding areas. However, on the coast the most favoured sites are Hamford Water (particularly Horsey Island) Tollesbury Marshes and Foulness. The species' ideal winter habitat is relatively flat grazing land, river flood plains, reclaimed grassland and coastal grazing marsh with a propensity for surface flooding, habitat typical of much of coastal Essex. Much has been enhanced recently by the introduction of the Essex Coast ESA but has largely been ignored by passage grey geese.

Inland, Abberton is the only site visited with any regularity, although numbers are variable and, apart from 1979, three-figure counts have been noted on just one further occasion with 118 on 1st March 1956. Hanningfield occasionally holds flocks for short periods with 29 from 1st–5th January 1997 the largest to take up residence. Here, as at many inland sites, most records involve over-flying skeins with 50 on 12th January 1985 the largest. Whilst high-flying skeins are regularly reported from well inland, it is unusual for flocks to linger, thus 40 at Fishers Green on 15th–16th February 1993 were notable.

White-fronted Geese begin to arrive as early as September, the earliest record thought likely to relate to genuine wild birds being 15 in Hamford Water on 15th September 1975. However, the species does not tend to appear in numbers until late December through to February, with returning migrants noticeable in March. The latest spring record involved 15 at Colne Point on 21st April 1975.

Three White-fronted Geese ringed at Slimbridge WWT, Gloucestershire, have been recovered in Essex as well as two Dutch-ringed birds, all typical of the species' movements across the country.

Drainage of wet pastures could pose an immediate threat but coastal reclamation and the provision of goose refuges in the Netherlands have reduced the numbers of White-fronted Geese in southern England and Wales with birds often arriving later in the season (Prater 1981). However, numbers at Heigham Holmes, Norfolk, have risen sharply in recent years probably as a direct consequence of sympathetic wetland management and this could become a key wildfowl site (Cranswick *et al.* 1999), offering the possibility of regular exchange between the Norfolk and Kent populations. Whilst it would seem little more can be done to conserve the species within Essex, flyover records may well increase.

Greenland White-fronted Goose   *A. a. flavirostris*

Vagrant: four records involving eight individuals

The Greenland White-fronted Goose breeds in western Greenland and winters in Ireland and west and northern Scotland.

1962	Abberton	18th October–1st December	Two
1977	Hanningfield	5th December	An escape?
1994	Leigh/Two Tree Island	25th October	
1996	Wat Tyler CP	11th February	Four

Although very rare in southern England, it is possible that the race's similarity to the nominate form means that it is under-recorded.

Lesser White-fronted Goose   *Anser erythropus*

Vagrant: one record involving three individuals

The monotypic Lesser White-fronted Goose breeds in the Palearctic region in the Willow and Birch forest belt between the arctic tundra and taiga zone (European Atlas). The species winters discontinuously between southeast Europe and China.

1986	Foulness	12th October	Three immatures

These three were in the company of newly arrived Dark-bellied Brent Geese, although most occur with White-fronted Geese. This globally threatened species (Tucker & Heath 1994) has been recorded 131 times in Britain, the last of which was in 2003 (BBRC 2004) with 66% coming from Slimbridge WWT, Gloucestershire. The species has become much rarer in recent decades due to a severe decline of the Scandinavian breeding population since the 1940s, the reasons for which are unclear, but may lie in the wintering grounds where habitat change and hunting pressure may be contributory (European Atlas). A reintroduction programme in Swedish Lapland from 1981–91 had some limited success, the small wintering population in the Netherlands originating from there; around 50 were present during 2003/04 (van den Berg 2004), the most likely source of any future county records.

In addition, there have been a total of eight records of individuals that were almost certainly escapes: Hanningfield, 22nd June–14th August 1977; Liston, 26th January and 5th–6th February 1985; Abberton, many dates from 28th January–24th April 1985; Walthamstow, November 1986–January 1987; Fishers Green, 4th April–4th May 1987; Horsey, 23rd May 1992; Hanningfield, two, 26th March 1995; and Walthamstow, 22nd February 1998.

Greylag Goose   *Anser anser*

The Greylag Goose breeds across Europe and Asia, from Iceland, Britain, Scandinavia and eastern Europe across central and southern Russia and south into Mongolia and northern China. Two races are recognised, the nominate western race *anser* and the eastern race *rubrirostris*. In winter, birds generally move south or southwest.

(Western) Greylag Goose   *A. a. anser*

**A common, introduced resident with a fast-increasing
population – wild birds may visit occasionally**   Amber List

The Western Greylag has the widest European distribution of the 'grey' geese; the race occurs from the Arctic Circle south to 40° N (European Atlas). In Britain, it is principally an introduced resident. Although less numerous during the last 30 years than the Canada Goose, a marked increase took place in the 1990s. The only truly native and generally sedentary population survives in the far northwest of Scotland. The entire Iceland breeding population winters in Britain, primarily in Scotland (Historical Atlas).

Fossil remains of Greylags have been found in the Pleistocene brick-earths at Grays, Ilford and Lawford (Glegg). The Greylag Goose is generally recognised as the ancestor of most domestic breeds. Prior to the 20th century, the only way of moving large numbers of geese to the London markets was to 'drive' or walk them to the market. In 1783, one of these droves, numbering 9,000, passed through Chelmsford (Christy). In 1740, Lord Orford bet the Duke of Queensbury that a drove of geese would beat an equal number of Turkeys in a race from Norwich to London. The geese won: "… the Geese kept on the road with a steady pace; but the Turkies, as every evening approached, flew to roost in the trees adjoining the road, from which the drivers found it very difficult to dislodge them. In consequence of [their not] stopping to sleep the Geese arrived two days before the Turkies".

The earliest documented reference involved eight at Shoebury in the severe winter of 1822/23. To Christy, the Greylag was "A winter visitor, most often seen during severe weather". One correspondent referred to vast flocks passing over in spring and autumn heading northeast and southwest, whilst another noted 600–

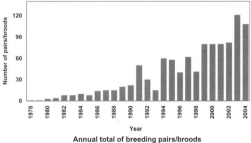

Annual total of breeding pairs/broods
of Greylag Geese from 1978-2004

1,000 heading northeast in the spring of 1880 and that "I have repeatedly seen them sometimes passing for whole days …". What remains uncertain is the true identity of these birds. Glegg made light of this difficulty and concluded that the Greylag was "… one of the least common of the four species of grey geese which have been recorded in

Essex". In severe weather in 1895, two were shot in the Lea Valley, whilst two, perhaps three, were at South Weald in March and April 1918 and one was at Snaresbrook in February 1919; these are probably the first documented records of feral birds in Essex.

Atlas	Survey Area	% of 10km squares or tetrads in which bred/probably bred	possibly bred or present
First National 10km	Essex	0.0	0.0
Second National 10km	Essex	26.3	24.6
First London Tetrad	Met. Essex	0.0	0.0
Second London Tetrad	Met. Essex	6.0	5.5
Essex Tetrad	Essex	3.5	2.2

Summary of results of Atlas surveys for Greylag Geese

In the early 1940s, a flock of domestic geese, including some greys, was introduced onto Horsey Island. Whether the grey geese were pure Greylags is not known, but numbers declined from 14 in 1958 to just four in 1962. However, in the early 1970s a pair of pure Greylags was introduced and subsequently bred. Their progeny were mixed with at least 40 birds caught in Norfolk during the period of flightless moult and released on Oakley Marshes in the late 1970s (Cox).

Introduced	60/61-64/65	65/66-69/70	70/71-74/75	75/76-79/80	80/81-84/85	85/86-89/90	90/91-94/95	95/96-99/00	00/01-04/05	Peak counts		Peak Month
WeBS totals	5^	0	8	22	168	275	672	1,027	1,960^	Jan 02	3,430	Nov
Stour	0	0	0	0	0	0	19	21	126^	Jan 02	277	Jan
Hamford Water	5	0	2	7	48	65^	183	157	287^	Mar 02	392	Feb
Colne	0	0	0	~	~	37^	26	72	133^	Nov 02	200	Nov
Blackwater	0	0	3	6	38	2	13	108	170^	Mar 02	174	Dec
Dengie	0	0	0	0	0	0	0	2	3	Jan 04	11	Dec
Crouch-Roach	0	0	0	0	44	127	179	176	180^	Mar 91	223	Dec
Thames	0	0	0	0	0	0	161^	125	199^	Dec 94	247	Dec
Ardleigh	~	~	~	0	3	13	75	227	455^	Nov 02	560	Nov
Abberton	0	0	0	17	71	63	145	356	748^	Jan 02	2,500	Jan
Coleman's	~	~	~	~	~	31	100	168^	320*	Dec 02	320	Nov
Hanningfield	0	0	0	0	0	0	9	41	65^	Nov 01	94	Dec
Lea Valley	0	0	0	0	0	0	0	31	149^	Nov 02	242	Nov
Met. Essex Waters	~	~	~	~	~	~	~	~	175^	Jan 04	244	Feb

Five-year average of peak WeBS counts (Nov-Mar)
of Greylag Geese from 1960/61-2003/04

Away from Horsey, Greylags were scarce in Essex during the 1950s. Five at Abberton in February 1953 were thought to be from the Hamford Water flock, whilst others at Abberton, Hanningfield and on the coast between Bradwell and Dovercourt through the 1950s were considered escapes. A pair at Hanningfield from 1964–67 was known to have escaped from a collection near Harlow. However, 17 at East Mersea on 4th March 1956 and 31 on Dengie on 17th December 1966 may have been genuinely wild and there were apparently grounds for believing that two at The Naze on 28th January and again on 18th February 1968 were also wild (*EBR* 1968). Two at East Mersea with White-fronted Geese in February 1970 and five at Tollesbury on 22nd March 1971 may have also been wild birds. Nonetheless, by 1965 there were "… so many feral Greylags in the British Isles that it is not possible to claim any particular record refers to a wild bird or birds" (*EBR* 1965). Countywide, numbers continued to increase slowly through the 1960s and 1970s. Between 1975 and 1981, more than 150 were released by the BASC on the marshes at Tollesbury, Goldhanger and Tillingham and also at Abberton.

Away from Horsey, breeding was first confirmed in 1978, when a pair nested at Heybridge GP, although breeding had probably been overlooked elsewhere. Subsequently, there has been a steady expansion across much of the county, although it remains scarce in central and

Introduced	1975-1979	1980-1984	1985-1989	1990-1994	1995-1999	2000-2004	Peak counts		Peak Month
WeBS totals	30^	146	284	857	961	1,477	Sep 02	1,755	Sep
Stour	0	0	1	4	11	40	Jan 02	277	Oct
Hamford Water	0	37	63	311	314	314	Sep 95	576	Sep
Colne	~	~	27	57	120^	124	Oct 95	350	Oct
Blackwater	0	18	4*	6^	74	268	Oct 04	566	Oct
Dengie	0	0	0	0	0	0	~	0	~
Crouch-Roach	0	42	110	187	135	228	Sep 03	256	Oct
Thames	0	0	12*	147^	19	163	Sep 92	227	Oct
Ardleigh	~	30*	22^	125	197	282	Nov 00	610	Oct
Abberton	45*	63	59	132	353	187	Sep 99	589	Oct
Coleman's	0	0	42^	129^	172*	130	Oct 94	203	Sep
Hanningfield	0	3	1	9	53	74	Aug 00	110	Sep
Lea Valley	0	0	0	0	36^	140	Oct 02	231	Oct
Met Essex Waters	~	~	~	~	~	170	Sep 03	201	Aug

Five-year average of peak WeBS counts (Jul-Oct)
of Greylag Geese from 1975-2004

northwest Essex. Breeding first took place at Abberton and Walthamstow in 1981 but not at Hanningfield until 1998. Greylag Geese are surprisingly catholic in their choice of breeding sites having been recorded using saltings, operational and disused gravel-pits, reservoirs, park lakes, natural ponds and irrigation reservoirs.

The Essex Atlas survey found Greylag Geese in 5.7% of tetrads. From about 20 pairs in 1990, the population increased rapidly to 60 pairs in 1994 and 86 in 2002. However, the species is almost certainly under-recorded, the naturalised population in Britain having increased by some 50% during the 1990s.

After the breeding season, Greylags form moult flocks. The largest used to be in Hamford Water, but more recently significant counts have come from Abberton, Ardleigh and along the Crouch.

During winter, Greylags do not disperse to the same extent as Canada Geese, most sites tending to have only slightly lower numbers in autumn than in winter, although in Hamford Water average winter counts are up to half those in autumn. Some dispersal out of Essex may occur but perhaps the species merely spreads itself more thinly across the county? There has been a threefold increase in the wintering population during the 1990s.

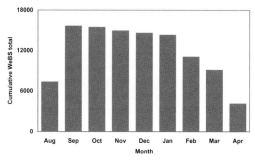

Seasonal occurrence of Greylag Geese from 1981-2004

Despite huge increases in the British population over the past ten years, little is known about the species' movements. The recent observation of a neck-collared bird from the Dutch feral population at Maldon on 15th March 1997, which was also seen in Kent in the winters of 1996/97, 1997/98 and 1998/99, suggests that the British and European mainland breeding populations are not as discrete as previously thought. Several Kent-ringed birds have also been recovered in the county. These observations, together with the fact that flocks along the Thames are regularly noted flying south to the north Kent marshes, suggest some interchange between the Kent and Essex populations.

Hybrid progeny of Greylags with Canada Geese and farmyard varieties occur with some regularity, particularly at sites where the species meet in some numbers and where well-meaning members of the public often release feral birds.

[Eastern Greylag Goose]   *A. a. rubrirostris*

Possible vagrant: one record

Eastern Greylags breed over much of the species' Asiatic range, west to western Russia and Turkey (Madge & Burn 1988).

1993	Dengie	19th February	Three

This subspecies has not been officially recognised as occurring in Britain by the BOURC and it should be borne in mind that Greylags introduced into Belgium were '*rubrirostris*-type' birds (Madge & Burn 1988).

(Greater) Canada Goose   *Branta canadensis*

An common, introduced resident

This North American goose, primarily of the nominate race *canadensis*, was introduced into Britain around 1665 by agents of King Charles II. By 1785 it was breeding freely on the estates of wealthy landowners. However, by the time of the first national Canada Goose census in 1953 there were still just 2,600–3,600, many of them around Holkham Hall, Norfolk. Crop trampling was making the species unpopular with farmers and so moulting geese were

rounded up in July and moved to other parts of the country where it was hoped that the "small manageable flocks" would be less troublesome (Kear 1990). Wildfowlers were expected to control numbers in these new areas but this did not happen, as the species was simply too tame to consider as 'sport'. Little direct competition and a similarity of habitat to its native North America meant that population growth was rapid; southern England alone may now hold at least 82,000 individuals (Rehfisch *et al.* 2002).

Christy considered that the species had "… no right to a place on the British list…" and that those occurring periodically were probably from collections at Kimberley or Gunton in Norfolk. The earliest documented record involved one killed at Radwinter on 24th April 1836. Christy noted several others, mostly shot, including one during very hard weather near Wix that '… cost the shooter a severe frostbite at the end of his ten fingers…' A pair was seen and photographed at Walthamstow in 1907 or 1908 (Homes 1957) and by 1927 there were feral colonies on Gosfield, Hallingbury and Takeley lakes, although these were shot out of existence during WWII (Hudson & Pyman).

Two pairs bred at Walthamstow in 1936 and one in 1940. An introduced pair bred in Valentines Park, Ilford, in 1953 and a pinioned pair (the same two?) bred in 1961. During the 1950s, most records from Metropolitan Essex were thought to involve individuals from the London parks where introductions had recently taken place. A pair bred on the Stour near Liston from 1957–63 at least, whilst a year later eight were introduced to Hanningfield (Hudson & Pyman). Nesting occurred at Boreham in 1966 and at Abberton for the first time in 1967. By the mid-1960s, the species was reported right across the county, although the largest count was 30 flying over Great Horkesley on 8th September 1965.

There was significant population growth from the late 1960s, centred mainly on Hanningfield. Analysis of records from this period suggests that much of the early expansion derived from the original eight birds at Hanningfield, plus those from the London parks and perhaps also the Liston area, all augmented by continuing introductions by wildfowling clubs. At a national level, annual increases were in the order of 8% (Owen *et al.* 1986). However, the pesticide problems of the 1960s did not leave the species unaffected. In 1968 and 1969, a pair at Leez produced a proportion of deformed goslings, tests on which by the Wildfowl Trust found high levels of the organochlorine Aldrin.

Atlas	Survey Area	% of 10km squares or tetrads in which	
		bred/probably bred	possibly bred or present
First National 10km	Essex	43.9	10.5
Second National 10km	Essex	80.7	10.5
First London Tetrad	Met. Essex	2.0	0.5
Second London Tetrad	Met. Essex	30.0	14.5
Essex Tetrad	Essex	16.2	7.9

Summary of results of Atlas surveys for Canada Geese

Continuing population growth occurred through the 1970s and 1980s, Cox observing that the species was "… rapidly increasing". Increases were particularly marked during the mid-1980s, such that by the time of the Essex Atlas survey, Canada Geese were present in 24.1% of tetrads and the population estimated at 300 pairs, although it may have been nearer to 400 (*EBR* 1991). Since 1991, reported breeding numbers appear to have stabilised. This may be due to a number of factors including saturation at existing sites, intraspecific competition (primarily with Mute Swans) and also predation by Foxes and corvids. In some areas, damage to crops and ecosystems has resulted in population control, the most effective method being egg-pricking.

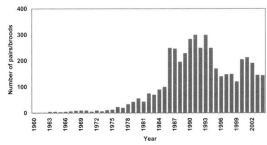

Annual totals of pairs/broods of Canada Geese from 1960-2004

The Canada Goose now breeds throughout Essex on almost any small body of water, although lakes and gravel-pits with islands often hold the largest numbers. Recently, Walthamstow and Foulness have been the most favoured localities with, at Walthamstow from 30–52 broods annually between 1985 and 2004, although there were 106 nests in 1990 and 120 in 1991. On Foulness, there were about 150 nests in 1986 and about 100–120 pairs from 1987–91, whilst 70 pairs were present in 2000. A total of 103 nests was located at Fishers Green in 1994 and about 250 goslings counted in Hamford Water in 1998.

After the breeding season large moult flocks form which, in recent years, have centred primarily on Abberton and the Lea Valley. Flocks tend to form earlier in the Lea Valley than at Abberton, peaking in the former during June and July, and at Abberton in August and September.

By late autumn the moult flocks have dispersed and total numbers decline. There is a general movement towards the coast, away from inland waters, although wintering numbers on the Lea Valley GPs often exceed those of autumn. Otherwise the Stour and Foulness are currently the principal wintering localities. The Essex winter population increased markedly in the 1980s, a seven-fold increase occurring in just ten years but, although still increasing, the rate has declined greatly. Recent comprehensive counts on the many small waters within Metropolitan Essex have identified a midwinter population of around 2,000, which has boosted the Essex midwinter population to around 5,500, representing about 6% of the population of southern England.

Introduced	1960-1964	1965-1969	1970-1974	1975-1979	1980-1984	1985-1989	1990-1994	1995-1999	2000-2004	Peak counts		Peak Month
WeBS totals	*15*	*46*	*86*	*223*	*1,065*	*2,906*	*2,430*	*2,657*	*3,965*	*Sep 02*	*4,924*	*Sep*
Stour	0	0	2	0	55	369	291	528	766	Sep 95	1,261	Oct
Hamford Water	0	0	1	7	72	89	383	290	63	Oct 95	569	Oct
Colne	0	0	0	~	~	116	64	49	174	Sep 02	362	Sep
Blackwater	0	0	0	95*	31^	120	139	179	324	Sep 02	545	Sep
Dengie	0	0	0	0	0	0	1	0	5	Oct 00	20	Oct
Crouch-Roach	0	0	3	5	89	127	156	81	77	Sep 92	356	Oct
Thames	0	0	37*	175*	244	449	427	310	403	Oct 04	701	Oct
Ardleigh	~	~	~	~	59*	132^	259	240	292	Oct 97	577	Sep
Abberton	9	2	25^	42^	287	976	706	702	660	Sep 92	1,251	Sep
Hanningfield	22*	46	78^	77	187	217	297	386	387	Sep 95	602	Sep
Lea Valley	0	0	1	39	353	565	649	901	992	Jul 02	1,452	Sep
Met. Essex Waters	~	~	~	~	~	~	~	~	2,050	Aug 02	2,289	Oct

Five-year average of peak WeBS counts (Jul-Oct)
of Canada Geese from 1960-2004

Canada Geese are surprisingly difficult to count accurately. Outside the county, marked individuals have been noted feeding beside several waters in the course of a day. In the late 1970s the presence of a feral Snow Goose in the Hanningfield flock allowed it to be tracked and it was seen as far away as Ingatestone. Hence only a rapid count is likely to accurately assess numbers (White-Robinson 1984) and this may be the reason for such variable numbers not only from year to year but from month to month as well, although hard weather may cause more than just local movements (Winter Atlas). For instance, numbers on the Stour around Sudbury are augmented from time to time in winter by a flock normally exceeding 500, which spends much of its time on the Suffolk side of the river.

Introduced	60/61-64/65	65/66-69/70	70/71-74/75	75/76-79/80	80/81-84/85	85/86-89/90	90/91-94/95	95/96-99/00	00/01-04/05	Peak counts		Peak Month
WeBS totals	*12*	*62*	*95*	*266*	*1,104*	*2,128*	*2,447*	*2,659*	*5,093^*	*Jan 02*	*7,393*	*Jan*
Stour	0	0	2	16	150	338	576	650	772^	Dec 02	1,026	Jan
Hamford Water	0	0	0	8	63	65	377	346	152^	Dec 96	857	Nov
Colne	0	0	0	~	~	44	41	87	181^	Nov 00	226	Nov
Blackwater	0	0	4	54	122	208	100	130	181^	Nov 87	357	Jan
Dengie	0	0	0	0	0	0	1	0	0^	Various	2	Mar
Crouch-Roach	0	0	4	6	97	121	81	73	140^	Jan 84	169	Nov
Thames	0	1	12	82	239	481	584	456	470^	Jan 01	650	Dec
Ardleigh	~	~	~	~	39^	56^	47	48	209^	Nov 00	480	Nov
Abberton	0	22	12	64	164	356	321	351	406^	Nov 98	665	Jan
Hanningfield	18^	51	69	53	124	177	268	273	346^	Jan 02	602	Jan
Lea Valley	0	0	3	86	364	853	711	758	808^	Jan 87	1,324	Jan
Met Essex Waters	~	~	~	~	~	~	~	~	2,357^	Dec 03	2,718	Nov

Five-year average of peak WeBS counts (Nov-Mar)
of Canada Geese from 1960/61-2003/04

Analyses of ringing recoveries indicate that Essex-bred Canada Geese remain almost entirely within the county. Some ringing of moulting birds has taken place at Hanningfield, in the Chelmer Valley and on Foulness. The majority of the recoveries from these locations involved movements within the county, the maximum distance travelled being 45km, most moving considerably less far. The few that moved further were all ringed on Foulness and travelled to: Rainham, Kent; Remenham, Berkshire; and—the farthest—225km northwest to Branston Water Park, Staffordshire. Of those moving into Essex, one from Stanborough, Hertfordshire, was shot on Horsey Island and another from Osterley, Greater London, was also shot, on Potton Island. Three ringed outside Essex have been found moving between the moulting flocks at Cavenham and Ixworth, Suffolk, and those at Abberton and Hanningfield.

Little attention has been paid to the races of Canada Geese occurring in Essex. However, with the recent split of Canada Goose into two species, Greater and Lesser Canada Goose (*Ibis* 147: 821-826), observers should be vigilant when searching through the Canada Goose flocks as examples of claimed vagrants of the races *parvipes* and *interior* have turned up in Scotland, Ireland and north Norfolk, with wintering flocks of Barnacle, Pink-footed and Greenland White-fronted Geese. Most Canada Geese in Essex have, however, been considered feral and of the nominate race.

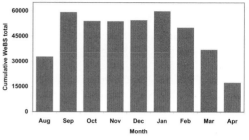

Seasonal occcurrence of Canada Geese from 1965-2004

Hybrids between Canada and other geese occur fairly regularly with birds showing characteristics of crosses with both Greylag, including its domesticated 'varieties', and Barnacle Geese not uncommon.

The Canada Goose has very successfully exploited a vacant ecological niche, so much so that it has, in some people's eyes, become a pest species as habitat degradation has occurred in many areas. Populations appear to have reached a plateau at present but the species' future may well depend on the outcome of the attempted control of another American 'import', the Ruddy Duck. A swift and effective campaign against that species may result in pressure to deal with other avian exotics in the same way.

Barnacle Goose   *Branta leucopsis*

Uncommon winter visitor with a small but increasing, presumed feral population   Amber List

The monotypic Barnacle Goose breeds in the coastal and island regions of the high-arctic and winters on coastal pastures. There are three breeding populations: the Greenland population (35,000) winters in western Scotland and Ireland; the Svalbard population (25,000) moves south through coastal Norway, crosses the North Sea and winters on the Solway Firth; and the Novaya Zemlya population (50,000) migrates through the White Sea and the Baltic to winter primarily in the Netherlands but occasionally along the English Channel coasts (European Atlas). Barnacle Geese are popular in wildfowl collections and until recently it was assumed that the increasing numbers of breeding and summering birds in East Anglia were of feral origin. However, the presence of birds ringed in Sweden and Svalbard in Norfolk and Suffolk during summer has thrown this theory into some confusion (Taylor *et al.* 1999, Piotrowski 2003).

One shot at Shoebury on 11th December 1830 is the earliest documented record. Christy described the Barnacle Goose as a "… rather uncommon winter visitor…". At Harwich in 1851 the species was "… a winter visitor here, appearing in considerable flocks, particularly in severe weather", whilst at Maldon in 1886 it was "… not uncommon in small lots" but apparently rare in Colchester and Paglesham districts at the end of the 19th century. Glegg considered the species a rare winter visitor, noting that there had been no records for 40 years. There was just one more record prior to 1950.

Since 1950 there has been a general increase in numbers, probably due to a combination of greater observer coverage and increases in both the wintering and 'feral' populations, the latter by the late 1990s perhaps and numbering 50–100 individuals.

The first breeding record involved an injured bird brought from the Solway Firth to a collection at Thorpe-le-Soken. It duly recovered and was present on Horsey Island during the winter of 1967/68. In January 1968, two birds of unknown origin joined it: two remained and subsequently bred, although Foxes raided the nest and the birds disappeared. Breeding has occurred annually there since 1983. Occasional breeding has occurred at Brightlingsea, Abberton, Braxted Park, Holyfield Marsh and Fishers Green; at the last mentioned site there is a small resident population. Separate counts of 27 were made at both Mersea Island and Hamford Water in July 1997 and there were 46 on Horsey Island on 15th February 2004, some of which were probably responsible for records of up to 20 along the Stour and in the Dovercourt area.

Increases in the 'feral' population have made it extremely difficult to confirm the presence of wild birds: as early as the 1970s it was thought that most single birds or small flocks probably involved feral birds. The origin of any Barnacle Geese is only likely to be confirmed in future by the presence of colour or metal rings on individuals as, whilst large feral populations (some of over 100 birds) occur in Norfolk and adjacent counties, the increase in Barnacle Geese numbers has coincided with increases in the breeding populations in the Baltic and the Netherlands, making it likely that at least some of the presumed 'feral' Barnacle Geese in East Anglia are actually wild birds (Batty *et al.* 2003). Colour-ringed birds have been noted on three occasions: two from the Svalbard population were in Hamford Water during early 1981; two (of five) at Old Hall from 19th–22nd January 1985 wore Dutch colour rings; and one of 16 at the same locality from 28th–30th November 1993 was colour-ringed.

Influxes in 1978/79 and 1980/81 were both assumed to involve wild birds but may have originated from different sources. The 1978/79 influx coincided with severe weather in eastern Europe and thus birds from the Netherlands may have been involved. The latter influx occurred

Atlas	Survey Area	% of 10km squares or tetrads in which	
		bred/probably bred	possibly bred or present
First National 10km	Essex	0.0	0.0
Second National 10km	Essex	0.0	0.0
First London Tetrad	Met. Essex	0.0	0.0
Second London Tetrad	Met. Essex	1.0	0.0
Essex Tetrad	Essex	0.5	0.3

Summary of results of Atlas surveys for Barnacle Geese

after severe weather in northern Britain and the presence of the two Svalbard-ringed birds suggested that the Solway population moved south. In 1979, a maximum of 60 was in Hamford Water on 22nd February, with about 40–42 on Foulness on 26th February and 14 at Rainham from 24th February–4th March. In 1981, 82 which flew over Colne Point on 25th February were thought to be the same as the 90 or so at Holland Haven the same day, whilst 40–50 were on Foulness also on 25th.

Other flocks of birds presumed to be of wild origin were: 22 at St Osyth, 22nd March 1953; 13 at Colne Point, 5th–9th February 1975 (they appeared at the same time that large numbers of White-fronted Geese arrived in the county); 18 on Foulness, 10th February 1985; 90 in Hamford Water, 7th January 1990; 40 at The Naze, 30th January 1993; and 27 at Old Hall, 11th November 1993.

The timing of influxes of 'wild' birds has usually been dependent on weather conditions in the respective wintering areas, although invariably the greatest numbers occur during the first two months of the year.

Apparent Canada x Barnacle crosses appear periodically, whilst a Barnacle x Emperor Goose *Anser indicus* hybrid nested successfully at Braxted Park in 1991 and 1992.

Brent Goose   *Branta bernicla*

The Brent Goose breeds across the Arctic on lowland tundra, usually near the coast. Three races are generally recognised (Lane & Miyabayashi 1997) and combined have an almost circumpolar distribution: Dark-bellied Brent *bernicla;* Pale-bellied Brent *hrota;* Black Brant *nigricans.*

Dark-bellied Brent Goose   *B. b. bernicla*

Abundant winter visitor and passage migrant: occasional in summer   **Amber List**

Virtually the entire population of Dark-bellied Brent Geese breeds in Asian arctic Russia, predominantly on the Taimyr peninsula, and winters in northwest Europe in the Netherlands, southern England and western France, with a few in Denmark and Germany. The population increased from 40,000 breeding pairs in the early 1970s to 300,000 in the early 1990s, although poor breeding seasons have since reduced the population to about 120,000 pairs. The increase, at least initially, was due to hunting bans in both breeding and wintering areas. In winter, approximately half of the world population is found in the estuaries of southeast England, from The Wash to the

Solent, with the remainder on the Continent from Denmark to France.

The huge flocks lifting off our estuaries in a cacophony of guttural calls is a familiar part of the winter scene in the county. Various research studies during the course of the last 50 years have provided us with a detailed knowledge of their lives.

Dale (1730) made the earliest reference to the species. From the evidence presented by Christy, the Dark-bellied Brent Goose appears to have been very numerous, particularly during severe weather, although few quantitative data were given. However, several correspondents

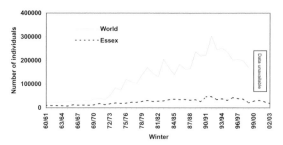

Peak winter counts of Dark-bellied Brent Geese in Essex and estimated World population from 1960/61-2002/03

provided graphic descriptions of what must have been very large gatherings: "I have seen it in inconceivable numbers on the Essex coast in hard winters, and the numbers reported to have been killed at one discharge of a heavy punt-gun seems simply incredible. In the very hard and long continued winter of 1837–8, I saw the ice which, in broken fragments of four or five feet square by three of four inches thick, covered the whole estuary of the Blackwater at Tollesbury (a space of very considerable width), black with them during high water. The expression made use by one of the sea-faring men of the neighbourhood was "There are acres of 'em"". Another correspondent noted that he had, at times, seen them on the coast in "… numbers sufficiently large to completely cover a ten acre field". Not surprisingly, these huge flocks attracted large numbers of wildfowlers and some remarkable numbers were reportedly 'bagged' (Christy). In 1860, 32 gunners firing simultaneously bagged at least 704, an average of 22 per gun, whilst on another occasion 18 guns bagged 360. The largest number bagged in one shot was achieved by a gunner by the name of 'Old Stubbins' of Maldon who killed 50 in one shot at the mouth of Thurslett Creek, Tollesbury, with his large punt gun known as 'Old Jubilee'. The decline of the species was noted in the latter decades of the 19th century and was blamed on the incessant disturbance by the gunners and the gradual disappearance of the *Zostera,* an important food source, from along the coast.

Glegg added little more. The world population fell substantially in the 1930s, perhaps to as few as 10% of the original total. By 1955–57, there were estimated to be just 16,500 left in the world and there was genuine concern for the long-term survival of the Dark-bellied Brent Goose (Ogilvie & St Joseph 1976). For many years this was thought to be the result of the failure, due to disease, of the eelgrasses. This has, however, recently been questioned as Brent seem to feed mainly on Dwarf Eelgrass (which was largely unaffected by the disease) and will also feed on a wide range of plant species. It is now considered more likely that the decrease was due to an increase in hunting mortality on the breeding grounds. One intriguing speculation is that moulting geese and eggs were collected in large numbers on their breeding grounds in order to provide food for Stalin's gulag camps in Siberia and that this contributed to the decline (Vickery & Sutherland 1996).

GB 1,000 / INT 3,000	50/51- 54/55	55/56- 59/60	60/61- 64/65	65/66- 69/70	70/71- 74/75	75/76- 79/80	80/81- 84/85	85/86- 89/90	90/91- 94/95	95/96- 99/00	00/01- 04/05	Peak counts		Peak month
WeBS totals	(3,872^)	(5,392)	8,869	11,228	17,334	24,133	29,411	28,617	39,870	31,801	23,023^	Jan 92	46,515	Jan
Stour	~	~	574	398	366	442	967	1,627	1,837	1,973	1,594^	Jan 87	2,371	Dec
Hamford Water	~	~	462	908	2,173	5,901	7,200	5,423^	5,377	6,829	3,820^	Mar 96	14,466	Jan
Colne	~	~	714	1,287	1,765	~	~	5,592	5,186	3,517	2,547^	Mar 87	7,748	Feb
Blackwater	~	~	1,734	2,781	4,604	9,282	8,618	8,292	11,625	8,891	7,059^	Feb 85	13,140	Jan
Dengie	~	~	844	970	2,310	2,005^	1,141	1,857	2,204	2,176	1,555^	Dec 70	3,000	Feb
Crouch-Roach	~	~	~	~	376	2,410^	4,936	4,416	5,892	4,421	3,479^	Jan 85	8,990	Dec
Thames	~	~	6,023	6,973	12,124	15,155	20,039	16,840	20,000	12,643	8,576^	Oct 90	33,109	Oct

Five-year average of peak WeBS counts (Oct-Mar) of Dark-bellied Brent Geese from 1950/51-2003/04

Since 1950, and almost certainly before, Essex has been of vital importance internationally for the Dark-bellied Brent Goose. At the time of lowest numbers in the mid-1950s, approximately 30% of the World and 65% of the British populations wintered in Essex. These proportions increased to 30–50% and 60–80% respectively during the 1960s and 1970s. The subsequent dramatic increase in the World population has not, however, been matched in Britain/Essex and in recent years the proportions have fallen to 15%–20% and about 50%, respectively. It is thought that the reason Britain has not attracted additional birds is that on the Continent management regimes of suitable habitat have recently allowed areas to accommodate increasing numbers, whilst a lack of hard winters in recent years has meant that large numbers have not been forced further west (Winter Atlas).

In recent years, Dark-bellied Brent Geese begin to arrive from their breeding grounds in late September, at which time birds are noted migrating south towards the eelgrass beds in the Thames Estuary. Some do not stop on the Thames but either continue south towards the Medway, Kent, or west, upriver, before crossing Kent and Sussex. Brent feed on a number of plants in sequence (Charman 1977). Their preference for eelgrasses is reflected in autumn concentrations in the Thames Estuary, principally off Foulness, Leigh/Two Tree Island and Canvey Point where it is particularly abundant. Here, 40–50% of the British population may be present, making it the single most important site in the country in late autumn. Non-breeders arrive first and families about 3–4 weeks later. At this time, feeding occurs at both high tide, when they will up-end, and at low tide when they paddle the mud to expose the rhizomes. By December, with the eelgrasses much depleted, the large concentration disperses to other estuaries and food selection becomes more catholic.

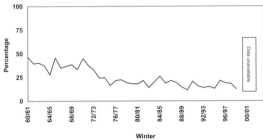

Peak winter counts of Dark-bellied Brent Geese in Essex from 1960/61-1998/99 expressed as a percentage of the World population

Whilst more than 1,000 moved onto Essex farmland in the severe weather of 1962/63, it was not until 1970 that over 3,000 were found feeding inside the seawalls; by 1975 approximately 14,000 were coming inland. Until the 1970s, most fed upon *Ulva*, *Enteromorpha* and saltmarsh vegetation but, with a rapidly increasing population causing food shortages, a new feeding habit developed—grazing of grass and cultivated crops such as Barley, Wheat and Oil-seed Rape (St Joseph 1979) and these now appear to have become the main food source. Not surprisingly this has brought the species into conflict with farming interests. Periodically licences are granted by DEFRA for limited shooting, although the action is intended purely to reinforce scaring and not as a means of culling. Wildfowlers have called for the species to be returned to the quarry list. However, as the species is fully protected under European law, this is not a legal option. In any case, as wildfowlers usually wish to hunt along the coast, this policy may simply encourage the geese to spend longer inland and so exacerbate the problem. Other possible ways of mitigating the problem, including paying farmers for the damage caused, are probably not cost-effective. In practical terms it seems likely that the establishment of feeding areas, perhaps on set-aside land or ESAs, in conjunction with cost-effective scaring, is probably the most viable solution to the problem (Vickery & Sutherland 1996).

The dispersal of such large numbers from the Thames frequently means that total numbers drop after November, although all the other estuaries achieve their peaks later in winter. In poor breeding seasons, peak numbers occur later in December–January. Marking of birds on Foulness has revealed that currently up to 40% of Brent move south to the estuaries on the south coast and into the Bay of Biscay. A similar number remain in the Thames Estuary with the remainder dispersing into Essex or to counties further north or to the German Waddensee, the main spring gathering ground for Essex Brent on their way east (St Joseph 1979).

There are at present nine separate large wintering flocks in Essex with little interchange between them. The largest is centred on Foulness but may be found anywhere between mid-Dengie and Wakering and occasionally on the Roach at times of high population. Moving north, the next population occupies the Crouch. The Blackwater is home to three populations and the Colne to two. Single flocks occur in Hamford Water and on the Stour. Severe winter weather will push birds from further east into Essex and so boost overall numbers. On more than one occasion, ringed birds have been noted at a particular site many years apart, but never in between.

In years of high numbers, Brent may move up to 4km inland to feed, particularly along the Blackwater, and are consequently missed by WeBS counters (Derek Wood pers. obs.).

The rapid increase has occurred against a background of extremely variable breeding success with the percentage of juveniles recorded in the flocks each winter varying from 0–50% between 1960/61 and 1998/99. Year to year variations are considerable with, for example, 49% in 1973/74, 0% in 1974/75 and 46% in

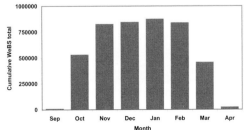

Seasonal occurrence of Dark-bellied Brent Geese from 1961-2004

1975/76. Successful breeding years tend to follow a three-year cycle linked to the Lemming cycle in the Arctic; low numbers of Lemming result in high predation of Brent Geese by Arctic Foxes. The prevailing winds in the Baltic at the end of May are another critical factor (Ebbinge 1989) as this may affect the migrating birds' condition and their subsequent ability to breed. Overall, numbers have declined by some 40% since the early 1990s; breeding success has been much reduced during the 1990s and early 2000s.

Most Brent leave our estuaries in late February and March, but severe weather in spring can delay departure significantly or even hold up large numbers passing through from further south. In March 1996, the WeBS total was one of the highest on record. Numbers were particularly high in the northeast where a record 14,466 were in Hamford Water. Careful observation of ringed birds suggested that up to 75% of the flock were from the French-wintering population that had been halted on migration by the weather conditions.

The long migratory flights are taken at night. During early March, large extended flocks pass along the Crouch for periods of up to four hours and many thousands can be heard passing over on still and misty nights. Small groups arriving in the Lea Valley or other western areas of Essex at this and other times are probably part of these large-scale movements.

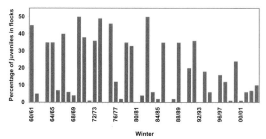

Percentage of juveniles in Dark-bellied Brent Goose flocks from 1960/61-2003/04

In spring, occasional small flocks will stay well into May, presumably still putting on weight for migration. In recent years, the principal flock at this time has been about 100–200 on the Stour. A few individuals and occasionally small flocks may summer. They are usually, but by no means always, sick, injured or old birds.

Abberton has in recent years attracted flocks of up to 200, probably part of the Old Hall flock. The species is, however, generally scarce on inland fresh water.

During four winters from 1973, more than 1,000 were colour-ringed in the county, and since 1976 several thousand have been ringed throughout the species' range. This has provided considerable data on the species' movements in general as well as extensive life histories of some of these individuals. Numerous individuals seen in Essex have been observed in the German Waddensee, Archangel, Russia (a known stopping-off point, 2,000km west of their breeding areas) and on the breeding grounds on the Taimyr peninsula, Siberia. The most easterly recovery of an Essex-ringed bird involved a female ringed at Great Oakley on 11th February 1976 and recovered 5,443km east-northeast in the Faddeya Gulf of the Laptev Sea, Taimyr. Many birds show a considerable degree of site fidelity from year to year. Remarkably, at least three marked individuals have reached over 20 years of age, although the majority will not reach half this age. One, first seen as an adult on Foulness on 21st January 1976, occurred in the interim at Archangel and was last observed on 11th November 1995 on the south Dengie. Another ringed as a yearling on 26th February 1974 was present on the Crouch in February 2001, making it nearly 27 years old (Derek Wood pers. obs.). At this age, these birds will have travelled at least 200,000km between breeding and wintering sites.

The increase in the Dark-bellied Brent Goose populations is one of modern conservation's success stories. Sites in Essex are sufficiently protected to assure the species' future and positive conservation measures based upon provision of high quality grass meadow either grazed or mown to the right length just inside seawalls, together with extensive saltings (and their creation using managed retreats) and neighbouring mud-flats with good growths of algae and safe roost-sites are all available. Provided international protection continues, the future of the species seems assured, although the consequences of rising sea levels and global warming are difficult to predict on both breeding and wintering grounds.

Pale-bellied Brent Goose   *B. b. hrota*

Uncommon winter visitor

One population of Pale-bellied Brent Geese breeds principally in Svalbard but also Franz Joseph Island, in the Arctic Ocean; the entire population winters in Denmark and northeast England. A second population breeds in arctic Canada and Greenland and, in part, winters in Ireland.

Christy recorded large numbers during February 1879, when "... a great many were shot for five days, but these were very thin". Otherwise Pale-bellied Brent Geese were only recorded in very small numbers and Glegg added no further information.

Since 1950, very small numbers are usually recorded in most winters with occasional influxes occurring, usually during hard weather. In early 1954, perhaps 10% of all the flocks were Pale-bellied Brent Geese. In 1958, counts included 40 in Hamford Water in February. Other influxes occurred in 1979, 1982, 1996 and 1997. The influx in 1996 was the largest in recent times and included 49 in Hamford Water on 22nd February. This race, more than any, undergoes marked fluctuations in population and this may explain the considerable annual variation in numbers.

A Pale-bellied Brent sporting a white ring at Steeple on 1st January 1998 was ringed on Jutland, Denmark, on 12th May 1988, which suggests that birds occurring in the county are most probably from the Svalbard population.

Black Brant   *B. b. nigricans*

Uncommon winter visitor: over 60 records although many returning birds probably involved

The Black Brant breeds in eastern Siberia through Alaska to northern Canada, wintering on the eastern seaboard of the USA and principally on both sides of the Pacific Ocean, although it is being recorded increasingly in northwest Europe.

Since the first British record on Foulness on 9th and 17th February 1957, with presumably the same individual present on 8th February 1958, have occurred with increasing regularity in Britain. As a result, Black Brant was removed from the list considered by BBRC from 1st July 2005; there were around 171 records nationally to the end of 2004 (BBRC 2005).

Not surprisingly, given its importance for Dark-bellied Brent Geese, a significant proportion of national occurrences are in Essex where, by the early 2000s, perhaps 4–5 individuals were resident each winter. Whilst the increase may in part be due to greater observer coverage, it is possible that following the rapid increase in numbers, the range of Dark-bellied Brent Geese may now overlap with that of Black Brant and occasional individuals are 'picked up' by the migrating flocks of Brent Geese (van den Berg *et al.* 1984). Just how many birds have been involved in the series of records is impossible to assess. Some individuals have undoubtedly returned to the county in several successive winters.

All the records bar one, at KGV on 18th March 1990, have occurred on the coast, where individuals are typically located amongst the large Dark-bellied Brent Goose flocks.

Although the majority of records have involved single birds, two have occurred at The Naze on 3rd February 2002; and Old Hall on 9th and 19th December 2001, 9th November 2002–end of the year and early November 2003 into 2004. Three were at Old Hall on 30th January and 13th February 2002, 9th November 2003 and 7th January 2004.

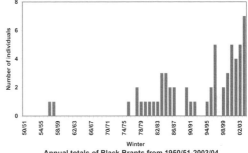

Annual totals of Black Brants from 1950/51-2003/04

The earliest autumn arrival was at Leigh/Two Tree Island on 1st October 2002 and the latest on Two Tree Island on 18th April 2004.

A possible hybrid showing characteristics of Black Brant and Dark-bellied Brent was at Goldhanger on 19th December 2004.

Sponsored by Derrick Lord

Red-breasted Goose   *Branta ruficollis*

Very rare winter visitor: 15 records involving 5–13 individuals

The monotypic Red-breasted Goose breeds principally in Siberia, with the majority wintering around the Black Sea area and smaller numbers in the Netherlands, Greece and Turkey.

| 1871 | Ray Sands, Dengie | 6th January | Shot |
| 1970 | Potton Island | 29th December | 1st-winter, shot |

	Foulness/Wakering/ Leigh/Two Tree Island	12th October–7th November	
1984	East Mersea	25th January	Adult
	Hamford Water/The Naze	21st–24th February	Same as previous
1985	Foulness	3rd February	
1986	Blackwater and Colne	28th January–27th March	Adult
1986/87	Creeksea/Canewdon	28th December–13th February	Adult
1993	Old Hall	12th January–12th February	Adult
1994	Crouch and Roach	2nd January–5th February	Adult
1996	Old Hall	3rd–20th January & 11th March	Adult
	Holland Haven	21st February	Same as previous
	Steeple	28th January & 14th February	Same as previous
1996/97	Mersea Island	21st December–16th February	Adult
1997	Brightlingsea	16th February	Same as previous

Remains of Red-breasted Geese have been found in the brick-earth deposits at Grays (Michael Daniels pers. comm.).

Nationally, there were 70 records to the end of 2004 (BBRC 2005), a marked increase having occurred since 1984, although there have been fewer in the last five years. The species has undoubtedly benefited from greater protection on its breeding grounds over the last two or three decades and, whilst increased observer coverage is undoubtedly a factor, it is likely that the substantial increase in Dark-bellied Brent Geese since the 1960s has caused some overlap of ranges, so allowing odd Red-breasted Geese to be 'picked-up' by the huge Brent flocks. Whilst Essex records account for some 20% of the national total, it is quite possible that only two birds were responsible for the series of records in the 1980s and 1990s.

The 1970 record was recently accepted by the BBRC (Rogers *et al.* 2003). It had originally been considered an escape but research for this book indicated otherwise. Both the 1871 and 1970 specimens are in Colchester Museum (Accession Nos, COLNH: 1958.11.6 and COLNH: 2004.2). The 1975 individual was found on Farlington Marshes, Hampshire, on 8th November.

In addition, Montagu referred to one shot near London, very likely Essex, in the "severe winter of 1776", although it is possible that the record referred to the north Kent marshes as he was quoting Lattham, who lived there for some considerable time (Harrison 1953).

One at Fairlop CP on 22nd March, Hanningfield on 8th–9th April and Holyfield Marsh from 18th May–3rd September 2000 was an obvious escape.

Egyptian Goose   *Alopochen aegyptiaca*

Uncommon resident with a small but increasing number of confirmed breeding records

The monotypic Egyptian Goose's natural distribution covers much of Africa south of the Sahara. First introduced into Britain at the end of the 17th century, probably from Africa (it still bred in southeast Europe at that time), the species became quite widespread in semi-domestication by the 19th century with particularly large flocks in Norfolk at Blickling Hall, Gunton Park, Holkham Hall and Kimberley Park (Taylor *et al.* 1999). Little of its subsequent history prior to the latter half of the 20th century is known, although most populations outside Norfolk became extinct and the species became largely confined to Norfolk, where in 1991 there were estimated to be 380–400 pairs (Sutherland & Allport 1991). Over the last two decades the species has shown signs of spreading south and west out of Norfolk, although the reasons remain unclear (Second National Atlas). In Europe, the species prefers gravel-pits, ponds, small lakes, meadows and woodlands and, although some have adapted to life in city parks, most prefer rural areas (Migration Atlas). Egyptian Geese often nest in holes in old trees and also thick vegetation (Second National Atlas).

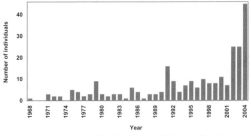

Annual totals of Egyptian Geese excluding goslings from 1968-2004

Christy did not mention the species but Glegg referred to singles shot at Heybridge in January 1868 and in Chingford parish prior to 1905. Neither Hudson & Pyman nor Cox referred to these records, the latter noting that the 'first' Essex record occurred around 1937 when a pair was on Connaught Water, Epping Forest (Homes 1957). The next documented record was not until 1968 when an immature stayed at Abberton from 13th June until the end of August, although this may have been one of the original Abberton 'collection'.

Atlas	Survey Area	% of 10km squares or tetrads in which	
		bred/probably bred	possibly bred or present
First National 10km	Essex	0.0	0.0
Second National 10km	Essex	0.0	5.3
First London Tetrad	Met. Essex	0.0	0.0
Second London Tetrad	Met. Essex	0.5	1.0
Essex Tetrad	Essex	0.4	0.4

Summary of results of Atlas surveys for Egyptian Geese

In 1971 the species was admitted to Category C of the British List (*Ibis* 113: 420–423) and since then, apart from 1976 and 1981, has been reported annually. However, numbers remained low until the 2000s with at least 16 in 1991 by far the highest annual count prior to then with usually no more than ten present. Recently there has been a notable increase, which has coincided with the increase in breeding records (see below); perhaps the milder late winters/early springs that now occur are improving breeding success?

Annual numbers fluctuate markedly, suggesting that some movement into and out of Essex may be of regular occurrence and, although the source of these movements is not known, it is likely to be Norfolk and Suffolk. There are, however, some 1,300 pairs in the Netherlands and 50–100 pairs in Belgium (Migration Atlas).

Breeding first occurred in 1979 with single pairs at Fishers Green and Holyfield Marsh, since when there have been further records from the Lea Valley at Fishers Green in 1981 and 1986 and Nazeing GP in 1992 and 1993. There are also breeding records from Boreham GP, 1992; the Stour, 1997; Little Totham and Chigborough Lakes, 1998; along the Colne (two), 1999; South Park, Ilford, 2001; near Cattawade (two), 2002 and 2003; Earls Colne, 2003; and Flatford, 2003. In addition, a pair was noted mating at Willingale in 1990. Individuals have made extended stays at a number of sites but nowhere has a thriving colony been founded. Despite high numbers in 2004, there were no confirmed breeding records, although perhaps 6–8 pairs were resident during the breeding season. A female present at South Park, Ilford, since 1987 was unfortunately killed during the park's centenary firework display in June 2002.

The rate of increase has been far below that of both Canada and Greylag Geese. Its rate of spread from Norfolk has been very slow, with just two young per pair reared due to predation by Carrion Crows and competition with Canada and Greylag Geese. Indeed, it almost seems ill-adapted to our climate; it breeds early, in late February and March, and the young stay in the downy stage for a month, resulting in high losses and relatively low productivity (Second National Atlas).

Analysis of records since 1968 suggests a slightly higher rate of occurrence in March and April, a time when breeding Egyptian Geese become far more secretive than at other times of year. There is also a smaller peak in August/September, again suggestive of some form of movement into/out of Essex.

The largest flocks have occurred during late summer/early autumn and may well involve family parties. The largest gathering, 12 at Cattawade in July 2002, was made up of two families, whilst there were 17 there on 31st July 2004. Away from the Stour, seven flying north past The Naze on 10th August 1991 is the next largest flock (excluding parents with goslings). Otherwise there were: six at Barling, 25th August and 7th September 1991; five at Nazeing GP, 24th September 1992 and during June 1994; five on the Stour, 3rd December 1995; and five at Newport, 11th August 2000.

It is quite likely that some records refer to escapes from local wildfowl collections, where it is known that several free-flying individuals occur. Indeed, when seven were ringed in the Lea Valley in the summer of 1993, the owner of one of the birds subsequently reported it back in his collection later that autumn with a BTO ring on its leg.

Whilst there is much apparently suitable habitat for the Egyptian Geese, its breeding strategy is likely to mean that further colonisation may be slow. If, however, global warming has the effect of producing earlier and warmer springs then a faster rate of increase may occur. However, with the increasing concern regarding the impact of introduced species on the environment, its long-term future appears uncertain.

(Common) Shelduck   *Tadorna tadorna*

Locally common resident, common passage migrant and winter visitor   Amber List

The monotypic Shelduck is a Palearctic species having a wide distribution from western Ireland across to China, generally in a broad band between 40°–60° N. Two fairly discrete populations occur in Europe: in the northwest one population is centred principally on the countries bordering the Atlantic, North Sea and Baltic with smaller numbers further south; in southeastern Europe the other population extends from eastern Greece through the Ukraine and Turkey and into Asia (European Atlas). The northwestern population increased in the 20th century notably in Britain due to greater protection at home and on the Continent. The British breeding population numbers around 5,800–11,000 breeding pairs, 18% of the European population. The species is well known for its spectacular moult gatherings in the Helgoland Bight, off the coast of northwest Germany, where up to 180,000 may congregate in July (Nehls *et al.* 1992). The current British wintering population is around 74,000.

The earliest claimed reference to Essex was in 1666, but in fact involved Kent, when Merrett noted: "… the Shelduck I have never seen other than in the Thames river, never-the-less they frequently go to Essex to an island called Thanet where they nest in rabbit burrows in the dykes";

Atlas	Survey Area	% of 10km squares or tetrads in which	
		bred/probably bred	possibly bred or present
First National 10km	Essex	42.1	8.8
Second National 10km	Essex	56.1	10.5
First London Tetrad	Met. Essex	2.0	0.0
Second London Tetrad	Met. Essex	14.5	3.5
Essex Tetrad	Essex	13.5	2.6

Summary of results of Atlas surveys for Shelducks

other early writers who referred to Shelducks included Dale (1730), Albin (1731–38) and Donovan (1799–1819). Up until the early 1800s the species appears to have been common. However, it declined through the 19th century, only to recover in the early years of the 20th century.

Christy described the species as "A resident on our coast, though not common and certainly decreasing. Without doubt it used to breed much more commonly than at present". The decline in other counties was probably due to persecution, possibly by those who farmed Rabbits. Shelducks regularly used Rabbit warrens for nesting and the warreners who saw them responsible for disturbing the Rabbits attempted to eradicate them (Historical Atlas). Whilst there is no written evidence to suggest that this occurred in Essex, the decline in Rabbit farming at the end of the 19th century saw corresponding increases in the county, suggesting that this may have been a factor limiting local populations.

Glegg considered that the Shelduck was increasing "… the reason probably being that the bird is not sought by the sportsman, as it does not eat well". He believed it commonest from the Blackwater to the Stour, both during the breeding season and in winter. The largest flock was 166 on Mucking Flats on 15th January 1928. Inland records were unusual, Glegg noting just one on the Lea Valley reservoirs on 8th January 1907.

Increases in the breeding population continued throughout the 20th century with Hudson & Pyman describing the Shelduck as a common resident and Cox

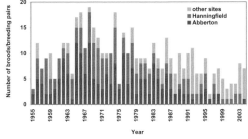

Inland breeding records of Shelducks from 1955-2004

confirming the ongoing increase. The first full county survey (Blindell 1977) located 188–209 pairs. In 1984 Cox suggested that there were 200–250 pairs, whilst in 1992/93 a comprehensive WWT survey arrived at a total of 298 pairs on the coast which, allowing for 30 pairs inland, gave a total breeding population of around 330 pairs (Essex Atlas), a figure which probably holds true today. It equates to approximately 3% of the UK population. The highest concentrations are found on the larger estuaries and adjacent marshes. Many non-breeding birds remain

GB 750 / INT 3,000	50/51-54/55	55/56-59/60	60/61-64/65	65/66-69/70	70/71-74/75	75/76-79/80	80/81-84/85	85/86-89/90	90/91-94/95	95/96-99/00	00/01-04/05	Peak counts		Peak Month
WeBS totals	(3,337)	(4,588)	4,892	7,437	8,076	8,324	8,852	7,512	9,984	9,871	8,227^	Jan 79	17,834	Jan
Stour	~	~	1,913	3,434	2,190	1,934	1,931	1,714	2,323	2,049	1,671^	Oct 66	6,800	Jan
Hamford Water	~	~	750	1,330	1,055	3,702	2,595	1,237	1,402	2,219	1,797^	Jan 79	10,000	Jan
Colne	~	~	324	913	1,578	~	~	975	1,625	1,219	889^	Mar 93	2,337	Jan
Blackwater	~	~	1,575	2,328	2,547	1,930	2,347	2,264	3,007	3,096	2,277^	Jan 96	4,356	Jan
Dengie	~	~	193	300	337	481^	159	331	204	195	293^	Feb 02	773	Jan
Crouch-Roach	~	~	91*	430*	382	456^	646	439	854	639	422^	Feb 92	1,119	Feb
Thames	~	~	1,012	586	630	1,001	1,808	1,436	1,577	1,608	1,862^	Jan 02	2,394	Jan
Ardleigh	~	~	~	~	1	1	1	2	3	8	3^	Mar 99	13	Mar
Abberton	(23)	(46)	22	18	32	51	49	52	27	18	13^	Mar 81	117	Mar
Hanningfield	~	(6)	19	28	32	29	18	14	10	14	9^	Mar 77	59	Mar
Lea Valley	~	~	1	1	1	2	2	6	12	13	14^	Mar 04	25	Mar
Met. Essex Waters	~	~	~	~	~	~	~	~	~	~	9^	Mar 02	19	Mar

Five-year average of peak WeBS counts (Oct-Mar) of Shelducks from 1950/51-2003/04

in Essex throughout summer and thus, whilst many pairs may appear to be present at individual sites, only a very small proportion of these breed. Thus breeding success in relation to birds present can appear very low. Although the species breeds all around the coast, in recent years particularly favoured locations have been: Old Hall (up to 20 broods annually); the Crouch; Foulness (66 pairs in 2000); and the inner Thames Estuary from Rainham to Barking. In 2002, 45 pairs bred on Horsey Island.

Inland breeding was first noted at Abberton prior to 1949, the drains in the slopes of the concrete margins being utilised as nest holes. About 20 pairs bred in 1950, a count not repeated since. Hanningfield was colonised soon after construction. The number of broods raised at both sites have declined since the mid-1970s. Away from the two main reservoirs, inland breeding first occurred at Woodham Walter in 1951, with the majority of inland breeding records now coming from the Lea Valley. Overall numbers have declined since the mid-1980s, whilst nationally the trend has been one of increase (Owen *et al.* 1986). Breeding first occurred along the inner Thames marshes in 1954 at Rainham with breeding annual from 1959 (Second London Atlas); in 2001, 17 females and 106 young were in Barking Bay.

Other inland nesting sites have included gravel-pits and farm reservoirs, whilst occasional nesting may occur at some distance from either fresh or tidal waters.

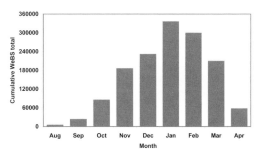

Seasonal occurrence of Shelducks from 1961-2004

Reasons for the initial increase in inland breeding are unclear but may have been due to the increased population causing saturation of original shore and estuary habitats; breeding success decreases sharply with increased population density (Patterson 1982) and more dispersed populations have significantly higher fledging success (Pienkowski & Evans 1982). Thus some individuals may have been forced inland where nutrient enriched waters provide an attractive habitat, whilst the cleaning of the Thames may have encouraged populations back into areas previously deserted. The fact that few are now found at what used to be the principal site, Abberton, means that overall numbers have declined recently.

From late July, most adult Shelducks migrate to their moulting grounds, principally in the German Waddensee, with smaller numbers heading for the Dutch Waddensee and a few British sites, the nearest being The Wash. A few adults remain to look after the ducklings, which at this time often form large crèches, the biggest being 275 in Seafield Bay, Stour, in July 1975 and 205 along the Crouch/Roach in July 1979. However, these are exceptional and few other three-figure counts have been noted. After fledging, the young disperse widely in Britain and sometimes abroad; birds from the same broods have been found at widely dispersed wintering sites (Second National Atlas).

Moulting birds begin to return during October and it is likely that many then move to the north and west. In turn, others arrive and replace them, not only local birds but Continental individuals, too. Thus every estuary tends to be used by a succession of individuals rather like a winter holiday resort (Winter Atlas). Unlike the substantial passage and hard-weather movements noted off the Suffolk coast (Piotrowski 2003), only small movements have been noted along the Essex coast.

The county winter population continued to increase in line with the national trend until the first half of the 1990s, since when there has been a decline of around 20%. Severe weather on the Continent can produce significant mid-winter influxes and a remarkable count of approximately 10,000 in Hamford Water in January 1979 is well in excess of the normal WeBS total for the county and contributed to an exceptional total that month.

The majority of Shelduck ringed in Essex have been ducklings, although adults have been ringed at Abberton. A number have subsequently been recorded in the Weser Estuary, Germany, at the eastern end of the Dutch Waddensee in autumn. Two juveniles ringed on Horsey Island have shown typically widespread dispersal, being found in January in Loiret, France, and near Dundalk, Louth, Ireland. A total of 15 foreign-ringed Shelduck has been reported in Essex, all typical of birds moving west in winter.va

	Jan	Feb	Mar	Apr	May	Jun	Jul	Aug	Sep	Oct	Nov	Dec
Sweden							2	1				
Germany						1	1	5	3			
The Netherlands								1				
Belgium								1				
Total	*0*	*0*	*0*	*0*	*0*	*1*	*5*	*6*	*3*	*0*	*0*	*0*

Month of ringing and origin of Shelducks ringed abroad and recovered in Essex

The Shelduck breeding population continues to increase slowly. With many of its principal sites on the coast already protected and signs that these populations may have reached saturation, significant increases are unlikely. Its adaptability and willingness to use new inland habitat may mean that further increases can be expected there; declines in the wintering population mirror that of some other wildfowl and waders and may be due to the unusually mild winters of the last 15 years or so.

Mandarin Duck   *Aix galericulata*

Introduced resident—slowly increasing

The monotypic Mandarin Duck's natural range is the Far East, principally Japan, China, Korea and the former USSR. The species normally nests in holes in deciduous trees up to 18m above ground (European Atlas). Although introduced into Britain as early as 1745 (Lever 1977), its current population and that in Continental Europe are descended from escapes and deliberate releases in the 20th century (Lever 1987). The British population is estimated at some 3,500 breeding pairs (European Atlas) found mainly in southern England.

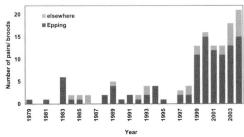

Annual totals of breeding pairs/broods of Mandarin Ducks from 1979-2004

The Mandarin was admitted to Category C of the British List in 1971 (*Ibis* 113: 420–423). Prior to then the Essex record is likely to be incomplete as the species was probably largely ignored. The first documented record involved a drake at Connaught Water, Epping Forest, from 15th November 1947–February 1948 (*Essex Naturalist* 28:75), whilst the next was a pair that investigated nestboxes at Margaretting in April 1950 but moved on. Between 1953 and 1955 at least six were in the Epping Forest area and breeding was suspected but never proven. In 1959 a 'wild' male paired with a pinioned female at Margaretting and bred. In 1979

Atlas	Survey Area	% of 10km squares or tetrads in which	
		bred/probably bred	possibly bred or present
First National 10km	Essex	5.3	3.5
Second National 10km	Essex	8.8	10.5
First London Tetrad	Met. Essex	0.0	0.5
Second London Tetrad	Met. Essex	2.5	3.0
Essex Tetrad	Essex	0.7	1.0

Summary of results of Atlas surveys for Mandarin Ducks

the first confirmed breeding involving 'wild' birds occurred: a female with two young at High Beech, Epping Forest, on 31st May and 22nd July. Since then, breeding has been confirmed in all but four years with most records coming from Connaught Water and some of the larger waters in Epping Forest.

The marked increase after 1998 is almost certainly due to greater observer coverage: the ELBF Mandarin surveys began in 1999 (Ian Woodward pers. comm.).

Elsewhere, three broods and 16 adults were in Braxted Park in 2003; this population has probably been in existence for some years but has rarely been counted. The only other sites where breeding has been confirmed (all single pairs) are: Weeley (1984–86); Thorpe-le-Soken (1999 and 2003-04); Wake Valley (1986); Coleman's (2003–04); Tillingham GP (1992); Southchurch Park, Southend-on-Sea (1997); Noak Hill (2003); Ingatestone/Mill Green (1993, 2000 and 2004); Weald CP (1999); Cornmill Meadows (1998-99); Fishers Green (1999); Romford GC (2001); Dagnam Park (1992–93); and Gidea Park (2004). The Essex Atlas survey revealed a presence in 1.7% of tetrads, almost entirely in the southwest. Whilst there would seem to be a well-established and slowly increasing breeding population in Epping Forest and perhaps Braxted Park, colonisation of the rest of Essex appears to be progressing very slowly. Generally, the lack of suitable stands of mature trees adjacent to lakes and ponds is likely to be the reason for the dearth of records; it is probably no coincidence that the two main sites hold many mature oaks.

Outside the breeding season, numbers typically peak during the late autumn with Connaught Water being the most favoured location. Counts of 104 on 5th November 2000 and 101 on 15th November 1998 are by far the highest to date. A total of 118 was counted on five Forest ponds on 8th December 2002.

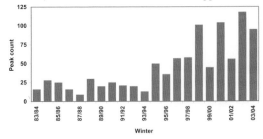

Annual peak counts of Mandarin Ducks at Connaught Water from 1983/84-2003/04

Away from Epping Forest, numbers are generally small and until very recently few had occurred in northern Essex. There were 20 at Girling in January 1985, 12 in February 1986 and 15 in January 1987; Connaught Water was frozen at these times. There were up to 31 at several sites around Ingatestone in the early 1990s. These originated from the ornamental wildfowl collection of the late Rosemary Upton, a former EBS President, at Coptfold Hall, Margaretting; after her death in the late 1980s Mandarins (and Wood Ducks) began to appear in the Ingatestone area (Smith 2005). There was a crèche of 23 young and three adults on Mill Green Common in 2003 (Smith 2005). At Braxted Park, there were 32 on 7th January and 9th February 2003.

Winter records have come from a wide spread of locations, suggesting that some dispersal may occur, although there remains a distinct bias to the corridors of the Lea and Thames valleys.

Sponsored by Derrick Lord

(Eurasian) Wigeon   *Anas penelope*

Abundant passage migrant and winter visitor: an erratic breeder   Amber List

The monotypic Wigeon has a northern Palearctic breeding range, occurring in the subarctic and boreal zones. In Europe, the species breeds principally in Scandinavia, Iceland and northern Russia with small numbers further south in northern Europe. The British breeding population appears fairly stable at 300–500 pairs, most being found north of the rivers Mersey and Humber; further south it is a rare breeder, the Second National Atlas survey confirming breeding in just seven 10km squares. European Wigeons winter principally in the North Sea countries where large numbers from the Siberian population join them.

This medium-sized duck, whose evocative whistling calls are such an integral part of the atmosphere of our coastal marshes in winter, is the most numerous duck to occur in Essex. The species is unique among the regularly occurring British ducks

Atlas	Survey Area	% of 10km squares or tetrads in which	
		bred/probably bred	possibly bred or present
First National 10km	Essex	3.5	7.0
Second National 10km	Essex	1.8	7.0
First London Tetrad	Met. Essex	0.0	0.0
Second London Tetrad	Met. Essex	1.5	0.5
Essex Tetrad	Essex	0.5	0.5

Summary of results of Atlas surveys for Wigeons

in its goose-like grazing habits. Historically, the Wigeon was a coastal species feeding on eelgrasses and algae found on mudflats, various saltmarsh grasses and short swards within adjacent grazing marshes. The 20th century saw an increasing use of inland sites, a move linked to the large reduction in the 1930s in eelgrasses due to disease (Batten *et al.* 1990).

The Wigeon is an extremely rare breeder in Essex. Christy gave a few rather inconclusive references, whilst Glegg confirmed the first breeding record, one brood being raised at Old Hall in 1927. The next six records also came from there in 1934, 1938, 1950, 1969 (two), 1970 and 1971 with others at Hamford Water in 1979, Langenhoe in 1984 and 1988 and Old Hall in 1989. Since the late 1980s, birds have been recorded in suitable breeding habitat in most years but breeding was not proved during the 1990s. In 2000, however, three pairs bred on Langenhoe Ranges and produced two broods and single pairs bred there in 2002–03. Given that the species is on the edge of its breeding range (Second National Atlas), it seems likely that the Wigeon will remain an extremely rare breeder.

Christy described the species as a common winter visitor, although Wigeons were apparently far more numerous in the 18th century than at any time since. The Steeple decoy, built in 1714, caught a total of 44,677 Wigeons in the period 1714–26, an average of 3,438 per annum, far more than the average WeBS count for the whole

Month	Aug	Sep	Oct	Nov	Dec	Jan	Feb
Total	1,085	15,897	18,671	7,655	1,085	275	9
Percentage	2	36	42	17	2	1	0

Seasonal occurrence of Wigeons caught in Steeple Decoy from 1714-26

Blackwater today. Interestingly, the majority were caught in September and October, with very few in January and February, the peak months since the late 19th century. It appears that at this time the Wigeon was principally a passage migrant and only wintered in small numbers. The early 18th century was a period of colder winters across Europe, the Little Ice Age as it was known, reaching its peak at the end of the 17th/early 18th centuries; perhaps Essex was too cold for Wigeons to winter and they migrated further south and west?

Glegg referred to the Wigeon as the most numerous of wintering ducks and Hudson & Pyman considered the species common in both winter and on passage. The Stour was considered the most important site, with the latter authors including Hamford Water, the Blackwater and Dengie coast as other important areas.

Cox described the Wigeon in a similar vein and added Foulness and the Leigh/Two Tree Island/Canvey Island area to the list of important sites and noted an increase at Abberton from the mid-1970s, where they fed on stubble, winter cereals and pasture. Increases at Abberton coincided with a relative fall in the estuarine population, the move inland perhaps prompted by increased competition with Brent Geese for limited food resources.

The British wintering population during the period 1960–82 was about 200,000. Since then, and allowing for the effect of severe weather, there has been a significant increase of around 40% to 280,000 (Cranswick *et al.* 1999). The west European wintering population appears to have increased much more rapidly from 400,000 in 1974 to around 1.25 million (Cranswick *et al.* 1999). The British proportion of the west European population has therefore fallen from 40% to 22% since 1982/83, possibly due to the reduction in the number of severe winters since 1987/88 that has resulted in large numbers remaining on the Continent.

Severe weather influxes aside, total numbers in Essex have remained relatively stable since the mid-1970s contrary to the national trend. However, numbers overall are greatly influenced by counts at Abberton; numbers here have decreased significantly during the 1990s and perhaps mask a general increase around the county?

A wintering population of 20,000 represents around 7.1% of the British and 1.6% of the European populations (Gregory *et al.* 2002). The species' distribution has changed little over the last two decades, although the relative importance of individual sites has varied. At Abberton, the declines since the late 1990s may be a result of the combination of the end of the 1988–92 drought, which produced ideal feeding conditions, the

GB 2,800 / INT 12,500	50/51-54/55	55/56-59/60	60/61-64/65	65/66-69/70	70/71-74/75	75/76-79/80	80/81-84/85	85/86-89/90	90/91-94/95	95/96-99/00	00/01-04/05	Peak counts		Peak Month
WeBS totals	*(9,058)*	*(12,932)*	*10,746*	*16,460*	*10,099*	*13,234*	*19,349*	*14,187*	*13,155*	*13,837*	*19,313^*	*Jan 85*	*48,060*	*Jan*
Stour	~	~	5,054	7,920	3,060	2,621	2,406	2,230	3,232	2,679	2,834^	Oct 66	11,800	Dec
Hamford Water	~	~	1,481	3,482	438	1,711	6,356	868	2,030	4,150	3,699^	Jan 85	**20,000**	Jan
Colne	~	~	91	352	197	~	~	277	616	709	1,677^	Feb 03	2,318	Jan
Blackwater	~	~	2,463	2,871	2,155	1,587	1,669	1,580	2,602	3,068	7,640^	Feb 03	10,781	Jan
Dengie	~	~	940	830	1,640	433^	153	68	92	118	148^	Nov 72	3,000	Nov
Crouch-Roach	~	~	42*	1,620*	838	1,118^	2,125	2,679	1,883	1,506	2,641^	Jan 85	5,035	Jan
Thames	~	~	1,472	3,863	2,761	1,957	4,055	1,695	2,087	2,377	3,297^	Jan 85	11,189	Jan
Ardleigh	~	~	~	~	1	4	4	14	0	10	1	Mar 87	33	Jan
Abberton	(2,213)	(2,526)	2,128	1,454	2,724	6,132	5,985	7,221	2,910	1,627	788^	Feb 85	11,830	Jan
Hanningfield	~	(329)	326	307	274	208	235	152	238	565	484^	Feb 99	810	Feb
Lea Valley	~	~	12	13	7^	11	24	162	147	238	447^	Jan 87	610	Jan
Met. Essex Waters	~	~	~	~	~	~	~	~	~	~	140^	Jan 03	190	Jan

Five-year average of peak WeBS counts (Oct-Mar) of Wigeons from 1950/51-2003/04

reduction in pasture land around the reservoir and significant improvements in the management of nearby key wetland coastal sites, e.g. Old Hall and Tollesbury Wick, the former contributing significantly to the increasing numbers in the Blackwater. Hamford Water is now the most important site, although interchange must occur with the nearby Stour.

The species' movements are complex and still not fully understood, although there is a progressive movement south and west through winter, with colder weather producing more pronounced movements. The British wintering population usually peaks in January, following a midwinter influx from the Netherlands and Germany, stimulated by cold weather (Winter Atlas). Cox mentioned several exceptional cold weather counts (non-WeBS), most significantly 25,300 in Hamford Water in January 1979 and 6,500 on Holland Marshes in December 1981. Since then, there have been two significant cold weather influxes: January 1982 when the WeBS totalled 24,490 and January 1985, when the WeBS total for the month represented a county record of 48,060. However, this did not include a truly exceptional (non-WeBS) count of 40,000 at Abberton on 26th January 1985.

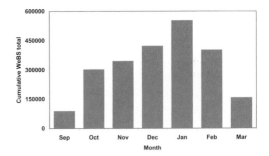

Seasonal occurrence of Wigeons from 1961-2004

When weather is severe in this country, numbers are much reduced. In the winters of 1978/79 and 1981/82, significant numbers moved south to Spain (Batten *et al.* 1990). A total of 13,480 at Abberton in September 1989 was exceptional for the time of year.

The data amassed from the ringing of Wigeons have built up a reasonable picture of the origins and movements of our wintering birds. The early results were summarised by Prater (1981), who stated that Icelandic birds winter in Scotland, with some moving on to Ireland. Continental birds from Finland through to Siberia move via the Baltic, Denmark and the Netherlands and on to southeast England. The British breeding population is thought to be resident. Around 20% of British-ringed Wigeons recovered abroad were ringed at Abberton. Essex data gathered to date broadly confirm Prater's summary.

Of the Essex-ringed recoveries, the farthest was from Tomsk, Russia, some 5,140km distant. Essex-ringed Wigeons have also been recovered on their wintering grounds in England, Scotland and Wales as well as Counties Donegal and Wexford, Ireland. Only one has subsequently been recovered again in Essex, implying little site fidelity; this is perhaps not surprising given the species' sensitivity to cold weather. There have been over 30 recoveries of foreign-ringed birds, although most have been Dutch-ringed. However, four have come from Finland and two from Russia, typical breeding areas, and also France and Spain, where presumably they had been wintering when ringed. One ringed at Abberton on 17th July 1965 and shot in the Somme, France on 15th November 1986 remains the oldest British-ringed Wigeon recorded by the BTO.

Batten et al. (1990) stated that there are no significant threats to Wigeons, though a number of potential threats, all relevant in Essex were suggested: land claim; reduced intertidal areas; disturbance/drainage; and other changes in land use. The most significant, and very real threat is the loss of both mudflat and saltmarsh feeding areas to rising sea levels. If our obligations under the European Birds and Habitats Directives are met, then the lost intertidal habitats will have to be replaced and our threatened grazing marshes either protected or replaced. This, combined with a more enlightened attitude to drainage and habitat creation within the Essex Coast ESA, should ensure that the species will remain the commonest wintering duck well into the future.

	Jan	Feb	Mar	Apr	May	Jun	Jul	Aug	Sep	Oct	Nov	Dec
Iceland									1			
Spain	1									1		1
France	12	14	3						2	1	6	8
The Netherlands	4		1	1					1	5	7	8
Denmark								2	17	11	4	4
Germany	1	1		1			1	1	1	7	5	4
Poland				1								
Norway									1			
Sweden						1	1	2	4	1		
Finland					3	1	1	4	7			
Baltic States									3	3		
Russia				19	84	10		18	24	16	1	
Italy		1	3							1	1	1
Greece		1										
Turkey			1									
Total	18	17	8	22	87	12	3	27	61	46	24	26

Month and location of recovery of Wigeons ringed in Essex

Sponsored by Derrick Lord

American Wigeon   *Anas americana*

Vagrant: four records involving two individuals

The monotypic American Wigeon breeds across northern North America and winters on both the north and western seaboards of North America, the Gulf of Mexico and south as far as Colombia.

1962	Foulness	20th December	1st-winter male, shot
2002	Stour at Cattawade	2nd–28th March	Immature male
2003	Stour at Cattawade	5th–14th April	Same as previous
2004	Stour at Cattawade	20th February–14th March	Same as previous

The skin of the 1962 individual remains in Southend-on-Sea Museum (Accession No. N75.165). There had been 359 British records of this former BBRC rarity by the end of 2002 (Fraser & Rogers 2005). Many occur in autumn and winter and show a surprisingly wide geographical spread.

One at Heybridge GP from 4th–26th December 1983 that was originally thought to be a first-winter male was, after it was shot, found to be a hybrid, probably a first generation Wigeon x American Wigeon (Ekins 1984).

A further 19th century record remains unsubstantiated: Christy considered the record of one shot on the Essex coast in around January 1864 as "... very vague and unsatisfactory... the whole record is so utterly unsubstantiated that no reliance must be placed on it", although Harting (1872) published the record, quoting Mr Carter of Tottenham: "I shot on the Essex coast last Saturday [? Jan., 1864] a beautiful female specimen of the American Wigeon".

A female at Hanningfield on 4th May 1966 and May 1967 was known to have escaped from a local collection (per the late Stan Hudgell). In addition, a series of records from 1986–90 of a male and one, possibly two, females were attributed to local escapes. The female(s) were only reported from Hanningfield, where one mated with a Gadwall in 1988. The male, however, was seen at both Hanningfield and Abberton and, although noted mainly in winter, was at Hanningfield on 12th–13th September 1987 and 8th July 1990.

Gadwall   *Anas strepera*

Uncommon resident, increasing passage migrant and winter visitor   Amber List

The monotypic Gadwall breeds across the Palearctic and Nearctic in relatively small areas in the mid-latitudes of the temperate and Mediterranean zones, farther south than any other dabbling ducks (European Atlas). The species has increased significantly in the 20th century. The British population numbered at least 1,123 pairs in 2002 (RBBP 2004). The winter population, which has increased markedly since the 1970s, may be as high as 12,500 (Cranswick *et al.* 1999). Gadwalls generally move south in winter, although a proportion of the British population is resident.

Remains attributed to Gadwalls have been found in the 300,000-year-old 'elephant bone beds' of the Hoxnian Interglacial at East Mersea (Urquhart 2000).

For most of the 19th century, this was one of the rarest of English winter ducks and keenly sought after by collectors (Historical Atlas). Christy described the Gadwall as "A decidedly uncommon winter visitor to our coast from autumn to spring". Of the few records, only around Harwich were there more than a handful of mostly spring reports. The earliest was shot at Wenden in February 1837 (one shot around 1836 on the Stour would have been in Suffolk).

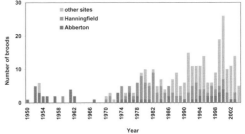

Annual number of Gadwall broods from 1950-2004

Around 1850, a pair that had originally been caught in the Dersingham decoy, Norfolk, was pinioned and released at Narborough, Norfolk. This pair's stock, probably assisted by other releases, but perhaps also by pairing with wintering birds, spread through Norfolk and Suffolk (Taylor *et al.* 1999). However, even by Glegg's time, the species remained a scarce winter visitor, although breeding was noted along the Crouch in 1921.

The colonisation of Essex was slow; by the mid-1960s Gadwalls were still very scarce residents, passage migrants and winter visitors (Hudson & Pyman). Breeding was almost entirely restricted to Abberton

Atlas	Survey Area	% of 10km squares or tetrads in which	
		bred/probably bred	possibly bred or present
First National 10km	Essex	10.5	1.8
Second National 10km	Essex	15.8	19.3
First London Tetrad	Met. Essex	1.0	0.0
Second London Tetrad	Met. Essex	4.5	3.0
Essex Tetrad	Essex	2.8	1.6

Summary of results of Atlas surveys for Gadwalls

GB 80 / INT 300	1950-1954	1955-1959	1960-1964	1965-1969	1970-1974	1975-1979	1980-1984	1985-1989	1990-1994	1995-1999	2000-2004	Peak counts		Peak Month
WeBS totals	(5)	(11)^	17	14	79	267	371	679	805	785	1,146	Sep 02	1,726	Sep
Stour	~	~	0	0	0	0	0	1	1	0	7	Sep 04	14	Sep
Hamford	~	~	0	0	0	5	5	0	3	4	14	Sep 02	21	Sep
Colne	~	~	0	0	0	~	~	9	6	1	6	Oct 87	31	Oct
Blackwater	~	~	0	0	0	4	35	59	36	34	35	Sep 87	110	Oct
Dengie	~	~	0	0	0	1	1	0	1	1	1	Several	4	Oct
Crouch-Roach	~	~	0	0	0	1	1	2	16	13	24	Sep 02	34	Oct
Thames	~	~	0	0	0	2	6	2	41	55*	75	Oct 00	136	Oct
Ardleigh	~	~	~	~	~	~	35	5	1	1	1	Sep 80	90	Sep
Abberton	(5)	(7)	16	9	65	174	236	437	399	459	605	Sep 89	846	Sep
Hanningfield	~	(5)	12	13	44	110	73	83	140	149	105	Oct 91	245	Sep
Lea Valley	~	~	0	2	1	4	71	162	326	232	478	Oct 02	859	Oct
Met. Essex Waters	~	~	~	~	~	~	~	~	~	~	121	Oct 04	143	Sep

Five-year average of peak WeBS counts (Jul-Oct) of Gadwalls from 1950-2004

and Hanningfield. Nationally, during the 1950s and 1960s, releases of birds by wildfowling clubs and escapes from wildfowl collections were widespread (Fox 1988). However, it was not until the 1970s that both breeding and wintering numbers in the county (and nationally) increased significantly. Thus it seems that it was not just introductions that fuelled the increases and, given that 27% of British-ringed Gadwalls are recovered on the Continent (Fox 1988), it seems likely that the rapidly increasing northwest European population augmented numbers in winter and perhaps the breeding population as well. Reasons for the increases in the northwest European population are unclear but climatic amelioration and increases in suitable habitat are likely factors.

Hanningfield particularly, but also Abberton, held the core of the population, at least until the 1990s. Confirmed breeding has occurred almost annually at the latter site since 1950 and at the former since it was flooded with up to nine pairs at Hanningfield (1982) and five (1952) at Abberton. Only since 1980 has breeding occurred away from these two localities with any regularity, some 20 or so sites being involved, mainly along the coast or in the Lea Valley. Most records have been of 1–3 broods, but there were: four at St Osyth Priory in 2003, Old Hall in 1994, along the Crouch in 1995, Rainham in 1999 and Hooks Marsh in 1995 and 2000;

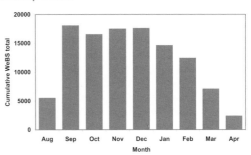

Seasonal occurrence of Gadwalls from 1961-2004

5–6 at Rainham, 2000; and six at Old Hall in 1988 and Hooks Marsh in 1999. In recent years, 10–20 pairs have summered at Old Hall, making it one of the most important sites; it is possible that declines at Abberton are due to more suitable habitat now being available at Old Hall. More recently 15 non-breeding pairs summered at Rainham in 2003. Breeding success is, however, low. In line with the general increase in breeding records, numbers of summering individuals have also increased.

The most broods reported in any year was 26 in 1991. The average of 12 broods per annum over the last 15 years represents around 1% of the British population.

GB 80 INT 300	50/51- 54/55	55/56- 59/60	60/61- 64/65	65/66- 69/70	70/71- 74/75	75/76- 79/80	80/81- 84/85	85/86- 89/90	90/91- 94/95	95/96- 99/00	00/01- 04/05	Peak counts		Peak Month
WeBS totals	(8)	(12)	14	33	82	225	333	671	860	650	1,403^	Jan 2003	1,540	Dec
Stour	~	~	0	0	0	2	1	1	5	0	10^	Nov 00	25	Mar
Hamford Water	~	~	0	0	0	5	4	1	6	18	41^	Feb 02	108	Feb
Colne	~	~	0	0	9	~	~	28	35	14	56^	Feb 01	145	Feb
Blackwater	~	~	0	0	3	22	34	63	50	66	58^	Dec 85	113	Dec
Dengie	~	~	0	0	0	0	1	0	1	2	1^	Dec 95	5	Dec
Crouch-Roach	~	~	~	5	8	0	21	11	76	31	29^	Jan 92	115	Jan
Thames	~	~	0	1	1	6	27	35	64	60	291^	Feb 02	361	Feb
Ardleigh	~	~	~	~	~	16	15	1	1	3	37^	Jan 02	104	Jan
Abberton	(5)^	(12)	11	27	66	143	152	248	229	123	74^	Dec 88	784	Nov
Hanningfield	~	(3)^	4	5	13	55	24	87	95	92	131^	Nov 86	226	Nov
Lea Valley	~	~	0	4	4	18	125	308	422	364	627^	Dec 01	734	Dec
Met. Essex Waters	~	~	~	~	~	~	~	~	~	~	173^	Jan 01	183	Nov

Five-year average of peak WeBS counts (Nov-Mar) of Gadwalls from 1950/51-2003/04

Gadwalls require generally undisturbed, still, eutrophic waters that have a combination of open water and emergent vegetation: lakes, gravel-pits and reservoirs are therefore favoured but well-manicured lakes in country parks that receive a lot of human disturbance are generally avoided.

Outside the breeding season, Abberton regularly holds numbers of international significance. It is important as a late summer post-breeding and moult location with males arriving from as early as mid-June and females and juveniles arriving in August. Until the late 1990s it was, after Rutland Water, Rutland, the second most important site in the country but lower counts in the late 1990s have seen it slip to eighth (Pollitt *et al.* 2003), although there has been a recovery in the 2000s. The highest count at Abberton (non-WeBS) was 1,072 on 8th October 1989, which at the time was about 12% of the British population. Variable water levels may influence prey levels, although nationally Gadwall numbers at individual sites may fluctuate considerably between years (Pollitt *et al.* 2003).

Numbers in the Lea Valley have at the same time been increasing markedly; it was the fifth most important site nationally in 2000/01 (Pollitt *et al.* 2003). Many other sites not in the WeBS tables have from time to time recorded counts of national importance, the majority being on the coast or in Metropolitan Essex. Recent comprehensive counts of the many waters in Metropolitan Essex have revealed a population of around 150 birds, some 10% of the

Essex total. The current WeBS total of around 1,400 Gadwall represents about 8% of the British wintering population of 17,350 and around 4.5% of the northwest European population of 30,000 (Gregory *et al.* 2002).

Gadwall numbers generally peak between September and December with a rapid decline in the New Year and a small increase in spring suggesting a return movement. Numbers on the coast are generally at their highest in winter, whilst those inland tend to peak during autumn.

Since 1950 more Gadwalls have been ringed at Abberton than at any other site in Britain with young birds having been recovered during autumn and winter in Denmark, the Netherlands, France (the greatest number) and Italy (once). The latter record is particularly far east for a British-reared Gadwall. Adults that arrive to moult at Abberton have been shown to move on subsequently to Spain and France as far southeast as the Camargue. Others have been recovered on their breeding grounds in subsequent summers in Poland, Latvia and Russia, indicating where some of our wintering Gadwalls originate. Gadwalls ringed as nestlings in the Netherlands, the former Czechoslovakia, Latvia and Estonia have also been recovered in Essex.

	Jan	Feb	Mar	Apr	May	Jun	Jul	Aug	Sep	Oct	Nov	Dec
Ireland												1
France	11	9					1	4	3	8	26	15
Spain	1	1	1							1		1
Italy		1	1									
The Netherlands									4	3		3
Germany										2		1
Denmark								2				
Poland								1				
Baltic States					1	1						
Russia				1				1				
Total	*12*	*11*	*2*	*1*	*1*	*1*	*1*	*8*	*7*	*14*	*26*	*21*

Month and location of recovery of Gadwalls ringed in Essex

The most distant ringing recovery was one at Karelia, Russia, 2,368km to the east in April 1976. Recent years have seen an increasing number of Abberton-ringed Gadwalls shot over southern Britain in late autumn and early winter. Some were juveniles when ringed and were presumably wintering locally, whilst others were presumably Continental birds dispersing to wetland sites in southern Britain.

Batten *et al.* (1990) noted the principal threats to the Gadwall to be disturbance and water pollution. Given that increased environmental controls on water pollution are hopefully improving water quality, the main threat is human disturbance, as long periods are required for foraging (Mayhew 1988). Many existing breeding areas are on nature reserves or reservoirs where disturbance can be controlled. The ever-increasing number of gravel-pits may provide additional opportunities and are likely to offset any losses caused by local disturbance. With annual growth in southern England estimated to be 9% in the late 1980s, it is likely that the breeding population will continue to grow, whilst the increase in the northwest European population as a whole is likely to mean that wintering numbers continue to rise for the foreseeable future.

(Eurasian) Teal   *Anas crecca*

Very common passage migrant and winter visitor: very scarce breeder   Amber List

The monotypic Teal is an abundant species which breeds throughout the middle latitudes of the western Palearctic in Europe and northern Asia. The species breeds on all kinds of shallow waters which have some dense fringing vegetation, both inland and on the coast. Both natural and man-made sites are used (European Atlas). In Britain, the Teal is thinly distributed, although it favours moorland pools, bogs and patterned mires of northern and upland Britain (Second National Atlas). Large numbers, principally from the Fennoscandian and Russian breeding populations, winter in Britain and can be found on almost any wetland areas.

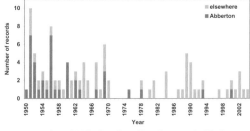

Annual totals of confirmed breeding records of Teal from 1950-2004

Christy described the Teal as being "Best known as a common winter visitor ... but also a resident, breeding with us in small and apparently decreasing numbers". In the first half of the 19th century as many as 30 pairs bred on Old Hall, but by the late 1880s there were fewer than one or two. The species also bred on Northey Island until the 1880s. Around the same time, breeding was noted at Harwich and in the Paglesham district. Glegg described the species similarly, although his statement that it was "... a not uncommon resident", albeit confined to the coast, suggested an increase since Christy's time. Up to a dozen pairs were nesting annually on Old Hall, together with a few on the Crouch, Reeveshall, Langenhoe and St Osyth marshes. The reduction in wildfowling from the beginning of the 20th century may have enabled the species to increase. In 1938, around 30–40 pairs were present on Old Hall (Pyman 1938e).

By the 1960s, breeding numbers had declined, Hudson & Pyman noting: "The Essex breeding population … is very small". At Old Hall in particular the population had fallen and continued to do so, with just 1–2 pairs by the early 1980s (Cox). Since then rarely more than a pair has bred at Old Hall with occasional pairs elsewhere. In most years, additional summering birds are noted and, given the species' extremely secretive nature whilst nesting, it is possible that some of these also breed.

The various Atlas surveys revealed a bias to the coastal regions, although the Lea and Rainham/Ingrebourne Valleys have also been favoured. Comparison of the two National Atlases

Atlas	Survey Area	% of 10km squares or tetrads in which	
		bred/probably bred	possibly bred or present
First National 10km	Essex	15.8	24.6
Second National 10km	Essex	8.8	28.1
First London Tetrad	Met. Essex	0.0	1.5
Second London Tetrad	Met. Essex	3.5	6.5
Essex Tetrad	Essex	1.2	2.8

Summary of results of Atlas surveys for Teal

suggested a decline, principally on the coast. In Metropolitan Essex breeding numbers have been fairly stable (London Atlases). The overall trend is in line with that nationally, where a decline of 40–50% occurred between the two Atlases (Second National Atlas). Causes for the decline, particularly in lowland Britain, are considered to be habitat loss or modification, pollution and increased human disturbance.

The Essex Atlas suggested that the breeding population was probably no more than ten pairs; currently perhaps no more than five breed annually. The current British population is estimated to be 1,500–2,600 pairs (Second National Atlas), of which Essex holds just 0.2–0.3%. The Teal is an opportunistic breeder and rainfall and temperature are probably the two most important factors affecting the timing and success of the species during the breeding season (Population Trends).

In recent years, apart from Old Hall, breeding has been noted at: Hornchurch CP in 1997; Rainham, single pairs on three occasions since 1980 and annually from 1999–2002 with two in 1989 and 1990; and Langenhoe, since 1980 single pairs have bred three times with two pairs on three occasions and three pairs in 1989.

GB 1,400 INT 4,000	1950-1954	1955-1959	1960-1964	1965-1969	1970-1974	1975-1979	1980-1984	1985-1989	1990-1994	1995-1999	2000-2004	Peak counts		Peak Month
WeBS totals	*(462)*	*(2,395)*	*4,307*	*2,492*	*2,907*	*2,977*	*3,577*	*4,885*	*9,027*	*8,672*	*9,193*	*Sep 90*	*15,639*	*Oct*
Stour	~	~	74	48^	91	44*	248	413	202	199	1,124	Sep 02	2,990	Oct
Hamford Water	~	~	80	73	228	453	581	565	2,555	1,096	2,164	Oct 91	**4,048**	Oct
Colne	~	~	~	21^	173	~	~	284	331	239	325	Oct 93	684	Oct
Blackwater	~	~	46	61	510	269	317	649	1,346	1,119	1,689	Oct 93	2,487	Oct
Dengie	~	~	104	137	244	238^	499^	187^	134	86	105	Oct 83	1,500	Oct
Crouch-Roach	~	~	~	361*	649^	354*	773	497	399	436	843	Oct 82	1,609	Oct
Thames	~	~	24^	60^	91	170	930	889	648	534	1,934	Oct 02	2,229	Oct
Ardleigh	~	~	~	~	~	~	0	19	18	0	2	Sep 90	64	Oct
Abberton	(685)	(2,200)	3,955	1,885	1,214	1,733	746	1,774	4,132	5,014	692	Sep 90	11,843	Sep
Hanningfield	~	(139)	191	173	173^	174	133	165	427	716	624	Sep 90	913	Oct
Lea Valley	~	~	14	2^	62	112	145	269	404	503	399	Oct 98	815	Oct
Met. Essex Water	~	~	~	~	~	~	~	~	~	~	148	Oct 04	242	Oct

Five-year average of peak WeBS counts (Jul-Oct) of Teal from 1950-2004

Moulting birds may begin to arrive as early as mid-June. However, only at Abberton do significant flocks gather; during the 1990s, 50–60% of all Teal present in Essex during autumn congregated here.

From August, numbers increase significantly as migrants and winter visitors arrive. As Cox noted, the timing of the main influx varies considerably from year to year. Countywide, numbers peak markedly in December. Most coastal locations also see peak counts between November and January. Inland, at Abberton following the autumn peak, there is a smaller one in December, whilst at Hanningfield peaks generally follow the pattern of those on the coast. However, in the Lea Valley, numbers peak in January and February with nearly 70% of all high counts occurring in this period. No peak count has occurred prior to November.

Total wintering numbers have in general shown a significant increase particularly since the 1980s, a trend seen right across the country and northwest Europe (Cranswick *et al.* 1997). A midwinter population of 17,000 represents around 12.5% of the British population of 136,000 and 4.25% of the European population of 400,000.

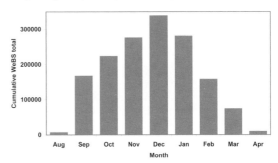

Seasonal occurrence of Teal from 1961-2004

Other significant non-WeBS counts included a gathering of some 20,000 on Dengie in October 1983, feeding on grain left after the accidental burning of the crop. Such a gathering is unprecedented, being almost 25% higher than the largest WeBS total. If the count is accurate and the assumption is made that Teal from all surrounding estuaries were attracted to the area, it suggests a significant under-recording by regular monitoring.

Old Hall has been the most favoured location along the Blackwater and numbers here can form a significant proportion of the Blackwater total; four-figure counts are regular, the highest being 3,100 on 11th December 1988, although during the 1990s numbers have been lower perhaps as a result of the drought conditions during the early years of the decade (Hawkins 1995). The cleaning of the Thames resulted in significant increases in the late 1960s and 1970s with four-figure counts between Woolwich and Rainham (on both shores) where Tubifex worms were the main prey item (Harrison & Grant 1976). Away from the principal estuaries, the marshes at Holland Haven attracted 660 on 5th February 1988.

GB 1,400 / INT 4,000	50/51- 54/55	55/56- 59/60	60/61- 64/65	65/66- 69/70	70/71- 74/75	75/76- 79/80	80/81- 84/85	85/86- 89/90	90/91- 94/95	95/96- 99/00	00/01- 04/05	Peak counts		Peak Month
WeBS totals	(1,916)	(7,010)	4,505	2,012	3,231	6,757	10,313	8,556	12,265	13,121	16,863^	Jan 03	18,366	Dec
Stour	~	~	153	89	56	120	311	513	472	397	1,343^	Jan 02	1,806	Jan
Hamford Water	~	~	536	267	249	2,364	4,335	2,260^	3,862	3,852	3,805^	Dec 90	7,211	Dec
Colne	~	~	28^	122^	381	~	~	345	664	740	932^	Jan 02	1,123	Dec
Blackwater	~	~	358	300	363	1,025	662	2,020	2,325	2,334	3,494^	Feb 01	4,864	Dec
Dengie	~	~	210	194	432	451^	484	123	358	191	396^	Nov 74	990	Dec
Crouch-Roach	~	~	150*	392*	898	1,194^	1,533	759	787	952	1,236^	Dec 77	2,058	Dec
Thames	~	~	66	97	240	1,157	2,159	1,624	1,247	1,522	5,259^	Jan 03	6,942	Dec
Ardleigh	~	~	~	~	~	~	20	27	68	21	9^	Feb 91	235	Feb
Abberton	(1,977)	(6,037)	3,267	1,072	967	1,381	1,941	1,427	2,600	4,547	1,380^	Dec 61	10,104	Nov
Hanningfield	~	(476)	409	306	253	765	255	352	1,052	985	471^	Jan77	1,800	Dec
Lea Valley	~	~	75	63	162	369	520	615	643	613	635^	Jan 85	904	Jan
Met. Essex Waters	~	~	~	~	~	~	~	~	~	~	390^	Feb 03	470	Feb

Five-year average of peak WeBS counts (Nov-Mar) of Teal from 1950/51-2003/04

Numbers at Abberton and Hanningfield are strongly influenced by water levels, with particularly low water providing ideal feeding conditions: numbers at a particular site have been shown to be linked to the depth of water and human disturbance (Cranswick *et al*. 1992). In the Lea Valley, numbers have risen consistently every five-year period perhaps due to the ongoing creation of suitable habitat.

Many thousands of Teal have been ringed in Essex, principally at Abberton, and the subsequent recoveries have provided a wealth of information on wintering and breeding areas. In the period 1949–77, 37,000 of the 55,000 Teal ringed in Britain were caught at Abberton (Migration Atlas).

The majority of Teal visiting Essex in autumn and winter originate from Russia (the furthest travelled being recovered at Surgut, Khanty-Mansi, Russia, 4,541km east northeast of Abberton), the Baltic States and Fennoscandia and pass through Denmark, Germany and the Low Countries on their way to/from Essex. Some carry on to winter in Eire and France, although in subsequent years some clearly remain on the Continent. Teal from Iceland may also winter here; one ringed in October 1952 was recovered there in August 1953. Cold weather appears to cause movements out of

Country	Jan	Feb	Mar	Apr	May	Jun	Jul	Aug	Sep	Oct	Nov	Dec
Iceland								1				
Ireland	196	67	5	1				4	27	47	49	115
Portugal	4	4	1						1	1		3
Spain	42	32	9					1	1		8	16
France	293	276	93		2	1	12	48	51	28	63	172
The Netherlands	34	6	1	2			2	31	52	36	22	23
Belgium	9	15	1			1	2	4	2	4	2	7
Germany	4	1	2	1	1		3	39	54	35	17	11
Denmark	1	1	2	4	1	3		124	137	51	17	5
Norway	1			1	9	6	1	5	6	1		
Sweden					5	14	5	5	58	28	12	3
Finland					15	73	16	8	180	57	8	
Poland					1	1		1	15	8	1	
Baltic States					5	4			56	25	3	1
Russia	2	2		40	117	6	4	130	94	24	6	2
Austria	1											
Switzerland												1
Italy	4	2	7	1		1		1	4	3	1	5
Yugoslavia		2										
Hungary									1		1	
Romania										1	1	
Czechoslovakia										2		
Bulgaria											1	2
Greece	4											
Turkey	1		2									
Georgia	2											1
Morocco	1											
Azores												1
Totals	596	408	123	76	222	39	38	698	548	258	190	362

Month and location of recovery of Teal ringed in Essex

Essex, hence the number of recoveries in winter in France, particularly in the south. A study of Teal ringed at Abberton (Migration Atlas) showed that females in particular showed a marked reduction in body condition in response to hard weather and the proportion of females caught there declined with increasing severity of the weather.

Recoveries have also proved that individuals from populations from further east, perhaps from west-central Russia and the Ukraine, occur but in subsequent years reorientate themselves to their normal wintering areas in Bulgaria, Greece and west Turkey (*BWP*). A female ringed in October 1952 was recovered in the Azores, some 2,625km to the southwest, two months later. Additionally, hundreds of Abberton-ringed Teal have been shot across Britain from Cheshire south to Hampshire and across to Wales in the same and subsequent winters. Around 50 foreign-ringed Teal have been recovered, mostly from the Netherlands but also Finland, Sweden, Poland, Denmark, Germany, Belgium and France. A female ringed at Abberton on 2nd October 1970 and shot on Hyde Marsh on 22nd October 1988 is the oldest British-ringed Teal to be reported to the BTO.

Hybrids of Teal with other species are not unknown; Christy referred to the earliest example noting "The Bimaculated Duck (*Querquedula bimaculata*) is a spurious species, described from a cross between a Teal and a Wild Duck [Mallard], which used to appear on the British List. Yarrell quoted (*Zoological Journal*, i. 585; and 14. iii. 166) that the male and female from which he took "his description" were sent up from a Decoy near Maldon in "Essex, to Leadenhall Market in the winter of 1812–13".

The Teal has never been a numerous breeding bird despite an apparent wealth of suitable habitat. Even with the creation of (potentially) suitable habitat at sites such as Abbotts Hall, Rainham and Wallasea Island, the breeding population is likely to remain small. Wintering numbers continue to increase in line with national trends, despite losses of salt marsh due to rising sea levels and it is to be hoped that restoration at the previously mentioned sites will provide further suitable habitat.

Sponsored by Patricia and Anthony Harbott in memory of George Gerard Thorp

Green-winged Teal   *Anas carolinensis*

Very rare winter visitor and passage migrant: 19 records involving 17 individuals

The Green-winged Teal is found throughout North America and winters throughout America into Central America and the West Indies. Throughout the 20th century the Green-winged Teal was treated as a race of Eurasian Teal. However, taxonomic studies indicated that each should be treated as a separate species and they were split in 2001 (Sangster *et al.* 2001).

1956	Abberton	2nd January	Male
1985	Walthamstow	28th February–27th March	Male
1987	The Naze	27th November	Male
1989	Abberton	12th November	Male
1991	Abberton	21st January	Male
	Hanningfield	17th March–4th April	Male
	Old Hall	14th April & 8th December	Male
1992	Abberton	14th & 18th–19th January, 26th February & 20th–28th April	Male
1996	Abberton	16th–22nd November	Male
1999	Old Hall	12th January	Male
	Hooks Marsh GP	11th February	Male
	Cornmill Meadows	12th–24th February	Same as previous
2001	Rainham	22nd November	Male
2002	Wat Tyler CP	8th February	Male
	Tollesbury Wick	8th–9th December	Male
2003	Walthamstow	16th February–10th March	Male
	Cornmill Meadows	19th March	Same as previous
2004	East Tilbury	28th March–10th April	Male
	Fobbing Marsh	5th–6th May	Male

Flocks of (Common) Teal have undoubtedly received far more attention since the Green-winged Teal was made a full species and its true Essex status has been confirmed over the last few years. A total of 563 was recorded nationally to the end of 2002, with around 40 annually (Fraser & Rogers 2005); all have been adult males. The years 1999 and 2002 were, nationally, the best years on record.

Mallard   *Anas platyrhynchos*

Very common and widespread resident, passage migrant and winter visitor

The Mallard has a Holarctic distribution and is the most abundant and widespread European duck with a stable population of some 2–3.4 million pairs, the British population numbering around 63,000-159,000 pairs. In Europe, the species is represented by the nominate race *platyrhynchos*. In western Europe, most wintering birds congregate in the countries bordering the southern Baltic Sea and in the Netherlands, Belgium and northern France. In the ten years to 1998, the British wintering population declined by 40% (Cranswick *et al.* 1999).

Mallard remains have been found in the Pleistocene brickearth deposits at Grays and in the peat at Walthamstow (Glegg).

The status of the Mallard as a breeding bird appears to have changed little since the mid-19th century. Christy and Glegg both indicated that the species was widespread as a resident, the latter noting that despite apparent declines in wintering numbers, the Mallard was "… probably holding its own, as it readily adapts itself to altered nesting conditions". The one detailed count, of 40–50 pairs at Old Hall at the end of the 19th century, is remarkably similar to the modern figure of up to 45 pairs (Hawkins 1995).

The last 55 years has seen little change in status. In the National and Essex Atlas surveys, breeding was proved in every 10km square; in the latter, breeding was proved in 64.4% of all tetrads with birds present in a further 4.5%. The map shows that the sparsest distribution was in the uplands of the northwest, the densest along the estuaries and the inland river valleys. The Mallard reaches its greatest abundance in East Anglia, the Midlands and Essex (Second National Atlas).

Cox estimated that the breeding population was "well in excess of 1,000 pairs". Unfortunately, breeding Mallards are very much under-recorded and little data are available. Estimated populations of 4,000–6,600 pairs in Hertfordshire (Smith *et al.* 1993) and over 1,000 in Suffolk (Piotrowski 2003) equate to markedly different breeding densities in each county. However, as adults and young birds show little post breeding dispersal (Migration Atlas), the September WeBS total perhaps gives a fair indication of the post-breeding population in Essex. Taking a WeBS total of 6,000 and allowing a 10% uplift for uncounted birds and an average of 1.8 young per pair (see Owen *et al.* 1986), a figure of 1,735 pairs results; the Essex population may therefore lie in the region of 1,500–2,000 pairs, which equates to about 2–3 pairs per tetrad occupied during the Essex Atlas survey and 1.5–2% of the British population.

Over the 25 years to 2002, the CBC/BBS (England) Index has increased steadily whilst the BBS

Atlas	Survey Area	% of 10km squares or tetrads in which bred/probably bred	possibly bred or present
First National 10km	Essex	100.0	0.0
Second National 10km	Essex	100.0	0.0
First London Tetrad	Met. Essex	49.5	11.5
Second London Tetrad	Met. Essex	63.5	25.0
Essex Tetrad	Essex	64.4	4.5

Summary of results of Atlas surveys for Mallards

(England) Index for 1994–2003 increased by 28%; releases may be responsible, at least in part, for this trend. The majority of breeding counts have come from well-watched sites, from where peak counts have been: 50–70 pairs (17 broods) at Rainham (2002); 26 at Walthamstow (1999); 25 at Coleman's (1994); 23 on Foulness (2001); and 20 on Langenhoe (1989).

As a winter visitor, the status of the Mallard appears to have changed little since Christy's and Glegg's times, although a steady decline has been evident since the 1980s. Christy observed: "… resident birds are … enormously

GB 5,000* INT 20,000**	1950-1954	1955-1959	1960-1964	1965-1969	1970-1974	1975-1979	1980-1984	1985-1989	1990-1994	1995-1999	2000-2004	Peak counts		Peak Month
WeBS totals	(1,746)	(2,634)	4,572	7,431	5,986	6,473	6,675	6,193	5,771	5,185	5,507	Sep 82	9,345	Oct
Stour	~	~	543	1,221	66	1,054^	358	1,107	1,195	455	208	Aug 88	2,270	Oct
Hamford Water	~	~	109	89	103	231	298	320	367	472	687	Oct 01	809	Sep
Colne	~	~	135	203	484	~	~	487	357	159	163	Aug 88	767	Oct
Blackwater	~	~	198	522	589	468	570	652	576	584	411	Sep 89	1,172	Oct
Dengie	~	~	462	750	817	575^	475^	307	259	134	123	Oct 70	1,100	Oct
Crouch-Roach	~	~	~	145*	179^	284*	412	453	354	319	330	Oct 82	798	Oct
Thames	~	~	295	195	314	313	954	642	739	410	749	Sep 83	1,148	Oct
Ardleigh	~	~	~	~	~	~	206^	180^	191	155	144	Sep 83	297	Oct
Abberton	(1,300)	(1,888)	2,475	4,865	3,422	3,563	3,148	2,058	1,234	1,807	686	Sep 67	7,380	Sep
Hanningfield	~	(550)	379	931	1,019^	493	545	403	419	787	762	Oct 70	1,415	Oct
Lea Valley	~	~	259	462	698	796	799	993	818	500	736	Oct 86	1,229	Oct
Met. Essex Waters	~	~	~	~	~	~	~	~	~	~	1,605	Oct 00	1,930	Oct

Five-year average of peak WeBS counts (Jul-Oct) of Mallards from 1950-2004

recruited during winter from arrivals elsewhere". Huge numbers used to be taken in the various decoys. At Harwich in the early 18th century, Mallard were "… in winter time abundantly caught in the decoy-ponds, from whence they are carried to supply markets". On the 0.5ha Great Oakley Hall decoy, some 4,800 were caught in one season in the early 18th century. Elsewhere, however, numbers were not as large and were outnumbered by catches of Wigeon by the order of ten to one. Thus a total of 4,576 caught in the Steeple decoy in the period 1714/15–1726/27 compared to 44,677 Wigeon (Christy). Although the evidence suggested a decline by Glegg's time, he was not convinced as he considered that counts from the old decoys were "… never very exact". He noted gatherings of several hundred Mallard on the Lea Valley reservoirs in the 1920s.

Mallard numbers are heavily influenced by the release of captive-reared birds for wildfowling. Harrandine (1985) estimated that nationally as many as 400,000 may be released annually. With a number of wildfowling clubs operating on the coast it must be assumed that released birds make up a proportion of winter counts in Essex. Between 1950 and 1981, the Essex Federation of Wildfowlers put down 7,000 Mallards and many others are likely to have been released by other groups affiliated to BASC (Cox). Many released birds are sedentary and all previous authors have commented on the number of feral birds and hybrids with domestic forms found on village ponds, lakes and reservoirs.

GB 5,000* / INT 20,000**	50/51-54/55	55/56-59/60	60/61-64/65	65/66-69/70	70/71-74/75	75/76-79/80	80/81-84/85	85/86-89/90	90/91-94/95	95/96-99/00	00/01-04/05	Peak counts		Peak Month
WeBS totals	*(2,086)*	*(3,491)*	*5,297*	*6,595*	*8,355*	*7,576*	*8,316*	*7,222*	*6,554*	*4,604*	*6,104^*	*Jan 79*	*11,130*	*Jan*
Stour	~	~	579	1,775	1,445	1,371	1,914	1,467	1,672	1,000	519^	Nov 81	3,207	Jan
Hamford Water	~	~	1,024	373	415	404	899	269	274	345	597^	Jan 82	2,800	Jan
Colne	~	~	490	438	972	~	~	592	519	280	283^	Jan 73	1,306	Jan
Blackwater	~	~	464	712	1,094	975	863	888	890	725	561^	Jan 79	1,817	Dec
Dengie	~	~	1,016	920	1,438	1,046^	618	548	611	208	241^	Nov 74	2,130	Jan
Crouch-Roach	~	~	51*	215*	356	356^	695	504	557	396	384^	Nov 82	1,056	Nov
Thames	~	~	735	365	502	507	1,301	1,095	713	606	889^	Feb 86	1,657	Nov
Ardleigh	~	~	~	~	66	96	198	174	169	213	238^	Dec 76	480	Dec
Abberton	(1,005)	(2,336)	1,888	2,468	2,616	2,707	2,395	1,502	955	580	388^	Jan 79	4,298	Dec
Hanningfield	~	(409)	644	871	685	716	585	546	384	345	271^	Nov 63	1,150	Nov
Lea Valley	~	~	414	591	832	1,078	1,335	1,423	975	531	1,044^	Jan 82	2,466	Jan
Met. Essex Waters	~	~	~	~	~	~	~	~	~	~	1,838^	Nov 03	2,031	Nov

Five-year average of peak WeBS counts (Nov-Mar) of Mallards from 1950/51-2003/04

Only at Abberton and Hanningfield does it appear that moult flocks form after the breeding season; at both sites numbers peak in September then decline before peaking again in December/January. On the coast and in the Lea Valley, numbers peak in midwinter. This pattern probably reflects a balance between high shooting mortality during autumn and newly arrived immigrants from Continental Europe (Owen *et al.* 1986). Counts at Abberton have fallen from a peak in the mid-1960s to a low in the early 1990s, and the site is no longer of national importance; in the early 1980s it was one of the most important in Britain. A similar pattern has been noted at Hanningfield and on the coast and indeed nationally, with counts the lowest since records began by the beginning of the 21st century. In Essex the decline has been masked by greater coverage of the Lea Valley and Metropolitan areas over the last 5–10 years. Although the absence of national statistics on released stock for hunting and shooting clouds the picture, similar declines in several other species triggered considerable concern in the conservation community (Cranswick *et al.* 1999): possibly the number migrating from further east has declined (Mitchell *et al.* 2004). It has long been thought that large numbers of Mallards were missed by WeBS counts as the species tends to be found over a wide number of small inland sites. Indeed, recent comprehensive counts of all the small waters within Metropolitan Essex have revealed a substantial winter population of 1,500–2,000, which represents some 25% of the Essex wintering population of around 6,750. The latter figure itself represents about 1.35% of the British population of 500,000 (Stone *et al.* 1997). Non-WeBS peak counts have included: 1,715 at Hanningfield, September 1966; 650 at Coleman's, 14th November 1999; and 432 at Ardleigh, 31st August 2001.

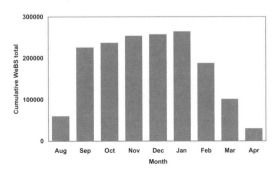

Seasonal occurrence of Mallards from 1961-2004

Mallards are nocturnal feeders principally because, as they feed in small numbers, they are vulnerable to attack and because many of the areas they exploit are disturbed by day. From Abberton, usually under cover of darkness, but occasionally just before sunset, birds fly off to feed in any direction inland, on routes between southwest and north, although during winter large numbers will head for the estuaries. Other small roosts are often present on the intertidal flats of the north Blackwater (Glover 1979).

Many thousands of Mallards have been trapped and ringed at Abberton in baited traps developed there and subsequently installed at other sites (Wainwright 1957). National ringing recoveries suggest that up to 75% of wintering Mallards are immigrants (Migration Atlas) with birds coming from a wide area including Fennoscandia, Russia, Poland, Denmark, Germany, the Netherlands, Belgium and France. This is typical of the situation in Essex. The most distant recovery was from Komi Assr, Russia, a distance of 3,543km to the east-northeast. Mallards also pass through Essex on their way further south and west, explaining the number of records from Ireland, France and Spain. Around 50 foreign-ringed Mallards have been recovered in Essex, generally reflecting the wide area from which immigrants are drawn. One ringed at Peakirk, Cambridgeshire, on 8th September 1965 and recovered at Steeple on 25th February 1986 is the oldest British-ringed Mallard to have been reported to the BTO.

	Jan	Feb	Mar	Apr	May	Jun	Jul	Aug	Sep	Oct	Nov	Dec
Scotland	3			2					2	1	5	2
North England	16	2	1		1	1			2	13	10	6
South England	255	44	14	12	14	9	3	5	89	161	167	199
Wales	4					1			2	1		
Ireland	4	1						1	2	7		1
Finland			1	1	7	4	3	38	20	17		
Norway					1	1		1	1	4	2	1
Sweden				4	5	3	2	41	33	19	4	
Baltic States			1	2			1	19	11	8		
Russia		1		10	10	1		16	20	16	2	
Poland						3	1	15	5	3	1	
Denmark	2	1	2	1	1	3		43	34	42	43	13
Germany	3	3	3	1	3	2	3	28	24	44	25	11
The Netherlands	28	7	4	7	3	3	15	61	68	52	39	29
Belgium	2	2					1	4	3	2	6	5
France	41	47	2				12	12	16	18	27	36
Spain		1										2
Italy										1		1
Czechoslovakia									1		1	
Total	*358*	*109*	*28*	*44*	*45*	*28*	*41*	*284*	*336*	*407*	*330*	*306*

Month and location of recovery of Mallards ringed in Essex

The Mallard is a highly adaptable species that happily lives alongside man even in urban areas and is likely to remain successful for the foreseeable future. However, to what extent numbers are maintained by releases by wildfowlers is not clear and, given the declines seen in wintering populations, attention should be directed towards monitoring breeding numbers on a systematic basis.

(Northern) Pintail   *Anas acuta*

Passage migrant and winter visitor: a very rare breeder   Amber List

The Pintail, the most northerly breeding of all dabbling ducks, has a Holarctic distribution. The nominate race *acuta* occurs across most of the species' range, which covers the northern and temperate regions of Europe, Asia and North America. The species' typical habitat is shallow tundra wetlands, eutrophic lakes and seashore meadows and, on North Sea coasts, brackish or salty waters (European Atlas). In Europe, the population is concentrated in Finland and Russia, where serious declines have been noted (Cranswick *et al.* 1999), with smaller numbers in Sweden and Norway. Elsewhere the distribution is patchy with rarely more than a few dozen pairs present in each country (European Atlas). In Britain, Pintails are extremely rare breeders with rarely more than 50 pairs present and 10–15 confirmed breeding (RBBP 2003), the majority in the Orkney Islands, although records have been country-wide. The Pintail is highly migratory, with northern populations moving south to winter on marshes, wetlands and estuaries. Some 47% of the European wintering population occurs in Britain (Gregory *et al.* 2002).

Prior to the 1950s, summering records of Pintails were very rare. Since then, however, odd pairs and single birds have occurred, with four pairs in 1993. Breeding first occurred in 1970 on Langenhoe Ranges where summering was first noted in 1966. All subsequent breeding records bar one (on nearby Rat Island in 1971, which may have involved the 1970 pair or its offspring) have come from Langenhoe Ranges. In 1970 five young were reared, whilst in 1971 breeding was attempted but the nest was washed away by a high tide. In 1983 one pair bred, with nine ducklings on 14th July, whilst in 1992 one pair fledged four young; all survived until at least 29th June. Breeding may have taken place at Hanningfield in 1965 and at Old Hall in 1985 where there were 2–3 pairs present in 1993. Six fully-grown juveniles at Holland Haven on 2nd–3rd June 1994 may have indicated local breeding. In addition, an apparently feral pair raised three young in a wildfowl collection in northern Essex in 1989. Such feral breeding may be making an increasing but unquantifiable contribution to the national breeding population (Second National

Atlas). Single pairs also summered: on Horsey Island, 1997; at The Naze, 1959; Old Hall, 1976, 1996, 1997 and 1999; and Rainham, 1975 and 1998. Two were at both Hanningfield and Abberton in June 1959.

Christy described the species as "A not uncommon winter visitor to the Essex coast … occasional individuals occur inland", although he detailed few records. At Steeple Decoy, Pintail made up less than 1% of the catch with just 138 caught in the 14 winters from 1714/15. Glegg considered the species to be an uncommon winter visitor. A wildfowler, who shot over the Thames in the early 1900s shot just three in 20 years, whilst Glegg referred to several records of small flocks as if they were significant. He listed just seven inland occurrences.

Since 1950, Pintail numbers have increased, although counts from individual sites vary considerably from year to year and, whilst changing water-levels at inland sites such as Abberton and Hanningfield are clearly responsible for annual fluctuations, those at the principal coastal sites are less easy to interpret. During the 1950s and early 1960s by far the largest gatherings were on the Thames between East Tilbury and Mucking where counts of 300+ were regular. Numbers peaked in the early 1960s with 840 on 13th December 1960 and 915 on 24th February 1963 (non-WeBS). Later in the 1960s, up to 300 fed on the abundance of Tubifex worms between Barking and Woolwich Reaches further upstream (Cox). Numbers subsequently declined.

GB 280 / INT 600	50/51-54/55	55/56-59/60	60/61-64/65	65/66-69/70	70/71-74/75	75/76-79/80	80/81-84/85	85/86-89/90	90/91-94/95	95/96-99/00	00/01-04/05	Peak counts		Peak Month
WeBS totals	(294)	(428)	783	689	988	1,148	1,088	882	1,092	1,245	1,249^	Jan 82	1,991	Jan
Stour	~	~	287	578	595	464	217	224	460	501	562^	Jan 73	940	Jan
Hamford Water	~	~	32^	27^	172	646	699	125^	176	384	231^	Jan 82	1,450	Jan
Colne	~	~	~	30*	11	~	~	26	47	25	8^	Mar 93	88	Jan
Blackwater	~	~	32	103	223	120^	163	167	311	282	412^	Dec 93	639	Jan
Dengie	~	~	55	65	171	79^	120^	22	43	26	28^	Nov 74	564	Nov
Crouch-Roach	~	~	~	28*	91	40^	125	297	65	205	278^	Mar 86	583	Jan
Thames	~	~	408	70^	15	124^	96	96	39	17	45^	Jan 63	817	Jan
Ardleigh	~	~	~	~	1	0	0	0	0	0	0^	Feb 72	5	Feb
Abberton	(106)	(145)	196	49	200	56	24	149	390	288	50^	Sep 90	652	Oct
Hanningfield	~	14	4	15	45	104	176	241	172	68	33^	Nov 91	407	Nov
Lea Valley	~	~	1	2	1	1	2	3	2	0	1^	Dec 89	8	Feb
Met. Essex Waters	~	~	~	~	~	~	~	~	~	~	0^	~	0	~

Five-year average of peak WeBS counts (Sep-Mar) of Pintails from 1950/51-2003/04

An increase on the Stour from the mid-1960s was perhaps linked to the decline on the Thames. The Stour quickly became—and has generally remained—the principal Essex site, regularly holding around 40% of the wintering population; most feed in the upper reaches of the river. A total of 1,500 (non-WeBS) was present in December 1978, the largest single count from a site in Essex. In recent years, Hamford Water has become of increasing importance and, although numbers are erratic, it is the only site to have held four-figure counts on more than one occasion: 1,150, December 1978; 1,450, 10th January 1982; 1,117, January 1997; and 1,000 (non-WeBS), 8th December 2002. The northwest section of Hamford Water is most favoured; here Laver Spire Shells and Glasswort seeds are eaten (Cox).

Elsewhere, all the other estuaries regularly attract a few hundred Pintails, although there were 700 (non-WeBS) at Goldhanger on 13th January 1985 and a total of 1,259 (non-WeBS) along the Blackwater in December 1993.

Inland, numbers at the two main reservoirs are greatly influenced by water levels and, at times of low water, counts can be significant. At Abberton, relatively few are noted when water levels are high but, when large areas of mud become exposed, three-figure flocks are regular. Although WeBS counts have tended to suggest that Hanningfield generally holds fewer than Abberton (even when water levels are low), it is typically used as a roost site with few present in early mornings and birds flighting in from the northeast perhaps from the estuaries at dusk. This may explain why few of the large gatherings are picked up by the WeBS counts: 747, 8th December 1985; 800, 30th November 1983; and 800, 5th January 1986. The last two are the largest inland counts. Very few are noted in the Lea Valley, numbers rarely reaching double figures. The highest counts (non-WeBS) have come from KGV: 23 flying west on 27th August 1989 and 31 on 25th September 1990, all presumably migrant birds. Increasing numbers are wintering at Rainham, with 88 on 2nd January 2003.

At present, no Essex site holds numbers of international importance but the Stour, Hamford Water and Abberton currently hold numbers of national importance. The most recent five-year WeBS average represents about 4.5% of the UK population of 28,000 (Gregory *et al.* 2002) and almost 2% of the European population.

Typical of other dabbling ducks, the Pintail has a distinct pattern of arrival with numbers generally peaking between November and January, but at Abberton it is principally an autumn migrant with counts generally highest in September and October; no peaks have occurred after the turn of the year. At Hanningfield, significant numbers do not start to arrive until October with numbers not peaking until December, followed by a rapid decline thereafter. Timing of peak counts from coastal localities varies considerably from site to site and, whilst numbers tend to peak in December and January, they vary

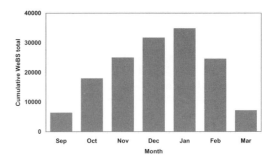

Seasonal occurrence of Pintails from 1961-2004

from year to year. This may be due to the timing of movements of different sub-populations and their relative occurrence both in Britain and within Essex (Cranswick *et al.* 1999).

Pintails are wary and difficult birds to catch but several hundred have been ringed since 1950. The distribution of recoveries is typical of the national situation with breeding birds from Finland and Sweden across to Siberia moving west through Germany and the Low Countries to reach Abberton. The most easterly recovery was from Yaguryakh, Khanty-Mansi, Russia, 4,204km east-northeast of Abberton. Some onward westward movement also occurs with one ringed at Abberton in November 1962 shot at Malltraeth, Anglesey, in January 1963, whilst another ringed at Abberton in October 1972 was shot in Senegal, 4,453km south-southwest, in December 1972. Other recoveries of Pintail ringed in Britain have also shown ongoing movements to southern Europe and northwest Africa, although the Senegal record is one of only two from that area. Nine foreign-ringed Pintails have been recovered in Essex, all but two from the Netherlands.

Country	J	F	M	A	M	J	J	A	S	O	N	D
Finland					1							
Sweden					1	1						
Baltic States									1			
Russia			1		6			2	3			
Denmark								3		1		
Germany								2	1			2
France	2		2				1			2	1	
Spain		2	1									1
Italy		1	1									
Senegal												1
Total	2	3	4	1	8	1	0	3	8	2	3	5

Month and location of recovery of Pintails ringed in Essex

The Pintail is never likely to be other than a rare breeder in Essex. In Europe the species has an 'unfavourable conservation status', reflecting declines in both breeding and wintering areas. In Essex, wintering numbers have increased slowly over the last few decades; if this trend continues the county's importance in European terms will increase. Potential port development on the Stour may have a detrimental affect on Pintails if the ecology of the river is altered in any way.

Garganey

Anas querquedula

Uncommon passage migrant: a sporadic breeder

Amber List

The monotypic Garganey is a trans-Palearctic breeding species that is distributed through the boreal, temperate, Mediterranean, steppe and desert climatic zones east to Sakhalin Island and Kamchatka (European Atlas). The species is found throughout Europe but numbers decreased sharply in central and western Europe during the 1970s. In Britain, Garganeys are on the northwestern edge of their range and numbers fluctuate annually. Between 1993 and 2002, 55–163 pairs were recorded annually (RBBP 2004). Most Garganeys winter in sub-Saharan Africa.

Remains attributed to Garganeys have been found in the 300,000 year old 'elephant bone beds' at East Mersea (Urquhart 2000).

Yarrell (1845) observed that the Garganey was "... rare ... in Kent and Essex". Christy described the species as "An uncommon visitor,

Atlas	Survey Area	% of 10km squares or tetrads in which	
		bred/probably bred	possibly bred or present
First National 10km	Essex	3.5	8.8
Second National 10km	Essex	3.5	3.5
First London Tetrad	Met. Essex	0.0	0.5
Second London Tetrad	Met. Essex	0.0	3.0
Essex Tetrad	Essex	0.3	1.4

Summary of results of Atlas surveys for Garganeys

chiefly when on migration. I know of no instance of it breeding ..." At Harwich in 1851 it was "... rather a rare species"; otherwise he detailed just three records. Glegg described the species similarly. However, he noted five breeding records, the first relating to a brood of six on the "Crouch marshes" in 1896, although breeding was suspected near St Osyth in 1890. A wildfowler who regularly shot over a Thames marsh from 1902–29, at least, considered that the Garganey was increasing and stated that "… during three or four days shooting in August, two or three, to six at most, would be obtained, and that some were shot during the first week of September, but rarely later". At Old Hall, 4–5 pairs were present in 1938 (Pyman 1938e).

Garganeys are exceptionally secretive whilst nesting and proving breeding is notoriously difficult. Since 1950, a total of 50–55 pairs has been confirmed breeding, at least 28 during the 1950s, 14–15 in the 1960s, 3–4 in the 1970s, none in the 1980s, four in the 1990s and four in the 2000s.

Locality	No. of years with summering/breeding pairs						Total	Years with confirmed breeding	No. of confirmed breeding pairs	Peak counts
	1950s	1960s	1970s	1980s	1990s	2000s				
Old Hall	10	4	0	0	6	4	24	9	10	3-4 pairs summered, success unknown, 1963
Abberton	10	5	5	0	6	1	27	11	26-29	4-5 pairs bred, 1952 & 1960
Hanningfield	5	4	0	1	1	0	11	3	4**	13 pairs summered, "several bred" 1957

** "several" pairs not included in this figure

Principal Garganey breeding sites from 1950-2004

During the 1950s, the Garganey was more common than at any other time. Hudson & Pyman suggested that at least 18 pairs bred in 1957, although this was probably an overestimate: the *EBR* 1957 mentions a total of 16–17 pairs that summered. Nonetheless from 1952–57 a total of 7–17 pairs summered annually. In 1957 the partially flooded Hanningfield provided ideal habitat with some 13 pairs and several broods resulting. There were also 2–3 pairs at Abberton. None summered in 1962 for the first time in the EBS's history, and after 1964 there was a steady decline. Occasional pairs were reported

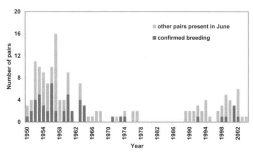

Annual totals of breeding Garganeys from 1950-2004

through to the late 1970s, after which the Garganey became rare with no summering pairs from 1978–88 and few migrants. Since 1988 there appears to have been a reversal of this trend. Breeding was confirmed in 1990 for the first time since 1974, since when it has occurred in five years with a peak of three broods in 2001.

Since 1950, Abberton and Old Hall have been the most favoured breeding localities, with the former having far more confirmed breeding records, perhaps due to the relative ease of surveying. Hanningfield was used with some regularity, from its flooding until the mid-1960s, but rarely since. Breeding or summering pairs have been noted from a further ten localities, but only at three of these was breeding confirmed. On the North Fambridge marshes birds summered from 1952–55, 1963 and 2002 (Blue House Farm) but only in 1963 was breeding (three pairs) confirmed. At Langenhoe, three pairs bred in 1956 with single pairs in 1992 and 2001. At Rainham, breeding was confirmed in 1988 (one pair) and 2001 (two pairs), whilst summering has occurred annually since 1998.

Spring migrants, often in pairs, begin to arrive around early March with passage lasting until early June. Numbers are generally small and vary from year to year. In 1974, 11 were at North Fambridge on 6th April with perhaps a further 10–15 passing through elsewhere, and in 1990 38 were reported, including five at Abberton on 14th March and seven at East Tilbury on 18th May. In contrast, there were no records until 21st June in 1987. Larger numbers may coincide with warm springs and anticyclonic conditions (Clarke & Eyre 1993). Cox felt that there was no evidence to suggest that passage birds were more numerous in earlier years. However, the 1980s saw comparatively low numbers of spring migrants, with increased numbers during the 1990s. Apart from the wintering individuals detailed below, the earliest arrivals were at Walthamstow on 3rd March 2002 and Heybridge GP on 4th March 1978 (male and two females). Numbers tend to peak around early April, although in most years there is no clear influx, the period early April to late May being peak arrival time.

In contrast to the situation in Suffolk (Piotrowski 2003), numbers of Garganeys are generally higher in autumn than spring. Large late summer and early autumn gatherings at Abberton and Hanningfield were typical during the 1950s but declined in parallel with the breeding population, perhaps suggesting that these gatherings involved locally-bred birds. There were 63 at Abberton at the end of August 1953 with 66 there in mid-August 1955, at which time there were 30 at Hanningfield. In 1957 there were at least 50 at Hanningfield in late July/early August following the exceptional numbers that summered there. In 1959,

35–40 were at Abberton on 8th August. Through the 1960s peaks were lower, although there were 29 at Hanningfield on 17th August 1967 and 35+ on 16th August 1969. Subsequently, there were no counts in excess of 20 for 25 years. A total of 13 at Hanningfield on 18th June 1967 was unusual; no breeding attempts were known that year. Away from these two sites, Garganeys have occurred at many sites, although on only four occasions have double-figure counts been noted, and these came from only two locations: Rainham, 12, 23rd August 1960 and 16, 3rd August 1961; and Heybridge GP, 12, 7th August 1967 and 13, 3rd August 1971.

The slight increase in breeding records in the 1990s saw a corresponding rise in autumn gatherings. There were 21 at Abberton on 20th–21st August 1994 at a time of very low water levels, and 19 at Hanningfield on 26th August 1996.

Most Garganeys have departed by the end of September, although odd birds occur into October. There are three November records, all involving singles, the latest being at Roydon GP on 16th with presumably the same at Netherhall GP on 18th in 1984.

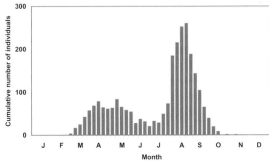

Seasonal occurrence of Garganeys from 1971-2004

There have been five winter records: Lea Valley, 16th February 1890; Kelvedon, 11th December 1926; Corringham, 20th December 1955; Little Oakley, 8th February 1970; and a female, the Lea at Spitalfields, 5th January 2002. The Corringham bird had been ringed in the Netherlands in August 1953. One present at Wanstead Park throughout 1966 was probably an escape.

Much of our knowledge of Garganey movements to and from Britain is due to the large numbers ringed at Abberton since 1954 with 332 up to the end of 1991, 73% of the national total; 48 were ringed in 1948 alone. Western Palearctic birds winter mainly in Africa between the Equator and 20° North. The only African recovery of an Essex-ringed Garganey is from Lac Niangaye, Mali, 4,013km south of Abberton; it falls within the Garganey's typical wintering area. The female involved was almost 15 years old when killed and is the oldest British-ringed Garganey to be reported to the BTO. An analysis of Essex ringing recoveries suggests a distinct bias to a southeast migration route with few recorded from Iberia at any time of year. The concentrations of spring recoveries in northern Italy spreading across northwest France to the Channel coast are marked.

The recovery of three locally-bred Garganeys in eastern Russia during the

	Jan	Feb	Mar	Apr	May	Jun	Jul	Aug	Sep	Oct	Nov	Dec
Russia				1				1	1			
Germany			1					1				
The Netherlands								2				
Belgium										1		
France		1	14				2		3	1		
Spain		1										
Italy		2	14	1				1	2	1	1	
Austria								1				
Hungary			1									
Bulgaria			1									
Yugoslavia		1										
Turkey					1							
Algeria									2			
Mali		1										
Total	0	6	31	2	1	0	2	6	8	3	1	0

Month and location of recovery of Garganeys ringed in Essex

breeding season/late summer suggests that they may have paired with eastern birds on their wintering grounds and moved to an adopted breeding locality (*BWP*), the furthest east being recovered in Tselinograd, 4,636km from Abberton. Two autumn-ringed Garganeys have been recovered later in Russia, suggesting that some eastern birds reach Essex in autumn.

Britain is on the northwest edge of the Garganey's world breeding range and this species is unlikely ever to be a common breeder in Essex. At present, the majority of breeding records come from nature reserves and so the potential for increasing the breeding population is not great. Raising water levels may well benefit the species where this is possible, but otherwise there is little that can be done to encourage the species. Global warming may make the county more attractive but its likely effects are at present little understood.

Blue-winged Teal   *Anas discors*

Vagrant: six records involving five individuals

The monotypic Blue-winged Teal breeds throughout North America and winters in southern North America, central America and northern South America.

1989	Stanford Warren	10th–12th May	Male
1996	Abberton	14th–21st September	Male
1999/2000	Hanningfield	9th September–22nd January	Male
2000	Walthamstow	5th November	Female/immature
2001	Old Hall	14th May	Male
	Abberton Manor/		
	Roman River	20th–26th May	Same as previous

Up to the end of 2004 there had been 228 British records (BBRC 2005), which showed a wide geographical spread. Most occur in spring and autumn. As it is the New World equivalent of the Garganey, its pattern of occurrence in Europe is quite different from other Nearctic ducks, with very few winter records. Autumn records probably relate to freshly arrived transatlantic vagrants, whilst those in spring are probably individuals moving, which have wintered further south, having arrived in Europe in a previous year.

A series of records that probably involved escapes came from Connaught Water between 1994 and 2000 and 2002–03; three birds were reported in 1995 and nest-building was reported in 1996.

(Northern) Shoveler   *Anas clypeata*

Fairly common resident, common passage migrant and winter visitor   Amber List

The monotypic Shoveler is a Holarctic lowland species that breeds mainly in the northern and temperate region, roughly between 40° and 70° N, from Iceland to 162° E in the Palearctic and from Newfoundland to Alaska in the Nearctic. The current European population is in the region of 35,000–40,000 breeding pairs (*HBW*) with perhaps 1,000–1,500 in Britain (Stone *et al.* 1997). The winter distribution of European birds is centred on north Africa and the Mediterranean with smaller numbers in the Sahel region of Africa; increasing numbers are remaining in northwest Europe. The British winter population is in the region of 10,000.

Christy considered that "… a few pairs nest annually among the marshes on our coast". Breeding occurred around Harwich but the principal site was Old Hall, where in 1889 it was noted "… a considerable number bred … it is becoming commoner as a breeding bird". This increase continued through the early years of the 20th century, possibly helped by the Bird Protection legislation of the late 1800s and early 1900s. Thus Glegg was able to detail seven nesting localities where breeding occurred annually. At Old Hall, 20–30 pairs bred, whilst at another unnamed location, perhaps 15 pairs bred. On one Thames marsh the species was considered by one wildfowler to be commoner than the Mallard. Around 30 pairs were present on Old Hall in 1938 (Pyman 1938e). Hudson & Pyman estimated that 60–70 pairs were breeding during the 1920s and 1930s. However, drainage of suitable habitat saw the population fall to 30–35 pairs in the 1950s and 15–20 pairs during the 1960s. The extent of the decline was, however, masked by the numbers that bred on the 'island' that existed at Abberton for a few years after it was flooded.

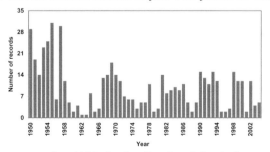

Annual totals of confirmed breeding pairs/broods of Shovelers from 1950-2004

Shovelers prefer poorly drained treeless meadows interspersed with eutrophic shallow, stagnant freshwater pools and lakes, rivers with undisturbed creeks and muddy bottoms usually possessing lush emergent and floating vegetation. As a result of its specialised filter-feeding methods, its habitat choice is therefore restricted (Dittberner & Dittberner 1987).

It is consequently very vulnerable to drainage and changes in land use and it is on unprotected, small marginal wetlands that most losses have occurred over the last 50 years, protected sites on the whole maintaining or even increasing numbers. Annual numbers of Shoveler broods

Atlas	Survey Area	% of 10km squares or tetrads in which	
		bred/probably bred	possibly bred or present
First National 10km	Essex	22.8	17.5
Second National 10km	Essex	17.5	19.3
First London Tetrad	Met. Essex	0.5	0.5
Second London Tetrad	Met. Essex	5.5	6.0
Essex Tetrad	Essex	2.7	1.7

Summary of results of Atlas surveys for Shovelers

vary considerably, the drought in the late 1980s and mid-1990s in particular appearing to have had an adverse effect on breeding success. Up to 15 pairs have bred successfully in recent years, representing around 1.0–1.5% of the UK population. Up to 47 pairs (2002) have summered at Old Hall in recent years; 100 pairs were present in Essex during 2002, including 20 on Horsey Island, 15 at Langenhoe and 13 at Rainham.

GB 100 INT 400	1950-1954	1955-1959	1960-1964	1965-1969	1970-1974	1975-1979	1980-1984	1985-1989	1990-1994	1995-1999	2000-2004	Peak counts		Peak Month
WeBS totals	(58)	(158)	506	484	755	722	888	1,004	1,352	945	1,250	Sep 90	2,177	Oct
Stour	~	~	0	0	4	0	12	6	2	3	1	Sep 82	30	Oct
Hamford Water	~	~	0	1	4	12	2	3	13	26	11	Oct 95	73	Oct
Colne	~	~	0	0	9^	~	~	8	18	6	16	Aug 91	33	Oct
Blackwater	~	~	2	4	7	9	39	26	68	43	50	Oct 83	119	Oct
Dengie	~	~	~	1	0	8	1	1	0	2	5	Sep 77	25	Oct
Crouch-Roach	~	~	~	11*	22*	~	23	82	92	20	53	Sep 94	135	Oct
Thames	~	~	0	0	7*	51^	176	39	53	7	127	Oct 81	380	Oct
Ardleigh	~	~	~	~	~	~	19	10	34	8	9	Sep 90	80	Oct
Abberton	(54)	(126)	455	304	504	412	350	438	683	594	376	Sep 61	1,387	Sep
Hanningfield	~	(39)	50	209	233^	82	82	51	132	201	172	Sep 67	392	Sep
Lea Valley	~	~	14	32	124	184	282	425	401	197	423	Sep 90	675	Oct
Met. Essex Waters	~	~	~	~	~	~	~	~	~	~	122	Oct 03	212	Oct

Five-year average of peak WeBS counts (Jul-Oct) of Shovelers from 1950-2004

Since 1950, breeding has been confirmed at about 35 locations either on marshes or gravel-pits adjacent to the coast or at the main reservoirs. At Abberton up to 25 pairs bred, mainly on the 'island', in the early 1950s but numbers have fallen subsequently. Nine pairs bred in 1971 but there have been few records in the last decade or so. This decline is a very good example of how a well-protected location, in this instance a Ramsar site, can be degraded in value for a particular species by the change in use of adjacent non-designated land. Cutting of silage right up to the reservoir edge has left little rough pasture adjacent to the reservoir, so important for nesting (Second National Atlas). At Old Hall, arguably the principal Essex site today, nine pairs bred in 1951 with eight in 1969 and seven in both 1992 and 1998. Small numbers breed at Hanningfield, although Shovelers were most numerous in the 1950s; ten pairs bred in 1957. In 1991, ten pairs bred successfully at Langenhoe/Fingringhoe Ranges, although 1–4 is more usual. In the Lea Valley as a whole, nesting has been confirmed in 13 years, mainly from Walthamstow where there were 1–2 pairs from 1967–84. Other notable records have included four broods on Mersea Island and at Fleet Head in 1953 and 1991 respectively.

GB 100 INT 400	50/51-54/55	55/56-59/60	60/61-64/65	65/66-69/70	70/71-74/75	75/76-79/80	80/81-84/85	85/86-89/90	90/91-94/95	95/96-99/00	00/01-04/05	Peak counts		Peak Month
WeBS totals	(254)	(384)	209	308	572	768	890	701	888	786	1,271^	Nov 02	1,346	Nov
Stour	~	~	3	2	13	22	17	25	31	11^	6^	Feb 93	67	Feb
Hamford Water	~	~	3	3	12	41	7	26	38	40	110^	Feb 02	214	Dec
Colne	~	~	1	3	44	~	~	35	58	28	66^	Feb 72	136	Feb
Blackwater	~	~	10	29	27	54	38	47	93	100	140^	Mar 04	209	Mar
Dengie	~	~	0	12	8	2	3	5	19	5	14^	Nov 92	54	Jan
Crouch-Roach	~	~	1	4	29	6	190	32	99	68	82^	Dec 82	302	Dec
Thames	~	~	12	19	31	147	138	168	63	79	323^	Nov 85	475	Feb
Ardleigh	~	~	~	~	2	6	20	12	17	44	15^	Jan 97	73	Dec
Abberton	(181)	(342)	143	117	320	378	288	184	246	326	367^	Nov 76	649	Nov
Hanningfield	~	(47)	59	144	171	94	53	50	126	90	209^	Nov 02	422	Nov
Lea Valley	~	~	18	47	154	204	364	313	321	224	264^	Nov 82	438	Nov
Met. Essex Waters	~	~	~	~	~	~	~	~	~	~	229^	Feb 03	239	Jan

Five-year average of peak WeBS counts (Nov-Mar) of Shovelers from 1950/51-2003/04

Although Christy considered Shovelers to be fairly common from autumn to spring, Glegg noted that they usually disappeared after September and reappeared in February with very few seen during winter. Hudson & Pyman thought that the largest numbers were present during spring and autumn and particularly the latter. Cox, however, referred to an increase in wintering numbers in coastal localities. Today, the largest numbers still occur in autumn, but there is now a significant wintering population and spring passage appears to be less evident than in the past.

Shovelers begin to arrive in Essex in late July/early August. Most gather at inland waters, particularly at Abberton, which during September may hold 50% of all the Shovelers in the county, some 3% of the British and 1% of the European populations, making it one of the most important sites in the country. The peak count of 1,387 at Abberton in September 1961 is the largest single WeBS count ever reported in Britain. The only other four-figure count was also at Abberton with 1,085 (non-WeBS) in September 1990. Recent comprehensive counts in the Lea Valley and Metropolitan Essex show that numbers may approach those at Abberton, particularly in autumn.

Generally numbers in Essex decline after October; nationally, numbers fall after November (Pollitt *et al.* 2003), although more recently this reduction has been less obvious as the winter population has increased. The recent Essex wintering population represents around 13% of the British and 2.25% of the European wintering populations.

Shovelers show a strong preference for freshwater. Thus, whilst it appears that there has been an increase in numbers in estuarine localities during winter in Essex, it should be borne in mind that many actually occur on the various freshwaters immediately adjacent to the tidal estuaries; few are found with regularity on the estuaries themselves.

Along the Thames, the largest counts have tended to come from either Foulness or Rainham, 463 at the former on 17th November 1985 and 415 at the latter on 10th February 2002 being of particular note. Occasionally, when suitable habitat exists, large gatherings have been noted at other sites along the Thames such as Vange Marshes.

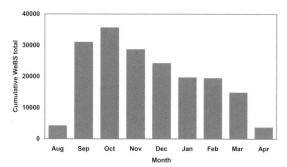

Seasonal occurrence of Shovelers from 1961-2004

Nationally, the ringing of Shoveler in the breeding season has largely been confined to Abberton; the 168 recoveries are therefore significant. Birds ringed in summer moved east to Belgium and the Netherlands and south into France, Iberia and northern Africa (Algeria and Morocco). This movement begins in August following the moult. Birds recovered in Italy and Algeria in late winter/early spring are possibly British breeders (Prater 1981). The absence of any recoveries from Scandinavia suggests a more southerly breeding distribution than for Teal, Pochard and Tufted Duck. With eight ringed Shoveler turning up as far east as Russia in subsequent years, the furthest being 4,008km distant from Abberton at Chelyabinsk, it seems likely that some British summer-ringed Shoveler do not return to Britain to breed (Migration Atlas).

Country	Jan	Feb	Mar	Apr	May	Jun	Jul	Aug	Sep	Oct	Nov	Dec
Ireland	1	1							1	2	1	1
Russia					2	4		2				
Denmark								5	1			
Germany								2	2	2		
The Netherlands									2	2	4	1
Belgium												1
France	6	9	8					6	3	6	4	5
Spain	2	1	1							1	1	3
Portugal	1		1							1		
Morocco	1	1									1	
Italy	1	1	3									
Algeria	1										1	
Total	13	13	13	2	4	0	0	15	8	15	12	11

Month and location of recovery of Shovelers ringed in Essex

Three Latvian birds, ringed as ducklings on Lake Engure during June, were controlled later at Abberton (two) and Grays, providing evidence for the origin of both moulting and wintering Shoveler. Another ringed at Puhtu, Estonia, in June was trapped at Abberton in June, suggesting that some of our breeding birds may come from breeding populations well to the east. In addition, two Dutch-ringed birds have been recovered in Essex.

Occasionally, presumed eastern birds continue to migrate after ringing at Abberton, one ringed in October turning up in Strathclyde the same autumn, likewise a juvenile ringed in September subsequently occurred on Anglesey.

Batten *et al.* (1990) listed the principal threat to individual Shoveler populations as disruption of habitats due, for example, to drainage or flooding. As has already been shown, specific site designation does not necessarily protect the species' habitat. However, their localised distribution and more sensitive management of key areas together with the potential for further habitat creation mean that overall there are no significant threats to the species. However, its very selective habitat requirements mean that the species is only likely to breed in relatively small numbers.

Sponsored by Patricia and Anthony Harbott in memory of George Gerard Thorp

Red-crested Pochard   *Netta rufina*

Scarce (feral) resident, uncommon passage migrant and winter visitor

The monotypic Red-crested Pochard is a Palearctic species that breeds principally in the steppe and deserts east of the Caspian Sea as far as central Asia. In Europe, populations are widely scattered and small. Since the late 1800s there has been a range extension into central Europe with numbers slowly increasing, although trends are variable. Around 20–30 pairs bred in the Netherlands in the early 1990s (European Atlas). Occurrences have increased in Britain. Most European birds winter either in Spain or the Danube delta and Black Sea (European Atlas).

Christy and Glegg considered that during the 19th and early 20th century genuine migrants might have occurred periodically. The earliest documented record involved one shot at Colchester in January 1844, whilst there was another on the Lea Valley reservoirs on 16th February 1924; both may have been genuine vagrants, the latter coinciding with an apparent influx along the east coast (Glegg).

The Red-crested Pochard has always been a popular species with aviculturalists as it is very easy to breed, and in the early 1990s at least 200 British collections were known to hold specimens (Second National Atlas). It is therefore not surprising that individuals have escaped or been deliberately released throughout the country and feral populations have become established, the largest centred on the Cotswold Water Park, Wiltshire, where there were 20 pairs in 1996, but smaller populations also occur in south and east England and the London parks.

Breeding took place at St Osyth in 1958 but probably involved feral birds (Hudson & Pyman), the first known instance of feral breeding in Britain. A breeding record in Lincolnshire in 1937 is now thought to have involved wild birds following an influx earlier that year (Historical Atlas). Since 1999, a small feral breeding colony has become established at Hanningfield with two pairs breeding in 2003 and 2004. Other breeding records, all of single pairs that were assumed to be feral birds, have come from Abberton in 1974 and 1977, and Horsey Island in 1995. The apparent feral flock referred to in Lack (1986) at Audley End (14 on 21st February 1982 but not subsequently) may have related to genuine wild birds as it coincided with the occurrence of eight at Minsmere, Suffolk (Piotrowski 2003), suggesting that some wild birds may be displaced from the Continent in winter given the appropriate conditions.

Annual numbers have increased recently, perhaps due to a combination of increased observer coverage and the incidence of feral birds. The large numbers in the mid-1950s and early 1960s occurred almost entirely at Abberton. They were considered to be migrants from the northwest European population, most likely from the large post-breeding flocks that assembled on Veluwemeer, the Netherlands, at the time (Pyman 1959). Indeed, the sharp drop in numbers at Abberton after 1962 coincided with the sharp decline of the Dutch flock, which was caused by water pollution that killed the stonecrop that Red-crested Pochards fed upon. The largest flocks were: 22, November 1956; around 25, September and October 1957; and 19, 16th October 1960.

Abberton has remained the most favoured locality with reports in every year except 1970/71.

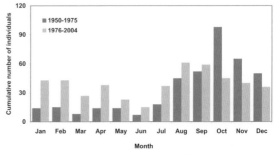

Seasonal occurrence of Red-crested Pochards for the periods 1950-75 and 1976-2004 (excluding 2003 and 2004 records from Hanningfield)

118

However, geographically the records have become increasingly widespread, with individuals recorded from all manner of waters, which may suggest that increasing numbers of feral birds are occurring. Indeed, a comparison of monthly records for the periods 1950–75 and 1976–99 shows a significant shift in timing of occurrence away from late autumn. However, a bias towards autumn arrivals remains, individuals perhaps originating from movements off the Continent. Apparent influxes of what may have been wild birds occurred in 1973/74 when amongst others, nine were at Abberton on 15th August. After Abberton, Hanningfield is the most favoured site, although in recent years records have become almost annual in the Lea Valley, perhaps because of the proximity of this area to the London parks; even here, however, there is a slight bias to autumn arrivals. Given that the Dutch breeding population is slowly increasing due to water quality improvement and the return of stonecrop (European Atlas), increases may be expected, particularly if a wintering flock is re-established in the Netherlands. However, any trends are likely to be masked by the increasing feral population and indeed differentiating feral from wild birds is now almost impossible. Harrop (1992) concluded that is was reasonable to assume that individuals or small parties in Britain are not truly wild unless there are particular grounds for thinking otherwise.

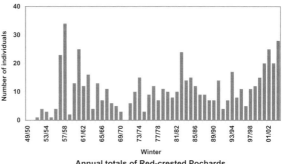

Annual totals of Red-crested Pochards from 1949/50-2003/04

Aside from inland sites, the species has occasionally occurred on tidal waters, always singly, apart from seven in Salcott Creek on 9th November 1956, which were probably part of the Abberton flock.

Hybrids with other wildfowl species are reported periodically, although crosses with Mallards appear to be the most prevalent.

Four ringing recoveries involve no more than local movements, the furthest to Tunbridge Wells, Kent, and involving the oldest British-ringed Red-crested Pochard reported to the BTO.

(Common) Pochard — *Aythya ferina*

Locally common resident, common passage migrant and winter visitor — Amber List

The monotypic Pochard is a Palearctic diving duck that breeds from the Lake Baikal region in the east, to Iceland, Ireland and Spain in the west, mostly between 45° and 60° N (European Atlas). The species' typical breeding requirements are relatively deep freshwater lakes with extensive open water and with a fair cover of fringe or emergent vegetation around the margins (Madge & Burn 1988). Since the 1850s the species' range has expanded through Europe, where it is currently most numerous in central and eastern countries. The Pochard probably only colonised Britain in the early 19th century and was very rare, and perhaps restricted to East Anglia, until around the 1840s (Fox 1991). The species remains a scarce breeder in Britain with numbers varying annually over the last decade or so from 293–638 pairs (RBBP 2002). The Pochard's wintering grounds extend from northwest Africa in the west to southern China and Japan in the east. Those wintering in Britain originate from central Europe as far east as Russia.

Although the Pochard may have bred on the coast some time around the 1830s, it was not until 1886 that breeding was first confirmed, at Old Hall. Christy observed: "During the last two or three years a small though increasing number have become resident and have bred (for the first time as far as I know) on the marshes of the Blackwater estuary": an apparently injured individual paired with another and reared young. In 1887, some 5–6 pairs nested with 17–18 the following year. Breeding was also noted on Northey Island in 1887.

By Glegg's time, breeding was still restricted to Old Hall: around 15 pairs bred annually, a similar number to the 1880s. Around 20–30 pairs were present in 1938 (Pyman 1938e).

Little had changed by the 1960s, Hudson & Pyman reporting that the "... breeding population ... is small, having fluctuated between 14 and 25 pairs for many years". Up to 20 pairs bred annually at Old Hall, but the Pochard had spread to Abberton, the only other site at which it bred regularly. Here there were usually 3–5 pairs, although there were nine in 1964. From around 1967, a general increase occurred, perhaps influenced in part by the start of survey work for the First National Atlas. An important breeding population was found on Langenhoe Marshes, although, as the site was subject to access restrictions, it may have existed for some years previously. Additionally, and for the first time, pairs were breeding successfully well inland, for example at Walthamstow and Hanningfield. Breeding between pinioned drakes from St James' Park and unpinioned females perhaps aided the increase in London/Metropolitan Essex (Homes 1957).

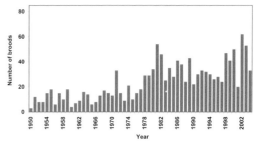

Annual totals of Pochard broods from 1950-2004

The breeding population has increased steadily to this day, 60 broods in 2002 being the highest annual total to date, with 54 in 1981 and 50 in 2000. The number of pairs breeding successfully each year vary markedly, perhaps due to weather conditions; numbers declined around the time of the drought in the late 1980s and early 1990s but increased at the end of the 20th century perhaps in response to the above-average rainfall that created suitable wetland habitat. The Pochard is, however, very sensitive to disturbance and suffers from low breeding success nationally (Fox 1991). The Essex Atlas suggested a breeding population of 30 pairs with breeding or probable breeding in 3.4% of tetrads and birds present

Atlas	Survey Area	% of 10km squares or tetrads in which	
		bred/probably bred	possibly bred or present
First National 10km	Essex	28.1	8.8
Second National 10km	Essex	24.6	29.8
First London Tetrad	Met. Essex	2.0	3.0
Second London Tetrad	Met. Essex	5.5	10.0
Essex Tetrad	Essex	3.4	2.7

Summary of results of Atlas surveys for Pochards

in a further 2.7%. By the turn of the 21st century, a figure of 60–70 breeding pairs would seem reasonable. Additionally, increasing numbers of presumed first-year birds are summering, resulting in a resident population of perhaps 130–140 pairs, which represents around 20% of the current British population and makes Essex one of the most important counties in Britain for the species.

Today, Old Hall and Walthamstow are the principal breeding sites, the relative importance of Abberton and Hanningfield having declined recently. Increases have also occurred in Metropolitan Essex, particularly in the Lea and Roding Valleys. The majority of breeding sites are close to the estuaries, typically on coastal grazing marshes, but more recently on gravel-pits and reservoirs. Away from the main sites, on Foulness 22 pairs bred in 2000, 11 in 2001, whilst 23 pairs were present in 2002, whilst eight broods were noted at both Berwick Ponds in 1992 and on Dengie in 2001 with seven at Rainham GP in 1991.

Christy considered the Pochard "A common winter visitor … to our coast …", the earliest reference to the species being made by Dale (1730) who noted: "This is frequent in the sea and places adjoining". Pochards, or Dunbirds as they were known locally, were caught in large numbers on the coast in some of the decoys, particularly on Mersea Island. However, Pochards are very shy and wary birds and it was rarely possible to drive them up the decoy pipes. Around the middle of the 19th century, Mersea Island was "… a great place for taking Dunbirds. After a strong south wind, immense

	Year of 1st breeding	No. of years when 10+ broods raised	No. of years when 5+ broods raised	Peak count
Langenhoe Marshes	1970	6	13	23 in 1981
Old Hall	1886	14	25	23 in 1998
Abberton	1953	0	8	9 in 1964
Hanningfield	1956	0	4	9 in 1964
Walthamstow	1967	11	30	18 in 1981

Principal Pochard breeding sites from 1950-2004

numbers were taken … Flight poles were used …They were like the masts and topmasts of ships: as soon as the gun was fired, a trigger was pulled; up went the poles; and the birds, striking the nets, fell down into the bags or pockets at the bottom. On one of the last occasions when they were used, a waggon-load of birds was taken". The description of the nets bears a passing resemblance to modern mist-nets. The numbers certainly appear to have been considerable, one author noting (Folkard, *The Wildfowler*): "… the capture of Dunbirds on one or two occasions within present memory, has been so great at a drop that a waggon and four horses were required to remove them from the yard …". At this time, inland records were relatively uncommon, presumably due to the lack of large inland waters.

Glegg considered that the wintering population had declined, with limited numbers found along the coast. He saw no more than 12 in a flock, whilst just four were obtained on a Thames marsh during 20 years of shooting and just one on the Crouch from 1921/22–1926/27. Inland, however, up to 110 gathered on the Lea Valley reservoirs.

GB 440 INT 3,500	1950-1954	1955-1959	1960-1964	1965-1969	1970-1974	1975-1979	1980-1984	1985-1989	1990-1994	1995-1999	2000-2004	Peak counts		Peak Month
WeBS totals	*(520)*	*1,019*	*1,524*	*2,780*	*1,990*	*2,630*	*2,000*	*2,469*	*2,777*	*3,621*	*4,781*	*Aug 00*	*5,709*	*Aug*
Stour	~	~	1	0	1	0	1	1	1	0	3	Oct 00	10	Oct
Hamford Water	~	~	0	0	0	85	139	0	10	2	6	Sep 82	350	Sep
Colne	~	~	0	1	17	~	~	43	8	1	11	Sep 88	102	Sep
Blackwater	~	~	0	30*	43	31	43	46^	23	38	43	Sep 88	116	Oct
Dengie	~	~	0	0	0	0	0	0	0	0	3	Oct 02	7	Oct
Crouch-Roach	~	~	0	0	6	0	21	12	21	31	47	Sep 00	139	Oct
Thames	~	~	0	0	1	3	39	8	13	14	15	Oct 80	77	Oct
Ardleigh	~	~	~	~	~	~	8	9	18	3	18	Sep 93	45	Sep
Abberton	(387)	(971)	1,371	2,727	1,990	2,591	1,814	2,427	2,431	3,351	4,363	Aug 00	5,296	Aug
Hanningfield	~	(87)	98	130	69	188	171	167	375	325	202	Aug 91	503	Oct
Lea Valley	~	~	78	204	428	423	215	223	195	226	299	Oct 74	629	Oct
Met. Essex Waters	~	~	~	~	~	~	~	~	~	~	130	Oct 02	308	Oct

Five-year average of peak WeBS counts (Jul-Oct) of Pochards from 1950-2004

The construction of the large reservoirs in the 1940s and 1950s created much suitable habitat for the Pochard that had previously been lacking. As early as 1952, there were large numbers at Abberton during late autumn passage, with 3,870 in October. Since then, numbers have increased steadily.

GB 440 INT 3,500	50/51-54/55	55/56-59/60	60/61-64/65	65/66-69/70	70/71-74/75	75/76-79/80	80/81-84/85	85/86-89/90	90/91-94/95	95/96-99/00	00/01-04/05	Peak counts		Peak Month
WeBS totals	*(2,534)*	*(1,720)*	*1,318*	*1,836*	*2,541*	*1,849*	*1,762*	*1,609*	*2,167*	*2,531*	*1,894^*	*Dec 98*	*3,594*	*Nov*
Stour	~	~	10	11	10	95	6	58	26	3	12^	Jan 79	423	Jan
Hamford Water	~	~	0	14	27	82	204	36	22	21	28^	Jan 82	950	Jan
Colne	~	~	0	17	159	~	~	302	64	180	14^	Feb 87	803	Mar
Blackwater	~	~	0	70	141	90	137	143	167	206	113^	Mar 75	316	Feb
Dengie	~	~	0	0	4	0	0	0	3	2	1^	Dec 70	20	Nov
Crouch-Roach	~	~	0	0	15	1	79	45	147	188	116^	Jan 93	231	Jan
Thames	~	~	156	34	56	101	226	168	81	154	153^	Jan 91	418	Jan
Ardleigh	~	~	~	~	65	14	23	29	81	56	235^	Jan 02	484	Jan
Abberton	(1,891)	(1,432)	874	1,117	896	943	606	641	1,090	1,230	928^	Dec 98	2,163	Nov
Hanningfield	0	(476)	362	433	152	345	337	289	428	473	220^	Dec 95	1,084	Nov
Lea Valley	~	~	178	536	1,212	697	585	535	512	507	477^	Jan 74	1,771	Jan
Met. Essex Waters	~	~	~	~	~	~	~	~	~	~	285^	Feb 02	379	Feb

Five-year average of peak WeBS counts (Nov-Mar) of Pochards from 1950/51-2003/04

As early as June, large numbers gather on the principal inland waters. This phenomenon is relatively recent, although it is perhaps no more than coincident that it was in 1968, a year after a noticeable increase in breeding numbers, that the first large gatherings were noted. Most flocks are comprised of drakes; females typically winter further south (*BWP*). By far the largest gatherings occur at Abberton with perhaps 80–90% of the Essex population present during autumn. The reasons for the increase and preference for Abberton are unclear but may perhaps be linked to an increase in stoneworts, an important algal food-plant, during the 1960s (Cox). Other non-WeBS counts at Abberton have included 4,000 on 2nd August 1968, *c.* 5,000 during July/August 1969, 3,500 on 8th August 1979, and 2,796 on 26th July 1992, whilst at Hanningfield there were 1,355 in September 1997, 800 on 22nd July 2001 and three counts in excess of 600, the highest being 636 on 28th June 1983.

After September, numbers decline then increase again to a peak in November as birds from further east arrive; most wintering birds have reached Britain by this time (Migration Atlas). From November to January, numbers remain relatively constant. In the Lea Valley, numbers peak later than at Abberton and Hanningfield, perhaps suggesting that some birds may disperse from the latter reservoirs. Away from these localities, Pochards may be found on most larger water bodies such as gravel-pits, lakes and freshwater coastal marshes. Counts of 300 or so from such localities are not uncommon.

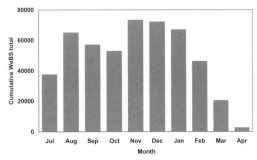

Seaonal occurrence of Pochards from 1961-2004

The British wintering population is around 44,000; Essex thus currently holds around 11% of the British population in autumn and 4.3% in winter, 1.4% and 0.5% respectively of the European population of 350,000.

The extent to which Pochards feed on tidal waters is unclear but the species regularly flies out to the coast after dark (Glover 1979). Many Pochards appear to spend most of the daylight hours sleeping at Abberton, so it is possible that many make this nocturnal movement. When inland waters freeze, Pochards move to inshore coastal waters. A total of over 5,800 was on the inner Thames (Essex and Kent) during the severe weather of January 1979 (Migration Atlas), around 2,000 were in Hamford Water on 3rd January 1982 and in early 1986 1,500 were in Pyefleet Channel, Mersea Island, on 23rd February. During the period of exceptional Tubifex worm abundance that peaked around 1968–74, large numbers fed on the Thames, mainly between Barking and Woolwich, with 3,000 off Barking alone in December 1972 (Cox). Some of the biggest roost counts at Walthamstow occurred at this time, suggesting some interchange between the two sites.

Numbers decline rapidly through February and March with only very small numbers remaining into April. Spring passage is not obvious.

Country	J	F	M	A	M	J	J	A	S	O	N	D
Ireland	12	2	1						2	3	2	2
Finland				1				1				
Sweden		1										
Baltic States					2			1			1	
Russia				2	5			7	4			1
Poland			1	1				6	1	1	1	
Denmark								1	1	3	1	
Germany	1	1	1	1	1	1		2	2	2	1	1
The Netherlands	2				2			2	5	1	4	4
Belgium							1			1	1	
France	14	12						1	3	4	10	14
Spain		1	2	1						1		2
Morocco												1
Austria	1											
Switzerland	1											
Italy	1											
Yugoslavia							1					
Czechoslovakia							1		1			
Totals	32	17	5	6	10	1	3	21	19	16	21	25

Month and location of recovery of Pochards ringed in Essex

Large numbers of Pochards have been ringed at Abberton and in national terms these have proved most important in unravelling the complex movements of the species. In autumn, some Essex-reared Pochards migrate south to France, Spain and North Africa. Large numbers then arrive from Eastern Europe, some of which, after a short stay, continue west to Ireland. Some appear to remain further east and southeast in subsequent winters; the reasons for this are unclear but may be due to milder weather allowing them to stay nearer their usual breeding grounds or simply a nomadic approach to wintering ground selection. The most easterly recovery of an Abberton-ringed bird involved one ringed during August 1965 and killed in Petropavlovsk, Russia, some 4,036km east-northeast in September 1968.

A total of 17 foreign-ringed Pochards has also been recovered in Essex. Nine were ringed at Lake Engure, Latvia, mostly as nestlings, whilst a further three, also ringed as nestlings, came from the former Czechoslovakia. Of the remainder, there were two from the Netherlands with singles from France, Denmark and Switzerland. Although some Pochards appear to vary their wintering quarters, some show site fidelity during winter; for instance, one of the Lake Engure ducklings that was ringed in July 1966 was controlled at Abberton in January 1967 and then shot at Langenhoe the following winter. One ringed at Abberton on 5th September 1977 was at least 22 years old when shot in Odessa, Russia, around 15th September 1999, the oldest British-ringed Pochard to have been reported to the BTO.

Whilst the Essex population is important in national terms, it is but a small fraction of the total European population of 200,000–250,000 breeding pairs (European Atlas). With an apparently steadily increasing population, the Pochard appears to be consolidating its position in the county. The main threats to this continuing success are disturbance and drainage and/or destruction of suitable habitat.

Canvasback   *Aythya valisineria*

Vagrant: six records of one, presumed returning, individual

The monotypic Canvasback breeds across northern North America from Alaska south to northern California and east to Minnesota. It winters south from the Great Lakes and British Columbia along the east and west seaboards.

1997	Abberton	23rd–24th and 30th November	Adult male
	Ardleigh	29th November	Same as previous
1999	Abberton	6th–16th April	Same as previous

1999/2000	Abberton	8th November–15th February	Same as previous
2000/2001	Abberton	12th November–1st January	Same as previous
2001	Abberton	24th January–13th February	Same as previous

The 1997 record was the third for Britain, following individuals in Kent in December 1996 (Larkin & Mercer 2004) and Norfolk in January 1997; the latter individual is assumed to be the same as the Abberton bird. To the end of 2002, there had been seven British records (BBRC 2005). Canvasback populations have been increasing in North America in recent years.

Ring-necked Duck   *Aythya collaris*

Very rare passage migrant and winter visitor: eight records involving 7-8 individuals

The monotypic Ring-necked Duck breeds across North America and winters mainly along the Atlantic and Pacific coasts and also Central America and the Caribbean.

1979	Abberton	26th April	Female
	Heybridge GP	27th April–5th May	Male
	Hanningfield	2nd May	Male
1995/1996	KGV	25th September–17th April	Female
1997	Walthamstow	24th January	Male
1999	Valentines Park, Ilford	20th February–2nd May	Female
2001/2002	Hanningfield	25th November, 31st December & 5th January	Male
2002	Old Hall	16th May	Male

This former BBRC rarity, which was removed from the British List after 1993, has been recorded 470 times nationally since 1958 (Fraser & Rogers 2005). Occurrences increased significantly from the mid-1970s, possibly linked to the species' eastward expansion in North America. The 1979 records may refer to just two individuals but did occur in one of the best years nationally for the species, when 26 newly-arrived birds were recorded; 49 in 2001 is the greatest annual number reported to date. Nationally, most occur during winter but four of the eight Essex records fall completely outside this period.

Ferruginous Duck   *Aythya nyroca*

Rare passage migrant and winter visitor: 44 records involving around 38 individuals, although some possibly escapes

The monotypic Ferruginous Duck is a Palearctic species found in wetlands in forest steppe, steppe and semi-desert zones. Although there are relict populations in a few places in Spain and central Europe, the species' main range stretches from central Europe eastwards towards the Black and Caspian Seas with two further separate populations

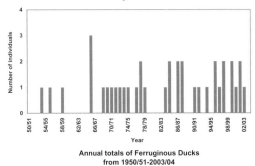

Annual totals of Ferruginous Ducks from 1950/51-2003/04

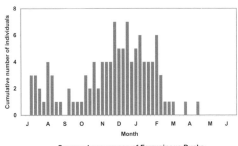

Seasonal occurrence of Ferruginous Ducks from 1950-2004

further east. Numbers appear to be decreasing in eastern Europe, probably due to habitat change (European Atlas). Most European birds winter in North Africa.

about 1880	Marshhouse Decoy, Dengie	Undated	shot
1947	River Chelmer at Beeleigh	23rd February	
1953	Abberton	11th October	Male
1956	Abberton	15th January	Male
1958	Abberton	29th October	Male
1965	Abberton	29th October–1st November	Male
1965/66	Abberton	18th & 25th November & 4th & 8th December	Immature
		4th–5th December with one until 2nd February	Immature (different)
1969	Fishers Green	2nd April	Male, escape?
1970	Fishers Green	2nd February	Same as previous
		29th October	Same as previous
1971	Alresford GP	21st September	Male
1973	Walthamstow	18th–25th February	
		15th December	
1974	Abberton	19th–31st July	Male
1977	Abberton	13th February	Male
		19th-20th November	Male
		& 21st & 28th December	Male
1979	St Osyth GP	3rd–15th March	Male
	Brightlingsea GP	17th March	Same as previous
1983/84	Walthamstow	31st December–18th February	Female
1984	Abberton	7th August–4th September	Male
1985	Weald CP	16th February	Male
1986	Netherhall GP	15th November–31st December	Immature male
	Roydon GP	23rd December	Same as previous
1987	Walthamstow	6th January–25th February	Same as previous
	Abberton	10th–20th August	Female
1987/88	Walthamstow	2nd December–31st December	Immature male
		5th January and 21st January-23rd February	
1990	Hanningfield	17th–26th August	Male
1991	Hanningfield	16th November	Male
1994	Fishers Green	9th & 15th January & 6th February	Male
1995	Coleman's	9th–10th December	Male
1996	Hanningfield	28th April	Female
		19th July	Male
1997	Abberton	1st August	Male
	Hanningfield	19th–26th October	Immature male
1999	Abberton	18th–25th September	Male
1999/00	Seventy Acres Lake	28th October into 2000 and 11th April	Female, escape?
2000	Abberton	17th & 19th October	Male
2001	Donyland GP	9th January	Male
	Netherhall GP	6th-17th October	Male
	Boreham GP	2nd–9th December	Male
2002	Hanningfield	21st July–18th August	Male
2004	Heybridge GP	28th December	1st-winter male

Despite the large increase in observers over the last 30 years or so, numbers reported have remained relatively constant suggesting that, in real terms, the actual number of occurrences has declined. This mirrors the national trend, where it has become so scarce in recent years that in 1998 the species was readmitted onto the BBRC List (it was originally on the List until 1968). Whilst the possibility of escapes must be borne in mind, the pattern of occurrence suggests that most are, however, genuine vagrants that tag along with the large flocks of Pochard and Tufted Duck that arrive from the east from late summer. Most have occurred at Abberton (15) with six from Hanningfield and five at Walthamstow.

Tufted Duck   *Aythya fuligula*

Common resident, passage migrant and winter visitor

The monotypic Tufted Duck breeds right across the Palearctic where it nests in the boreal, temperate and steppe climatic zones. Its range extends to 70° N in Norway and parts of Siberia and reaches 45° N in southern Europe. Almost exclusively a lowland species, Tufted Ducks breed on freshwater lakes with abundant floating vegetation, ponds, quiet stretches of rivers, sheltered coastal areas and—because of its tolerance of human presence—on a variety of man-made water bodies (European Atlas). Since the 1950s, the species has greatly expanded its European breeding range, coinciding with the spread of the alien Zebra Mussel which has flourished in freshwater areas (Olney 1963). In Britain, the species first bred in 1849 and is now fairly widespread. Significant concentrations occur in northern East Anglia, south Suffolk, Essex, west Midlands/Welsh borders, southeast Scotland and the northeast tip of Scotland (Second National Atlas). The Tufted Duck's main wintering areas are in northwest Europe where moult gatherings also occur on large freshwater bodies (European Atlas).

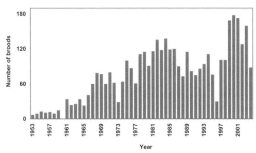

Annual totals of Tufted Duck broods from 1953-2004

Tufted Duck remains have been found in the Pleistocene brickearths at Walthamstow (Michael Daniels pers. comm.).

Christy was not aware of successful breeding but considered it very likely, as the species appeared to be resident and increasing. Breeding was first recorded at Walthamstow in 1905 (Homes 1957), with three pairs by 1914 (Glegg). Elsewhere, breeding was noted at Connaught Water in 1913 and Snaresbrook, Waltham Forest, in 1916. It is not clear to what extent the introduction of Tufted Ducks to St James' Park, London, in the mid-19th century contributed to increases in the area, although fully-winged birds were present in 1913. The species remained a relatively rare breeder for the first few decades of the 20th century, its chief haunts being the Lea Valley reservoirs (Glegg).

By the 1950s, 5–10 broods were reported annually from Abberton, Hanningfield, and Walthamstow and around Nazeing/Fishers Green. Many non-breeding individuals also began to summer. Around 65–75 pairs were present annually during the mid-1960s, the majority at Hanningfield but with an increasing number of sites used elsewhere (Hudson & Pyman); there were up to 42 pairs in the Nazeing/Fishers Green area in the 1970s. By the early 1980s the Tufted Duck was relatively widespread. Numbers in Metropolitan Essex in particular increased during much of the 1980s, the species taking advantage of the many lakes in urban parks. Around this time, however, and, despite increased observer coverage as a result of the Essex Atlas survey, there was a decline in

Atlas	Survey Area	% of 10km squares or tetrads in which	
		bred/probably bred	possibly bred or present
First National 10km	Essex	63.2	22.8
Second National 10km	Essex	68.4	19.3
First London Tetrad	Met. Essex	11.0	9.5
Second London Tetrad	Met. Essex	25.0	18.5
Essex Tetrad	Essex	13.3	9.0

Summary of results of Atlas surveys for Tufted Ducks

breeding numbers, which coincided with the period of exceptionally dry weather. Since the mid-1990s, with the return of wetter conditions, the species has flourished, such that by the start of the 21st century record numbers of broods were reported. During the last ten years or so other important sites have been located. On Foulness there were 33 broods in 2000 and on Horsey Island, where nests were located in grass along edges of borrow dykes and even on the top of seawalls, there were 25–30 pairs in 1996. Within Metropolitan Essex, 16 broods were in Goodmayes Park, Barking, in 1999 and ten in Valentines Park, Ilford, in 2003. At Fairlop CP, ten broods were noted in both 1994 and 1997, whilst a total of 13 was around East Tilbury in 1995. The Essex Atlas survey located the Tufted Duck breeding in 13.3% of all tetrads and present in a further 9%. Breeding pairs were irregularly scattered across Essex although clearly correlated to the presence of man-made waters.

The reasons for the increase in Tufted Ducks are probably two-fold: the number of reservoirs and gravel-pits created since 1950 and the spread of the Zebra Mussel, which was first reported in Britain from London Docks in 1824. Increasing eutrophication of fresh-water may have also aided the spread, as this has produced an increase in invertebrate biomass (ducklings feed on chironomid larvae from the moment they hatch), plant growth and nesting sites (European

	Decade					
	1950s	1960s	1970s	1980s	1990s	2000s
Abberton	3	3	9	5	11	13
Hanningfield	6	35	22	27	12	12
Walthamstow	5	25	40	47	55	31

Peak number of broods of Tufted Ducks at principal breeding sites from 1950-2004

Atlas). The current Essex population probably lies in the region of 200 breeding pairs, which represents 1.7–2.0% of the British population of 10,000–12,000. In addition, there are often several hundred non-breeding birds present during summer.

Christy described the Tufted Duck as "A somewhat rare and irregular winter visitor, occasionally met with on lakes or rivers in various parts of the county, but most often near the coast". It was clearly a rarity in the early 19th century with only four records prior to 1867. One record involved several trapped in a decoy near Maldon: "During their confinement … they uttered a hissing noise like the Common Goose, and were continually snapping their bills. They have many of the actions of the Teal, but are a far less elegant species". By Glegg's time, the species' status appeared little changed, although increases had occurred in the Lea Valley, with peak counts probably reaching four figures during winter and reasonable numbers present throughout the year. An influx occurred there before the end of August. Elsewhere, Glegg recorded the species on just four occasions in seven years along the coast and knew of two further records from central Essex.

By the mid-1960s, three-figure gatherings were "… quite usual …" on inland waters (Hudson & Pyman). Moult gatherings have continued to increase since then, but wintering numbers have remained remarkably stable since the 1970s following significant increases in the late 1960s.

As Cox pointed out, there are many parallels between Pochards and Tufted Ducks, large mixed flocks of which commonly occur: both form large moulting flocks, mainly of males, from June onwards, a phenomenon that began around the late 1960s. Tufted Ducks are more widely dispersed than Pochards, however.

GB 600 / INT 10,000	1950-1954	1955-1959	1960-1964	1965-1969	1970-1974	1975-1979	1980-1984	1985-1989	1990-1994	1995-1999	2000-2004	Peak counts		Peak Month
WeBS totals	(117)	(165)	617	1,291	2,954	3,725	3,305	3,923	4,341	6,601	8,577	Aug 00	10,247	Sep
Stour	~	~	0	0	12	4	8	1	2	1	3	Sep 73	45	Sep
Hamford Water	~	~	0	0	3	49	50	54	44	51	39	Oct 75	150	Oct
Colne	~	~	0	0	39	~	~	37	21	8	1	Oct 73	84	Oct
Blackwater	~	~	1	6	49	28	69	93	97	114	71	Sep 99	224	Sep
Dengie	~	~	4	0	0	0	0	0	2	0	0	Oct 61	20	Oct
Crouch-Roach	~	~	0	0	4	1	31	11	36	34	17	Sep 81	91	Sep
Thames	~	~	0	0	3	20	61	39	122	53	106	Oct 00	321	Oct
Ardleigh	~	~	~	~	~	~	25	56	61	27	91	Oct 02	121	Oct
Abberton	(82)	(81)	150	605	1,726	2,678	2,637	3,227	2,102	2,820	3,520	Oct 04	5,112	Aug
Hanningfield	0	(87)	119	136	323^	433	482	625	1,358	1,460	1,914	Sep 03	3,109	Sep
Lea Valley	~	~	441	900	1,674	1,848	1,447	1,755	2,451	2,513	3,643	Aug 03	4,051	Sep
Met Essex Waters	~	~	~	~	~	~	~	~	~	~	495	Oct 02	651	Oct

Five-year average of peak WeBS counts (Jul-Oct) of Tufted Ducks from 1950-2004

The considerable annual variation in the number of moulting birds is perhaps due in part to water levels and their influence on prey availability. On the whole, however, numbers have increased steadily, although during the 1990s numbers at Abberton declined and those in the Lea Valley increased and now rival those at the former in autumn (and exceed them during winter). Cox suggested that the reason for the increase in the size of the Pochard moult flock at Abberton was the increase in stoneworts as Pochards eat mainly vegetable matter. Tufted Ducks are, however, mainly carnivorous, animal material forming more than 80% of their diet (Second National Atlas). Thus whilst the increase in moulting numbers of both species may be no more than coincidence, it is possible that another, as yet unidentified factor, is responsible. Up to 15% of the British non-breeding population is present in Essex during autumn and just under 1% of the northwest European population.

Tufted Duck numbers generally peak in August, then decline slightly during September and October, before increasing slightly in November. Numbers then generally remain constant until February and decline thereafter.

Wintering numbers have remained relatively stable since the 1970s after a period of rapid increase in the 1950s and 1960s. Nationally, the population has been amongst the most stable of all wildfowl over the last 25 years (Waters *et al.* 1998) with an estimated British population of 60,600 (Stone *et al.* 1997), which is some 10% of the northwest European population. An Essex wintering population of 5,500 represents around 9% of the British population.

The majority of wintering Tufted Ducks are found at Abberton, Hanningfield and in the Lea Valley, each site regularly holding some of the largest gatherings in Britain. Away from these sites, gatherings of up to 500 are not uncommon. However, recent comprehensive surveys of the numerous Metropolitan waters have revealed a significant non-breeding population that accounts for some 20–30% of the entire wintering population.

Although small numbers are regularly reported from estuarine localities, it is only during severe weather, when the reservoirs are frozen over, that large numbers occur, although rarely more than a few hundred are reported. Larger gatherings have, however, occurred during fair weather. About 750 were on the Thames at East Tilbury during the early 1960s and up to 800 further upstream at the end of the 1960s (cf. Pochard).

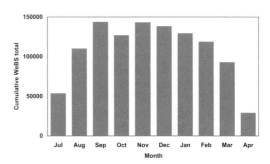

Seasonal occurrence of Tufted Ducks from 1961-2004

Spring migration is not obvious, although small increases at some reservoirs, particularly in March suggest a small return movement, a fact confirmed by ringing recoveries.

Several thousand Tufted Ducks have been ringed at Abberton since 1950 and the recoveries have proved to be of national significance. Most British breeding birds remain within the country all year (Ogilvie 1987). Many breeding birds from Russia, Finland and to a lesser extent Scandinavia pass through or winter in Essex, whilst some continue further west or south to Ireland, France and Spain. The most easterly recovery involved a first-year female ringed in October 1983 and shot 5,042km east-northeast at Korliki, Khanty-Mansi, Russia in May 1985. A return passage of eastern birds through Abberton appears to take place from March with birds arriving back on their breeding grounds mainly during May. Birds that have previously wintered at Abberton remain on the Continent during some subsequent winters perhaps in response to weather conditions. The Russian recovery, during February in Georgia on the eastern shore of the Black Sea, suggests a more significant change in wintering location. Remarkably, one ringed at Abberton on 28th May 1969 was recovered over 6,000km away in Lahore, Pakistan, on 14th April 1971, the only British ringing recovery from the Indian subcontinent. It may have still been on migration to its breeding grounds having wintered in India; it is a common winter visitor to northern India with most birds leaving by the end of March (Grimmett *et al.* 1998).

GB 600 / INT 10,000	50/51-54/55	55/56-59/60	60/61-64/65	65/66-69/70	70/71-74/75	75/76-79/80	80/81-84/85	85/86-89/90	90/91-94/95	95/96-99/00	00/01-04/05	Peak counts		Peak Month
WeBS totals	(516)	(590)	1,329	1,977	3,800	3,365	4,268	4,225	4,151	3,472	5,243^	Jan 01	7,168	Nov
Stour	~	~	4	14	16	87	29	1	64	13	2^	Jan 79	347	Jan
Hamford Water	~	~	0	0	2	70	83	14	66	72	65^	Jan 82	300	Mar
Colne	~	~	0	24	103	~	~	104	87	116	14^	Jan 85	470	Jan
Blackwater	~	~	6	44	87	100	147	159	164	144	75^	Dec 78	227	M
Dengie	~	~	1	0	0	0	0	0	0	0	1^	Dec 61	4	Jan
Crouch-Roach	~	~	0	3	5	4	59	22	87	83	60^	Feb 91	176	Feb
Thames	~	~	135	31	45	92	174	165	337	318	276^	Jan 95	579	Jan
Ardleigh	~	~	~	~	50	16	52	75	96	94	410^	Dec 02	556	Dec
Abberton	(445)	(258)	405	441	1,297	1064	1,782	1,381	1,377	730	611^	Dec 88	3,987	Nov
Hanningfield	~	(389)	429	397	493	418	428	506	519	880	1,255^	Feb 01	1,840	Dec
Lea Valley	~	~	738	1,319	2,147	2,036	2,301	2,279	2,209	1,578	1,793^	Feb 91	3,406	Nov
Met. Essex Waters	~	~	~	~	~	~	~	~	~	~	1,126^	Feb 03	1,218	Feb

Five-year average of peak WeBS counts (Nov-Mar) of Tufted Ducks from 1950/51-2003/04

A total of 12 foreign-ringed birds has been recovered in Essex, four from the Baltic States, two from Switzerland and singles from Finland, Sweden, Denmark, Germany, the Netherlands and France. The Swiss birds were males and were controlled at Abberton in May 1981 and May 1984; they were probably heading back east to Russia. One of the longest-lived Tufted Ducks was ringed at Abberton as a first-year male in June 1980 and shot in October 1995 in Northern Ireland.

Tufted Ducks appear to be prospering in Essex and northwest Europe generally. This situation has arisen because the species has taken readily to man-made water bodies, is tolerant of disturbance and is generally omnivorous. Further increases in the breeding population are to be expected.

	J	F	M	A	M	J	J	A	S	O	N	D
Ireland	17	2	1						5	15	12	9
Iceland					1							
Finland					34	3	2	14	5	3		
Norway					1	1		3	1	1		1
Sweden	1			5	2			6	1	5		
Baltic States							1				2	1
Russia		1	1	2	79	14	1	10	22	15		
Poland									5			
Denmark	2		1						1	12	3	
Germany	5	3		2	3	2		1	2	1	1	2
The Netherlands	28	12	8	2	2	1	2	10	9	16	23	27
France	11	6	2				2	4	5	7	11	8
Spain	3				2					1	1	2
Italy												1
Switzerland											1	2
Czechoslovakia								1		1	1	
Pakistan				1								
Totals	*67*	*24*	*13*	*12*	*125*	*22*	*7*	*48*	*56*	*74*	*59*	*52*

Month and location of recovery of Tufted Ducks ringed in Essex

(Greater) Scaup

Aythya marila

Fairly common passage migrant and winter visitor, occasional in summer

Amber List

The Scaup breeds widely throughout the Holarctic, principally in the tundra regions, its European range extending from Iceland through Scandinavia and the Baltic, east to the Urals and totalling 8,000–11,000 pairs. The nominate race *marila* occurs throughout northern Eurasia from Iceland to the Lena River, Siberia. The Scaup is Britain's rarest breeding duck with, during the last 20 years, no more than 0–2 pairs nesting annually (RBBP 2003). The majority of the European wintering population of 300,000 (Laursen *et al.* 1992) are found along the coasts of Denmark, Germany and the Netherlands (European Atlas). The British wintering population numbers some 11,000.

The Scaup was considered by Christy to be "… common on our coasts from autumn to spring; seldom met with inland". The earliest documented record involved one shot at Audley End on 2nd February 1830. On the coast "A large flock of about a hundred frequented Leigh Ray during January and February [1871]. Although constantly shot at they refused to leave the cockle-grounds". Glegg was less confident of its regularity, rather considering it to be a winter visitor to the coast in small numbers and then less than annually. Whether this represented a change in status is difficult to assess. However, the breeding range contracted northwards in Europe during the 19th century (Voous 1960). Glegg also considered the species rare inland quoting just nine records, all singles apart from 7–8 on Wanstead Basin for a few days on an unspecified date. One lingered on the Lea Valley reservoirs from March 1924–February 1926.

Since 1950, Scaup numbers have typically been erratic with the largest influxes generally occurring with the onset of severe mid-winter weather. Around 1,100 were present in early 1963, with 700 off East Tilbury on 17th February, 220 off Brightlingsea on 24th February and 150 in Hamford Water on 3rd March. In 1997 a similar number was present, although almost the entire influx was accounted for by a single flock of around 1,000 seen from a boat off Stansgate/Osea Island on 12th January, with 600 remaining off Steeple on 17th. Around 90 were also present in Hamford Water. Other influxes were in: 1953/54, 750 including 430 off East Tilbury; 1955/56, 575 including two flocks off The Naze on 24th February 1956 totalling 489; 1981/82, 350 including 280 in Hamford Water on 10th January 1982; and 1990/91, 500 including 217 in Hamford Water on 17th February 1991.

Whilst numbers on tidal waters are generally significantly higher than inland, in years of low numbers overall more may be reported inland than on the coast. High inland numbers do not necessarily coincide with influxes on the coast. For example, of the 1,112 in 1962/63 only 23 were inland and in one of the best years for inland records, 49 in 1988/89, there were only 66 reported from tidal waters. The majority of inland counts have involved flocks of ten or less, although there have been four larger: Abberton, 22, 26th December 1972 with some staying well into 1973; Hanningfield, 15, 22nd January 1961; Walthamstow, 12, 17th February 1991; and Abberton, 11,

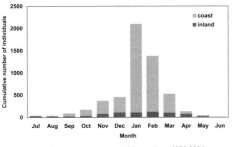

Seasonal occurrence of Scaup from 1971-2004

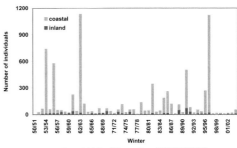

Annual totals of Scaup from 1950/51-2003/04

30th December 1969. In addition, there were 15 at Heybridge GP on 1st January 1997. Many inland records, particularly in late spring, are characterised by a very short stay, often of just a few hours.

Although primarily a winter visitor and passage migrant, Scaup have occurred in every month with midsummer records not uncommon; these usually occur inland and have involved 1–3 birds. However, 6–7 males were at Abberton from 9th–12th July 1954. Two individuals have made extended stays over spring: a female at Abberton from 2nd April–24th July 1980; a male at Girling from 24th April–3rd September 1988. The only other June records have come from: Old Hall, a pair, 8th May to mid-June 1955; Hanningfield, a pair, 25th in 1972; Abberton, one, 10th–18th in 1989; Rowhedge, a female, 20th in 1995; Girling, one, late June 1997; Abberton, one, 24th in 1998; and Walthamstow, a male, 21st March–24th June 2001.

The Ijsselmeer in the Netherlands holds about 1,000 moulting birds during July and it seems likely that inland occurrences during spring may involve individuals *en route* to this location; most of the moulting flock are males as females stay on or near their breeding grounds to moult (BWP). The majority of midsummer Essex records have involved males.

Abberton was one of the few sites in Britain to trap Scaup regularly, resulting in three foreign recoveries, two from Germany (January and February) and one from Lithuania (October), all within the species' typical wintering area. As yet there is no evidence to link Essex with Icelandic birds, which form the majority (96%) of recoveries of foreign-ringed Scaup in Britain (Migration Atlas).

Lesser Scaup   *Aythya affinis*

Vagrant: two records

The monotypic Lesser Scaup breeds from central Alaska through Canada and south to Washington and South Dakota and winters along both coastlines of the USA south to central America.

2003	Seventy Acres Lake	23rd–25th March	Male
2004	Abberton	11th–31st December	1st-winter male

This was a long overdue addition to the Essex List, the first British record being in 1987 since when the species has turned up with increasing regularity; there have been 75 records to the end of 2004 (BBRC 2005).

Only a few years earlier Seventy Acres Lake would have been in Hertfordshire and not Essex (Harris 2004). This individual was also seen on nearby Police Pit GP and Friday Lake and proved quite mobile and elusive; the second individual was far more obliging (Kettle 2006).

(Common) Eider   *Somateria mollissima*

Locally common passage migrant and winter visitor with small numbers usually present in summer

Amber List

The Eider is a Holarctic species that has a circumpolar distribution, breeding up to 80° N. It is the most numerous and widespread seaduck in Europe, the nominate *mollissima* occupying most of the European distribution, *faroeensis* the

Faeroe Islands and *borealis* on Franz Josef Land, Svalbard, Iceland, Greenland and Baffin Island. Since the 1950s, the Eider has extended its breeding range south (European Atlas). The current European population is around 850,000 breeding pairs of which around 31,000 occur in Britain, mostly in Scotland (Second National Atlas). The main winter concentrations are off the coasts of Denmark, Germany, the Netherlands, Norway, Iceland, Britain and Ireland and the White Sea, the Western Palearctic winter population being about 3 million birds (Laursen 1989).

Christy described the species as an uncommon winter visitor, although one correspondent considered it "common in heavy weather". The first documented Essex record was not until 1865 when two males were shot at Maldon on 3rd January; they were originally thought to be King Eiders. In all, Christy detailed just 11 records to the end of 1890, all occurring in the period 7th October–3rd January. Glegg added just six more records, including the only double-figure count prior to the 1950s, ten on the Roding "… close to where it joins the Thames …" on 10th March 1917. The Eider's status changed little until the 1950s, Hudson & Pyman noting: "Until 1950 this species was a considerable rarity". Indeed, the *EBR* 1950 contained brief field notes of one at Little Oakley on 26th August, suggesting that it was still regarded as exceptional, at least at that season.

The early 1950s saw a rapid increase such that the 1952 *EBR* noted: "Nothing could be more obvious than the continued increase of this species in Essex waters". Double-figure counts quickly became regular with the first three-figure count coming from The Naze with 100 in April and June 1958. The severe winter weather of early 1963 produced three-figure counts in Hamford Water with 125 in February and off Southend Pier where there

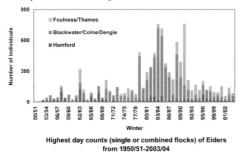

Highest day counts (single or combined flocks) of Eiders from 1950/51-2003/04

Seasonal occurrence of Eiders from 1971-2004

were 138 at the end of January. The latter was by far the largest count from the Thames at that time; previously, numbers had rarely reached double figures. Up until the end of the 1970s, there were just three more three-figure counts, all from the Blackwater/Colne/Dengie area, the peak being 140 off Bradwell in early April 1973. The severe weather of 1978/79 brought a huge influx into the Blackwater Estuary but surprisingly few were reported from elsewhere. From a peak of 200 in January, numbers rose steadily to 420 off Bradwell in March, a total almost three times the previous county high. Whether this influx contributed to a change in the wintering distribution of, for instance, a proportion of the Dutch population is unknown. Nonetheless from 1978/79 and for the next decade or so, the species was more numerous than at any other time; three-figure counts became annual in the Blackwater/ Colne/Dengie complex. The largest single-day total (WeBS) from here was 704 in February 1984, whilst there were 583 in March 1985 and 435 in March 1989. By the early 1990s, numbers in this area had begun to decline, at which time there was a corresponding increase off Foulness. Although gatherings were generally smaller than in the Blackwater, the largest single flock ever recorded in Essex, of some 600 birds, was present off Maplin on 30th March 1991. As numbers appear to have declined over the last decade whilst those in Suffolk have perhaps increased (Piotrowski 2003), it is possible that, like Common Scoters (q.v.), the main flocks have moved south to an offshore locality where observation is very difficult. Milder winters may also be a factor.

The Winter Atlas confirmed the Eider's preference for the outer estuaries, although small numbers are occasionally recorded well up the Thames and Blackwater; 340 were off Goldhanger on 6th April 1985 and there were 79 off East Tilbury on 29th November 1993.

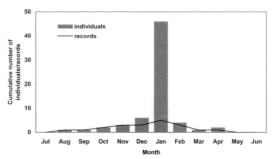

Seasonal occurrence of inland Eiders from 1950-2004

The largest numbers tend to occur in late winter and early spring perhaps as individuals gather prior to heading back to the breeding grounds. Small flocks of non-breeding, immature Eider summer in Essex waters. Most gatherings are in the range of 1–50 but there were 100 off The Naze in June 1958 and Bradwell during June 1972.

Movement along the coast, both during spring and autumn, is evident in some years although, in general, passage is not pronounced, the presence of wintering and summering birds often obscuring the situation.

Inland records are scarce. Prior to the end of 1981 there were just five records. Subsequently, records have become more regular, presumably linked to the increase along the coast. In all, Eider have occurred inland on 18 occasions, involving a total of 64 individuals, some of which made extended stays. A remarkable influx occurred on 9th January 1982 when, during a spell of severe weather 17 (five male and 12 females/immatures) arrived at Hanningfield with 25 (six male and 19 females/immatures) at Walthamstow. Other counts of more than one have been: Walthamstow, four, 21st–29th December 1997 with two, 30th December–4th January 1998; Dagenham Chase, two flew east, 21st January 1992; KGV, two, 26th April 1997; Hanningfield, two, 19th February 2000. Of the 18 records, the majority have come from the Lea Valley, at Girling (two), Netherhall (one), Walthamstow (two), KGV (two) and Nazeing (two), with the remainder records coming from Abberton (four), Hanningfield (three) and Dagenham Chase (two).

Not surprisingly, given its maritime habitat, there have been no ringing recoveries involving Essex. The breeding populations of northern England and Scotland are largely resident (Prater 1981) and the origin of the Essex population is thought to include wandering birds from the Baltic and Dutch and German Waddensee. The 13 foreign-ringed birds recovered in Britain have come from Denmark, Germany and the Netherlands (Migration Atlas) and lend support to this theory.

King Eider   *Somateria spectabilis*

Vagrant: one record

The monotypic King Eider has a circumpolar distribution across the Arctic Ocean and winters just south of its breeding range.

1977	Colne Point	18th July	Adult male

Of the 190 British records to the end of 2004 (BBRC 2005), almost all were from Scotland. An occurrence so far south is, however, not without precedent, not only in this country but on the Continent, too. However, despite this individual occurring after a period of very strong northerly gales and King Eiders being very expensive and rare in captivity, there must remain the possibility that, given the timing of the record, it was an escape.

Long-tailed Duck   *Clangula hyemalis*

Uncommon passage migrant and winter visitor   Amber List

The monotypic Long-tailed Duck has a circumpolar breeding range extending through the Arctic zone. The majority of the European population breed on the islands and coasts of high-arctic western Russia. Outside the breeding season, it occurs in exposed offshore saltwater habitats. The northwest European population of some 4.7 million birds is found almost entirely within the Baltic (European Atlas). In Britain, where the winter population is estimated at some 24,000 individuals, the majority occur in Scotland in the Shetland Islands, Orkney Islands, Outer Hebrides and along the east coast, notably the Moray Firth (Winter Atlas). In contrast to other sea duck, whilst often found inshore, large numbers also occur well offshore and it is almost certainly under-recorded by casual observation.

Yarrell (1845) observed that the Long-tailed Duck was "… considered a rare bird but has been killed on the coasts of Kent, Essex, Suffolk and Norfolk". Christy described the species as "An

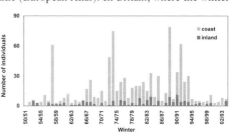

Annual totals of Long-tailed Ducks from 1950/51-2003/04

uncommon winter visitor only to the Essex coast", although at Harwich in the 1880s "... young birds are common every winter". Typically all records involved shot birds, the earliest obtained on the coast prior to 1832. The species' status in Glegg's time was similar: "... recorded from Essex on only rare occasions, and is almost unknown to the field observer. It would seem, however, that it occurs almost annually" (Glegg). In all, Christy and Glegg detailed only 11 records involving 14 birds.

Numbers since 1950 have, apart from occasional influxes, been relatively stable although there are annual variations. However, a run of mild winters since the early 1990s has seen lower than average numbers. The increase from the late 1960s was probably due to increased observer coverage. The highest numbers generally occur when Long-tailed Ducks are displaced from the Baltic after severe weather has caused it to freeze; since the early 1990s this has not happened and probably explains the reduced numbers.

Birds have been recorded from all around the coast, although the Colne/Blackwater complex has been particularly favoured. There have been relatively few records south of Dengie where counts of more than three are rare, although there were 19–20 off East Tilbury on 1st December 1957, at a time when small numbers had been reported regularly from the area. The largest flocks have been: 39, off Fingringhoe Wick, 6th April 1974; 36, Hamford Water, 6th December 1988; 36, Hamford Water, 19th January 1992; 33 off Goldhanger/Tollesbury, February/March 1989; 30, Hamford Water, January 1989; 30, off The Naze, 8th December 1957; and 30, East Mersea, 21st January 1973. Flocks this large are the exception rather than the rule, with the majority being of 1–10 individuals.

There have been inland records in all but 13 winters since 1950/51. Excellent adaptation to living in the exposed offshore zone means that they are less prone than many species to being blown inland by severe storms. Usually, numbers peak during spring and autumn passage. Numbers on the coast usually exceed those inland, although occasionally the opposite occurs. Only in 1988/89 have more than ten been recorded, the total of 12

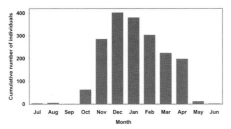

Seasonal occurrence of Long-tailed Ducks from
1950/51-2003/04

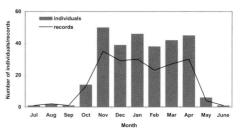

Seasonal occurrence of inland Long-tailed Ducks
from 1950/51-2003/04

birds, however, including seven at Hanningfield on 9th January 1989. Records have come from 11 locations, although only at Abberton, where it has occurred in 35 winters since 1950/51, can it be described as regular. Here, around 100 individuals have occurred, with the highest counts being four on three occasions: February–March 1953; 8th February 1976; and 26th April 1986. At Hanningfield, where 34 have occurred in 13 winters, most have involved 1–2 individuals but an unprecedented influx of five on 24th November 1988 increased to seven by 9th January 1989. Away from these two localities, reports have been scarce, with records from KGV in seven winters involving 1–2 birds and other records coming from Fairlop CP (three), Fishers Green (two) and single records from Ardleigh, Leez, Walthamstow and Nazeing GP, Grange Waters Complex and Stubbers OPC.

Long-tailed Ducks generally begin to arrive in late October, with passage apparent until December after which numbers steadily decline. There is evidently an occasional small spring passage with numbers increasing in early/mid-April on the coast as well as inland in some years; the county's largest flock occurred at this time. Numbers decline rapidly through April, although occasionally birds remain into May, there being nine records all of singles, except for two males on the Lea Valley reservoirs until 4th May 1968.

There have been three June and two July records, all involving singles: a male in Hamford Water, 11th June 1989; off Foulness, 13th June 1992; a summer-plumaged male on KGV, 18th–23rd June 1996; a female at Abberton, 25th July 1972; and a freshly dead bird at Beaumont, 29th July 1981. The three August records have come from: Abberton, a female/immature on 8th in 1967 and one from 19th August–16th September 1965; and, off The Naze, four, 26th August 2003. Apart from the previously mentioned Abberton record, the only other September record came from Mayland on 3rd in 2000. The next earliest arrival was one at Abberton on 1st October 1966.

There are no ringing recoveries involving Essex. Nationally, there is just one overseas ringing recovery; those wintering around Britain are thought to come from northern Fennoscandia and northwest Russia.

Common Scoter
Melanitta nigra

Common passage migrant and winter visitor with a small non-breeding population in summer   Red List

Although a maritime species during winter, the monotypic Common Scoter breeds inland across the boreal and low-arctic zones of Eurasia where it can be found in tundra and scrub habitat to alpine terrain. Common Scoters breed from Iceland, northwest Ireland and Scotland across Fennoscandia to Russia and east to central Siberia (European Atlas). The British population is small and probably declining, the last full survey locating a maximum of 195 pairs (Underhill *et al.* 1998). Outside the breeding season, the species undergoes an extensive moult migration, beginning as early as June, with upwards of 100,000

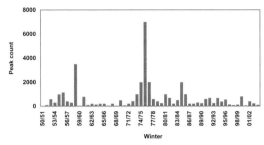

Largest single day counts of Common Scoters from 1950/51-2003/04

birds assembling in the western Baltic, eastern North Sea and offshore Britain and Ireland and western France (European Atlas). Up to 940,000 have been counted in the western Baltic alone, including one flock of 800,000 (Cranswick *et al.* 1995). Around 35,000 winter along the coast of Britain.

Christy described the Common Scoter as a common winter visitor, very rare inland, the first documented Essex record occurring prior to 1730: "It was sent to Braintree some years past from Tendring Hundred". The largest gatherings were noted offshore: "Immense gatherings are to be seen all winter on the Foulness and Maplin Sands ... The ducks often rival the Geese [Brent] in numbers and ... are frequently seen in spring and summer". During the Jubilee yacht race on June 14th 1887 the Swin Middle Lightship "... was surrounded with Black Ducks, as far as could be seen with a telescope". Yarrell (1871–85) noted: "At times the waters between the Eastern counties and Holland are black with them". Glegg considered the Common Scoter to be a winter visitor and, although not commonly seen from the shore did, on occasions, occur in large numbers offshore, although he added nothing to Christy's narrative.

Since 1949, the species' status appears to have changed very little. Common Scoters are found principally on the shallow waters over and around the offshore

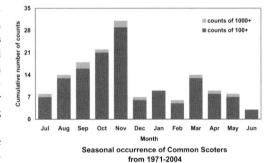

Seasonal occurrence of Common Scoters from 1971-2004

sandbanks, especially at the mouth of the Thames. It is here, off Maplin Sands, that 3,500 gathered on 30th August 1958, whilst there were 7,000 in mid-February 1976, a large flock having been present during the 1975/76 winter. Off The Naze, three-figure flocks were noted with regularity in the 1950s, peaking at 1,160 on 18th March 1956. Large gatherings were also off Clacton-on-Sea, peaking at 2,000–2,500 in late March 1975. Subsequently, numbers have been much reduced, the last four-figure flocks having occurred in 1985 with 2,000 in several loose flocks off

Bradwell on 14th April, 1,500 off Jaywick on 21st May (presumably part of the same flock) and 1,000 off Maplin in early November.

The apparent large annual fluctuations at each site may be due to either variable observer coverage and/or changes in use of feeding areas by Common Scoters. Certainly there is some correlation between the large counts off Walton and Frinton-on-Sea and abundance of Soft Clams near the Gunfleet Sands, whilst Foulness and Maplin Sands are prolific in Cockles (Cox). Common Scoters feed mainly on molluscs during winter, principally the Blue Mussel (*BWP*). However, in excess of 80,000 Common Scoters winter off the

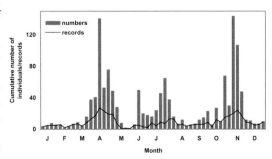

Seasonal occurrence of inland Common Scoters from 1950-2004

Dutch and Belgian coasts and an influx of just a small proportion of these would have a significant effect on the numbers off the Essex coast (Cranswick *et al.* 1997).

Small numbers regularly occur in offshore waters during summer although, apart from up to 2,000 a few kilometres off the Dengie coast from late July to September 1976 (see above), most counts have been in double figures. However, off the northeast coast, three-figure flocks were noted during June and July with some regularity during the mid- to late 1990s. Numbers peaked in 1995 with 550 on 14th July. These were probably immature birds and it is possible that they had stayed to moult in offshore Essex waters.

Counts by land-based observers have, by comparison, been small, although some of the larger rafts of roosting birds do occasionally move towards the coast in favourable weather conditions, usually with onshore winds. In colder winter weather small numbers will move well up the estuaries of the Blackwater and Thames, most flocks involving single-figure but occasionally double-figure totals. However, three-figure flocks have been observed on several occasions, with 420 off Brightlingsea in January 1973 being the largest. Early spring may also see small movements along the estuaries, although 150 at the head of the Blackwater at Mundon on 16th March 1958 were exceptional.

Although small numbers can be seen moving along the coast, it is only in the Thames and particularly from Southend Pier, Canvey Island and East Tilbury, that any significant passage has been observed. During the 1990s, with increased observation, it became apparent that Common Scoters regularly moved up the Thames, although the largest numbers perhaps coincide with onshore winds and/or cold weather. In 1993, nearly 2,000 passed East Tilbury between 14th October and 22nd November, with peaks of 692 on 17th November and 405 on 16th. In 1991, 400 passed there on 22nd October with 600 on 23rd November 1990, coinciding with similar numbers off the north Kent coast. A total of 560 passed Canvey Island on 22nd October 1990.

Numbers offshore peak in November, as they do nationally (Winter Atlas). Largescale movements have been noted along the English Channel in autumn and to a greater extent in spring, and many of Essex's largest gatherings have coincided with these movements; they probably involve flocks of birds that have wintered off the French and Iberian coasts and are heading back north to breed.

Every year, a few Common Scoters occur on inland waters, albeit usually briefly. Records show strong peaks in spring, midsummer and autumn. The midsummer peak may relate to movement to/from the moult flocks that form in the Baltic at this time. Most occur at Abberton and Hanningfield and in the Lea Valley with the latter particularly favoured. The majority of records have involved 1–3 birds but there have been several large flocks, with double-figure counts not unusual. The largest was 79 at Walthamstow on 6th November 1980, and there were 65 at Girling on 7th April 1996. Other counts in excess of 30 have been: 40–45 at Hanningfield, 16th July 1984; 39 females/immatures at Fairlop CP, 24th October 1991; and 33 females/immatures at Girling, 11th–13th November 1988.

Not surprisingly, it being such a marine species, there have been no ringing recoveries involving Essex, except that two birds ringed at Abberton were found dead there within days of being trapped.

Surf Scoter   *Melanitta perspicillata*

Vagrant: one record

The monotypic Surf Scoter breeds throughout northern Canada and Alaska and winters south along the east and west seaboards of the USA.

| 1997 | Bradwell | 21st September | Immature male |

This individual did not linger; it flew north past BBO then into the Blackwater Estuary before flying out a few minutes later and heading north (Sutherby 1998). A marked increase in records during the 1980s led to the species' removal from the BBRC List in 1990. To the end of 2002 there had been 376 British records (Fraser & Rogers 2005), the majority associating with flocks of Common and/or Velvet Scoters. In good years, 20–30 can be present during winter, principally in east and northeast Scotland but with occasional birds wintering further south around the entire British coastline.

In addition, Ticehurst (1909) referred to two Surf Scoters that were seen at the mouth of the Thames during one winter between 1875 and 1880, although as the birds were not obtained, he felt that the record should be placed in 'square brackets'.

Velvet Scoter

Melanitta fusca

Uncommon passage migrant and winter visitor: rare in summer

Amber List

The monotypic Velvet Scoter has an almost circumpolar distribution and breeds throughout Eurasia and northern North America, although it is absent from Iceland. In Europe, the main breeding populations are in Finland, Sweden and Estonia. The total northwest European wintering population exceeds 550,000 individuals (Durinck *et* al. 1993) with 20% wintering in Denmark. On migration up to 200,000 have been recorded in a single day moving along the Estonian coast (Rusanen 1993). Around 3,000 winter off the British east coast (Stone *et al.* 1997), mainly in Scotland.

Christy considered the Velvet Scoter an uncommon winter visitor to the coast and cited seven records. The earliest documented record involved a flock of about 30 in the Stour near Harwich in the winter of 1829/30 "... they were so expert in diving that but few [five] were shot." Another correspondent noted that "From its habits of diving rather than flying when approached, it is ... caught in the nets of ... sea fishermen". Glegg described the species as a winter visitor to the coast, although he thought that it was probably overlooked in the large Common Scoter flocks. Of the six records Glegg added, all bar one came from the Blackwater.

Since 1950 the species has been an uncommon but regular passage migrant and winter visitor (Cox, Hudson & Pyman). Occasional influxes have occurred, although overall numbers have remained relatively constant. Numbers are, however, never large with the most recorded in any winter being 58 in 1984/85. Velvet Scoters are often found feeding in association with Common Scoters.

The species was relatively abundant during the mid-1950s, a period when there was a large flock of Common Scoters off the northeast coast (q.v.). The largest flocks were 27–31 off The Naze on 24th February 1956 and 27 off Bradwell on 25th April 1954, whilst other flocks of 20+ all came from The Naze: 26, 26th December 1954; 26, 30th December 1956; 23, 28th January 1955 (20 on 23rd); and 20, 18th October 1958. Subsequently the scoter flock moved further south off Dengie, making observation difficult and numbers reported declined (Cox). The only subsequent counts in excess of 20 have been: 26 off Dovercourt, 31st January 1985; 25 along the north Blackwater, 25th September 2000; 24 in the mouth of the Blackwater, 12th August 1979, an exceptionally early date; and 22 off Holliwell Point, 24th November 1991, where the flock remained for the rest of the year, with a few still present in the New Year. There appears to be no correlation between Velvet Scoter numbers and the severity of winter weather.

Although they are sea duck, Velvet Scoters will readily use shallower coastal waters and individuals are regularly recorded some way up the main estuaries, with regular reports off Goldhanger in the Blackwater and East Tilbury in the Thames in recent years. Although most are reported from the Dengie coast northward, the species has become more regular in the Thames recently, although eight is the largest count: off Southend Pier, 22nd March 1985 and 11th November 1999; and Mucking, 11th March 1956.

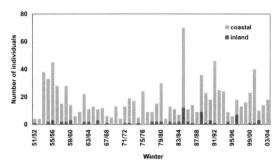

Annual totals of Velvet Scoters from 1951/52-2003/04

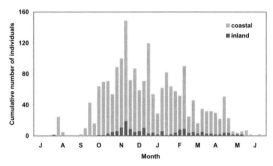

Seasonal occurrence of Velvet Scoters from 1950-2004

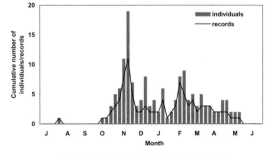

Seasonal occurrence of inland Velvet Scoters
from 1950-2004

Small numbers of Velvet Scoters occur regularly inland with almost 50 records involving around 75 individuals since 1950. Inland records peak in November and again in February/March, closely following the pattern seen on the coast.

Few Velvet Scoters occur before October, although some of the largest flocks have occurred in August/September. Numbers tend

	No. of winters with records	Total number of individuals	Peak counts
Abberton	10	10	Singles only
Hanningfield	12	26	Five on 17/12/96
KGV	5	7	Three on 19/2/66
Walthamstow	5	7	Two on 19/2/80 & 18-26/11/85
Girling	12	26	Seven on 20/11/88
Nazeing GP	1	1	One on 22/11-7/12/58

Summary of inland Velvet Scoter records from 1950/51-2003/04

to peak in late October/early November and again in late winter/early spring when presumably those that have wintered further south are heading back towards their breeding grounds. There have been three June records: off Bradwell, two, 9th in 1975; Blackwater Estuary, one, 19th in 1977; and off Tollesbury, one, 30th in 1998. Apart from these and one off Canvey Island on 2nd July 1998, extreme dates have been 31st May (an oiled male off West Mersea in 1972) and 30th July (a male at Hanningfield in 1983).

The origin of our wintering birds is unclear although birds from Finland, Norway and northern Russia may be involved (Migration Atlas).

(Common) Goldeneye *Bucephala clangula*

Common passage migrant and winter visitor: occasional birds summer **Amber List**

The Goldeneye's breeding distribution extends principally over the coniferous zone between 55° and 70° N in Europe, northern Asia and North America. It is a hole-nesting species, preferring older forests that contain woodpecker nest sites and natural holes. The nominate race *clangula* occurs across Europe where there are around 250,000 pairs. Following the provision of nestboxes, small but increasing numbers have bred in Scotland since 1976. Breeders from northern Europe migrate to their main wintering areas in Denmark, the western Baltic, the Netherlands and Great Britain. Some 300,000 winter in western Europe (Scott & Rose 1996) with around 17,000 in Britain during the 1990s (Stone *et al.* 1997).

Breeding has never occurred in Essex, nor even been suspected, due to the absence of suitable natural nesting localities. However, following the first summer record of one at Hanningfield on 15th July 1972 (considered a pricked bird), others have occurred with increasing regularity, although only at Abberton can the species be described as regular. Up to five were present in 1967 with up to four in 2001, although 1–2 is more usual. Three to four summered on the Lea Valley reservoirs in 1984 and 1985. Odd birds have also been noted in midsummer at Hamford Water, Colchester, the Colne, Old Hall, Heybridge GP and Hanningfield.

Christy described the Goldeneye as a winter visitor chiefly to the coast, although sometimes met with inland. The earliest documented Essex record involved two shot prior to 1777 (Pennant 1777). The species was rare around Southminster in 1835 but was latterly noted as common on the coast by one observer. Glegg's description of the species' status was very similar, although he noted that the species was occasional on the Lea Valley reservoirs. However, the Goldeneye was not seen in the large numbers occurring on some of the other London reservoirs at that time, Glegg seeing no more than three on any occasion. On the coast the largest gathering was 40 in Pyefleet Channel on 24th January 1926.

GB 170 / INT 3,000	50/51-54/55	55/56-59/60	60/61-64/65	65/66-69/70	70/71-74/75	75/76-79/80	80/81-84/85	85/86-89/90	90/91-94/95	95/96-99/00	00/01-04/05	Peak counts		Peak Month
WeBS totals	(306)	(300)	462	719	768	796	1,041	1,033	1,208	953	948^	Feb 91	1877	Feb
Stour	~	~	46	84	51	110	100	65	149	119	221^	Jan 01	291	Feb
Hamford Water	~	~	1	19	43	61	117	64^	44	69	16^	Feb 85	250	Jan
Colne	~	~	151	198	184	~	~	234	207	82	32^	Feb 91	477	Feb
Blackwater	~	~	125	126	177	270	454	347	309	283	216^	Jan 82	799	Jan
Dengie	~	~	1	1	14	11	19	10	1	2	4^	Feb 82	80	Jan
Crouch-Roach	~	~	0	2	2	2	8	5	52	34	3^	Jan 97	81	Jan
Thames	~	~	1	1	2	3	11	4	18	6	2^	Feb 94	40	Feb
Ardleigh	~	~	~	~	0	0	2	2	5	4	6^	Jan 01	12	Feb
Abberton	(185)	(254)	253	468	353	462	542	557	507	607	492^	Mar 89	1,002	Mar
Hanningfield	~	(21)	34	32	40	48	45	41	67	45	49^	Dec 93	75	Mar
Lea Valley	~	~	27	34	47	51	64	95	114	98	99^	Mar 91	161	Feb
Met. Essex Waters	~	~	~	~	~	~	~	~	~	~	1^	Twice	1	~

Five-year average of peak WeBS counts (Nov-Mar) of Goldeneyes from 1950/51-2003/04

Although a maritime species, the Goldeneye was quickly attracted to the newly built Abberton Reservoir, 200 being noted there in 1945. Since then, Abberton has consistently held more Goldeneye than any other site in England and any other inland location in Britain. The large increase at Abberton saw a corresponding decline in numbers during the 1950s on tidal waters, where it became relatively rare with no flocks of more than 50 recorded (Hudson & Pyman). Exceptionally, 500 were on the Colne in February 1963, coincident with total ice cover at Abberton. However, numbers on tidal waters increased through the 1960s, particularly after the severe winter of 1962/63, the Blackwater being particularly favoured.

Subsequently, numbers on the coast and inland have generally increased, mirroring the significant growth in the northwest European population which increased by as much as 50% between 1985 and 1995 (Rose 1995). However, numbers have been reduced over the last decade, perhaps as a result of the run of warmer winters recently.

Numbers at Abberton are of national importance, although in international terms are not significant. The only other sites regularly holding numbers of national importance are the Blackwater and Colne. A population of 1,000 represents almost 6% of the British wintering population but just 0.3% of the west European population.

Linsell (1969) described large pre-dusk gatherings at Abberton, although Glover (1979) noted that, unlike other sawbills, Goldeneye never formed large communal roosts and virtually no interchange occurred between the reservoirs and the coast,

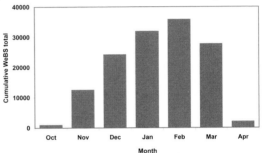

Seasonal occurrence of Goldeneyes from 1961-2004

except in hard weather. On the estuaries, rafts may form late in the evenings on the Blackwater, most often in Tollesbury Fleet, Goldhanger Creek and Pyefleet Channel. Linsell (1969) in his three-year study confirmed the proportion of adult males occurring at Abberton to be in the range 13–17%, reflecting the fact that males generally migrate shorter distances than females; many stay in the Baltic through winter and only occur in large numbers when severe weather forces them west. However, these proportions can vary markedly and consistently between adjacent sites (Campbell 1977) perhaps reflecting differences in the relative importance to adult males and others of factors such as shelter and disturbance.

Many birds moult in the Baltic from June and only start to return to their wintering grounds from late August, although the main movement does not occur until November and is virtually complete by December (*BWP*, Migration Atlas). In Essex, the main arrival begins in November, although small numbers occur through October with some arriving as early as late August/September. Numbers on the coasts and estuaries generally peak in December/January with a later peak on inland waters in February/March. The highest WeBS totals generally occur in late winter, perhaps due to a combination of late-winter weather-related influxes and birds passing through and heading back to breeding grounds. The majority have left by late April, although stragglers are reported into May with some regularity.

There is little ringing information available and very few studies published (Cranswick *et al.* 1995). Boyd (1959) found that birds breeding in Sweden move firstly south into the Baltic and later into Britain, which concurs with a general build up to a peak nationally in February. The wintering population as a whole is probably drawn from the entire Fennoscandian breeding population (Migration Atlas).

Whilst it is possible that the provision of artificial breeding sites at the main reservoirs could tempt summering individuals to breed, it seems unlikely that it will occur in the foreseeable future. Most of the species' wintering areas are protected and the species is tolerant of humans, often allowing close approach. For the foreseeable future therefore, the Goldeneye's status seems assured.

Smew   *Mergus albellus*

Uncommon winter visitor in variable numbers

The monotypic Smew breeds in the Palearctic boreal taiga zone from northern Sweden and Finland, eastward through Siberia. The species is a tree-hole nester, although it will use nest boxes. Most of the European population of 7,000–15,000 pairs occur in European Russia where there may have been a range contraction between 1970 and 1990 of 20–50%, although numbers vary annually by at least 20%. Elsewhere, the species' range contracted

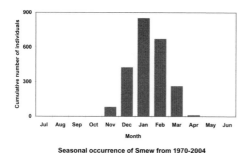

Seasonal occurrence of Smew from 1970-2004

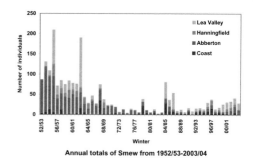

Annual totals of Smew from 1952/53-2003/04

markedly in eastern Europe during the latter part of the 19th century and again from 1920–70, probably due to deforestation. Up to 15,000 winter in northwest Europe, including 10,000 in the Dutch Ijsselmeer and along the Rhine, with a further 50–60,000 in the Baltic (Migration Atlas).

Fossil bones of Smews dating back 300,000 years have been uncovered at East Mersea in the "elephant bone beds" (Urquhart 2000).

Christy described the Smew as an uncommon winter visitor to the coast, although occasionally met with inland and usually occurring in twos and threes. He noted: "... in severe seasons the Smew has been taken in the nets of the fishermen in the Thames. Two males were taken alive in the winter of 1819–20 in Bow Creek, but although abundantly supplied with food, [they] refused all sustenance and perished". Glegg considered the Smew an annual winter visitor in small numbers, perhaps suggesting an increase over the previous 40 years. Indeed, he observed that since 1924 the Smew had become regular on the Lea Valley reservoirs. His observations revealed that the species rarely appeared until the second week of December, later than at the other London reservoirs. The largest count was 12 in 1924. Numbers on the London reservoirs increased during the 1930s (Homes 1957).

Hudson & Pyman described the Smew as an uncommon passage migrant and winter visitor. However, numbers during the 1950s and early 1960s were the highest ever recorded. In the Lea Valley, there were 85 on KGV on 3rd March 1956 and an exceptional 124 on Walthamstow on 4th March 1963, probably the second largest concentration recorded in England. At this time, numbers at Abberton were also high with 113 on 22nd February 1954 and an average peak count for the four winters 1952/53–1955/56 of 92. All of the largest counts coincided with extremely cold weather (Cox). Smaller numbers were regular at Hanningfield, the peak count being 30 in February and March 1956. In the 1950s, the London reservoirs held about 30% of the British population.

Numbers have subsequently declined, in line with the national trend (Winter Atlas), Cox noting that the Smew was a "Winter visitor, now scarce".

Reasons for the decline are unclear. Numbers recorded from the late 1960s through to the early 1980s were unexceptional, although intermittent cold-weather influxes caused by severe weather in the Baltic at times boosted counts. With most inland waters frozen during the 1978/79 winter, many moved to the coast and a count of 12 at Goldhanger on 6th January 1979 equalled the second highest coastal count from the Stour at Manningtree in January and February 1955. A total of 15 off East Tilbury on 13th January 1968 remains the largest single tidal count and coincided with the freezing of many inland waters; around 35 occurred on tidal waters at this time.

Severe weather in early 1985 produced the largest influx since the mid-1960s. Most occurred in the Lea Valley, particularly at Fishers Green with 40 on 24th January, but higher than average numbers were also recorded from the main reservoirs and tidal waters. Numbers remained at a higher level for the next few winters, and included 40 at Fishers Green on 8th February 1987, suggesting that influxes may influence subsequent wintering patterns. By the end of the 1980s, numbers were again low and generally remained low until another cold-weather influx in 1996/97, since when numbers have shown an upward trend. Nationally, 90-130 are reported each winter; in January 1979 there were 400 with 390 in early 1985.

In recent years, most Smews have occurred in the Lea Valley, particularly around the Fishers Green area, one of the most important sites in the country for the species.

Elsewhere, Smews have occurred across Essex on gravel-pits, farm reservoirs, ornamental lakes and ponds, even in heavily built-up areas e.g. Eagle Pond, Snaresbrook; Valentines Park, Ilford; and Hackney Marshes. A lack of suitable habitat in the north and west means Smews are scarce there. Most records away from the main sites have involved 1–3 individuals. However, there were: 16 on the Stour at Flatford, 2nd February 1955 (Hudson & Pyman); 14 on Heybridge GP, 6th January 1997; ten on Langford Reservoir, 2nd January 1963; and ten on Lofts Farm GPs, 22nd December 1996.

Smews appear to be very mobile on their wintering grounds with daily counts at individual sites varying markedly. WeBS counts therefore tend not to record the species particularly well. In addition, at complex sites, such as those in the Lea Valley, there appears to be considerable interchange between waters.

As with other species of duck, the males generally migrate shorter distances than females/immatures and so most records involve the latter. Only when pushed west by severe weather do larger numbers of males occur.

Smews generally start to arrive in November, although an exceptionally early individual was at Walthamstow on 18th September 1953. Most, however, do not arrive until the end of the year and numbers generally peak from late January/mid-February and decline rapidly after the end of February with very few left by April, 23 at Abberton on 4th April 1966 being exceptional. There have been two May records: one on Ulting GP until 7th in 1979; one redhead on the Stour, 19th–20th in 1989. Two birds have summered, although both were almost certainly injured, one at Hanningfield in 1960 and another at Abberton in 1962.

Those occurring in southeast England are thought to originate from the Dutch wintering population but a lack of ringing recoveries precludes confirmation (Toms & Clark 1998).

Red-breasted Merganser   *Mergus serrator*

Common passage migrant and winter visitor

The monotypic Red-breasted Merganser has a widespread Holarctic distribution, mostly above 50° N and covering Eurasia, North America and southern Greenland. In Europe, the species is common in Iceland, Ireland, northwest Britain, Fennoscandia, Estonia and northern Russia. Unlike other sawbills, it is not a tree-hole nester and thus has more catholic habitat requirements. Its European range has remained largely unchanged since the 19th century apart from a southerly shift in Britain and Ireland caused by population increases, although the latest studies suggest a possible slight contraction of the population (Armitage *et al.* 1977). The British population numbers 2,500 pairs. Northern populations move south in winter to more temperate areas where they are almost exclusively maritime. Birds in southeastern Britain are thought to derive from the major breeding areas in Fennoscandia (Scott & Rose 1996). About 100,000 are thought to winter in northwest Europe with 10,000 in Britain (Stone *et al.* 1997).

Glegg referred to remains of Red-breasted Mergansers being found in post-Tertiary deposits in the Lea Valley. The earliest documented record referred to by Christy stated that it was "… not uncommon on the Essex coast", an observation made prior to 1826. Otherwise, he described the species as a not uncommon winter visitor, occasionally met with inland; a pair summered off Northey Island in 1888. The species' status changed little in the next 40 years (Glegg). It was most common from the Blackwater around to the Stour but rare between the Crouch and Thames. Flocks of more than 15 were considered rare.

Although its general status remains largely unchanged, peak WeBS counts have increased since the end of the 1980s.

Nationally, wintering numbers have shown a gradual increase with near record numbers in the winter of 1997/98 (Cranswick *et al.* 1999); Essex data suggest a similar trend, although numbers have recently declined slightly. The population increased most rapidly between 1966/67 and mid-1980s with some stabilisation since. Annual numbers vary greatly, perhaps as a result of factors that include the size of autumn passage, the severity of weather on the Continent and the abundance of fish stocks in inshore waters. The largest Essex influx occurred during the severe weather of early 1979 and included the largest single site count of 215 in Hamford Water on 14th January. Other three-figure mid-winter

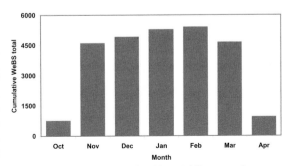

Seasonal occurrence of Red-breasted Mergansers from 1961-2004

counts (non-WeBS) have included: around 200 in the Colne/Blackwater complex, December 1953; 175 in Hamford Water, December 1978; 140 off Fingringhoe Wick, 31st January 1971; and 120 in the Blackwater, 4th January 1958.

Spring passage has seen: 200 off Dengie, April 1996 and 12th March 2000; 150 off Dengie, March 1981; 114 in the Blackwater, 11th March 1956; and 103 off East Mersea, 10th March 1999. The flock off Dengie in 1996 was attracted, along with divers and other sea birds, to a huge shoal of Sprats.

Glover (1979) noted that Red-breasted Mergansers made nightly roost flights out of the Colne/Blackwater and Roach/Crouch complexes to spend the night on some of the most exposed areas of coast, often 2km or so off Dengie and perhaps Mersea Island. Quite why a species that prefers the quietest waters of the coast should forsake these for these rough waters is unclear, but Glover (1979) suggested that dissemination of information regarding feeding areas, social interaction (when display may occur) and possibly loose pair-bonding were all factors. Visible migration along the coast has rarely been recorded.

GB 100 INT 1,250	50/51- 54/55	55/56- 59/60	60/61- 64/65	65/66- 69/70	70/71- 74/75	75/76- 79/80	80/81- 84/85	85/86- 89/90	90/91- 94/95	95/96- 99/00	00/01- 04/05	Peak counts		Peak Month
WeBS totals	*(105)*	*(130)*	*92*	*116*	*156*	*176*	*136*	*132*	*211*	*252*	*207^*	Jan 79	363	*Feb*
Stour	~	~	0	0	0	1	0	12	34	70	69^	Nov 99	<u>103</u>	Dec
Hamford Water	~	~	15	15	43	81	29	18^	48	36	25^	Jan 79	<u>215</u>	Jan
Colne	~	~	35	78	69	~	~	49	62	60	40^	Dec 65	<u>200</u>	Jan
Blackwater	~	~	41	64	82	70	68	52	63	71	72^	Mar 02	<u>116</u>	Nov
Dengie	~	~	5	10	23	29^	19	13	31	34	21^	Nov 91	58	Nov
Crouch-Roach	~	~	1	3	8	2	10	10^	19	20	10^	Jan 98	35	Feb
Thames	~	~	12	3	6	17	19	14	23	29	15^	Jan 94	40	Jan

Five-year average of peak WeBS counts (Oct-Mar) of Red-breasted Mergansers from 1950/51-2003/04

Numbers along the Thames are generally small and rarely exceed 20, a count of 79 off East Tilbury on 8th November 1992 being exceptional. In recent years, increasing numbers have been recorded from the inner Thames and, whilst this may be due to increased observer coverage, it is possible that the cleaning of the river is also a factor. Very recently, a few have been recorded within the East London docks.

A wintering population of around 200 represents approximately 2% of the British and 0.2% of the European populations.

Males often leave the breeding grounds from early June (*BWP*); Essex records in July/early August may therefore involve males that have moulted locally together with non-breeders. The main arrival occurs during October and November with peak counts between November and April.

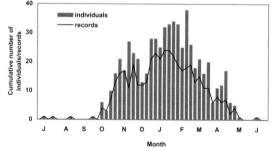

Seasonal occurrence of inland Red-breasted Mergansers from 1960-2004

Return passage usually peaks in February/March with numbers declining rapidly after the end of March/early April, although stragglers are recorded with some regularity into May. One or two are normally recorded during summer in most years, usually from the coast. However, six flew past Rat Island on 30th June 1968 and four were in Hamford Water on 2nd July 1998.

Although principally maritime during winter, Red-breasted Mergansers occur inland with regularity, often at times of severe weather locally or on the Continent. Numbers are generally small and rarely exceed five at any local-ity. However, an exceptional influx in early 1956 saw 34 at Girling on 25th February, 36 at Walthamstow on 25th February and 33 at KGV on 3rd March. Other double-figure counts have come from: KGV, 17,

	No. of winters with records	Total no. of individuals	Peak no of individuals recorded annually						Peak counts
			1950s	1960s	1970s	1980s	1990s	2000s	
Abberton	37	109	14	5	6	12	3	5	14 on 22/12/57
Hanningfield	22	68	5	0	3	7	7	4	6 on 2/11/97
Lea Valley	37	208	60	3	14	9	10	18	60 in Feb/Mar 1956

Summary of inland records of Red-breasted Mergansers from 1950/51-2003/04

20th November 2002; Abberton, 14, 22nd December 1957; Nazeing GP, 14, 18th February 1979; Walthamstow, 11, 18th February 1979; and Abberton, 12, 20th February 1988.

Very few national ringing recoveries have been made and none have involved Essex. The directions and orientations of migratory flights of central European birds make it likely that those wintering off the east coast of Britain include both local breeders and birds from central Europe (Robinson 1999).

There are no discernible threats to the wintering population of Red-breasted Mergansers, although disturbance within the estuary complexes caused mainly by various leisure activities are a potential problem, unless existing controls are maintained and perhaps increased.

Sponsored by Kevin and Isobel Marsden

Goosander   *Mergus merganser*

Locally common passage migrant and winter visitor

The Goosander inhabits clear water lakes and is typically a hole-nesting species, the breeding range of which broadly overlaps that of the Red-breasted Merganser. The nominate race *merganser* occurs in Iceland, north and west Britain, Fennoscandia, Russia and Siberia. Since the 1850s, the species' range has moved south with Scotland colonised in 1871 and England in 1941. The current British population is estimated to be 2,900–3,600 pairs. Northern populations are generally migratory, with Scandinavian birds wintering along the shores of the North Sea and Baltic. Almost the entire European population of some 30,000 males gathers to moult in the mouth of the Tana River in Norway in early September (Second National Atlas); it has been suggested that this is the centre of the species' original range (Little & Furness 1985).

Christy described the Goosander as an uncommon winter visitor to the coast adding that it was "… not unfrequently met with inland". The earliest documented reference (Dale 1730) to the species being frequently met with in Harwich harbour may result from confusion with Red-breasted Merganser. Thus, the earliest definite documented record involved a female shot at Debden Hall on 30th January 1830. The majority of Christy's records came from inland, the largest count being 15 on Wanstead Basin in the winter of 1884/85. Glegg added little further regarding the species' status but noted that there had recently been a marked increase in the London area, although it was generally scarce on the Lea Valley waters in comparison with others across London, the largest count being eight on 27th December 1927. Records from tidal waters were scarce.

Both Hudson & Pyman and Cox considered the Goosander a bird of the reservoirs with few reported in other habitats and that is the situation today. Since Glegg's time, however, the creation of Abberton and Hanningfield has provided alternatives to the Lea Valley, which has held far more birds since the 1930s and this, together with the species' range expansion, means that since 1950 numbers have been far greater than at any time previously.

Annual numbers vary markedly with the largest counts usually occurring after severe weather on the Continent. The species is very difficult to census accurately as it is extremely mobile and flocks often appear at sites for only short periods.

In addition to the counts in the table, there were 100 at Hanningfield (non-WeBS) on 20th January 1982.

Goosanders are primarily fish-eaters and prefer waters of depths greater than 4m. Thus, birds may use different waters to feed and roost, again making censusing difficult. Counts in the Lea Valley in the 1970s and 1980s showed that about 50 individuals dispersed to feed on sections of flood relief channels during the day and only appeared in significant numbers in the evening when returning to the reservoirs to roost. Roost counts would therefore give the best estimate of numbers (Cranswick *et al.* 1997). Few sites in Britain hold more than 50 birds (Winter Atlas). The most recent estimate of the British wintering population is about 8,900 (Stone *et al.* 1997), with the northwest European population being around 100,000. The current average of around 110 individuals therefore represents about 1.3% of the British but less than 0.1% of the northwest European populations.

GB 90 INT 2,000	60/61- 64/65	65/66- 69/70	70/71- 74/75	75/76- 79/80	80/81- 84/85	85/86- 89/90	90/91- 94/95	95/96- 99/00	00/01- 04/05	Peak counts		Peak month
WeBS totals	75	79	48	110	90	131	91	134	108^	Mar 89	229	Jan
Abberton	44	64	26	33	42	44	38	56	46^	Feb 96	173	Jan
Hanningfield	8	8^	22	33	18	19	13	15	3^	Jan 79	49	Feb
Lea Valley	34	7	12	50	41	63	49	63	59^	Jan 63	111	Jan
Met. Essex Waters	~	~	~	~	~	~	~	~	6^	Jan 01	8	Jan

Five-year average of peak WeBS counts (Oct-Mar) of Goosanders from 1960/61–2003/04

The general increase mirrors the national trend over the last three decades, although the population appears to undergo cyclic fluctuations with regular, large troughs every 4–5 years (Kirby *et al.* 1995). National data suggest that whilst there has been a general increase in all habitats, it has been above average on gravel-pits and rivers, a trend mirrored in Essex. Like Smew, there is some suggestion that following a cold-weather influx, a number of birds continue to arrive from the Continent in subsequent winters despite milder conditions, perhaps having become accustomed to wintering further west (Cranswick *et al.* 1997).

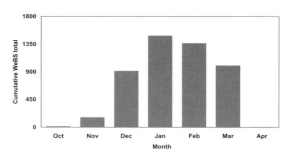

Seasonal occurrence of Goosanders from 1961-2004

Away from Abberton, Hanningfield and the Lea Valley reservoirs, Goosanders are regular in small numbers on many gravel-pits, rivers, ornamental lakes and pools and occur in built-up areas. The highest counts away from the three main sites have come from the complex of gravel-pits to the north of the Lea Valley reservoirs; it is highly likely that there is much interchange between all the sites along the Valley. The largest count by far was 93 at Nazeing GP on 31st December 1996, counts of up to 40 being far more usual. Elsewhere, the highest counts have been: 44 at University of Essex Lake, January 2001; 42 at Alresford GP, 5th February 1997; 40 northeast over Colchester, 23rd February 2003; and 30 at Great Baddow, 17th March 1996. Recently there has been a trend for Goosanders to occur on a greater number of inland waters. Whilst this may be due to increased observer coverage, numbers at Hanningfield have been much reduced in recent years and redistribution from here may have occurred; why this should be is unclear.

Away from inland locations, numbers are usually small with a few occasionally frequenting sheltered estuaries and, sometimes, coastal waters. The largest numbers occur in severe weather when inland waters freeze. Six double-figure counts have been reported from tidal waters: Pyefleet Channel, 20, 14th February 1969; Foulness, 18 west, 24th October 1994; Hamford Water, 15, 11th January 1978; Colne Point, 12, 30th November 1953; The Strood, Mersea Island, 12, 19th January 1969; and Hamford Water, 12, 21st March 1964. Those passing Foulness were almost certainly migrants and it is not unusual to see occasional individuals passing by offshore during migration periods.

The main arrival of Goosanders occurs from mid-November with numbers peaking during January and February and occasionally March. Very small numbers occur in November and the species is extremely rare prior to October, although there was a very early female at The Hythe from late August 1989. Numbers begin to decline from mid-March with a rapid decline after the beginning of April and a handful staying into May, the latest being off Bradwell on 29th May 1976. There have been four summering records, all possibly involving sick birds. A disabled female stayed at Walthamstow from 1961-January 1967, whilst another female stayed there during 1969. Also in 1969 a male summered at Abberton and what was possibly the same individual was at Heybridge GP on 6th July. In 1990, a female was at Beeleigh from 25th June to 10th July with possibly the same bird in Colchester in mid-July.

Most birds winter within 150km of their natal or breeding sites (Migration Atlas). Thus whilst some individuals in Essex may include British birds, of which there is one Essex recovery (Migration Atlas), particularly when northern waters freeze over, many probably come from the near-Continent or Scandinavia. The latter is borne out by the recovery of one ringed at Abberton on 21st December 1965 at Saaler Bodden, Rostock, East Germany, on 14th April 1966 and another ringed as a duckling in Sweden and found at Little Wigborough in January 1962.

Ruddy Duck   *Oxyura jamaicensis*

Fairly common introduced resident, common passage migrant and winter visitor

This native of North America was introduced into British wildfowl collections during the 1930s. In 1948, the Wildfowl Trust imported three pairs of the race *jamaicensis* to Slimbridge WWT, Gloucestershire. Following difficulties rearing young in artificial environments, parents were allowed to rear young in a 'natural' state. Being extremely difficult to catch and pinion, some young birds escaped—four in 1953 and some 70 between 1956 and 1963—leading to the formation of a breeding colony in the Chew Valley, Somerset, in 1960 and Staffordshire a year later (Historical Atlas). Expansion was rapid, the species apparently exploiting a vacant niche in the avifauna, and by 1975/76 the national population was estimated to be 375 birds (Vinicombe & Chandler 1982). There were around 350–400 pairs by 1991 (Population Trends) and 780–974 females in 1994 (Hughes *et al.* 1998), mostly in the Midlands and central England. Since

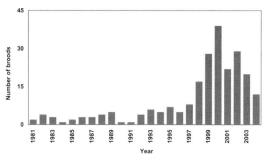

Annual number of Ruddy Duck broods from 1981-2004

then, populations have continued to increase, although in recent years WeBS organisers have felt unable to make current population estimates as some counters, opposed to ongoing control measures, have declined to submit counts. However, they concluded that increases were continuing, particularly in the form of colonisation of new sites (Cranswick *et al.* 1999). The species was admitted onto Category C of the British List in 1971.

The first Essex records came from Hanningfield in 1958, a male present on 24th and 30th August (*EBR* 2002), whilst in 1960 a male summered at Walthamstow with at least two on Lea Valley waters during 1963. Following two records in 1966 and one in 1971, Ruddy Ducks have occurred annually from 1973. The majority of early records involved wintering individuals. However, small but increasing numbers occurred during summer and in 1979 a pair defended a territory and may have nested at Abberton; in 1981, three broods were seen there although the first perished and it was thought only two pairs were involved. Subsequently the number of confirmed breeding pairs have increased steadily, although given the secretive nature of the species the total is probably an underestimate of the true population size.

Counts vary markedly from year to year. Numbers of reported broods fell during the early 1990s, perhaps due to a reduction in suitable breeding sites caused by the drought; virtually no broods were noted at the main reservoirs where water levels were particularly low. With the end of the drought in the late 1990s, breeding resumed. Although Abberton and Hanningfield were the species' strongholds in the early years of colonisation, their importance has decreased as the population has expanded. Breeding has occurred at many sites, principally in the southern half of Essex. Chigborough Lakes have been used consistently since breeding first occurred in 1983. At Old Hall, the county's principal site in most years since 1989, there were 11 broods in 2002. Many

Atlas	Survey Area	% of 10km squares or tetrads in which	
		bred/probably bred	possibly bred or present
First National 10km	Essex	0.0	0.0
Second National 10km	Essex	10.5	8.8
First London Tetrad	Met. Essex	0.0	0.0
Second London Tetrad	Met. Essex	3.0	4.0
Essex Tetrad	Essex	1.9	1.0

Summary of results of Atlas surveys for Ruddy Ducks

other sites have held 1–2 pairs, but in recent years there has been a bias to the southwest; several pairs have bred on some of the smaller waters within urban Metropolitan Essex. Whether the decline in broods reported recently is as a result of the cull beginning to have an effect (see below) or because observers are not reporting them because of the cull is unclear.

The 1994 national survey ranked Abberton as the sixth most important site in the UK and Hanningfield the thirteenth, despite "poor coverage" across Essex. The ranking was based on the number of males and females present at the site during summer. Taking just females present, Abberton ranked second with nine (Hughes *et al.* 1998). The Essex Atlas survey found Ruddy Ducks in 2.9% of all tetrads, with breeding thought to have occurred in 1.9%.

Ruddy Ducks do not appear to form large post-breeding flocks, possibly due to their highly aquatic nature (Hughes *et al.* 1998). In winter, however, they become highly gregarious and form large flocks on suitable inland waters. Hanningfield was, until the late 1990s, the most favoured locality but Abberton has since become more popular. Sites in the Lea Valley and Lofts Farm GPs have also held significant numbers in recent winters with peak counts increasing almost annually.

Non-WeBS counts have included 780 at Abberton during October 2003 (with 740 in November) and individual site counts of 352 at KGV on 17th January 2004 and 118 at Walthamstow on 21st February 2004. Away from these sites there were 84 at Heybridge GP on 21st November 1999 and 104 at Old Hall on 5th February 2004; the extent of interchange between sites along the Blackwater, Abberton and Hanningfield is unknown.

Numbers at Abberton tend to peak in late autumn and at Hanningfield in mid-winter. Based on the 1994 estimate of 3,300 birds (Hughes 1998), the midwinter population lies in the region of 10% of the British population. However, the national population has undoubtedly increased since then so 5–10% would seem a more reasonable estimate.

Introduced	75/76-79/80	80/81-84/85	85/86-89/90	90/91-94/95	95/96-99/00	00/01-04/05	Peak counts		Peak month
WeBS totals	1	18	60	150	255	777^	Feb 03	1,074	Dec
Blackwater	0	1	12	11	40	88^	Feb 02	152	Feb
Ardleigh	0	0	0	0	0	0^	~	0	~
Abberton	0	13	28	50	196	504^	Nov 03	678	Oct
Hanningfield	0	12	38	126	92	451^	Feb 03	664	Jan
Lea Valley	0	3	3	3	38	122^	Feb 03	193	Feb
Met. Essex	~	~	~	~	~	24^	Jan 03	38	Sep

Five-year average of peak WeBS counts (Sep-Mar) of Ruddy Ducks from 1977/76-2003/04

Abberton has probably been the only site in Britain and western Europe where the species has been ringed with any consistency. Up until 1997, more than 200 were metal-ringed and a further 35 wing-tagged. However, the recovery rate for the species is extremely low at around 2%. Ducks in general have an average recovery rate of about 20%; the Ruddy Duck's nocturnal habitats and general reluctance to fly are perhaps the reason for this. Wing-tagging was discontinued in 1997 as it was discovered that the species was strong enough to pull the tags off whilst preening after only a few weeks. It was not until 1997 that movements of more than a few kilometres were recorded and a link finally established with the Midlands and central England populations (Ekins 1998). Evidence suggests that in hard weather the species will move to the coast or occur at sites where it is not regularly recorded (Winter Atlas) and indeed in America the species is known to migrate some considerable distances.

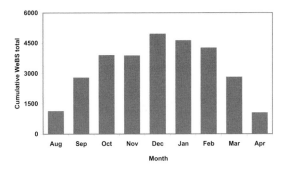

Seasonal occurrence of Ruddy Ducks from 1981-2004

The Ruddy Duck is probably the most controversial species on the British List due to its apparent spread onto the Continent and the likely effect this may be having on the globally threatened White-headed Duck *O. leucocephala*. The upsurge in European records correlates with the increase in the British population. Between 1965 and 1996, some 1,500 Ruddy Ducks occurred in 19 Western Palearctic countries outside the UK (Hughes *et al.* 1998). Many that reached Spain were shot; those reaching France in recent years have met the same fate. Inter-breeding with White-headed Ducks has occurred in Spain, where 51 hybrids have been shot. A record of inter-breeding in Turkey, the centre of the eastern population, has been withdrawn (King 1999). An International Ruddy Duck workshop, held at Arundel WWT in 1993, first recommended that action be taken to control the spread of the species, since when it has been widely accepted that by the professional conservation bodies that the arguments in favour of control were overwhelming. In 1999, the Government gave approval to three pilot areas where control measures were taken; these were considered a success and culling began at Abberton and Hanningfield in January 2004. These developments have been accompanied by both strong opposition and support from the public, and the popular birding press has seen letters from former RSPB members urging others to terminate their membership in protest, or questioning the true extent to which hybridisation would occur (e.g. Vinicombe 2003).

Although the Essex breeding and wintering populations have continued to grow, the long-term culling operation is likely to depress significantly numbers locally; whether this will completely wipe out the Ruddy Duck remains to be seen.

Red-legged Partridge   *Alectoris rufa*

An introduced resident—fairly common and widespread

The Red-legged Partridge is a resident of southwest Europe, occurring naturally in Portugal, Spain, France, Corsica, northern Italy, Elba and the Balearics (European Atlas). The nominate race *rufa* was first introduced into Britain during the 18th century, although it is only since the 1930s that it has attained its present distribution (Second National Atlas). The species occurs throughout much of England, reaching the greatest densities in eastern counties and although found in Scotland and Wales, it is generally absent from the most westerly areas. Annually, around 800,000 are released and 400,000 shot in Britain.

Although the earliest attempts to introduce Red-legged Partridges to Britain were made as far back as the reign of Charles II (1660–85), it was not until 1770 that the species was successfully introduced at two localities in Suffolk (Yarrell 1845). William Henry de Nassau, the fourth Earl

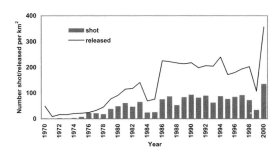

Annual numbers of Red-legged Partridges shot and released per km² from 1970-2000
(data courtesy of The Game Conservancy)

of Rochford, who was Ambassador Extraordinary to the Court of Spain, made several apparently unsuccessfully attempts to introduce the Red-legged Partridge into Essex using birds from Spain some time after 1763 (Christy). In 1777, a covey of 14 was found within 3.2km of Colchester with five killed over the next three days. In 1821 the species was described as being found "... in those parts of Essex bordering on Suffolk ...", although in 1838 it was described as uncommon near Sudbury with records from Saffron

Atlas	Survey Area	% of 10km squares or tetrads in which	
		bred/probably bred	possibly bred or present
First National 10km	Essex	91.2	5.3
Second National 10km	Essex	87.7	10.5
First London Tetrad	Met. Essex	22.0	17.5
Second London Tetrad	Met. Essex	46.5	22.5
Essex Tetrad	Essex	64.1	17.9

Summary of results of Atlas surveys for Red-legged Partridges

Walden between 1831 and 1835. In 1848, a nest was found at Saffron Walden, the first confirmed Essex breeding record, although Red-legged Partridges very probably nested before then. In 1855 several coveys were present around Runwell Hall. It appears, however, that it was not until the latter half of the 19th century that the Red-legged Partridge became widespread and common. In 1887, it was noted: "It is only quite recently that the ... Red-legged Partridge has become common in the Essex Marshes and islands, and I know several sportsmen still living who well remember the first specimen they ever shot, and have heard them relate how carefully they smoothed it down and wrapped it up in their handkerchief, pocketing what they considered a rare and beautiful prize". In 1890 Christy described the species as "An abundant resident ... Round Chelmsford it is now at least as abundant as the Common Partridge".

To Glegg, the Frenchman, as it has sometimes been called, was "... a not uncommon game bird which breeds in some numbers throughout the county". From correspondence with shooting men he concluded that the species was very unevenly distributed with, at one unnamed locality, just 5% of the birds shot being Red-legged Partridges, whilst at another unnamed site the proportion was 50%. He concluded that "Taking the county as a whole, the Red-legged is much less numerous than the Grey Partridge". Just how much the variation in numbers at this time was due to the release of captive-bred birds is unknown.

Hudson & Pyman considered the Red-legged Partridge to be resident and widespread. An enquiry conducted by the EBS from 1952–56 looked into the status of Red-legged and Grey Partridges. It concluded that the proportion of Red-legged to Grey Partridges in limited areas of northwest and southwest Essex was 4:1 with numbers fairly equal elsewhere. Nationally, Greys outnumbered Red-legs by 20:1 until the 1950s (Second National Atlas). A study during March 1965 revealed an average of 69 pairs per 1,000ha, compared to 52 for Grey Partridge (Middleton 1965).

The various atlas surveys have revealed little change in distribution with breeding confirmed in almost all 10km squares. The Essex Atlas survey located the Red-legged Partridge in 82% of tetrads, with confirmed breeding in most, compared with just 23.9% for Grey Partridge. Although generally absent from many urban and suburban areas, a notable increase occurred in Metropolitan Essex between the two London Atlases. More recently, the generally low level of partridge records received by the EBS has meant that it has not been possible to comment on trends.

The successful colonisation of Essex by the Red-legged Partridge has probably been due to its catholic habitat requirements, the species occurring on most types of agricultural land as well as rough grasslands and scrub, both inland and on the coast, and occasionally allotments within urban areas, the upper reaches of saltmarshes, sand or shingle ridges. Since chicks are less dependent on insectivorous food, the Red-legged Partridge has in general successfully adapted to modern farming methods. In addition, as Cox noted, the decline of the Grey Partridge, which has always presented a more challenging target for sportsmen, has resulted in an overall decline in partridge shooting which has benefited the Red-legged Partridge. However, its abundance since the 1970s has been due to increasing numbers of hand-reared birds being released. Several shoots in Essex specialising in the species put down a total of 10,000 chicks in two areas of central Essex in 1981 alone. In 1993 one estate in northeast Essex released 4,500.

From the 1970s large numbers of Chukars *A. chukar* and Red-legged Partridge x Chukar hybrids were released: a survey of central Essex farmland in 1984 revealed that up to 50% of *Alectoris* partridges present were Chukars. The practice was stopped with the last issue of release licences in 1992, as the Wildlife and Countryside Act made the introduction of alien species illegal. Reports of apparent hybrids, however, continue.

Releases undoubtedly influence the size of larger coveys that congregate periodically in arable fields, 575 at Bovingdon Hall, Braintree, on 9th November 1999 being the biggest gathering reported.

Although Red-legged Partridges are generally considered sedentary, very rarely and usually during spring, odd birds occur at coastal localities in situations that suggest at least some local movement. Such records include two in April 1962, one tired and exhausted in a cliff-top garden at Walton and a freshly dead bird, well below the average weight, on the beach nearby. Similar movements have been noted in Norfolk (Taylor *et al.* 1999) and perhaps involve English birds that had flown out to sea and then turned back to the coast. Local dispersive movements are known to take place during spring when winter social groups break down (Migration Atlas).

The Red-legged Partridge has adapted well to the considerable changes in the modern countryside and remains common. Just how much the existing population relies on continuing releases is difficult to say. Nonetheless, its catholic tastes and habitat requirements should ensure that, even if the total number of birds released falls, the Red-legged Partridge will survive as a breeding species.

Grey Partridge *Perdix perdix*

Much declined now scarce resident Red List ~ Essex BAP

The Grey Partridge, which was originally a bird of short steppe and open grassland, has adapted itself to farmland as its main habitat. It is found across Europe from Ireland to the Urals and from northern Sweden to the Mediterranean, and in Asia it reaches eastern Mongolia. The species has declined over much of its range since the 1950s, although it still remains widespread (European Atlas). The Grey Partridge has declined markedly in Britain and its range contracted eastward and is now nearly absent from

Atlas	Survey Area	% of 10km squares or tetrads in which	
		bred/probably bred	possibly bred or present
First National 10km	Essex	96.5	1.8
Second National 10km	Essex	63.2	19.3
First London Tetrad	Met. Essex	24.5	11.5
Second London Tetrad	Met. Essex	20.0	12.0
Essex Tetrad	Essex	14.7	9.2

Summary of results of Atlas surveys for Grey Partridges

Ireland, large parts of southwest Scotland, northwest England, Wales, Cornwall, Devon and parts of Dorset (Second National Atlas). In the 20th century, annual stocks fell by around 5.5 million birds or 95% (Migration Atlas) to 70,000–75,000 pairs. The species is represented in Europe by the nominate race *perdix*.

Christy noted that the Grey Partridge was "An abundant resident, especially where well protected. It does not appear in Essex to have in any way diminished since the introduction of the Red-legged Partridge, as is often supposed". He gave little indication of its actual abundance, concentrating instead on the size of clutches and certain shooting exploits. Nationally, numbers increased dramatically from the mid-19th century due to rising cereal production and gamekeeping such that the species was reckoned to be one of the ten most common birds. Forty years later its status appeared to have changed very little with Glegg observing that it "… is a very common resident gamebird, which breeds freely throughout the county, persisting to the outlying marshes along the coast … It is at all times a much commoner bird than the Red-legged Partridge, the introduction of which does not seem to have had any adverse influence on the indigenous species". Individual bags of 3,160 at Audley End in the winter of 1858/59 and 370 in one day at Thaxted in 1905 give some indication of its former abundance (Ruggles-Brice 1933). A few years later, on the Coptfold Hall estate, Margaretting, an average of 240 birds per annum was shot through the 1920s and the ratio of Grey to Red-legged was at least 5–6:1 (Cox).

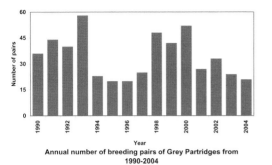

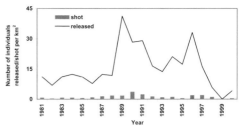

Annual number of breeding pairs of Grey Partridges from
1990-2004

Annual number of Grey Partridges shot and released
per km² from 1981-2000
(data courtesy of The Game Conservancy)

As late as the 1950s, the Grey Partridge outnumbered the Red-legged in most areas. However, there was a dramatic decline throughout England in the early 1960s, apparently due to poor chick survival in a succession of wet summers, with numbers in Essex distinctly lower than Red-legged Partridge by the mid-1960s (Hudson & Pyman). During 1961/62, Game Conservancy analysis of data from estates across Essex produced mean Grey Partridge bags of 20 per km² and of Red-legged Partridges, 27 per km². The highest Grey Partridge density was at Chrishall, where bags numbered 77 birds per km²; by 1981/82 the highest density had fallen to just seven per km² at Debden.

During the 1960s and 1970s numbers nationally remained fairly stable (Population Trends). However, from around 1980 a catastrophic decline set in that has continued to this day. Between the two National Atlases, confirmed breeding records across Essex declined by around 35%, whilst significant losses occurred in Metropolitan Essex between the two London Atlases. The Essex Atlas survey found Grey Partridges in 23.9% of tetrads with breeding confirmed in just over 60% of these. There were obvious concentrations of population in the open estuarine habitats of Thames-side, Colne, Hamford, and Dengie, whilst inland another population centre existed in the triangle formed by Epping, Brentwood and Witham. Urban and wooded areas were generally avoided. Small populations also existed between Bishop's Stortford in the west and Halstead in the east. Today, the Grey Partridge remains extremely thinly spread across Essex; only in coastal regions are any reasonable numbers reported with regularity. Unfortunately because the species has historically been overlooked, EBRs provided little comment upon specific trends until the decline was well under way. By the early 2000s, fewer than 100 records were received annually by the EBS.

Grey Partridges have been hand-reared and released for many years. Information available prior to 1981 was incomplete but since then, the number released and shot annually has remained relatively constant. About 100 were released on one estate near St Osyth in 2004.

The modern decline of the Grey Partridge can be traced back to the end of the 19th century; only in regions such as East Anglia where gamebird management, with gamekeeping, was paramount were maximum population levels maintained into the 1940s (Population Trends). A reduction in cereal farming due to the agricultural recession and reduced keepering prompted the initial declines but by the 1940s, with considerable reductions in gamekeeping during WWII, the decline became general.

The reduction in gamekeeping has allowed nests, eggs and incubating females to be increasingly targeted by predators. Perhaps half of the post-1940s decline has been attributed to this cause. The other main modern impact, estimated to account for 43% of the decline, has been the effect of farm chemicals, initially herbicides but more recently insecticides, on the June densities of arthropods on which the chicks depend for food (Population Trends). For instance, the use of insecticides on winter wheat, a predominant practice since 1985, can halve chick survival, sending it far below the level required to maintain numbers. Grey Partridges avoid winter cereals, ploughed land and intensively managed pasture; rotational set-aside is selected, particularly fallow land (Buckingham *et al.* 1999).

Although generally sedentary, the Grey Partridge exceptionally makes relatively longer distance movements. One, found at Stanford-le-Hope in May 1968, had been ringed four months earlier at Hoddesdon, Hertfordshire, a movement of some 40km.

Extensive work by The Game Conservancy has shown that chick survival rates can be restored towards the mean levels seen prior to the introduction of herbicides, and above 30%, either by the use of selective unsprayed 'conservation headlands' or by the traditional system of under-sowing cereals with ley pasture. The latter is of great benefit to sawflies, a favourite chick food (Second National Atlas). However, both systems are not without cost to the individual farmer and, without an appropriate system of grants to compensate the individual, their widespread uptake is unlikely. Only on farms with a keen shooting interest are such proposals going to receive immediate acceptance and use.

The Grey Partridge is one of five species included within the Essex Biodiversity Action Plan; failure to act may see the species heading for extinction in Essex within the next two decades.

Sponsored by Keith Leeder

(Common) Quail   *Coturnix coturnix*

Scarce summer visitor and passage migrant, subject to periodic influxes   Amber List

The Quail is generally distributed throughout much of the west and central regions of the Palearctic, the nominate race *coturnix* occurring throughout its European range. Although fluctuating markedly from year to year, numbers in Britain declined throughout the 19th and first half of the 20th centuries due principally to intensive hunting (Moreau 1951, Nicholson 1951) and habitat change. However, since 1942 there has been an upward trend (Population Trends). Whilst individuals have been known to winter as far north as Britain and Germany and with some regularity around the Mediterranean, most Western Palearctic populations winter south of the Sahara, mainly in the Sahel zone.

Pennant (1777) referred to Quail arriving in Essex during October and remaining to winter! Christy described the Quail as "Not a rare bird,

Atlas	Survey Area	% of 10km squares or tetrads in which	
		bred/probably bred	possibly bred or present
First National 10km	Essex	14.0	7.0
Second National 10km	Essex	3.5	8.8
First London Tetrad	Met. Essex	0.0	0.5
Second London Tetrad	Met. Essex	0.0	1.0
Essex Tetrad	Essex	0.6	1.9

Summary of results of Atlas surveys for Quails

though very sparingly distributed, never abundant, and much less so than formerly. It occurs from time to time, and has also bred, in most parts of the county, but can never be counted upon to do so regularly". In 1831, it was noted: "The Quail was formerly found in this [Great Totham] and other parts of Essex, but its occurrence now is very rare". The species' status had changed little by Glegg's time "It is probable that at one time it was a regular nester, without being really common". Glegg could cite just eight definite breeding records: Witham, 1833 and 1892; Romford, 1866; Ingatestone, 1867; Heath Place Farm, Orsett, 1885; Mucking, two in 1885; and Great Oakley, 1924. However, the species may have been more numerous than Glegg suggested "In one district in Essex, numerous eggs have been found during the mowing season and as many as sixty couples have been killed in the course of a few days shooting in one manor in that county [Essex]" (Jesse 1844). Even as late as 1860, "large bevies" were met with in the Rochford Hundred.

Since 1950 breeding has been confirmed just four times: Wicken Bonhunt, 1955; Corringham, 1960; Epping, 1974; and Chrishall Grange, 1993. However, further sightings of adults and the presence of birds calling from the same areas in consecutive years suggest that breeding may occur irregularly at a wide number of sites. Indeed, both the wide open 'prairies' of Dengie and the chalk uplands of the far northwest provide records almost annually. Typically, birds are heard calling from cereal fields, Barley being particularly favoured. As males tend to call frequently after arriving but less so after mating (unless there are other males nearby), it is likely that lone males calling for more than a week are unpaired and therefore not proof of breeding; they may also move considerable distances which makes assessment of breeding numbers very difficult (First National Atlas).

Numbers recorded annually vary markedly, with very lean years interspersed with good ones known as 'Quail years'. These tend to occur after a warm dry spring with plenty of southeast winds which cause overshooting of migrants, although a good breeding season the previous year and low mortality rates may also be factors. In a breeding strategy not dissimilar to some butterflies and moths, e.g. Painted Lady and Silver Y, Quails breeding in Europe in summer may include young hatched at more southerly latitudes earlier the same year. Many arrive in Britain in June and July and are clearly associated with this onward migration and may therefore include many young (Migration Atlas).

The general pattern over the last 50 years has been of very gradual increase which may in part be due to increased observer coverage, but also to reduced hunting pressure, particularly in the Mediterranean, since WWII (Population Trends).

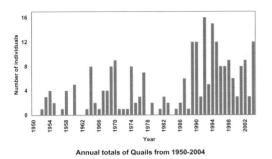

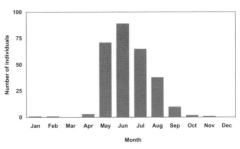

Annual totals of Quails from 1950-2004

Seasonal occurrence of Quails from 1950-2004

The first calling males generally arrive in mid-May. However, there were singles at Fleet Head on 11th April 1999, Abberton on 28th April 1958 and at Old Hall on 30th April 1997.

Birds may be heard regularly into August but few are noted after the middle of the month. There has been a total of nine September records and two in October: Dengie on 15th in 1982, and Great Dunmow on 17th in 1954. The sole November record involved one at Rainham on 12th in 2001. Since 1950 there has been just one winter record, one near Romford SF from 16th January–26th February 1967, although there were five in January prior to 1950: in 1827, 1918, 1923, 1928 and 1946.

Quails are likely to remain scarce in Essex for the foreseeable future although global warming may result in increasing numbers moving further north in Europe than at present.

(Common) Pheasant

Phasianus colchicus

A very common resident, probably introduced

The Pheasant's native European range covers western Georgia, the west Caspian shore plain, Armenia and Azerbaijan, from where it then extends east along the northern slopes of the Himalayas, north into Manchuria and Korea and south towards Vietnam, also being found on Taiwan and the Japanese archipelago. Across much of Europe it is an introduced species. The Romans probably introduced the Pheasant to Britain, although it was probably not well known or feral prior to 1500. Stock introduced by the Normans was therefore the likely basis of the population, which did not spread across the whole of Britain until the late 1700s (European Atlas). In Britain today it is widely distributed although absent or occurring at very low densities in much of Wales and northwest Scotland. Especially in southern and eastern England, numbers are greatly increased by the release in autumn of hand-reared birds for shooting (Second National Atlas). Around 20 million are shot annually in Britain and Pheasant shooting is, in parts of the country, an important rural industry,

Christy described the species as "An abundant resident wherever it is sufficiently preserved". He detailed one of the first written records of the species in Britain, which came from Essex; the Pheasant was mentioned on the bill of fare drawn up by King Harold for the guests of the Canon of Waltham Abbey in 1059.

The earliest birds introduced into Britain were of the race *colchicus* ('Old English') from the Caucasus. The race *torquatus* ('Ring-necked'), which was brought from China in the late 18th century, now predominates; the males have a white neck-ring (Glegg). Hybrids of these two and other forms occur from time to time. Apparent melanistic individuals may in fact be distant hybrids with the Green Pheasant *P. versicolor* from Japan.

The Pheasant is probably the most

Atlas	Survey Area	% of 10km squares or tetrads in which bred/probably bred	possibly bred or present
First National 10km	Essex	96.5	1.8
Second National 10km	Essex	93.0	7.0
First London Tetrad	Met. Essex	38.5	14.5
Second London Tetrad	Met. Essex	63.0	16.0
Essex Tetrad	Essex	82.5	2.6

Summary of results of Atlas surveys for Pheasants

under-recorded bird on the Essex List; it was not even mentioned in the Systematic List of the *EBR* until 1988. The species was and remains a very common bird, the commonest and most widespread of the gamebirds, which becomes scarce only in the most built-up areas. Notwithstanding its general absence from urban areas, it will nonetheless visit gardens in search of food, particularly in times of severe weather.

Both National Atlas surveys recorded the species in virtually every 10km square with breeding confirmed in the majority, whilst the Essex Atlas located the Pheasant in 85.1% of tetrads, with breeding confirmed in most. Apart from Metropolitan Essex, the species was absent only from the built-up areas around Southend-on-Sea and Basildon, Canvey Island and the centres of the principal towns such as Chelmsford and Colchester. Numbers increased in Metropolitan Essex, particularly in the southwest, between the two London Atlas surveys. Although this increase may in part be due to greater observer coverage, it seems that the Pheasant may increasingly be using urban and suburban areas to breed and feed, perhaps because there is a year-round supply of food there that the somewhat sterile modern winter farmland cannot provide. National CBC/BBS data revealed a 66% increase in the Pheasant population over the period 1977–2002 with a 41% increase in the BBS (England) Index from 1994 –2003; perhaps warmer summers are aiding chick survival so that greater numbers are present in the subsequent summer to breed.

Although naturalised, Pheasant numbers are boosted significantly by the release of thousands of artificially reared birds. Cox detailed releases of the order of 5,000–10,000 chicks per annum by one of the county's largest shooting syndicates. An average of 110 birds per km^2 was shot during the 1960s and 1970s on one north Essex estate, whilst those syndicates releasing thousands of birds per annum may see a season's bag in the order of 500 birds per km^2. Game Conservancy data for the period 1961–94 suggest a ratio of birds shot to birds released of around 7:1. What impact this has on the population as a whole is unclear, although over 60% of reared birds are shot within 400m of their release point, less than 1% disperse more than 2km and many succumb to natural forces, especially predation (Winter Atlas).

The Pheasant is almost completely sedentary, although the fact that ringing of this species is prohibited in Britain means little is known of movements of birds once they are released.

Although the Pheasant is not a native bird, its positive impact on the countryside due to creation and management of habitat in order to encourage its

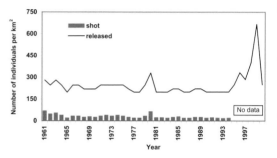

Annual numbers of Pheasants released and shot from 1961-2000
(data courtesy of The Game Conservancy)

numbers is significant. A survey of Essex landowners in 1995 showed that 250 farms with driven gameshooting represented 10% of all holdings in the county "… lowland driven game shooting influences the consideration of less intensive land management practices such as hedge retention and maintenance, field spraying or woodland planting" (Howard & Carroll 2001).

The future of the Pheasant in Essex seems secure given the large amounts of habitat suitable for the species and the high numbers put down by shooting syndicates. Locally, numbers may fluctuate where disturbance is significant, declines during the 1990s at Rainham being attributed, at least in part, to the activities of falconers. However, on the whole the outlook for the Pheasant is good.

has on the population as a whole is unclear, although over 60% of reared birds are shot within 400m of their release point, less than 1% disperse more than 2km and many succumb to natural forces, especially predation (Winter Atlas).

The Pheasant is almost completely sedentary, although the fact that ringing of this species is prohibited in Britain means little is known of movements of birds once they are released.

Although the Pheasant is not a native bird, its positive impact on the countryside due to creation and management of habitat in order to encourage its numbers is significant. A survey of Essex landowners in 1995 showed that 250 farms with driven gameshooting represented 10% of all holdings in the county "… lowland driven game shooting influences the consideration of less intensive land management practices such as hedge retention and maintenance, field spraying or woodland planting" (Howard & Carroll 2001).

The future of the Pheasant in Essex seems secure given the large amounts of habitat suitable for the species and the high numbers put down by shooting syndicates. Locally, numbers may fluctuate where disturbance is significant, declines during the 1990s at Rainham being attributed, at least in part, to the activities of falconers. However, on the whole the outlook for the Pheasant is good.

Red-throated Diver   *Gavia stellata*

Common winter visitor and passage migrant   Amber List

The monotypic Red-throated Diver has a circumpolar and Holarctic distribution and is one of the most northerly breeding aquatic birds, typically nesting in treeless tundra or heath terrain near oceanic coasts, as well as in the boreal coniferous forest zone (European Atlas). In Europe, the species breeds through Iceland, Scandinavia and into northern Russia, as well as Scotland and Northern Ireland, where the population was estimated to be 935–1,500 pairs in 1984 (Stone *et al.* 1997). A significant proportion of the Western Palearctic population winters in British and Irish waters, some 4,300–5,400 birds (Daneilsen *et al.* 1993), particularly along the east coasts of Scotland and England.

The earliest documented Essex records were prior to 1777 when Pennant (1777) referred to them on the Thames. Christy described the "Sprat Loon", as it was known colloquially, as fairly abundant off the Essex coast during winter. He listed just five inland occurrences, one of which deserves detailing in full: "Early on the morning of Dec. 2nd 1876, during a heavy fall of rain and a high wind which had blown all night from the S. E., a female (?) specimen alighted in the garden of a cottage at Springfield ... to the great surprise of the occupants ... It had no doubt been blown inland by the gale, but from the first it exhibited little or no fear of human beings, and lived contentedly for a fortnight in a pig-pen in the garden, without making any attempt to fly away. It was fond of Sprats and earthworms. In the end it was killed for stuffing." An almost pure albino specimen was shot at an unnamed site in 1862.

Glegg considered the Red-throated Diver the most numerous of the three divers and thought it more frequent out to sea. Although very common in the mouth of the Thames, the species was frequently found in the Colne Estuary during winter. Hudson & Pyman found the Red-throated Diver to be a much less common winter visitor and passage migrant than previously; the species was particularly scarce during the mid-1960s. Inland, reports were regular, although all too frequently oiled birds were involved, many subsequently being picked up dead.

By the early 1980s, the species' status had become clear (Cox), with the highest numbers occurring during December and January, coincident with the annual winter influx of Sprats into coastal waters. Unfortunately, the effects of discharged and spilt oil were evident particularly from the 1960s to mid-1980s, with many birds succumbing regularly to this pollution. More recently, stricter maritime pollution controls have meant that oiled individuals are noted with far less regularity.

In the 1950s, numbers reported in the first four winters were modest and 80–100 off East Mersea on 1st April 1955 were considered exceptional. In 1956, 104 were off Colne Point on 30th March with 120 there on 26th March 1959.

After large counts off Colne Point in the early 1960s, peaking with 142 on 19th March 1961, numbers crashed with no more than three together in 1963, although 17 were found dead between Harwich and East Tilbury early in the year. By now, many records involved oiled birds; in early 1966, 21 corpses were found along the north shore of the Blackwater. Subsequently, numbers recovered slowly with 55 off Colne Point on 13th April 1969, although oiling remained a problem, eight being picked up at Bradwell during the first three months of 1972, whilst six oiled individuals were on Heybridge GP on 12th February 1972. A count of 80–100 at Bradwell on 26th February 1977 was the highest for 16 years but numbers returned to more modest levels by the end of the decade.

On 17th February 1980 there were 204 off the Dengie coast. On 17th January 1982 approximately 150–200 were observed from a boat in the Thames Estuary, with most towards the Kent shore, whilst on 24th February 1982 an aerial survey of all Essex offshore waters found 256, then a county record. Notable influxes occurred in December 1985, with 80 off Southend Pier on 22nd, and 1986 with 53 off Dengie on 14th December. There were 300 in the Blackwater Estuary on 27th March 1989 and 180 off Southend Pier on 3rd January 1989.

During December 1992 numbers were exceptional, with 134 flying southwest in an hour at Holland Haven on 4th, about 220 at East Tilbury

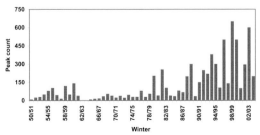

Peak annual day-counts of Red-throated Divers from 1950/51-2003/04

on 20th (two flocks of 106 and 112 flying high to the northeast) and 175 off Bradwell on 13th. Numbers again reached 300 along the Dengie coast on 1st January 1994 and increased to 380, a new county record, on 2nd February. At the same time, 233 flew past The Naze and 175 were off Colne Point on 19th January. Another count of 300 was achieved in 1995 off the Dengie coast on 19th February, but on 3rd February 1997 some 500 were reported a few kilometres off the northeast coast, including a single raft of 345. The peak Essex count increased still further in 1999 with 650 off the the Dengie coast on 31st

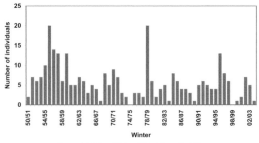

Annual totals of inland Red-throated Divers from 1950/51-2003/04

January. Over 500 were off the northeast coast on 27th January 2000. In 2002 there were 296 off Foulness on 27th January, with at least 600 passing southwest along the Gunfleet Sands on 22nd December, whilst in 2003 there were 264 off Sunk Sands/Long Sands on 6th February. The largest counts have generally coincided with huge gatherings in the Sole Bay area, off the Suffolk coast, where there were 1,500–3,500 in consecutive winters between 1993/94 and 2000/01, including an unprecedented 3,760 off Covehithe on 15th December 2001 (*Suffolk Bird Report* 2003); these are believed to be the largest concentrations ever reported in the Western Palearctic (Piotrowski 2003.). A recent environmental impact assessment in the outer Thames suggests that the area may hold as many as 7,500 Red-throated Divers or 1.5 times the previously assumed British wintering population (Gibson 2005).

Red-throated Divers are generally scarce throughout September (15 records since 1950) and October, early arrivals perhaps involving Scottish individuals. By the end of October and early November, numbers increase, with direct movement from Scandinavia possibly occurring (Winter Atlas). Numbers tend to peak in late winter; as winter progresses the species may move further south in the North Sea and, given certain conditions, large numbers wintering further offshore may move closer to land (Taylor *et al.* 1999). The northerly movement of individuals that have wintered further south may also boost numbers. By early April most Red-throated Divers have departed, although stragglers are recorded occasionally into May and June, there being 14 May and four June records since 1950. One off The Naze on 27th July 1968 is the only record for that month, and the only August record is one off Dengie on 29th in 1993.

Inland, Red-throated Divers have been recorded in every winter since 1950/51 except for 1974/75 and 1998/99. Many prior to the mid-1980s were either dead or oiled and found dead subsequently. Of the three diver species, Red-throated is, perhaps not surprisingly, recorded in the greatest numbers inland, although as a proportion of the wintering population, the percentage involved is far smaller than for the other two divers, a trend similar to the rest of the country (Migration Atlas).

The majority of inland records have come from Abberton, with Hanningfield and the reservoirs along the Lea Valley also visited regularly. It is interesting to note that the numbers of Red-throated Divers recorded in the Lea Valley are barely in excess of those of Black-throated Divers, a far rarer species (q.v.).

	No. of winters with records			Estimated totals			Peak counts		
	RTD	BTD	GND	RTD	BTD	GND	RTD	BTD	GND
Abberton	45	19	11	135	26	13	14 on 18/03/79	3 on 18/01/57 & 02/02/58	Singles
Hanningfield	35	19	15	78	23	16	8 in early 1956	4 on 18/02/85	Singles
KGV	15	13	14	16	17	15	Singles	3 on 25/02-04/03/56	2 from 25/11/72 to 10/03/73 and 17-29/01/98
Girling	14	11	8	19	18	9	2 on 20/01/63	4 on 25/02/56	Singles
Walthamstow	14	9	8	16	9	9	2 on 19/02/66 & 06/10/68	Singles	Singles
Ardleigh	3	1	Nil	4	1	Nil	2 on 30/12/70	1 on 13/2-26/03/03	Nil

Summary of inland diver records from 1950/51-2003/04

During the 1950s, numbers at Abberton were higher than at any time since with 4–5 on 19th February 1950, four on 3rd and six on 17th February 1952, six during March 1953, five on 27th December 1953 and seven on 18th January 1957. However, 14 there on 18th March 1979 remains the largest inland count. At Hanningfield, maxima have been eight in March 1956 and five in early 1960, all of which were found dead subsequently. Away from those sites mentioned in the table, single records (unless stated otherwise) have come from: over Friday Wood (three); central Colchester; Beeleigh; Gosfield Lake; Leez Reservoir (two); over Danbury Lakes; High Easter; Langdon Hills; Weald CP; Hornchurch; Audley End (two); Little Chesterford; Holyfield GP; Waltham Abbey GP; Hylands Park; Wanstead Flats; and Leyton Flats. Individuals also occur with some regularity on gravel-pits adjacent to the coast and estuaries as well as up the Thames as far as East Tilbury, but only occasionally beyond. Singles were in the Royal Albert Dock on 18th March 1996 and from 7th January–2nd February 1997, with two on 22nd–23rd January and 2–3 during January 1998. Numbers occurring inland peak from January to March with slightly higher numbers in February and March, suggesting some overland return passage through Essex; it is late April/early May before most breeding areas are reoccupied (*BWP*).

One ringed as a nestling at Ikamiut, Christianshab, Greenland, on 5th July 1950 was found dead 3,400km southeast at North Fambridge on 15th September 1959, whilst another found dead at Old Hall had been ringed 1,261km to the northeast as a nestling at Orvikskölen, Lima, Kopparberg, Sweden, on 31st July 1988; the latter was the first British recovery from the Swedish population. Another ringed as a nestling in the Orkney Islands on 20th July 1979 was found dead on Foulness on 9th June 1983. It is therefore likely that those visiting Essex are from mainland European, Iceland, Greenland and northern Scottish populations. Very few foreign-ringed Red-throated Divers have been recovered in the country (Migration Atlas).

Sponsored by Gerry Johnson

Black-throated Diver

Gavia arctica

Uncommon winter visitor and passage migrant

Amber List

The Black-throated Diver is a northern Holarctic breeding species that occurs mainly in the arctic and boreal zones in Europe, Asia and North America. The species' European distribution has a southern limit of 55° N, although the Great Northern Diver replaces it in Iceland (European Atlas). The nominate race *arctica* occurs across the Western Palearctic (*BWP*). The Scottish population numbers 155–189 pairs (Stone *et al.* 1997). The Black-throated Diver winters mainly on coastal waters in the North, Baltic, Black and Caspian Seas and also in the Mediterranean, although large inland lakes are used

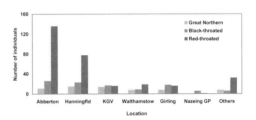

Summary of inland diver records from 1950/51-2003/04

throughout. The British wintering population has been estimated at approximately 700 (Danielsen *et al.* 1993), the majority found along the south and east coasts (Winter Atlas).

Christy described the Black-throated Diver as a "... somewhat rare visitor to the ... coast during winter, when individuals are occasionally found ... inland, after high winds or storms". Whether more or less common than Great Northern Diver in Christy's time is not stated, but Glegg concluded that the Black-throated Diver was the least common of the three divers. The first documented county record (assuming it was in Essex), in March 1840, involved two adults "... shot near Sudbury in nearly full nuptial plumage." A further 13 were noted up to 1889, two of which were inland including one at Chignal Smealey where "On the morning of 4th December 1876, during an extraordinary flooding, a man ... observed a large bird swimming on the flood in a meadow close to Pengy Mill Farm. On approaching and finding that it did not seem inclined to fly, the man set his dog upon it, and after about twenty minutes, managed to kill it. During this time it never once attempted to fly, but dived frequently." There were just four more records between 1890 and 1929.

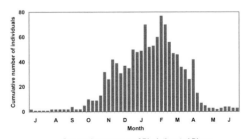

Seasonal occurrence of Black-throated Divers from 1950-2004

Currently, the species is slightly less common than the Great Northern Diver, although apparently less prone to influxes, at least in recent years, than its larger cousin. Numbers have increased in recent decades, almost certainly due to increased observer coverage, better optics and a much better understanding of its most important identification features.

The pattern of high numbers in the 1950s followed by fewer in the next two decades seems to have been mirrored elsewhere in southern England (e.g. Hampshire and Surrey). Few were, however, reported from Norfolk prior to the late 1970s (Taylor *et al.* 1999). The other divers and rarer grebes have shown similar patterns of occurrence.

Essex records during the 1950s included a significantly high proportion from inland sites, some involving long-staying individuals, a situation also observed elsewhere in southern England at that time (e.g. Surrey). Indeed, Hudson & Pyman noted that over 50% of occurrences had been at the major reservoirs. Cox suggested that this was due to increased observer coverage. However, numbers appearing inland have actually decreased subsequently, despite increased observer coverage and fewer are now reported inland than in the 1950s. Quite why this should be is unclear, but it may suggest that fewer are now visiting Essex than before.

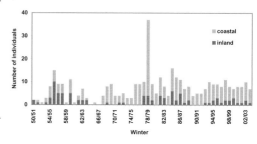

Annual totals of Black-throated Divers
from 1950/51-2003/04

Above average numbers were present in the winter of 1978/79, following severe weather on the Continent. An unprecedented flock of 25–30 off Bradwell on 13th April 1979 was perhaps a gathering of birds moving north. The only other counts of more than five together are: seven off Tollesbury on 18th February 1976; seven off Southend Pier in February 1986; and six off Canvey Island on 25th January 1998.

The species is recorded regularly around the coast, with the Blackwater/Colne complex being particularly favoured. Numbers on the Thames have increased in recent years and, whilst this may be due to increased observer coverage, the cleaning of the Thames may have made it a more attractive habitat than in the past. The general spread of records around the coast points to a more widespread distribution than that of Great Northern Diver.

The first autumn arrivals are usually in October with the main arrival from November onwards. However, there was one at Girling on 11th and 20th August 1956, with perhaps the same individual at Walthamstow on 24th September, which remained until 22nd June 1957. One in full summer plumage off Canvey Island on 14th in 2002 is the only other September record. Numbers peak in late February/early March and perhaps suggest a small return movement through Essex. In spring, the majority have left by mid-April with a few lingering into early May. However, in addition to the Walthamstow record above, one at Nazeing GP from 11th February 1983 moved to Fishers Green in early May and stayed until 2nd July. Otherwise, the latest spring records are: two at Girling on 4th May 1985; one in Hamford Water from 30th May–6th June 1988: and one at Hanningfield from 4th June 1960–14th May 1961.

Except for the previously mentioned records, a winter-plumaged individual in Tollesbury Creek on 27th June 1981 and one off Holland Haven on 17th June 1994 are the only summer records.

Since 1950 just over 100 have been recorded inland, principally at the major reservoirs, a significantly higher total than Great Northern Diver occurrences. Totals recorded in the Lea Valley are significant and outnumber those at both Abberton and Hanningfield; they perhaps hint at an overland migration route between the south coast and The Wash. Other records, all of singles, have come from: Ardleigh, 13th February–26th March 2003; Ulting GP, 5th–22nd March 1995; Tillingham GP, 4th March 1979; Fishers Green, 15th November 1981 and early May–2nd July 1983; South Ockendon, 19th–29th November 1977; Gobions Pit, East Tilbury, 31st January 1996; Buckhurst Hill GP, 8th–30th December 1987; and Dagenham Chase, 7th January 1986. Additionally, whilst not truly a non-tidal occurrence, one in India and Millwall Docks, London, on 16th and 22nd February 1979 is notable.

Whilst there are no Essex ringing recoveries, it is likely that those occurring in the county are from the Scottish and Scandinavian populations (Migration Atlas).

Sponsored by Gerry Johnson

Great Northern Diver

Gavia immer

Uncommon winter visitor and passage migrant

Amber List

The monotypic Great Northern Diver is a predominantly Nearctic species that also occurs in Greenland. In Europe, its only regular haunt is Iceland where there are about 300 breeding pairs (European Atlas). The species winters principally in the North Sea and along the Atlantic coasts of France and Spain, with around 3,000 in British waters.

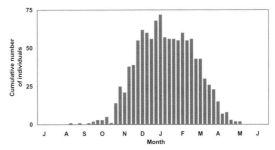

Seasonal occurrence of Great Northern Divers from 1950-2004

Christy considered the Great Northern Diver to be "A fairly common visitor..." However, as Glegg pointed out, this assumption was based on erroneous correspondence, which muddled the names of this and Red-throated Diver: Glegg believed it to be the rarest of the divers. The first documented Essex record of the 'sprat-loon', a local name it shared rather unhelpfully with the other two diver species, concerned two captured on the Thames just below Woolwich in the winter of 1814/15.

Currently the species is marginally more common than the Black-throated Diver, despite being considered the rarest of the three divers to occur regularly in the North Sea (Stone *et al.* 1997). The species tends to feed a greater distance offshore than other divers (Barrett & Barrett 1985, Camphuysen & Leopold 1994) and it is possible that it is under-recorded, although few are observed from fishing boats off the Essex coast. Occurrences have increased generally over the last few decades, presumably due to increased observer coverage; however, numbers vary quite markedly from year to year. During the last 20 years or so, the winter population has been of the order of 3–10 individuals, with as many as 11 in 1985/86, 12 in 1996/97, 13 in 1991/92 and 14 in 1993/94.

Great Northern Divers occur around the entire coast, the Blackwater/Colne complex being the most favoured location with 4–6 present in most winters; five were along the north Blackwater during the February 2000 WeBS count. Occasional counts of up to four off Dengie may involve those from the Colne/Blackwater. The species has occurred up the Thames as far as the Royal Albert Dock and Albert Basin. Like the Black-throated Diver, Thames records have increased noticeably in recent years, presumably for the same reasons (q.v.). An influx into the Thames in late 1996 saw four off Southend Pier from 31st December with five on 1st and 10th January 1997.

Most Great Northern Divers typically start to arrive in November. Just 14 have been observed in October (ten since 1990) and two in September: off St Osyth on 17th in 1994; and Hanningfield on 24th–25th in 1977. Numbers peak between early December and late February and decline through March and April, with no obvious signs of passage through Essex (cf. Red-throated and Black-throated Divers). There have been five May records, all of singles, the latest on the Crouch and then off Bradwell 17th–18th May 1980 and at Abberton on 18th May 2002 (from 16th February).

More than 60 have occurred at inland localities, mostly at the main reservoirs (see table with Red-throated Diver text). Other records have come from: Alresford GP, 8th–26th December 1970; Leez, 26th–27th December 1968; Margaretting, 20th February–12th March 1994; Basildon, 26th–29th December 1996; Fishers Green, 30th November 1974–4th January 1975; Roydon GP, 20th November 1988; Fairlop CP, 21st November–9th December 1988 (probably the Roydon bird); Netherhall GP, 12th December 1991–5th January 1992; and Essex Arena GP, 3rd December 2003–12th January 2004. Whilst not strictly inland, one in Royal Albert Dock and Albert Basin, London, from 8th–11th January 1997 was notable. Why so

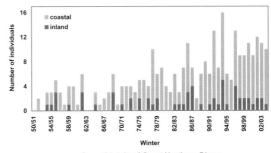

Annual totals of Great Northern Divers from 1950/51-2003/04

relatively few have been recorded at Abberton is unclear; perhaps it is too close to the coast to 'lure' the species. Hanningfield has been visited most frequently, whilst the combined Lea Valley sites have recorded similar numbers to those at Abberton; perhaps like the other divers there exists an overland route between the English Channel and The Wash?

There are no ringing recoveries involving Essex or indeed Britain, so it is impossible to be certain of the origin of individuals occurring in the county, although they are probably from Iceland, Greenland and possibly Canada (Migration Atlas).

Sponsored by Gerry Johnson

Little Grebe   *Tachybaptus ruficollis*

Locally common resident, fairly common passage migrant and winter visitor

The Little Grebe is a widespread species breeding throughout much of central and southern Eurasia, southeast Asia and southern Africa with the nominate race *ruficollis* occurring through western Europe. In the central Western Palearctic the species is generally widespread and common, the British population of 5,000–10,000 pairs being one of the most important in Europe (European Atlas). The Little Grebe frequents still or slow-moving waters and for breeding requires submerged and emergent vegetation (Second Atlas). Northern and eastern European populations are migratory (European Atlas).

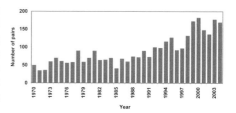

Reported annual totals of breeding pairs of Little Grebes from 1970-2004

The earliest records came from Shoebury where in 1843 the species was considered a "… constant resident ". Christy described the 'Dobchick' or 'Dobchicken', as it was known locally, as "… widely distributed, but not common and seldom found breeding except on or near the coast". Glegg believed that the Little Grebe was the most common of the grebes, noting that it "… breeds on the lakes, suitable streams, and particularly on the fleets in the vicinity of the coast". Hudson & Pyman considered the species thinly distributed in suitable habitat but not a common species, particularly because of high mortality during the severe winter of 1962/63; populations through-

Atlas	Survey Area	% of 10km squares or tetrads in which bred/probably bred	possibly bred or present
First National 10km	Essex	73.7	12.3
Second National 10km	Essex	75.4	10.5
First London Tetrad	Met. Essex	8.0	6.0
Second London Tetrad	Met. Essex	28.0	5.0
Essex Tetrad	Essex	17.7	2.2

Summary of results of Atlas surveys for Little Grebes

out Europe fluctuate markedly according to winter weather conditions (European Atlas). The First and Second National Atlases and the Essex Atlas survey confirmed a breeding distribution encompassing much of the county with a complete absence only in the chalk uplands of the northwest. The Essex Atlas confirmed a presence in 20% of tetrads, with breeding confirmed in most. The Little Grebe's range reflects the distribution of suitable habitats which include a wide variety of freshwater sites bearing enough vegetative cover: for example, quite small ponds, slow-running streams and flooded coastal borrow dykes may be utilised as well as larger inland waters. Increased extraction of chalk, principally in southwest Essex, and of gravel, and the creation of new habitats during the construction of the M25

GB 30* INT ?	1985-1989	1990-1994	1995-1999	2000-2004	Peak counts		Peak Month
WeBS totals	82	142	202	428	Sep 03	477	Sep
Stour	~	~	2*	3	Sep 03	5	Sep
Hamford	~	~	19*	15	Sep 00	37	Sep
Colne	12^	12	7	10	Sep 04	18	Sep
Blackwater	21^	28	50	58	Sep 03	75	Sep
Dengie	~	~	0*	5	Sep 03	6	Sep
Crouch-Roach	11^	10	23	42	Aug 03	60	Sep
Thames	20	33	41	88	Sep 02	115	Sep
Ardleigh	4	3	0	0	Sep 90	11	Sep
Abberton	17^	14	40	20	Sep 99	96	Sep
Hanningfield	54*	33	26	17	Sep 88	85	Sep
Lea Valley	17	34	31	99	Sep 04	138	Sep
Metropolitan Essex	~	~	~	122	Aug 03	143	Sep

Five-year average of peak WeBS counts (Jul-Sep) of Little Grebes from 1985-2004

motorway, have contributed significantly to the substantial increase in suitable habitat. There are perhaps 1,000 inland waters currently in the county (Essex Atlas). The Second London Atlas recorded a significant spread into the many gravel-pits in the west and southwest, since the First Atlas.

The *EBRs* have documented annual numbers of probable or confirmed breeding pairs, but the species' secretive nature whilst nesting, together with the large number of potential breeding sites, must mean that the breeding population is underestimated. However, numbers appear to have increased since the late 1960s and, whilst this may be due to increases in suitable habitat, greater observer coverage must also be a factor.

With no recent severe winters, 183–184 pairs were located in 2000, compared to the 130–170 pairs suggested in the Essex Atlas: allowing for under-recording, the current population perhaps lies in the region of 180–225 pairs. Numbers at individual sites can vary markedly from year to year, presumably in response to water levels. For instance,

at Old Hall, 17 pairs in 1996 fell to nine in 1997, increased to 16 in 1998 and 28 in 1999, declined to 12 by 2003 but climbed to 24 pairs in 2004. The marked increase towards the end of the 1990s has coincided with a period of above-average rainfall. It will be of interest to see if numbers decline should rainfall return to nearer the average.

Shortly after it was flooded, Hanningfield apparently provided ideal conditions for Little Grebes, probably as a result of the proliferation of small fishes, e.g. sticklebacks, as well as insect larvae and plenty of nesting sites (the late Stan Hudgell pers. obs.).

GB 30* INT ?	85/86- 89/90	90/91- 94/95	95/96- 99/00	00/01- 04/05	Peak counts		Peak Month
WeBS totals	62	152	184	418^	Oct 04	492	Oct
Stour	1^	9	5	8^	Jan 03	15	Dec
Hamford	7^	30	36	55^	Jan 02	100	Dec
Colne	17^	19	15	15^	Feb 92	28	Dec
Blackwater	14^	18	38	47^	Oct 03	69	Oct
Dengie	7*	3	2	4^	Oct 88	13	Oct
Crouch-Roach	6^	20	25	31^	Oct 03	43	Dec
Thames	27	51	62	128^	Jan 02	158	Dec
Ardleigh	3	5	0	0^	Twice	2	Oct
Abberton	3*	1	6	6^	Oct 97	13	Oct
Hanningfield	4^	7	12^	13^	Oct 88	36	Oct
Lea Valley	17	23	25	90^	Nov 02	118	Oct
Metropolitan Essex	~	~	~	112^	Oct 02	136	Oct

Five-year average of peak WeBS counts (Oct-Mar)
of Little Grebes from 1985/86-2003/04

An estimated 30 nests were counted in 1956, with 15–20 in 1958, although by the early 1960s there were only up to three pairs. Since 1970, up to ten pairs (1984 and 1992) have bred annually with numbers generally remaining stable. Counts have been made across Dengie since 1973 with between five and 23 (in 1977) pairs recorded annually, although numbers have been lower during the 1990s. At Rainham, numbers increased during the 1990s to around 20 pairs recently. Counts from the Stort, principally between Bishop's Stortford and Harlow, and therefore not entirely in Essex, from 1974–82 revealed a population of 15–25 pairs. Here changes in vegetation on a flood alleviation scheme resulted in an increase in breeding numbers (Raven 1986). Otherwise maximum counts from the other principal sites have been: Ardleigh, ten, 1973; Fingringhoe Wick/Langenhoe, 12, 2002 and 2003; Abberton, 11, 1998 and 1999; Tollesbury Wick, 12–15, 2001; Goldhanger, 12, 1999; South Woodham Ferrers, 11, 2000 and 2001; St Osyth Priory Estate, ten, 2003; Wat Tyler CP, ten, 1986 and 1999. In addition, 16 pairs were noted throughout the gravel-pit complex around Maldon in 1983; similar numbers are probably present today (Simon Wood pers. obs.).

In late summer/early autumn, small flocks congregate on several waters across Essex; these may be moult gatherings (Cox). At Hanningfield, large flocks occurred in the early years after flooding. In 1955, 80–100 were present from mid-September to the end of October, whilst in 1957 there were 150–200 from late August to mid-October. The

largest ever gathering recorded in Essex, around 300, was present from late August to the end of October 1958 with 260–300 from mid-August to mid-September 1959. These are some of the largest gatherings observed in the Western Palearctic (*BWP*). A rich food source, created by the flooding of the reservoir, is likely to have been a significant factor in attracting such numbers. About 175 were noted on 21st August 1960 but such large gatherings have never been repeated. Since the mid-1970s, counts have generally peaked at 50–85 annually. At least 110 were on Ardleigh on 31st August 1976, with 90 there on 19th September 1971. Few large gatherings have been noted elsewhere, although

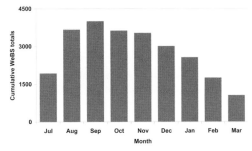

Seasonal occurrence of Little Grebes from 1985-2004

there were: 75 on East Tilbury GP, 5th October 2003; 67 at Walthamstow, 16th October 2004; 61 at Paglesham Lagoon, 5th September 2004; 60 at East Tilbury, September 1989; and 57 at Abberton, September 1989.

Little Grebes have only been counted on WeBS surveys since the mid-1980s and thus only relatively short-term trends can be discerned. Generally, numbers have increased although this may in part be due to increased observer coverage. For example, recent comprehensive counts of the many small waters in Metropolitan Essex have revealed a significant population in excess of 100, around 25% of the total population.

In winter, the majority of Little Grebes leave their summer haunts and frequent the more sheltered tidal waters (Vinicombe 1982). In Essex, however, a significant proportion of the wintering population is to be found on inland waters, particularly in Metropolitan Essex and the Lea Valley where up to 50% of the total has occurred in recent years. Also, Mason and Macdonald (2000c) found that it was likely that riverine populations of Little Grebes (and Mute Swans, Mallards and Moorhens) were larger overall than those on the main reservoirs and estuaries within the catchment (22 1km reaches of rivers in northern Essex and southern Suffolk).

Away from the sites mentioned in the WeBS table, there were 70–80 on the River Cam at Audley End on 10th December 1956.

A mid-winter population of 450 represents around 14% of the British-wintering population of 3,290 (Stone et al. 1997).

Many Little Grebes have been ringed at Abberton and most national ringing recoveries originate from there (Migration Atlas). One ringed on 1st November 1950 and subsequently found at Grand-Fort-Phillipe, Gravelines, France, on 22nd March 1951 was the first foreign recovery of a British-ringed Little Grebe. Others have been found in Germany, at Munster, 436km to the east and the Netherlands, implying that some wintering birds have a Continental origin. Within Britain, juveniles ringed at Abberton and presumably dispersing away from natal areas, have been found in: Lancashire, on Aintree Race course; Northamptonshire; Lincolnshire; Kent; Suffolk; and Norfolk. A total of 18 was ringed at Abberton between August and October 1992, none of which was re-trapped, suggesting a regular movement through the site not obvious from daily observations.

At present, the Little Grebe population seems to be steadily increasing as a result of the species' exploitation of the proliferation of gravel-pits and farm irrigation reservoirs. Ultimately, however, sympathetic management of new and existing habitat and the extent of pollution-free waters will determine the species' future in Essex.

Great Crested Grebe   *Podiceps cristatus*

Locally common resident, fairly common winter visitor and passage migrant

The Great Crested Grebe is found throughout Europe, Africa, west and central Asia, Australia and New Zealand; the nominate race *cristatus* is found in Europe and Asia. Most birds breed on large shallow waters with some fringing vegetation in which the nest is usually sited (Second National Atlas). West European populations have increased markedly in the 20th century, due probably to a combination of eutrophication of water bodies which increases small fish populations and reed beds,

Atlas	Survey Area	% of 10km squares or tetrads in which	
		bred/probably bred	possibly bred or present
First National 10km	Essex	42.1	5.3
Second National 10km	Essex	63.2	5.3
First London Tetrad	Met. Essex	8.5	3.0
Second London Tetrad	Met. Essex	21.5	7.0
Essex Tetrad	Essex	9.7	2.9

Summary of results of Atlas surveys for Great Crested Grebes

reservoir construction and reduced hunting pressures (European Atlas). In Britain, the species shows a preference for breeding in lowland areas (Second National Atlas), the population being around 8,000 individuals (Stone et al. 1997). Northern populations are fully migratory (European Atlas).

The first documented record involved one shot near Sudbury in 1838. From 1851 to the 1870s, extensive persecution to provide 'grebe-fur' that was made into ladies' boas and muffs decimated the British population (Historical Atlas). Christy knew of only one breeding record, at Walton-on-the-Naze in 1888 and described it as "An uncommon visitor, chiefly to our coast, from autumn to spring". Subsequent protection, brought about by a successful campaign by a group that went on to form the RSPB, allowed a recovery and rapid

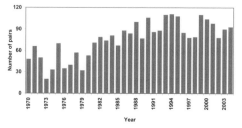

Reported annual totals of breeding pairs of
Great Crested Grebes from 1970-2004

expansion across the country. Glegg described the species as a common breeder having its main nucleus in the Lea Valley, a status that had "... altered during recent years in a very marked manner". National breeding censuses produced Essex totals of 97 adult birds in 1931 (Harrison & Hollom 1932), 271 in 1965 (Prestt & Mills 1966) and 194 in 1975 (Hughes *et al.* 1979), although these figures included some non-breeders.

Both Abberton and Hanningfield held exceptional breeding numbers in the early years after flooding, with peaks of 45 pairs in 1950 at the former and 115 in 1958 at the latter. Like Little Grebe, the species undoubtedly benefited from the considerable amount of small fish and insect larvae produced as a direct effect of the flooding. Such concentrations have not been repeated but, from a rather low base in the early 1970s, there has been a steady increase that was well illustrated by the two National Atlases. In Metropolitan Essex, there were significant increases between the two London Atlases due to the proliferation of small sand and gravel-pits,

GB 100 INT 1,500	1980-1984	1985-1989	1990-1994	1995-1999	2000-2004	Peak counts		Peak Month
WeBS totals	418^	665	788	852	810	Nov 89	1,098	Nov
Stour	92^	131	212	227	130	Nov 89	322	Oct
Hamford Water	~	5^	9	8	6	Nov 92	26	Nov
Colne	~	56^	34	20	7	Nov 95	67	Nov
Blackwater	~	97^	104	109	85	Nov 95	171	Nov
Dengie	~	47^	15	7	7	Sep 88	70	Sep
Crouch-Roach	~	3^	12	7	11	Oct 04	36	Nov
Thames	5^	17	24	15	29	Nov 92	49	Nov
Ardleigh	~	23^	96	87	48	Jul 90	120	Oct
Abberton	109^	178	117	205	129	Nov 89	303	Nov
Hanningfield	62*	133^	164	98	88	Nov 91	233	Sep
Lea Valley	276^	226	201	263	306	Sep 00	335	Oct
Met Essex Waters	~	~	~	~	86	Aug 03	114	Oct

Five-year average of peak WeBS counts (Jul-Nov) of Great Crested Grebes from 1980-2004

GB 100 INT 1,500	80/81-84/85	85/86-89/90	90/91-94/95	95/96-99/00	00/01-04/05	Peak counts		Peak Month
WeBS totals	272^	561	851	545	587^	Dec 92	1,040	Dec
Stour	42^	63	99	90	79^	Dec 91	146	Dec
Hamford Water	~	5*	11	12	8^	Feb 91	24	Dec
Colne	~	226^	231	40	21^	Feb 93	614	Feb
Blackwater	~	99^	88	63	69^	Feb 88	190	Mar
Dengie	~	41^	124	16	23^	Dec 91	312	Dec
Crouch-Roach	~	5^	19	17	9^	Mar 93	31	Mar
Thames	8^	29	55	29	60^	Mar 02	123	Dec
Ardleigh	~	26^	70	89	61^	Feb 98	171	Dec
Abberton	48^	109	75	73	57^	Dec 89	213	Dec
Hanningfield	~	89^	133	39	50^	Dec 93	298	Dec
Lea Valley	213^	161	144	201	237^	Dec 01	281	Dec
Met Essex Waters	~	~	~	~	76^	Mar 03	94	Dec

Five-year average of peak WeBS counts (Dec-Mar) of Great Crested Grebes from 1980/81-2003/04

whilst the Essex Atlas estimated a breeding population of 90–110 pairs, with a few other summering individuals usually present. About 110 pairs were reported in the *EBR* 1999; allowing for some under-recording the current population is perhaps in the region of 125–150 pairs.

The distribution map in the Essex Atlas, which confirmed the species' presence in 12.1% of all tetrads, with breeding in most, showed a cluster of occupied tetrads in the southwest, where many park lakes and flooded chalk and gravel-pits exist, and good representation across central Essex to the Colne Estuary. The most favoured sites in recent years have been in the Lea Valley (Holyfield Lake complex, Walthamstow, Fishers Green and Nazeing GP) and both Hanningfield and Ardleigh, all of which may hold from 10–20 pairs.

As early as June, non-breeding birds may gather at the main reservoirs. In autumn and early winter, there are sometimes impressive gatherings on the large reservoirs, although during the 1990s peak counts averaged somewhat lower than the previous 25 years; numbers in 2003, however, returned to pre-1990 levels. Maxima are: 551, Abberton, 18th October 1970; 500, Abberton, 22nd November 2003; and 500, Hanningfield, 30th September 1961. Ardleigh and the combined Lea Valley waters also host three-figure flocks occasionally. In general, winter numbers are slightly lower than in autumn although the extent varies from year to year. A total of 500 in the Lea Valley on 15th January 1967 is particularly notable.

Although the precise timing and distribution may vary, large concentrations on tidal waters have been a regular feature of the last 30 years. Recently, the Stour has attracted 100–300 from September to November/December with slightly lower peaks in the Blackwater at the same time. After the turn of the year, numbers tend to be the greatest in the Colne/Blackwater complex

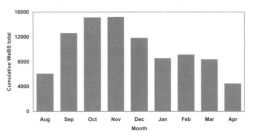

Seasonal occurrence of Great Crested Grebes from 1985-2004

and off the Dengie coast with a modest presence some years along the Thames. Record totals occurred in early 1989, with 600 off East Mersea and 500 off Bradwell on 22nd January and an estimated 1,300 or more in the whole county (all non-WeBS counts). Slightly lower peaks of 1,000+ were recorded in the winters of 1991/92 and 1992/93; there were 614 in the Colne on 7th February 1993.

The inclusion of recent counts from Metropolitan Essex appears to have masked a general decline in Great Crested Grebes over the last 15 years, with overall numbers similar to those 20 years ago. Nationally, maximum counts declined fairly steadily from 1992/93 (Cranswick *et al.* 1999), although 2000/01 saw the highest numbers yet recorded (Pollitt *et al.* 2003).

Overall, numbers peak in November and decline steadily thereafter, with data suggesting a passage through Essex in February.

Despite a significant number having been ringed at Abberton, there are, as yet, no recoveries to confirm long-distance movements involving Essex birds, the furthest being recovered in Lincolnshire; the bird in question was at least 12 years old when found dead on 3rd March 1978 and is currently the oldest ringed Great Crested Grebe to have been recovered in Britain. Nationally, however, there are several examples of individuals moving between Britain and neighbouring North Sea countries, so it is possible that birds of Continental origin visit Essex waters (Migration Atlas).

Like the Little Grebe, the Great Crested Grebe has benefited from the creation of gravel-pits and farm irrigation reservoirs. It should therefore continue to prosper provided that sympathetic management and pollution-free waters can be maintained.

Red-necked Grebe   *Podiceps grisegena*

Uncommon passage migrant and winter visitor   Amber List

The Red-necked Grebe is a Holarctic species that nests mainly in boreal, but also in temperate and steppe climatic zones (European Atlas). The nominate western race *grisegena* inhabits the Baltic area, central and eastern Europe, Turkey, Kazakhstan and western Siberia (Migration Atlas). Since 1988, occasional breeding attempts have been made in England and Scotland, with successful breeding first recorded in 2001 (RBBP 2003). In winter, the species becomes predominantly maritime, the largest numbers being found in the Baltic, off the central west coast of Norway, the North Sea and Dutch delta as well as the Black and Caspian Seas. Small numbers, in the region of 150 birds, winter off the south and east coasts of Britain between the Firth of Forth, Fife, and Poole Harbour, Dorset.

Christy described the species as a "… somewhat rare visitor, chiefly to our coast from autumn to spring". The first documented county record involved one at Wethersfield in the winter of 1837/38. Of the 11 or so records mentioned, six came from inland and three from the coast; on the Blackwater it was described as common. Christy noted: "One caught by a dog in a pool of water on the seashore at Dovercourt" and "Another … captured at Bradwell [-on-Sea], after half an hour's exciting chase …" Glegg reckoned that the species was recorded more frequently than the Slavonian Grebe and listed 13 records, including two together on the Lea Valley reservoirs in February 1924, 16th January 1926 and 27th November 1927.

Today, the Red-necked Grebe is the rarest of the three non-breeding grebes to visit Essex. Despite apparent declines at the edge of its breeding range (European Atlas), increasing numbers have summered in Britain since the 1970s. In 1997 a pair was present at Hanningfield from 26th May–8th June but, despite display being noted on one occasion, breeding was not attempted; one stayed into August. Single birds have summered on

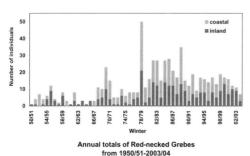

Annual totals of Red-necked Grebes
from 1950/51-2003/04

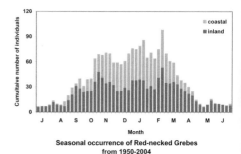

Seasonal occurrence of Red-necked Grebes
from 1950-2004

a further five occasions: Girling, 11th April–27th November 1982 and 20th February–12th November 1983 (possibly the same individual); KGV, 9th February–31st July 1985; and KGV and Girling, 1st June–16th August 1994 and intermittently during June and July 1998. A number of individuals have made brief appearances in June and July.

Overall, numbers have increased since the 1950s and particularly so since 1978/79, following an unprecedented influx involving around 49 birds that occurred as a result of a sustained spell of severe weather and easterly winds over the Continent (Chandler 1981). Around 60% occurred around the coast but records came from ten inland localities, all in the Lea Valley apart from Abberton and Hanningfield.

Prior to 1978/79, the average number occurring in each winter was about 6–7, but since then this has increased to around 15–20. The reasons for the increase remain unclear but, whilst increased observer coverage may be a factor, it is possible that—following the influx—Red-necked Grebes continued to return to Essex waters each year, thus resulting in a shift of part of the Continental wintering population.

Seven off Southend Pier on 27th December 1988 is the largest single site count to date, with six there on 26th November 1988 and six off St Osyth beach on 23rd November 1952. In early 1985 up to seven passed through Hanningfield.

Red-necked Grebes have been reported from the entire coast, from the Stour around to and including much of the Thames Estuary. No particular preference for any estuary is apparent.

Inland, records have come principally from the major reservoirs. Abberton has been the most favoured with records in 37 winters since 1950/51, all involving 1–2 birds. At Hanningfield, records have occurred in 33 winters with four on 21st–22nd October 1991 the highest count. In the Lea Valley, the species occurs almost annually and, whilst most records have come from the main reservoirs, some have occurred at other regularly watched sites. Away from these three localities the species is rare.

Normally, individuals begin to arrive in September with numbers peaking initially in late October and early November. Whether early migrants stay to winter in Essex is not known and indeed the fact that individuals probably wander throughout the county during winter makes an accurate assessment of numbers difficult. Peak winter counts are generally attained by the end of December and remain fairly stable until February, at which time, inland at least, there are signs of a return passage.

Very little ringing information is available for the species and little is known of the Red-necked Grebe's movements in Europe (Migration Atlas). It is assumed that most Essex individuals are from the Swedish, Finnish and Baltic populations.

Slavonian Grebe *Podiceps auritus*

Locally common passage migrant and winter visitor Amber List

The Slavonian Grebe is a boreal, almost circumpolar, species and the most northerly breeding grebe. The species prefers shallow, fairly small eutrophic lakes but other habitats are used, even man-made gravel-pits. In western Europe outside Russia, the principal breeding areas are in Norway, Sweden and Denmark. A marked range expansion has occurred since 1900, although local declines have been noted (European Atlas). Slavonian Grebes have bred in the Scottish Highlands since 1908 where there are currently around 46 pairs (RBBP 2004). Scottish birds show characteristics of the race *arcticus*, which also breeds

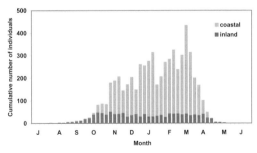

Seasonal occurrence of Slavonian Grebes from 1950-2004

in Iceland and northern Norway; the nominate race *auritus* breeds elsewhere in Europe (Migration Atlas). In winter, European populations move to the North Sea, southern Baltic, and lakes of central Europe and the Mediterranean (European Atlas).

Christy described the species as an uncommon winter visitor, chiefly to the coast, although the first documented county record involved one shot at Audley End in 1838. One of his correspondents, however, described the species as "… common in Essex, especially on the Blackwater". Glegg considered the Slavonian Grebe to be the rarest of the three non-breeding grebes and detailed just seven records. Hudson & Pyman felt that the species was more common than the Red-necked but scarcer than the Black-necked Grebe. This apparent increase in numbers may perhaps be linked to the range expansion across Europe. Since the late 1960s, it has been the commonest of the three rarer grebes, principally due to the large numbers found on the Blackwater in late winter/early spring (Cox). However, numbers here have in general declined from the peaks seen in the early 1980s.

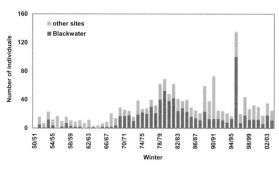

Annual totals of Slavonian Grebes from 1950/51-2003/04

The significant peak in 1995/96 was due to an unprecedented flock of 100 in the Blackwater on 16th March 1996, one of the largest flocks ever reported in the country and equivalent to about 25% of the estimated British wintering population. Otherwise the highest counts have been: 56 off Dengie, 20th January 1991; 52 in the Blackwater, 16th March 1980; 42 off Dengie, 11th December 1988; and 42 in the Blackwater, 7th March 1982. Apart from the huge count in 1996, numbers present in Essex appear to follow a ten-year cycle with peaks occurring around 1970, 1980 and 1990. The recent decline in the Blackwater may be due to the flock moving southeast to waters off Dengie (cf. Common Scoter), as high counts there have coincided with smaller numbers in the Blackwater. Around other parts of the coast, numbers have generally been small, although there were 11 off Wakering Stairs on 13th March 1982. Individuals are regularly recorded within the inner Thames.

On the coast, records after mid-April and before mid-October are rare. Inland, however, small numbers regularly occur until early May and again from late July with passage through inland waters peaking during October and November and small numbers occurring throughout winter. Abberton and Hanningfield are the most regularly visited with peak counts of five (4th January 1952 and 16th March 1961) at the former and four (4th November 1973, 11th November 1976, 14th December 1986, 20th December 1987, 20th February 2000 and 14th–28th April 2000) at the latter. The species is also regular in the Lea Valley, the highest counts being four on KGV on 10th April 1979 and at Walthamstow from 14th–17th March 1956.

The Slavonian Grebe tends to arrive later than the Black-necked Grebe, with numbers peaking in late spring, perhaps as birds from further south head north.

The sole mid-summer record involved one at Walthamstow on 16th June 1934. Otherwise, extreme dates are 20th May in 1981 and 28th July in 1985, both at Abberton. It has been suggested, with some supporting evidence, that individuals of the nominate race winter predominately off the east coast of Britain, along the Dutch coast and off Denmark (Migration Atlas).

Black-necked Grebe

Podiceps nigricollis

Locally common passage migrant and winter visitor - single pairs bred annually from 1999–2002   Amber List

The Black-necked Grebe is a colonial breeding species found from Spain east to China, in southern and eastern Africa, and central and western North America. In Europe, the species' core range runs from central France to southern Russia, with 70% of the European population found in the Ukraine and southern Russia. The Black-necked Grebe is a scarce breeder in the west of its range. The nominate race *nigricollis* occurs in Europe (European Atlas). In Britain, around 20–50 pairs breed annually (RBBP 2004), principally in central and northern England. In winter, European birds disperse widely, but most are found in the Mediterranean, Black, southern Caspian and northern Red Seas and on Turkish lakes, with far smaller numbers along Atlantic and North Sea coasts (European Atlas).

Of previous avifauna authors, only Cox referred to any breeding season records, a pair displaying at Abberton from 10th June–14th July 1973. However, with the steady increase in the British population, a corresponding rise in breeding season records has occurred, although it was not until the very end of the 1990s that such occurrences became annual. Initially, odd birds occurring for just a few days in suitable breeding habitat were involved.

In May 1991, breeding behaviour was noted at three sites, perhaps only two pairs being involved: at Abberton a pair present from 10th–26th was carrying nesting material on several days but then left; at Paglesham Lagoon a displaying pair was present from 6th–9th; and at East Tilbury a pair was nest-building from 19th–30th. Three birds were at Abberton on 20th June 1993, and one was at Hanningfield on 27th June 1993. In 1997 two were at Abberton on 3rd June, with one on 29th, and at Hanningfield there were three on 5th June. It was not

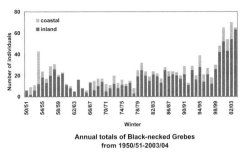

Annual totals of Black-necked Grebes
from 1950/51-2003/04

until 1999 that breeding finally occurred, albeit unsuccessfully, when a pair nested on a farm reservoir in northeast Essex. Two eggs were laid but the nest was subsequently deserted. In 2000 three adults frequented a gravel-pit in eastern Essex; their behaviour suggested that breeding had occurred (one disappeared for about 20 days), but a sudden fall in water levels may have caused any nest to be lost. Successful breeding took place in 2001 when a pair raised two young on a small lake in Metropolitan Essex (Morrison 2002). What was assumed to be the same pair returned in 2002 and raised a further two young.

Christy described the species as an uncommon winter visitor, the first documented Essex record being one shot on the coast between 1811 and 1821. Amongst a handful of records he detailed were "A young male in poor condition … taken on the lake in Debden after an hour's chase on 15th October 1881" and "… one … taken from a Water Rat's hole, into which it had been seen to creep for shelter". Black-necked Grebes were considered common on the Blackwater in the latter decades of the 19th century and "… not rare at Mersea in winter". Glegg considered the Black-necked Grebe the commonest of the three non-breeding grebes and almost certainly of annual occurrence in the Blackwater; his review of the records of both Black-necked and Slavonian Grebes showed that the former were recorded more regularly on the coast than the latter, a clear reversal of the situation today. Indeed, two flocks totalling some 35 individuals were counted on the Blackwater on 20th December 1928. Like Glegg, Hudson & Pyman described the species as the commonest of the rarer grebes but noted that it had become far more irregular in the Blackwater, perhaps due to the counter attraction of Abberton. Whilst the possibility of misidentification must be borne in mind, it should be noted that a flock of 20 off East Mersea on 4th April 1954 included five in full breeding plumage. Given that Black-necked Grebes occur in even larger numbers on tidal waters elsewhere—for example Langstone Harbour, Hampshire, regularly holds up to 30% of the current British wintering population—it does seem likely that the significant increase in reservoirs over the last 50 years has attracted Black-necked Grebes away from the estuaries to inland freshwater sites (Cox).

After relatively high numbers in the 1950s, a general decline was evident during the 1960s and 1970s since when an increase has taken place, particularly at the end of the 20th century. This trend is in line with the general increase that has occurred in Britain as part of a general spread north and west through Europe during the 20th century (*BWP*).

The increase since 1998/99 has been largely due to significantly greater numbers occurring in the Lea Valley, and particularly at Girling, during autumn and winter. From the mid-1970s Girling was known principally as the species' main wintering site in Essex with 3–5 usually present although, after becoming more erratic in occurrence in the early 1990s, the winter of 1993/94 became the first in almost 30 years that Black-necked Grebes were not present. Numbers remained low until an influx occurred in autumn 1998 that built to a peak of 13 on 2nd October (equalling the largest count previously recorded in Essex at Abberton on 24th November 1957). None, however, wintered but a return passage saw six during March 1999. In autumn 1999 the peak was 16 on 14th October with two overwintering. In autumn 2000 a total of 28 was present on 14th November, including 17 on Girling, seven on Walthamstow and four on KGV; a total of 14 was still present on Girling on 16th December, with 10–11 during January and February. By 2001, Girling was established as the principal site, with a peak of 18 on 23rd October 2001 and 10–13 during January and February 2002. By far the largest ever site count was made in autumn 2002: 25 at Girling on 31st October; 13 wintered. Subsequently, there has been a wintering population of around 15 individuals. In the same period, there has not been a significant increase at either Abberton or Hanningfield.

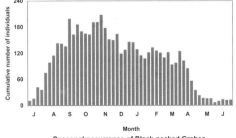

Seasonal occurrence of Black-necked Grebes
from 1950-2004

Although most Black-necked Grebes occur on inland waters, small numbers continue to be reported from around the coast, and the mouth of the

No. of winters with records		Peak counts in each decade						Date of highest count
		1950s	1960s	1970s	1980s	1990s	2000s	
Abberton	50	13	4	3	5	6	7	24/11/1957
Hanningfield	46	5	3	5	6	6	12	01/04/2004
Girling	44	4	3	6	7	13	25	21/10/2002

Summary of inland records of Black-necked Grebes from 1950–2004

Blackwater, especially from Tollesbury Wick to Rolls Farm, continues to be favoured. Since 1950 rarely more than 1–4 have been reported together. Apart from the count off Mersea Island in 1954 (see above), the only counts of five or more have been: 5–6 off St Osyth beach, 20th–22nd December 1956; eight in Bridgemarsh Creek, 13th January 1968, with six still there in early February and six from 28th–31st December; six in the Althorne area, 5th February 1973; and six off Rolls Farm, 5th November 2002.

Black-necked Grebes tend to arrive earlier in Essex than Slavonian Grebes and also show a more distinct peak during the late autumn period, after which numbers decline to a relatively stable winter population. Birds apparently remain loyal to a site throughout the winter unless forced to move by extreme weather. Return passage is evident in March and April.

The first Black-necked Grebe to be trapped and ringed in Britain was caught at Abberton on 23rd December 1969, one of only eight ringed in Britain to the end of 1997: recoveries of individuals in Britain that had been ringed in Europe suggest that those wintering in southeast England may originate from Europe (Migration Atlas).

(Northern) Fulmar *Fulmarus glacialis*

Fairly common non-breeding visitor and passage migrant Amber List

The nominate race of Fulmar, *glacialis*, breeds in Svalbard, the Barent Sea, Jan Mayen, the Faeroe Islands, Britain, Ireland, Norway, Helgoland, Normandy and Brittany, as well as western Greenland and the islands of the eastern Canadian Arctic (Migration Atlas). Over the last 250 years the Fulmar has undergone a dramatic population increase and range expansion. It has spread from its original boreal distribution in Iceland to the Faeroe Islands and subsequently all around the coast of Britain and Ireland and to small colonies elsewhere in northwest Europe. There are now 506,000 pairs breeding in Britain (Mitchell *et al.* 2004). Southeast England remains the least densely populated region, although an expansion has occurred here too with, significantly, the first successful breeding in Suffolk in 1983. Up to 40 have frequented a site at Bawdsey, Suffolk, only a few kilometres north of the county boundary (Piotrowski 2003).

Although the Fulmar is now a regular visitor to coastal waters, principally from mid-March to September, prior to the 1950s this was not the case. Christy described the Fulmar as a rare winter visitor and detailed just four records, the first being killed at Chrishall in 1834. Glegg added just three more records. Since 1951 the species has occurred annually (Hudson & Pyman) with numbers steadily increasing since the late 1960s. Fulmars are most regular off the northeast coast, probably because of the area's proximity to the Suffolk breeding sites.

Although the Fulmar has been described as "prospecting" the cliffs and occasionally the block of flats at The Naze, there is no evidence to date of any serious breeding attempt.

Fulmars occur in every month, but between October and February reports are infrequent and rarely involve more than 1–2 individuals, although there have been occasional reports of up to seven and one report of 12 flying north past The Naze in one hour on 23rd February 1986. Six Fulmar corpses were also found along the adjacent coastline that day, with another four elsewhere soon after. The largest ever wreck occurred in early March 1962 when, following a series of easterly gales, more than 40 corpses were found. A significant proportion of records during the 1950s and 1960s involved dead birds.

Currently, reports become more frequent from around mid-March, with a regular presence through to September, although sightings were significantly higher than the norm in October 2003. Land-based observations suggest that fewer are present during mid-summer. This pattern is repeated offshore where a few interested fishermen have logged sightings, principally from Harwich south to Dengie. Total numbers are impossible to calculate, as it is not known to what extent the same individuals are seen repeatedly, but there is a presence of a few birds, possibly no more than

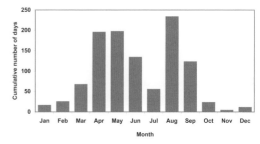

Number of days per month that Fulmars have been recorded from 1971-2004

ten, on most days throughout summer. Single day counts of ten or more have been recorded just ten times—and from just two areas—by land-based observers: The Naze, ten on 2nd September 1962, 12 on 23rd February 1986, 13 on 28th April 2002, 14 on 25th August 1995 and 16 on 30th August 1997; Southend Pier/Canvey Island, ten on 18th and 21st September 1996 and 14th October 2003, 12 on 7th September 1993 and 14 on 10th September 1989. Although numbers offshore are generally higher, double-figure counts are far from regular. Further offshore still, 100 were about 40km from the coast on 14th–15th March 1988, 120 some 40–50km offshore on 5th June 1991 and 138 in the mouth of the Thames near the Kentish Knock Lightship on 15th May 2003; such numbers may be more regular here.

From time to time, individuals penetrate some distance up the estuaries and, in particular, records are now annual from the Thames as far upstream as Canvey Island and sometimes East Tilbury, especially in late July and August or following northeasterly gales in September.

Inland sightings are rare. Of just 17 since 1950, six came from Hanningfield, including two on 1st August 1986, and three from Abberton, with singles from Girling, KGV and Walthamstow. In addition, singles have been recorded at: Rowney Wood, Debden, 30th August 1952; Holyfield Marsh, 10th–11th April 1986; Matching Green, Harlow, 12th June 1997; and Newport, freshly dead, 13th April 2004. All inland records have fallen in the period March–June or August except for one at Girling on 1st January 1979.

Single examples of the blue colour phase that form the majority of populations in the High Arctic have occurred three times: The Naze on 10th August 1981 and 17th August 1983; and offshore off the northeast coast on 21st April 2001.

Information on the origins of Essex Fulmars is limited to one ringed as a nestling on North Ronaldsay, Orkney, that was found dead at Holland Haven on 18th January 1997. This may give an indication of the origins of the very few birds wintering off the coast. After fledging, young Fulmars spend perhaps four years at sea and disperse widely; they may never visit land in that time (Migration Atlas).

Cory's Shearwater   *Calonectris diomedea*

Vagrant: four records

The Cory's Shearwater breeds on islands in the Mediterranean and off the coast of northwest Africa and winters principally through the central and southern Atlantic Ocean. The nominate race *diomedea* breeds on Mediterranean islands, whilst *borealis* breeds on the Azores, Madeira, Canary and Berlinga Islands.

1978	Foulness	24th September
1989	Bradwell	10th September
	East Tilbury and	
	Canvey Island	22nd November
1999	Coate Outfall, Dengie	26th September

Although relatively common in most years off the western seaboard of Britain in late summer and early autumn, only small numbers move into the southern North Sea. However, Cory's Shearwaters have become more common over the last decade or so with greater numbers recorded from the North Sea than was traditional, possibly as a result of increased observer coverage. Remarkably, the East Tilbury bird was first seen swimming alongside barges marked "CORY"! Nationally, 1999 was the second-best year on record (Fraser & Rogers 2005). The East Tilbury individual was particularly late as numbers usually peak in August and September.

In addition, the following large shearwaters were probably Cory's: Foulness, 19th September 1987; St Osyth, 8th September 1993; and Deal Hall, Dengie, two, 12th October 2003.

Great Shearwater   *Puffinus gravis*

Vagrant: two records

The monotypic Great Shearwater breeds at just four sites (*HBW*) in the south Atlantic in the austral summer, then migrates northwest on a circular route up the eastern American seaboard as far as Nova Scotia, across the Atlantic to western Europe, down to the African coast and then south to its breeding islands.

| 1990 | Stour Estuary | 22nd September (from Landguard Point, Suffolk) |
| 1995 | offshore Maplin | 11th September |

Both were following fishing boats. The species typically occurs off the western seaboard of Britain, sometimes in greater numbers than Cory's Shearwater with numbers peaking in August and September. Very few are recorded in the North Sea. Nationally, numbers were unexceptional in both years.

Christy referred to one shot at Debden around 1870 but gave no further information. In addition, Christy (1903) described the species as "An occasional autumn and winter visitor", but without further comment; this must have been a mistake. Glegg dismissed the records.

Sooty Shearwater   *Puffinus griseus*

Uncommon passage migrant – one June record

The monotypic Sooty Shearwater breeds on islands off South America, Australia and New Zealand. It is a transequatorial migrant, which moves into the north Pacific (where it is more abundant) and the north Atlantic. Large numbers head first for the northwest sector of the respective ocean and then move east with the prevailing winds, so that they arrive along the west coast of Europe late in the local summer, before heading south again (*HBW*).

The first documented Essex record was not until 1969, when one was off Brightlingsea on 1st October and Colne Point the next day, with two more offshore later in the month. Increased observer coverage has probably been responsible for the upsurge in records, Sooty Shearwaters having been recorded annually since 1985. At least 163 had occurred up to the end of 2004, with the highest annual totals being 65–70 in an unprecedented influx in 2002, 11 in 2003 and ten in 2000. Numbers vary considerably from year to year probably due to weather conditions: most occur after gales, often with an easterly element, but some have occurred after strong

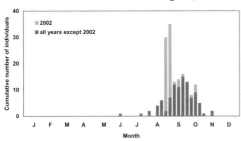

Seasonal occurrence of Sooty Shearwaters
from 1969-2004

northerlies and a few on quiet, warm days with only moderate onshore breezes. The 2002 influx coincided with unprecedented numbers, perhaps as many as 10,000, moving into the North Sea during September (*Birding World* 15: 355).

The earliest Sooty Shearwater was off Maplin on 16th June 1979 and the latest off Colne Point on 17th November 1997. The majority occur in September.

The September 2002 influx saw peak counts of eight off Canvey Island and 11 off The Naze/Walton Pier on 1st and 15 off the latter on the 9th with four off The Naze/Walton Pier, Holland Haven and Bradwell on 2nd. Otherwise, the only other counts of 4+ have been five off Holland Haven on 14th September 1994 and six off Canvey Island on 30th September 2000. The largest number recorded on any one day is around 20 on 9th September 2002.

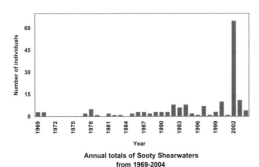

Annual totals of Sooty Shearwaters
from 1969-2004

The majority of the records have come from the northeast coast, particularly The Naze and Holland Haven, with most others coming from the Thames Estuary where singles have occurred as far upriver as East Tilbury on 11th October 1988 and 19th October 1991.

Sponsored by Simon Cox

Manx Shearwater

Puffinus puffinus

Uncommon, principally autumn passage migrant

Amber List

Approximately 81% of the World population of 350,000–390,000 pairs (Mitchell *et al.* 2004) of the monotypic Manx Shearwater breed in western Britain, particularly on the islands of Rhum, northwest Scotland (the largest breeding colony in the world), and Skokholm and Skomer Islands, Wales. Other large colonies occur in Iceland, Ireland and the Faeroe Islands (European Atlas). All large colonies are on rat-free islands or on cliffs inaccessible to them. In July, after breeding, adults move south to winter off eastern South America with juveniles following in September.

Christy detailed just three definite records, all inland, the earliest being one found at Epping on 21st September 1866, although a shearwater picked up dead at Epping prior to 1835 may have been a Manx. Glegg added five records, including two inland. There were just two more prior to 1950, since when a total of 336 has occurred, although there were just three from 1950–65. It was not until the advent of modern optics, increased interest in sea-watching and the presence of several birding-orientated fishermen working our offshore waters that the species' true status became apparent.

Numbers occurring each year fluctuate markedly, as would be expected of a species that is uncommon in the southern North Sea, and it is the occurrence of gales with an easterly and/or northerly element at the appropriate time of year that drives those that do make it this far south, near enough for land-based observers to see them. The largest influxes occurred in 1997 (40), 1988 (36) and 1987 (34). There were nine off Canvey Island on 14th September 1994, 8–10 off Colne Point on 19th September 1987 and nine off Brightlingsea on 9th September 2002, with seven off Maplin Sands on 9th September 1987. The highest Essex day totals are: 23–25 on 19th September 1987; 19 on 9th September 2002; 13 on 14th September 1994; and nine on 26th September 1981.

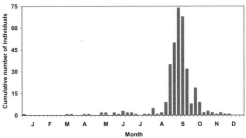

Seasonal occurrence of Manx Shearwaters from 1950-2004

Around 75% of all records occur in September. Nationally, records between December and February are rare, so it is not surprising that there are just two county records: off Southend Pier on 4th January 1997; and off Wakering Stairs on 7th December 2003, a year in which passage was generally late with four off Southend Pier on 16th October being unusual. Otherwise, extreme dates are 15th March (off Southend Pier in 1992) and 27th November (3km off The Naze in 1967).

Records have occurred all around the coast, although recently the majority have come from the well-watched Thames Estuary where the species has been recorded as far upriver as Rainham on 29th May 1987 and 28th August 1994, and Dagenham Reach on 11th September 1976 (a sick bird).

There have been 21 inland records since 1950, from 15 widely scattered localities. Singles have been recorded on three occasions at both Hanningfield (9th September 1983, 31st August–4th September 1988

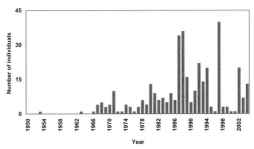

Annual totals of Manx Shearwaters from 1950-2004

and 2nd September 1997) and KGV (20th September 1987, 29th August 1988 and 30th July 1991) with two recorded from Weeley (15th September 1980 and 22nd September 1992). Singles, unless stated otherwise, have been reported from: Cooksmill Green, Writtle, 13th September 1963; Loughton, 11th November 1978; Plaistow, 12th September 1980; Girling, two (one dead), 14th September 1980; Mount Bures, 1st September 1982 (dead); Great Bromley in 1982; Little Baddow, 8th September 1985; Sheering, 16th September 1985; Brentwood in 1985; Stanway Green, 6th September 1988; White Roding, 19th September 1989; Romford High Street, 11th September 1998; Hornchurch, "September" 2004. The Plaistow individual had been ringed at Penally, Dyfed, Wales, on 2nd September 1980: nationally, inland records have involved individuals ringed at the major west coast colonies, such as Skokholm Island, Wales. Those off the Essex coast are more likely to originate from the large colonies in the Firth of Forth, Scotland.

Balearic Shearwater   *Puffinus mauretanicus*

Very rare passage migrant: nine records

The monotypic Balearic Shearwater breeds around the Balearic Islands in the western Mediterranean with 70% of the population on Formentera (European Atlas). After breeding, almost the entire population moves north into the Atlantic, with most moulting in the Bay of Biscay; some move further north into the western English Channel (Hobbs 2003).

1975	Foulness	28th September
1978	Foulness	1st October
1980	Bradwell	16th September
1992	Canvey Island	17th September
1994	East Tilbury	11th July
	Canvey Island	14th September
1996	Canvey Island	4th August
1998	Canvey Island	10th September
2000	Foulness	29th May

In 2002 Balearic Shearwater was split from Mediterranean Shearwater *P. yelkouan* (Sangster *et al.* 2002), the latter having been split from Manx Shearwater in 1991. Most occur at the time of peak Manx Shearwater passage. The May record is particularly early as numbers generally peak in July and August in southern and western Britain. Few have been reported in Suffolk (Piotrowski 2003) but more than 150 have been recorded in both Kent and Norfolk.

(European) Storm-petrel   *Hydrobates pelagicus*

Rare passage migrant: substantial influx in 2000   Amber List

The monotypic European Storm-petrel is a pelagic species that is endemic to the Western Palearctic, being found along the rocky European coasts of the Atlantic Ocean and Mediterranean Sea (European Atlas). Like all petrels it is extremely difficult to census. The British population, which nests on rocky islands in the west, numbers some 21,000–34,000 pairs (Mitchell *et al.* 2004). After breeding, the species disperses into the open ocean and migrates south to winter principally off the coasts of western and southern Africa.

The first documented Essex specimen was shot at Walthamstow at the end of the 18th century (Christy). Another occurred on the Stour on the unusual date of 29th May 1820 and one was taken at Marshhouse Decoy, Dengie, on an unknown date. At Harwich in the late 19th century "... some are seen every winter"; several were in the harbour on 29th October 1880. One was picked up at Audley End in 1836, as was another at Elmdon prior to 1845. Between 1880 and 1887, the European Storm-petrel was reported from the Swin, Galloper and Kentish Knock Lightships, "a dozen" being noted from the Galloper on 6th November 1880. Glegg added records of one shot on the Stour on 20th November 1893 and another taken at Colchester around 22nd November 1902. One preserved by a Braintree taxidermist may have come from Essex. It seems, even from the small number of records, that the European Storm-petrel was perhaps more common in the 19th century than today; this was certainly the case in Norfolk and Suffolk (Taylor *et al.* 1999, Piotrowski 2003).

The next record was not until 1955, since when at least 53 have occurred, with 25 in 2000 and the most in any other year being just four, in 1983. All records are of singles unless stated otherwise:

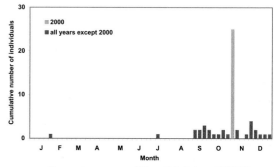

Seasonal occurrence of Storm Petrels from 1950-2004

1955	Abberton	1st October	
1956	Epping Forest	9th December	
1962	Woodford Green	26th November	
1964	KGV	25th December	
1965	Tollesbury Wick	7th November	
1966	Walthamstow	23rd October	
1972	off Clacton-on-Sea	17th December	
1974	St Osyth	February	dead
	Maplin Sands	18th September	
1977	Hamford Water	11th October	moribund
1978	Tilbury Docks	about 7th November	died in care on 13th
	off Clacton	29th November	
1979	Bradwell	30th September	
1983	Girling	3rd September	
	Bradwell	23rd October	
	Rolls Farm, Tollesbury	6th November	
	Colne Estuary	mid-December	
1985	off Frinton-on-Sea	19th October	
1986	Hanningfield	11th September	
	The Naze	13th September	
1987	Dengie	19th September	
	Colne Point and Estuary	30th September	
1990	Becontree, Dagenham	8th December	
1991	Parkeston	27th November	exhausted
1992	West Thurrock	14th July	
1994	Colne Point	29th November	
1998	Marshhouse Outfall, Dengie	20th September	
2000	Jaywick	30th October	3–4
	Canvey Island	30th October	15–20
	Barking Bay/Creekmouth	30th October	
	Hanningfield	30th October	Three
		31st October	
	Canvey Island	31st October	
	Rainham	31st October	Two
2004	Canvey Island	7th September	
		11th October	

In addition, several were noted 65km off the coast in May 1979. It is only recently, due to increased seawatching, that the species has been seen by land-based observers, rather than from fishing boats offshore or picked up, wrecked inland (excluding 2000, almost 25% of records occurred inland). It is usually only in, or shortly after extreme weather, particularly gales with an easterly or northerly element, that European Storm-petrels are reported. However, still, foggy conditions have been known to cause individuals to become lost: the 1983 record involved one flying east out of the Blackwater Estuary as fog dispersed. Numbers recorded in Suffolk from 1950–99 were remarkably similar to those in Essex, 28 being noted (Piotrowski 2003), compared with 27 in Essex.

The exceptional 2000 influx saw more recorded in a two-day period than in the previous 50 years. It is possible that two periods of severe southwesterlies that originated deep in the eastern Atlantic and Bay of Biscay at a time when many European Storm-petrels were in those areas, swept them up the English Channel and into the North Sea (Bond 2001). Numbers in Suffolk were unexceptional (Piotrowski 2003), which suggests that Essex was on the northern limit of the influx.

Since 1950 all records have fallen in the period September–December, apart from the corpse at St Osyth in February and one at Thurrock in July.

Although European Storm-petrels have occurred all around the coast, it is surprising that prior to the 2000 influx just three had occurred in the Thames Estuary.

Leach's Storm-petrel

Oceanodroma leucorhoa

Scarce, principally autumn passage migrant

Amber List

Leach's Storm-petrels breed on oceanic islands in the north Atlantic and north Pacific. The nominate race *leucorhoa* occurs in Europe (*HBW*), where the species probably has a more oceanic distribution than any other, breeding only on Atlantic islands comparatively close to the edge of the Continental shelf (European Atlas). The principal British colonies are in northwest Scotland. The species is notoriously difficult to census, as it only returns to its burrow at night, having spent the day feeding beyond the Continental shelf. The total British population of 36,000–65,000 pairs (Mitchell *et al.* 2004) is only a small propor-

Seasonal occurrence of Leach's Petrels from 1950-2004

tion of the estimated 7–9 million pairs worldwide. Western Palearctic populations move south after breeding and winter off the west coast of Africa.

The first documented Essex record involved one taken alive on the coast in November 1823, to which Christy added five inland occurrences and one near Bow Creek on the inner Thames. In addition, it was sometimes seen in Harwich harbour during winter. One record in early December 1867 is worth detailing: "... during the first week of Dec., 1867, which was exceedingly rough and stormy, a boy was cleaning an engine at the Colchester Railway Station about five o'clock in the morning, when a bird of this species flew against his lantern with great force and was stunned". Glegg added just three coastal records, the last in 1922. Leach's Storm-petrels therefore appear to have been less common than European Storm-petrels in the 19th and early 20th centuries.

The next record was in October 1952 when six occurred following a wreck in the southwest of England after severe westerly gales (Boyd 1954). The species, however, remained very rare until the late 1970s but thereafter, with the increase in seawatching, it was revealed as an almost annual visitor, albeit in very small numbers. A total of 193 was recorded in the period 1952–2004; 105 occurred in Suffolk between 1950 and 2000 (Piotrowski 2003). There have been four significant influxes: 44 in 1997, 23% of the 53 year total; 32 in 2004; 20 in 2003; and 19 in 1989.

The 1997 influx occurred around the 18th–21st September and included nine off Dengie on 21st and six on 19th. Day totals of ten occurred on 19th, 11 on 20th and 12 on 21st September. In 2004 there was a total of 14 on 10th October and 12 on 12th October. Ten off Southend Pier on 10th September 1989 is the largest single site count with other totals of six coming from Canvey Island on 21st October 1999, 13th October 2003, and 10th and 12th October 2004.

Leach's Storm-petrels have occurred all around the coast, although in recent years most have been recorded from the Thames, with Canvey Island and East Tilbury particularly favoured. Four have been recorded off Rainham and two from Barking, on 4th September 1983 and 21st October 1989.

There have been 21 inland records, mostly from the large reservoirs, with those in the Lea Valley particularly favoured: Girling, two, 3rd September 1983 and singles on 2nd October 1977, 27th September 1989, 12th November

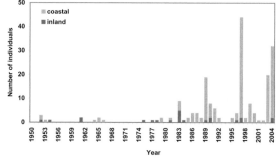

Annual totals of Leach's Petrels from 1950-2004

1997 and 8th November 2004; KGV, singles, 26th April 1981 (the only Essex spring record), 3rd September 1983, 22nd September 1990 and 12th November 1997 (same date as at Girling); and Waltham Abbey GP, 25th November 1984. Away from the Lea Valley there have been records from: Hanningfield, 8th November 1975, 8th September 1983 (dead), 8th September 1990, 29th October 1996 and 1st November

2004; Abberton, 7th November 1952, 24th September 1961 and 3rd October 1997; Romford, 2nd November 1954; Felsted, 19th October 1961 (long dead); and Cressing, 29th September 1978.

Most Leach's Storm-petrels occur between September and November, with peaks in mid-September and mid-October: does this suggest different origins for the influxes? Most records occur after gales, usually from a north or easterly direction, although some have occurred after severe southwesterlies.

There have been no ringing recoveries involving Essex. Nationally, the only recoveries have involved the Faeroe Islands and Iceland. The fact that the species often occurs in Britain with Sabine's Gulls after the passage of vigorous westerly depressions suggests that some autumn birds may be from the Canadian population displaced eastward into the Atlantic Ocean by westerly gales. Virtually no ringing of this population has occurred.

(Northern) Gannet

Morus bassanus

Common passage migrant

Amber List

The monotypic Gannet is restricted mainly to the temperate waters of the North Atlantic and adjoining seas. In the east, its range covers Norway, Iceland, Britain and Ireland, and northern France (European Atlas). Approximately 54% of the world population (72% of the European) breeds in British waters, mostly in huge colonies off the west coast, the largest being St Kilda with 60,000 pairs. Somewhat fewer colonies occur on the east coast, the largest being 48,000 on Bass Rock, Lothian (Wanless *et al.* 2005). The Gannet population increased by about 3% per annum during the 20th century (Nelson 1978),

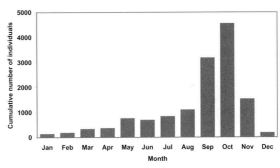

Seasonal occurrence of Gannets from 1981-2004

although the rate of increase has now slowed; reduced human persecution and climate improvements may have aided this increase.

Christy described the Gannet as "A fairly-common bird on the coast from autumn to spring … After severe storms in winter, it is sometimes found in an exhausted state far inland". He listed some ten records, the earliest "… picked up in the snow at Terling…" in 1830. Six came from inland, including one caught alive at Willingale on 10th December 1881, which "… was very savage, and bit a piece out of the hand of its captor". At Harwich "A few are seen every year". Glegg considered the species an occasional visitor to the coast and added a further nine records, including three inland. He noted that it was probably more frequent farther from the coast; adult Gannets were seen moving south from the Kentish Knock Lightship during September and October 1903.

In the mid-1960s the Gannet was considered a scarce but regular visitor (Hudson & Pyman) with annual totals rarely exceeding ten, although 37 (22 offshore) occurred in 1961 and "large numbers" were reported 8km off Brightlingsea in January and February 1964. Many coastal records involved dead, sick or oiled individuals. From the late 1960s, one birding-orientated fisherman collected many offshore records; his reports continue to provide a pattern of offshore numbers to this day.

It was not until 1970 that the first land-based double-figure counts occurred with 17 off St Osyth/Clacton-on-Sea on 15th October, whilst six days later 31 flew east out of the Thames in strong northwesterlies. Increasing observer coverage and the awareness that strong winds with a northerly element caused coastal sea bird movements, saw increasing numbers reported and by the end of the decade the first land-based three-figure count occurred with 200 moving northeast off Foulness Point on

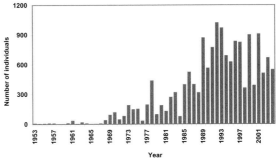

Annual totals of Gannets from 1953-2004

1st October 1978 during strong northerlies. Offshore, at least 100 were between Walton and St Osyth on 3rd October 1977, a calm day following 48 hours of northwesterly gales.

Counts continued to increase during the 1980s, especially following the discovery of the importance of the Thames as a seabird migration route. In 1986, 200 flew out of the Thames in a northerly gale on 2nd November and in 1989, during a period of northeasterlies, 151 passed Canvey Island on 9th September and 171 passed Southend Pier on 10th September.

Although increased coverage must be a significant factor in the greater numbers observed, the Bass Rock gannetry increased from 8,077 pairs in 1968–70 to 48,065 in 2004 (Wanless *et al.* 2005).

By the 1990s, three-figure counts were regular. In 1990, 111 flew by Southend Pier on 7th October, with 127 on 8th. In 1991, 157 passed Canvey Island on 10th October. Until 1992, three-figure counts have been restricted to autumn. However, 195 passed Southend Pier on 15th March 1992, representing 56% of the cumulative total recorded in March from 1981–2003. The next highest March count was 26 off East Tilbury on 13th in 1988. December 1998 saw another unusual movement, the flock of 60 passing Southend Pier on 12th being 31% of the cumulative total of December records for 1981–2003: 14 off there on 27th December 1985 is the next highest count. Also in 1992, 115 passed Canvey Island on 17th September. In 2003, an exceptional movement along the Thames of around 70 individuals on 1st January represents 50% of the cumulative total for the period 1981–2003. Also in 2003, 118 flew north past The Naze on 24th August. Totals of 30 off Bradwell on 6th February 1994 and 46 off East Tilbury on 20th February 1996 are by far the largest recorded in that month.

The largest ever influx occurred in 1993 following strong northeasterlies in mid-October, with counts on 14th of that month of 379 off Canvey Island, 246 off Southend Pier and 85 off East Tilbury, the last particularly remarkable so far upriver; around 400 individuals were probably involved. In 1997, 242 passed Canvey Island on 3rd November, whilst in 1999 326 (the second highest individual site count) flew by Shoeburyness on 15th October. The 1992 total of 1,022 is the largest in any year (cf. Suffolk, 9,660 in 1995 (Piotrowski 2003)).

The Gannet has been well studied and the pattern of its complex movements is well known (Nelson 1978). The species is recorded in Essex waters in all months, although it is in autumn that the biggest numbers occur. In contrast, in Suffolk five out of six of the county's largest movements were in spring (Piotrowski 2003). In autumn, firstly young (non-breeding) birds and sub-adults occur, followed by the year's juveniles and finally breeding adults. Most first-year birds winter off tropical Africa where they remain for two winters, although it is known that some remain in European waters. Adults tend to remain further north in European waters, depending on the level of fish stocks. Numbers present in Essex waters are lowest during winter. The northward migration, initially involving adults with immatures thereafter, can begin as early as January and lasts until May. A small spring movement is discernible off the Essex coast but on a much smaller scale than during autumn. In addition to migratory movements, adults are known to forage up to 500km from their breeding colonies and non-breeders can range much further, so summer sightings off the Essex coast could refer to either breeding or non-breeding individuals.

Since 1949, when one was recorded at Langham on 6th June, there have been 25 inland records, all singles apart from two at Hanningfield on 28th–29th September 1981 and two over Walthamstow on 3rd September 1987. A total of six in the period 24th–29th April 1981 was part of an exceptional seabird influx across southern Britain after severe southwesterlies (Nightingale & Sharrock 1982). All inland records have fallen in the periods April–June or September–November, except for one at Havering on 29th January 1996 and another over Great Baddow on 2nd January 2004. Although not truly inland, one caught in a cowshed at Bradwell-on-Sea on 10th April 1970 deserves mention.

A total of eight Gannets ringed within Britain and Ireland has been recovered in Essex. Several have come from the large gannetries at Grassholm Island, Wales, Bass Rock, Fife, and Ailsa Craig, South Ayrshire, and suggest the likely origin of many of the passage birds that pass down our coast.

(Great) Cormorant
Phalacrocorax carbo

Locally common resident, common winter visitor and passage migrant
Amber List

The Cormorant has an extensive range that covers Eurasia, Australasia, Africa and part of eastern North America. Two races breed in Europe: nominate *carbo*, which is found along the coasts of the North Atlantic from easternmost Canada and the Norwegian coast in the north to southwest France in the south; it is only partially migratory. The

Continental race *sinensis*, which is primarily a tree-nester and inhabits central and southern Europe and much of Asia, is migratory throughout much of its range (Migration Atlas). In Britain, the species is represented primarily by the nominate race and is typically a western bird. However, it is now known that the Continental race constitutes part of the tree-nesting population that since 1981, when breeding first occurred at Abberton, has increased rapidly in southeast England and the Midlands.

Remains of Cormorants have been found in the brick-earth deposits at Grays (Michael Daniels pers. comm.).

During the late 17th century Sir John Barrington fished with a tame Cormorant in Hatfield Forest (Rackham 1989). To Christy and Glegg, the Cormorant was a common visitor to the coasts from autumn through to spring. Apart from the Lea Valley reservoirs, where 1–2 were observed annually, the Cormorant was very rare inland.

Hudson & Pyman noted that a pair feeding half-grown young was seen on the Stour some time during the 1920s, and that around 1926 a nest with eggs was found on a buoy off Wrabness. In addition, an adult and two half-grown young were seen further upstream at Bures, Suffolk, in 1937 suggesting that breeding may have occurred locally, although it was likely to have been in Suffolk (Payn 1962). In 1948, a pair built a nest on the old loading jetty at what is now known as Colne Point, although the success was unknown (Cox).

In 1981, following summering by a few individuals in previous years, nine pairs nested in willows bordering Abberton and reared 15 young. It was the first instance of successful tree nesting in Britain since 1916; five pairs had nested at Stodmarsh, Kent, in 1947 but the nests were raided (Taylor *et al.* 1981). The Abberton

Atlas	Survey Area	% of 10km squares or tetrads in which	
		bred/probably bred	possibly bred or present
First National 10km	Essex	0.0	0.0
Second National 10km	Essex	3.5	0.0
First London Tetrad	Met. Essex	0.0	0.0
Second London Tetrad	Met. Essex	0.5	6.5
Essex Tetrad	Essex	0.2	1.4

Summary of results of Atlas surveys for Cormorants

colony grew rapidly to 526 nests in 1993. In 1994, a slight decline occurred (possibly due to cold weather in March and April) before numbers rose to the peak count to date, 551 nests in 1996, since when the colony, on average, has declined by around 7% per annum. The decrease in size of well-established colonies has been documented in several Dutch studies (Bregnballe *et al.* 2003).

The colony success seemed, at one point, likely to cause its demise, as it appeared that the huge amount of guano produced was likely to kill the very trees the Cormorants were nesting in (Ekins 1995). However, the willows showed rapid rates of regrowth and this, combined with subsequent higher water levels, has meant there has been no shortage of nesting sites. The cause of the decline in 1997 was considered to be low water levels that allowed Brown Rats to climb some trees and eat the young and Foxes to patrol under the trees and continually disturb the sitting adults.

In 1991, ten years after the founding of the Abberton colony, trees on an island at Walthamstow were colonised, since when the colony has grown on average by around 50% per annum although yearly increases have varied considerably and in one year (1999) a 21% decrease occurred. In 1997 the trees were cut down on the northern island, causing the colony to move to the southern island where considerable room for expansion exists. It is currently one of the fastest growing colonies in the country (Graham Ekins' personal data) and is now larger than the Abberton colony.

The "other colonies" referred to in the graph are at: Hanningfield, ten pairs nested in 1995 but breeding success was very poor with just one young fledged and the colony deserted; single pairs nested in 2000 and 2001 and two nested in 2002; Holyfield Lake, nine pairs nested in 2001, ten in 2002, 16 in 2003 and 27 in 2004; and Netherhall GP, a single pair bred in 2002 with two in 2003.

The total of 694 pairs in 2004 represented 52% of the national inland Cormorant breeding population of 1,334 pairs (Mitchell *et al.* 2004).

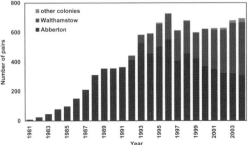

Annual totals of breeding Cormorants from 1981-2004

The colony at Abberton has been the subject of much study since the late 1980s (e.g. Ekins 1995, Sellers *et al.* 1997). Colour-ringing and direct observation of birds at or close to the nest have been the principal methods of data collection. Abberton has provided the nucleus for the expansion into inland England (Sellers *et al.* 1997). A Dutch-ringed *sinensis* and a *carbo* from Dyfed both raised young at Abberton in 1993 and provided the first documented occurrences of successful tree-nesting in Britain of both races, although *carbo* bred in trees in southern Ireland (Bannerman

GB 130 INT 1,200	85/86- 89/90	90/91- 94/95	95/96- 99/00	00/01- 04/05	Peak counts		Peak Month
WeBS totals	773^	1,368	1,559	2,367^	Oct 02	2,914	Oct
Stour	205^	131	131	133^	Sep 88	244	Oct
Hamford Water	35^	51	48	70^	Oct 01	91	Oct
Colne	254^	339	99	241^	Feb 94	676	Feb
Blackwater	272^	286	268	311^	Feb 94	501	Feb
Dengie	56^	178	98	133^	Mar 93	401	Mar
Crouch-Roach	21^	22	21	39^	Jan 03	66	Dec
Thames	101^	142	188	699^	Dec 03	935	Oct
Ardleigh	15^	34	36	24^	Jan 95	88	Nov
Abberton	307^	362	528	450^	Nov 94	600	Mar
Hanningfield	~	262	401	349^	Oct 98	758	Oct
Lea Valley	178^	578	545	769^	Oct 02	1,230	Oct
Met Essex	~	~	~	133^	Oct 02	121	Dec

Five-year average of peak WeBS counts (Sep-Mar)
of Cormorants from 1985/86-2003/04

& Lodge 1959). Subsequent ringing studies have confirmed the regular presence of both races at Abberton, and although the continental form predominates (Sellers *et al.* 1997), the proportion of *carbo* present at Abberton is higher than at other inland colonies (Migration Atlas). Birds reared at Abberton were reported breeding in colonies in Belgium and the Netherlands in 1998. A recent study has confirmed that the shape of the gular pouch angle is the only diagnostic feature for separating *carbo* and *sinensis* (Newson *et al.* 2005).

During the 1950s, outside the breeding season the largest Cormorant flocks were found at the mouths of the Colne and Blackwater Estuaries, the highest count during that decade being 290 off Colne Point on 2nd March 1958. Inland, only at Abberton did any large numbers occur, although the species was unusually numerous there dur-

ing the early 1950s with counts of 250 on 2nd February 1954 and 200 on 21st January and 3rd December 1950. Otherwise, only occasional birds turned up at other inland localities, mostly during winter. By the 1960s, the highest count from the coast had increased to 400, although this was 2km off the northeast coast. Numbers at Abberton were, for reasons that remain unclear, much reduced during the 1960s, and there were no three-figure counts there after the severe winter weather of 1962/63. The peak count at Hanningfield was just 33 (December 1969) by the end of the decade. During the 1970s, increasing numbers began to occur in the Lea Valley, 112 being at Walthamstow in late December 1975, whilst on the coast

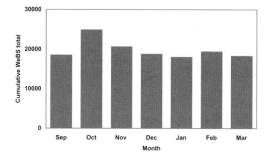

Seasonal occurrence of Cormorants from 1986-2004

numbers remained on a par with those during the 1960s. By the mid-1970s a few individuals had begun to summer at Abberton, a prelude to breeding early in the next decade.

With the formation and rapid increase of the Abberton colony, peak counts there and at other inland sites grew rapidly during the 1980s. Birds from the newly established inland colonies have contributed to the enlarged winter population, as around 75% remain in Britain for the winter (Hughes *et al.* 2000). Peaks counts were: 829 at Abberton in May 1989; 550 at Hanningfield in December 1990; and 400+ at Girling in October 1989. With breeding numbers increasing across Essex during the 1990s, inland peak counts continued to climb. At Abberton, four-figure totals occurred annually between 1993 and 2000, with the peaks in May and then again in June as young fledged, 1,860 in June 1996 being the highest. At Hanningfield, the peak was 758 during October 1998, whilst there were 586 at Walthamstow in April 2001. Coastal counts have also increased in magnitude and have included: 750 off the Colne Estuary in December 1994; 720 off Bradwell in January 1996; and 650 off Canvey Island on 11th January 2001. However, some 3,000 off the Maplin Sands and roosting on the Redsands Tower during the first two weeks of January 1992 remains without precedent. It was probably one of the largest, if not *the* largest, single count of Cormorants ever reported in Britain and at the time represented a significant proportion of the entire British wintering population.

Counts of all known winter roosts have been carried out in Essex since the 1980s and have revealed a steady rise to a relatively stable winter population over the last five years of around 1,500 birds, 11.4% of the British winter population of 13,200 (Stone *et al.* 1997). The WeBS counts have located larger numbers of Cormorants than those at known roosts and point to a current autumn/winter population of around 2,500 individuals.

Prior to the formation of the Abberton colony, counts along the coast showed a strong March peak. It is unclear why this peak was so prominent but may have been due to a build-up in numbers caused by the annual arrival of Sprats close offshore from late December. Subsequently, many of the largest counts have been during May and June. In May, numbers are boosted by the presence of non-breeding birds at the colonies (although there is evidence to suggest that some birds will nest in their first summer), whilst by June young Cormorants swell the numbers still further. An analysis of WeBS counts, which are available since 1986, also shows numbers peaking in March and again in October and November, suggesting an autumn passage through the county.

Bradwell Bird Observatory ringed many full-grown adults during the 1960s and 1970s. Birds roosting on an old radar wall off Dengie were caught at night when the tide was out; as they jumped off the wall and ran across the sand they were caught by hand. Many were recovered at south coast and Welsh localities, the latter during the breeding season. One, however, moved to an inland Dutch lake, strongly suggestive of it being of the race sinensis of which there had been many sight claims since the 1950s.

Many of our wintering birds come from Wales and north to Highland region, Scotland (Graham Ekins pers. obs.). In addition, Continental birds from Sweden, Denmark and the Netherlands have wintered in Essex. Both Dutch and Belgian birds have nested at Abberton and birds from Sweden and Denmark have attempted to. Young birds dispersing from Abberton have provided the majority of British records from the Netherlands, Belgium and Germany as well as the only record from Tunisia, 1,799km to the south-southeast. Abberton-bred birds also form the majority of those identified inland in Spain and France.

Analysis of Abberton ringing recoveries and observations of colour-ringed birds have shown

	Jan	Feb	Mar	Apr	May	Jun	Jul	Aug	Sep	Oct	Nov	Dec
Wales					1		1				1	
Germany					1		1	4	2			
The Netherlands	2		1		2	1		2	2		1	
Belgium			1									
France	1	1	1					1	1	1		
Spain	1		1									1
Tunisia											1	
Totals	4	1	4	0	4	1	2	7	5	1	3	1

Month and location of recovery of Cormorants ringed in Essex

that fewer than 10% of the local population remains at Abberton during winter, the majority dispersing across the Midlands, East Anglia and eastern south coast counties with 10% reaching the near-Continent. They are largely replaced by Cormorants from the principal British west coast and northern colonies together with around 15% of *sinensis* from Europe (Ekins 1995).

In the past, man has persecuted Cormorants because of the detrimental effect that they were thought to have on fish stocks (Second National Atlas). The huge increase in the Essex population has once again brought them into direct competition with fisherman. Dietary studies undertaken at Abberton during the springs and summers of 1992, 1993 and 1995 (Carss & Ekins 2002) suggested that cyprinids (Roach and Rudd), eels and flatfish were predominant in their diet, with Garfish taken during April and May; Brown and Rainbow Trout were taken in small quantities throughout the breeding season. Estuarine habitats from the Crouch north to the Blackwater/Colne are the favoured feeding areas, but a wide variety of inland habitats are also used, the commonest being gravel-pits, followed by reservoirs, lakes and rivers (Essex Atlas).

There is still considerable opportunity for breeding Cormorants to spread to other freshwater localities in Essex. For example, in 1994 it was estimated that the Abberton colony had the potential to grow to around 1,000 nests (Ekins 1995), although recent decreases there suggest that the site has a maximum load-carrying potential far lower than this. Indeed, food may be the limiting factor (G. R. Ekins pers. obs). Conflict with fisheries and fishermen will remain a potential problem and illegal shooting will remain a local threat. The recent licensed culling of Cormorants by the Government is a disturbing development that is being opposed by conservation organisations. Overall, however, it would seem that the future of the Cormorant as an Essex breeding species remains secure.

Sponsored by Graham Ekins

(European) Shag

Phalacrocorax aristotelis

Fairly common winter visitor and passage migrant

Amber List

The Shag is confined to the northeast Atlantic and Mediterranean where it is commonest along rocky coastlines. Three subspecies are recognised: the nominate race *aristotelis* breeds in Iceland and Scandinavia south to the

Iberian peninsula; *desmarestii* breeds in the central Mediterranean east to the Black Sea; and *riggenbachi* breeds along the Moroccan coast (*HBW*). Unlike the Cormorant, the Shag is rarely found in estuaries or freshwater, generally preferring deeper waters in which its main prey, the Lesser Sandeel, thrives (First National Atlas). In Britain, the species breeds on rocky coasts as far east as the Isle of Wight on the south coast and as far south as Flamborough Head on the east. The British population of 29,000 pairs (Wanless *et al.* 2005) fluctuates but represents around 37% of the European population. Northern populations are truly migratory; elsewhere Shags tend to be more sedentary or make only small-scale movements away from colonies (European Atlas).

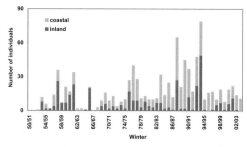

Annual totals of Shags from 1950/51-2003/04

Christy considered the Shag a very occasional winter visitor to the coast but documented just one record: one on the Stour on 30th September 1820. Glegg described the species similarly and added five records, including three inland. Numbers increased over the next 40 years or so as Hudson & Pyman considered the species almost annual, but added: "… more Shags are seen inland than on the coast …" a statement that was perhaps prompted by the periodic inland wrecks that were a feature of the 1950s and early 1960s. The majority of Shags involved in these wrecks were probably first-year birds from the east coast colonies of England and Scotland (Winter Atlas). Sudden food shortages after periods of easterly gales can cause immatures to travel further afield than is usual and then weakened birds, sometimes in flocks, may occur on low-lying coasts and inland (*BWP*).

Until the late 1960s inland records outnumbered coastal records. Cox suggested that increased observer coverage and the burgeoning interest in seawatching probably accounted for reversing the coastal:inland record ratio. Since the mid-1980s, larger numbers have been reported. A major wreck in early 1988 saw a marked increase subsequently, which peaked in 1993/94, since when numbers have declined. The overall increase must have been strongly influenced by the growth in the British population, combined with greater observer coverage.

Following the 1988 influx, a roost was founded on the barrier wall off Bradwell Power Station. It seems likely that, having been wrecked into Essex waters, small numbers subsequently 'adopted' the area and acted as a nucleus that periodically attracted other individuals. The subsequent decline suggests that recruitment has not been sufficient to overcome mortality and desertion. The roost counts were at their greatest in autumn and early winter and peaked at 24 on 25th October 1993. By 1999 numbers had, however, declined virtually to nil, although occasional individuals continue to be attracted to the barrier wall; its similarity to the Shag's typical habitat is, perhaps, the reason for this.

Elsewhere, small numbers wintered regularly in the Rainham area and 30 roosting there following severe weather on 26th January 1991 represented Essex's largest ever gathering. Otherwise, small numbers are recorded around the coast from the Stour and into the Thames, with one wintering in Royal Albert and Victoria Docks in 1998/99.

Notable inland wrecks have occurred during several winters and these have sometimes, but not always, coincided with above-average numbers on the coast. In early 1958 there were 11 at Abberton on 26th March and, in early 1962, 21 immatures were at Walthamstow on 10th March. In late 1965, 15 were at Walthamstow from 22nd November–4th December and there were ten at Hanningfield on 24th March 1988, whilst the 22 that paid a brief visit there on 14th October 1993 remains the largest inland flock. A total of 14 was in the Wanstead/Epping Forest area during January 1993, and the most recent double-figure count was 16 at Abberton on 6th February 1994.

Many of the victims of these wrecks soon died, although some survived and made extended stays: one that arrived at Walthamstow in the March 1958 influx remained until 31st January 1959, and another was present for some 28 months from November 1965. Individuals have turned up in unusual locations such as gardens and farm sheds, whilst three adorned a fountain in the middle of an ornamental lake at Little Easton Manor on 3rd March 1962. Inland records have come most regularly from Hanningfield (in 25 winters) and Abberton (23). The Shag is nearly as regular in the Lea Valley, with Walthamstow (23) the most favoured locality.

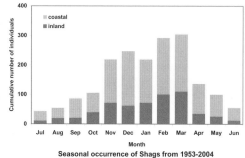

Seasonal occurrence of Shags from 1953-2004

Overall numbers begin to increase in early October and remain fairly constant during winter. In February and March, an early spring passage is evident. Numbers at the Bradwell roost tended to peak a month or so later, in mid- to late April.

Prior to the formation of the Bradwell roost, summer records were uncommon and usually involved singles, although there were four off The Naze on 22nd July 1978. From 1988, up to eight were present around the Bradwell barrier wall during the summer months, but numbers usually tailed off by late summer. With the decline of the Bradwell roost, summer records are once again rare.

Over 70 British-ringed Shags have been recovered in Essex. With the exception of one ringed on Lundy, Devon, on 26th June 1957 and found dead in Ongar on 10th September 1957, the recoveries have all originated from the east coast colonies on the Farne Islands, Northumberland, the Isle of May and Bass Rock, both Fife, and Sule Skerry, Orkney. The lack of recoveries from the west coast colonies, despite a substantial ringing programme, suggests that few reach Essex waters. There is little known movement between the Continent and Britain, with most adults remaining within 100km of their breeding colonies. Immatures, however, may move up to 200km (Winter Atlas).

Sponsored by Andrew Bryce

(Great) Bittern *Botaurus stellaris*

Uncommon but annual winter visitor and passage migrant - bred around 1944   Red List - Essex BAP

The Bittern is a very secretive heron that breeds throughout the warmer boreal and temperate zones from western Europe through central Russia to the Pacific. The nominate race *stellaris* occurs throughout much of its range. During the 19th century the species was common throughout west and central Europe but subsequently underwent a drastic decline caused by habitat change and destruction, although some gains were made in the first half of the 20th century (European Atlas). The declines have continued to this day, although in England conservation measures are beginning to meet with success. From a low of 11 booming males in 1997, numbers increased to 31–37 in 2002 (RBBP 2004). South and west European populations are probably resident around ice–free waters, but those in central and eastern Europe disperse south and southwest to unfrozen waters (European Atlas). Around 120 Bitterns winter in Britain (Migration Atlas).

Christy stated that the species was "Once a common resident before the draining of the extensive swamps ... and [is] now only a winter visitor". However, he produced no evidence to support his statement. That it was probably more widespread is most likely; for instance, the origin of the name of Purleigh near Maldon is 'pur', the Old English name for Bittern (Reaney 1969).

There has been just one confirmed breeding record, a nest found at Old Hall around 1944, although the outcome was unknown. One, possibly two, birds were also present in mid-summer 1951, whilst singles were noted there in mid-summer 1953, 1960 (booming), 1961 and 1962. Singles were heard booming at Hanningfield on 7th April 1968 and at Abberton on 2nd June 1992.

In the early 19th century, the species was clearly not uncommon outside the breeding season, if comments made by some of Christy's correspondents can be relied upon. Thus around 1834, the Bittern was ".... not unfrequently met with upon the marshes by the side of the river that runs to that town [Maldon]..." and "... specimens are not unfrequently shot from some of the numerous beds of reed growing by the sides of the Thames on the shores of Kent and Essex" (Yarrell 1845). More unusually, one was shot at Walthamstow town in January 1850 as "... it rose first from among some cabbages in a garden". From the second documented Essex record (Glegg referred to an earlier one), one shot at Audley End in 1831 [an 1826 record referred to by Christy was in fact an American Bittern (q.v.)], Christy detailed some 34 Bitterns that had been shot and several more either seen or heard. Most occurred between December and February and occurred across Essex: four were shot at Sturmer Mere around 1850. Glegg noted: "The Bittern has been recorded so often ... as to suggest that it is almost an annual winter visitor"

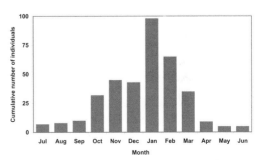

Seasonal occurrence of Bitterns from 1950-2004

177

and listed some 70 records, spread widely across the county from the earliest documented Essex record, at Maldon on 30th December 1820, to the last in 1926. All the dated records fell between November and May. Only four were reported between 1905 and 1926 and very few from then until 1949.

Since 1950 Bitterns have been recorded in all but three winters. A large influx occurred during the severe weather of early 1979 when at least 13 arrived, at least two of which died. They were probably displaced as wetland froze in northwest Europe, from where many

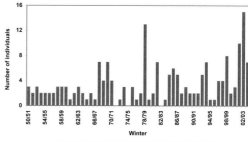

Annual totals of Bitterns from 1950/51-2003/04

of our wintering birds are thought to originate (Bibby 1981). Individuals occurring in late summer are more likely to be from the British population dispersing from breeding grounds. Increased observer coverage is the most likely explanation for the greater numbers reported at least until recently, as since 1950 the British population has fallen from 100 pairs (Parslow 1973). In the last few years, the growing numbers wintering in the Lea Valley have largely been responsible for the increase in the Essex wintering population. Habitat creation around the Bittern Watchpoint at Seventy Acres Lake has resulted in a steady increase in wintering birds. There were seven at roost on 11th January 2003 with four present on 9th January 1999 and 2nd February 2003, whilst the last decade or so has seen 1–3 in most winters.

Since 1950, and away from Seventy Acres Lake, Bitterns have occurred at more than 50 widely scattered locations, split fairly equally between the coast and inland. On the coast, 18 individuals have been reported from Old Hall (assuming one bird was responsible for the records from 1960–63) with five from Langenhoe and four at The Hythe. A total of 26 has been reported at Abberton and 13 at Hanningfield.

Numbers tend to peak markedly in January and February.

A female radio-tagged in the Lea Valley during the winter of 2002/03 was tracked to Lincolnshire where she bred successfully before returning in 2003/04.

American Bittern   *Botaurus lentiginosus*

Vagrant: one 19th century record

The monotypic American Bittern breeds across much of North America and winters in the southern United States, Central America and the West Indies. The species has been declining in the USA for many years, probably due to loss of marsh habitat (*HBW*).

1826	Wendens Ambo	Date unknown	Immature shot

This record was accepted by the BOURC in December 2001 as the second British record; the first was in Dorset in 1804. The mounted specimen was discovered at Saffron Walden Museum (Accession No. NB135) during routine research for this book. Acceptance came following extensive research (Green 2002). Ironically, Henry Seebohm, the eminent Victorian ornithologist, correctly identified the specimen following a visit to the museum around 1891. Unfortunately, the record never reached ornithological circles as the only written reference to it was in a local newspaper. There were 62 British records to the end of 2001, only 11 of which have occurred since 1958 (BBRC 2000).

Sponsored by Nick Green

Little Bittern   *Ixobrychus minutus*

Vagrant: 11 records involving 13 birds

The nominate race of Little Bittern, *minutus*, breeds over much of south and central Europe and North Africa, east to western Siberia and through Iran to northeast India, with populations wintering from Africa to India (*HBW*). Other races occur in Africa and Australasia.

about 1835	Near Billericay	Date unknown	
1860	Near Coggeshall	Date unknown	Shot
1866	Colchester, North Bridge	13th August	Male shot
1867	"Essex"	15th June	Two shot
1874	Near Stapleford Tawney at Passingford Bridge	15th September, but present several days previous	Immature male shot
1879/80	Ashdon	winter	Shot
1884	Near Colchester	autumn	Killed, hit telegraph wires
1954	Nazeing GP	30th May	Male
1958	Tillingham	late May	Moribund female
1968	Hanningfield	11th August	Immature
1970	Fingringhoe Wick	27th April	Male and female

There had been 466 British records to the end of 2004 (BBRC 2005), although there has been no increase in vagrancy over the last 40 years, despite increased observer coverage, which suggests a decline in real terms. This correlates with marked declines on the near-Continent, particularly the Netherlands, the likely origin of Essex individuals, where a population of 225 pairs in the 1960s had fallen to 12 territories by 2002 (*Dutch Birding* 25:130).

The 20th century records neatly follow the national trend for spring occurrences. Interestingly, the 19th century pattern of occurrence in the latter half of the year also followed the national trend of the time (Cottridge & Vinicombe 1996); the reasons for the change are not obvious.

(Black-crowned) Night Heron   *Nycticorax nycticorax*

Very rare passage migrant and winter visitor: 14 records of 13 individuals

The Night Heron is a cosmopolitan species found throughout much of the world. The nominate race *nycticorax* breeds in central and southern Europe, eastwards to central and southern Asia and north to Japan and south to Timor, as well as Africa (*HBW*). The species is a summer visitor to much of Europe and winters principally south of the African Sahara.

1839	New England Island	31st October	
1880	Dovercourt	29th November	Immature female
1891	Brightlingsea	5th December (for ten days)	Immature male
1946	Abberton	April	Adult
1953	Steeple Stone	21st November–24th December	1st-winter
1953/54	Foulness	late October–7th January	1st-winter
1956	St Osyth	11th November	Immature
1980	Walthamstow	11th October	Juvenile—dead
	Northey Island	25th October	Adult
1980/81	Foulness	6th December–21st February	Juvenile
1983	Fingringhoe Wick	16th–20th April	Adult
1987	Fingringhoe Wick	16th May–21st July	1st-summer
	Ardleigh	19th August	Same as previous
1990	Holland Haven	7th May	Adult

There had been 436 British records to the end of 2002 (Fraser & Rogers 2005), after which the Night Heron was removed from the list of species considered by BBRC. The majority are overshooting spring migrants, although records exist for every month. Interestingly, nine of the 13 Essex records occurred in the period October–December, with three overwintering: only since 1983 has the pattern of occurrence been more typical of the rest of the country. Nationally, 1987 and 1990 were exceptional years, with 53 and 61 records respectively.

Despite being regularly kept in collections in Britain and Europe, it is likely that most records refer to genuine vagrants from populations on the near-Continent, particularly the Netherlands. However, the recovery of one ringed as a nestling on the Black Sea coast of Russia, at Skegness, Lincolnshire, in January 1980 (Lorand & Atkin 1989), suggests a somewhat more distant point of origin for at least some winter occurrences (Cox).

Squacco Heron   *Ardeola ralloides*

Vagrant: one record

The monotypic Squacco Heron has a small and fragmented Western Palearctic breeding range in southwest and central Europe, eastwards to the Aral Sea and southeast Iran with other populations in Africa (*HBW*). Western populations winter in northern tropical Africa.

2004	Abberton	5th June

There had been 134 national records of Squacco Herons to the end of 2004 (BBRC 2005). Like other herons, the species suffered serious declines in the 20th century and has generally become less regular in its occurrence nationally.

Although present for only 2.5 hours, most county listers were able to connect with this individual before it flew into cover and was never seen again (Ransdale 2006b). It was probably the bird seen previously on both the south and north Kent coasts.

Cattle Egret   *Bubulcus ibis*

Vagrant: two records

The Cattle Egret is a cosmopolitan species, widespread throughout the world. In Europe, where the species is represented by the nominate race *ibis*, the majority breed in Iberia with small populations in France and Italy. European populations are partially migratory, wintering in southern Iberia and north Africa.

1995	Abberton	15th June	Adult
1998	Wanstead Park	10th May	

Up until 1970 there had been just 11 British records. However, by the end of 2002 this had increased to 125 (BBRC 2005). The Cattle Egret's European range has increased this century: it has spread through France in recent decades and now breeds as close as the Baie de Somme in the northwest. The occurrence dates are typical, national records predominantly involving overshooting spring migrants and winter visitors.

In 1995, an individual of the Asiatic race *coromandus* was at Hanningfield on 15th–16th August, Pitsea on 26th August and Theydon Bois on at least 6th and 21st September. It was assumed to have been an escape.

Little Egret   *Egretta garzetta*

Increasingly common resident, passage migrant and winter visitor: first bred in 2000   Amber List

The Little Egret is a widely distributed species, breeding throughout the tropical and temperate latitudes of the Palearctic, African and Oriental regions and Australasia. The nominate form *garzetta* occurs in Europe where its principal range is in the south and east, although in recent years the species' range has expanded along the Atlantic coast of France (Lock & Cook 1998). British records increased from the 1970s but an influx in 1989 provided the impetus for the first stage of colonisation (re-colonisation?—see Bourne 2003) of Britain. Breeding was first confirmed on Brownsea Island, Dorset, in 1996. Continuing post-breeding dispersal from the French Atlantic colonies has led to more birds wintering in Britain and subsequently staying to breed (Musgrove 2002). The majority of Little Egrets winter in Africa, although increasing numbers are staying on the European side of the Mediterranean (European Atlas).

The first Essex and only the 11th British record involved one at Abberton on 18th August 1950. By 1990, 15 had occurred with ten since 1980, mostly during summer. The subsequent increase has been rapid, with an almost exponential increase from the late 1990s. With the steady year-round increase in numbers, breeding soon followed. In 2000, seven pairs nested at a site in the south of the county and raised 14 young; in 2001, 20 pairs raised 45 young, and by 2002 32 pairs reared 46 young. Breeding occurred at a second site in the east of Essex from 2003, when two pairs nested. In 2004, there was a total of three colonies, all within heronries and involving 62 pairs (51, nine and two).

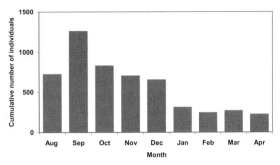

Seasonal occurrence of Little Egrets from 1950-2003

Estimating the size of the non-breeding population has become increasingly difficult (graphical data are presented up to 2003 only for this reason) with roost and WeBS counts probably providing the most accurate information. Individuals appear to feed over quite a large area and, despite their rather obvious colouring, their habit of feeding along the water line means that, unless there are particularly high tides, they can be difficult to detect in the creeks and gullies that bisect the saltings. Seven main roosts have been located to date although, due to their proximity to each other, there is probably much interchange between Chigborough Lakes and Lofts Farm GPs. Recent WeBS count totals have been slightly higher than the roost totals, perhaps suggesting that not every roost site has been identified. By 2004, an autumn population of 500–750 existed.

	Peak counts									
	1995	1996	1997	1998	1999	2000	2001	2002	2003	2004
St Osyth*	6	4	5	6	21	50	118	110	186	98
Lofts Farm GPs	0	0	0	0	0	2	32	51	68	141
Chigborough Lakes	0	0	0	0	0	0	0	0	55	50
North Fambridge Hall	0	0	2	4	nc	nc	21	nc	35	?
Foulness	0	0	1	1?	14	14	93	96	132	206
Two Tree Island	0	0	1	5	nc	23?	32	43	80	80
Abberton	0	0	0	0	0	0	0	40	107	120

* roost at Langenhoe in 1995

Principal Little Egrets roosts from 1995-2004

Little Egret numbers peak in late summer/ early autumn at the same time as the build-up in southern coastal counties, involving what are assumed to be individuals dispersing from the French Atlantic colonies.

Although the majority of records have come from the coast, the Little Egret is now regularly recorded inland, principally at the main reservoirs but increasingly along many of the county's river systems.

The success of the Little Egret as a colonist

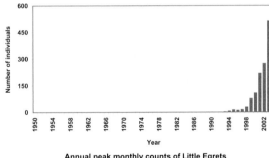

Annual peak monthly counts of Little Egrets from 1950-2003

has been exceptional and, although its range will never be as expansive as that of the Collared Dove, its rapid spread mirrors that species' arrival. The Little Egret's future in Essex is likely to depend on the severity of winter weather, as mortality at this time may be an important factor controlling populations (Lock & Cook 1998); if global warming means warmer winters, its future seems assured.

Great White Egret (Great Egret) *Ardea alba*

Vagrant: two records involving four individuals

The Great White Egret is a cosmopolitan species found throughout the temperate and tropical areas of the world (European Atlas). The nominate race *alba* occurs across Europe and central Asia, south to Iran (*HBW*). In Europe, the species is largely confined to east and southeast Europe, although it has bred in the Netherlands since 1978 and northwest France since 1994. Most of the European population winters in northern Africa and the eastern Mediterranean. Increasingly, however, birds are wintering in central Europe and the Netherlands.

| 2002 | Stone Point, The Naze | 11th May | Three |
| 2003 | Abberton | 26th July | One, colour-ringed |

The first Essex record of this increasingly regular visitor to Britain was long overdue, the species having already visited many inland counties. Nationally, 274 had been recorded to the end of 2004, the majority since 1988 (BBRC 2005). There were 37 in 2002 and 42 in 2003. A flock of three is the largest recorded in Britain to date. The colour-ringed Abberton bird was ringed as a pullus at Lac du Grande Lieu, Loire Aquitaine, France, on 26th June 2001 and was also seen in South Yorkshire on 19th–22nd July 2003 and Devon on 31st August 2003.

Christy referred to one along the Stour on 3rd October 1823 "… it appeared to be pure white, and to stand rather taller than some common Herons which were feeding not far off". A similar bird was seen the following spring at Oakley and subsequently on the banks of the Orwell, Suffolk: neither Payn (1962) nor Piotrowski (2003) mention the latter. Glegg dismissed the record, together with one allegedly seen on many occasions in Lexden Park, Colchester, in June and July 1901.

Sponsored by Pete Davis

Grey Heron   *Ardea cinerea*

Common resident, passage migrant and winter visitor

The Grey Heron breeds across most of the Old World, apart from Australasia. In Europe, where the nominate race *cinerea* occurs, the species breeds from Ireland, east through central Europe to Russia and from the Arctic Circle in Norway, south to Portugal and Spain. In Britain, systematic nest counting began in 1928 with further full censuses in 1954, 1964, 1985 and 1997, making it one of the most closely monitored species in the country. There are around 15,000 pairs in Britain (Marchant *et al.* 2004), around 7% of the European population. Northern populations are migratory, generally moving south and west in winter; British populations are largely sedentary (Migration Atlas).

Christy and Glegg documented the early history of the Grey Heron in some detail. The oldest known heronries were at "Towleshunt Darcye: nere wch is a fayre Heronry" (Norden 1594) and at Belhus, Aveley, where Morant (1768) described a former heronry which was once protected for the purpose of flying hawks against the herons, at one time a popular 'sport of princes'. The decline in the sport's popularity resulted in less protection for the site and it was abandoned.

Large heronries were noted throughout the 19th century. The oldest and, at that time the nearest to London, was in Wanstead Park, which was described as of "long establishment and very populous" in 1834. The Conservators of the Forest protected the heronry during the breeding season, resulting in a steady increase from 43 nests in 1884 to 74 in 1914. Thereafter, there was a gradual decline such that by 1957 it was extinct. However, as is so often the case, it appears that the heronry simply moved over time and a new one was established at Walthamstow around 1914, initially on No.

Atlas	Survey Area	% of 10km squares or tetrads in which	
		bred/probably bred	possibly bred or present
First National 10km	Essex	36.8	31.6
Second National 10km	Essex	29.8	64.9
First London Tetrad	Met. Essex	0.5	0.0
Second London Tetrad	Met. Essex	2.5	50.0
Essex Tetrad	Essex	1.6	0.0

Summary of results of Atlas surveys for Grey Herons

5 reservoir, although it has shifted location a couple of times subsequently. After a relatively slow increase, numbers rose to 60–80 nests in the 1950s and, despite setbacks caused by severe winters, increased to over 100 nests annually during the 1990s, making it on occasions the second-largest heronry in the country after Northwood Hill, Kent. A slight decline has occurred in the early 21st century. Recently the site of the heronry has shifted to other islands on the reservoir, following the arrival of breeding Cormorants, although two pairs have nested within the Cormorant colony. The Walthamstow heronry accounts for around 50% of the Essex breeding population.

Location	Founded	Max. no. of nests	Peak 1950-59	Peak 1960-69	Peak 1970-79	Peak 1980-89	Peak 1990-99	Peak 2000-04	Comments
EXTANT (since 1990)									
St Osyth	1872	75 (1928)	15	14	20	14	14	26	Transferred from Brightlingsea. Colony moved a short distance in mid-1950s
Walthamstow	about 1914	138 (1993)	80	84	115	128	138	110	Transferred from Wanstead. Britain's second largest heronry
Paglesham	pre-1939	12 (1946)	n/a	n/a	n/a	n/a	2	2	Extinct 1954 but 1-2 nests intermittently 1990-2002
Beazley End	1967	28 (2001)	n/a	3	13	9	26	28	Transferred from Gosfield?
Foulness	1970	38 (1995)	n/a	n/a	17	24	38	22	
Waltham Abbey	1974	36 (1994)	n/a	n/a	25	30	36	22	
North Fambridge Hall	1975	26 (2000)	n/a	n/a	19	25	25	26	
Goldhanger	1978	9 (1990)	n/a	n/a	2	8	9	1	Used 1978-82, 1988-92 & 2000
East Donyland	1980	12 (90/98)	n/a	n/a	n/a	7	12	4	
Witham	1988	6 (1998)	n/a	n/a	n/a	3	6	nc	Nesting in 1988, 1990 & 1998 only
Osea Road	1992	12 (1992)	n/a	n/a	n/a	n/a	12	6	Transferred from Osea Island?
Chigborough	1992	5 (1992)	n/a	n/a	n/a	n/a	5	4	Intermittent use -site has moved some years
Copt Hall	1998	24 (1998)	n/a	n/a	n/a	n/a	24	11	Discovered 1998; A heronry existed in Copthall Grove until at least 1938
Holyfield Lake	1999	9 (01/02)	n/a	n/a	n/a	n/a	3	9	
Mayesbrook Pk, Dagenham	1999	5 (2002)	n/a	n/a	n/a	n/a	2	5	Nesting 1999 - 2004
Ingrebourne Valley	2001	14 (2004)	n/a	n/a	n/a	n/a	n/a	14	Nesting in 2000-04
EXTINCT SINCE 1950	**OCCUPIED**								
Tollesbury Wick	1982-90	8 (1990)	n/a	n/a	n/a	5	8	0	Off-shoot of Osea Road colony?
Barling GP	1980-87	7 (1983)	n/a	n/a	n/a	7	0	0	Off-shoot of Foulness Is. heronry?
Osea Island	ca. 1963-86	42 (1975)	n/a	32	42	11	0	0	Formed from Rolls Farm colony, moved to Osea Road?
Great Wigborough	1975-84	5 (1975)	n/a	n/a	5	3	0	0	Nested 1975 & 1982 - 83
Layer Breton	1961-78	16 (1970)	n/a	14	16	0	0	0	Transferred to Donyland?
Hylands Pk Chelmsford	1927-77	28 (1961)	25	28	22	0	0	0	
Mundon Hall	1913-74	35 (1928)	3	2	22	0	0	0	Used until 1949, then 1950-5, 1965 & 1972-74
Rolls Farm Tollesbury	1890s-1966	38 (1954)	38	29	0	0	0	0	Transferred to Osea Island
Gosfield/Gosfield Place	pre-1949-63	6 (1951/56)	6	3	0	0	0	0	Transferred to Beazley End?
Skippers Is Hamford	ca.1930-62	11 (1954)	11	7	0	1	0	0	One pair also nested 1989
Little Parndon	??-1962	14 (1950/52)	14	4	0	0	0	0	
Peldon	ca.1945-1959	13 (1952)	13	0	0	0	0	0	Transferred to Layer Breton
Wanstead Park	pre-1834-1957	74 (1915)	7	0	0	0	0	0	Transferred to Walthamstow
Tillingham	pre-1951-55	5 (1951-52)	5	0	0	0	0	0	Location moved around 1950
Latchingdon, Stamfords Fm	1949-52	5 (1952)	5	0	0	0	0	0	

Other sites with less than five nests (max. in brackets) in any year since 1950:
Gt Hallingbury Pk 1950-55 (3); Hatfield Broad Oak [two sites] 1951-63 (4); Canewdon 1951(1); Danbury Park 1954 (1); Creeksea 1974-76 (1); Elsenham 1954 (1); Langenhoe 1975-78 (3); Gt Chesterford 1957 (1); Littlebury 1960-61 (1); Terling 1973 (1); River Pant, nr Braintree 1972 (2); E. Mersea 1962 (2);Terling 1973 (1); Roman River Valley 1970 & 74 (3); Gt Maplestead 1969 (1); White Notley 1976-79 (4); Stock 1984 (1); Copperas Wood 1986 (1); Langham 1987 (1); Heybridge 1988-91 (3); Abberton Manor 1988-89 (3); Rainham 1990 & 2000 (1); Stanway 1991 (1); Fishers Green 1991 (1); Two Tree Island 1999 (1); Barrows Wood, Highwood 2000-04 (4); Watts Wood, Purfleet 2000 (3); Netherhall GP 2002-04 (3).

Grey Heronries in Essex from 1950-2004

Christy and Glegg mentioned a large heronry at Brightlingsea, 400m west of the church which numbered some 100 pairs in the first half of the 18th century, but by 1870 it held just 30 nests and became extinct in 1872, due to tree-felling, hunting and competition from Rooks. Herons from this site probably transferred to St Osyth Priory in 1872, the oldest surviving heronry in Essex.

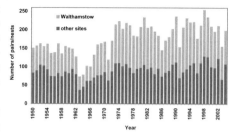

Annual totals of breeding Grey Herons from 1950-2004

The largest heronry in Essex was located in Calves Pasture Wood, Birch, and numbered some 170 nests in 1890; it is quite possible that herons from Brightlingsea founded this, too. It was originally in nearby Chest Wood but a pair of Peregrines apparently caused the move to Calves Pasture Wood in 1878. Somewhere between 1890 and 1892, however, the heronry moved back to Chest Wood where it was still doing well in 1902, but by 1928 there were just 19 nests. When it was abandoned entirely is not recorded, but it was gone by 1950. The only other heronries mentioned by the two early writers that remained in use were located at Boreham House, where despite intense persecution there were 32 nests in 1927, and Mundon Hall, which held 35 nests in 1928. The former became extinct before 1937 (Pyman 1938b), whilst the latter went the same way in 1951, although it was used briefly in the mid-1970s, peaking at 20 pairs in 1974. The Copt Hall heronry was described as the "... largest heronry of all ..." in 1938 (Pyman 1938d).

Christy, Glegg and Hudson & Pyman mentioned other heronries extinct prior to 1950 and not subsequently reoccupied: Lawling Hall, Latchingdon; the Nursery, Bradwell Glebe; Old Farm, Burnham-on-Crouch; Steeple; Scot's Grove, Tollesbury; Great Wood, Tolleshunt Major; Barton Hall, Paglesham; Chigwell; Waltons Hall, Mucking; Mundon Furze; Bower Hall Grove, Mersea Island where 12–15 pairs occurred until ca 1850 when the trees were chopped down; Tofts, Little Baddow; and Woodham Walter Lodge.

Since 1950, between 6–20 heronries have been occupied annually, although in recent years 10–12 has been the norm. More than 60 sites have been used since 1950, from the old, long-established ones to those used just once. In that time, fortunes of each individual heronry have been mixed with the loss of large, old heronries (e.g. Wanstead and Hylands Park, Chelmsford) but the establishment of new ones (e.g. Waltham Abbey, Foulness and Copt Hall). Various factors play on each one and result in declining or improving fortunes. Disturbance in one form or another is probably the main cause of desertion.

The late 1990s saw an increase in the number of heronries reported, particularly from Metropolitan Essex, although it is possible that this was due to increased observer coverage rather than any other cause.

Severe winters can have a serious impact on Grey Heron populations. Virtually no first-winter birds survived the winter of 1962/63 and numbers were suppressed for several years thereafter. At Walthamstow, numbers virtually halved and took around five years to recover. At Hylands Park, the number of nests in 1963 were just 30% of that in 1962 and it was the final blow to already declining heronries at Little Parndon, Skippers Island, Gosfield and Hatfield Broad Oak. Meadows (1972a) gave details of the effects of severe weather on Essex Herons. He estimated that there had been a 40% reduction in the population between 1958 and 1966, a period of colder than average winters. He also suggested that the slow return in numbers was due to high insecticide residues, which for a top of the food-chain predator were far higher than in other water bird species.

The winter of 1978/79 was probably the last when really severe weather affected the county, although the effects were not so great as in 1962/63. The subsequent run of generally milder winters has seen breeding numbers increase steadily, such that by 1998 an estimated 255 pairs were recorded, a similar level to that seen in the late 1920s, compared with just 73 in 1963. Nationally, numbers have increased in recent years, although it is unclear whether this is because of climatic amelioration or reduced persecution and pollution. Botulism, often caused by particularly hot, dry weather, can cause severe mortality in young birds.

Most Grey Herons are tree-nesters, showing a particular preference for certain species such as Oak, Alder and Ash. However, some have bred in Hawthorn thickets (e.g. Foulness, the heronry originally being in Elms) and there is one record, albeit an unsuccessful attempt, of ground nesting at Rainham in 1990, the nest being in dense Sea Aster and Common Reed. Man-made structures have occasionally been used, as on Foulness where several pairs have used artificial platforms.

Outside the breeding season, the largest individual site count has been 150 at Hanningfield (including a loose flock of 120) on 6th July 1957, where there were also 96 on 9th August 1958 and 100+ on 28th June and 19th

July 1959. Subsequently, the largest count there was 57 during September 2000. Winter roost flocks were noted on the pits and lagoons near West Thurrock Power Station between 1980 and 1993. A total of 135 was present on 3rd January 1992, 126 on 7th December 1991 and 110 in December 1990, with counts of 100 on two further occasions and counts of 50+ annually between 1980 and 1993. A total of 73 was present between Foulness and Leigh/Two Tree Island on 9th October 1994.

There has been very little evidence of visible migration. Occasionally, small flocks of up to 20 have been noted along the coast in autumn. Single birds are often seen heading out to sea or coming in off the sea: the presence of the sandbanks off the coast, however, provide large areas of relatively undisturbed feeding and it is possible that many records refer to birds moving to/from there. The origin of five birds about 13km offshore, beyond Maplin Sands, on 20th August 1989, is even less clear; they may have been migrants but perhaps they were local birds utilising a plentiful food source.

In the 1950s and 1960s ringing was carried out at Walthamstow and in the 1980s and 1990s on Foulness. Recoveries from both colonies have revealed that some birds stay relatively close to the natal site, yet others disperse widely. Individuals from Walthamstow have all moved south or west to Oxfordshire, Gwynedd, Hampshire, Greater London and Berkshire, apart from one first-year bird which was found the same year it was ringed in Lanarkshire, Scotland, an exceptional within-Britain movement. Herons from Foulness have also moved south and west to northern France (three), Kent (two), Sussex, Greater London, Herefordshire, Worcestershire and Oxfordshire, although one moved north to Lincolnshire. Grey Herons ringed as nestlings in Sweden, Norway (two), Denmark (three) and the Netherlands (five) have reached Essex in autumn and winter, suggesting that our population is augmented at this time by Continental birds from further east. One ringed as a nestling at Wytham, Oxfordshire, on 20th May 1955 was recovered at Shalford during July 1978.

Sponsored by John Fitzpatrick

Purple Heron   *Ardea purpurea*

Very rare passage migrant: 26 records involving 25 individuals

The Purple Heron is a widespread species found in the Palearctic, Oriental and Ethiopian regions. In Europe, where the nominate race *purpurea* occurs, the species is found predominantly through central and eastern areas and winters in equatorial Africa, mainly north of the Equator.

1839	In a wood near Maldon	April, second week	Shot
1953	Abberton	13th June	
1955	Abberton	22nd August–20th September	Immature
1956	Fishers Green	12th May	
1958	Walthamstow	25th May	
1959	Flatford/Cattawade	2nd October	Juvenile
1969	Walthamstow	16th September	
1970	Fingringhoe Wick	2nd–18th August	
	Hanningfield	15th and 30th November	
1971	Hamford Water/The Naze	29th April	
	Sewardstone GP	16th October	Adult
1972	Rainham	1st June	
1973	Orsett	26th May	
1975	Rainham	31st May	
	Hanningfield	15th June	
1976	Bradwell	29th August	Immature
1978	Rainham	26th May	
1980	Southminster	19th–20th April	Immature
	Lamarsh	2nd–6th September	
1987	Rainham	2nd May	
1989	Wat Tyler CP	22nd July	
1990	Dagenham Chase	27th April	

1996	Abberton	27th April	Immature
	Southminster	5th May	
2004	Holland Haven	6th–7th September	Juvenile
	East Mersea	15th September–3rd October	Same as previous

Populations in central Europe and the Netherlands increased from the 1950s to the 1970s but since then there has been a steady decline, particularly in France from 1974–83, possibly attributable to reduced survival rates in their wintering quarters (European Atlas). This has been reflected in a decline in numbers reported in Essex from the early 1980s, a similar trend to that seen nationally, despite increased observer coverage; nationally, there were 745 records to the end of 2002 (Fraser & Rogers 2005).

The pattern of occurrence is typical of the national trend, with a peak in April and May as migrating birds overshoot their typical breeding ranges. A smaller peak in autumn involves juveniles dispersing from breeding areas.

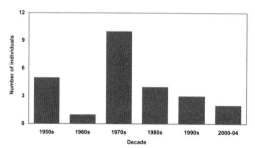

Ten-year totals of Purple Herons from 1950-2004

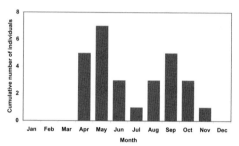

Seasonal occurrence of Purple Herons from 1839-2004

Black Stork   *Ciconia nigra*

Very rare passage migrant: ten records involving eight individuals

The monotypic Black Stork is principally an Asian species but with populations in central and eastern Europe, Iberia and France, where in 1999 the species nested within 300km of Essex. Black Storks are highly migratory and, whilst a few remain in Spain, the majority winter in Africa, principally in the east and northeast.

1881	Stour	April or May	Shot
1983	Little Hallingbury	12th June	
1989	Waltham Abbey	14th May	
1990	Old Hall	25th-26th August	Juvenile
	Hamford Water	26th August	Same as previous
1991	Epping Forest	7th July	
	Frinton-on-Sea	30th September	
2002	Newport	15th May	
2004	Abbots Hall,		
	Fingringhoe Wick,	16th August–4th September	Juvenile
	Langenhoe, etc.		
	Westcliff-on-Sea	15th September	Same as previous

Up to the end of 2004, there had been 161 British records (BBRC 2005). Nationally, numbers have increased recently and 1991 was the best year on record with some 23 occurrences, at a time when there had only been a grand total of 84. The trend mirrors the expansion of the European population following significant declines in the early years of the 20th century (European Atlas); most occur during spring with a lesser peak in autumn.

Christy included the 1881 record, albeit noting: "Strictly speaking, this is a Suffolk specimen" whilst Glegg stated quite clearly that "I do not consider that the species should be included on the Essex list". Hudson & Pyman and Cox included the record. There is little evidence to suggest this individual definitely wandered into Essex; it was seen at Boxford and shot on the Suffolk side of the Stour at Stoke-by-Nayland after being seen "... flying down the river valley to the sea ...". Just which river valley was being referred to is unclear as a flight from Boxford to Stoke-by-Nayland takes one down the Box Valley not Stour: the former is entirely in Suffolk, whilst the latter forms the Essex/Suffolk boundary in this area.

White Stork   *Ciconia ciconia*

Very rare passage migrant: 28 records involving 27–30 individuals

The White Stork is a Palearctic species widely distributed through east and central Europe and Iberia with a patchy distribution in northwest Europe. Throughout much of its range the species is represented by the nominate race *ciconia*. White Storks are highly migratory with western populations wintering in west Africa.

1842 or 1852	"Essex"	date unknown	Shot
1879	Tillingham	January	Two shot
1924	Braintree	March	
1938	Tollesbury	11th August	
1971	Boreham	18th August	
1974	Foulness/Hadleigh area	13th October	Two
1975	Leigh/Two Tree Island	week ending 16th March	
1976	Ilford/Hornchurch	25th and 30th September	
1977	Sewardstone	3rd April	
	Ramsden Heath	9th-22nd June	
	Rowhedge/Great Bromley/ Clacton-on-Sea	20th and 26th June	
1986	Ingatestone	26th May	
1988	Stow Maries	18th-21st April	Two on 18th, then one
	Stock	2nd-6th September	
1998	Oozedam Farm, Fobbing	4th-8th May and intermittently 14th May-5th July	
	West Bergholt	7th September	
1999	Finchingfield	5th September	
	Rayleigh	8th September	
2001	Black Notley	1st-2nd May	
	Berwick Ponds	2nd May	
	Bradwell	1st July	
2002	Pratt's Farm, Chelmsford	21st-26th July	Adult
2003	Wrabness	25th April	
	Margaretting	26th April	Same as previous
	North Fambridge	27th July	
	Orsett	16th September	
2004	South Ockendon	18th March	
	Whipps Cross Marsh	18th and 24th May	Flew south

Despite recent signs of an increase in the northwest European population, overall there was a substantial decrease in the 20th century. In the east of its range, however, numbers have continued to increase (European Atlas).

White Storks are regularly kept in and escape from captivity and in recent years known escapes have been tracked across the country. The 1998 Fobbing individual had a metal ring on its leg, which was never deciphered.

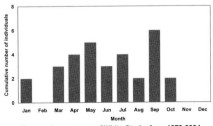

Seasonal occurrence of White Storks from 1879-2004

Probably the same individual was seen at Wat Tyler CP, Layer-de-la-Haye and over the A12 and was perhaps the individual on the Isle of Sheppey, Kent, from 24th–25th April. One at Abberton on 17th–19th July 2000 bore a ring marked 'AX' and was seen in several counties; it was assumed to be an escape. It is possible that some of the more recent records refer to individuals dispersing from the Netherlands and Belgium where reintroduction schemes began in the 1960s; in the Netherlands the project was so successful it was stopped in 1995.

The pattern of occurrence is typical, mirroring that seen across the country with peaks in spring and autumn.

Glossy Ibis   *Plegadis falcinellus*

Vagrant: eight records involving at least 14 individuals

The Glossy Ibis is a monotypic, cosmopolitan species that is a local breeder in southeast Europe. Although many migrate south to sub-Saharan Africa, the species is prone to randomly dispersive and nomadic movements (*HBW*).

1872	Paglesham, South Hall Marshes	15th October	Immature, shot
1912	The Naze	14th October	Two adults and three immatures shot from six
1920	Fobbing Creek	November	Shot
about 1943	Bradwell	Date unknown	One shot from a small flock
	Abberton	Date unknown	
1974	Grays, but mostly Kent	11th April–12th May	
1984	Little Clacton	26th December	Two adults
2004	Hanningfield	25th June	

Although there were many old British records, there have been just 87 since 1958 (BBRC 2005) as a result of a marked decline and range contraction on the Continent early in the 20th century, though there have been signs of a slow recovery recently; the species is no longer a national rarity in the Netherlands. The 1984 record almost certainly involved the pair that stayed in Kent for much of the period 1975–85; one survived until 1992. The 2004 individual was one of a small influx in 2003 that wandered around many sites in southern England.

Sponsored by Frances Hall

(Eurasian) Spoonbill   *Platalea leucorodia*

Uncommon passage migrant and rare winter visitor: about 90 records involving approximately 163 individuals   Amber List

The Spoonbill is found in shallow wetlands from the temperate and steppe zones in the north to the dry tropics in the south. The species breeds across Europe, central and east Asia, the Persian Gulf, the Indian subcontinent and Africa. The nominate race *leucorodia* occurs throughout Europe and much of its range (European Atlas). The Dutch population has increased over the last 40 years following declines in the first half of 20th century, but decreases have occurred across much of the rest of Europe. European populations winter in the Mediterranean and in North Africa.

Christy noted: "That it formerly bred ... in Essex is more than probable, although there is, I believe, no actual record of its doing so". Spoonbills bred in Britain until the 17th century, the last nests being at Trimley, Suffolk (Piotrowski 2003). Christy listed six records from the first, of three birds shot on the Stour in the winter of 1815/16, to the last in 1889 (a seventh was in Suffolk). These included the largest parties recorded in Essex, nine at Harwich in June 1877, of which two were shot, and seven at Burnham-on-Crouch, three of which were shot, in December 1889. Glegg described the species as a rare visitor and added just two records, the last in July 1918 on the Stour at Bradfield. Of the total

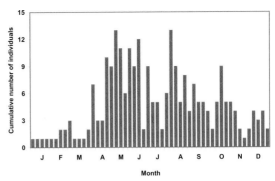

Seasonal occurrence of Spoonbills from 1950-2004

of eight records, two were undated, one was taken in "winter" and singles were recorded in each month from June–August, October and December.

Apart from one on Rochford Marsh on 27th December 1929, the next was at North Fambridge in late 1947 (Pyman 1947). The species has since become an almost annual visitor, with 139 recorded from 1952–2004.

Recently, national records have increased and, although greater observer coverage must be partly responsible, breeding numbers have increased in the Netherlands recently from 60 pairs in the 1960s to over 600 in 1993 (Voslamber 1994), so the increase is probably genuine. The record numbers in 1996 were part of a substantial influx into East Anglia that included up to 19 at Minsmere, Suffolk, during the summer. Unsuccessful breeding occurred in Suffolk in 1997, 1998 and 2002 (Piotrowski 2003).

Most records since 1950 have been of 1–3 individuals, with five on Two Tree Island on 16th June 2002 the largest flock since the 19th century. Records of four birds have come from: Foulness, 12th June 1977; Old Hall, 18th October 1990; The Hythe, 1st April 1991; Abberton, 8th September 1991; Old Hall, 26th April–14th May 1996; Tollesbury Wick, 10th–12th May 1996; Colne Point, 2nd June 1996; and Old Hall, 1st June 2000. Some of the 1996 records may relate to the same wandering flock.

Numbers are generally higher in spring than autumn, although not significantly. Spoonbills have occurred in every month, although the only one in January involved a long-staying individual that arrived on 19th November 1978 and wandered along the north side of the Blackwater until found dead on 20th February 1979.

Individuals recorded in spring are probably overshooting migrants or even failed breeders (Migration Atlas), whilst those arriving during summer are likely to be wandering non-breeders. Autumn and winter records presumably involve adults and young dispersing from breeding grounds.

Spoonbills have been recorded all around the coast, the Old Hall/Tollesbury area being the most favoured locality (20 records of 33 birds). Inland records have come from the main reservoirs at Abberton (eight records of ten individuals), Hanningfield (four of four) and Walthamstow (two of two), and also from Fishers Green (three of three); there have been singles at Stansted, Waltham Abbey and Dagnam Park.

Few birds stay long at any locality. However, in addition to the 1978 individual mentioned above, a first-summer bird lingered at Hanningfield from 3rd May–14th September 1958 and one was at Fleet Head from 26th February–10th April 1996.

A Spoonbill bearing a Dutch ring was picked up dead at Fishers Green Goose-field in mid-September 2001. In recent years, most sightings in East Anglia have been of colour-ringed birds originating from the Netherlands where the government is funding an ongoing research programme, so this is the likely source of many of our Spoonbills, although an old national ringing recovery of one from the former Yugoslavia indicates that some come from further east.

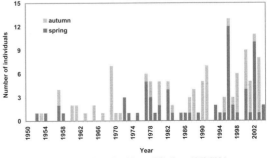

Annual totals of Spoonbills from 1950-2004

(European) Honey-buzzard

Pernis apivorus

**Uncommon passage migrant, except for an unprecedented influx
in autumn 2000: one 19th century breeding record**

Amber List

The monotypic Honey-buzzard breeds across Europe and
western Asia and winters in Africa, south of the Sahara.
In Britain, which is on the edge of its breeding range, a
total of 50–60 pairs breeds annually (Roberts *et al.* 1999)
out of a total European population of 160,000 pairs
(European Atlas).

The sole confirmed breeding record relates to a clutch
that was taken from a nest near The Rodney pub in Little
Baddow in June 1847 (Jourdain 1918). A pair may have
nested in the same wood in 1888, whilst in 1895 there was
evidence to suggest a nest was built at Little Baddow but it
came to nothing. A single bird summered at Margaretting
from 24th May–22nd July 1950. In 2003, breeding
may have occurred at a site in the county but was not
confirmed.

Between 1837, when one was shot at Debden Hall (an 1831 record was in fact in Suffolk), and 1927 a total of
24 was recorded in 19 years, including two in a year "around 1850", five in autumn 1881 (an influx also occurred
in Norfolk and Suffolk) and two in both 1888 and 1927 (Christy, Glegg). Of the dated records, five were in May,
two in June, nine in September and two in October.

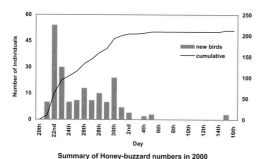

Summary of Honey-buzzard numbers in 2000

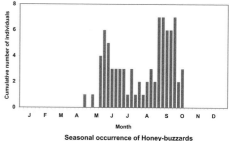

**Seasonal occurrence of Honey-buzzards
from 1950-2004 (excluding 2000)**

The next documented record was not until 1950. Numbers remained low with only 12 between 1950 and
1981, although with six occurring after 1976, Cox was prompted to note: "… there is a suggestion that the species
is beginning to visit the County more frequently". The increase has continued with, up to the end of 2003, a total
of 308, although 212 (69%) occurred in the exceptional influx in 2000.

A combination of greater observer coverage and an apparent increase in the size of the British population
(Roberts *et al.* 1999) are both likely factors accounting for the increase during the 1990s. Records show a
typical pattern of occurrence with peaks in late May and early/mid-September. Extreme dates have been 17th
April, at Weald CP in 1976, and 15th October,
two south into Essex from Landguard Point,
Suffolk, in 2000.

Apart from in 2000, all records have been of
single birds except for two over Foulness on 17th
August 1996, two at Tiptree on 22nd September
2002 and two at Langley on 28th August 2004.
Over 70% have come from the coast, including 13
from Dengie, with others at widely scattered sites
from Hamford Water in the north to East Tilbury
in the southwest.

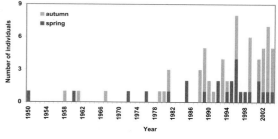

Annual totals of Honey-buzzards from 1950–2004 (excluding 2000)

The 2000 influx involved some 212 individuals and was some three times the total previously recorded It was part of an exceptional arrival along the east coast of England from the third week in September (Gantlett & Millington 2000). Ekins (2002) described the influx in detail. The first birds arrived on 21st September with the 22nd being the peak of the movement with some 54 new individuals reported, the Abberton area alone recording 19. Birds were seen across Essex with notable concentrations around Abberton and along the mid-Thames. The majority were juveniles, almost all following a south-southwesterly course. It appears that the birds were drifted west/northwest from the Continent by adverse weather conditions, with most making a northerly landfall before moving south *contra* Rossiter (2000).

Sponsored by Graham Ekins

Black Kite   *Milvus migrans*

Very rare passage migrant: 19 records involving 18 individuals

The Black Kite breeds throughout much of the Old World with western populations wintering in tropical Africa. The nominate race *migrans* occurs throughout northwest Africa and Europe, east to central Asia and south to Pakistan.

1971	Fingringhoe Wick	2nd June	
1977	Bradwell	6th May	
1979	South Ockendon refuse tip	19th–20th April	
1980	Navestock	circa 1st October	Adult freshly dead
1988	West Clacton	12th June	
1989	Stanway Green	26th May	
	Birch	27th May	Same as previous
1992	South Woodham Ferrers	17th May	
	East Tilbury	24th May	
	Shoeburyness	2nd June	
	Great Wakering	21st August	
1993	The Naze	20th April	
	Hadleigh Downs	24th June	
1994	Great Wakering	28th April	
	Rayleigh	9th May	
	Colne Point	10th May	
1999	Salcott	11th May	
2003	Gunners Park	24th April	
2004	Goodmayes	24th June	

There had been 345 British records to the end of 2004 (BBRC 2005) with 30 in 1994 the most in any one year. The majority of records involve 'fly-overs', making it a very difficult species to catch up with in this country. The BBRC describes the Black Kite as an "easy-to-identify but difficult-to-prove" species; it had the highest rejection rate of any BBRC rarity. National records have increased markedly since 1971, linked to an increase on the near-Continent. Most occur in spring with numbers peaking in late May/early June and involving presumed over-shooting migrants head ing north. A few are recorded through summer and autumn, sometimes as late as mid-November. Essex records follow this pattern very closely with all but two in spring between 19th April and 25th June.

Several were released from London Zoo in 1957 and subsequently seen twice over Stratford on 24th October (Homes 1957). Odd birds were also known to have escaped from Colchester Zoo in 2003 and 2004.

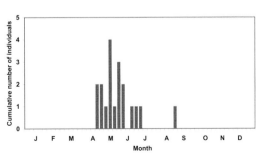

Seasonal occurrence of Black Kites from 1971-2004

Red Kite   *Milvus milvus*

Uncommon but increasing passage migrant: last bred in 1854   Amber List

The Red Kite primarily inhabits the temperate and west Mediterranean zones of the southwest Palearctic; it is very much a European species (European Atlas). The nominate race *milvus* occurs throughout much of the species' range. Some areas of Europe have shown increases in populations in recent years, whereas in others there have been declines. In Britain, until recently, the species was confined to mid-Wales but since the late 1980s introduction schemes have successfully returned the species to many areas.

The earliest reference to the species is prior to 1768 at "Leighs Priory". From the surprisingly scant written evidence available, the Red Kite was probably a common resident until the end of the 18th century. By the early 19th century, many were commenting on its decline (Christy).
At Witham in 1834 the species was probably still breeding but it was noted: "There used to be a good many of them round here once, but there are not many of them now". Red Kites were reckoned to be extinct around Epping Forest by 1835 "... thanks to the gamekeepers ..." and by 1838 had disappeared from around Saffron Walden where once they had been common. The species was still nesting around Kelvedon until the mid-1830s and occurred in Stroodland Grove, Mersea Island, in 1845. Red Kites also bred at High Woods, Writtle (dates unknown) whilst Great Wood, Hempstead, was appar-

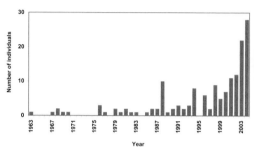

Annual totals of Red Kites from 1963-2004

ently a famous haunt; Red Kites were regularly slain there when attempting to take chickens and their wings and tail feathers half filled a drawer. The last documented nesting took place at Maldon in 1854, when eggs were taken from a nest; Christy donated the eggs to the EFC Museum where they remain (Accession No. 11342) (Christy 1903). However, it is quite possible that odd pairs survived until about 1870 when breeding may have occurred at Finchingfield. Occasional birds were recorded up to about 1880, either the last Essex residents or migrants. Thereafter there were just three records prior to 1950, in 1925, 1948 and 1949.

Between 1950 and 1980, the Red Kite remained rare with just 12 records (Cox). Subsequently, its incidence has increased steadily, and the species has been recorded annually in small numbers since 1985, apart from 1995. The 2003 total was almost double that recorded in any previous year. If numbers continue to increase, there is every possibility of the Red Kite once again breeding in Essex. Indeed, one pair was resident in the northwest of the county during 2004, although breeding was not confirmed.

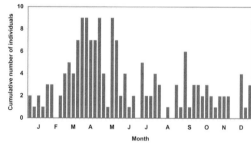

Seasonal occurrence of Red Kites from 1963-2004

The recent increase has probably been due largely to the success of the reintroduction programmes. Wing-tagged birds from these schemes have been noted on occasions. One of two at Abberton from October–December 1992 was found poisoned in Bedfordshire in spring 1993, and two were in the Waltham Abbey/Upshire area in August 1994. However, it is clear that Continental Red Kites reach Essex, as two German-ringed birds have been found dead: Havering, 6th April 1976; The Naze, 24th December 1987. Both were ringed as nestlings in the former East Germany; there are just three other British recoveries of foreign-ringed nestlings, two from Germany and one from Denmark (Migration Atlas). Minor influxes in spring 1988 and autumn 2001 occurred during/after easterly winds and presumably involved Continental birds. Multiple occurrences have been rare, three at Great Braxted on 19th May 2002 being the most reported together.

Records generally peak around late March/early April with no obvious autumn passage.

Records show a wide geographic spread across Essex with no sites particularly favoured; more are, however, recorded inland than on the coast.

Sponsored by John Davis, Mid-Wales Birdwatching Holidays

White-tailed (Sea) Eagle

Haliaeetus albicilla

Vagrant: occasional 19th century winter visitor but just four 20th century records, the last in 1928

Red List

The monotypic White-tailed Eagle breeds across the northernmost Palearctic region as well as southeast Europe, Asia Minor and Greenland. Adults are generally sedentary unless severe weather forces them to move, but juveniles are prone to wandering. Severe persecution was responsible for eliminating the species from many areas of Europe during the 1800s (European Atlas). White-tailed Eagles were more common than the Golden Eagle but by 1916 the species was extinct in Britain. A long-term reintroduction programme has been underway in Scotland since 1975.

1829/30	Stour Wood	Winter	One of four shot
about 1832	Shoeburyness	Undated	Shot
1835	near Shoebury	1st August	Adult shot
prior to 1845	Epping Forest	Undated	Shot
1867	Hylands Park, Chelmsford	11th January	Shot
1868	Alresford	December	Immature
1890	near Colchester	End of year	Immature, shot
1892	Virley	Undated	Shot
1906	Great Oakley	Undated	Immature, shot
1909	Weald CP	16th February	
1926	Finchingfield	January and February	Immature
1928	Navestock Lake	1st February	

Remains attributed to White-tailed Eagles have been found in the brick-earth deposits at Walthamstow (Michael Daniels pers. comm.). Eagles, almost certainly White-tailed Eagles, are referred to in "The Battle of Maldon", an Anglo-Saxon poem dating from 991; this is the oldest text to mention a species of bird in Essex.

A 1908 record referred to by Glegg as a probable White-tailed Eagle was actually a Spotted Eagle (Green 2003), whilst the 1868 individual was later trapped at Thornham, Suffolk (Green 2004a). Old writers often referred to White-tailed Eagles as Golden Eagles, a species that possibly occurred in the early 19th century. This undoubtedly caused confusion over the identity of early specimens. However, Christy and Glegg described the species as an occasional winter visitor, principally to the coast, and White-tailed Eagles may have been almost annual in very small numbers in the early decades of the 19th century if the few confirmed records are representative. In correspondence, Sheppard (1836), the son of the vicar of Wrabness, wrote: "Almost every winter we see eagles at Wrabness. Once, walking ... on the banks of the river Stour, we saw four together. They were then principally preying upon the Coots. It is a curious sight to see the Eagle drive up a flock of many thousands of Coot ... into a thick knot, and to see then with fluttering wings scrambling over each other, some under water, some above. The eagle then very deliberately, picks one up, and flies to the ooze, or, if in very severe weather, perhaps to some floating ice, where he devours his victim ... I used to try all manner of schemes to shoot an Eagle, but I never succeeded ... They were sometimes shot by the fowlers on the river and the gamekeepers in the woods". The species was seen " ... on the shore, but very rarely" in Rochford Hundred prior to 1832, although in Christy's time his correspondent, G. P. Hope, stated that the species was " ... often seen passing up the coast and is not uncommon off the main".

A number of other reports of eagles are probably attributable to this species:

1839	Forest Hall, Ongar	Shot	
1879	Manningtree	December	
1880	Hatfield Forest	December	
about 1883	Danbury	Six months during winter	
1887	Wivenhoe	November and December	
1929	Stapleford Tawney	15th December	Immature

Glegg did not mention the 1868, 1883 or 1887 records detailed by Christy and subsequent writers therefore omitted them.

There have been a number of recent records of White-tailed Eagles in Kent, Suffolk and Norfolk; a modern county record is therefore long overdue. However, despite the success of the Scottish breeding programme, it is likely that any records will probably involve wandering individuals from the northwest European wintering population.

One at Epping on 13th August 1992 had escaped from Whipsnade Zoo, Bedfordshire.

Egyptian Vulture   *Neophron percnopterus*

Vagrant: one 19th century record

The Egyptian Vulture breeds in Iberia and north-west Africa and discontinuously east to southwest Asia with western populations wintering south of the Sahara in Africa. The nominate race *percnopterus*, occurs throughout Europe.

| 1868 | Peldon | 28th September | Immature, shot |

"On the 28th September last the labourer who had charge of an off-hand farm of Mr. Woodward of Stanway Hall, situated at Peldon, Essex, had been killing his Michaelmas Geese. On going some time after in the yard where the said Geese had been slaughtered, he saw a strange bird feeding upon the blood. The bird flew away, and the man loaded his gun. Presently, the bird came and hovered over the spot in the hopes of another spell at the blood; but his fate was sealed, and he fell dead to the labourer's shot" (Christy). The respected Colchester taxidermist, Ambrose, preserved the specimen. It was lent to John Gould, who used it as the model for the illustration in his *Birds of Great Britain* (1862–73). It was sold at auction in 1910 for £38 17s, a considerable sum of money. The specimen is now in the Booth Museum, Brighton (Accession No. 207175).

The first and only other accepted British record is of one at Kilve Cliffs, Somerset, in October 1825.

Christy made another rather intriguing reference to "… a flock of Vultures, for several days amongst the large trees …" on a farm at Burnham-on-Crouch many years previous, "… they were known by their bare heads, and were most probably the Egyptian Vulture".

(Eurasian) Marsh Harrier   *Circus aeruginosus*

Uncommon summer resident, with breeding occurring annually since 1999, common passage migrant and uncommon winter visitor   Amber List

The Marsh Harrier has a wide distribution, the nominate race *aeruginosus* occurring in the lowlands of Europe and Asia with others occurring in northern Africa, Indian Ocean, Australian and Pacific regions (European Atlas). The species is widespread in Europe and occurs in open wetlands, although it will adapt to drier conditions locally. Across Europe, numbers have generally increased steadily since the 1970s, particularly in the north. Increases have been attributed to the banning of DDT, which reduced the British population to just one pair at Minsmere, Suffolk, in 1971, the creation of new reed beds and a reduction in hunting pressures (European Atlas). The British population numbered 222–246 breeding females in 2002 (RBBP 2004). Northern populations are generally migratory, wintering mostly in west and east Africa.

The earliest reference to the species involved one at Littlebury on 1st August 1823. Christy considered the Marsh Harrier a rare winter visitor that had once bred commonly, although even by the 1830s it appeared to have been lost from many areas, presumably due to drainage of the marshlands and perhaps disturbance. Around 1830, the species bred around an old decoy at Tolleshunt D'Arcy, whilst in 1832 it was described as "Frequent in all the marshy districts [of Rochford Hundred] and formerly very common, remaining to breed in the corn or long grass on the marshes at Barling, Foulness … now rarely seen but in the winter months" (Glegg). The reference to breeding in corn is interesting as this habitat accounts for about 10% of breeding records in Britain today (Second National Atlas). Around 1840 in the Paglesham district "… the Marsh Harrier would sometimes be found nesting … few of these nests escaped destruction … all … were rifled".

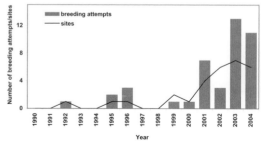

Annual totals of breeding Marsh Harriers from 1990–2004

Despite the significant increase in the British population and the fact that some of the largest breeding concentrations were in adjacent counties, there were few breeding attempts until the mid-1990s. The first Essex breeding record for around 150 years occurred on Foulness in 1992 when two young fledged from a nest of three eggs (Lewis 2000). Breeding also occurred there in 1995 and 1996 but, following nest building in 1999, no further attempts have been made. However, since 1999 breeding has occurred at several sites in the northeast and in the south. Given the increased use of small reed beds and arable crops in adjacent counties and the increasing

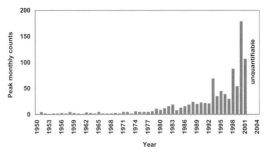

Annual peak monthly counts of Marsh Harriers from 1950-2004

numbers now summering, the somewhat overdue colonisation appears to be in progress; by 2003, at least 14 young were raised from nine nests at three sites in the northeast with breeding activity noted at four other localities.

Outside the breeding season, numbers declined through the 19th century. Glegg considered the Marsh Harrier no more than an occasional winter visitor, although ten were shot around Tollesbury in the winter of 1880. The decline in the British population was mirrored by a lack of Essex records, just six being noted between 1900 and 1949; numbers remained low during the 1950s and 1960s. Subsequently the species has increased at all seasons as the British population has recovered. Numbers recorded on migration, however, vary considerably from year to year. This may be due to a number of factors including breeding success and weather conditions, both locally and on the Continent during migration.

The Marsh Harrier is not known to migrate in flocks and most Essex records of apparent migrants usually involve 1–2 birds. The majority occur along the coast where recently significant movements have been noted at some sites: day counts of up to five individuals are now regular at many. The largest single site counts have been: 15–25 through Wakering Tip, 22nd September 2000; 15 on Foulness, 8th September 2002; ten on Foulness, 13th August 2000. Passage in autumn 2000 was exceptional, and the total of around 142 during the fortnight 17th–30th September was greater than every other complete autumn passage bar 2001 and 2002. This two-week period was exceptional for several species of migrant raptor.

Spring migration begins as early as late February/early March but the main movement does not occur until late April, with numbers peaking in late May/early June. Autumn passage begins around late July, although the increasing number of summering birds has masked this in recent years. Migrants peak in late August/early September with the majority having left by the end of the month. Winter records are scarce, albeit almost annual although only 1–2 individuals are normally involved; up to five were, however, present in 2000/01 and 2001/02 and perhaps as many as ten in 2002/03 and 15 in 2003/04. Most winter records in Britain involve females close or near to their nest site (Winter Atlas).

Marsh Harriers are recorded regularly from all around the coast and along the main estuaries. Inland records are now regular and, although the majority have come from Abberton and Hanningfield, reports have come from across Essex.

There have been no ringing recoveries involving Essex, except for a nestling ringed at Benacre, Suffolk, in July 1997 that was found dead in Epping Forest one month later. However, recoveries in Britain of birds ringed in Denmark, Germany and the Netherlands suggest that some of our passage birds are Continental. The majority, however, probably come from the British population.

The main threats to the continued recovery of the Marsh Harrier in Britain and its regular establishment in Essex as a breeder are deliberate disturbance of nesting sites, egg collecting and persecution and predation, principally by Foxes (Batten *et al.* 1990). Given the healthy breeding populations in 2001 in Norfolk (106 nests), Suffolk (41 pairs) and Kent (16 pairs), (RBBP 2003 & 2004), it is to be hoped that there will be a steady increase in Essex. However, close liaison with the farming community will be required as nesting in crops is almost inevitable: on the Isle of Sheppey, Kent, in 1997 almost 50% of breeding attempts were in either Wheat or Oil-seed Rape (Rowlands 1999).

Hen Harrier   *Circus cyaneus*

Fairly common passage migrant and winter visitor   Red List

The Hen Harrier is a widespread species typical of open habitats, and is found throughout many of the northerly areas of the Northern Hemisphere. The range of the nominate subspecies *cyaneus* stretches from Eire in western

Europe to Kamchatka and Sakhalin Island in Siberia (European Atlas). Across Europe, most populations are declining, possibly due to habitat destruction or deterioration and, locally, persecution. In Britain, it is typical of the undulating moorlands of Scotland, northern England and Wales, although young forest plantations are also favoured (Second National Atlas). The latest national survey located 749 pairs in 2004 (RSPB). Following declines in Britain caused by persecution in the late 19th and early 20th centuries, the species increased after the 1930s, although persecution on grouse moors appears to be a limiting factor in populations expanding further (European Atlas). Hen Harriers are entirely migratory in north and east Continental Europe, but only partial and short-distance migrants in western Europe (Ferguson-Lees & Christie 2001).

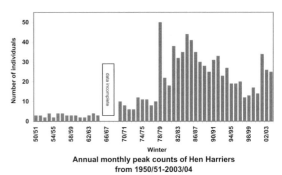

Annual monthly peak counts of Hen Harriers from 1950/51-2003/04

Although Christy stated "… there can be no question that it once bred commonly in Essex", he presented no firm evidence to back up his assertion. Around 1821 Hen Harriers were "not uncommon about the marshes of Kent and Essex, bordering on London" and in 1832 "… frequent on the marshes and seashore from Shoebury eastward …", whilst it was frequently taken around Sudbury about 1845. Unfortunately, no mention is made of the season these observations were made. The Hen Harrier bred in the Fens and Broads of Norfolk until 1861 (Taylor *et al.* 1999) and in northwest Suffolk in the 1830s (Piotrowski 2003). Although there have been no subsequent breeding records, a female summered in the far northwest from 5th May–27th September 1985 with perhaps the same bird from 20th June–13th July 1986. A ring-tail was at Old Hall on 6th June 2001.

The earliest documented record involved a male shot somewhere in Essex prior to 1738 (Christy). Most early specimens were shot, including one at Harwich in 1879 "… the one that was shot had just struck down and killed a Gull that was teasing it. It did not attempt to follow the Gull, which was picked up by a man who then shot the Harrier".

Glegg added few records, noting that the Hen Harrier was "… now a scarce winter visitor to Essex, to which its visits are becoming less frequent". Numbers may have increased by the 1960s when Hudson & Pyman suggested that 4–5 regularly wintered and described the species as a scarce passage migrant and winter visitor. Numbers continued to increase with at least ten wintering throughout the 1970s (Cox) and a significant influx in early 1979 after which numbers rose to a peak in the mid-1980s before declining through the 1990s, only to increase again in the early 21st century. Do raptors, as appears to be the case with wildfowl, change their subsequent wintering areas following a severe weather event?

The severe weather of early 1979 saw the greatest influx of Hen Harriers yet recorded with around 50 counted at roosts, with 12 at Old Hall the largest. In all, some 750 were reported across England in 1978/79 (Davenport 1982).

Accurate counts of Hen Harriers are difficult because individuals hunt over large areas. This, together with Essex's long, indented coastline, means that individuals can easily visit a number of widely dispersed sites within one day. Organised counts at winter roosts therefore probably provide the most accurate assessment of wintering numbers but, prior to the 1980s, a lack of such counts hampered knowledge of its status (Cox). Roosts have been located at various times at Hamford Water, Langenhoe, Old Hall, Dengie and Foulness. Foulness held the largest single roost with peak counts of 24 in the 1983/84 winter and 28 in 1984/85; more recently there were 18 on 13th January 2002. Elsewhere, there were 12 at Old Hall on 17th February 1979 and ten in January 1983 and 14 on Langenhoe from November–December 1985 and ten in November and December 1990.

Hen Harrier numbers generally peak from November to February but individuals occur with some regularity as early as August and as late as April and early May. In some years, numbers peak in November and again in March, suggesting onward movement through Essex. Excluding the previously mentioned summering individuals, there have been three (all ring-tails) in July: Bradwell, 30th July–6th August 1994; Bradwell, 4th in 1995; Old Hall, 7th in 1995. One at Bradwell on 29th May 1983 is the latest in that month. Around 4–5 were present on Dengie and in the adjacent Blackwater Estuary in August 2004.

Hen Harriers hunt over the marshes and adjacent farmland along the entire coastline and occur with regularity along all the principal estuaries, including the Thames to Rainham and beyond. A noticeable decline at Rainham in the late 1980s may be due to disturbance by falconers (*EBR* 1990). Prior to the 1970s, inland records away from Abberton were rare. However, through the 1970s occasional singles were reported from a number of sites, and during 1978/79 several were noted several kilometres inland, since when occurrences have been almost annual. The majority have involved singles observed on one day only. However, records from Writtle in 1988, 1991 and 1993 and again from 1998–2001 suggest some site fidelity to inland sites. Three were in northwest Essex in the winter of 1983/84, whilst a female stayed in the Ashdon/Hadstock area from mid-October to the end of November 1973.

An individual at Bradwell on 17th September 1989 showed bright orange underparts that are more typical of the American race (Marsh Hawk *C. c. hudsonius*).

Until the start of the British Hen Harrier project in 1988, it was assumed that most passage and wintering Hen Harriers in southeast England were of Dutch origin. This was supported by the recovery at Peldon in October 1980 of one ringed as a nestling at Ballum, Ameland, in June 1980. However, since 1988 six Scottish, one English and one Welsh wing-tagged birds have occurred in Essex: four from Perthshire and singles from Tayside and the central highlands; one from the Forest of Bowland, Lancashire; and one from the very small Powys, Wales, population. These birds disappeared in late autumn suggesting that they were still on migration. Indeed, at least one marked bird from this study has been seen in France and furthermore the BTO has details of eight others that have travelled as far as Spain and Portugal. Thus the winter population appears to be made up of both British and Continental birds (Migration Atlas).

Pallid Harrier   *Circus macrourus*

Vagrant: one record

The monotypic Pallid Harrier breeds from Eastern Europe, east as far as Mongolia and winters in Africa, the Middle East and India.

1993	Dengie	13th–15th June	2nd-summer male

Despite its three-day stay, this individual was extremely elusive (Miller 1994). Up to the end of 2004, there had been just 21 British records (BBRC 2005), although until 1993 there had been just three, the last in 1952. There were five in 1993, four in 2003 and three in 2002. A juvenile wintered in Norfolk during 2002/03. The reason for the remarkable change in status is unclear but may be due to habitat change within the Asian breeding grounds (BBRC 2004).

Montagu's Harrier   *Circus pygargus*

Uncommon passage migrant: has bred on four occasions   Amber List

The monotypic Montagu's Harrier is a Palearctic species that breeds from western Europe across to central Siberia with western populations wintering in sub-Saharan Africa. In Britain, the species declined during the 19th century, increased in the first half of the 20th century but then declined again from the mid-1950s (Batten *et al.* 1990). Originally a species of steppe and marsh it has, during the 20th century, adapted to a wider variety of breeding habitats and in Britain is increasingly using cereal crops (European Atlas). It is a rare breeder in England and Wales with 7–11 pairs in 2002 (RBBP 2004) and with never more than 40–50 pairs recorded (*BWP*).

Christy described the Montagu's Harrier as "A rare and accidental visitor, though once common in fenny districts". Whether "fenny districts" refers to Essex is unclear but there were no definite 19th century breeding records as Glegg felt that a report of a summering pair at Hornchurch in July 1889 had "… an element of uncertainty" about it. Ticehurst (1932) considered the species to be the commonest harrier in East Anglia in the early 19th century. Of the eight records Christy detailed, the earliest involved one shot at Colchester prior to 1832. Glegg detailed nine satisfactory records and noted that the species was occasionally recorded on passage, chiefly in autumn. There were very few records between 1930 and 1949.

Montagu's Harriers have nested successfully in Essex on three occasions with single pairs on Horsey Island in 1939 and 1940 (Hudson & Pyman) and on Dengie

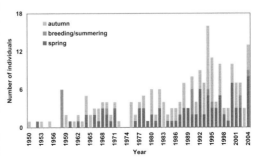

Annual totals of Montagu's Harriers from 1950-2004

in 1990 where two young fledged from a nest in a field of Oil-seed Rape (Pease & Sutherby 1991). A pair bred unsuccessfully on Dengie in 1964. Summering birds were noted in 1958 (an exceptional year nationally, with two pairs at Old Hall, a pair on Foulness and 2–3 females elsewhere) and in 1966, 1969, 1990 (two), 1994 (two) and 1995, all on Foulness. In 2002, two first-year females toured northeast Essex, whilst a pair summered on Fobbing Marshes in 2004.

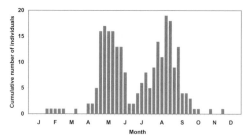

Seasonal occurrence of migrant Montagu's Harriers from 1950-2004

Hudson & Pyman knew of 24 records of migrants between 1950 and 1966 to which Cox added 35–37 for the period 1967–81. Records have been annual since 1958, apart from 1973 and 1974, when the British population reached a low point, with no breeding pairs present in 1974 and 1975 (Batten *et al.* 1990). Since 1981, numbers have increased steadily probably as a result of increased observer coverage and a very slow recovery of the English breeding population.

Numbers passing through peak in early May and again in late August/early September. Apart from a male on Foulness from 4th February–3rd March 1968, the earliest arrival was a female at Burnham-on-Crouch on 19th March 1978. In autumn, the latest individual was at Old Hall on 30th November 1995, whilst one was trapped at Paslow Hall, High Ongar, in the third week of November 1887. The former was believed to have been the controversial individual previously at Stiffkey, Norfolk (Forsman 1995).

Most records come from coastal areas, many from the wide open spaces of Dengie and Foulness. Only 17 (all singles) have occurred inland: Abberton, a total of nine; Rainham, a male, 30th May 1986, a ring-tail, 15th-16th June 1990 and an immature male, 28th May 2001; Hanningfield, a juvenile, 29th August 1964; Hornchurch CP, a male, 2nd May 1988; Strethall, a female, 2nd June 1981; Marks Tey, 28th September 1999; northwest chalk, a second-summer male, 17th June 2000.

There have been no ringing recoveries involving Essex and indeed there is a paucity of such records from other areas of eastern and northern England, suggesting that many sightings relate to British-bred birds. However, the erratic numbers of migrants occurring each year suggest that at least some may be of Continental origin.

(Northern) Goshawk   *Accipiter gentilis*

Uncommon resident (breeding not yet proven) and passage migrant

This large and powerful raptor has a widespread Holarctic distribution and occurs throughout much of Europe where it is represented by the nominate race *gentilis*; northernmost European populations are of the race *buteoides*. The British population has increased in recent years, despite continuing persecution, to 217–297 pairs in 2002 (RBBP 2004).

The Goshawk has some of the earliest written references of any Essex bird. In the Court 'fines' of the 12th and 13th centuries there were a surprising number of references suggesting that Goshawks were probably relatively common (Glegg). Edmund Bert of Collier Row successfully trained Goshawks and wrote a book entitled *An approved treatise of Hawks and Hawking* in 1619. Escaped Goshawks were recorded as early as 1822 when a female with jesses was shot at Audley End.

By the end of the 19th century, the Goshawk had all but died out as a British breeding species due to heavy persecution and deforestation (Batten *et al.* 1990). Christy gave only two records; a third was just in Suffolk. Glegg, without explanation, dismissed records at Potton Island in 1881 and Hutton Hall around 1898, considering just one record acceptable, one at Harwich in the winter of 1895. One was seen near Braintree on 19th March 1942, but its identification was not considered proven by H. F. Witherby; Hudson & Pyman considered none of the early records acceptable.

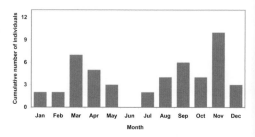

Seasonal occurrence of Goshawks away from known summering sites from 1982-2004

From the mid-1960s, Goshawks began to breed again at very low density throughout Britain, principally in the large state-owned forests. However, continuing persecution probably slowed any spread and it was not until 1982 that the first modern Essex record occurred, one at Hadleigh Downs on 6th November. It is thought likely that the re-established population derived almost entirely from escaped or released falconers' birds, the population growing noticeably in the 1970s at a time when large numbers were imported with many being released (Historical Atlas). According to DEFRA statistics, there are more falconers' Goshawks kept in Essex than in any other county and at least 12 have escaped over the last 14 years (Graham Ekins pers. obs.); individuals with jesses are regularly reported.

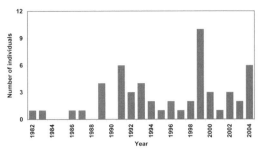

Annual totals of Goshawks away from known summering sites from 1982-2004

The first signs of breeding activity occurred in 1989, when a pair displayed at Hanningfield, whilst a male displayed regularly at a site in central Essex in spring 1991. From 1994, a pair was present and periodically displayed over a north Essex wood for a time but from 1999–2003 only a male was present; a female appeared in 2004. Breeding behaviour was also noted at single sites in 1996 and 2001 and at two sites in 2003. Two juveniles were over Little Clacton on 27th August 2004.

Goshawks have been recorded annually since 1991 with by far the most reported in a year away from known summering sites being ten in 1999.

Records show distinct spring and autumn peaks. The spring peak may, at least in part, be due to the species being more conspicuous whilst displaying but in autumn, dispersal from local breeding grounds may be a significant factor. However, one Scandinavian-ringed bird has been recovered in Britain, so some individuals may be genuine vagrants from further east. It seems from the lack of records that Goshawks leave known summering localities during winter — or is observer coverage poor at this time?

(Eurasian) Sparrowhawk   *Accipiter nisus*

Common resident, passage migrant and winter visitor

The Sparrowhawk breeds in the Palearctic, from Madeira and Europe to eastern Siberia, Sakhalin Island and Japan. In Europe, where the nominate race *nisus* occurs, the species inhabits all woodland types, but prefers 15–40-year-old conifer plantations interspersed with farmland and villages. However, it has increasingly utilised pure deciduous woodlands, copses, marshes and urban areas (European Atlas). Populations collapsed in northwest Europe during the 1950s due to the use of organochlorine pesticides but following a ban on their use, numbers have increased significantly since 1970. In Britain the recovery was rapid with east and central England recolonised within ten years; the species now nests at some of the highest densities in Europe (European Atlas), the current population being 40,000 pairs. Central and southern populations tend to be generally sedentary but migratory tendencies increase further north in the species' range.

Remains of Sparrowhawks and thrushes found at a Roman site at Great Holts, Boreham, may suggest early hawking, although the Sparrowhawk may have been used as a decoy (AML Report 9/97).

Christy described the Sparrowhawk as "… a fairly common resident, but decreasing through incessant persecution". Glegg considered the species "an uncommon resident, sparingly distributed throughout the county", although more common in the north than the south, but added "There can be little doubt that it is a much-decreased species …" He blamed gamekeepers for the decline and considered further decreases likely. Protection was, however, not advocated as any advantages gained by it destroying "… injurious birds … is outweighed by the amount of destruction of poultry, game birds and insectivorous birds". Declines in gamekeeping during the two world wars undoubtedly relieved pressure on Sparrowhawk populations, and following WWII gamekeeping never regained its former prevalence and continued to decline. A random survey during 1949–51 revealed that the Sparrowhawk was sparsely distributed and that in some extensively wooded areas several pairs were nesting in close proximity. It was absent from only the most highly populated areas.

Anecdotal evidence suggested that by the late 1950s the Sparrowhawk was in serious decline. In 1959 and 1960, about ten pairs were reported across Essex but just two in 1966. Between 1967 and 1973 there was just one breeding record, at Navestock in 1969; the nest was destroyed. In 1969, there were just ten sight records.

The cause of the decline was attributed to the introduction into agriculture of organochlorine pesticides, which are easily absorbed by body fat and are very persistent and accumulate within birds' bodies. As a bird-eating raptor, the Sparrowhawk accumulated sufficient residues to depress its reproduction and survival. DDT, first used in 1947, caused eggshell thinning that reduced breeding success. However, the more toxic cyclodiene products, such as aldrin and dieldrin which came into use in 1956, directly poisoned many Sparrowhawks. Thus by 1960 the species disappeared from many of the

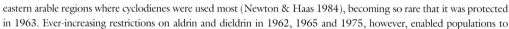

Annual totals of breeding pairs/territories of Sparrowhawks from 1957-2004

eastern arable regions where cyclodienes were used most (Newton & Haas 1984), becoming so rare that it was protected in 1963. Ever-increasing restrictions on aldrin and dieldrin in 1962, 1965 and 1975, however, enabled populations to recover. In Essex, the recovery was very slow and it was not until the 1980s that a marked increase occurred. Nationally, it is now more abundant than at any time since the 19th century (Second National Atlas) and the same is probably true in Essex where it may now be more common than the Kestrel.

Atlas	Survey Area	% of 10km squares or tetrads in which	
		bred/probably bred	possibly bred or present
First National 10km	Essex	14.0	28.1
Second National 10km	Essex	36.8	36.8
First London Tetrad	Met. Essex	1.5	2.5
Second London Tetrad	Met. Essex	54.5	24.0
Essex Tetrad	Essex	30.1	18.2

Summary of results of Atlas surveys for Sparrowhawks

The apparent rapid increase at the end of the 1980s was perhaps due, in part, to greater observer coverage during the Essex Atlas survey, which found Sparrowhawks commonest in well-wooded areas of the southwest and central parts and scarcest in the northwest and coastal areas. Subsequently, the species has continued to increase and expand its range and can now be found in most suburban areas of the southwest: of 151 pairs reported in 2000, almost half were in Metropolitan Essex. It has also spread into coastal regions and the northwest. Based on breeding densities of 12–18 pairs per 100 km² in Suffolk (Wright 2001), the Essex population lies in the region of 475–715 pairs, which correlates well with the species' presence in 515 (48.3%) tetrads during the Essex Atlas survey.

Such resilience to the efforts of gamekeepers and poison, and the ability to bounce back rapidly, results from the species' high reproductive rate, an early age of first breeding and strong density dependent factors that control numbers — there is a high proportion of non-breeding, non-territorial birds that are able rapidly to occupy vacant territories (Historical Atlas).

Outside the breeding season, Sparrowhawks appear to disperse from breeding areas and it has been suggested that winter numbers are smaller than the breeding population (*EBR* 1991). Glegg noted: "… there is said to be a certain amount of movement, if not migration in October and March, the empty woods receiving new tenants in the spring. My dated records from the marshes along the coast and estuaries suggest that there is a certain amount of movement to this area chiefly in autumn". This appears to be true today with coastal records suggesting both dispersal from breeding areas and immigration. At the main coastal watchpoints, increased numbers are noted in spring and autumn with individuals regularly noted arriving off or heading out to sea. Counts of nine at The Naze on 31st March 2002, eight on 4th September 2002 and 12 on 31st August 2003, and totals of 19 through Colne Point in August and September 1993, 13 through The Naze in October 1994, 12 through Bradwell in October 1992 and ten there in August 1993 and September 1998, strongly suggest movement through Essex. These movements are not restricted to coastal areas: there were 20–30 on both 30th September and 1st October 2000 at Oliver's Orchard, Colchester, during the unprecedented movement of Honey-buzzards and other raptors, and 16 moved south at Newport over five days in late October 2001 with seven heading south in just under two hours on 5th October 2002. Numbers of presumed migrants have increased as the British population has recovered. As the British population is supposedly very sedentary (Newton 1986), birds from elsewhere must be assumed to be responsible for the increases, suggesting that populations on the Continent may be increasing as well.

Three foreign-ringed Sparrowhawks have been recovered in Essex, all during winter, two from Germany and one from the Netherlands. All were ringed in spring or autumn and thus may have involved north European birds on passage to Britain; most Continental Sparrowhawks that winter in Britain come from Norway and Denmark with fewer from Sweden and Finland (Migration Atlas). Two birds controlled in Essex are strongly suggestive of onward migration: one ringed at Spurn in September 1955 was found a month later at Earls Colne, whilst one ringed at Ickburgh, Norfolk, was controlled two months later at Pitsea in November 1993. A second-year bird ringed on North Ronaldsay, Orkney Islands, in May 1993 was found dead at Eastwood in May 1996.

The Sparrowhawk has been accused of causing the decline of songbird populations and calls have been made to control its numbers. However, the decline in songbirds pre-dated the increase in Sparrowhawk numbers and some of its commonest prey species, for example Great Tit, have in general increased. With its continued spread, the amount of territory available for new pairs is diminishing and it is possible that the population is close to an upper limit set by prey availability, although the Woodpigeon, upon which the Sparrowhawk preys, is abundant. Continuing declines in farmland birds may also affect numbers overall. Apart from these two possible problems its remarkable resilience should ensure that the species is secure for the foreseeable future.

(Common) Buzzard   *Buteo buteo*

Uncommon but increasing resident, passage migrant and winter visitor

The Buzzard is widespread throughout the Palearctic, the nominate race *buteo* occurring in the west and in northern Fennoscandia and eastern Europe where it intergrades with *vulpinus* which, unlike the largely resident or partly migratory nominate race, is a long-distance migrant wintering mostly in east and south Africa (European Atlas). The British population, which is steadily increasing, numbers some 44,000–61,000 pairs (Clements 2002).

Once abundant throughout Britain, the Buzzard was declining rapidly by the mid-18th century because of relentless persecution. In Essex, written evidence of its status is rather thin and vague and, although it appeared to breed in several areas in the early 19th century, it seems to have been uncommon. Christy noted that it bred uncommonly in the woods of Rochford Hundred and around the coast to about 1830–35 but had ceased to do so around Epping Forest, Sudbury and other inland districts by that date. Christy's correspondent Rev. J. C. Atkinson recalled: "I well remember as a schoolboy [at Kelvedon] ... some thirty odd years ago [about 1830], that the nests of the "Puttock", as the Buzzard was invariably called in that district, were more frequently found by us than those of any other wood-building Hawk; and many a hatch of young "Puttocks" it fell to my lot to see brought within the old school gates". This record was, however, not confirmed by other writers of the time (Glegg). The last 19th century breeding record came from Purleigh where a nest with two eggs was taken in 1865; they remain in the Essex Field Club collection (Accession No. 11341). To Glegg the Buzzard was an uncommon and irregular winter visitor.

No further breeding attempts occurred until 1950 when nest-building was noted at Littlebury, although both birds left before laying. Despite the very slow eastward spread of the British population very few were noted in Essex and it was not until 1977 that a pair summered again at Margaretting with another pair there in 1983. During the 1990s, but particularly around the turn of the 21st century, the Buzzard became re-established as a regular breeder. To the end of 2002, a total of eight pairs had definitely bred with the first successful breeding for nearly 130 years occurring in 1994, when a pair fledged two young at a site in the northwest. Since then, the breeding population has expanded at a relatively rapid rate.

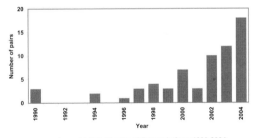

Annual totals of pairs of Buzzards from 1990-2004

Along with the increase in breeding/summering records, annual numbers of Buzzards have increased, particularly since 1993, following what was at the time the largest influx of Buzzards into Essex. Whilst increased observer coverage may have been a contributory factor, the rapid increase in the last ten years or so suggests that other factors have been involved. Given the expansion of the breeding population, it has become impossible to differentiate resident birds from migrants.

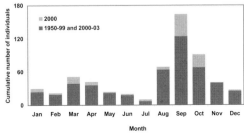

Seasonal occurrence of Buzzards away from known breeding areas from 1988-2003

There have been several apparent influxes and the timing and frequency of some at least point to a Continental origin; large scale movements have been noted in recent years along the Suffolk (Piotrowski 2003) and Norfolk (Taylor *et al.* 1999) coasts. Whether these are also linked in some way to population growth is unclear. However, the species is doing well in Norfolk with a maximum of 33 breeding pairs in 2003 (*Norfolk Bird Report*); the origin of these is uncertain as, apart from rumoured illegal releases, the Institute of Terrestrial Ecology has been carrying out a controlled release scheme in Norfolk to assess habitat requirement (Taylor *et al.* 1999). Currently there is no evidence to suggest whether our population is derived from other counties, from the Continent where perhaps populations are increasing, or from released birds.

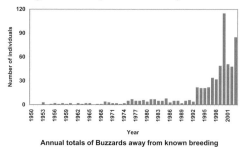

Annual totals of Buzzards away from known breeding areas from 1950-2003

It should be borne in mind that given the species' propensity to wander over large areas the figures given in the graph might overestimate numbers. The influx of 60–65 individuals in autumn 2000 coincided with the huge influx of Honey-buzzards and other raptors.

Most occur during autumn passage with numbers peaking significantly around the end of August and early September. A smaller spring passage is also evident with numbers generally peaking in March and April. Breeding birds from the northwest of Essex appear to disperse away from summer territories during winter.

Records have come from across Essex. In influx years, more are recorded inland than on the coast, except in 1993. Unlike Norfolk and Suffolk, where day counts of up to 32 from individual sites have been recorded (Taylor *et al.* 1999, Piotrowski 2003), there have been no multiple arrivals of Buzzards along the coast and almost every record away from breeding/summering areas has involved single birds and rarely 2–3. However, in late September and early October 2000 there were seven over Galleyhill Wood on 15th October with four at Abberton on both 22nd September and 6th October, and Oliver's Orchard on 30th, with counts of two or more from eight sites. Near to breeding areas counts of 5–7 have become regular with 14 on 22nd April 2004 and 12 on 8th September 2004 over Newport notable.

The origin of the Buzzards now breeding and occurring in increasing numbers in spring and autumn remains unknown. Nationally, ringing recoveries of British Buzzards have shown that they do not travel very large distances, most moving less than 100km. The single national recovery from mainland Europe makes it difficult to assess the origins of the regular influxes along the east coast (Migration Atlas).

The Buzzard is probably more common in Essex now than it has been at any time in the last 200 years. With numbers steadily increasing and no obvious threats to its continued success, the species' future, for the time being, seems assured.

Rough-legged Buzzard   *Buteo lagopus*

Scarce passage migrant and winter visitor

The Rough-legged Buzzard has a Holarctic distribution in the arctic and subarctic zones but also nests in the south Scandinavian fells; the nominate race *lagopus* breeds in Europe (European Atlas). It is a migratory species; the timing of autumn departure and distance travelled largely dependent on rodent numbers and the extent of snow cover in breeding areas (Ferguson-Lees & Christie 2001). Most Rough-legged Buzzards winter to the east of the Netherlands with few normally reaching Britain.

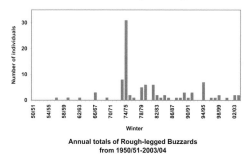

Annual totals of Rough-legged Buzzards
from 1950/51-2003/04

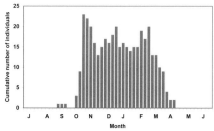

Seasonal occurrence of Rough-legged Buzzards
from 1950-2004

Christy described the Rough-legged Buzzard as "A somewhat rare and irregular visitant chiefly during autumn and winter", the earliest documented occurrence being 1st March 1836 at Saffron Walden. One of Christy's correspondents gave a description of the species' status that holds true of the periodic influxes today, although the numbers he described have not been approached subsequently: "[the Rough-legged Buzzard was] ... common on the coast, first arriving at the end of September, but coming in flocks in very cold weather. I once saw 25 hawking rabbits, over a tract of sand-hills within three miles of Harwich and obtained three of them. In early autumn they seem to come from the east, but in winter from the north". In all, Christy detailed a further 16 or so records including two from inland, one beside the Chelmer at Broomfield in December 1879 and another at Birdbrook around November 1888. Both were shot as were most others reported. Glegg listed around 35 occurrences including one inland at Roxwell in February 1908; most occurred between October and December, with a few between January and March. Just one was recorded between 1930 and 1949 (Hudson & Pyman).

Since 1950, Rough-legged Buzzards have been recorded in 28 winters, with by far the largest influx in 1974/75 and smaller ones in 1973/74 and 1994/95.

Populations of Rough-legged Buzzards in Fennoscandia fluctuate with the rodent populations. When numbers are high, there is a marked southerly migration. In 1974/75, at least 30 birds were recorded, out of a national total of 250 (Scott 1978). The influx began on 22nd October when about six arrived to be followed on 25th by eight, including three at both Fingringhoe Wick and on Foulness. Further arrivals in early November included three at Rolls Farm, Tollesbury, on 3rd that remained for the rest of the year, and two at Tiptree. A final arrival occurred around 17th November, with five on Foulness, four of which remained into January. This influx followed a minor one the previous autumn, suggesting that populations built up over the previous two summers. Numbers fell back the following winter and have been generally low ever since, the most recent influx in autumn 1994 involving around seven individuals, of which only one wintered.

Nationally, numbers typically peak in autumn as migrants arrive on the east coast before dispersing. The earliest arrival was at Abberton on 4th September 1983, the latest at Colne Point on 23rd April 1974.

Most records come from coastal areas with Hamford Water, the mouth of the Colne/Blackwater and Foulness particularly favoured. Since 1950, there have been 20 inland records involving 22 birds, all singles except for two at Long Wood, Tiptree, on 3rd November 1974 and two soaring over Ingatestone on 27th February 1980. Four records have come from Abberton, three from Weeley and two from Margaretting with singles at 11 other sites. Almost all have been observed for just 1–2 days, but singles were at: Weeley, December 1973–early January 1974; Margaretting, 25th October–8th November 1974; Margaretting, March 1977; Great Horkesley, 22nd–31st December 1989; Strethall area, 17th November 1994–1st April 1995.

(Greater) Spotted Eagle *Aquila clanga*

Vagrant: three records

The monotypic Spotted Eagle is a much declined species that breeds from northeast Europe east across to Siberia and winters mainly in the Middle East and northeast Africa.

1891	Elmstead	29th October	Captured alive
	Leigh/Two Tree Island	3rd November	Juvenile, shot
1908	Rettendon/Downham	10th and 13th–14th April	Immature male, shot

All were originally reported as Lesser Spotted Eagles *A. pomarina* but investigations by H. F. Witherby identified the first two as *A. clanga*, whilst Glegg confirmed the identification of the third as *A. clanga*. There are only nine other British records, the most recent being in 1915. The two in 1891 were part of a small influx of four individuals; the others were in Suffolk. The Elmstead specimen was kept alive for some months and Lord Lilford had a drawing made of it by the young Archibald Thorburn for his coloured plates of British birds (Lilford 1885–97). The Leigh/Two Tree Island specimen, currently on display in Southend-on-Sea Museum (Accession No. SOUSM: 660), is in first-class condition.

The corrected dates are now shown for the Rettendon/Downham individual (Green 2003). Glegg listed only 14th April, which was followed by Hudson & Pyman and Cox. The 10th April sighting by P. M. Meeson was published in British Birds but listed by Glegg as a probable immature White-tailed Eagle (q.v.). Naylor (1996) listed the correct dates.

An eagle around the Thaxted area during November and December 1891 may have been of this species; the *Essex Chronicle* newspaper of 11th December 1891 quoted: "The eagle is described as a rusty black character" (Glegg).

Osprey

Pandion haliaetus

Uncommon passage migrant

Amber List

The Osprey is a cosmopolitan species, found on every continent except Antarctica. The nominate race *haliaetus* breeds across the Palearctic. Ospreys are principally summer visitors to the Western Palearctic, breeding mainly in northern and eastern Europe and in some Mediterranean countries and wintering in central and southern Africa, although some stay in the Mediterranean. Until the early 19th century, the species was a common breeder in Scotland but severe persecution reduced the population to extinction in 1917 and

it was not until 1954 that breeding resumed. The current population numbers 163 breeding pairs (RBBP 2004); successful breeding has occurred in Cumbria since 2000 and at Rutland Water, Leicestershire, since 2001, the latter as part of a reintroduction scheme.

According to Glegg, Osprey remains had been found in the peat-beds of Walthamstow.

Christy detailed some 12 records (three others were obtained just inside Suffolk), the earliest both prior to 1730 and involving individuals shot at Maldon and St Osyth. Glegg detailed 13 occurrences, the latest at Weald CP

from 11th–24th October 1903, the few dated records all falling within the typical migration period. However, there are references to one obtained near Colchester in January 1850 and two were reputed to have visited Gosfield Lake "... during one or two winters ..."

One at Gosfield Lake in 1908 was only the 14th Essex record (Hudson & Pyman) and it was 44 years before the next at Boreham on 19th September 1952. The next two records were in 1958 and the species occurred annually from 1965. Numbers have risen steadily since, as the British and Scandinavian populations have increased.

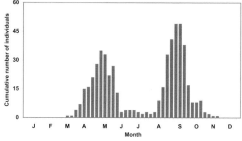

Seasonal occurrence of Ospreys from 1950-2004

Adult Ospreys arrive back on their breeding grounds in Scotland as early as late March but usually April (Thom 1986). Spring passage through Essex peaks in mid-May; second-summer birds migrate north on average a month later than experienced breeders (*BWP*) and probably make up a large percentage of this total.

However, ringing recoveries have shown that Scandinavian birds may occur (Migration Atlas). Indeed this is strongly suggested at Hanningfield where birds that arrive on southeasterly winds and are held up by bad weather during April, invariably move off in a northeasterly direction when they are able (Graham Ekins pers. obs.).

There have been six records during March: Manningtree, 15th in 1981; Holyfield Lake, 24th in 1996; Netherhall GP, 29th in 1987; Weald CP, 30th in 1997; Nazeing, 31st in 1986; and Brentwood, 31st in 1993. Several have occurred in late June and may involve wandering non-breeders.

In autumn, passage peaks in mid-September. A few occur regularly through October but five have been recorded in November: Frating, 2nd in 1999; Maldon area, 8th in 1998 (from 1st October); Steeple Creek, 9th in 1976; Dengie, 11th in 1984; East Mersea, 23rd in 1999.

Whilst Ospreys have been recorded widely, Hanningfield has been particularly favoured, accounting for around 20% of the total since 1950. The fact that it is well stocked with trout and has many substantial trees

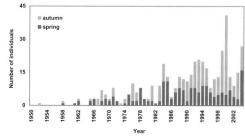

Annual totals of Ospreys from 1950-2004

surrounding it suitable for roosting must be important factors in its favour. Abberton is the next most favoured site, whilst on the coast Br adwell and Dengie are regularly visited.

All records have been of singles, or very occasionally two birds together. A total of six, including a group of three at 1630hrs, flew south from Landguard Point, Suffolk, into Essex on 16th September 2000 (Piotrowski 2003).

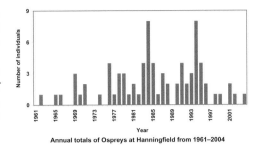

Annual totals of Ospreys at Hanningfield from 1961–2004

Lesser Kestrel   *Falco naumanni*

Vagrant: one record

The monotypic Lesser Kestrel is distributed from southern Europe and north Africa, east through Asia to China. Its European breeding range is mainly Mediterranean (European Atlas). The species has suffered a catastrophic decline, perhaps linked to changing agricultural practices, throughout the western half of its ranges and perhaps, less markedly, in the east too (Ferguson-Lees & Christie 2001).

| 1974 | Rainham | 31st July–3rd August | Adult male |

There are only 18 British records with just two since 1992 (BBRC 2003); until the most recent, a first-summer male on the Isles of Scilly in 2002, the Rainham individual was the last twitchable bird.

(Common) Kestrel   *Falco tinnunculus*

Common resident, passage migrant and winter visitor   Amber List

The Kestrel is widespread across Europe, Asia and Africa. In Europe, where it is represented by the nominate race *tinnunculus*, the species breeds almost everywhere apart from Iceland. It utilises most terrestrial habitats although open country is preferred and dense forests avoided (European Atlas). Like many birds of prey, it declined in parts of Europe in the 1960s and 1970s when organochlorine use was the greatest. This trend, however, was reversed after the chemicals were banned but declines have been noted again in many areas, with a reduction in the breeding population of around 28% in the last 25 years (Gregory *et al.* 2002). Around 37,000 pairs breed in Britain. Whilst northernmost populations are entirely migratory, elsewhere the species is partially migratory or sedentary.

Christy devoted just 20 words to the Kestrel: "A fairly common resident, though partially migratory, and rapidly decreasing on account of the senseless persecution it has to undergo". This persecution by gamekeepers was widespread across Britain (Historical Atlas). Glegg considered the species a not uncommon resident, sparingly distributed across the county and the "… only Hawk to be seen with any degree of regularity by the field observer … It is probably maintaining its numbers."

Hudson & Pyman believed that the Kestrel had "… decreased markedly of late years but may now have begun to recover". The decline began in the 1950s at the time of widespread use of organochlorines with an apparent recovery begin-

Atlas	Survey Area	% of 10km squares or tetrads in which	
		bred/probably bred	possibly bred or present
First National 10km	Essex	89.5	10.5
Second National 10km	Essex	91.2	8.8
First London Tetrad	Met. Essex	21.5	40.5
Second London Tetrad	Met. Essex	71.5	28.0
Essex Tetrad	Essex	73.4	12.4

Summary of results of Atlas surveys for Kestrels

ning in the mid/late 1960s, a similar pattern to that noted across the country. The reduction in some areas in the early 1960s was rapid; for example, five sites regularly occupied in the Lea Valley until 1960 were vacant in 1961. The extent of decline was, however, variable with some areas noting little population change. Despite requests from the editors of the *EBR* for all Kestrel records, the species was reported from just 15 localities in 1963.

The banning of organochlorines saw a reverse in fortune and a steady recovery began; by 1980, 63 pairs were reported, almost certainly a considerable underestimate of the population. Nationally, between 1963 and 1978, the CBC Index increased five-fold. Although Kestrels were recorded in every 10km square in both National Atlas surveys, the number with confirmed breeding increased marginally. The Essex Atlas survey recorded breeding in 73.4% of all tetrads and a presence in a further 12.4%. Populations in urban areas also increased steadily after the pesticide bans, perhaps more so than in the open countryside. In Metropolitan Essex there was an overall increase between the two London Atlas surveys. These apparent increases have, however, been offset in recent years by declines that seem to be taking place in the countryside where intensive agricultural practices may be reducing vole populations, the species' main prey (Essex Atlas), although the problem of organochlorines seems to have persisted at least into the early 1990s, as a Kestrel found dead at Danbury in 1991 contained traces of a breakdown product of DDT known as DDE with traces of mercury and PCBs also present.

Although largely arable, Essex held some of the highest breeding densities during the Second National Atlas survey. Village (1990) gave breeding densities in intensive arable farmland of around 12–32 pairs per 100 km² in Scottish grasslands. In Suffolk, the breeding population was estimated at 660–970 pairs (a density of around 17–25 pairs per 100 km²) between 1995–98 (Wright 2001); Piotrowski (2003), however, suggested a population of 1,200, a density of 31 pairs per 100 km². Extrapolating the Suffolk data to Essex produces a population range of 675–1,225 pairs. Allowing for differences in habitat between the two counties, it would seem reasonable to assume an Essex population of around 600–1,100 pairs.

Kestrels will utilise a wide variety of nesting sites either in natural or man-made locations, particularly derelict buildings. Several parish churches have their own resident Kestrels, as do some of the few castles in Essex. At Colchester Castle, where the species appears to have nested since at least 1920 (Glegg), recesses were left in the wall faces during substantial restoration works to the external walls in the 1980s and early 1990s to encourage the resident birds to stay. The Kestrel takes readily to nest boxes: at the Colchester Garrison Training Area a total of 11 out of 13 was used successfully in 1983; ten clutches were completed and 40 young fledged.

Glegg, unlike Christy, considered the Kestrel to be sedentary, although he acknowledged that irregular movements perhaps took place, noting that 33 were killed in three weeks in March (date unknown) on an estate near Chelmsford. A male was present on the Kentish Knock Lightship on 18th–19th September 1903. More recently there have been reports of visible migration from coastal watchpoints. Occasionally, individuals are watched coming in off the sea or heading out to sea during spring/autumn but obvious movements appear to have largely gone unnoticed, although ten were observed flying south from Landguard Point, Suffolk, on 23rd–24th September 1989 (*EBR* 1989).

The highest daily counts along the coast tend to occur during August and September; presumably these are mainly local birds gathered to take advantage of ideal feeding conditions. The highest counts have been 36 on Foulness on 13th September 1981 and 33 in the Colne/Mersea Island area on 11th August 1991 with

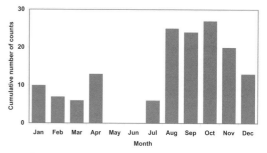

Seasonal occurrence of counts of 10+ Kestrels from 1980–2004

double-figure counts noted regularly on Foulness, along the Blackwater and at Rainham and occasionally from other coastal sites. Counts vary from year to year; local survival rates probably determine the numbers present in autumn and winter, starvation being the main cause of death amongst first-year birds at this time of year (Village 1990). The pattern of occurrence of counts of 10+ Kestrels points to an increased incidence of birds in October.

The large numbers of ringing recoveries provide a good indication of the origin of Kestrels occurring in Essex and confirm that, whilst many occurring during late autumn/winter are local birds, British and foreign-bred birds augment their numbers. Juvenile Kestrels disperse in a random direction after fledging (Village 1990), although most recoveries are within 150km of the ringing site. The speed of dispersal is quite rapid with nestlings ringed in Essex in late June found outside the county by August. True autumn migration begins in September and lasts until November with juveniles generally migrating further than adults in winter. Whilst birds from southern Britain are generally sedentary, many northern birds winter in the Midlands and East Anglia (Village 1990); five Essex recoveries of Kestrels from Scotland and 11 from northern England confirm this. Some Essex-bred birds move abroad for winter, five having been recovered in France, including one ringed as a nestling at Fingringhoe Wick on 5th July 1982 and found dead around 15th August 1982, near Chartres. One ringed at East Hall Farm, Bradwell, on 25th June 1989 was recovered at Mafra, Lisbon, Portugal, 1,628km to the south-southwest on 24th November 1991.There have also been seven foreign-ringed birds recovered within the county, each ringed in the year of hatching in their respective countries. Three originated from the Netherlands and two from Sweden, with singles from Finland and former Czechoslovakia. The Finnish bird was ringed at Kauhajoki, Vaasa, on 3rd July 1997 and found dead at Stickling Green, Clavering, on 10th October 1997, a distance of 1,750km southwest of its natal area. Many juveniles originating from Fennoscandia have been recovered in Britain (Migration Atlas); one ringed at Holland Haven in October was recovered in Finland in a subsequent breeding season.

Kestrels will take a wide variety of prey items. More unusually, one preyed on free-flying Budgerigars at Margaretting during December 1968 and another took a Grass Snake at Mundon in mid-July 1978. During February 1985, near Essex University, one was seen to drop to the ground in the usual way as if to seize prey. However, it failed to take to the air again. On approaching the area in which it had disappeared, the observer disturbed a Stoat, which ran away. The Kestrel was found dead with its throat torn out. One individual made itself particularly unpopular by allegedly catching the Richard's Pipit at The Naze on 26th October 2001.

The Kestrel is our only declining breeding raptor. Increasing agricultural intensification appears to have had a detrimental affect on rural populations although the species seems to have adapted to using quieter semi-urban and urban environments. Proposed changes to the European CAP that should bring more environmentally friendly farming methods could help the Kestrel. At present, however, large-scale change seems unlikely. For the foreseeable future the fate of the Kestrel seems uncertain, although it is likely to remain relatively common.

Sponsored by Martin Henry

Red-footed Falcon   *Falco verspertinus*

Rare passage migrant and summer visitor: 31 records involving at least 29 individuals

The monotypic Red-footed Falcon is a Palearctic species that breeds in eastern Europe and west, central and north-central Asia and winters entirely in southern Africa (Ferguson-Lees & Christie 2001).

1873	Alresford	31st May	Adult female, shot
1897	Stanford Rivers	21st May	Adult female, shot
1901	Bradwell	about 17th October	Immature male, shot from two or three
1973	East Tilbury	29th July	Adult female
1974	Ingatestone, Mill Green	1st July	Adult male
	The Naze	21st July	Adult male
1976	Old Hall	2nd–5th June	Sub-adult male
1985	Abberton	31st October	Adult female
1987	Abberton	23rd July–12th August	Immature female
	Hanningfield	25th July	1st-summer male
	Holland Haven	5th September	Immature male
1989	Bradwell	21st May	Adult male
	Old Hall	1st June–15th July	Same as previous
	Colne Point	2nd June	Same as previous
	Langenhoe	5th June	Sub-adult male
1990	Barling	5th May	Adult male
	Bradwell	27th May	Adult female
	Rainham	31st May–17th June	1st-summer female
	Boreham/Sandon	19th June–10th July	1st-summer female
	Hadleigh Downs	2nd August	Adult female
1991	Rainham	8th–17th June	Sub-adult male
1992	Abberton	21st–24th May	Sub-adult male
	Barling	22nd May	1st-summer female
	Fingringhoe	23rd May	Same as Abberton bird
	Walthamstow	2nd June	1st-summer female
	Latchingdon	23rd–29th August	1st-summer female
1996	Walthamstow	14th September	Juvenile
1997	Colne Point	5th May	Adult female
2001	Stansted Airport area	27th May	Adult male
2003	Old Hall	10th June	1st-summer male
	Great Leighs	2nd August	2nd-summer female

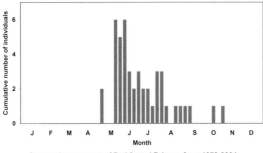

Seasonal occurrence of Red-footed Falcons from 1873-2004

The Red-footed Falcon is an annual, principally spring, vagrant to Britain with 766 records to the end of 2004 (BBRC 2005). Numbers vary considerably from year to year, depending mainly on the prevalence of easterly winds in May and early June. The species has a far more westerly migration route in spring than in autumn, hence the paucity of autumn records.

The arrivals in spring 1992 were part of a huge influx into northern Europe caused by an unusual meteorological situation that resulted in a very long spell of exceptionally warm easterly winds in late May and early June (Nightingale & Allsopp 1994). The Essex records accounted for only 4% of this, the largest British influx to date. However, the five in 1990, representing 20% of national records that year, suggested a much narrower arrival corridor.

Whilst many have occurred along the coast, there is a wide geographic spread of inland records, although just one has come from the northwest of Essex, perhaps because of the lack of observers.

Merlin   *Falco columbarius*

Uncommon passage migrant and winter visitor   **Amber List**

The Merlin has a circumpolar distribution and is a bird of upland and high altitude moorland or open countryside (European Atlas). From northern Europe across to central Siberia, the species is represented by the race *aesalon*, whilst those breeding in Iceland are of the race *subaesalon*. The British population, which is found throughout the upland regions of Scotland, northern England, Wales and parts of Ireland, numbers some 1,300 pairs (Rebbeca & Bainbridge 1998) and is unusual in having a high prevalence of ground-nesting. Most populations are entirely migratory but *subaesalon* is partially migratory and *aesalon* may be sedentary or no more than an altitudinal migrant (Ferguson-Lees & Christie 2001).

Christy described the Merlin as an uncommon winter visitor. However, he presented evidence to suggest that the species formerly bred at least until around 1865: "From Essex, Dr C. R. Bree writes that the Merlin breeds in the marshes of the Rochford Hundred. Mr Laver his informant has brought up young birds from the nest". Laver confirmed: "There can be no mistake about their breeding ... They bred on the Paglesham Marshes, as well as on Foulness, in the rank grass beside the marsh ditches, but I have not heard of a nest for years, as I now never visit that district". If correct, Essex was the only location in southeastern England where Merlins still bred in the 19th century (Historical Atlas). Glegg dismissed a breeding record from near "Ongar Wood" in 1867 (and perhaps in 1857) as it relied entirely on the word of a known egg-dealer. Interestingly, the eggs

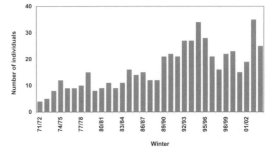

Annual totals of Merlins from 1971/72-2003/04

were apparently taken from a nest on the ground. There have been no other breeding records, although a female carrying food was observed on Foulness on 20th June 1992 and a male was seen just north of there, at Holliwell Point, a fortnight earlier.

Glegg's description of the Merlin as no more than an irregular winter visitor suggested a continuing decline, in line with the national trend. Unlike most other raptors, which were able to recover their numbers in the early 20th century as gamekeeping decreased, the Merlin continued to decline. Glegg detailed 39 records from the first in 1829 but very few in the 20th century.

The Merlin's status had changed very little by Hudson & Pymans' time, when it was described as a very scarce passage migrant and winter visitor. They estimated that no more than 5–6 were present at any one time and that a decline had occurred particularly since 1958. This decline coincided with the introduction of organochlorine products into agriculture. Unlike other raptors, however, the Merlin showed no obvious recovery after the chemicals were banned, possibly because the British population's ground-nesting habitat had a lower success rate than more northerly populations that nest in trees. Thus even small reductions in breeding success through pesticides (which are still present even at low levels), habitat loss and disturbance can tip the population into decline (Newton & Haas 1988). More recently, Merlins have taken to using old crows' nests in forests and the population is now increasing with declines in productivity apparently reversed (Crick 1993).

In Essex, numbers remained relatively low through the 1960s but thereafter a steady increase became apparent with numbers peaking in the early 1990s before declining markedly thereafter. Above-average numbers occurred during the cold spell in early 1979. In the mid-1980s, Merlins were counted at roosts, which undoubtedly increased the numbers reported; Hen Harriers used the same roost sites and were the actual target of the counts. Only at Langenhoe (maximum eight in 1990/91 and 1998/99), Old Hall (maximum four in 1993/94) and on Foulness (maximum five in 1984/85) were roosts identified that were used for more than just 1–2 winters. The Langenhoe roost probably remains in use but the other two appear to have been used very little during the 1990s.

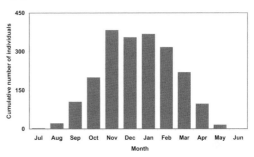

Seasonal occurrence of Merlins from 1971-2004

The recent decline has not been noted nationally and the cause is unclear. However, in Norfolk it has been calculated that almost 50% of the Merlin's winter diet is Skylarks (Clarke & Hewitson 1993) and it is possible that the recent significant reductions in Skylark numbers may have caused fewer Merlins to visit Essex, although the Skylark's decline has been common to all counties.

Merlins are reported regularly from around the coast with no site particularly favoured. Inland records, which have increased in the last decade, have been widespread, although few are now reported from the northwest, from where regular sightings occurred in the 1950s and 1960s. The increase may be due to greater observer coverage but perhaps Merlins have changed their habits as prey availability has changed on the coast. Abberton is the most favoured inland site: of 27 inland records in 1994 (the greatest county total in a single year), 21 came from there.

Most Merlins begin to arrive in October when migrants are noted regularly along the coast. Small numbers occur in September, whilst August records have increased significantly since the early 1990s, suggesting that Merlins are arriving earlier than before. In addition, there have been six July records, five during the last week and one on 11th in 2002 at Old Hall. Passage appears to occur through Essex during November with the wintering population mainly present from then until February and departing during March and April with a few birds in May. There have been seven June records, including the Foulness records mentioned above, the others being: Mundon, a pair, 18th in 1955; Stambridge, a male, 19th in 1955; Holland Haven, a male, 8th in 1992; Holland Haven, one, 4th in 1994; and Old Hall, a female, 23rd in 1996.

Three recoveries of birds ringed on their breeding grounds in northeast and northwest England suggest that the origins of our wintering and passage birds are relatively local. A nestling ringed on 27th June 1984 in Durham was recovered at Westcliff-on-Sea on 1st January 1992; a nestling ringed in Lancashire on 30th June 1989 dispersed rapidly south to Writtle, being found dead on 12th August 1989; and an adult female ringed in North Yorkshire on 8th June 1993 was found at Bradwell in February 1994. The latter flew into a window clutching a Meadow Pipit; the Merlin survived, the pipit did not. There is no ringing evidence to indicate that Icelandic or Scandinavian birds reach Essex. However, the 1979 influx coincided with influxes of other species from Fennoscandia suggesting that at least some of our wintering Merlins may at times be of a Continental origin.

Whilst it would seem that the British breeding population is making a slow recovery, the noticeable decline in the Essex wintering population is of concern. However, until the cause is identified few positive conservation measures can be taken to reverse the trend, which it is to be hoped, is no more than a temporary setback for the species.

(Eurasian) Hobby   *Falco subbuteo*

Fairly common summer visitor and passage migrant

The Hobby has a very wide breeding range, covering much of Eurasia from Europe through north Africa, central Asia and north China to Kamchatka, Sakhalin Island and northern Japan. The nominate race *subbuteo* occurs over much of the range and is highly migratory, with European birds wintering mainly in southern Africa. Hobbies are essentially lowland birds that occupy a wide range of habitats (European Atlas). In Britain, the species was traditionally considered a bird of southern heathlands with most occurring south of the Thames, although it is now thought likely that it was overlooked in farmland and woodland (Fuller *et al*. 1985). However, the Hobby has increased markedly since the mid-1980s and now occurs throughout much of England, albeit principally the south, with the latest population estimates being 2,200 pairs (Clements 2001).

Christy noted that the Hobby was "A summer visitor which used to breed commonly in the county, but is now scarce, though instances of its having nested here within the last year or two are not unknown". Confirmed breeding was noted at: Debden in 1829 and 1835; Hockley in 1842; Saffron Walden in 1843; around Epping Forest in 1846–47, although it was described as "... very rare" in 1835; Felsted in 1877, Belhus Park in 1879; Birch in 1885. In 1832, the Hobby was "rare" in the Rochford Hundred but the following year was described as "very destructive to the Larks" round Southminster as though the species was fairly common there. Around 1838 it was rare in the region of Sudbury. In 1875, the species was "not uncommon at Havering". Many records involved birds shot during the breeding season. Thus, Christy's assertion that it was once common appears to be based on relatively few records. Glegg's description of the Hobby as "... a very rare summer visitor ... [that] at one time was a less rare bird, which bred in different parts of the county" is probably a better description of its former status. He added several other breeding records, single pairs nesting at Great Chesterford around 1860–70, White Notley in 1878–79, Farnham in 1887, Danbury Park in 1890 and the latest at an unnamed locality in 1898; young Hobbys were still taken to fly at larks in the last few decades of the 19th century. The apparent decline was in part due to persecution by gamekeepers as, despite not known to prey on game, the species was often mistaken for the Sparrowhawk and shot. Persecution of Carrion Crows and Magpies particularly in eastern England may have also resulted in a lack of suitable nest sites for it to take over (Historical Atlas). The relative rarity of the Hobby meant that collectors prized it and, whenever the species attempted to nest, the pair was shot.

Hudson & Pyman considered the Hobby a rare and irregular passage migrant and went as far as to doubt whether, despite Christy and Gleggs' evidence, the species had ever bred regularly. From 1949–66, the species was noted in

Atlas	Survey Area	% of 10km squares or tetrads in which	
		bred/probably bred	possibly bred or present
First National 10km	Essex	1.8	3.5
Second National 10km	Essex	17.5	35.1
First London Tetrad	Met. Essex	0.0	0.5
Second London Tetrad	Met. Essex	10.0	33.5
Essex Tetrad	Essex	5.6	12.4

Summary of results of Atlas surveys for Hobbies

11 years, usually in late summer/autumn, although there were three June records; just 20 birds were involved. Throughout the 1960s and 1970s, the number of migrants increased, Cox noting that there were 2–3 annually until 1974, rising to at least ten each year from 1978–81. This increase coincided with a resumption of breeding. In 1978, an adult and a juvenile were found in the Wid valley in the Doddinghurst/Mountnessing area, although breeding was not proved. In 1979, a pair raised three young in the same area and did so successfully for the next nine years (Essex Atlas). Breeding numbers increased slowly through the 1980s but accelerated markedly in the early 1990s. By the end of the 20th century, the population appeared to have peaked at around 30–50 summering pairs with perhaps 50% confirmed breeding. Subsequently, there appears to have been a slight decline, although perhaps reduced observer interest in the species due to its changed status has reduced reporting levels. Chapman (1999) gave a breeding density of between 1–5 pairs per 100 km²; applied to Essex this gives a theoretical population of 40–200 pairs.

The pattern of increase has been remarkably similar to that of the Sparrowhawk. Unlike that species, however, the Hobby was not significantly affected by organochlorine pesticides (Fiuczynski & Nethersole-Thompson 1980) and it has been suggested that the increase has been due to the increased post-fledging survival during August and September, brought about by the increased abundance of at least two dragonfly species, Common Darter and Migrant Hawker, which are associated with gravel-pits and reservoirs (Prince & Clarke 1993). Indeed the Hobby's breeding distribution closely follows that of both dragonflies (Benton 1988). However, the fact that Essex has for many years had a considerable number of gravel-workings and reservoirs suitable for dragonflies and that the Hobby has shown a similar pattern of increase to the Sparrowhawk, a raptor with a very different lifestyle, suggests that, in Essex at least, some other unknown factor or factors may be at work.

Breeding is invariably difficult to prove, although a visit to a likely area in late August will confirm breeding success if the very vocal young are about. In autumn, Hobbies generally become more conspicuous as they feed on roosting hirundines. The Essex Atlas survey confirmed breeding in 61 tetrads with birds present in a further 139, a distinct bias being shown to the southwest where a significant increase occurred in Metropolitan Essex between the two London Atlas surveys. Fewer pairs were also present towards the coast and northwest. Favoured breeding areas include river valleys, gravel-pits and reservoirs. Old Carrion Crows' nests on electricity pylons have been used close to Abberton.

Sizeable counts have been reported recently, both in spring and autumn. A total of 13 at Cornmill Meadows on 26th May 1999 is the highest during spring. A peak of 12 at Berwick Ponds on 6th July 2000 was probably a response to a local abundance of prey, which was, in this instance, thought to be thousands of Summer Chafers.

Migrants arrive during April and May with the earliest at East Tilbury on 1st April 2001, whilst there were two at Ardleigh on 3rd April 2003. Most arrive in late April and early May. In autumn, Hobbies pass through in the greatest numbers during September, although a few are recorded in October. Exceptional numbers were reported in September 2000 during the Honey-buzzard passage; although there was undoubtedly an influx from the Continent at this time, there was also a significant increase in coverage due to the large number of observers looking out for raptors.

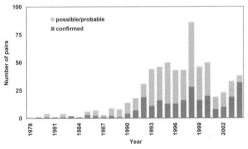

Annual totals of breeding Hobbies from 1978-2004

The latest records include one that hunted the sparrow roost at Burnham-on-Crouch railway station from 1st October–8th November 1997, whilst singles were at Holland Haven on 6th November 1999 and Abberton from 26th October–3rd November 1955. Remarkably, there is one wintering record, one of very few known in Britain: one, probably a female, at Abberton from 21st December 1953–3rd January 1954.

There is just one ringing recovery involving Essex, one ringed as a chick at New Yatt, Oxfordshire, on 8th August 2002 being found at The Naze on 5th May 2004. Unfortunately, a ringed specimen (ring no. 3035277) found at Lexden on 13th August 1961 and now in the Colchester Museum collection (Accession No. 1984.16) was not traceable at the BTO. The few national recoveries indicate movement through to the near-Continent.

With the likelihood of more gravel-workings being created, the trend towards individual farms constructing their own reservoirs, the possibility of longer term reservoir construction/expansion and global warming, the amount of suitable habitat in Essex is likely to increase and, whilst events outside the county will impact on numbers returning annually, for the medium term at least, the Hobby's future seems assured.

Sponsored by Scott Johnson

Peregrine Falcon   *Falco peregrinus*

Increasing but uncommon passage migrant and winter visitor: bred in 1998 and 2004   Amber List

The Peregrine is a cosmopolitan species and one of the most widespread of all birds. In the Northern Hemisphere, the species occurs from the Equator north to 77°. There are currently 16 recognised subspecies (Ferguson-Lees & Christie 2001). The nominate race *peregrinus* occurs across much of Europe and Asia south of the tundra, whilst *calidus* is found on the tundra and arctic islands of Eurasia and is highly migratory. The species' habitat ranges from treeless to quite heavily wooded country, although there is a general dependence on cliffs for nest sites (European Atlas). Most central and northern European populations collapsed during 1956–65, due to the toxic effects of organochlorine pesticides. Following the withdrawal and banning of the pesticides, most populations are increasing with the UK population of 1,492 occupied territories in 2002, the highest on record (Crick *et al.* 2003). In the UK, most breed in Scotland, northern England and Wales.

Both Christy and Glegg considered the Peregrine to be an uncommon and irregular winter visitor, Glegg noting at least 66 records between 1823 and 1926. Neither gave any firm breeding evidence and, although there is a vague reference by Christy to "… a gentleman resident near Harwich" taking several from their nests prior to 1821, it is not clear whether this was at Harwich or elsewhere. In addition, a pair was supposed to have bred and raised three young in a tree at "Sampford" in 1843; they were all shot in July and donated to Saffron Walden Museum but are not now in the collection.

The Peregrine has been recorded annually since 1950, although its status has varied markedly from decade to decade. In the 1950s and 1960s, perhaps 3–5 were present during the winter. From 1969, however, there was a marked decline, the nadir being 1971 with just three reports. The collapse in the national population, which occurred during the 1950s and early 1960s, saw a decline to just 360 pairs in 1962, many not breeding (Population Trends). The pesticides reduced breeding success and increased adult mortality (Newton 1979). Essex records therefore reached a low point some ten years after the lowest ebb nationally and this may be due to a remarkable series of observations of wintering birds in the Chelmer Valley and Blackwater Estuary throughout the 1960s. These birds may have wandered widely and were perhaps responsible for many other reports. The first occurrence was in 1955 and the last in 1965, with over 50% of the records during the winters of 1960/61, 1962/63 and 1963/64. The observations formed the basis for the award-winning book *The Peregrine* (Baker 1967), which detailed the analysis of 619 kills over four winters. Of the 45 species involved, 38% were Woodpigeons, 14% Black-headed Gulls and 6% Lapwings. Chiefly, number and conspicuousness of birds within the Peregrine's territory governed prey selection. This series of records even today seems remarkable; the editors of the *EBR* 1968 even went as far as to suggest that the birds were not of wild origin.

From the mid-1970s, the number of records very slowly began to rise, although most appeared to involve passage migrants with few wintering. A noticeable increase occurred in the very late 1980s and early 1990s (cf. Hobby and Sparrowhawk), such that by the mid-1990s at least ten individuals wintered or passed through and, by the end of the decade, nearer to 20. Initially the increase was primarily during autumn but wintering numbers soon increased markedly too.

Summering records also increased in the early 1990s, and from 1989 1–2 pairs bred in north Kent. In 1992, a pair was displaying at a coastal oil refinery but breeding was not observed. In 1998, three sites were occupied during the breeding season and at one of these, in Silvertown, a pair bred on a redundant grain mill and raised two young (Dally 2000). At a further

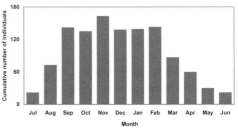

Seasonal occurrence of Peregrines from 1965-2002

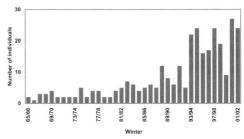

Annual totals of Peregrines from 1965/66-2001/02
(after 2001/02 numbers incalculable due to large increase in records)

site, a pair mated but the female disappeared and, at the third, a pair summered and was seen displaying. From 2001–03 a resident pair may have bred, whilst 1–2 pairs bred regularly just beyond the county boundary. In 2004, a pair bred on Tilbury Power Station and successfully raised one young whilst another pair almost certainly bred; in all there were five territories along the Thames in 2004.

The nature of the Essex coastline and the large areas that such an aerial species can cover in a day make it very difficult assessing numbers, particularly since the early 1990s.

Numbers remain relatively constant from September through to February, with a slight peak being evident in November. High numbers in September and October and a small peak in November are suggestive of passage at that time; immature Peregrines disperse away from their natal grounds from August to early November (*BWP*). The consistency of numbers throughout suggests that many arriving in autumn may well winter in Essex.

There have been no ringing recoveries involving Essex. Nationally, recoveries have shown that Scandinavian birds reach Britain and this may indicate the origins of some of the Peregrines seen in Essex in autumn (Migration Atlas). A number have been observed from fishing boats off the coast during the passage periods. However, the majority of British recoveries have involved movements of less than 100km, so it is likely that most Peregrines are from our native population. The origin of our breeding/summering birds is unclear, although it is probable that they involve individuals from populations in western and northern Britain.

As a breeding bird, the Peregrine is never likely to be common in Essex. That said, the species has shown itself to be remarkably adaptable and has colonised many American cities, nesting on skyscrapers and living off the large feral pigeon flocks. This habitat is readily available in Essex and it is likely that further breeding attempts will occur.

Water Rail
Rallus aquaticus

Scarce resident, winter visitor and passage migrant

Amber List

The Water Rail breeds in Eurasia, from Ireland and Portugal as far east as China, and from Iceland and central Finland south to North Africa and Iran. The nominate race *aquaticus* occurs throughout Europe (Taylor & van Perlo 1998). It is an elusive species, typical of water-fringe vegetation and other permanently waterlogged habitats (European Atlas). In Britain, the Water Rail breeds extensively, if thinly, over much of the country. Although such an elusive species is very difficult to census, the minimum number of breeding pairs in Britain is probably in the region of 700–1,400 pairs, a serious decline from 2,000–4,000 pairs revealed by the First National Atlas. North and northeast European populations are mostly migratory and winter in west and southwest Europe, mainly in Britain and Ireland, France, Portugal and also in the Mediterranean and Black Sea areas (European Atlas).

Christy noted that the Water Rail was "A resident, though local and by no means common. It evidently used to breed in the county, and may still do so, though I have no evidence of that fact",

Atlas	Survey Area	% of 10km squares or tetrads in which	
		bred/probably bred	possibly bred or present
First National 10km	Essex	15.8	40.4
Second National 10km	Essex	12.3	10.5
First London Tetrad	Met. Essex	1.5	2.0
Second London Tetrad	Met. Essex	3.0	1.5
Essex Tetrad	Essex	1.7	0.9

Summary of results of Atlas surveys for Water Rails

although he added "… its skulking habits making it … appear less common than it really is". Despite being under pressure from land drainage and waterways clearance, there was no clear indication of a change in status nationally during the 19th century, although local extinctions took place (Historical Atlas). Glegg considered the species to be a resident but chiefly a winter visitor, noting: "The evidence of breeding is scanty". He gave just six breeding records, from the earliest at Tolleshunt D'Arcy around 1830. Neither Christy nor Glegg provided quantitative data on wintering birds.

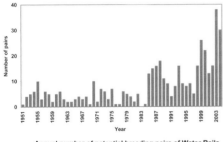

Annual number of potential breeding pairs of Water Rails
(broods and birds present) from 1951-2004

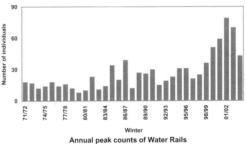

Annual peak counts of Water Rails
from 1971/72-2003/04

Ideal habitat is not common in Essex, but as well as reed beds, river margins, ponds and reservoirs are used with regularity. Hudson & Pyman considered that at least 2–3 pairs bred at both Abberton and Old Hall with probably larger numbers in the Cam and Stort valleys between Saffron Walden and Bishop's Stortford, although most were at Stansted and Bishop's Stortford SFs. Occasional nesting was noted from a wide spread of localities elsewhere. A marked decline seemed to occur between the two national Atlas surveys, a trend mirrored nationally. However, this does not appear to be borne out by the number reported annually in the *EBR*, a significant increase having occurred from the mid-1980s. It is possible that the Second National Atlas survey coincided with a time of low population levels, caused by habitat loss, due to below-average rainfall during the 1988–90 drought.

A small breeding population was established in southwest Essex between the two London Atlas surveys, but otherwise there was little change in distribution. However, without more accurate assessments of the population, absolute trends are difficult to assess; recent use of tape-luring in breeding population assessments has led to large increases, some of up to 100%, at supposedly well-monitored sites.

The most regular breeding locations have been: Old Hall, up to 12 pairs (1987) in the late 1980s, although fewer since; Berwick Ponds/Ingrebourne Valley, up to 23 pairs (in 2003); Langenhoe/Fingringhoe Ranges; Abberton; Stanford Warren; and Dagenham Chase.

Based on an estimate of 2–4 pairs per occupied 10km square (Second National Atlas), the county population at the time of the Essex Atlas survey was around 18–36 pairs, about 4% of the national total. A similar figure probably holds true today.

The Water Rail appears to be far more widespread outside the breeding season, although this may in part be due to the species becoming less skulking, die-back of reed bed vegetation and more catholic winter habitat requirements. The species becomes quite common on salt marshes during winter (Cox). Hard weather also causes Water Rails to venture from cover in search of food, mortality being high when shallow water and mud freezes. Numbers recorded annually vary markedly, possibly in response to the severity of the weather but, in general, have steadily increased; recently improved coverage during WeBS counts, particularly in Metropolitan Essex, has resulted in a significant increase in the known wintering population, some 30% being reported from there.

Given its skulking behaviour, it is not surprising that double-figure counts are rare. The largest concentrations were noted in the early 1960s at Stansted SF, where numbers peaked at 20 from 25th–26th December 1961. The only other locations to have held double-figure gatherings have been: Bishop's Stortford SF, up to 15 between September and December 1961; Ingrebourne Valley, 14, 17th November 2002; the Cam between Saffron Walden and Audley End, 13, 30th December 1962; Dengie, 10–12 flushed from 0.5km of borrow dyke, 8th December 1990; Stanford Warren, ten, 31st December 1961; Seventy Acres Lake, a maximum of ten, 23rd December 2001; and Berwick Ponds, 8–10, October–December 1989.

Between 1950 and 1980, a total of 227 was ringed at Abberton (Cox) suggesting that considerable numbers move through this and other sites. National ringing recoveries suggest that there is an influx from the Continent in October/November and departures in March/April. At these times, Water Rails have been noted in unusual locations and include one that fell down a chimney in foggy weather at Colchester on the night of 20th/21st November 1954. There have been several recoveries of Abberton-ringed birds (all prior to 1975), which represent a significant proportion of national recoveries. Singles have come from Germany and the Netherlands, whilst two have been recovered in France. One ringed on 4th December 1957 was recovered at Broumov, Hradec Kralove, in the former Czechoslovakia, 1,087km to the east on 24th April 1958, whilst another ringed on 22nd February 1955 was recovered 1,208km eastnortheast at Vastervick, Kalmar, Sweden, on 25th July 1956. As Water Rails breeding in Britain and Ireland are resident (*BWP*), and assuming natal dispersal over short distances, all recoveries on the Continent probably represent migrants that have wintered in Britain (Migration Atlas). By inference therefore, our wintering population is larger than that in summer and, although it is not quantifiable, it is thought to be considerable (Winter Atlas).

It is difficult to speculate on the future of such an elusive species when there are so few quantitative breeding or wintering data, although anecdotal records suggest a steady increase over the last two decades. Fortunately, many breeding Water Rails are found in protected areas where conditions can be managed for them (Essex Atlas); perhaps the species may even benefit from the various ongoing Bittern reed bed restoration projects. Outside these areas, drainage and disturbance remain potential threats. It is to be hoped that increases in suitable habitat will result from the agri-environment schemes, such as the Essex Coast Environmental Area and more enlightened attitudes towards drainage and the management of riverbank vegetation.

Spotted Crake   *Porzana porzana*

Very rare passage migrant: one confirmed 19th century breeding record   Amber List

The monotypic Spotted Crake breeds across much of the west and central Palearctic, from western Europe and southern Fennoscandia across to central Siberia. The species has declined over much of west and central Europe during the 20th century. In Britain, significant declines occurred during the first half of the 19th century (Alexander & Lack 1944), prior to which Spotted Crakes probably bred throughout the country. In the 20th century the species only bred in very small numbers, although there were signs of an increase towards the end of the 1990s, with perhaps 75–80 pairs nationally (Gilbert 2002). The Spotted Crake's wintering range is not well known but most European birds cross the Sahara to east and southeast Africa (European Atlas).

Christy described the species as "A rare and local summer or autumn visitant ... by no means common". He referred to two possible breeding records, a female shot on Northey Island (undated) that was carrying a perfectly formed egg and "several" killed on Pitsea Marshes in 1889 "... some of which were obviously

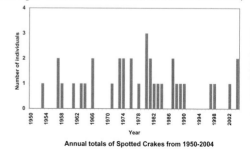

Annual totals of Spotted Crakes from 1950-2004

young birds, probably bred in the district". The first documented Essex record came from around 1838 when one was shot at Maldon, at which time it was considered rare at Sudbury. At Newport several were picked up dead after flying into electric telegraph wires prior to 1845, whilst it was an occasional visitor to Epping Forest where "… it is occasionally met with in the soft low-lying parts of the Forest, such as would be attractive to Snipe". Christy detailed a further 11 records, all the dated ones occurring from August to November, including three shot on Hackney Marshes during October 1863.

Glegg described the only confirmed Essex breeding record, a pair raising five young at Dobb's Weir on the Lea at Roydon in 1891: "The young brood, five in number, was frequently observed during June and July, and on the 1st August his [E. J. Wills] spaniel caught two of them and he shot another". Interestingly, two were also taken at Leabridge in 1890 and nine were shot near Waltham Abbey in 1896; it is tempting to suggest that there may have been a small breeding population in the Lea Valley at this time. Glegg noted records during autumn passage in 11 years from 1841–1916, but only three in spring: Bradfield in April 1905 and 1907; and Chingford in May 1911. In addition, Glegg knew of a number of undated records.

The next documented record was not until 1953 when one was trapped and ringed at Abberton on 1st September. There have been just 34 since, an average of fewer than one a year, and it has become particularly scarce since 1990. Quite why there has been a dramatic decrease in the last decade is unclear, particularly as national occurrences have not declined and observer coverage has increased. Much of the 1990s has, however, been particularly dry and low water levels may have reduced the amount of suitable habitat. Additionally, some sites that held Spotted Crakes in the past have been altered or are now inaccessible.

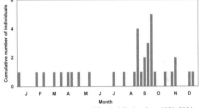

Seasonal occurrence of Spotted Crakes from 1950–2004

Records show a strong autumn peak. During the early 1970s there was a run of what were assumed to be wintering individuals, although all records since have occurred during passage periods. The apparent break in autumn migration in mid-September has also been noted nationally (Fraser *et al.* 2000).

Since 1950 the records have shown a wide geographical spread with four each from Bradwell and Abberton (all trapped in 1953, 1958, 1964 and 1966), two each at Two Tree Island, Heybridge GP, Hanningfield, Hornchurch CP and Sewardstone and singles at 18 other sites. All records have involved singles except for two together at Heybridge GP on 12th–13th September 1981 and an adult and juvenile at Hornchurch CP on 25th September 2004 (the juvenile was present from 19th–26th), although two may have been at Dagenham Chase from 28th August–11th September 1988 and at Great Wakering Boatyard, Fleet Head, from 13th April–mid-May 1990.

Although there is no ringing evidence, it is assumed that in autumn birds from Germany, Poland, the Netherlands and presumably Britain move south and southwest towards their wintering grounds (Migration Atlas). One came aboard the S. Y. *Argonaut*, 65km off the Essex coast in September 1899 (Glegg).

Little Crake   *Porzana parva*

Vagrant: three records involving four individuals

The monotypic Little Crake breeds discontinuously across Europe, east to Kazakhstan, wintering mostly south of the Sahara (European Atlas).

1873	Witham	8th August	Shot
1965	Battlesbridge/Hullbridge	3rd April	Female caught alive
1973	Two Tree Island	28th–31st March	One, with two on 29th

Fossil remains attributed to Little Crakes have been found in the 300,000-year-old 'elephant bone bed' of the Hoxnian Interglacial at East Mersea (Urquhart 2000).

The Little Crake is typically an early spring migrant; of the 107 British records, only 33 have occurred since 1958 (BBRC 2005). The decline has been attributed to considerable population decreases on the Continent caused, principally, by habitat destruction (European Atlas). The 1873 individual was not identified for 56 years, Glegg only locating the specimen in 1929. The Battlesbridge individual flew into overhead wires and, after being caught, was released unharmed. The two on Two Tree Island were present at the same time as a Spotted Crake.

Christy also referred to one shot during October at Paglesham, around 1885, but Glegg felt that the "… evidence of identification is incomplete", although he did not explain why.

Baillon's Crake   *Porzana pusilla*

Vagrant: two 19th century records

The Baillon's Crake has a fragmented breeding range through Europe, where the species now appears to be rare, east to China and Japan, as well as Africa and Australasia. The race *intermedia* occurs in Europe. The species winters in Africa, India and southeast Asia.

1874	Dagenham Gulf	3rd October	Immature
1891	Waltham/Cheshunt	24th October	Shot

The 1874 individual was found and caught by a dog in a thick reedy ditch in Dagenham Gulf that is now in the middle of the Ford motor works (Christy). The specimen is in the EFC collection (Accession No. 11318). According to Hudson & Pyman, Sage (1959) showed that the 1891 specimen was obtained within Hertfordshire. However, Sage presented no evidence to confirm this and as the marsh is bisected by the county boundary, the record is included here; Christy and Glegg included the record. One at Abberton on 13th June 1953, which was for many years accepted by the BBRC, has now been deemed unacceptable, as the published account was second-hand (Wallace *et al.* 2006).

In the 19th century, the Baillon's Crake was far more common in Britain than the Little Crake and even bred on occasions. Like the Little Crake, it has declined significantly on the Continent (European Atlas) but it is now much the rarer of the two nationally, with just 15 records since 1958, the last in 2001 (BBRC 2002). Recent national records have occurred during spring and autumn migration.

Crake sp.   *Porzana sp.*

The following small crakes were not specifically identified

1975	The Naze	19th October	Probably either Little or Baillon's
1978	Hanningfield	5th March	Probably Spotted
1981	Hanningfield	19th December	
1986	Pitsea	31st December	Probably Spotted

Corncrake (Corn Crake)   *Crex crex*

Very rare passage migrant - last bred in 1948   Red List

The monotypic Corncrake breeds through west, central and eastern Europe, where it is commonest in the Baltic States, then east as far as western Siberia. The species has declined dramatically in Britain and Europe during the 20th century, probably due to loss of habitat and reduced breeding success caused by the modernisation and mechanisation of farming practices. There were 676 pairs/singing males in Britain in 2002 (RBBP 2004), almost all in the Scottish islands where, thanks to much research (RSPB 1995) and habitat management, populations are now stable and showing signs of increasing. The species winters principally in the savannahs of south, central and southeast Africa.

Confirming the historical status of the Corncrake is difficult, as early writers left little documentary evidence. Christy noted: "I have been assured that it was once common with us", whilst Glegg considered that "The evidence to prove that this species ever bred commonly does not seem to exist, but this view appears to be generally accepted". Breeding records were extremely few and far between. In 1838, the Corncrake was "not a very common bird" around

Sudbury and bred occasionally around Saffron Walden prior to 1845, but thereafter breeding was noted only once, in 1881. In the late 1870s, it seems that the species was still regularly recorded on the eastern side of Chelmsford (Smith 1996). During the 1880s, the Corncrake was "... a summer visitor, nesting and remaining until the middle of September" in Epping Forest, breeding "... not uncommonly" around Harwich and not common around Orsett. Breeding was also noted at Mucking in 1887, the only known instance in that area, and at Feering in 1888. Christy heard the species during

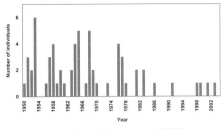

Annual totals of Corncrakes from 1950-2004

the breeding season five times: Chignal St James, 16th June 1876, 5th May and 11th June 1882; Newport, 9th June 1881; and Stanford Rivers, 19th June 1883. Alexander (1914) stated that in Essex decreases were first noted in the 1850s or 1870s. It seems therefore that the Corncrake was a rare summer visitor to Essex during much of the 19th century, at which time the species was still common throughout much of Britain (Historical Atlas).

As late as 1910, Corncrakes were still present in several areas, around Shenfield, Felsted, the Eastons and Colchester and a pair bred at Theydon Bois in 1917. However, by the 1920s it had become very rare. The species probably still bred at Easton in 1924 and one pair probably bred at Priory Bridge, Felsted, in the same year and also at the Lea Valley reservoirs in 1927. Breeding was last confirmed in 1948, when a dead juvenile was found at Strethall, where birds were also present in 1949 and 1955. Subsequently, there have been only five breeding season records: two at Great Clacton in August 1952, in an area where 1–2 were present throughout summer; one on Almshouse Plain, Epping Forest, on 3rd June 1968; two flushed from a wheat field just south of Sudbury in the first week of July 1972; and singles at Abberton on 3rd June 1972 and 8th June 1977 (dead).

Relatively large numbers were still recorded in autumn in the last few years of the 19th century with, for example, 15 shot in mid-September 1887 near Messing and ten at Little Waltham in early September 1885, whilst similar numbers were present on Northey Island from 20th-25th September 1897. Even as late as 1926 at Stambourne "... a pair had been seen on nearly every field that had been cut in the autumn ...". Christy and Glegg cited single records in November (1826), December and February.

Numbers of migrants declined rapidly as the dramatic contraction in the Corncrake's range throughout Britain and Europe continued.

Migrants peak in late April to early June and again in September, with the extreme dates during the 20th century being 27th February at Writtle in 1951 and 7th November on Foulness in 1999.

No foreign-ringed Corncrakes have been recovered in Britain (Migration Atlas), so it seems most likely that the majority seen in Essex are from the British population, although some records during migration periods may refer to drift migrants off the Continent.

The Corncrake has now been extinct as an Essex breeding species for nearly 60 years. Whilst there are now signs of a recovery in numbers in the Scottish Islands, it is unlikely that the species will return to Essex to breed in the foreseeable future. Increasing populations further north and perhaps also the reintroduction programme currently under way in eastern England may, however, result in increased numbers of migrants occurring.

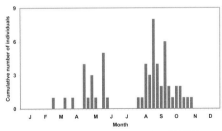

Seasonal occurrence of Corncrakes from 1950-2004

(Common) Moorhen $\qquad$ *Gallinula chloropus*

An abundant resident, winter visitor and passage migrant

The Moorhen is a cosmopolitan species that occurs across five of the six major zoogeographical regions, being absent only from Australasia. The nominate race *chloropus* breeds throughout Europe. Around 270,000 pairs occur in Britain, some 17–32% of the European population of 800,000–1.6 million pairs. Here the species is widespread, although absent from upland areas; it reaches its greatest abundance in eastern and central England (Second National Atlas). The Moorhen exploits a wide range of natural and man-made eutrophic freshwater wetlands with fringe vegetation, on both still and moving waters. The species occurs alongside Coot at wetland margins but is less prone to venture far out into open water (Taylor & van Perlo 1999). Across Europe, the species is principally a year-round resident, although Moorhens migrate from much of northwest Europe, particularly Sweden and Denmark, to avoid winter conditions.

The Moorhen appears to have always been an abundant or very common species with little change in status to this day. Loss of traditional habitat during the 20th century has probably been offset by the creation of reservoirs and gravel-pits and it is possible that the species is as numerous as it has ever been.

Moorhens can be found on virtually any still or running water, including rivers, canals, gravel-pits, lakes, reservoirs, ponds and coastal borrow dykes. They are not shy and will nest in areas of seemingly high vehicular and pedestrian disturbance. Unfortunately, as a breeding species it was not reported in the *EBR* prior to 1980 and regular census figures prior to then appear not to exist. Even after 1980, few sites have been regularly monitored. The largest counts of pairs have come from: Old Hall, 79 in 1987; Abberton, 60 in 1993 and 63 in 1999; and Rainham, around 100 pairs. Breeding numbers vary considerably from year to year, perhaps as a result of harsh winter weather and variable rainfall. However, Moorhens are multi-brooded with 30% of all pairs attempting a second brood and occasionally third and fourth broods (Second National Atlas); therefore numbers tend to recover rapidly following severe weather.

Atlas	Survey Area	% of 10km squares or tetrads in which	
		bred/probably bred	possibly bred or present
First National 10km	Essex	100.0	0.0
Second National 10km	Essex	98.2	1.8
First London Tetrad	Met. Essex	54.0	9.0
Second London Tetrad	Met. Essex	75.5	9.5
Essex Tetrad	Essex	80.4	1.9

Summary of results of Atlas surveys for Moorhens

Little change was evident between the two National Atlas surveys, the Moorhen being present in every 10km square in both, whilst there was a slight increase between the two London Atlas surveys. The Essex Atlas survey confirmed breeding in 80.4% of all tetrads and in every 10km square, Moorhens being absent only from the most built-up areas and areas of intensive agriculture, and least widespread in the northwest where suitable habitat is particularly lacking. WBS plots have shown average densities of 3.3 pairs per km along waterways, the maximum being 10.9 pairs per km along the Roding, whilst Cox noted densities of up to 7.2 pairs per km along the Stort. Using breeding densities suggested in the Second National Atlas, the Essex population perhaps lies in the region of 4,000–5,000 pairs, which represents 1.7–2% of the British population.

Moorhens pass through a flightless moult, with juveniles dispersing from breeding grounds in July and the main migration occurring from September to December, although there is no evidence of a separate moult migration (Taylor & van Perlo 1999). Unlike Coot, large gatherings are rarely observed, by far the largest being about 1,000 at the west end of Abberton in late autumn 1955, at a time of very low water levels. There were 223 at the same site on 7th August 1994. Otherwise reports of more than 150 anywhere are exceptional. Around 200 were counted along a 14.5km stretch of the Chelmer during the winters of 1984/85 and 1985/86. Large gatherings may involve mainly young, together with some adults wintering away from their breeding areas (Winter Atlas). A total of 160 was present on Berwick Ponds in December 1993 (non-WeBS). By February, gatherings tend to break up as birds return to their breeding areas (Winter Atlas).

The British population appears to be resident but migrants arrive in winter from northwest Europe and thus increase the population. However, with few regular year-round counts made anywhere, there is little direct evidence of higher winter numbers. Christy noted that the Moorhen was "… especially common during winter when its numbers are greatly increased by arrivals from elsewhere". The species has only been regularly included in WeBS counts since the 1990s and these provide insufficient data to discern trends; recent comprehensive counts of the many waters in the Lea Valley and Metropolitan Essex have revealed a substantial winter population of around 1,000 birds that regularly represents over 60% of the county WeBS total in any month. Nonetheless, WeBS must locate only a small fraction of the wintering population, many being present on the multitude of inland waters that are not surveyed.

A considerable number have been ringed at Abberton, from which there have been several recoveries. The recoveries in southern Britain are typical of British Moorhens dispersing away from natal areas and include movements northwards with recoveries from Suffolk, Norfolk, and Lincolnshire. One recovered at Skien, Telemark, Norway, 1,022km to the northeast on 28th December 1986 had been ringed at Roydon on 1st March 1986. A total of ten foreign-ringed Moorhens has been recovered

	Jan	Feb	Mar	Apr	May	Jun	Jul	Aug	Sep	Oct	Nov	Dec
Southern England	6		2	1	1		2				1	1
Norway												1
Denmark				1								
The Netherlands									2			
France	1										1	
Totals	7	0	2	2	1	0	2	0	2	0	2	2

Month and location of recovery of Moorhens ringed in Essex

in Essex, seven from the Netherlands, two from Denmark and one from Germany. The Netherlands and Denmark are important sources of winter immigrants (Migration Atlas).

Although a very common species, threats remain. Sympathetic management of waterways can increase numbers. Dredging and removal of potential nesting vegetation from banks, however, reduces both density of breeding pairs and the proportion that lay second clutches (Taylor 1984): dredging rivers just one side at a time can be less damaging. The impact of Mink is unclear. Nationally, low breeding densities have been attributed to Mink, as Moorhens are an important part of the species' diet (Birks 1990). However, Otters are slowly increasing and are known to drive off Mink, so any effect that Mink are currently having on populations may be reduced. Overall, given the species' adaptability and its readiness to utilise the smallest of waters, the future for the Moorhen looks secure.

(Common) Coot   *Fulica atra*

A common resident, passage migrant and winter visitor

The Coot is widespread across Eurasia, northern Africa, India, the Far East and Australia. The nominate race *atra* breeds throughout the Palearctic as far south as North Africa, as far east as Japan, and north to 65° N in Fennoscandia and Siberia; it also breeds as far south as Sri Lanka (Migration Atlas). Amongst its most important habitats are eutrophic and mesotrophic lakes, fishponds, large artificial reservoirs and river deltas (European Atlas). In Britain, the Coot is commonest and most widespread in lowland areas of England, especially the Midlands, southern and southeast England (Second National Atlas). In much of Europe, the species is sedentary or a partial migrant but populations from Fennoscandia and from east of the Czech Republic are mostly migratory (Migration Atlas).

In the 19th century, the Coot appeared to be largely restricted to the coast, Christy describing the species as "An abundant resident frequenting large sheets of water near the coast. It is sometimes, but not often, seen inland on the lakes in Skreens Park, Audley End, Wanstead and other parks, where it occasionally breeds … It is probably decreasing in numbers, through the draining of its haunts". Glegg considered the Coot a fairly common resident and, whilst confirming its affinity for coastal freshwaters, noted the increasing use of inland waters, although it remained somewhat local, its chief haunts still being the larger artificial lakes such as Gosfield, Hallingbury and Navestock. Very small numbers were by now breeding on the Lea Valley reservoirs.

Hudson & Pyman described the Coot as locally common, the largest populations being on the main reservoirs, with smaller numbers on park lakes and some mature gravel-pits, particu-

Atlas	Survey Area	% of 10km squares or tetrads in which	
		bred/probably bred	possibly bred or present
First National 10km	Essex	100.0	0.0
Second National 10km	Essex	91.2	1.8
First London Tetrad	Met. Essex	25.0	5.5
Second London Tetrad	Met. Essex	51.5	3.0
Essex Tetrad	Essex	30.7	3.7

Summary of results of Atlas surveys for Coots

larly in the Lea Valley. Whilst Coots still bred on coastal freshmarshes, numbers had declined and the habitat was no longer the principal one. Up to 100 pairs bred at Hanningfield in 1957 with around 50 pairs at Abberton in 1962.

Cox described the Coot in a very similar vein to Hudson & Pyman and gave breeding populations of 70–100 pairs at Hanningfield, 30–50 at Abberton and 20–30 at Ardleigh. In the Lea Valley in 1982, at least 124 broods were counted (40 on Walthamstow and 84 around Nazeing). Cox estimated that the breeding population was probably in excess of 500 pairs and perhaps of the order of 750–1,000 pairs.

In Essex, Coots tend to avoid breeding adjacent to running water or the very small areas of standing water that Moorhens favour, instead preferring large open bodies of water. A considerable number of the latter have been created in recent years as a result of gravel extraction and construction of irrigation reservoirs. It seems likely, therefore, that the Coot has increased as a breeding species in the last 50 years. Despite this, comparison of the National Atlases suggests a very slight range contraction, albeit restricted to northwest Essex, although between the two London Atlases there appears to have been a local range expansion. The Essex Atlas survey recorded the Coot in 34.4% of tetrads with breeding confirmed in most and suggested that the breeding population was in the region of 2,000–3,000 pairs, a figure that probably holds true today.

Essex WBS data are very limited with densities on the Stour of 0.22–1.78 pairs per km and on open water, along the Lea Navigation/Lea, of 12–14.7 pairs per km. Surprisingly for such a common and obvious species that is fiercely territorial, there is little data on breeding densities. In Hertfordshire, densities on open water WBS sites have been recorded in the range of 12–41 pairs per km and on rivers 1.3–3.7 pairs per km (Smith *et al.* 1993). Although but a fraction of the estimated population, numbers of breeding Coots reported in the *EBR* have been rising steadily in recent years, perhaps in part due to increased observer coverage, particularly in Metropolitan Essex.

The Coot is a prolific multi-brooded species and 181 pairs reported in 2000 raised some 750 broods, 662 of them in Metropolitan Essex.

In recent years, peak counts of pairs/broods have come from: Abberton, 86 in 1999; Rainham, 74 in 1999; Walthamstow, 66 in 2000; and Seventy Acres Lake, 53 in 2000. In addition, 20 or more pairs have been recorded from Old Hall, Tollesbury Wick and several sites in the Lea Valley.

By late summer, large flocks form on the main reservoirs. Prior to their construction, however, it appears that coastal sites and the Stour in particular were favoured; a switch from salt to freshwater has occurred over the last 60 years or so. However, it seems that the gatherings found on coastal waters had declined through the 19th century, prior to the creation of the reservoirs, one of Christy's correspondents noting that: "In former days, I have sometimes seen them in straggling flocks of several hundreds or thousands, on the tideway on the Essex coast". In the early 19th century, it was also noted: "In the autumn and winter, these birds make their appearance on the rivers in vast flocks, and upon an appointed day all the boats and guns are put into requisition, and a general attack is made upon them" (Christy). Gulls and White-tailed Eagles often attacked such gatherings.

GB 1,100 INT 15,000	1980-1984	1985-1989	1990-1994	1995-1999	2000-2004	Peak counts		Peak Month
WeBS totals	*12,775*	*16,052*	*17,144*	*13,160*	*14,243^*	*Sep 94*	*23,708*	*Nov*
Stour	7	16	23	17	9^	Nov 94	52	Nov
Hamford	~	~	~	~	63^	Nov 82	89	Nov
Colne	~	78	119	91	94^	Nov 94	311	Nov
Blackwater	~	310	301	411	208^	Nov 89	502	Nov
Dengie	0	0	0	1	9^	Twice	10	Jul
Crouch-Roach	~	43	98	56	108^	Nov 01	158	Nov
Thames	157	87	503	65	132^	Sep 94	754	Sep
Ardleigh	~	105^	341	188	278^	Oct 91	568	Sep
Abberton	9,552	11,545	12,188	7,883	8,180^	Sep 94	**18,632**	Oct
Hanningfield	2,557	3,178	2,749	3,513	2,876^	Nov 83	4,930	Oct
Lea Valley	2,738	2,695	3,113	2,737	3,624^	Oct 90	5,744	Nov
Met. Essex Waters	~	~	~	~	2,364^	Oct 03	2,298	Nov

**Five-year average of peak WeBS counts (Jul-Nov)
of Coots from 1980-2004**

Glegg considered the numbers on the Stour to be remarkable, although he noted that the Lea Valley reservoirs also held good numbers, the first signs of the move to inland waters: neither Abberton nor Hanningfield existed at this time. Regular wintering flocks of around 4,000 were reported from the Stour, although numbers varied annually with more being seen in severe weather. The stretch of tidal water between Bradfield and Wrabness was always favoured. Large numbers were not, however, limited to the Stour; in around 1840, a 'gunner' from Tollesbury bagged no fewer than 50 with a single discharge of his gun (Christy).

After the building of Abberton and Hanningfield during the 1940s and 1950s the species appeared to have entirely adopted these new inland freshwater sites by Hudson & Pymans' time, with up to 8,000 recorded from Abberton, although 2,000–2,500 was more usual. It is quite likely that the Stour was abandoned when Abberton was flooded in 1940 (Cox). Today, only in severe weather, when inland waters ice over, do large gatherings occur on tidal waters.

The large autumnal flocks are presumed to be moult assemblies (Cox); adult Coots are in heavy wing moult and flightless for a period between July and September (Migration Atlas). The largest counts have come from Abberton, which is by far the most important site for Coots in Britain, whilst Hanningfield is the third most important. Together, Abberton and Hanningfield may hold 10% of the national wintering population, all the more remarkable for this is generally a dispersive species (Pollitt *et al.* 2003). The Lea Valley and Metropolitan Essex areas have received comprehensive coverage in recent years and the combined counts from these areas often exceed those at Hanningfield. Perhaps 15% of the national population may therefore winter at these four sites. Numbers vary considerably from year to year and, although the reasons are unclear, weather-related movements and changing water levels at the main sites may be factors.

Numbers usually peak in September and then decline steadily through winter. The mid-winter population is about 30% of the September total.

During winter, Coots tend to disperse widely, with regular wintering populations across the county, with even relatively small waters having populations of several hundred at this time. At Abberton, numbers tend to decline rapidly after October with only around 10–15% of the peak autumn numbers present in January. Rarely do counts exceed 1,000 after the turn of the year. However, in the winters of 1988/89 and 1993/94 large numbers remained, encouraged by shallow waters that presented ideal feeding. In late 1993, there were nearly 11,000 in December (typically 400–800 in other years), whilst there were over 7,000 in January 1994. A total of 8,000 was present during December 1960. A similar pattern has been observed at Hanningfield, the largest winter numbers occurring in 1988/89 and 1994/95. Away from these two localities, numbers tend to peak later perhaps suggesting dispersal from Abberton and Hanningfield to sites both within and outside the county. Spring passage is not obvious.

GB 1,100 INT 15,000	80/81- 84/85	85/86- 89/90	90/91- 94/95	95/96- 99/00	00/01- 04/05	Peak counts		Peak Month
WeBS totals	3,950	7,764	7,561	5,303	9,107^	*Dec 93*	15,746	*Dec*
Stour	27	30	23	38	11^	Feb 96	87	Feb
Hamford	~	~	~	~	66^	Mar 02	77	Feb
Colne	~	116	144	213	114^	Dec 98	624	Dec
Blackwater	~	350	363	480	392^	Jan 01	710	Dec
Dengie	0	0	3	1	2^	Mar 95	11	Mar
Crouch-Roach	~	43	94	59	166^	Dec 02	194	Jan
Thames	423	251	453	101	293^	Jan 85	650	Jan
Ardleigh	~	187^	279	338	521^	Dec 01	718	Jan
Abberton	1,277	3,448	3,193	1,389	842^	Jan 89	10,959	Dec
Hanningfield	1,550	1,196	1,138	1,754	1,952^	Dec 96	4,986	Jan
Lea Valley	2,324	2,837	2,459	2,489	3,776^	Dec 03	4,224	Dec
Met. Essex Waters	~	~	~	~	2,364^	Jan 01	2,482	Jan

**Five-year average of peak WeBS counts (Dec-Mar)
of Coots from 1980/81-2003/04**

The annual variation in numbers at Abberton is marked. The magnitude of these variations is greater than for the national total, suggesting that Abberton birds are redistributing within Britain on a fairly broad scale (Cranswick *et al.* 1999).

Kirby *et al.* (1990) suggested that a genuine increase had occurred in Britain, rather than redistribution from moult flocks elsewhere on the Continent. In Essex, this increase may be related to habitat creation over the last two decades (*EBR* 1990). Indeed, if it is the case that the Essex breeding population is of the order of 2,000–3,000 pairs and each pair on average fledges two chicks (some pairs will raise a second or even third brood), a minimum autumn population of 8,000–12,000 now exists. The number of birds, whether British or foreign, occurring in Essex each winter are not known, but assuming most locally-bred Coots remain in Essex during September, in peak years it appears that perhaps 8,000–12,000 British and foreign Coots arrive in autumn.

Coots are presumed to be fairly sedentary during the breeding season and observations suggest that some may stay on the same waters all year (*BWP*). The species is, to many observers, not an obvious passage migrant, but clearly there are marked fluctuations in numbers throughout the year. Cox noted that as there is a year round presence in Essex and that the Coot is generally a nocturnal migrant, the extent of any passage tends to be largely masked. Even short-distance movements between waters must take place at night (Migration Atlas).

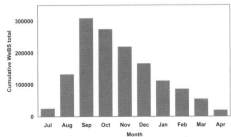

Seasonal occurrence of Coots from 1980-2003

Several thousand Coots have been ringed at Abberton since 1950. Ringing evidence suggests that some young reared at Abberton move to northwest France in late autumn and winter of the same year. Six of the recoveries show very rapid movement into France, some just 17 days after ringing, possibly triggered by severe weather locally. Some birds move further south still, with recoveries coming from Spain, Portugal and Morocco. Those from the latter two countries are the only recoveries of British-ringed birds from there.

	Jan	Feb	Mar	Apr	May	Jun	Jul	Aug	Sep	Oct	Nov	Dec
Northern England	1		1	1					1	1		
Southern England	38	19	9	14	3	1	5	6	1	5	8	1
Sweden								1				
Russia							3					
Poland						1	1				1	
Denmark	1		1	1			1	1	1	3	3	1
Germany	1	2		1	2			2			1	2
The Netherlands	2	6	4	1	1		3			2	1	4
Belgium		1										
France	10	8	3						1	6	5	7
Spain					1					1		
Portugal											1	
Morocco					1							
Total	53	36	19	19	7	2	9	12	5	18	20	15

Month and location of recovery of Coots ringed in Essex

Autumn immigration is known to occur from the Continent between October and the second half of November (*BWP*). Interestingly, a Coot was observed sitting on the sea 10km off St Osyth on 18th July 1990, perhaps suggesting that Continental birds begin to arrive as early as mid-summer to moult. Recoveries of birds ringed during winter at Abberton, in Sweden, Poland and Russia confirm that Essex receives, probably on a regular basis, a proportion of the south and westerly movement that eastern populations make; Russia is, however, unusually far east.

The Coot has responded well to the increase in available habitat and appears to spread rapidly to new sites when they become suitable. This may have been aided by the fact that an unknown percentage of the population does not breed in any one year and can therefore respond quickly to the formation of new habitat or vacant sites (Winter Atlas). Even in urban areas the Coot seems to have adjusted to the presence of humans and, provided there is somewhere that is relatively undisturbed, will nest on lakes in busy urban parks.

(Common) Crane   *Grus grus*

Rare, principally autumn passage migrant: 46 records involving up to 121 individuals   Amber List

The monotypic Crane breeds from central Europe and Scandinavia across to the Far East, from the northern taiga to the central Asian steppes and winters in southwest Europe, north and east Africa and from the eastern Mediterranean east as far as China. Throughout much of west and southern Europe the species had become extinct by the 17th century although since the 1970s most national populations have begun to increase (Migration Atlas). A small resident population exists in the Norfolk Broads where breeding has occurred annually since 1981 (Taylor *et al.* 1999). It is likely that some recent county records relate to wanderers from this population.

Christy commented, "… there is every probability that it was fairly common on our coast several centuries ago" but gave no evidence to back up this comment. Palin (1872) stated that Cranes were "common … in the then-un-drained lowlands about Aveley" but this may have been rather fanciful thinking as the author incorrectly believed that the name of nearby Cranham was derived from the Crane (Reaney 1969). That said, Cranbrook is derived from the 13th century "Cranebroc" meaning, "Crane or heron brook", so perhaps there is a grain of truth in his belief? Christy gave just two records, including one of eight at Elmstead Market on 9th November 1888. Glegg added just one record of a single bird. Subsequently, Cranes have been recorded in 20 years since 1950, the best being 1977 with 26 individuals and 2003 with 30.

The largest flock involved 26 that flew over Tollesbury/Bradwell/Foulness on 16th October 1977. It was also seen over Higham, Suffolk, and several sites in Kent; at Folkestone they headed south over the English Channel. Other flocks of 4+ have been at: The Naze, four, 3rd November 1963; Colne Point, four, 9th January 1985; Southend-on-Sea, four, 16th May 1986; Holland Haven, four, 27th February 2002; Hanningfield, nine, 8th September 2003; and Prittle Brook, Leigh/Two Tree Island, 14, 2nd October 2003. In 1987 a pair summered in Essex. They were first seen at Foulness on 27th May and finally at Fleet Head on 20th September. In between they were observed at five sites, although only at Latchingdon

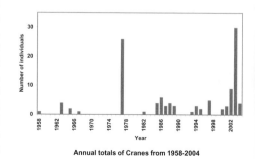

Annual totals of Cranes from 1958-2004

(18th June–8th July) and Potton Island (12th July–31st August) were the stays longer than a day; display was noted at Hanningfield on 14th June. Singles that summered in the Foulness area in 1988 and 1989 may have been one or other of this pair.

Due to increases nationally, linked to greater breeding numbers on the Continent since the mid-1970s, the species was removed from the BBRC List at the end of 1987. Nationally, 2,332 had been recorded to the end of 2002 (Fraser & Rogers 2005), with 685 in 1963, 243 in 2002 and 199 in 1982. Such influxes are typical of birds moving out of the near-Continent following abrupt temperature decreases and then drifting across the North Sea in poor visibility and easterly winds (Cottridge & Vinicombe 1996).

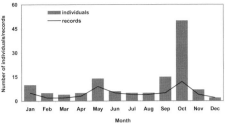

Seasonal occurrence of Cranes from 1950-2004

Most national records occur between October and November, with another peak in April and May, so Essex occurrences are typical.

Little Bustard   *Tetrax tetrax*

Vagrant: ten records involving 11 individuals, but only one since 1885

The monotypic Little Bustard has a fragmented range over the Western Palearctic with discrete populations in the Iberian peninsula and the Ukraine to western Siberia. The species has declined dramatically over much of its European range during the 20th century due to agricultural intensification and has consequently become extremely rare in Britain. The nearest breeding populations in France are mostly migratory, whilst those in Spain are predominantly resident. More easterly populations, as far as the Russian steppe, winter in the southern part of their range.

1823	Harwich	January	Female, shot
1824	Clacton-on-Sea	Winter	Shot
1837/38	Writtle	Winter	Shot
prior 1840	Landwick, Dengie	September	Shot
prior 1860	Berechurch	Undated	Shot
1860	St Osyth	17th December	Female, shot
1874	The Naze	28th December	Pair, shot
1882	Little Oakley and Ramsey	21st November for one week	
1885	Tillingham	Early September	Female, shot
1969	Bridgewick Farm, Dengie	28th January	Female/immature

The Writtle specimen generated much interest at the time, being left by its owner at the offices of the *Essex Chronicle* in Chelmsford for exhibition, whilst the pair in 1874 "... was shot by Mr Eagle, of Walton Hall ... from a field of turnips and cabbages ... They were in full winter plumage ... Mr Eagle shot one in the morning when after game, and finding it a rarity, he went back later in the day and shot the other". A third bird may have been present in the area (Christy).

There were 92 British records prior to 1958, the majority during the 19th century, with just 19 since (BBRC 2003). The most recent Essex occurrence was part of the largest national influx this century with two recorded in Norfolk and another in Pembrokeshire. Most records probably involve individuals from eastern populations which, when winters are particularly severe, move west well beyond their normal range, although it is just possible that individuals from France and Iberia may also be involved.

Great Bustard   *Otis tarda*

Vagrant: three 19th century records

The Great Bustard is a globally threatened species, with a widespread Palearctic distribution. The nominate race *tarda* occurs from Iberia and northwest Morocco to central Siberia, and *dybowskii* is found from the Altai and Lake

223

Baikal to Mongolia. The species has declined dramatically since the mid-18th century and has disappeared from much of western Europe (European Atlas). Great Bustards formerly bred across many parts of Britain, the last record coming from Icklingham, Suffolk, in 1832 (Piotrowski 2003). Central European populations have declined rapidly since the mid-1970s. Most western and central populations are generally sedentary, although subject to hard-weather movements, whilst eastern populations generally move south in winter.

about 1830	near Saffron Walden	Undated	Male, shot
1879	River Crouch,		
	Woodham Ferrers	5th December	Female, shot
1890	Bridgewick Farm, Dengie	6th December	Female, shot

A further specimen, reported by Christy to have been shot at Manningtree in the winter of 1879/80, at a time of an influx into the country (Witherby 1920), was dismissed by Glegg who felt that the evidence was incomplete. Christy (1903) referred to an unsubstantiated record of one at Hatfield Broad Oak on 31st October 1899, during frosty weather.

Whilst there is no hard evidence to suggest that Great Bustards once bred in Essex, it is possible that they did so in the far northwest, where there were large areas of uncultivated downs that would have suited the species. Indeed, there would seem to be written evidence of it being quite abundant in that area in the early 18th century, as an advertisement in Addison's Spectator for the 4th March 1712 stated: "Heyden [sic], in Essex, near Walden and Royston. The seat of Sir Peter Soame, Bart., deceased, situate on a gentle hill, with a very large and pleasant prospect, fair gardens, canals, fish ponds, dove coate, and all sorts of offices without door, woods of large timber, and where is all game in great plenty, even to the Bustard and Pheasant, is to be Let…". At this time Heydon was in Essex — it was transferred to Cambridgeshire in 1895 when the political boundary was moved.

The description of the 1879 occurrence makes interesting reading: " On the morning of Friday, Dec. 5th, soon after daybreak, Mr. Albert Pertwee … was "laid up"… on the north side and under the wall of the River Crouch, for the purpose of shooting Wildfowl. While so stationed, he was surprised to observe a very large bird fly leisurely across the river and over his head at a small height. Being loaded with No. 2 shot, he fired, and brought down the bird, although but slightly wounded. Mr. Pertwee had no idea of the species to which the bird belonged, but brought it with him on the day of its death to Chelmsford market, where it was purchased by Mr. Charles Smoothy. Mr. Travis of Walden preserved the bird, which was a female weighing about ten pounds. On the night of the day following its death, there occurred one of the sharpest frosts of the century" (Christy).

Nationally, there were just five records between 1910 and 1963, followed by a slight increase in the 1980s, perhaps linked to increased observer coverage, but a decline since. In total there have been 20 since 1958, the last in 1987 when two occurred in Norfolk and five in Suffolk (BBRC 1988). Like Little Bustards, most occurrences appear to be caused by displacement due to severe weather.

(Eurasian) Oystercatcher   *Haematopus ostralegus*

Resident, passage migrant and winter visitor   Amber List

The Oystercatcher is a large Palearctic wader, the nominate race *ostralegus* occurring principally along the coasts of western Europe and the Mediterranean. The species breeds in a variety of coastal habitats, along lakesides, in river valleys, on farmland, heath and rough grazing and, increasingly, on shingle-covered roofs in suburban areas near to food sources. The European population is of the order of 200,000–300,000 breeding pairs (European Atlas). The species is widespread in Britain, in the south breeding principally on the coast but increasingly inland, whilst in Scotland and northern England it is found both on the coast and inland. The population has increased from 19,000–30,000 pairs in the early 1960s (Dare 1966) to 99,000–127,000 pairs. Northern populations show a stronger migratory tendency than southern ones (Migration Atlas). Around 315,000 winter in Britain and Ireland.

The Pyefleet Channel, north of Mersea Island, and Pye Sands, off Harwich, are so named from the 'Sea Pie', a local Essex name for the Oystercatcher (Reaney 1969).

Atlas	Survey Area	% of 10km squares or tetrads in which	
		bred/probably bred	possibly bred or present
First National 10km	Essex	26.3	5.3
Second National 10km	Essex	33.3	12.3
First London Tetrad	Met. Essex	0.5	0.5
Second London Tetrad	Met. Essex	2.5	1.0
Essex Tetrad	Essex	6.2	2.6

Summary of results of Atlas surveys for Oystercatchers

Christy considered the Oystercatcher a "... scarce resident on our coast, where it formerly bred not uncommonly, but best known as a fairly-common visitor to our shores from autumn to spring". Apart from Harwich, where the species may have continued to breed, all other breeding records that Christy detailed were prior to 1850 (Shopland, Paglesham and Tollesbury, Wigborough and Peldon saltings). By the early 20th century, the Oystercatcher probably no longer bred in Essex, the last definite occurrence being around Harwich in 1889. Glegg's only records came from the shingle beaches between the Colne and Stour, with no more

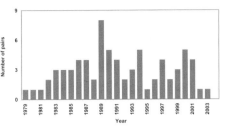

Annual number of breeding pairs of Oystercatchers at Abberton from 1979-2004

than six observed together. Nationally, numbers declined throughout eastern and southern England in the 19th and early 20th century, possibly due to persecution (Population Trends) and the increasing use of beaches for leisure purposes (Historical Atlas). One pair bred in the northeast in 1929 (Pyman 1938c).

Perhaps as a result of reduced persecution, numbers slowly increased with ten pairs breeding in 1950 and 52 by 1955–56 (Hudson & Pyman). The majority were found around Hamford Water (19 pairs) and the Blackwater and Crouch Estuaries (14 and 12 pairs respectively). Survey work for the BoEE from 1973–74 found at least 150 pairs of which 30 were in Hamford Water, 20 along the Colne, 35 along the Blackwater, 20 along the Crouch and 35 on Foulness. On account of apparent increases in the late 1970s, Cox suggested that in the early 1980s the population was around 200 pairs.

GB 3,200 INT 9,000	70/71-74/75	75/76-79/80	80/81-84/85	85/86-89/90	90/91-94/95	95/96-99/00	00/01-04/05	Peak counts		Peak month
WeBS totals	6,499^	10,164	10,806	13,689	19,194	18,284	24,440^	Jan 03	31,028	Jan
Stour	165^	314	337	1,020	1,440	1,890	1,585^	Jan 99	2,596	Jan
Hamford Water	406^	497	733	414^	884	1,079	1,072^	Jan 84	1,446	Feb
Colne	440^	~	~	1,049	1,062	1,179	883^	Jan 97	2,246	Feb
Blackwater	544^	488	297	508	901	1,409	1,149^	Feb 97	1,903	Jan
Dengie	1,007^	1,395^	899	1,155	1,948	2,253	2,868^	Jan 02	5,271	Jan
Crouch-Roach	33^	37*	112	214	173	228	177^	Mar 95	270	Mar
Thames	4,579^	8,321	9,491	11,343	14,797	12,216	19,453^	Jan 03	25,951	Jan

Five-year average of peak WeBS counts (Dec-Mar) of Oystercatchers from 1970/71-2003/04

Results from the Essex Atlas survey suggested that by the 1990s the population had increased to 300 pairs. Since then, numbers have increased further, with the population perhaps as high as 500 pairs, about 1–1.5% of the British population. A significant part of this increase has been due to the discovery of a large colony on Horsey Island where there were 213 pairs in 2002. Just how long such numbers have been present on the island is unknown but the colony had clearly been overlooked. Elsewhere, significant but variable numbers have occurred on Foulness where during the 1980s and early 1990s some 50% of the Essex breeding population occurred. However, from a peak of 157 pairs in 1993 numbers crashed to just five in 1998 (Lewis 2000), although there were 112 in 2000. Away from Foulness, up to 67 pairs have bred at Old Hall, in 2002, with smaller numbers along the Colne Estuary and at Bradwell and all around the coast and on adjacent gravel-pits. Breeding first occurred in Metropolitan Essex at Rainham in 1971, since when Oystercatchers have bred periodically at several sites as far upriver as Silvertown and Beckton.

GB 3,200 INT 9,000	1970-1974	1975-1979	1980-1984	1985-1989	1990-1994	1995-1999	2000-2004	Peak counts		Peak month
WeBS totals	6,595	8,184	11,096	13,135	14,510	16,121	19,275	Oct 04	24,192	Nov
Stour	115^	82*	433	783	1,176	1,571	1,227	Nov 96	2,053	Nov
Hamford Water	333^	337^	438	382	787	854	890	Sep 00	1,478	Nov
Colne	409^	~	~	949	970	903	1,076	Oct 00	1,402	Oct
Blackwater	609*	779^	222	181	950	966	940	Nov 79	1,561	Nov
Dengie	2,585^	2,788^	1,031	1,032	1,364	1,675	1,675	Oct 78	6,000	Oct
Crouch-Roach	15^	~	7	2	8	38	33	Oct 00	73	Oct
Thames	4,172	5,815	9,165	10,703	10,973	11,982	14,551	Nov 01	17,560	Nov

Five-year average of peak WeBS counts (Sep-Nov) of Oystercatchers from 1970-2004

Although the majority of nesting locations have been on coastal sand and shingle, an increasing number have utilised coastal farmland and grasslands, a habit first noted at Foulness in the 1960s and now regular in Hamford Water/Horsey Island and Old Hall.

In 1979, inland breeding first occurred at Abberton, with breeding attempted there every year since. The Essex Atlas noted that the breeding cycle at Abberton has tended to be several weeks in advance of that on the coast, a similar tendency in Lancashire being linked to the necessity to meet the peak abundance of soil invertebrates (Briggs 1984). Single pairs have also bred at: Coleman's, 1989, 1990 and 1997; Chelmer Valley, 1990 and 2001; Boreham GP, 1991, 1992 and 2002; Stanway GP, 1997; and Russell Green GPs, 2003.

During the 19th century, wintering and passage numbers appear to have been small, if counts around the mouth of the Thames in the 1830s were typical (Christy). Glegg knew of only single-figure counts. The first three-figure

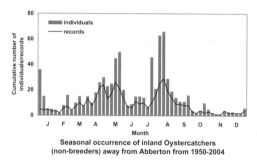

Seasonal occurrence of inland Oystercatchers
(non-breeders) away from Abberton from 1950-2004

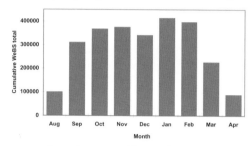

Seasonal occurrence of Oystercatchers from 1970-2004

counts occurred in 1951, with the first four-figure flocks reported from Foulness just five years later. Wintering numbers increased markedly from the early 1970s, the most recent five-year average being some four times that for 1970/71–1974/75. Nationally numbers have also increased considerably; the East Atlantic flyway population has grown by 19% since the mid-1980s (Cranswick *et al.* 1999).

Passage occurs through October and November with wintering numbers peaking during January and February before declining rapidly during March.

Some 70% of the Essex-wintering population is found off Foulness, reflecting the abundance of Cockles, Mussels and other bivalves; numbers here are regularly of international importance. The record count of 25,951 in January 2003 was considerably above the site average, but still less than half the average count at Britain's most important site at Morecambe Bay, Lancashire/Cumbria. Cox estimated that based on an average peak of 11,500, Essex regularly supported 4% of the British and 1.5% of the European population of wintering Oystercatchers. At this time Britain supported some 45% of the European population. Today, the five-year average for the most recent five-year winter period equates to 7.7% of the British population of 315,200 (Rehfisch et al. 2003) and 2.8% of the European wintering population of 875,000 (European Atlas).

Inland records are regular and come principally from the main reservoirs, with most during passage periods. The largest counts have come from Hanningfield, 34, 20th July 1984 and 25, 2nd January 1982, the latter during severe weather.

Although most are likely to move south, perhaps as far as Africa (*BWP*), some Essex breeding birds probably winter locally on the coast (Migration Atlas) where they are joined by large numbers of immigrants, mostly of Norwegian origin (Winter Atlas). These populations generally inhabit coastal areas west of North Cape-Porsanger and migrate southwest along the Norwegian coast to winter chiefly in Britain (Waters & Cranswick 1993). However, recoveries in southern Britain suggest that birds from breeding areas in Iceland east to Estonia may also be present (Migration Atlas). Increasingly, birds from the much enlarged Dutch population have been recovered in Britain, particularly in southeast England. A single Oystercatcher ringed in Denmark and three from the Netherlands have been recovered in Essex. Relatively few Oystercatchers have been ringed in Essex and the seven recoveries have all been within Kent and East Anglia. All were marked as nestlings. One ringed at Snettisham, Norfolk, in August 1967 was found dead at Mistley in April 1993, making it at least 26 years old.

The Essex population has increased considerably in the last 20 years, although the previously unrecorded Horsey Island colony and that on Foulness may each make up around 40% of the current county population. The marked increase in the wintering population appears to be continuing and with the species generally remaining faithful to wintering sites, protection of the bivalve mollusc populations is important to maintain wintering and breeding numbers. Potential threats include commercial shellfish fishing and offshore development proposals.

Black-winged Stilt

Himantopus himantopus

Very rare passage migrant: 14 records involving 22 individuals

The Black-winged Stilt has a huge world range. The nominate race *himantopus* occurs in Eurasia from southwest Europe to Mongolia and south to southern Africa. Nesting occurs irregularly as close to Britain as the Netherlands, Belgium, Germany and Denmark but regularly only in Spain, France (principally in The Camargue) and Portugal in western Europe. There have been four British breeding records, the most recent in Cheshire in 1993 being unsuccessful. Most of the European population moves south to the sub-Saharan wetlands in winter, although there is an increasing winter population in southwest Iberia.

1947	St Osyth	17th and 27th November	
1948	St Osyth	12th April	Two
1961	Havengore Island	4th June	Two
	Eastwood	3rd November	
1962	Little Oakley	10th August	
1968	Hamford Water	5th September	Two adults and three juveniles
1970	Fingringhoe Wick	3rd August	
1971	Coate Outfall, Dengie	7th August	
1974	Cripplegate, Southminster	14th September	
1980	Wakering	8th–13th June	Male
1987	East Tilbury	31st May	Female
1995	Hanningfield	10th May	Male and female
	Vange Marsh/Coryton	19th–22nd May	Male and female
1997	Rainham	10th–20th September	Juvenile

The records in 1995 referred to different pairs.

To the end of 2004 there had been 347 British records (BBRC 2005) of this predominantly spring migrant. Periodic spring invasions occur nationally with records increasing in recent years as populations in France and Spain have expanded. The largest influx was in 1987 and involved 38 records. These influxes may occur as a result of varying breeding success on the Continent, which is dependent on water levels in their breeding ranges (Cottridge & Vinicombe 1996). However, in 1987 a large anticyclone over Europe during April produced ideal conditions for overshooting spring migrants. November arrivals are unusual, although there are several national records of wintering birds.

Christy also made reference to one seen around 1820 near Saffron Walden, Mr J. Clarke having been hurriedly called by a man to see "a bird with legs a yard long" but was only in time to see it fly away; Glegg considered that the evidence was unsatisfactory.

(Pied) Avocet

Recurvirostra avosetta

Increasing summer visitor, passage migrant and winter visitor

Amber List

The monotypic Avocet breeds locally from southern Sweden to southern Spain and northwest Africa, east to southern Ukraine, the Black Sea and across central Asia and Outer Mongolia; other significant populations occur in east-central and southern (European Atlas). In England, the Avocet breeds principally in East Anglia and the southeast where shallow brackish coastal lagoons with bare or sparsely vegetated low islands are favoured (Second National Atlas). In the region of 1,262–1,266 pairs bred nationally in 2003 (RBBP 2004).

The Avocet almost certainly bred in Essex prior to the 19th century. Although Christy gave no specific reference, he quoted Dale (1730) who noted that the "Crooked-bill" was met with "... in these eastern parts [about Harwich] frequently. The first time I did see it, was on an island below Maldon, called Northey, anno 1700. In the summer time".

Christy also noted that there was a creek on Northey Island, marked on some late 19th century maps, called "Awl Creek", perhaps "...a relic of the time when the Avocet or "Awl-bill" bred on its banks". Although one correspondent noted that Avocets "... often land in the winter time" there appears to

Atlas	Survey Area	% of 10km squares or tetrads in which	
		bred/probably bred	possibly bred or present
First National 10km	Essex	0.0	0.0
Second National 10km	Essex	10.5	3.5
First London Tetrad	Met. Essex	0.0	0.0
Second London Tetrad	Met. Essex	0.0	0.0
Essex Tetrad	Essex	0.5	0.2

Summary of results of Atlas surveys for Avocets

be just one, undated 19th century record, involving eight killed with one shot at the mouth of the Blackwater. Given the number of gunners working the coast in the 19th century, the Avocet must have been very rare for there to be so few records. Avocets allegedly obtained at Canvey Island in 1901 and Leigh/Two Tree Island in 1908 were actually in Kent (Glegg).

Between 1930 and 1949, there were just five records, one involving a pair that bred at Langenhoe in 1944. This coincided with the recolonisation of England at a time when the Dutch population was increasing rapidly, seawalls had fallen into disrepair during WWII and large areas were closed off to the public for security reasons (Second National Atlas). Breeding probably also occurred at Old Hall in 1953. Despite the presence of the large breeding colony at Havergate Island, Suffolk, which numbered some 100 pairs by the end of the 1950s (Piotrowski 2003), it was not until 1975, on Potton Island, that breed-ing occurred, although the location was withheld at the time and zealously guarded by the tenant farmer, military police and conservation agencies (Essex Atlas). Avocets have bred there almost every year since with nearby Foulness colonised in 1988; up to 62 pairs (1996) have bred. It was, however, not until 1993 that breeding occurred away from this area when six pairs bred at Old Hall where breeding is now annual: 49 pairs bred in 2002. Since 1993, other coastal sites have been established, by far the largest on

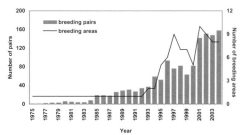

Annual totals of breeding pairs of Avocets from 1975–2004

Horsey Island where at least 60 and possibly 80 pairs bred in 2000. Lack of disturbance on this private island must be an important factor in the colony's success, although numbers have been lower more recently. Elsewhere, 28 pairs bred just north of The Naze in 2002, 20 at Tollesbury Wick in 2002, 20+ on Two Tree Island in 2003 (breeding annual since 1997) and ten at Coate outfall, Dengie, in 1997. Breeding was reported from a further 12 sites by the end of 2004. The breeding population currently stands at around 150 pairs.

Breeding success varies considerably from site to site and from year to year. At larger sites the average number of young raised has been well below one young per pair. Fox predation has been the principal cause of losses; in 1996 all 26 pairs that nested at Old Hall failed to rear young. Studies at Havergate Island and Minsmere, Suffolk (Hill 1988), have shown that as colony size increases, so the number of young per pair declines. Thus new sites generally produce more young per pair than older, established ones. Annual fluctuations in the breeding numbers have been related to the level of chick mortality in the previous year and the main factor regulating population size, competition for breeding space (Second National Atlas). Colour-ringing has revealed that Avocets do not show strong attachment to natal sites when they breed for the first time, but tend to return to the same breeding sites once they have bred. Thus immigrants from outside the county may have assisted the increase in the Essex population.

GB* 35 / INT 700	70/71-74/75	75/76-79/80	80/81-84/85	85/86-89/90	90/91-94/95	95/96-99/00	00/01-04/05	Peak counts		Peak month
WeBS totals	2^	3	7	62	447	984	1,562^	Mar 02	1,730	Dec
Stour	1^	0	0	0	1	3	1^	Nov 99	9	Dec
Hamford Water	0^	2	5	58	295	420	495^	Dec 02	670	Nov
Colne	0^	~	~	1	49	284	373^	Feb 02	465	Dec
Blackwater	0^	1	1	1	33	30^	186^	Feb 04	294	Nov
Dengie	0^	0	0	0	2	2	1^	Sep 92	6	Mar
Crouch-Roach	0^	0	0	0	6	7	23^	Nov 01	43	Nov
Thames	0^	1	4	24	175	415	787^	Jan 02	1,223	Jan

Five-year average of peak WeBS counts (Sep-Mar) of Avocets from 1970/71-2003/04

Since 1949 Avocets had been recorded annually in ever-increasing numbers outside the breeding season. Hudson & Pyman described the species as a very scarce passage migrant and winter visitor with 4–5 recorded annually. During the 1950s numbers were small and appearances generally irregular, the largest flock being seven at Goldhanger on 27th September 1953, shortly after breeding probably occurred at Old Hall. Numbers in the 1960s and early 1970s continued at a similar level to those previously, despite the continuing population growth in Suffolk, seven at Hanningfield from 29th–30th May 1963 and off the Colne on 10th April 1961 being the highest counts.

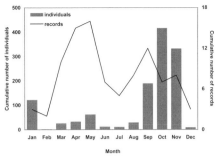

Seasonal occurrence of inland Avocets from 1950-2004

Prior to re-colonisation, most records occurred during spring or autumn migration periods, with more reported in spring than autumn. Despite the subsequent increase in numbers year round, passage is still discernible at most sites and remains strongest in spring.

Wintering began as a phenomenon only after colonisation in 1975. Early records were usually of single birds around the Foulness area with odd birds occasional further up the Thames. Counts of 100–200 are now regular at Foulness. Today, the two principal wintering sites are at opposite ends of the county: Hamford Water and particularly East Tilbury. The former col-

Seasonal occurrence of Avocets from 1971-2004

ony was founded in the early 1980s and grew rapidly from a peak of 20 in late 1985 to 670 in December 2002, although numbers are variable. The East Tilbury flock, originally part of the Cliffe, Kent, wintering population, formed around 1984 and has also grown rapidly, the peak being 1,200 (non-WeBS) on 30th January 2002. Geographically between these two sites is the third most important locality, the Colne Estuary, where up to 465 have occurred (in February

2002). Smaller numbers (up to 100) are also beginning to winter in the Blackwater Estuary.

The increase in wintering numbers has occurred in tandem with the increase in the breeding population. The fact that wintering began soon after the founding of the first breeding colonies and that it has been suggested that those wintering on the Alde Estuary in Suffolk are

	First record	Years with records	Peak counts
Abberton	5 on 15/09/59	20	120 in Oct 1998 & Jan 2000
Hanningfield	7 on 29/05/63	20	23 on 29/11/03
Walthamstow	1 on 14/04/56	5	Six on 01/05/83
KGV	1 on 08/05/88	4	Four on 18/08/90
Girling	2 on 30/04/90	3	Eight on 21/09/96
Stansted Airport Lagoon	3 on 19/05/92	3	Three on 19/05/92

Summary of inland Avocet records from 1950-2004. Also single records from Ardleight, Great Holland Pits, Coleman's, Fairlop, Berwick Ponds, Holyfield Lake and Cornmill Meadows.

probably local breeders (Winter Atlas) suggests that many Essex birds are year-round residents.

Inland, records have come principally from Abberton and Hanningfield. At the former, large numbers were attracted by the exceptionally low water levels during 1996–2000 culminating in peaks of 115 in November 1997, 120 in October 1998, 106 in October 1999 and 120 in January 2000. Almost half of all records occur in April and May.

Marked birds from Minsmere, Suffolk, have been found wintering on the Devon/Cornwall estuaries and also further south in south and southwest France and Iberia (Prater 1981). Three recoveries fall neatly into this pattern: a juvenile shot from a flock of eight at Langenhoe on 8th August 1934 that had been ringed at Etang de Vaccares, Camargue, France, in May 1934; and two ringed on Foulness in June 1995 and July 1996 and found in Charente-Maritime and Gironde, France. At the present time, the percentage of the East Anglian population that winters on Essex estuaries is not known.

Most of the county's Avocets breed on or near nature reserves, MoD-restricted areas or remote coastal areas where it is relatively easy to control human disturbance. However, predator pressure remains a severe problem at most locations. Nesting localities are limited by the species' habitat requirements, although in the Netherlands the Avocet has bred inland on arable land, alongside ditches in open farmland or muddy sections in meadows (European Atlas). Here, success has been shown to vary from year to year due to flooding, rainfall, vegetation succession and ease of access to sites for predators. Therefore, provided disturbance from humans and Foxes can be minimised, the Avocet is likely to spread to other breeding locations, perhaps even inland.

Sponsored by David and Wendy Preston

Stone Curlew (Stone-curlew)   *Burhinus oedicnemus*

Very rare, probably extinct summer resident, and very rare passage migrant   Red List - Essex BAP

The Stone Curlew, a crepuscular and nocturnal wader, has a breeding range that covers much of the southwest Palearctic and Mediterranean and Oriental regions. Within Europe, the nominate race *oedicnemus* is found from southern England east to Poland and southern Russia, and from Iberia to Italy, the Balkans and the Caucasus. The Iberian peninsula, France and Russia together hold 95% of the European population. In England, the Stone Curlew is almost entirely restricted to two main population centres, one in the Brecklands and the other on Salisbury Plain. There are several other precariously small sub-populations. The species' distribution is limited to free-draining, sandy soils with a high proportion of chalk rubble or flints (Second National Atlas). Following years of decline, which had begun by the mid-19th century (Historical Atlas), the population has stabilised and shown signs of recovery, with 272–297 pairs breeding in 2002 (RBBP 2004).

Christy noted: "In Essex, although it seems formerly to have bred not uncommonly, it now only does in one locality..." In 1838, around Sudbury, the Stone Curlew was described as "a not uncommon summer visitant but of extremely retired habits", whilst in 1845 it was still breeding in Saffron Walden district, which Christy took to mean the wide open downs that were still in existence to the north and south of the town around Heydon and Chrishall. The species was still breeding at Chrishall Grange in 1889 where nesting continued until 1902, but with what regularity is not known (Glegg). Despite making inquiries and searching the area himself, Glegg could not confirm that breeding continued. The species was probably only ever found in any numbers in the far northwest, although it seems that the Stone Curlew may have bred as far east as Sudbury district in the early 19th century.

In 1949 the species was 'rediscovered' in the northwest with local farmers confirming that Stone Curlews had been present since at least 1932. It is therefore likely that the species had always been present in the area, despite Glegg's assertion to the contrary (Pyman 1967). The first modern attempt at a census in 1952 located ten pairs and Pyman (1967) considered that annually the number of breeding pairs probably attained double figures. Subsequent records indicated an annual presence with five pairs up until the late 1960s, declining to 3–4 during the 1970s and 1980s and subsequently to only 1–2 pairs in the 1990s.

In 1999 a pair that may have nested on Essex soil was subsequently observed over the county boundary in Cambridgeshire with two young, which fledged successfully (*per* RSPB). This was the first successful breeding attempt in the county since 1992, when one young was raised. However, no birds have been reported since 1999 and it must be assumed that this small population is now extinct.

In a national context, the Essex/south Cambridgeshire birds were the remnants of a population that once stretched along the chalk belt from Royston in Hertfordshire northeast to the Brecklands of Norfolk and Suffolk. In 1952, the same year as the first Essex census, there were estimated to be more than 70 pairs breeding in the whole of Cambridgeshire, including 13 pairs in south Cambridgeshire (Bircham 1989). From the 1960s, this population declined rapidly. This long-term decline has been well documented nationally. From an estimated national population of 1,000–2,000 pairs in the late 1930s, just 150–200 pairs remained at the time of the Second National Atlas. Whilst the species was able to adapt to the conversion of downland to farming, the last 30 years of agricultural intensification has meant that the species has faced an increasingly adverse environment. The trend towards extensive production of cereals and Oil-seed Rape has meant that by spring crops are too advanced to allow feeding or breeding. In addition, even where habitat is available, nests are extremely vulnerable to modern farming operations and, although nest marking has helped at the egg stage, chicks remain vulnerable until fledged. However, following considerable research and conservation measures by the RSPB, the national population appears to be increasing.

Stone Curlews form post-breeding flocks and these may provide an indication of numbers formerly present in the northwest. Counts of 24 on 27th September 1953 at Strethall and 40 on 18th October 1955 at Littlebury Green were the largest, although both may have included birds from south Cambridgeshire. The last autumn count of any size was 18 just over the border at Ickleton in late September 1987.

Outside the breeding season, the Stone Curlew has always been relatively scarce as a passage migrant. In the 19th century, the species occasionally wintered (Christy). Around the Shoebury area in the early part of the 19th century, it was recorded in every month from September to March. Five were at Shoebury in December 1844, whilst in the late 19th century four were at Heybridge on 11th December

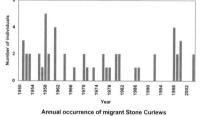

Annual occurrence of migrant Stone Curlews
from 1950-2004

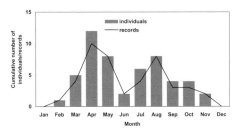

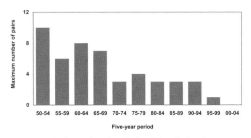

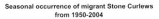

**Seasonal occurrence of migrant Stone Curlews
from 1950-2004**

**Peak annual number of pairs of Stone Curlews in
five-year periods from 1950-2004**

1890 (Colchester Museum archive) with singles at Bulphan and Stifford in late November 1887 and Stratford in January 1889. Birds occasionally winter in southern England today.

Surprisingly for a species that is usually considered an early migrant, there have been almost as many records in May as in April. Sightings have been widely scattered, but have shown a bias to the coast, with the northeast (from The Naze to Colne Point) being particularly favoured. Passage numbers have fallen as the breeding population has declined and in recent years records have become particularly rare. Extreme dates, apart from Christy's winter records, are 28th February 2000 at Sewardstone and 14th November 1976 at Rolls Farm, Tollesbury.

There have been three ringing recoveries involving Essex: one ringed as a chick in Norfolk in May 1980 and found dead two months later at Wicken Bonhunt; a juvenile ringed near Icklingham, Sussex, found dead at South Ockendon on 23rd September 1980; and a colour-ringed bird at Abberton on 7th July 1998. Interchange with the Brecklands population has also been reported from Cambridgeshire breeding sites (*Cambridgeshire Bird Report* 1993).

Disappointingly, the most recent declines in the Essex/south Cambridgeshire population have taken place despite a decade of conservation measures by the RSPB and volunteers. Measures have included giving advice to farmers, marking and monitoring of nests and chicks and provision of Stone Curlew-friendly habitat. Considerable research into prey availability has also taken place to try to ascertain whether this is affecting breeding success. A low rate of chick production over many years has meant that a probably ageing population has had an extremely difficult time maintaining itself in the few remaining niches. The decline and apparent extinction may prove more difficult to reverse than in the Brecklands, and indeed any help may now be too late given the lack of recent records. Recolonisation, if it occurs, may depend not only upon continuing increases in the Brecklands, but also a return to the pattern of farming that sustained the species in the past. The availability and take-up of stewardship-type schemes could play a crucial part in any recovery.

Cream-coloured Courser   *Cursorius cursor*

Vagrant: two records

The Cream-coloured Courser is a desert and arid grassland species that breeds across North Africa, including the Canary Islands, East Africa and east to western Pakistan. The nominate race *cursor* occurs in the Canary Islands and from Morocco to southwest Iran and Socotra (*HBW*). Most populations make extensive southerly movements in winter to the southern limit of winter frosts (*BWP*).

1858	Temple Mill Marshes, Stratford	19th October	Shot
1984	Hadleigh Marshes	29th September–2nd October	2nd-winter

The first record was originally assigned to Middlesex but Christy was subsequently advised by a man who knew the person who had first seen it, that it was actually shot on Temple Mill Marshes, which are on the Essex side of the River Lea: "It was shot on the morning of October 19, 1858, and the story is that a working man came full of excitement … to say that he had just seen a strange bird, looking like a piece of whity-brown paper blowing about on the Marsh; whereupon the late Mr. George Beresford took down his gun, went out, and secured the wanderer" (Hudson 1898).

Nationally, there were 27 records prior to 1958 compared with just seven since (BBRC 2005), all in late September–October, the most recent being in the Isles of Scilly in autumn 2004, the Hadleigh individual (Cottridge & Vinicombe 1996) being the last previous. The Hadleigh bird caused the first mass twitch to Essex, involving some 2,000 people. It was

231

in fairly poor condition, in somewhat 'moth-eaten' plumage and sporting—at least some of the time, a clod of earth on the tip of its bill (Todd 1985). The main trans-Saharan movement occurs in late-September and early October, tying in well with many of the British records and suggesting reverse migration out of northern Africa (Cottridge & Vinicombe 1996).

Collared Pratincole *Glareola pratincola*

Vagrant: two records

The Collared Pratincole has an Afrotropical and southwest Palearctic breeding distribution. In Europe, it breeds around the Mediterranean, Black and Caspian Seas, and in Asia as far as east Kazakhstan. Palearctic populations winter in Africa (European Atlas). The nominate race *pratincola* occurs throughout Europe to Pakistan (*HBW*).

| 1861 | Old Hall | mid-August | Adult female, shot |
| 1958 | Hanningfield | 31st May | |

The first specimen was obtained during a duck-shoot: "… it was a fine bird, and had much the appearance of having recently sat on eggs … Its appearance on the wing was much like that of the genus hirundo" (Christy). Christy and Glegg concluded that it was shot at Old Hall, despite the individual who shot it being unable to recall the locality.

The Collared Pratincole is the most regular of the three pratincoles to occur in Britain with 90 records, the last in 2003 (BBRC 2004), averaging just fewer than two per annum. The dates are typical, although most occur in spring and probably relate to overshooting migrants from southern Europe.

In addition, a species of pratincole was at Steeple on 8th June 1985.

Oriental Pratincole *Glareola maldivarum*

Vagrant: one record

The monotypic Oriental Pratincole breeds from India east through southeast Asia and northeast China, with the eastern populations wintering south to Indonesia and northern Australia; Indian populations are mostly resident (*HBW*).

| 1981 | Old Hall | 2nd August–11th October | 1st-summer/adult winter |

This was the first British record, although it was initially present at Dunwich, Suffolk, from 22nd June–8th July before moving to Old Hall. Originally in first-summer plumage, it stayed long enough to moult into adult winter plumage (Burns 1993). This was a seemingly remarkable occurrence given its breeding and wintering ranges which, until the more recent British records, had the spectre of being an escape hanging over it. There have been two subsequent records: Kent in 1988; and Norfolk, Suffolk and Sussex in 1993.

Black-winged Pratincole *Glareola nordmanni*

Vagrant: one record

The monotypic Black-winged Pratincole has a Palearctic distribution, mainly in the steppe zone from Hungary and southeast Romania eastwards across south Ukraine and south Russia to eastern Kazakhstan; it winters in sub-Saharan Africa (European Atlas).

| 1960 | Abberton | 28th August–14th September |

The water levels at Abberton were exceptionally low at this time and would have provided ideal feeding conditions for aerial insectivores such as pratincoles. Nationally, the species is only about one-third as common as Collared Pratincole, with just 35 records, the last in 2002 (BBRC 2003). This was the sixth British record. The majority occur in August and September and are thought to relate to birds undertaking reverse migration from their breeding grounds (Cottridge & Vinicombe 1996).

Little Ringed Plover

Charadrius dubius

Summer resident and passage migrant

The Little Ringed Plover is a Palearctic species represented in Eurasia and North Africa by the race *curonicus*. In Europe it ranges from Scandinavia to the Mediterranean and breeds in every country except Ireland and Iceland. Originally a species of natural shingles, gravel and sand banks, the species declined in the 19th and early 20th century, probably as a result of climate change which was not conducive to breeding success, as well as loss of its traditional habitat of river shingles to improvement schemes. However, the species made an apparent change in habitat choice in the early 20th century (European Atlas). This, together with a return to a more favourable climate in the 1920s and 1930s and the proliferation of engineering schemes and gravel extraction (e.g. for autobahns), enabled the species to prosper and spread slowly westward in Europe. Prior to 1920, the Little Ringed Plover was an extremely rare vagrant nationally with only eight authentic records, and even by 1938, when the species bred for the first time in Britain at Tring, Hertfordshire, it was still a very rare vagrant. The Little Ringed Plover has, however, increased steadily and in 1991 the British population stood at 825–1,070 pairs (Second National Atlas).

The first documented Essex record was in 1947 when one pair bred at Girling, and since 1954 breeding has been annual. By 1957, there were at least 13 pairs, 8–9 of which bred successfully, a significant percentage of the British population at that time. Numbers rose to a peak of 34 pairs in 1987, although reported numbers have declined slightly since, perhaps due to the end of survey work for the Essex Atlas. The transient nature of the species' habitat makes regular and comprehensive monitoring difficult.

However, national surveys carried out in 1967 (18 pairs), 1973 (25–26 pairs) and 1984 (32 pairs) (Parrinder & Parrinder 1969, Parrinder & Parrinder 1975, Parrinder 1989) provided accurate assessments of the Essex population, the results of which confirmed that numbers reported to the EBS annually were fairly representative of actual breeding numbers. Overall, the current population probably lies in the region of 25–30 pairs, 3.0–3.5% of the British population.

Throughout Essex, as in the rest of England, the Little Ringed Plover's typical habitat is man-made. Gravel-pits are some of the most regularly used locations, but the species has also used reservoirs, sewage farms and even areas of rough ground in industrial areas. Only 10% of nesting sites across Europe are in traditional habitat (Vaughan 1980). The

Atlas	Survey Area	% of 10km squares or tetrads in which	
		bred/probably bred	possibly bred or present
First National 10km	Essex	38.6	0.0
Second National 10km	Essex	35.1	8.8
First London Tetrad	Met. Essex	12.0	1.5
Second London Tetrad	Met. Essex	14.0	6.0
Essex Tetrad	Essex	5.1	2.2

Summary of results of Atlas surveys for Little Ringed Plovers

Essex Atlas survey revealed that the main breeding strongholds were in southwest, central and eastern Essex with an almost entire absence from the north. The highest breeding densities were close to London, particularly around Rainham, the Ockendons, West Thurrock and along the Lea Valley. In the early 1980s, Rainham held the highest breeding numbers, peaking at ten pairs in 1984, approximately one-third of the population that year. Here, the drier lagoon beds were used but habitat change has seen far fewer recently. Little Ringed Plovers were also present in reasonable numbers along the Chelmer Valley and around the many small inland waters to the east of Maldon, but in recent years these have become largely unsuitable due to vegetation succession.

An unusual instance of mixed nest sharing with a Ringed Plover was noted in an Essex gravel-pit in 1968 (Parrinder & Parrinder 1969), one of only three known instances (*BWP*).

Little Ringed Plovers are one of the earliest returning summer migrants, usually arriving from mid-March, with passage peaking in the third and fourth weeks of April and continuing into early May. The earliest arrival was at Stansted Airport lagoons on 7th March 1993, and there was one at Abberton on 9th March 2000.

Autumn passage commences at the end of June as juveniles disperse away from breeding areas. Passage peaks relatively early, around the end of July and early August with the majority having left by late September. There have been two November records of single birds at Old Hall on 4th in 1985 and Wrabness on 21st in 1954.

Rainham and Hanningfield historically held the largest gatherings. During the late 1970s and early 1980s, very large congregations, amongst the biggest reported in the country at that time, occurred at Rainham with 70 on 12th August 1979 and 91 on 31st July 1980. However, habitat change has seen numbers much reduced in recent years. At

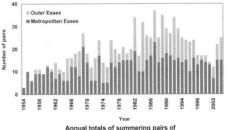

Annual totals of summering pairs of Little Ringed Plovers from 1954-2004

Hanningfield, the highest count was 41 on 4th August 1984 but no more than 20 have been noted since the mid-1980s.

Peak counts at Abberton occasionally reach double figures with 20 on 2nd September 1976 and 16 on 25th August 1998. The reservoirs and gravel-pits along the Lea Valley regularly record double-figure counts with peaks of: 27 at Walthamstow on 26th July 1979; 21 at Cornmill Meadows on 1st July 2000; and 18 at Netherhall GP on 2nd July 1988. The lagoons at The Hythe are also favoured with 23 recorded during August 1977 and 15th July 1993. Many

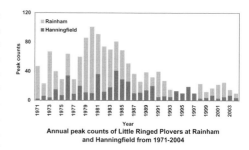

Annual peak counts of Little Ringed Plovers at Rainham and Hanningfield from 1971-2004

of these counts are likely to include local breeders. Smaller numbers are reported widely, sometimes from estuarine localities, although Little Ringed Plovers tend to avoid this habitat in favour of freshwater.

There have been relatively few national ringing recoveries, all suggesting migration through western Europe and across the Sahara into equatorial Africa. Two recoveries of Little Ringed Plovers ringed in Britain illustrate onward movement through the county whilst first-year birds ringed at Abberton on 21st July 1970 and found dead on 8th August 1970 in Somme, France, and from Rainham on 18th August 1979, controlled in The Camargue, France, on 26th August 1979, illustrate very rapid movement south.

The Little Ringed Plover's particular habitat requirement means that it will never be a common breeding bird. The species' choice of man-made habitats such as gravel-pits are, by their nature, transitory and once worked out are either 'restored' or eventually overrun with vegetation. Working pits may be used as the species tolerates a certain amount of indirect disturbance, whilst a worked-out pit surrounded by farmland in Suffolk supported a small population, some of which nested on adjacent fields (Essex Atlas). Conversion of gravel-pits to fishing lakes and recreational lakes has a detrimental affect on breeding Little Ringed Plovers through increased human disturbance. Thus, without direct management, sites can quickly become unsuitable. Despite being a Schedule I breeding bird, its habitat is not protected. Although it is likely that at present the number of sites lost to that gained probably balances out, direct management in the future may be necessary to maintain the species' small population, as new planning consents for sand and gravel may require the subsequent conversion of the land back to arable.

Ringed Plover   *Charadrius hiaticula*

Resident, passage migrant and winter visitor   Amber List

The Ringed Plover breeds along the coasts of the northern Palearctic, its distribution extending as far east as the Chukotsky peninsula and west to Greenland and Baffin and Ellesmere Islands. Two subspecies are recognised, the nominate race *hiaticula*, which breeds in western Europe, Greenland and Iceland, and *tundrae*, which occurs in northern Scandinavia and Russia. The species inhabits open, bare or sparsely vegetated areas adjacent to water, typically coastal sand and shingle beaches but also a wide variety of inland habitats from river valleys to bare industrial sites (European Atlas). In Britain, where the species is on the extreme southwest of its range, approximately 8,600 pairs breed, some

70% of the temperate breeding population of the nominate race. European and Nearctic populations winter principally along the coasts of west Africa, the Mediterranean and the Atlantic from southwest Europe to Britain (European Atlas).

Atlas	Survey Area	% of 10km squares or tetrads in which	
		bred/probably bred	possibly bred or present
First National 10km	Essex	43.9	0.0
Second National 10km	Essex	49.1	8.8
First London Tetrad	Met. Essex	3.5	0.0
Second London Tetrad	Met. Essex	10.0	6.5
Essex Tetrad	Essex	7.8	4.1

Summary of results of Atlas surveys for Ringed Plovers

Christy noted that the Ringed Plover was "A common resident on the coast, though its numbers are largely increased in autumn by the arrival of birds from elsewhere" and that "It breeds on all our beaches". The earliest reference to breeding involved one shot and a nest taken on Foulness on 23rd May 1838.

Glegg described the Ringed Plover as "... one of the common birds of the Essex coast..." and, although he gave no quantitative data, he considered that the species bred right around the coast, although there were many more north of the Colne "... at which point the shingle commences ..." than to the south and that it was especially numerous around Walton-on-the-Naze.

Populations nationally and in Essex were probably stable until the years between the two World Wars (Historical Atlas), after which there was a widespread decline. This period saw a rapid increase in recreational use of the coast, the development of many bungalow and caravan sites and sea-defence work. Many breeding sites were abandoned from the 1920s and, as the 20th century progressed, this effect became worse.

Surveys between 1953 and 1957 revealed 120–130 breeding pairs, but by the mid-1960s there were perhaps no more than 70–80 pairs. Hudson & Pyman considered that the cause of the decline was increased disturbance by day-trippers, particularly in the Hamford Water and St Osyth areas.

However, intensive wardening of Little Tern nesting colonies benefited the Ringed Plover and populations recovered such that by the early 1980s Cox estimated that the population was around 300 pairs, some 5% of the British population at that time. The BTO surveys in 1972–73 and 1984 produced breeding totals of 260 and 248 pairs respectively, suggesting a population of 250–300 pairs. No further comprehensive surveys have been carried out, although based on data collected for the Essex Atlas, the population was estimated to be 200–250 pairs. This represented a slight decline over the previous decade but was still some 3% of the total for Britain and Ireland. It should, however, be borne in mind that an extensive nest recording/ringing programme at Colne Point during the early 1980s (R. W. Arthur and B. C. Manning, unpublished) revealed up to twice the number of pairs present than suggested by casual observation. At this time, up to 75 pairs bred at Colne Point, and 70 around both Hamford Water and on Foulness.

During the 1990s numbers reported in the *EBR* declined by some 50% from those in the 1980s. Significant declines occurred at the three main sites, Hamford Water, Colne Point and Foulness. At the first two of these sites,

GB 300p / INT 500w	1970-1974	1975-1979	1980-1984	1985-1989	1990-1994	1995-1999	2000-2004	Peak counts	Peak	Peak month
WeBS totals	2,002^	1,298	1,530	2,572	3,922	4,261	3,068	Sep 95	5,634	*Sep*
Stour	162^	68*	177^	325	606	670	647	Sep 02	959	Sep
Hamford Water	460^	350^	156	450	1,177	1,664	765	Sep 95	2,592	Sep
Colne	243^	~	~	541	512	349	474	Sep 94	913	Sep
Blackwater	613^	419^	457	505	686	510	358	Sep 92	1,229	Oct
Dengie	143^	285^	106^	52^	157	158	188	Sep 92	302	Sep
Crouch-Roach	53^	~	152	139	226	168	84	Nov 90	375	Sep
Thames	615^	639	732	1,041	1,165	954	841	Sep 87	1,933	Sep

Five-year average of peak WeBS counts (Sep-Nov) of Ringed Plovers from 1970/71-2003/04

less intensive wardening and increasing predator pressure have significantly reduced numbers. The current Essex population probably lies in the region of 100–200 pairs, 1.2–2.4% of the British population (Prater 1989).

Although coastal populations have declined, there was an increase in inland breeding records during the 1980s; the two trends are probably not linked. Nationally, there has been a colonisation of inland sites, particularly in central and eastern England, possibly assisted by the drier weather experienced during the late 1980s and 1990s. The increase in gravel-pits, lakes and reservoirs may also have helped the spread. In Essex, however, inland breeding records peaked in the mid-1980s, a few years prior to the drought, and then declined, despite increased observer coverage during the Essex Atlas survey, and have continued to do so.

Prior to the 1970s breeding only occurred at Abberton and Hanningfield. At the former, some 20 pairs bred on the island in 1950, although very few have been reported since. At Hanningfield the odd pair nested from 1960 onward, and annually from 1972–85, with a peak of three in 1976. Other previously favoured inland locations, which have subsequently become unsuitable for breeding, have been: Coleman's, peaks of six pairs in 1989 and 1990; Chelmer Valley GPs, five pairs in 1985; Ulting GPs, single pairs occasionally during the 1970s and early 1980s; and Berwick Ponds, 2–3 pairs in the early 1980s.

More unusual nesting locations have included the gravel areas between the oil storage tanks at the Mobil refinery at Coryton (six pairs in 1960), on the dried out lagoons at Rainham and on grassland close to seawalls.

The species has a complex migration pattern through Europe, with the most northerly populations migrating the furthest south, effectively 'leap-frogging' British populations which either stay in the country or move short distances south (European Atlas). Thus, resident Essex birds of the race *hiaticula* are joined for the winter by many birds from northern Europe. Substantial numbers of the smaller and darker-mantled race *tundrae* probably

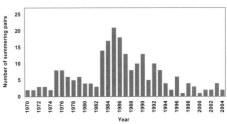

Annual totals of inland breeding Ringed Plovers from 1970-2004

GB 330w / INT 500w	70/71-74/75	75/76-79/80	80/81-84/85	85/86-89/90	90/91-94/95	95/96-99/00	00/01-04/05	Peak counts		Peak month
WeBS totals	914^	1,067	1,075	1,560	1,749	1,566	1,616^	Dec 90	2,279	Dec
Stour	100^	115	165	402	466	213	196^	Dec 92	**756**	Dec
Hamford Water	210^	194	90	122^	480	376	378^	Dec 90	**861**	Feb
Colne	164^	~	~	287	284	387	260^	Jan 96	**707**	Dec
Blackwater	176^	187	163	264	228	200	188^	Jan 89	**564**	Dec
Dengie	59^	165^	37^	44	60	67	95^	Mar 76	**500**	Feb
Crouch-Roach	54^	~	128	134	85	85	104^	Dec 83	196	Dec
Thames	313^	716	456	599	656	602	723^	Dec 76	**1,072**	Dec

**Five-year average of peak WeBS counts (Dec-Mar)
of Ringed Plovers from 1970/71-2003/04**

pass through in autumn and to a lesser extent in spring (*BWP*). It is in autumn, that the largest numbers of Ringed Plovers occur with the majority of p eak WeBS counts occurring from September–November.

Numbers in August may exceed those in September but little data have been available until very recently. During the passage period, most of the principal Essex sites hold numbers of national importance, with five holding numbers of international importance. Counts in Hamford Water during the 1990s were amongst the largest in Britain.

During winter, at least three sites have regularly held numbers of national importance, with those on the Thames being of international importance and currently the most important wintering site in Britain (Pollitt *et al.* 2003). A total of 3,500 (non-WeBS) at Canvey Point on 4th September 1955 remains the largest single-site count.

Seasonal occurrence of Ringed Plovers from 1970-2004

Although greater observer coverage may be a factor, there has been a significant increase in the number of Ringed Plovers both on passage and wintering, particularly since the mid-1980s. An eastward shift of the wintering grounds has been noted in several species of wader, including Ringed Plovers, possibly as a result of climate change (Rehfisch 2002) and this may explain why nationally Ringed Plover numbers have declined by some 28% over the last 25 years (Gregory *et al.* 2002) but doubled in Essex over a similar period. Further research on this point is, however, required (Rehfisch 2002). Essex currently holds around 5% of the estimated 32,450 British wintering population and just over 3% of the 47,500 European population (Gregory *et al.* 2002).

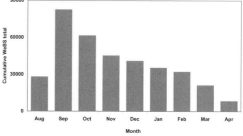

	J	F	M	A	M	J	J	A	S	O	N	D
Northern England				1								1
Southern England	3	1		1	1	1		4				
Wales												2
Denmark						1						
Germany						1						
The Netherlands				1	2	2	2					
France	2							2	3		1	1
Spain										2	1	
Portugal										1		
Total	5	1	0	2	3	5	2	6	3	3	2	4

Month and location of recovery of Ringed Plovers ringed in Essex

Birds showing plumage characteristics and biometrics of the northern race *tundrae* have been trapped in spring and autumn, primarily at East Tilbury in the late 1960s, but there have been no recoveries of Ringed Plovers from within the breeding range of *tundrae*. Birds trapped or found dead in Essex include individuals that had been ringed as breeding adults or chicks elsewhere in Britain; likewise there have been several from Scandinavia, the Baltic States and western Europe, which were either wintering here or on passage. Recoveries of Ringed Plovers ringed in Essex include: one marked on Foulness on 23rd June 1974, and subsequently controlled on Anglesey, Wales, in December 1977 and December 1980; three ringed at Canvey Point as part of an intensive cannon-netting programme by the BTO that were later controlled whilst breeding at sites in the Netherlands; and one found dead across the Thames at Cliffe, Kent, 18 years after having been ringed at East Tilbury, a longevity record from BTO ringing at the time.

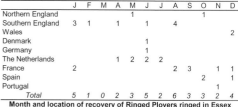

	J	F	M	A	M	J	J	A	S	O	N	D
Scotland					2							
Southern England	1			1	1	1	2	4	3	1		
Sweden					1							
Norway			1			1	1					
Poland							1					
Germany					1	2						
The Netherlands									1			
Totals	1	0	1	1	5	5	6	3	2	0	0	0

**Month of ringing and origin of Ringed Plovers
ringed abroad and recovered in Essex**

The Ringed Plover's habitat preference means that the species is a vulnerable breeding bird. Although numbers reached a peak in the mid-1980s, there has been a subsequent marked decline, contrary to the national trend. Reductions in intensive wardening at the species' principal breeding haunts would seem to be one of the main causes of the decline. The small inland population has also declined for less well understood reasons, although habitat change caused by vegetation growth around gravel-workings may be a significant factor. Passage and wintering birds are less prone to disturbance and have increased significantly in recent years and, based on current trends are likely to do so for the foreseeable future.

Sponsored by Dave and Kate Williams

Kentish Plover   *Charadrius alexandrinus*

Rare passage migrant: 46 records involving 49 individuals, one in winter

The Kentish Plover is a cosmopolitan wader that inhabits temperate and tropical coasts and inland wetlands in Eurasia, America and north Africa. In Europe, where the species is represented by the nominate race *alexandrinus*, the breeding population is essentially coastal. Most populations have been in long-term decline, resulting in range contractions in northwest and central Europe through the 20th century (European Atlas). Kentish Plovers bred in Britain regularly until 1935, principally in Kent and Sussex (Batten *et al.* 1990) but, despite subsequent sporadic records, it is now only a scarce but annual passage migrant. The species winters in the Mediterranean and Africa south of the Equator.

The first documented Essex record involved two seen and one shot at Dovercourt on 23rd August 1876. Christy listed three further records (he also detailed three records from Landguard Point, Suffolk) including two at Canvey Island on 10th September 1881 and two at Clacton-on-Sea, prior to 1890. Glegg, however, rejected two of the records, at Harwich and Clacton-on-Sea as "... open to suspicion", although it would seem that this was only because specimens were not obtained. He added two further records. Considering that the Kentish Plover bred on the south side of the Thames during the early 20th century, it is perhaps surprising that there were not more recorded.

Prior to 1950, there were just three further records, with two at Abberton in 1949, including one on 22nd December, the only winter record.

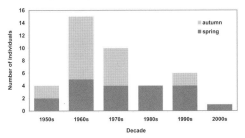

Total number of Kentish Plovers recorded in each decade
from 1950-2004

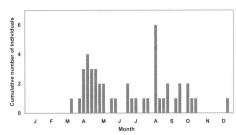

Seasonal occurrence of Kentish Plovers
from 1949-2004

Since 1950, there has been a total of 39 records, involving 40 individuals, but numbers have declined sharply in recent years:

1956	Horsey Island	4th September	
1957	East Mersea	5th April	
	Abberton	26th September	
1959	Walthamstow	9th April	Female
1961	Abberton	11th October	
1962	Rainham	1st July	Male
	The Naze	15th–16th July	Female
	Tillingham	1st August	Female
1963	Girling	7th September	

1965	Hanningfield	17th April	Female
	Abberton	5th May	
	The Naze	18th August	Two
1967	The Naze	30th April–1st May	Male
1968	Little Oakley	20th April	
	The Naze	18th August	Two
1969	Heybridge GP	19th October	
1970	Rainham	18th April	Female
	The Naze	27th September	
1974	Heybridge GP	27th July	Adult male
	Rainham	2nd–15th September	
1976	Girling	24th April	Male
1977	The Naze	24th–26th August	Male
	Colne Point	14th–15th August	
1978	The Naze	4th May	
	Bradwell	16th April	
	Hanningfield	15th May	Male
1979	Rainham	19th–27th August	
1983	Rainham	24th April	Female
1985	Hanningfield	18th April	Adult male
		4th–7th June	1st-summer
1989	Canvey Island	18th May	Adult male
1990	Abberton	13th May	Female
	East Tilbury	14th–18th October	Male
1991	The Naze	10th May	Male
1995	The Naze	9th–10th April	Female
1996	Bradwell	15th–16th April	
1999	The Naze	25th–27th October	
2003	The Naze	1st–3rd June	Adult female
		1st–2nd July	Same as previous

Given the general decline across Europe, the decrease is not surprising. Quite why records increased in the 1960s is unclear. Records peak from mid-April to mid-May and again in mid-August to mid-October.

Over 70% (28) have occurred along the coast with the most favoured location being The Naze with 13 individuals, then Rainham and Bradwell, Heybridge GP and Hamford Water each attracting two. Inland records have come from Abberton and Hanningfield, with four at each, Girling with two and Walthamstow (one).

Sponsored by Paul Wood

Greater Sand Plover   *Charadrius leschenaultii*

Vagrant: one record

The Greater Sand Plover breeds from east Turkey across to Mongolia and winters in the eastern Mediterranean, east and southern Africa and coastal areas of Asia and Australasia. Three races are recognised: *columbinus, crassirostris* and the nominate *leschenaultii* (Hirschfield *et al.* 2000); the nearest populations, in Turkey, are of the race *columbinus*.

| 1992 | East Tilbury | 10th–14th August | Female or 1st-summer |

There have been 14 British records (BBRC 2005), seven of which occurred in late July/August. This was the eleventh, on a typical date, and it was almost certainly the same individual as at Cley Marsh and Blakeney Harbour, Norfolk, from 5th–8th August, and for a few hours on the pools at Cliffe, Kent, on 14th (Kane 1993). If so, this is a remarkable but not unprecedented example of a rare vagrant being tracked across the country.

(Eurasian) Dotterel

Charadrius morinellus

Rare but almost annual passage migrant: around 56 records involving at least 258 birds   **Amber List**

The monotypic Dotterel is an arctic–alpine wader that has a rather limited European distribution, occurring mainly in northern Russia, Fennoscandia and Britain 690 pairs (Gregory *et al.* 2002), but having a world range that extends along the northern shores of eastern Siberia to the Bering Strait and to the mountain chains of Mongolia and central Siberia (European Atlas). The species winters in northernmost Africa and the Middle East.

Christy described the Dotterel as a rare passage migrant and documented nine records, the first being one shot in New England Creek in 1830. The largest flock was 14 at Forest Gate at the end of August 1871. He noted that the "... open chalk downs around Chesterford, Chrishall, Heydon and the Chishalls seem formerly to have been a rather favourite halting-place" but gave no further details. However, just over the border into Cambridgeshire, in the Gog Magog Hills, Dotterels used to be caught in large numbers in nets and the 10th May was known on the borders of Hertfordshire and Cambridgeshire as 'Dotterel Day' (Christy). This practice occurred at a time when Dotterels were far more numerous than today, before over-hunting caused a significant decline at the end of 19th century. Glegg added just one more record, in 1905.

Given the regularity of records from just over the border in Cambridgeshire, it is remarkable that 56 years elapsed before the next county record, one at Hanningfield on 7th–10th September 1961, and it was not until the 1970s and 1980s that regular searches of the northwest chalk and large open fields of Dengie confirmed its present status.

In recent years, many records have come from the prairie-like fields of Dengie, pea fields showing early spring growth being particularly favoured; since 1990, almost 100 have occurred there. In the mid-1970s, the northwest chalk received greater coverage and was found to be a regular stop-off point still.

Most Dotterels occur during spring but the species is regular in small numbers during autumn.

Extreme dates have been 20th April, by Steeple Creek in 2003, and 3rd November, at Potton Creek in 2002. However, a wintering individual was present in the Mersea Island/Wigborough area from 19th December 1982–23rd January 1983, the first known instance of wintering in Britain.

Although most records have involved counts of fewer than ten there have been eight double-figure counts, the largest being 26 at Wigboro Wick Farm, St Osyth, on 12th May 2004 (22 on 11th). The others came from; Canewdon, 24, 20th May 2004; Wendens Ambo, 23, 17th May 1975; Dengie, 22, 16th May 1993; Marshhouse, Dengie, 11, 3rd May 1999; Middlewick Farm, Dengie, ten, 7th May 1998; Burnham-on-Crouch, ten, 7th–9th May 1994; and Holliwell Point, ten, 13th–14th May 1990.

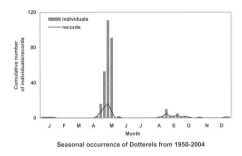

Seasonal occurrence of Dotterels from 1950-2004

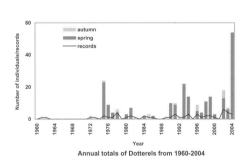

Annual totals of Dotterels from 1960-2004

American Golden Plover

Pluvialis dominica

Vagrant: one record

The monotypic American Golden Plover breeds on the coastal tundra of northeast Siberia, east across northern Alaska and Canada to Baffin Island and winters in southern South America.

| 2004 | Old Hall | 24th July–4th August | Moulting summer adult |

A total of 257 American Golden Plovers had occurred in Britain to the end of 2004 (BBRC 2005); an Essex record was therefore long overdue. It was one of 12 nationally in 2004. This individual remained faithful to Bale Field during its stay (Ransdale 2006a).

Pacific Golden Plover

Pluvialis fulva

Vagrant: two records

The monotypic Pacific Golden Plover breeds across northern North America and winters in South America. The two 'Lesser Golden Plover' species were separated by the BOURC in 1986 into Pacific and American Golden Plovers.

1896	Shellhaven Point, Coryton	6th August	Shot
2000	Old Hall	7th–9th May	1st-summer

A total of 58 Pacific Golden Plovers had been recorded nationally to the end of 2004 (BBRC 2005), the majority in the Northern Isles, Scotland and along the east coast. Most have involved post-breeding adults between late June and August.

The 1896 specimen, the third British record, has an interesting history. It was originally identified by the British Museum of Natural History as 'Asiatic Golden Plover, *Charadrius dominicus*', presumably meaning the Asiatic race of 'Lesser Golden Plover, *Charadrius dominicus fulvus*' as it was then known. H. F. Witherby (1920), however, referred it to *'Charadrius d. dominicus'* but following correspondence with Glegg, Witherby concluded that it was impossible to say to which form it referred. However, Glegg traced the specimen to the Booth Museum, Brighton, Sussex, where Dr. Hartert had identified it as the Asiatic form *C. d. fulvus*. There is, however, a further twist to the tale. A review of all old records of 'Lesser Golden Plover' in the early 1990s by the BBRC, resulted in the inspection of what was thought to be the correct specimen which was still in the Booth Museum: it was apparently a Dotterel. A further inspection in 2001, however, confirmed that a correctly identified and labelled specimen of Pacific Golden Plover existed (Nick Green pers. comm.)!

(European) Golden Plover

Pluvialis apricaria

Common passage migrant and winter visitor

The European Golden Plover is a Palearctic species that breeds mostly from Iceland in the west and as far east as central Siberia, although about 100 pairs breed in Greenland and on Ellesmere Island. The nominate race *apricaria* breeds in Britain, Germany, Denmark and southern Fennoscandia to the Baltic States, with *altifrons* occurring in Greenland and through northernmost Europe to the Taimyr peninsula. In Britain, it is a species of the flat or gently sloping moors of the north and west. The population has declined from an estimated 29,400 pairs during 1968–72 to 22,600 pairs during 1988–91 (Second National Atlas). Populations from Iceland, Scandinavia and Russia are wholly migratory and winter in Britain (250,000 birds) and Ireland, western Netherlands, western Belgium, western France and on Mediterranean coasts. There are two main migratory routes through Britain, down the east and west coasts with very few Icelandic birds present along North Sea coasts (European Atlas). British populations are relatively sedentary.

Christy knew the speciess as a winter visitor, noting: "After severe easterly gales and during hard weather, many large flocks appear in the inland parts of the county … often in company with the Lapwing". Glegg likewise considered that the Golden Plover was a winter visitor, albeit somewhat local and variable in numbers. Many of the

GB 2,500 INT 18,000	70/71- 74/75	75/76- 79/80	80/81- 84/85	85/86- 89/90	90/91- 94/95	95/96- 99/00	00/01- 04/05	Peak counts		Peak month
WeBS totals	*3,873^*	*2,631*	*2,444*	*5,502*	*14,853*	*21,968*	*21,538^*	*Feb 01*	*33,501*	*Jan*
Stour	117^	87^	156^	228	650	691	1,860^	Feb 02	4,167	Jan
Hamford Water	1,972^	696	649	560	3,266	4,843	3,054^	Jan 98	8,275	Dec
Colne	593^	~	~	919	2,593	3,136	2,330^	Feb 95	6,301	Feb
Blackwater	720^	901	669	1311	5,053	7,908	10,001^	Feb 02	18,826	Jan
Dengie	1,280^	356	305	764	1,424	1,783	2,206^	Jan 04	4,451	Nov
Crouch-Roach	368^	710*	795	1,881	2,022	2,227	2,544^	Feb 01	3,889	Jan
Thames	621^	895	853	2,046	3,371	3,555	4,530^	Feb 95	8,899	Jan

**Five-year average of peak WeBS counts (Sep-Mar)
of Golden Plovers from 1970/71-2003/04**

earliest records provided little quantitative data other than that flocks assumed "… very remarkable dimensions" but Glegg detailed flocks mixed with Lapwings of up to 30,000 at Felsted prior to the severe winter of 1917. A flock of Golden Plovers seen by Glegg at Bradwell on 14th April 1921 numbered some 10,000 birds. Ticehurst (1932) mentioned "huge flocks" on the Stour.

During the 1950s and early 1960s flocks rarely exceeded 200 (Hudson & Pyman), although concentrations of 500–1,000 were not unknown. Numbers increased steadily until the end of the 1980s, since when there has been a remarkable increase. From 1972–75 around 3,000 birds regularly wintered on the coast (Cox) with, exceptionally, 7,300 in December 1974; in January 1968 6,000–7,000 were estimated in the southern Dengie alone, along with several hundred birds scattered around inland localities. During the 1980s, 5,000–10,000 were usually present during winter. WeBS totals of 20,000–25,000 are now regular. Increases of the order of eight to ten times have occurred on several estuaries since the early 1970s.

The exceptionally high WeBS counts in February 1995 and February 2002 included 6,060 at Old Hall in the former year and 7,330 in the latter; prior to the 1990s these would have been high totals for the whole county. The total of 18,826 for the whole of the Blackwater in February 2002 is by far the highest number reported from a single Essex estuary.

An average of 21,000 wintering Golden Plover is approximately 8.5% of the British population and 1.2% of the European population. Flocks on inland farmland are generally not counted by the WeBS survey and hence total numbers present at any time are probably somewhat higher than WeBS figures suggest.

The reason for the substantial increase is unclear. Major influxes into Britain from the Continent occur between October and December. If the weather stays mild, these birds generally stay but they will undertake cold-weather movements to the south and southwest if severe weather occurs (Winter Atlas). The 1990s have seen some particularly mild winters, so it is possible that these influxes have not moved on but remained in Essex. Kirby & Lack (1993) found that in any

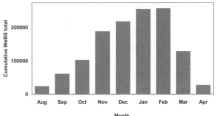

Seasonal occurrence of Golden Plovers from 1970–2004

particular winter the distribution and abundance of both Golden Plovers and Lapwings in Britain and Ireland were directly correlated to temperature patterns. During mild winters there is a relatively static population and distribution, whereas the onset of cold weather precipitates an exodus.

The majority of Golden Plovers counted by WeBS are found on farmland adjacent to the coast. Very few utilise coastal mudflats, although the use of estuaries for foraging may be more prevalent than realised (Mason & Macdonald 1999b). Golden Plovers regularly feed on arable land in early and late winter and arable land, especially ploughed, is strongly preferred for roosting. Many flocks regularly return to the same 'flock ranges', traditional wintering areas outside which they rarely occur (Winter Atlas). Fuller & Youngman (1979) and Fuller & Lloyd (1981) identified various types of agricultural land below 200m as the mainstay of wintering Golden Plovers in England, with grassland being the preferred feeding habitat. Permanent pasture was preferred over grass leys or winter cereals, indicative of greater invertebrate densities in the older sward, though there is a greater propensity for arable feeding in southern counties. On the Tendring peninsula, Golden Plovers and Lapwings showed a preference for larger fields, with cereal fields holding a greater ratio of Golden Plovers, but only when crop height did not exceed 90mm. Rapid crop growth in mild autumns precluded these fields from both feeding and roosting (Mason & Macdonald 1999a).

The earliest arrivals appear in late July with migrant flocks moving through until around September, after which numbers build steadily to a mid-winter peak before declining rapidly during March, with most having left by May. A small spring passage is usually marked by the appearance of small flocks from March–May after the local wintering birds have left. June records are uncommon and less than annual: there were 17 at Tollesbury Wick in 1992 and 15 at Old Hall on 23rd in 2001, other counts having rarely exceeded three.

Birds of the more southerly areas of the breeding range, *apricaria*, on average, acquire a less striking breeding plumage than northern ones but there is much variation and Prater *et al.* (1977) found it impossible to separate the two forms in winter plumage; possibly subspecific status is not fully justified (Mullarney *et al.* 1999). Birds showing characteristics of both subspecies have been identified in Essex, darker birds presumably of the northern race *altifrons* being most noticeable in spring.

There have been eight ringing recoveries involving Essex, seven being Dutch-ringed individuals, one of which was at least 14 years old when shot at Little Oakley in January 1974. Birds on passage in the Netherlands have been recorded breeding in Russia, Finland and Scandinavia (*BWP*). The eighth recovery involved one ringed at Bradwell in September 1973 that was shot at Braga, Minho, Portugal, 1,335km to the south-southwest in February 1981. Both populations winter in Portugal, so it is unclear whether it was Icelandic or Scandinavian in origin, although the latter is far more likely (Migration Atlas).

That wintering populations of Golden Plovers in Essex have risen dramatically during the 1990s is more likely a consequence of weather-related movements from Continental Europe than significantly increased productivity at breeding sites, at least in Britain (Brown 1993, Parr 1993). Significant fluctuations in passage and wintering populations of Golden Plovers are likely to be commonplace in Essex and nationally. The advent of the Essex Coast ESA in 1993 should ensure the species' continuing occurrence within the farming landscape, so long as a suitable mix of arable cropping and extensive grassland exists, though Mason & Macdonald (1999a) were a little more pessimistic, concluding that "if warm, dry autumns become the norm, allowing rapid growth of winter cereals, the implications for the long-term conservation of Lapwings and Golden Plovers in southern England could be severe". Adaptability may be the key to the species' future; a switch to intertidal feeding is possible and may already be a developing phenomenon (Mason & Macdonald 1999b).

Grey Plover   *Pluvialis squatarola*

Common passage migrant and winter visitor   Amber List

The monotypic Grey Plover has a circumpolar distribution and breeds over the whole Eurasian high-arctic mainland and on most offshore islands, from the Kanin peninsula in the west to the Chukotsky peninsula and Anadyr Bay in the east. The species' breeding range has expanded westward and increased since the 1950s (European Atlas). The Grey Plover's migrations are complex and occur throughout the non-breeding season. Adults begin to arrive in Essex in August with juveniles in September and October; in November (after moulting) some move south, whilst others remain all winter to be joined by new arrivals from the Continent. In February and March there appears to be an emigration, possibly to the Dutch Waddensee with spring passage in March and April (Winter Atlas). The species winters in many of the coastal regions of the world, with those in Britain originating in western Siberia.

Christy described the Grey Plover as "... fairly common ... seldom occurring inland, and never in large flocks". He gave no quantitative data. Glegg considered the species scarce when compared to Golden Plover: "It cannot be described as an abundant bird on any part of the coast ... Parties are not infrequent, but they are usually small, rarely exceeding twenty". The largest flock he saw was 45. He considered it most abundant from the Blackwater round to the Stour, where it was a bird of the coast or open waters of the estuaries. A count of 500–600 on the Stour on 23rd January 1924 was considered exceptional.

GB 530 INT 1,500	70/71- 74/75	75/76- 79/80	80/81- 84/85	85/86- 89/90	90/91- 94/95	95/96- 99/00	00/01- 03/04	Peak counts		Peak month
WeBS totals	*2,820^*	*3,334*	*5,415*	*8,219*	*15,168*	*16,903*	*15,687^*	*Feb 01*	*22,776*	*Feb*
Stour	439^	679	905	1,683	3,132	2,853	3,051^	Jan 92	4,279	Jan
Hamford Water	729^	1,034	1,135	959	2,646	5,710	2,665^	Nov 95	8,186	Jan
Colne	264^	~	~	992	1,121	1,090	1,141^	Feb 90	1,540	Jan
Blackwater	566^	594	1,104	1,419	3,720	4,146	2,608^	Dec 93	6,609	Oct
Dengie	840^	780^	1,732	1,714	2,427	3,106	4,607^	Feb 01	7,826	Feb
Crouch-Roach	25^	68*	84	157	659	1,009	591^	Jan 95	2,132	Jan
Thames	623^	1,129	1,901	4,675	5,945	6,178	5,350^	Dec 96	9,454	Jan

**Five-year average of peak WeBS counts (Sep-Mar)
of Grey Plovers from 1970/71-2003/04**

Grey Plovers appeared to have increased between 1930 and 1965; Hudson & Pyman observed that three-figure counts were regular and that concentrations of up to 1,000 had been recorded along Dengie. Cox noted that the BoEE counted an average of 2,500 in mid-winter, representing about 30% of the British and 4% of the western European wintering Grey Plovers. Since the early 1970s significant increases have occurred nationally. In Essex, the increases have been most marked since the early 1980s. Some sites have shown increases of eight- to ten-fold (cf. Golden Plover).

Essex is probably the most important county in Britain for wintering Grey Plovers, the 2000/01–2004/05 average peak count representing 30% of the estimated British wintering population of 52,750 (Rehfisch *et al.* 2003) and nearly 15% of the west European population of 105,000 (*HBW*). The highest WeBS total of 22,776 in February 2001 represented 43% of the British population that month, the count from Dengie being 15% of the national total. The considerable increase in the population has been reflected not only in Britain but also in western Europe, the East Atlantic Flyway population having increased six-fold in the period 1970–92 (European Atlas), with a 46% increase to around 170,000 since the 1980s. A decline in shooting and a series of good breeding seasons are perhaps the reason for the increase (Winter Atlas) but the scale of the increase tends to suggest that other factors may be at work, including perhaps a change in breeding distribution (European Atlas) and a northward shift in the wintering distribution (Wetlands International 1999). Mid-winter counts on the Dutch Waddensee in particular have also increased in line with numbers in Britain, although marked exoduses occur in hard winters (Cranswick *et al.* 1995). In May, almost the entire East Atlantic Flyway population congregates in the Waddensee; the importance of that area internationally and its proximity to Essex no doubt explains at least in part the importance of the county to the species.

Overall, numbers peak between December and February, with passage numbers boosting numbers during spring and autumn.

The majority of birds depart by the end of April, although small numbers may be present throughout summer. A count of 240 at Foulness on 6th July 1958 is the largest during the midsummer period; there have been several other smaller three-figure counts. A total of 810 was counted during the June 2000 WeBS count. Returning birds, presumably failed or non-breeders, begin to appear as early as mid-July with numbers increasing rapidly from late August.

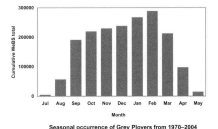

Seasonal occurrence of Grey Plovers from 1970–2004

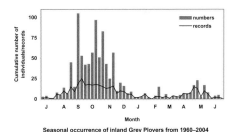

Seasonal occurrence of inland Grey Plovers from 1960–2004

Unlike Golden Plovers, Grey Plover do not appear to move south in the face of severe weather; this may be because an incomplete moult precludes this option (Branson & Minton 1976). This makes the species particularly susceptible to harsh weather and in some winters considerable numbers can succumb. In early 1986, 40 were picked up in Hamford Water and along the Stour.

Inland, the species has always been an uncommon passage visitor. Glegg knew of only three records, including, "a flock" at Stratford in the spring of 1890, one of which was killed. The construction of the major reservoirs saw a steady increase in records but, up until 1984 all were of 1–6 birds apart from 30 flying east over Navestock on 14th October 1982. However, a rapidly increasing winter population and a number of years of drought that produced ideal inland feeding conditions have seen numbers increase with records almost annual at Abberton and Hanningfield and within the Lea Valley. The largest counts have come from Abberton with peaks of: 59, 19th October 1990; 24, 15th September 1993; 23, 29th October 1996; and 11, October and December 1991. At Hanningfield, peaks have been: 22, 12th September 1993; 14, 11th November 1984; and ten, 21st February 1985. Elsewhere, 30 at KGV on 30th August 1992, 17 at KGV on 14th September 1988 and 15 the same day at Stansted Airport lagoons are the only other double-figure counts. The majority occur in autumn but a small passage is also detectable in spring.

A number of Grey Plovers have been ringed in Essex with, of the six recoveries, five recovered in subsequent winters within 7km of the place of ringing and the sixth only 24km distant, indicating that, normally, individuals return to the same wintering areas each year. Three birds recovered in Essex had been ringed in Norfolk, Lincolnshire and Shetland. Two birds ringed at Amager, Sjaelland, Denmark, during autumn passage and recovered in Essex mirror other recoveries in Norfolk (Taylor *et al.* 1999) and suggest that birds on their way from Russia to Britain may pause in Denmark. Grey Plovers are long-lived birds and one ringed at Friskney, Lincolnshire, in August 1977, as an adult was at least 21 years old when recaptured at Canvey Point in November 1997.

An eight-fold increase in the wintering population over the last 30 years begs the question as to just how many Grey Plovers Essex estuaries can hold. To date, there has been no evidence to suggest that populations on Essex estuaries are stabilising (Graham Austin pers. comm.) and therefore, provided that suitable habitat remains available and breeding success remains constant, there is every reason to believe that the wintering population will continue to increase.

Sponsored by Paul Levey

Sociable Plover (Sociable Lapwing)   *Vanellus gregarius*

Vagrant: three records

The monotypic Sociable Plover breeds on the steppes of Russia and Kazakhstan and winters in northeast Africa, parts of the Middle East and northern India and Pakistan.

1976	Hanningfield	24th–27th October	Adult
1977/78	Great Henny (and Suffolk)	25th December–21st January	Adult
2001	Old Hall	23rd–24th February	1st-winter

There have been 41 British records, the last in 2002 (BBRC 2003), and the earliest Essex record was the 18th nationally. The first and second records could, conceivably, have involved the same returning individual. The Hanningfield bird was particularly elusive (Miller 1977). The 2001 individual was discovered on the day that foot and mouth disease restrictions were first enforced.

Despite catastrophic declines in breeding populations (Belik 2005), there has been a general increase in national records, presumably due to increased observer coverage. Most have occurred between late September and early November, often arriving with Lapwings from the Continent.

Sponsored by David Acfield

(Northern) Lapwing   *Vanellus vanellus*

Abundant passage migrant and winter visitor and uncommon resident   Amber List

The Lapwing is a widespread, monotypic Palearctic wader that breeds across much of Europe and more sparsely across southern Russia and northern China to Ussuriland. A large variety of lowland habitats is occupied that historically the species colonised as its original habitat of marsh, bog and coastal grasslands was drained for conversion to farmland. Britain is internationally important for breeding Lapwings, but the population has been in decline for many years; that in England and Wales fell by around 50% between 1987 and 1998 to just 63,000 pairs (Wilson *et al.* 2001). The species winters from Britain and Ireland, south to Iberia and from the coastal plains of northwest Africa to the Mediterranean Basin and Mesopotamia (European Atlas). The current British wintering population is around 1,800,000.

In 1668 Charleton (1668) recorded the "Vanellus" on Foulness. Christy described the Lapwing as "A resident, breeding not uncommonly near the coast and at a few inland places, but nowhere abundant ..." Declines had already been noted inland, around Saffron Walden, for instance, prompting Christy to comment: "In all probability their absence from the inland parts of our county during the breeding season may be largely accounted for by the better farming now carried on... ". Organised egg collecting for the growing London markets must also have had a significant impact during the 19th century; Yarrell (1845) noted that many of the eggs sent to these markets came from the marshes of Essex, Lincolnshire, Norfolk, Cambridge and Kent. The high prices paid for Lapwing eggs, which were considered a delicacy, probably encouraged overzealous collecting, as one Lapwing egg was worth 20 Black-headed Gull eggs. Although no figures are mentioned for Essex, in 1839 alone some 200 dozen were taken from Romney Marsh, Kent, giving some indication of the former abundance of the species on the east coast marshes (Historical Atlas). A total of 22 nests was found on one day on Osea Island in 1879, and in 1887 upwards of 300 eggs were taken on one farmer's land around Maldon (Christy). On the coast, drainage of marshland for conversion to farmland was almost certainly another factor that caused declines.

Atlas	Survey Area	% of 10km squares or tetrads in which bred/probably bred	possibly bred or present
First National 10km	Essex	93.0	3.5
Second National 10km	Essex	71.9	22.8
First London Tetrad	Met. Essex	23.0	15.0
Second London Tetrad	Met. Essex	28.0	20.0
Essex Tetrad	Essex	17.1	16.2

Summary of results of Atlas surveys for Lapwings

According to Glegg "... the species is declined as a breeder" but "... still breeds all over the county, although in restricted numbers in inland localities... ". Lapwings remained common breeders on the marshy meadows near the coast and estuaries.

During the next few decades, numbers breeding inland continued to decline. By the late 1950s to mid-1960s, inland breeding was largely restricted to: Abberton, 100 pairs in 1953–55; Hanningfield, 24 pairs in 1958; and Romford SF, 15 pairs in 1964 (Hudson & Pyman). On the coast, however, numbers remained relatively high with, amongst others, concentrations around: St Osyth, 53 pairs in 1968; and Mersea Island, 80 pairs in 1952.

From the 1960s, ever-increasing agricultural intensification caused an acceleration of the declines already in progress. The BoEE produced a population of around 250 coastal breeding pairs during 1973–74 which, when added to the few inland records, produced a total of around 275–300 pairs. However, Cox concluded that by the early 1980s the population "may have fallen below 200 pairs". Numbers declined slightly between the two National Atlases, whilst there was little change between the two London Atlas surveys, although there was some redistribution of breeding pairs.

However, survey work for the Essex Atlas produced a breeding population of around 400 pairs, an apparently significant increase over the previous decade. It is difficult to be sure about the reasons

	1980-84	1985-89	1990-94	1995-99	2000-03
Horsey Island	8*	8*	21	19*	18
Old Hall	13^	35	29	28	55
Foulness	45*	62	63*	36^	21
Rainham	11	14	13	13*	21

Five-year average of breeding pairs of Lapwings at four coastal sites from 1980-2004

for this increase, but greater observer coverage may have been an important factor, particularly inland where many pairs were found along river valleys and around gravel-pit complexes. Habitat management on coastal reserves may have increased breeding numbers, although at most regularly monitored sites, except Old Hall where numbers have increased, numbers have generally been stable or declined since the early 1980s. Since 1990 there has probably been little overall change in the population.

The principal reasons for the decline are thought to be the dramatic reduction in suitable breeding habitat due to increased autumn tillage and the reduction in autumn pasture (European Atlas) that have removed or severely degraded the mosaic of arable and grassland on which Lapwings rely; many now breed in sub-optimal habitat and, whilst there has been no reduction in Lapwing survival, there has been inadequate production of fledged young to maintain population levels (Tucker *et al.* 1994). The south and east of England have seen the steepest declines (Shrubb & Lack 1991). In Essex, much of the remaining population is found on coastal nature reserves, although wet grazing meadows along river valleys and gravel-pits are also used; few areas of farmland remain that are suitable.

Outside the breeding season, Lapwings are very conspicuous passage migrants and winter visitors and can be found in meadows and marshlands, wet grasslands and farmland, whether ploughed or showing early growth, large sports fields and golf courses. Large numbers are also found on coastal mudflats and saltmarshes. Both Christy and Glegg referred to large winter numbers, the former observing, "... after strong easterly gales or during severe weather, enormous flocks appear in the inland parts of the county ..."

Subsequently, the overall status of the Lapwing outside the breeding season changed little until the 1990s when a phenomenal increase was recorded by WeBS surveys. Note that, like the Golden Plover, the Lapwing occurs inland in large numbers that are not counted by WeBS, although in recent years counts have been made at Abberton and Hanningfield. Counts of around 11,000 in the northwest in mid-November 1956, and 5,000 at Kelvedon on 8th February 1990 and Little Waltham/Boreham on 10th November 1990 and 25th November 1991 are the largest of many regular four-figure inland counts and give some indication of the numbers present away from the coast.

Apart from the truly exceptional count of 32,700 along the Blackwater in December 1992 and 22,550 along the Thames in January 1998, no site has qualified as either nationally or internationally important. Some 100,000 may have been present in Essex in December 1992 during the largest national influx recorded to date (Waters & Cranswick 1993). An average WeBS total of 40,000 represents 2.2% of the British and 0.57% of the European wintering populations respectively.

Nationally, wintering populations have shifted east/northeast since the mid-1980s, with increases in existing numbers predicted to occur across southern England in the future (Rehfisch 2002), a trend that ties in well with the large increases seen over the last decade or so in Essex. However, rapid growth of winter Wheat in mild autumns may preclude the use of fields for both feeding and roosting (Mason & Macdonald 1999a) and it may be that many Lapwings that formerly wintered in inland areas and hence were not counted by WeBS surveys have been forced onto the coast.

Numbers vary considerably from year to year depending on weather conditions; the Lapwing is probably the wader most prone to movements in response to temperature in western Europe (Pollitt *et al.* 2000). Such movements have on occasion

GB** 20,000 IN** 20,000	70/71-74/75	75/76-79/80	80/81-84/85	85/86-89/90	90/91-94/95	95/96-99/00	00/01-04/05	Peak counts		Peak month
WeBS totals	*8,049^*	*6,054*	*7,945*	*12,229*	*44,064*	*46,679*	*36,170^*	*Jan 98*	*70,386*	*Jan*
Stour	990^	1,093	919	1,793	5,160	5,088	5,224^	Feb 93	11,813	Jan
Hamford Water	2,551^	2,541	1,174	548	5,306	5,784	2,703^	Jan 94	11,635	Dec
Colne	1,105^	~	~	3,482	6,935	7,757	4,388^	Jan 98	12,440	Dec
Blackwater	1,992^	1,509	1,358	2,296	12,496	10,382	11,003^	Dec 92	**32,700**	Dec
Dengie	902^	615	722*	981^	2,415	2,098	1,784^	Nov 94	4,300	Feb
Crouch-Roach	1,742^	1,454*	3,085	3,092	7,659	5,456	5,140^	Dec 92	12,534	Jan
Thames	1,746^	1,241	2,193	2,562	7,681	10,389	9,935^	Jan 98	**22,550**	Jan
Abberton	~	~	~	~	4,731*	5,867	2,754^	Nov 95	12,425	Jan
Hanningfield	~	~	~	~	700*	1,466	557^	Dec 97	3,100	Dec
Lea Valley	~	~	~	~	~	~	448^	Nov 01	704	Dec
Met. Essex Waters	~	~	~	~	~	~	1,236^	Jan 03	1,990	Dec

Five-year average of peak WeBS counts (Sep-Mar) of Lapwings from 1970/71-2003/04

involved impressive numbers and on the coast there have been: 6,000 over Tollesbury/Salcott on 7th January 1967, and 6,000 southwest over Tollesbury in four hours on 5th January 1985. Inland, 3,000 flew south over Rainham and 2,500 southwest over Fairlop CP on 10th January 1987. During the extreme weather in early 1963, very few Lapwings remained in Essex.

Lapwings from Continental Europe begin to arrive as early as late May. By mid-June, three-figure flocks are not unusual: more than 400 were in the Chelmer Valley in June 1990. It is not until September through to early November, however, that the largest numbers begin to arrive and then build to a mid-winter peak. Flocks include both British and Continental Lapwings.

Although Lapwings undoubtedly move through during spring, passage is not readily discernible and numbers decline rapidly after February.

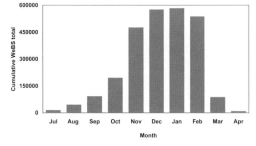

Seasonal occurrence of Lapwings from 1970-2004

Many Lapwings have been ringed in Essex. British breeding birds are only partially migratory with some wintering close to their natal area (*BWP*), whilst others may move substantial distances into France, Iberia and northern Africa. Two Essex-ringed fledglings have been recovered in Portugal with one in Morocco and another further east in Italy. Five recoveries in Russia of birds ringed in Essex during winter are typical of Lapwings returning to their breeding areas, the furthest east being at Ivanovo, some 2,700km distant.

Foreign-ringed Lapwing have been recovered in Essex from: Sweden, two; Denmark, two; Germany, one; the Netherlands, four; Belgium, two; and France, one. Most were ringed as nestlings and subsequently found wintering in Essex.

Across Essex and particularly inland, the Lapwing has declined over the last two centuries, initially as its habitat was drained and more recently due to agricultural intensification. Many breeding Lapwings are now restricted to coastal nature reserves. Here, improved habitat management has seen numbers stabilise and increase in places. Large new reserves at Abbotts Hall and Rainham also have the potential, with appropriate site management, to increase breed-ing numbers. On coastal meadows and grasslands numbers may well increase in the next few years. Inland, there is little hope that the Lapwing will return as a breeder in any numbers until such a time as the traditional mosaic of arable and grassland and spring-sown crops returns.

	Jan	Feb	Mar	Apr	May	Jun	Jul	Aug	Sep	Oct	Nov	Dec
Southern England			1		1	1						
Russia				2		1	1	1				
Denmark										1	1	
The Netherlands							1					
France	6	3	1	1								2
Spain	2	7									1	
Portugal	1									1		1
Morocco		1										
Italy		1										1
Total	9	12	2	3	1	2	2	1	0	2	2	4

Month and location of recovery of Lapwings ringed in Essex

The last 30 years have seen an almost nine-fold increase in Lapwings as winter visitors. Climate change may cause this increase to continue (Rehfisch 2002) assuming suitable habitat remains in Essex.

Sponsored by David and Wendy Preston

(Red) Knot   *Calidris canutus*

Common passage migrant and winter visitor: occasional during summer   Amber List

The Knot is a circumpolar tundra species that breeds mainly in North America, Greenland and eastern Siberia, where suitable habitats include dry rocky plateaux containing tufts of Mountain Avens (European Atlas). There are five subspecies worldwide, two of which, *canutus* and *islandica*, are encountered in the Western Palearctic. The latter inhabits Greenland and northeast Canada and winters in northwest Europe, whilst the former breeds on the coastal tundra of the Taimyr peninsula and perhaps the Yakutsk region of Siberia and migrates through Europe and winters in Africa (Migration Atlas). Around 85% of the European population of 345,000 *islandica* winter in Britain (Gregory *et al.* 2002). The occurrence of *canutus* in Britain is believed to be exceptional and has not definitely been recorded since 1984, despite the fact that almost the entire population stages in the Dutch Waddensee, just 250km from southeast England, in autumn (Migration Atlas).

It would seem that the overall status of the Knot has changed little over the last 200 years, except perhaps that its distribution along the coast has altered. Pennant (1777), who referred to the Knot as the "Red Sandpiper" noted that the species "... appeared in great flocks on the coast of Essex, on the estate of Col. Schutz", which was around Clacton-on-Sea. Christy described the species as "A common winter visitor to our coast, often appearing in August and remaining until spring". He gave little quantitative information but it would seem that large flocks occurred on the mudflats off Bradwell: "Mr John Balsham, jun., of Maldon ... informs me that, some 20 or 30 years ago, he and another gunner fired jointly into a flock resting on the mudflats near Bradwell chapel, and his companion's gun missing fire, he bagged to his own gun no less than nine dozen, which they sold at 4s. per dozen, sharing the proceeds". One of his correspondents noted that "... they are very common in vast flocks, generally arriving about Sept. 24th, and going north in May". The Knot was occasionally met with inland, being considered not uncommon around Sudbury in 1838.

Despite stating that numbers varied considerably from year to year, Glegg gave little quantitative information, although he referred to 320 shot by a single gun off the coast. He had only seen the species from the Colne north to the Stour, despite his regular visits to other areas further south; flocks of "hundreds" were all that he observed. Glegg harked back to the experiences of punt gunners, noting: "... parties of Knots must have been periodically very large". Did the species decline in Essex around the early years of the 20th century?

In the 1950s and 1960s the Knot was recorded regularly all around the coast with only small numbers frequenting the estuaries of the Colne, Crouch and Roach, moderate to large numbers on the Stour and in Hamford Water and the greatest numbers in the Blackwater/Dengie area and in part of the Thames Estuary (Hudson & Pyman). Prior to the regular wildfowl and wader counts that began in the early 1970s, flocks of 1,000–2,000 were reported with some regularity, the largest being 10,000 at Foulness Point in December 1960 and 8,000 in October 1964; up to 5,000 were noted as far up the Thames as East Tilbury.

Cox estimated that, based on the BoEE average of 11,000, Essex held some 4–5% of British wintering *islandica* and nearly 3% of those wintering in western Europe. Since then, however, numbers of *islandica* wintering in Essex have increased six-fold. Nationally, numbers of Knots wintering in Britain have declined by 15% over the last 30 years yet have increased by 40% over the last ten, the decline having been blamed on severe summer weather in the breeding grounds in the 1970s and 1980s (Pollitt *et al.* 2003). However, over-fishing of Cockles in The Wash and Dutch Waddensee may have caused a redistribution of birds to other sites in south and southeast England, which may explain, at least in part, the trend noted in Essex, where currently some 17% of the UK and 14% of the European wintering population occur.

Around 90% of Knots are concentrated along the sandflats of Foulness, the mid-Thames and Dengie coast. It is here that the small bivalve mollusc Baltic Tellin, the Knot's principal prey item, occurs in huge numbers (Cox). A change of diet from bivalves to snails may occur as winter progresses; such a shift may explain how estuaries can accommodate such large numbers of the species (Waters *et al.* 1993). Numbers using other estuaries are modest by comparison but even these have generally experienced considerable increases over the last few decades.

GB 2,800 **INT 3,500** *islandica*	70/71- 74/75	75/76- 79/80	80/81- 84/85	85/86- 89/90	90/91- 94/95	95/96- 99/00	00/01- 04/05	Peak counts		Peak month
WeBS totals	*12,719^*	*13,938*	*19,112*	*27,492*	*36,281*	*50,766*	*47,149^*	*Dec 97*	*65,318*	*Jan*
Stour	1,096^	536	1,115	986	3,136	5,416	4,943^	Nov 99	9,677	Jan
Hamford Water	868^	354	1,209	258*	1,457	3,752	4,561^	Jan 03	7,378	Jan
Colne	68^	~	~	139	228	767	931^	Jan 01	2,087	Jan
Blackwater	463^	370	86	112	1,216	2,669	3,595^	Jan 04	5,982	Jan
Dengie	**5,405^**	**3,888^**	**6,607^**	6,834	7,922	8,700	12,563^	Nov 00	19,400	Jan
Crouch-Roach	42^	1	9	4	3	2	51^	Nov 01	75	Nov
Thames	**7,247^**	**12,241**	**14,946**	22,808	27,232	37,490	32,457^	Dec 97	54,592	Dec

Five-year average of peak WeBS counts (Sep-Mar)
of Knots from 1970/71-2003/04

Numbers build up rapidly from October to a peak in January and February and then decline quickly during March.

The build up in midwinter also occurs at other sites in Britain. Ringing studies have shown that large numbers of Knots move out of their wintering grounds in the Netherlands at this time and augment the numbers already wintering on British estuaries (Winter Atlas).

Numbers present in midsummer are generally small and appear to have declined in recent years. Cox noted that a few hundred non-breeders occasionally summered but the last three-figure count during June was 300 off Foulness on 25th June 1967. In June 1963, unprecedented numbers were present off Foulness, with 720 on 9th and 1,100 on 11th. The largest counts in recent years have been a total of 60 in Essex during June 1996 and 24 at The Naze on 23rd June 2002. Most summering birds are probably non-breeding, first-year individuals.

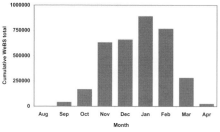

Seasonal occurrence of Knots from 1970-2004

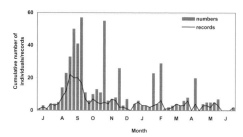

Seasonal occurrence of inland Knots from 1950-2004

Knots are recorded annually from inland locations, although numbers are usually small. The majority have occurred at Abberton, Hanningfield and the Lea Valley reservoirs. From 1950–2004, Knots were reported from Hanningfield in 34 years, Abberton in 28 and the Lea Valley reservoirs in 25, with a smattering of records from a few other sites, many further up the Lea Valley. The most unusual record involved one that spent 3rd–4th February 1966 in the gardens of Chelmsford Crematorium, feeding on the lawns and rose gardens. Inland records peak markedly around late August/early September, far earlier than the midwinter WeBS count peak. Knots make long non-stop flights between staging areas and first-year birds are especially prone to arriving in wintering areas in poor condition and it is this age group that probably accounts for many inland records, perhaps as tired birds drop out from long flights (*BWP*). The largest counts have occurred at times of low water levels at the main reservoirs. In all there have been nine double-figure counts, the highest being: Abberton, 50 on 30th October 1996, 25 on 28th November 1959 and 22 on 22nd September 1957; and Walthamstow, 21 on 2nd February 1992.

A total of nine foreign-ringed Knots has been reported, four from Norway, two from Germany and singles from Sweden, Iceland and Italy, whilst a single bird ringed in Essex has been recovered in the Netherlands. The Icelandic bird was almost certainly of the race *islandica* and it is likely that most of the others were also of this population. However, it is possible that the Swedish individual, which was found dead on Foulness in February 1958 and the Italian bird, which was trapped at Canvey Island in November 1997, were of the race *canutus* as they came from further east than *islandica* would normally be expected to occur, although wintering in western Europe is unusual for this subspecies. Both races occur together in southwest Norway and Denmark and the south Baltic coasts of Germany and Poland (Migration Atlas). Research by the WWRG over the last 20 years has shown that considerable movements occur between key estuaries in the course of a winter. Many birds arrive in Britain in spring and autumn on The Wash, Norfolk/Lincolnshire, complete their moults and fatten up and then migrate further north or disperse to key wintering sites; there have been three recoveries in Essex of birds ringed in The Wash.

The reasons for the increase in Knots occurring in Essex are unclear. The population increase has been apparent from early winter, rather than later in the season when it is known individuals from the Waddensee augment our population. It appears therefore that increasing numbers are migrating directly from their breeding grounds to Essex to moult and subsequently remaining to winter. Whatever the cause, the Foulness area and Dengie are sites of considerable importance internationally. The limited wintering areas make the species particularly prone to disturbance but despite the use of the Foulness area for regular munitions testing, the species appears to be unaffected. The Knot has been identified as a species that should provide one of the best early warning systems of a species' ability to cope with climatic change as this threatens every aspect of its life cycle both on its breeding and wintering grounds (Cranswick *et al.* 1999).

Sanderling   *Calidris alba*

Fairly common passage migrant and winter visitor – occasional in summer

Despite having a huge breeding range that encompasses the high-arctic regions of Canada, northern Greenland, Svalbard and north-central Siberia, the Sanderling is a monotypic species. In Europe, breeding is restricted to Svalbard but it is widespread as a passage migrant and winter visitor. The complex migration system of the species is poorly known with different breeding populations apparently overlapping in their winter ranges. Those migrating through Europe may be members of the Greenland or Siberian populations but those wintering in Europe are probably mostly from Greenland (European Atlas). In Britain, the Sanderling is widespread but found only in areas with long sandy beaches where it spends much of its time running along the tideline picking up small crustaceans that are active in the area disturbed by the lapping waves.

Historically, the Sanderling was considered to be principally a passage migrant in Essex; the first documented record coming from the mouth of the Thames in spring 1828 (Glegg). Christy noted that the Sanderling was "A not uncommon spring and autumn migrant, and to some extent also a winter visitor". Around Harwich the species was considered common particularly during spring. It would seem that over the next 40 years numbers declined as Glegg described the Sanderling as "… an uncommon bird of passage, which has been sparsely recorded on the autumn and spring movements". Despite many visits to the coast he saw the species just twice, both occasions at Colne Point: 3rd August 1925 (eight) and 1–2 on 15th June 1927.

Hudson & Pyman considered that the Sanderling had increased over the previous 30–35 years. Whilst this may have been, at least in part, due to greater observer coverage, it would seem that there was a genuine increase in numbers. By the early 1970s, the winter population was estimated at 375 and, based on figures then available, Cox estimated that Essex regularly supported about 4% of the British and 2–3% of the west European wintering population. Since then, WeBS counts have revealed a continuing increase.

The most recent estimate of the British wintering population lies in the region of 20,540 individuals (Rehfisch *et al.* 2003). Thus, Essex currently supports around 3.5% of the British and 0.6% of the east Atlantic population of 123,000, although these should perhaps be considered as conservative figures because it is likely that a percentage is missed from those areas of open coast not covered by WeBS surveys; at least 400 were estimated to have wintered between Walton and Frinton-on-Sea during 1972–73 and there were 531 (non-WeBS) along Southend-on-Sea seafront on 14th January 2002.

Sanderling numbers peak during autumn. The species starts to arrive in Britain in July and early August and, initially, congregates at a few major sites such as The Wash, Norfolk/Lincolnshire, and the Dee Estuary, Cheshire/Clwyd, where Sanderlings moult before dispersing around the coasts. However, a proportion does not moult but stays for 2–3 weeks to deposit enough fat to allow ongoing passage south, to west and southern Africa for winter. Given that the Siberian population is perhaps at least five times as large as the Greenland one (European Atlas), it seems reasonable to assume that the autumn peak is composed of mainly Siberian birds on their way south. Numbers recorded in autumn along the outer Thames increased markedly after 1990.

The recent WeBS average represents some 1.8% of the British migrant population of 40,000 (Stone *et al.* 1997), although this takes no account of the numbers present on open coastal areas.

GB 300p INT 1,000	1970- 1974	1975- 1979	1980- 1984	1985- 1989	1990- 1994	1995- 1999	2000- 2004	Peak counts		Peak month
WeBS totals	*353^*	*290*	*311*	*382*	*658*	*726*	*924*	*Oct 03*	*1,496*	*Oct*
Stour	0^	0	0	1	1	1	11	Nov 01	22	Nov
Hamford Water	105^	85	115	50	180	132	99	Nov 90	442	Nov
Colne	143^	~	~	290	231	132	125	Sep 89	406	Nov
Blackwater	0^	75	15	7	6	8	0	Oct 78	210	Oct
Dengie	185^	200	76	12	20	16	65	Sep 76	500	Oct
Crouch-Roach	0^	0	0	0	0	0	0	Sep 87	1	Oct
Thames	7^	32	46	61	345	517	781	Oct 03	1,387	Oct

Five-year average of peak WeBS counts (Sep-Nov)
of Sanderlings from 1970-2004

Many of the largest individual autumn counts have not been made on WeBS census days: 500 Dengie, September 1976, September 1977 and September 1983; 652 between Chalkwell and Shoebury, 29th November 2000; 720 on Shoebury East Beach, 6th September and 5th October 2001; and 844 along Southend seafront, 6th September 2002.

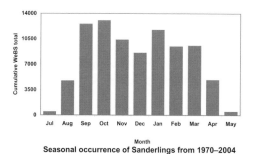

Seasonal occurrence of Sanderlings from 1970–2004

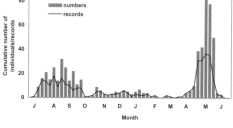

Seasonal occurrence of inland Sanderlings from 1954–2004

In spring, Sanderling numbers are probably augmented by an unknown number of birds from further south. WeBS counts suggest that numbers increase slightly after February but fall away again rapidly in April. Significant non-WeBS counts have included: 500 at Wakering Stairs, 20th May 1995; 540 at Shoebury East Beach, 31st March 2002; and 592 on Southend-on-Sea seafront, 11th March 2001. Small numbers of Sanderlings are present during summer, although rarely more than 20.

The species' distribution along the coast is directly influenced by the presence of sandy beaches. Thus, most Sanderlings occur in the northeast, with only the area between Foulness Point, where the species appears to congregate on autumn passage (Lewis 2000), and Southend-on-Sea seafront holding significant numbers further south.

Inland, Sanderlings are recorded in small numbers in most years, usually at the main reservoirs. Most records have involved 1–4 individuals but there have been two double-figure counts: 12 at Abberton on 20th September 1998 and 11 at Hanningfield on 28th May 1960, with a further two records involving nine, one of eight and four of seven. Inland passage peaks during May and coincides with the occasional occurrence of large flocks on the coast at

GB 210w INT 1,000	70/71- 74/75	75/76- 79/80	80/81- 84/85	85/86- 89/90	90/91- 94/95	95/96- 99/00	00/01- 04/05	Peak counts		Peak month
WeBS totals	*303^*	*373*	*350*	*193*	*424*	*569*	*712^*	*Mar 03*	*986*	*Dec*
Stour	0	0	0	5	4	7	49^	Feb 01	62	Feb
Hamford Water	122^	301	249	79^	172	220	90^	Jan 83	395	Jan
Colne	180^	~	~	145	159	213	143^	Jan 87	278	Jan
Blackwater	1^	25	12	22	23	8	0^	Jan 71	150	Dec
Dengie	37^	38	17	16	15	28	16^	Dec 76	75	Jan
Crouch-Roach	0^	0	0	0	0	0	0^	Feb 74	3	Dec
Thames	32^	26	27	14	160	256	537^	Mar 03	875	Mar

Five-year average of peak WeBS counts (Dec-Mar)
of Sanderlings from 1970/71-2003/04

that time; passage along the British west coast is greater in spring than autumn (Migration Atlas) and perhaps suggests that a small northwesterly passage through Essex may occur at this time. A smaller passage occurs in autumn, peaking in August and September, after which there is an apparent random scattering of records through the winter with a virtual absence in February and March. These winter movements may relate to onward movement from favoured moulting sites or movements between favoured coastal sites; recent colour-ringing studies suggesting that this occurs far more regularly than was previously thought.

Two foreign-ringed Sanderlings have been recovered in Essex, both ringed on 23rd September 1955 at Revtangen, Jaeren, Norway, and — remarkably — both shot on the same day, 14th October 1955, at The Naze; they are likely to have been newly arrived Siberian birds. The date of recovery does not indicate whether they were on passage or wintering birds. Three Sanderlings ringed on The Wash, Norfolk/ Lincolnshire, have also been recovered, demonstrating dispersal from one of the Sanderling's main moult sites. One of these found on the rela-

	Winters recorded	Counts of 4+	Peak count
Abberton	39	8	12 on 20th September 1998
Hanningfield	40	10	11 on 28th May 1960
Walthamstow	11	1	4 on 27th May 1984
KGV	20	4	6 on 26th May 2004
Girling	25	4	9 on 2nd-8th August 1959

Principal inland sites for Sanderlings from 1954-2004

tively early arrival date of August 1979 at Colne Point suggests that it may have originated from Greenland. One found dead at The Naze in January 1979 was over ten years old.

Although not a stronghold for Sanderlings, due to the limited amotunt of suitable habitat, there are three sites of national importance in Essex: Hamford Water; Colne Estuary; and Foulness. The species' habitat preference makes it particularly vulnerable to human disturbance, as man is also strongly attracted to sandy shorelines both for recreation and development. Thus, it may suffer more than many waders if disturbance of this habitat increases. Continuing protection of the stretches of coastal beach both within and outside nature reserves is therefore vital to maintain the current status of the Sanderling for the foreseeable future.

Sponsored by Albert Watson

Western Sandpiper *Calidris mauri*

Vagrant: one record

The monotypic Western Sandpiper breeds in north and west Alaska and extreme eastern Siberia and winters along the southern coasts of USA, the West Indies and Central and South America.

1973	Rainham	21st–23rd July	Adult

This individual was moulting into winter plumage.

The Western Sandpiper is the rarest American calidrid to occur in Britain with just seven records to the end of 2004 (BBRC 2005). This was the third, the first from England and also the first for the mainland; it almost certainly arrived in Europe in a previous year, as the date is probably too early for a transatlantic crossing in 1973. The majority have occurred between late July and September.

Little Stint *Calidris minuta*

Fairly common autumn passage migrant, scarce in spring – 1–2 usually winter

The monotypic Little Stint is the smallest breeding wader in the Western Palearctic. It breeds from northern Norway in the west to the River Lena in Siberia in the east, typically inhabiting the northern-most tundra zone. Most western Palearctic birds migrate down the Atlantic seaboard and through Africa to spend the winter in tropical Africa.

There appears to have been little overall change in the status of the Little Stint in Essex since the 19th century, apart from a general

	Years with records	First record	Years with counts 10+	Peak counts
Abberton	49	1952	13	170 w/c 29/09/96
Hythe	32	1960	1	11 on 22/09/60
Hanningfield	50	1955	20	108 w/c 08/09/96
Old Hall	25	1953	1	22 on 11/09/03
East Tilbury	24	1962	10	77 on 29/09/01
Rainham	39	1960	12	50 on 09/09/78

Principal sites for Little Stints from 1950-2004

increase in numbers since the 1950s that is probably due to increased observer coverage. Wintering numbers have, however, increased recently. The species' typical habitat is the muddy edges of freshwater bodies. However, small numbers also occur on coastal mudflats where they may mingle with flocks of Dunlins. The Little Stint and Curlew Sandpiper have close parallels in their occurrence, arriving at the same time and in broadly similar numbers.

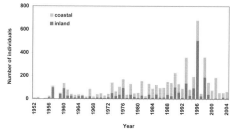

Annual totals of Little Stints from 1952-2004

The first documented Essex record occurred prior to 1826, the species having been "… killed … on Ray Island in the River Stour" (Christy). Christy considered the Little Stint to be a "… not uncommon shorebird when on migration in spring and autumn", although he makes only one reference to the species in spring: "… for a few days in April and again in October, when on migration, they may be seen about the ditches on the salting in parties of five or six". Glegg described the Little Stint as "… occasionally recorded from the Essex coast …", although he gave just one dated spring record involving two on the Stour on 30th May 1922. All autumn records fell in August and September. Hudson & Pyman considered the species a rather scarce passage migrant with usually no more than 3–4 occurring in spring. Likewise, Cox regarded the species as a regular autumn passage migrant that was very scarce in spring.

Autumn passage varies considerably from year to year, fluctuations probably being linked to population peaks and to weather encountered during migration. Unstable cyclonic conditions with easterly winds over Scandinavia and the Baltic have been present at the time of the larger influxes (Migration Atlas). More locally, the amount of suitable habitat, which is influenced principally by water levels at the reservoirs, may affect the numbers that halt in Essex during migration. Different sites are more attractive to Little Stints in some years than others.

By far the largest influx was in 1996, which produced the only ever three-figure counts. At its peak, more than 300 Little Stints were present with some 680 passing through that autumn, almost twice as many as in the previous peak year. Low water levels across Essex (and Britain), combined with a very good breeding season, were considered the main reasons for the influx (Cranswick *et al.* 1997). Very few were recorded prior to 2nd September, which suggests that adults and juveniles moved through together.

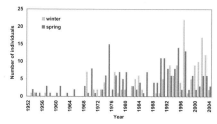

Annual totals of winter and spring Little Stints from 1952–2004

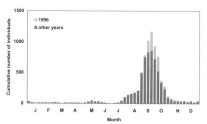

Seasonal occurrence of Little Stints from 1971-2004

Away from the principal sites, numbers are generally smaller but the species has occurred all around the coast and at many inland sites, the highest counts being: 60 in Bathside Bay, 21st September 1996; 32 flying north at Wakering Stairs, 3rd September 1989; 30 along the Stour, 23rd September 1996; and 30 at Blue House Farm, North Fambridge, 6th September 1998. Inland, away from Abberton and Hanningfield, small numbers regularly visit the Lea Valley, with 17 at Girling on 20th September 1996 the highest individual site count.

Adults pass through from late July to October (Prater 1981) with numbers peaking in September when juveniles begin to arrive in force (Migration Atlas). More recently Little Stints have remained much later than in the past, perhaps due to the run of warmer autumns and the establishment of a wintering area in Iberia since the 1960s (Winter Atlas). A total of 13 was still at Abberton on 7th November 1996.

Winter records have increased noticeably over the last 30 years: nationally, increases in the number of wintering Little Stints began as early as the 1930s (Winter Atlas). The first Essex winter record was in 1952 when one was at Abberton on 4th December. Hudson & Pyman were aware of two further winter records, whilst Cox noted a considerable increase after 1968. In the winter of 1967/68, up to seven were at Rainham, this locality holding most of the wintering Little Stints during the 1970s and 1980s, with up to five during 1976/77. More recently, most records have come from East Tilbury, which is probably one of the most reliable wintering sites in East Anglia, with seven in both January 1995 and March 2002, and nine on 18th November and eight on 2nd December 2001. Low water levels at Abberton saw up to five in December 1996 and 1999 and five at Hanningfield, also in December 1996, whilst there were five off Dengie on 10th January 1993 and four at Dovercourt on 14th December 1983, Foulness on 16th December 2000, and Wat Tyler CP on 3rd January 2001.

Spring passage, which generally lasts from May into June, is generally light with none recorded in some years. The greatest number occurred in 1991 when a minimum of 17 occurred at ten locations. There were 15 in 1975, 14 in 1995 and 13 in 1997. Eight at South Woodham Ferrers on 31st May 1997 is the largest single site count in spring; there were five, possibly six, together at Abberton on 3rd June 1975.

A few midsummer records have occurred, which are difficult to assign to either passage.

There have been two foreign recoveries of Essex-ringed birds. One ringed at Abberton on 27th September 1952 was shot at Mouchao da Povoa, Lisbon, Portugal, on 23rd September 1956 (this is also the oldest British-ringed Little Stint to have been reported to the BTO), and another ringed on Foulness on 19th September 1960 was recovered at Catarroja, Valencia, Spain, on 22nd November 1960. Both could have been either in their wintering area already or still on passage to the species' principal wintering area further south.

Sponsored by Paul Wood

Temminck's Stint   *Calidris temminckii*

Scarce but almost annual passage migrant: one winter record   Amber List

The monotypic Temminck's Stint breeds mainly in the tundra zone from east Siberia to Scandinavia, where it also breeds in the boreal zone. The Russian population is estimated at 1–10 million pairs (European Atlas); a few pairs breed annually in Scotland. Migrating birds occur singly or in small groups over much of Europe, although numbers are lowest in western maritime countries. Unlike most calidrids, Temminck's Stints move overland during migration (Migration Atlas). Western Palearctic birds winter mainly in the African savannah zone wetlands with some staying in Europe.

The earliest documented record involved one shot on New England Island on 25th August 1835, one of five obtained in Essex and detailed by Christy, although at Harwich it was "... occasionally to be seen on the oozy patches of our shore". Glegg added a single undated record of one shot on Mu cking Flats. Two on the "Blackwater freshmarsh" (Old Hall?) on 11th September 1943 was the only other record prior to 1950.

Since 1950 the Temminck's Stint has been an almost annual passage migrant with 185 reported to the end of 2004. Numbers have increased steadily, although this is probably due to more comprehensive coverage. Double-figure totals have only been recorded in 1990, 1992 and 1993, although these were followed by the poorest run of years since the 1950s; numbers have subsequently recovered.

Nationally, 1987 (176) and 2001 (137) were the best years on record, an average of 95 being recorded annually during the 1990s (Fraser & Rogers 2005). Prior to the 1980s more were recorded in autumn than in spring but this trend has reversed, although quite why this should be is unclear. Peak numbers have tended not to coincide with peak arrivals of other tundra breeders that periodically occur in large numbers, such as Little Stint and Curlew Sandpiper; numbers occurring in Britain are, however, likely to be correlated to breeding success (Migration Atlas).

In spring, Temminck's Stints begin to arrive in late April, the earliest being two at Hanningfield on 19th April 1976. Numbers peak markedly in the second half of May with a few late birds, perhaps non-breeders, occurring in June; the latest was at Hanningfield on 13th June 1970.

Autumn migrants begin to arrive during August, although birds periodically occur in July, the earliest returning migrant being an adult at Hanningfield from

	First record	Most recent record	Years with records	No. of individuals			Peak count
				Spring	Autumn	Total	
Hythe	1960	2000	9	5	5	10	All singles
Old Hall	1955	2004	15	24	8	32	Four from 14th-22nd May 1987 & 22nd May 1989
Heybridge GP	1971	1982	5	0	7	7	All singles
South Woodham	1990	1993	4	5	1	6	Two from 8th-11th May 1992
East Tilbury	1973	1993	6	6	2	8	Two on 17th May 1973 & 7th May 1990
Rainham*	1959	2003	14	9	15	24	Three on 26th August 1970
Abberton	1956	1993	12	14	9	23	Two on three dates
Hanningfield	1957	1991	18	10	23	33	Two on six dates

* includes wintering bird present 1970/71

Principal sites for Temminck's Stints from 1950-2004

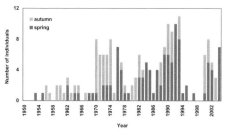

Annual totals of Temminck's Stints from 1950-2004

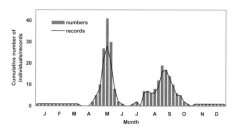

Seasonal occurrence of Temminck's Stints from 1953–2004

3rd–8th July 1989. Early arrivals are probably failed breeders (Migration Atlas). Autumn passage tends to be more protracted than in spring with a peak in late August–early September and occasional individuals lingering into October, the latest being at Hanningfield on 17th October 1971. The only winter record involved one at Rainham from 4th November 1970–20th March 1971.

The majority of spring records have involved individuals lingering no longer than 1–3 days. In autumn, however, Temminck's Stints may make longer stays. Singles at Hanningfield from 18th August–20th September 1959, 24th August–18th September 1960 and 3rd August–24th September 1961 (perhaps the same bird on each occasion) and at Heybridge GP from 29th August–15th September 1981 and East Tilbury GP from 23rd August–13th September 1981 were, however, exceptional.

Temminck's Stints have been recorded from over 25 localities with, in recent years, Old Hall the most favoured site.

In addition to the counts shown in the table, there were two at: Cattawade, 15th May 1982; Rainham Marshes, 2nd May 1983; Wat Tyler CP, 16th May 1993; Holland Haven, 10th–11th May 2001; Old Hall, 14th May 2001; Vange, 13th–14th May 2004; and Potton Island, 15th May 2004.

Inland, four passed through the Chelmer Valley in May 1984 and there were three on 14th May 1985, whilst there were two at Dagenham Chase on 15th–20th May 1988. Other inland records, all of singles have come from: Roman River Valley, 18th August 1971; Earls Colne GC, 14th August 1993; Girling, 26th April 1989; Netherhall GP, 10th May 1984 and 19th May 1985; Chingford Marshes, 8th September 2001; and Fairlop CP, 2nd May 2004.

White-rumped Sandpiper   *Calidris fuscicollis*

Vagrant: seven records

The monotypic White-rumped Sandpiper breeds principally along coastal arctic Canada and winters in southern South America.

1964	Hanningfield	27th August	
1967	Abberton	3rd September	
1972	Heybridge GP	31st August	
1977	Hanningfield	22nd–23rd August	
1984	Two Tree Island	2nd–5th September	Adult
2002	Old Hall	18th–21st July	Moulting adult
		11th and 13th August	Different adult

There had been 386 British records to the end of 2004 (BBRC 2005), averaging some ten per annum in recent years. Records have exhibited a wide geographic spread with, perhaps surprisingly, more recorded in Norfolk (46 to 1999, Taylor *et al.* 1999) than in any other county. Most occur between late July and October. The consistency of arrival dates of the first five is remarkable, just 11 days separating the earliest and latest. Early autumn arrivals along the east coast suggest a Continental origin, these birds having probably crossed the Atlantic in a previous year. Indeed, the Heybridge GP individual arrived at a time of Scandinavian drift migration (*EBR* 1972). However, it is also possible that birds occasionally associate with flocks of Ringed Plovers and Dunlins that regularly cross from Greenland over the Atlantic to Britain (Cottridge & Vinicombe 1996).

Baird's Sandpiper   *Calidris bairdii*

Vagrant: two records

The Baird's Sandpiper is a monotypic wader that breeds in the high-arctic of North America and also northwest Greenland and extreme eastern Siberia and winters in South America, south of the Equator.

1972	Abberton	19th August	Adult
1977	Rainham	3rd September	Adult

Both individuals occurred in years that White-rumped Sandpipers were recorded in Essex. There were 186 British records to the end of 2004 (BBRC 2005). The early autumn dates suggest that they either originated from the Siberian population or, perhaps more likely given the extremely small size of this population, were transatlantic vagrants that arrived in Europe in a previous year.

Pectoral Sandpiper   *Calidris melanotos*

Scarce, almost annual passage migrant: around 66 individuals

The monotypic Pectoral Sandpiper breeds from the western shore of Hudson Bay, Canada, west to the Taimyr peninsula of Siberia and winters principally in southern South America. The species is by far the commonest Nearctic wader to occur in Britain, averaging some 57 records a year in the 1990s (Fraser & Rogers 2005), although there were 131 in 1984 and 132 in 1999.

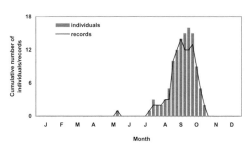

Seasonal occurrence of Pectoral Sandpipers from 1952–2004

One at Abberton on 18th September 1949 was the first Essex record. Since 1950 and up to 2004, the Pectoral Sandpiper has been recorded in 29 years and since 1976 in all but five. The increase in occurrence is probably due to greater observer coverage.

Most records involved singles. However, there were three, possibly five, at Abberton on 26th–31st August 1952, one of which became the first Pectoral Sandpiper to be ringed in Britain, and three juveniles at Abberton on 26th–28th September 2003. Two have occurred at: Hanningfield, 27th July 1957; Girling, 24th September–3rd October 1985; Chelmer Valley, 18th–19th September 1988; Abberton, 18th September 1999 and 29th September–5th October 2003; and Rainham, 21st–22nd September 2002.

Apart from an adult female at Old Hall from 23rd–24th May 1993, all records have occurred between 18th July, at Old Hall in 1991, and 24th October, at Abberton in 1986, with numbers peaking during September and early October.

Spring occurrences are rare and presumably relate to individuals that have wintered further south in Europe and are migrating north. It is possible that birds occurring on the east coast in autumn are actually undertaking reverse migration from the Siberian population, although it seems more likely that most are simply North American birds arriving from the Continent, having crossed the Atlantic in a previous year (Cottridge & Vinicombe 1996).

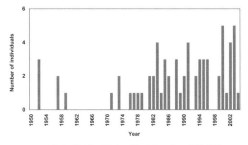

Annual totals of Pectoral Sandpipers from 1950-2004

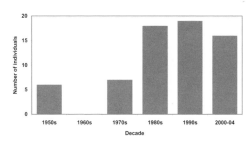

Totals of Pectoral Sandpipers in each decade from 1950–2004

Records have come from widely scattered locations, although there is a distinct preference for the two main reservoirs with 14 at Abberton and 11 at Hanningfield. Rainham and Old Hall, with nine each, are the next most favoured localities. Three have occurred at Girling, all in 1985, whilst there have been two at Heybridge GP, Chelmer Valley reservoir and Grange Outfall, Dengie (both in 1991), with singles at a further 14 sites.

Curlew Sandpiper   *Calidris ferruginea*

Fairly common, principally autumn passage migrant - rare in winter

The monotypic Curlew Sandpiper is a species of high-arctic coastal tundra and nests regularly only along the coast and on islands in the Arctic Ocean (Migration Atlas). Outside the breeding season the species can be found from sub-Saharan Africa through South Asia to Australasia. It is a common migrant in the Western Palearctic where three major routes are followed: one to the White Sea then down the western European coast to west Africa; another across eastern Europe via the Black Sea and Tunisia to west Africa; and the third via the Black and Caspian Seas through the Middle East to east and southern Africa (Migration Atlas).

The arrival of this species is frequently linked with that of the Little Stint. However, in comparison Curlew Sandpipers are more inclined to feed on tidal mudflats, sometimes mixing with Dunlin flocks. However, the species also occurs inland, in Essex principally at the two main reservoirs and exceptionally at other inland sites,

	Years with records	Years with counts of			Highest counts
		10+	30+	70+	
Colne Point	26	2	0	0	25 - 26/08/96
Fingringhoe/Langenhoe Ranges	26	8	3	0	50 - 09 &10/88 and 08/09/91
Old Hall/Tollesbury	29	8	1	0	50 - 15/09/85
Dengie	31	10	4	1	75 - 19/08/01
Foulness/Wakering/Fleet Head	29	7	2	0	35 - 10/09/88
East Tilbury	25	15	11	5	107 - 19/09/90
Rainham	24	6	1	1	70 - 17/09/78
Abberton	20	6	1	1	70 w/c 15/09/96
Hanningfield	30	3	1	0	48 - 19/09/90

Principal sites for Curlew Sandpipers from 1971-2004

particularly when low water levels provide ideal feeding conditions.

Christy described the Curlew Sandpiper as "Not very uncommon on our coast as a spring and autumn migrant. It is remarkable, as the only British Bird whose eggs still remain undiscovered". Of the records he detailed, all occurred in the period August to October, except for one shot at Bumpstead (sic) on 2nd February 1832. The first documented Essex record occurred prior to 1827 on Peewit Island. Christy gave little quantitative information, although the correspondence he received suggested that in some years numbers could be "... fairly plentiful ..." Surprisingly, Glegg did not know of any Essex records for the period 1898–1929.

Both Hudson & Pyman and Cox noted that numbers had increased, a trend that has continued to this day, although greater observer coverage must be a significant factor; particularly large influxes occurred in 1988 and 1990.

Birds returning to their breeding grounds from west Africa follow a route that takes them across eastern Europe, so few occur on Atlantic and North Sea coasts in spring. Only in three years since 1950 have there been ten or more recorded in spring, in 1990 (ten), 1993 (12) and 1997 (11). The fact that all of these counts occurred in the 1990s may be due to increased observer coverage but it may be that the milder run of winters over the last decade has allowed the Curlew Sandpiper to winter further north in Europe and so bring its spring passage route closer to Britain than before. The largest single spring flock was six at Abberton on 20th May 1965. In all, 155 have occurred in spring since 1950, all from the coast, Abberton or Hanningfield. Almost one-third of the records have come from Old Hall/Tollesbury.

A few have occurred from mid-June, either very early returning birds or perhaps lingering non-breeders.

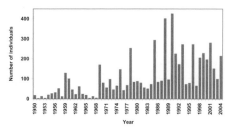

Annual totals of Curlew Sandpipers from 1950-2004

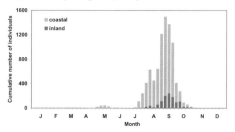

Seasonal occurrence of Curlew Sandpipers from 1971–2004

Males leave the breeding grounds as soon as they have mated (Underhill 1995) with females following once the young have become independent. Juveniles only start to leave at the end of July–mid-August. Thus, it is the red-breasted adults that arrive first at the end of July and early August, although some birds may be seen as early as the end of June. A far more westerly migration route through Europe is taken in autumn, explaining why autumn passage is more significant than that in spring. Adult passage peaks in early August (the first, smaller, peak in the graph), with juveniles peaking in mid-September although they may be noted as early as late July.

The principal factor controlling the number of Curlew Sandpipers occurring in autumn is the weather at the time of migration, and it has been suggested that influxes occur when unstable cyclonic conditions with easterly winds prevail over Scandinavia and the Baltic at the time of migration (Wilson *et al.* 1980). Whilst this has certainly been responsible for some of the influxes, those in 1985 and 1988 arrived on strong west/southwest airflows devoid of any drift migrants. Breeding success may, therefore, be another factor that determines numbers. The unpredictable arctic weather can severely affect breeding success—the complete lack of juveniles in 1989 was probably due to snow covering the breeding grounds in July (*EBR* 1989). Additionally, the breeding cycle of the Norway Lemming has been linked to breeding success; Arctic Foxes switch between Lemmings and waders depending on which are the more abundant.

Most of the large influxes have involved juveniles, although in 1992, a poor breeding year, large numbers of adults passed through particularly early, including the third largest flock reported in Essex. The species has a preference for coastal waters and this is where the largest flocks have occurred, although significant numbers have been found along the muddy edges of freshwater or brackish sites. East Tilbury has consistently attracted the largest gatherings over the last 20 years or so. Other high counts from East Tilbury have been: 100, 10th September 1988; 85, all adults, 14th August 1992; 76, 30th August 1999; 74, 5th September 2000. Away from the most favoured sites, the only counts of 30+ have come from Paglesham (40 on 17th September 1985) and Mersea Island (30 on 3rd September 1993).

Most have departed by mid-October but a few have lingered into November. Although records of the species wintering in Britain are rare, the nearest regular wintering areas being in northwest Africa, six have occurred in Essex, all singles: Langenhoe Point, 1st January 1984; East Tilbury, one with a damaged wing, 27th November 1990–26th February 1991 and another, 22nd February 1992; East Mersea, 26th December 1996; Roach, December 1998; and Fingringhoe Wick, 1st January 2004. Singles at Hanningfield on 30th March 1957 and The Hythe on 7th April 1979 may have wintered locally.

There have been no ringing recoveries affecting Essex. Elsewhere in Britain, ringing has shown that it is normally juveniles that are displaced furthest west in some autumns but that in subsequent years they will take a far more easterly migration route through Russia, Italy and the Ukraine.

Stilt Sandpiper   *Calidris himantopus*

Vagrant: one record

The monotypic Stilt Sandpiper breeds in northern Canada and Alaska and winters mainly south of the Equator in South America.

1973	The Naze	2nd September	Winter-plumaged adult

This was the 11th British record of one of the rarest North American waders to occur in Britain, with only 21 records, the last in 2002 (BBRC 2003). The majority show a late summer/early autumn arrival pattern. Unusually, most of the late summer occurrences have been on the east coast, suggesting that they are not direct transatlantic vagrants but perhaps reverse migrants out of Alaska or northern Canada (Cottridge & Vinicombe 1996).

Purple Sandpiper   *Calidris maritima*

Uncommon passage migrant and winter visitor   Amber List

The monotypic Purple Sandpiper breeds in mid- and high-alpine and arctic areas from the eastern Canadian high-arctic through Greenland, Iceland, Scandinavia and eastward to Severnaya Zemlya and the Taimyr peninsula in

Siberia. The species has the most northerly wintering range of any wader and, whilst in Europe it can be found as far south as Spain, large numbers can occur along the coast within the Arctic Circle (European Atlas).

Allowing for increased observer coverage, there seems to have been little significant change in the status of the Purple Sandpiper since the 19th century. However, modern sea defence schemes have undoubtedly provided additional habitat. Christy considered the species to be a "... rather rare winter visitor ..." with the

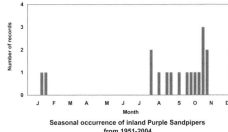

Seasonal occurrence of inland Purple Sandpipers
from 1951-2004

first documented Essex record coming from near Southminster in about 1833. Two of his correspondents felt that it was less common than previously. All the dated records fell in the period November–January and most were from the northeast, the highest counts being seven shot on the stone breakwater at Harwich between 6th and 10th November 1876 and five near Walton-on-the-Naze in December 1888. Records also came from Dovercourt, Mersea Island, New England Island, Shoebury, Southend-on-Sea and Canvey Island. Glegg added just three records, including four shot from a "... party of about a dozen ..." at Leigh/Two Tree Island on 19th November 1906.

Hudson & Pyman considered that the Purple Sandpiper was a winter resident was confined to Dovercourt and The Naze with normally 1–3 present (maximum six) from October to April. Away from the northeast coast, just 18 were recorded between 1950 and 1966.

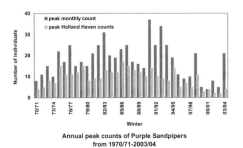

Annual peak counts of Purple Sandpipers
from 1970/71-2003/04

Seasonal occurrence of Purple Sandpipers
from 1970-2004

From 1970, there was a noticeable increase both in numbers and range. The Purple Sandpiper spread from the Dovercourt and The Naze area, south along the northeast coast with Holland Haven quickly becoming the principal site, the substantial rock sea defences and groynes undoubtedly proving particularly attractive for feeding and roosting. During the 1970s and 1980s, peak counts here were 17 on 15th April 1979 and 29th March 1986. Numbers remained relatively constant at Holland Haven from the early 1970s to the mid-1990s; Purple Sandpipers show strong site fidelity and will return each winter to the same stretch of shore (Winter Atlas). A count of 17 was also made in Hamford Water on 13th December 1992. Further south, small numbers were attracted to the seawalls around St Osyth and Jaywick. Small numbers have also occurred from the Colne around to the Thames, six at Deal Hall, Dengie, on 9th September 2001 being the largest count away from the northeast. Along the Thames, Southend Pier was favoured during the 1980s, with up to four during early 1985. Further upriver, the dredging pipe at East Tilbury attracted individuals on four occasions, with one from 14th January–1st April 1992. Records have also come from Rainham (three) and West Thurrock (one).

The reasons for the decline since the mid-1990s are unknown but may be due, at least in part, to increased disturbance caused by tidal defence and sewage treatment works, particularly in the northeast, and also to the run of very mild winters. Ironically, the largest single site count, of 20 at Dovercourt on 12th October 2003, occurred during one of the poorest winters for the species in many years. The Essex population is an extremely small proportion of the estimated 17,530 Purple Sandpipers that winter in Britain (Rehfisch *et al.* 2003), mainly in the northeast and becoming scarce south of Yorkshire (Winter Atlas).

Purple Sandpiper numbers peak in January, although in some years the largest counts have been in March and April, suggesting a return passage.

Midsummer records have come from: Dovercourt, 3rd June 1987; The Naze, 20th June 1983; Holland Haven, 21st July 1999; and The Naze, 27th July 1970.

Inland, there has been a total of 16 records, all singles except 2–3 at KGV on 7th February 1991, one of which also occurred at Girling from 7th–17th. Other records have come from: Abberton (six); Hanningfield (six); KGV; Girling; and Walthamstow. All bar two of the records fell in the period August–November.

There has been just one ringing recovery affecting Essex, that of a winter-ringed bird from Landguard Point, Suffolk, whose ring was read in the field at Holland Haven the following year. Nationally, ringing recoveries have shown that Greenland, arctic Scandinavian and Spitzbergen birds reach Britain. Along the east coast, the largest numbers controlled or recovered have been from Norway with smaller numbers from Sweden and Finland. Interchange with the Netherlands has been recorded on several occasions (Migration Atlas).

Dunlin   *Calidris alpina*

Very common passage migrant and winter visitor   **Amber List**

The Dunlin has a circumpolar distribution, breeding in arctic and northern temperate latitudes and occurring in open wet habitats such as alpine tundra, meadows, pastures and heaths. Six subspecies are recognised of which two breed in Europe: *schinzii* in Greenland, Iceland, the British Isles and southern Norway; and the nominate race *alpina* in northern Fennoscandia and Russia. The former winters primarily in west Africa, whilst the latter winters in western Europe and around the Mediterranean. The smallest and rarest race, *arctica*, breeds in Greenland and occurs as a passage migrant in Iceland and along the Atlantic coast of Europe (European Atlas).

The Dunlin appears always to have been the commonest wintering wader in Essex, although there are no historical references to the species ever having nested. One of the species' principal local names was 'Oxbird', the origin of which is obscure (Lockwood 1993). Christy stated that it was "The commonest Sandpiper on our coasts during autumn, winter and spring". The earliest reference to the species comes from Southchurch during the first quarter of the 19th century: "... about the middle of July the old ones arrive here, and the first of the young about the middle of August. All that month [they] continue to come, and during winter may be seen in immense flocks, traversing the surface of the water, or sometimes, rising higher, they appear like a dark cloud, and rapidly turning and presenting their breasts to the spectator, they all at once appear of a snowy white." Another of Christy's correspondents noted that "... on the oozes of the Essex Coast many tens of thousands of the there-called Oxbird be seen in a flock". Large numbers were shot by the gunners along the coast: "Mr John Balsham ... informs me of an enormous bag of these birds made by his father one night, about forty years ago, when he killed by a single discharge of his gun no less than 24 dozen out of a flock settled on the ice. This was the number actually obtained but he thinks that the gulls and the crows took several dozen for themselves" (Christy).

Glegg added little quantitative data but noted: "... the numbers that may be seen are very remarkable". He considered the Dunlin to be particularly abundant along the Stour "... where, on many occasions, it can be said without exaggeration, thousands can be seen".

Prior to the regular BoEE/WeBS surveys, there were up to 10,000 off Canvey Point in January 1957, whilst 4,000–5,000 were regularly reported off Goldhanger, Dengie and Foulness during the 1950s and 1960s. Since the 1970s regular counting has confirmed the international importance of Essex for Dunlins, which have increased markedly since the 1990s. Cox estimated that the Essex population represented around 12% of the British and 3.5% of the west European population. Based on a current population of 80,000, Essex now holds around 14.5% of the British

GB 5,600 / INT 14,000	70/71- 74/75	75/76- 79/80	80/81- 84/85	85/86- 89/90	90/91- 94/95	95/96- 99/00	00/01- 04/05	Peak counts		Peak month
WeBS totals	*66,667^*	*53,146*	*58,531*	*63,187*	*83,507*	*86,825*	*80,580^*	*Dec 97*	*99,264*	*Jan*
Stour	**15,880^**	12,558	**15,269**	**15,144**	**17,602**	**14,606**	11,940^	Jan 85	**20,854**	Jan
Hamford Water	10,250^	**11,450**	9,111	3,897	5,990	7,887	4,650^	Jan 79	**14,300**	Dec
Colne	7,890^	~	~	10,424	10,983	10,754	7,215^	Jan 96	**13,000**	Jan
Blackwater	12,513^	11,045	**15,523**	**16,677**	**22,786**	**24,547**	**21,452^**	Dec 00	**37,550**	Jan
Dengie	6,833^	6,900	5,602	5,520	9,890	7,970	8,992^	Feb 02	**15,720**	Feb
Crouch-Roach	2,743^	1,390*	4,049	2,560	3,976	3,393	2,300^	Feb 84	6,076	Jan
Thames	**21,092^**	**23,178**	17,377	**23,452**	23,026	**29,120**	**34,762^**	Jan 03	**46,431**	Dec

**Five-year average of peak WeBS counts (Sep-Mar)
of Dunlins from 1970/71-2003/04**

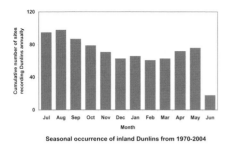

Seasonal occurrence of inland Dunlins from 1970-2004

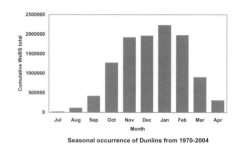

Seasonal occurrence of Dunlins from 1970-2004

and 5.6% of the European population. These increases have occurred despite an apparent decrease of 14% since the mid-1990s of the international Dunlin population, although current figures are still within the 24-year range of 900,000–1.5 million (Cranswick *et al.* 1999). The increases in the Blackwater and Thames are particularly marked.

The Dunlin is recorded regularly inland, being most widespread during migration. When water levels around the main reservoirs are low, numbers can be considerable. At Abberton, four-figure flocks have occurred on several occasions, the largest being 4,245 on 28th October 1990, in a year when there were at least 1,000 present from September–December. A maximum of 4,200 was present in November 1991, although four-figure numbers were present for just two months. Four-figure winter counts at Abberton have been noted in a further six years. At Hanningfield, the peak was 1,000 in November 1991, although this figure was exceptional with rarely more than 100 recorded, whilst in the Lea Valley, where numbers have only occasionally exceeded 30, the peaks have been 62 at KGV on 19th July 2004 and 55 on 14th September 1988. Otherwise, small numbers have occurred at a wide range of sites including reservoirs, gravel-pits, ornamental lakes, sewage farms, etc. Many of the large inland flocks have dispersed by the turn of the year, even when water levels have remained low, perhaps suggesting that by midwinter invertebrate populations in such temporary habitat are insufficient for the Dunlin's requirements.

Autumn migrants begin to appear from late July and numbers then increase throughout August and September. Data from birds trapped in Britain indicate that these probably refer mainly to passage birds of the races *schinzii* and *arctica*, although there have been no confirmed records of the latter in Essex. Studies have confirmed that Dunlins wintering in Britain are of the race *alpina*. After breeding, adults migrate through southern Scandinavia in July and early August and head directly to the Dutch Waddensee in the Netherlands and the Wash before moving on to wintering quarters in October and November. At this time very large flocks begin to form, with juveniles arriving a month or so later. Numbers are relatively constant from November to February.

Substantial numbers of *alpina* leave Essex in March and head for the Waddensee where they fatten up before leaving in mid-May. Presumably the arrival of spring passage *schinzii* (and *arctica*) from further south boosts numbers present into April.

It is unclear whether the records of several hundred Dunlins reported from time to time during June and early July are summering birds, presumably non-breeders, or simply late or early returning migrants.

The pattern of occurrence of inland Dunlins shows peaks in August and May, times when *schinzii* are heading south/north, ahead of the arrival of *alpina*.

Glegg provided details of a remarkably early ringing recovery, one ringed as an adult at Rybatschi, Kaliningrad, Russia (formerly Rossitten, Germany) on 3rd August 1909 and recovered at Southend-on-Sea on 15th December 1909. There have been a large number of recoveries of Essex-ringed Dunlins that shed light on the species' movements through Essex.

In the Essex-ringed Dunlin table, the only one that can be ascribed with certainty to the race *alpina* is the Russian individual, although it is likely that most of the Scandinavian and Polish records in September are *alpina*. The Icelandic recovery is more likely to refer to *schinzii* as very few *arctica* are recorded in Iceland (*BWP*) and the date suggests that the individual was already back on its breeding grounds.

	Jan	Feb	Mar	Apr	May	Jun	Jul	Aug	Sep	Oct	Nov	Dec
Finland							6	3	2			
Norway							1	2	12	2		
Sweden							25	32	11	1		
Baltic States								2				
Poland							3	4	9			
Denmark							4	4	1	1		
Germany							1	7	5	6	1	
The Netherlands					1		1	3	4	3		
Belgium									1			
Portugal					1							
Totals	0	0	0	0	2	0	41	57	45	13	1	0

Month of ringing and origin of Dunlins ringed abroad and recovered in Essex

The remainder fall within the breeding ranges and migration times of *schinzii*. Some *alpina* head further south and west in winter, particularly if the weather is severe; the records in France, Portugal and Morocco illustrate this. In some autumns, a proportion of the more eastern populations of *alpina* are displaced west, in much the same way as Curlew Sandpipers; although they normally winter in the eastern Mediterranean and northeast and east Africa, they do occur in Britain. In subsequent years, however, they reorientate and migrate on their more normal easterly route to the breeding grounds.

	Jan	Feb	Mar	Apr	May	Jun	Jul	Aug	Sep	Oct	Nov	Dec
Essex	11	2	4	2	1		1	3		3	7	10
North England					1							
South England	12	6	4	2	1		3	7	3	1	4	5
Wales	1				2							
Iceland						1						
Finland					3		7	1				
Sweden							17	11	1			
Estonia				1								
Russia					2	1		3	2	1		
Poland							5	2				
Denmark					1			1	1	1	1	
Germany			1	2	7	1	1	2	1			
The Netherlands					1	1		2	1			
France			1	1	1					1		1
Spain												1
Portugal		1										
Morocco			1									
Totals	24	9	11	8	20	4	34	32	9	7	12	17

Month and location of recovery of Dunlins ringed in Essex

There has also been a large number of foreign-ringed Dunlins recovered in Essex. Many of the Swedish and Danish birds in the foreign-ringed table of the race *alpina* were subsequently recovered in winter in Essex and show how important the county is for this race. The occurrence of birds ringed in Germany and the Netherlands suggests some interchange with the Waddensee, which is an important feeding and wintering area. The Portuguese-ringed bird was probably *schinzii*, ringed whilst on passage from northwest or west Africa.

At present and for the immediate future, there appear to be no significant threats to the Dunlin. Currently numbers of wintering birds are stable or increasing. Annual variations in numbers are more likely due to variable breeding success rather than factors at work within Essex. In the longer term, however, in common with other wader species, threats to the species include continuing coastal development, pollution and, in particular, rising sea levels.

Broad-billed Sandpiper   *Limicola falcinellus*

Vagrant: four records involving five individuals

The Broad-billed Sandpiper breeds across Fennoscandia east to Siberia, and winters principally through the Persian Gulf, India, Australasia and rarely in east Africa. The nominate race *falcinellus* breeds through Scandinavia and northwest Russia with the other recognised race *sibirica* occurring further east (Migration Atlas).

1988	Old Hall	22nd May	
	East Tilbury	23rd May	
		25th May	Two
1989	Old Hall	23rd–24th May	

A total of 211 had been recorded in Britain to the end of 2004 (BBRC 2005), although records prior to 1972 were rare, perhaps due to a poor understanding of its identification features (Cottridge & Vinicombe 1996). During the 1980s, national records averaged nine per annum, but numbers fell to about five per annum in the 1990s. The Broad-billed Sandpiper has a southeast to northwest spring migration route, so those recorded in Britain have possibly flown too far west and have then been displaced across the North Sea by easterly winds. However, it is possible that small numbers winter further west in Africa than currently supposed and they are simply migrating north (Cottridge & Vinicombe 1996). Most records involve adults along the east coast in spring.

After the rather uncooperative first bird, which revealed itself to just two people (Rhymes 1989), the trio at East Tilbury (the two present on 25th being considered different to the individual there on 23rd) were well received (Steward 1989). The consistency of dates is remarkable.

Buff-breasted Sandpiper   *Tryngites subruficollis*

Very rare passage migrant: 13 records involving 13–15 individuals

The monotypic Buff-breasted Sandpiper breeds in the high-arctic of North America and extreme eastern Siberia and winters on the grasslands of Argentina, Paraguay and Uruguay.

1975	Hanningfield	1st–11th September	
	Abberton	4th–5th September	
1977	Hanningfield	9th–17th September	
1982	Abberton	22nd August	
1984	Abberton	3rd October	
1986	Rainham	21st July	
1988	Foulness	3rd September	
1992	Dengie	19th–24th September	
1996	Hanningfield	17th–24th August	
		7th September	Two
	Abberton	8th–13th September with one until 22nd September	Two
1997	Abberton	5th September	
1999	Deal Hall, Dengie	5th September	

In addition, Christy (1903) referred to one shot at Walthamstow SF on 10th October 1903, although for some unknown reason Glegg did not accept the record. It is probable that only three were involved in 1996.

Nearly hunted to extinction in America in the 19th century, the species has subsequently recovered its numbers, although not to the "millions" estimated in the 18th century (Migration Atlas). A former BBRC Rarity, it was removed from the Rarities List in 1982, by which time there had been 445 recorded in Britain & Ireland. National records averaged 15 per annum during the 1990s (Fraser & Rogers 2005) but there are occasional influxes of which 54 in 1977, 48 in 1975 and 34 in 1996 are the largest. Most occur during September; all but four of the Essex records occurred between 1st and 24th September. The July record at Rainham probably involved an individual that crossed the Atlantic in a previous year.

Ruff   *Philomachus pugnax*

Common passage migrant and winter visitor   Amber List

The monotypic Ruff breeds from Scandinavia and Britain in the west, across Europe and Asia as far as the Bering Strait, mainly north of 60° N. In the temperate zone the species' typical breeding habitat is wet, low-lying grassy terrain at or below sea level, whilst further north it breeds on moorland and tundra. Serious declines have been noted in northern and east European populations since the 1980s; odd pairs occasionally breed in England. The majority of the population winter in sub-Saharan Africa, although small numbers winter in northwest Europe in coastal areas or inland floodplains in Germany, the Netherlands and Britain (European Atlas).

The Ruff was a widespread though uncommon breeding species throughout the east coast counties of England up until the end of the 18th century, but widespread drainage and ploughing for agriculture and collecting saw its extermination by the end of the 19th century (Historical Atlas). There is perhaps one Essex breeding record, Christy noting that: "Doubtless it once bred commonly in Essex, but I am not aware of more than one record of its having done so". In response to Christy's inquiry, Reverend Atkinson replied: "Yes, I did hear of the Ruff breeding on the Tollesbury Marshes and not far from the land end of Shingle Hill. But I did not know it of my own knowledge. My reminiscence is that it had been known to breed there on divers occasions. You see I have two sets of recollections, so to speak, my own and my father's". The date of the records would have been around 1830. Glegg felt that "There is no satisfactory evidence to show that it ever bred in Essex, though it may have done so", suggesting that he did not accept Reverend Atkinson's record. Although there have been no subsequent breeding records in Essex, on at least two occasions during the 1980s lekking was noted at suitable breeding localities, whilst in 1989, following lekking behaviour a very young juvenile was noted at Rainham. Lekking birds were also present at Rainham and Langenhoe in 1992. It is suspected that females join leks on passage but then breed further north (van Rhijn 1991). Despite an increasing summer population, there have been no further signs of breeding.

The Ruff's general status as a passage migrant has changed very little since Christy's and Glegg's times, although whilst Christy considered the species to be not uncommon in spring and autumn, Glegg thought the Ruff was an irregular passage migrant, occurring chiefly in autumn and rarely in spring, perhaps suggestive of a decline around the turn of the 20th century. From the 1950s, significant increases in autumn numbers occurred, although spring passage was light and only very small numbers were present in midwinter (Hudson & Pyman). The steady increase in numbers has continued to this day, although there was a sharp increase during the 1990s. Changing water levels at the main reservoirs have meant that annual totals vary considerably.

From the early 1970s, following a series of records from Thames-side, wintering numbers increased markedly (Cox) and have remained at a high level to this day with, in some years, more being present in winter than during autumn passage. The WeBS survey sometimes fails to do justice to this species with counts not always coinciding with peak autumn numbers or detecting wintering individuals that may disperse from favoured feeding and roosting areas during the day and only return at night.

The increases in passage and wintering numbers do not appear to be linked as, after autumn passage, numbers decline before rising again to a midwinter peak. Cox noted that numbers tended to peak in February. This peak has been less obvious in recent years. Prater (1973) noted that most Ruffs wintering in Britain were males and casual observations in Essex confirm this to be true. It is thought that the reason for the separation is that males tend to stay further north, nearer to the breeding areas.

The first autumn birds arrive in June and tend to be males, which play no part in parental care (van Rhijn 1991). Juveniles appear from around mid-August and passage peaks in August and September. Numbers generally decline in October and November but rise to a midwinter peak, perhaps as Continental Ruffs arrive after the onset of cold weather (Prater 1973).

Spring passage is normally light as Ruffs generally take a more easterly route to their breeding grounds at this time (*BWP*). Numbers reported in April and May 1994 were exceptional, with 220 passing through in May including 100 at Holland Haven on 3rd and 55 at Old Hall the same day; these were the largest flocks reported at this time of year. About 70 at East Tilbury during late March/early April 1976 may have been spring migrants or a late departing winter flock.

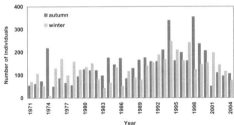

Peak autumn and winter counts of Ruffs from 1971–2004

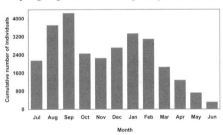

Seasonal occurrence of Ruffs from 1971-2004

Although Ruffs are generally widespread on the coast, three areas in particular have been favoured in recent years: Old Hall/Abberton; Hamford Water/Holland Haven; and Crouch–Roach/Potton Creek. Around Abberton and Old Hall, numbers tend to be highest in autumn. Water levels at Abberton appear strongly to influence counts at both localities with high counts at Abberton at times of low water levels corresponding with low numbers at Old Hall, the reverse occurring when levels are high at Abberton. A total of 238 at Abberton on 16th October 1994 remains the largest single count in Essex and occurred at a time of exceptionally low water levels that continued well into the winter. Six further three-figure counts have come from Abberton, the highest being 159 during the September 1995 WeBS count. Generally, numbers at Old Hall are lower than at Abberton, but this may perhaps be due to the greater difficulty of surveying Old Hall, the highest counts being: 115 on 22nd January 2003; 80 on 24th January 1993, 20th July 1993 and 18th July 2000; and a further five counts of 60+.

In the northeast, Hamford Water is a regular wintering location with smaller numbers on passage. Not far to the south, the marshes at Holland Haven are also favoured, although numbers vary considerably. There have been three counts of more than 70 from: Hamford Water, the highest being 87 on 19th January 1992; and Holland Haven, the highest being 100 on both 3rd May 1994 and 13th February 2002. The proximity of the two sites may mean some interchange occurs. Along the Crouch and Roach, the largest numbers occur during winter with the Fleet

Head area particularly favoured at present. Exceptionally, there were 150 at Oxenham Farm on 26th December 1997; otherwise there have been three counts of 70+.

Large numbers occurred around West Thurrock, Purfleet and Rainham during the early 1970s, the settling tanks near the power station attracting 130 during January and February 1971 with 100 nearby in January and February 1973. A count of 100+ at Hanningfield on 26th December 1956 was exceptional given the small numbers occurring at that time, the next highest count there being 52 during January 1981.

Five Ruffs ringed in Essex have been recovered in Kent, West Yorkshire, France (two) and Italy. The two found in France were likely to have been on migration from southern Europe when captured at Abberton and were both shot when heading back from southern Europe in subsequent winters. The Italian recovery at Fano in March 1971 illustrates the more easterly, northbound migration route taken in spring.

The reasons behind the recent increases, particularly during winter, are unclear, although milder weather may have allowed greater numbers to winter further north than previously. Despite these increases, however, there have been no observations which point to an imminent breeding attempt, though with habitat improvement continuing on many nature reserves, it is not unrealistic to suggest that the Ruff may one day breed in small numbers in Essex.

Jack Snipe *Lymnocryptes minimus*

Scarce passage migrant and winter visitor

The monotypic Jack Snipe's main European breeding populations are in northern Scandinavia and Russia; further east its range continues into central Siberia. Typical of watery bogs and floodplains, the species' diminutive size and crepuscular habits mean that its status even in Europe is not well known, although it is thought to have declined in the 19th century and continues to do so. Western populations winter in western Europe and north and west Africa (European Atlas).

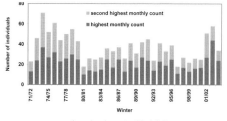

Annual peak counts of Jack Snipes
from 1971/72-2003/04

The 'Half Snipe', to give the species one of its local names, was described by Christy as "A fairly common winter visitor, most often seen during a frost". Glegg considered the species "... a regular and not uncommon winter resident ... but is a scarce bird as compared with the Common Snipe". In his experience he found that "... more ... are found on the sewage farms than in any other locality ... numbers vary[ing] with the conditions, more being seen during severe weather".

Early writers left little data with which to confirm that the Jack Snipe was in decline by the early 20th century. Even over the last 50 years or so, the secretiveness of the species has made it extremely difficult assessing trends. Hudson & Pyman considered the Jack Snipe a passage migrant and winter visitor, whilst Cox concluded that there was "... no evidence of any recent change in status..." However, data suggest that there was a decline of around 50% after 1979, since when numbers have remained relatively stable.

Many of the largest counts from earlier years came from the old style sewage treatment works where the species found the open settling beds particularly attractive. Few now exist and it is tempting to suggest that some of the apparent decline may be due to the loss of such habitat and the subsequent dispersal of the species to habitats more difficult to observe. In all habitats, the Jack Snipe is extremely difficult to detect, tending to sit tight on the ground until the very last moment before flying out from an observer's feet. The largest counts from treatment plants included 40 at Epping Forest SF from November–December 1974, when ten were ringed, with 20 there on 22nd November 1978 and 20 at Romford SF on 23rd November 1956. Silt and sludge lagoons are also favoured and The Hythe attracted up to 20 during December 1972, with double-figure counts regularly recorded through the 1970s. The two highest site counts have, however, come from reservoir and coastal locations, at the then still filling Hanningfield where the muddy areas attracted 50 on the relatively early date of 2nd October 1956 and 50 with Snipes on Ramsey Marsh, Steeple, on 30th November 1958.

There were no double-figure counts reported during the 1980s and 1990s, but in 2002 there were 12 along the Stour Estuary on 10th February, whilst at Rainham numbers built to a peak of 32 on 10th October, the third highest Essex count. Here, the species was found in very shallow, wet grazing marsh. Other sites used regularly during the 1990s included The Hythe, East Tilbury, Sewardstone, Dagenham Chase and Woodham Fenn.

Although Jack Snipes do not begin to arrive in any numbers until late September or early October, there have been four August records, the earliest at Goldhanger on 20th in 1910, whilst one at Heybridge GP on 28th in 1984 is the earliest since 1950. Numbers tend to peak prior to the turn of the year, suggesting that onward passage occurs through Essex.

Numbers remain relatively high until March but fall off rapidly thereafter. However, 34 were present during April 1974, including 15 at The Hythe. Occasional birds are recorded during May although there have been just three in the last week, the latest being singles on 28th at Rainham in 1977 and Dagenham Chase in 1992. Apart from a bird that summered in 1984 just over the border at Stanstead Abbotts, Hertfordshire, but which almost certainly crossed into Essex, there is just one June record, one flushed from Bradwell Brook on 21st in 1993.

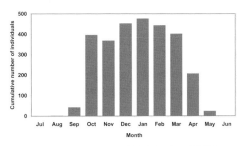

Seasonal occurrence of Jack Snipes from 1971-2004

Over 50 have been trapped and ringed since 1950, many at Epping SF and Abberton. One ringed at Epping SF on 5th November 1974 was shot at Montastrue, Lot-et-Garonne, France, on 6th November 1975 and was perhaps part of a cold-weather movement to the Continent. The relatively few national recoveries suggest that our passage and wintering populations have a Scandinavian origin. In addition, a number of records from Denmark, the Low Countries and Germany suggest onward movement into Britain in the same and subsequent winters; one ringed at Arzbacher Teiche, Marburg, Germany, on 8th April 1968 and found dead near Waltham Abbey on 14th December 1968 being typical. Several were noted at lightships off the Essex coast in the late 19th and early 20th centuries (Glegg). One ringed at Abberton in March 1958 and found dead there in January 1960 points to a degree of site fidelity in some birds.

(Common) Snipe
Gallinago gallinago

Common passage migrant and winter visitor: very rare breeder
Amber List

The Snipe is a widespread Holarctic wader. The nominate race *gallinago* has an extensive breeding range across northern and central Eurasia with other races occurring in Africa, South America, Canada and the USA. Many populations in Europe are in

Atlas	Survey Area	% of 10km squares or tetrads in which	
		bred/probably bred	possibly bred or present
First National 10km	Essex	36.8	28.1
Second National 10km	Essex	17.5	36.8
First London Tetrad	Met. Essex	1.0	6.0
Second London Tetrad	Met. Essex	3.0	10.0
Essex Tetrad	Essex	0.8	3.0

Summary of results of Atlas surveys for Snipes

decline. In Britain, the species decreased significantly during the 20th century but particularly since 1980, with a 62% decline recorded on lowland wet grassland between 1982 and 2002 attributed to habitat loss and degradation (Wilson & Vickery 2003). Eurasian birds winter in any parts of the breeding range that remain unfrozen, principally in Britain and the Low Countries and south to the Mediterranean (European Atlas).Snipe were hunted in Hatfield Forest in the early 18th century (Rackham 1989).

To Christy, the Snipe was "A common winter visitor, especially during a sharp frost or floods ..." As a breeding species, however, he noted: "It used to be a common resident, but it is now more scarce than formerly, though it still breeds in various places on the coast, and probably in Epping Forest." At Old Hall in 1889, however, it was thought to be becoming more common. Breeding was also noted in Hainault Forest CP until at least 1878 and at Harwich and Paglesham around 1890. Glegg stated that the Snipe was "... a not uncommon resident breeding throughout the county in suitable localities ... If the earlier reports are to be accepted the species has been increasing steadily as a breeder during the past forty years, and as such it may be said to be now generally distributed throughout the county, although perhaps in somewhat limited numbers". Unfortunately, he presented no data of his own.

Virtually no data exist for the period 1930-50 but in the early 1950s, the *EBRs* were reporting declines and in 1954 it was noted: "The conclusion is inescapable that the Snipe is now distinctly scarce as a nesting species in the

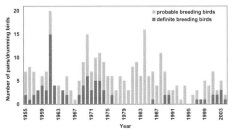

Annual totals of breeding Snipes from 1955-2004

county". The last significant breeding concentration was in the Lea/Stort valley, where in 1961 there were still up to 15 pairs on Hallingbury Marsh alone. However, the site was drained and lost its Snipes after 1963 and, by 1966, just 1–3 pairs were confirmed breeding annually from Writtle/Roxwell, Little Baddow, Newport, Bishop's Stortford and Beddall's End (Hudson & Pyman). Despite increasing observer coverage, Cox considered that perhaps no more than ten pairs nested annually, apart from in 1970 when 15 pairs were reported from 12 localities, the majority along the river valleys of the Stort, Colne, Roman River and Chelmer with a few still present on coastal marshes and odd pairs reported from gravel-pits and similar damp habitats.

The historical decline of the species in Essex has been mirrored nationally. In the last quarter of the 19th century, the introduction of the breech-loading shotgun and the reclamation and enclosure of wetlands had an adverse affect on lowland populations and breeding ceased in several counties (Historical Atlas). An apparent national recovery between 1900 and 1940, noted in Essex by Glegg, was perhaps encouraged by the agricultural depression that resulted in an increase in neglected pasture and winter flooding (Population Trends) and a reduction in shooting. In lowland Britain, Snipes are typical of wet pasture, fen and bog, particularly those with peaty soils. However, the species tends to be virtually absent from coastal grazing marshes with clay or silty soils (Green & Cadbury 1987) so typical of the Essex coast (Essex Atlas). Historically therefore, most Snipes breeding in Essex probably occurred inland, where drainage and conversion to arable and grassland have eliminated the vast majority of breeding sites. Comparison of the two National Atlases revealed a decline of around 50% in confirmed breeding records. Given that the Snipe had already declined drastically by the time of the first National Atlas, the overall decrease was catastrophic.

During the Essex Atlas survey, Snipes were reported from 14 possible breeding sites, of which no more than six were occupied in any one year. The maximum number of breeding pairs/drumming males in any one year was 11 in 1988, a wet year, including seven drumming males at Old Hall. Two pairs bred there in 1990. Since the Essex Atlas survey, the number of breeding/drumming birds reported has remained relatively constant although only in five years since 1990 has breeding been confirmed: at Sawbridgeworth Marsh (1997 and 1998); Thorley Wash (1999); Old Hall (2001); and Langenhoe Ranges (two pairs in 2002 and 2003). Most reports of drumming/summering birds during the 1990s came from a handful of sites in the south and west. Annual variations in the very small population are likely have been due to the prevailing weather conditions. Currently, no more than five pairs of Snipes are likely to breed annually across Essex.

Outside the breeding season, the Snipe is difficult to census accurately due to its secretiveness and preference for wet grassland and marshes. Thus, WeBS counts are not representative of the true numbers present. In addition, many Snipes occur at inland sites.

The sludge lagoons and settling tanks at the old style sewage farms and the silt lagoons along Thames-side were all important habitats during the 1970s and 1980s but, with their closure/degradation, numbers have been much reduced. Otherwise, most of the larger counts have come from coastal grazing marshes and it is here, when conditions are suitable, that significant gatherings occur. Countywide, the highest individual site count was 900 at Holland Haven on 9th March 1988, following counts of 600 there in January and February. A total of 500 was at Holland Haven on 28th November 1965 and 400 at the still filling Hanningfield on 11th December 1955. There

GB ? IN ?	70/71- 74/75	75/76- 79/80	80/81- 84/85	85/86- 89/90	90/91- 94/95	95/96- 99/00	00/01- 04/05	Peak counts		Peak month
WeBS totals	*471*	*206*	*151*	*334*	*280*	*133*	*395^*	*Nov 73*	*643*	*Nov*
Stour	19	71	33	53	45	37	135^	Jan 02	162	Nov
Hamford Water	82	88	39	40	53	35	28^	Dec 75	258	Nov
Colne	200	~	~	178	108	39	70^	Nov 73	520	Nov
Blackwater	93	30	41	66	46	26	42^	Oct 73	120	Nov
Dengie	7	4	14	4	3	2	2^	Dec 81	26	Nov
Crouch-Roach	31	10	29	35	34	11	37^	Jan 01	73	Dec
Thames	195	75	55	100	82	24	125^	Feb 73	230	Dec
Ardleigh	~	~	~	~	~	3	0^	Dec 96	6	Dec
Abberton	~	~	~	~	~	31	4^	Sep 96	61	Sep
Hanningfield	~	~	~	~	~	8	3^	Oct 03	12	Oct
Lea Valley	~	~	~	~	~	~	72^	Oct 01	106	Oct
Met Essex Waters	~	~	~	~	~	~	53^	Jan 03	58	Jan

Five-year average of peak WeBS counts (Sep-Mar) of Snipes from 1970/71-2003/04

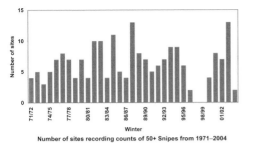

Number of sites recording counts of 50+ Snipes from 1971–2004

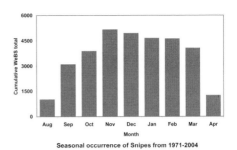

Seasonal occurrence of Snipes from 1971-2004

have been seven other counts of 300+: Stanford-le-Hope, 300+, 26th January 1969; Rainham, 300+, 2nd January 1972; Hamford Water, 300+, 15th November 1975; Bowers Gifford Marsh, 330, 10th March 1977; Holland Haven, 300, end of 1987; Colne/Mersea Island, 307, 12th March 1989; and Cudmore Grove CP, 300, 29th December 2002. A decline in the mid-1990s in the number of gatherings of 50+ may have been caused by the drought conditions prevalent at that time; numbers have subsequently recovered.

Although difficult to ascertain given the limited data available, Snipes appear to start moving through Essex from July, with the majority occurring in late autumn and early winter. Numbers remain relatively constant during winter, with spring migration occurring from February/early March, before numbers decline rapidly in April.

There have been numerous recoveries abroad of Snipes ringed in Essex during late summer and early autumn. Records from Norway, Sweden, Baltic States, Finland, Russia and Poland all fall within the known breeding range of passage and wintering birds moving through Britain (*BWP*), whilst those recovered in Denmark, Germany and the Low Countries probably involve passage birds from more northerly breeding grounds. Numerous recoveries from further south and west in England, and in Ireland and Wales illustrate onward movement through Essex by some Snipes, perhaps as the result of severe weather. Movement even further south into southern Europe and into northwest Africa is illustrated by the recoveries from Spain, Portugal and Morocco.

Six foreign-ringed individuals have also been recovered in Essex. Singles from Finland, Sweden and Poland were from likely breeding areas, whilst two from the Netherlands and one from Germany were likely to have been on passage when ringed.

	Jan	Feb	Mar	Apr	May	Jun	Jul	Aug	Sep	Oct	Nov	Dec
Essex	28						1	3	5	13	5	18
North England		1				1		2		1		
South England	9	2	1	2	1				3	1		2
Wales	1											
Ireland		1										2
Finland					1		1	1				
Norway								1				
Sweden									1			
Baltic States									1			
Russia				1				3		1		
Poland							1					
Denmark								2	2	1		
Germany				1				1	2	1		
The Netherlands								1	3	1	2	
Belgium									1			
France	12	9	4					1			2	4
Spain	1	2								1	1	1
Portugal	2										2	1
Morocco		1										
Totals	53	16	5	4	2	1	3	15	18	20	12	28

Date and location of recovery of Snipes ringed in Essex

With many areas of the coast and key inland sites protected or managed sympathetically, Essex should remain an important passage and wintering area for Snipes with no immediate threats to the species' future. The very small breeding population is unlikely to increase to any great extent unless substantial change in the wholesale management of the countryside occurs which, for the foreseeable future at least, seems unlikely.

Great Snipe   *Gallinago media*

Vagrant: 19 records involving 21 individuals but only three since 1900

The monotypic Great Snipe breeds in Scandinavia, Poland and the former Soviet Union east as far as the Yenesei. It winters across sub-Saharan Africa. The species has suffered substantial declines in the south and west of its European range since the 1850s, probably due to changing agricultural practices, although the Scandinavian population has apparently remained stable since 1945 (European Atlas).

19th century	Tiptree Heath	Undated	Shot
1836	Essex coast	Undated	Shot
1853	Newport	Undated	Shot
about 1869	Stanford Rivers	September	Shot
1879	Lexden	August	Found dying
1880	mouth of the Colne	November	Two shot
about 1884	Takeley	Undated	Shot
1887	Colchester	September	Killed when it hit wires
1888	Brentwood	November	Two shot
	Paglesham	about 30th December	Shot
1889	Langham	end of August	Shot
	Mucking	September	Shot
	Old Hall	13th September	Shot
	Forest Gate	Undated	Shot
1896	Thaxted	3rd September	Shot
1897	Waltham Abbey	27th February	Shot
1959	Girling	12th–17th September	
1969	East Mersea	15th February	
1989	Dagenham Chase	1st–2nd June	

The BBRC has recently rejected the previously accepted record of two at North Fambridge on 17th August 1958; another from Saffron Walden around 1825 is also no longer accepted.

Whilst the catastrophic declines on the Continent have clearly affected the number recorded, it may also be that the decline in Snipe and Woodcock shooting has reduced the number of this secretive species reported. Nationally, a total of 492 was noted prior to 1958 with just 120 since (BBRC 2005), although there has been a slight upturn in occurrence in recent years. The 1989 record is the only British record in June. It proved typically elusive during its two day stay (Barrett 1990). Recent national records have been in late August and September, principally down the east coast.

Long-billed Dowitcher   *Limnodromus scolopaceus*

Very rare passage migrant: seven records involving 5-6 individuals

The monotypic Long-billed Dowitcher breeds along the coasts of eastern Siberia and north and west Alaska and winters in the western and southern American states and Central America.

1979	Abberton	28th September–21st November	Juvenile
1980	Old Hall	22nd March–23rd April	Adult, same as previous
1983	Old Hall	17th–31st July	Adult
1985	Heybridge GP	29th September–6th October	Immature
	Langenhoe	30th September	Adult, same as previous
1985/86	Old Hall	14th October–26th January	Immature
1996	Holland Haven	1st–3rd August	Adult

The 1979 bird was ringed on 21st November.

Nationally, there were 171 records to the end of 2004 (BBRC 2005), with an average in recent decades of about five per annum. Most appear from late September to mid-November, although spring sightings are becoming more frequent and there are several records of wintering individuals. It seems likely that spring and late summer records relate to migrants that arrived in Europe the previous autumn and successfully wintered on the Continent. Nationally, 1985 was one of the best years with 15 recorded.

(Eurasian) Woodcock   *Scolopax rusticola*

A scarce resident, common winter visitor and passage migrant   Amber List

The monotypic Woodcock is a secretive and solitary wader that breeds in forests, woodland and scrub throughout the entire temperate and boreal Palearctic. The species' favoured habitat in Europe is deciduous or mixed woodland with approximately 30% of the World's population breeding in Europe, 90% of which are in Russia, Belarus, Finland, Sweden and Norway (European Atlas). The British population is of the order of 5,400–14,000 'pairs' (Woodcocks exhibit polygamy) but there have been significant declines in the last few decades, perhaps linked to recreational disturbance, modification of the field layer by deer and increasingly dry conditions in some woods (Fuller *et al.* 2005). The large Fennoscandian and Russian populations are migratory, wintering in south and western Europe, particularly in France, Spain, Italy, Britain and Ireland.

Given the species' extremely secretive nature and rather complex breeding behaviour, it is not surprising that confirmed breeding records are very few and far between.

Woodcocks were hunted in Hatfield Forest in the early 18th century (Rackham 1989).

To Christy, the Woodcock was "A fairly common winter visitor, much sought after by sportsmen. Plentiful in some years, but scarce in others. A few remain to breed ..." Nationally, there were few breeding records up to the 18th century but by the end of the 19th century almost every county

Atlas	Survey Area	% of 10km squares or tetrads in which	
		bred/probably bred	possibly bred or present
First National 10km	Essex	15.8	17.5
Second National 10km	Essex	8.8	14.0
First London Tetrad	Met. Essex	1.0	2.0
Second London Tetrad	Met. Essex	3.5	4.0
Essex Tetrad	Essex	1.8	1.7

Summary of results of Atlas surveys for Woodcocks

had a breeding population. This increase, which continued well into the 20th century, assisted by the availability of conifer plantations, has been attributed to climate change but perhaps also the cessation of shooting during the breeding season (European Atlas). The first Essex nesting records came from Wimbish in 1831–33, whilst Christy gave other areas in which the species bred during the 19th century as Colchester, both in the town and at High Woods, Laindon ("... common ..."), Burstead, Orsett District, Epping Forest and possibly Danbury. There was, however, nothing to suggest that Woodcocks had increased as a breeding species in the 19th century. Glegg, however, considered that, although the species bred in Essex, it did not do so annually. He added just two further breeding sites to Christy's: Hazeleigh Wood and Stour Wood.

There have been just 12 confirmed breeding records since 1950, six prior to 1961. However, the number of roding birds has, at least since the mid-1980s increased, although this may be due to increased observer coverage. Hudson & Pyman considered that Woodcocks were only regularly recorded in the summer months in the Thorndon/Warley CPs area; there were nine roding birds at Warley in 1965.

Cox noted that the majority of roding birds were reported from the area bordered by Hatfield/Harlow and Epping Forest in the west and Warley/Thorndon CPs to the east, with a few records from sites located across the county. Notable declines were suggested by the two National Atlas surveys. The Essex Atlas survey revealed a similar distribution, although Marks Hall, Coggeshall, was identified as important with five roding in 1991. Five roding Woodcocks were also in Ongar Park Wood in 1993, whilst there were three in Hatfield Forest in 1991,1993 and 1995 and at North Weald in 1989. In all, roding Woodcocks have been reported from 13 areas since 1990.

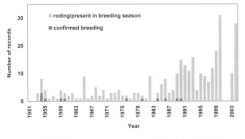

Breeding season records of Woodcocks from 1951-2004

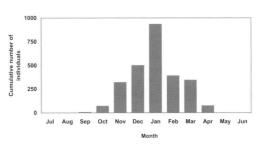

Seasonal occurrence of assumed non-breeding Woodcocks from 1971-2004

Against this background of casual observations, the ELBF organised a comprehensive survey of Epping Forest during 2000 and subsequently (Dent *et al.* 2001). The survey analysed Woodcock flightpaths (*BWP*) and concluded that there were 31 roding Woodcocks in the Forest, double the previous highest count from there (15 during 1999). A total of 28 roding Woodcocks was located in 2004. The suspicion that the species was severely under-recorded in Essex appears to have been borne out by the survey. Taking into account the number of roding birds reported from other sites during the 1990s, it is possible that the Essex population may be of the order of 50–60 'pairs' which, although a significant increase on previous estimates, represents no more than 0.25–0.70% of the national breeding population.

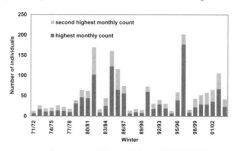

Peak counts of Woodcocks from 1971/72-2003/04

Outside the breeding season, Woodcocks become far more widespread but remain very secretive and estimating numbers is difficult, casual observation being shown to grossly underestimate the numbers present when compared to data available from shooting syndicates. At Danbury in the 1880s, bags averaged around 18 per winter (Christy), remarkably similar to the figures given by Cox for shoots across Essex during the 1970s, with an average of 18 shot per winter (range 13–26).

It has been noted that in years when casual observation suggests there has been an apparent influx, the number shot does not significantly increase. Perhaps Woodcocks involved in such influxes haunt more marginal sites such as roadsides, gardens and coastal marshes, where they are more visible, and not traditional woodland sites where shoots take place.

Counts at individual sites have generally been in single figures. However, exceptional numbers were present on Dengie in January 1997, with 100 at Curry Farm and 50 at Tillingham GP. Other high counts have been: Great Bromley/Elmstead Market, 32 put up during a shoot of two woods, 29th December 2004; Margaretting, 30 put up by a shoot, 25th January 1981; Pitsea, 20+, 14th February 1982; Hadleigh Downs, 20, 20th January 1985; Little Clacton, 40, January 1986; Mountnessing, 20, January 1986; and Stows Farm, Tillingham, 20, January 1996.

Continental Woodcocks make up approximately 90% of the British wintering population, with the largest numbers occurring in southern England and Wales (Hoodless 1995). Few migrant Woodcocks appear until the end of October, individuals recorded before then probably being dispersing local breeders. During October and November, Woodcocks are regularly observed arriving off the sea. Local wildfowlers hold that Woodcocks appear under a full moon in November (Tony Barnard pers. comm.). Traditionally, the species was thought to turn up on a full moon some time near All Hallows Day: in fact, prior to the modern theories of migration, the timing of the Woodcock's arrival led to the suggestion that the species migrated to the moon (Greenoak 1981). Although the moon's influence may be a factor, it is more likely that weather conditions, both here and on the Continent, are the primary influences on arrivals. Observations suggest that winds with an easterly element are ideal for the Woodcock's arrival, with birds often coinciding with falls of Goldcrests; in folklore, Goldcrests were thought to 'pilot' Woodcocks. Arrivals continue into January when numbers are strongly influenced by severe weather on the Continent, which may cause significant movements west across the North Sea. Most Woodcocks have departed by the end of February, but some may linger until the end of April, although there is no evidence to suggest that they ever stay to breed (Hoodless 1995).

Eight recoveries of foreign-ringed Woodcocks, the majority between November and February, from Russia (two), Norway, Sweden (two), Germany, Denmark and the Netherlands, lend support to the fact that the majority of birds passing through and wintering in Essex are from Scandinavia or western Russia, although one ringed in Carlisle, Cumbria, as a nestling and recovered at Witham in December 1911 suggests some may be of more local origin. Two birds ringed in winter in Suffolk and one ringed in Norfolk have been recovered in subsequent winters in Essex. There have been four recoveries outside the county of Woodcocks ringed in Essex between October and February: in County Wexford, Eire, France (two), and Germany, the first three illustrating the onward movement of some individuals to wintering grounds further west.

Uncertainty as to the size of the breeding population makes it difficult to suggest appropriate conservation measures. An extension of the ELBF survey to other known or suspected breeding sites should therefore be a priority.

Although many mature, damp woodlands and thickets have been lost to agricultural intensification over the last few decades, new areas of woodland have been planted as a result of permanent set-aside schemes, community woodland projects and so on. Thus, the current population would appear not to be under immediate threat. The wintering population probably does not receive the hunting pressures that it used to, although with eastern populations known to be in decline and winters becoming milder, it remains to be seen whether numbers will stay at the current level.

Black-tailed Godwit   *Limosa limosa*

Common passage migrant and winter visitor: has bred   **Red List**

The Black-tailed Godwit is restricted to the Palearctic, where it occurs as three discrete subspecies, two in Europe and one in Siberia. The two European races do not differ significantly in appearance but do so in terms of breeding and wintering habitat. The Icelandic race *islandica* breeds on subarctic tundra and moorland and winters in estuarine habitats along the Atlantic coast from Britain south to Morocco. The Continental race *limosa* breeds on temperate grasslands and moorlands and winters primarily in freshwater habitats south of the Sahara (European Atlas). The Icelandic population numbers some 5,000–15,000 and the Continental form 130,000–250,000 breeding pairs, approximately 50% of which breed in the Netherlands. In Britain, the race *limosa* is a scarce breeder, with up to 54 breeding pairs over the last decade (RBBP 2004). The British passage (*limosa* and *islandica*) and wintering populations (*islandica* only) have increased significantly in recent years.

GB 150 / INT 700	1970-1974	1975-1979	1980-1984	1985-1989	1990-1994	1995-1999	2000-2004	Peak counts		Peak month
WeBS totals	841^	416^	952	1,953	3,637	3,703	3,452	Oct 04	5,331	Oct
Stour	755^	493*	603^	896	1,501	2,051	1,467	Nov 95	2,617	Oct
Hamford Water	197^	282^	492	980	1,754	716	220	Sep 92	3,058	Sep
Colne	2^	~	~	286	418	399	300	Oct 89	812	Sep
Blackwater	3^	12	19	177	351	591	566	Sep 98	1,013	Sep
Dengie	4^	0	2	32	95	209	32	Oct 99	400	Oct
Crouch-Roach	2^	0	0	0	87	161	99	Nov 97	320	Nov
Thames	0^	2	2	1	164	326	1,252	Oct 04	3,263	Oct
Abberton	0^	0	0	0	158*	752	0	Sep 97	1,247	Oct

**Five-year average of peak WeBS counts (Sep-Nov)
of Black-tailed Godwits from 1970-2004**

Although Christy gave no evidence to back up his statement that the Black-tailed Godwit "… formerly bred with us, but has long ceased to do so", it is possible that the species may have done so until the early 19th century; Black-tailed Godwits apparently bred in abundance in East Anglia (Historical Atlas). No other breeding records occurred until, during the mid-1980s, increasing numbers of the nominate race *limosa* began summering in Essex, particularly at Old Hall. In 1992 breeding was confirmed on Langenhoe where a pair raised one young. The site was subsequently drained and no further breeding attempts have occurred. A pair attempted to nest at a site by the Crouch in 1996 but no young were seen. By the early/mid-1990s, significant numbers were summering at Old Hall with 76 in June 1996, 107 on 1st June 1995 (with 40 still present on 20th) and 57 on 10th June 1994, although recently numbers have declined with very few now present in midsummer.

Outside the breeding season, the Black-tailed Godwit appears to have increased noticeably since the 19th century and early 20th century, when the species was principally a passage bird with wintering records quite exceptional. To Christy, the species was a visitor to the coast in spring and autumn, whilst Glegg observed that the Black-tailed Godwit was an occasional visitor to the coast: "Most of the records refer to the autumn migration, but some to the spring movement, and one or two winter occurrences have been reported" . Based on current knowledge, this pattern of occurrence suggests that most of the records probably referred to *limosa* rather than *islandica*, unless the latter has changed its wintering areas. The species' status clearly changed after 1930, as by the 1960s it was not only a passage migrant, but a winter visitor as well (Hudson & Pyman). Even since the 1950s, increases had been noted in the northeast, particularly on the Stour where typically 500–700 occurred during the 1960s (exceptionally 850 in September 1963) between August and October, after which the flocks dispersed, mainly into Hamford Water where 200–400 were usually present from November–March.

During the 1970s there was an apparent decline in both numbers on passage and wintering in Essex, but subsequently there has been a significant increase.

271

This considerable increase has mirrored the situation nationally. Historically, numbers wintering in Britain have been related to the prevailing climatic conditions in Iceland that affect the population size of *islandica*. Since the 1930s, Iceland has experienced an amelioration of its climate that has resulted in increased breeding success and therefore greater numbers have occurred in Britain. A period of cooling in the late 1960s led to reductions in the number wintering during the 1970s, but since the mid-1970s there has been a steady increase—and since the mid-1980s the international population has increased by 62% (Cranswick *et al.* 1999). Essex is exceptionally important for the species, with the Stour and Blackwater the third and fourth most important sites respectively in Britain. During winter Essex holds around 26% of the British and 5% of the European population of *islandica*, based on the average WeBS for 2000/01–2004/05. Numbers at individual sites vary markedly from year to year and even month to month, a pattern also noted nationally (Cranswick *et al.* 1999).

Numbers on autumn passage generally exceed those present in winter. Until the mid-1980s, most Black-tailed Godwits occurred in the northeast but, as numbers have increased, so they have become more widespread, although it has only been since the mid-1990s or so that significant numbers have been recorded south of the Blackwater, with notable gatherings now occurring along the Thames at East Tilbury. Generally each site records its peak numbers during autumn. However, along the Blackwater numbers tend to peak in spring with many of the recent high counts not recorded by WeBS e.g. 2,020 off Maldon on 30th March 2002.

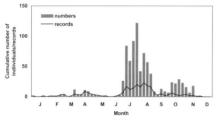

Seasonal occurrence of inland Black-tailed Godwits away
from Abberton from 1971-2004

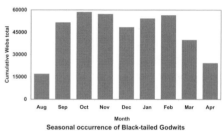

Seasonal occurrence of Black-tailed Godwits
from 1971-2004

Other significant non-WeBS counts have included 1,450 flying east past Canvey Island on 10th January 2001 and 2,000 at Fingringhoe Wick on 10th September 2002.

Inland, the majority of records have come from Abberton, but small numbers are regularly recorded from Hanningfield and along the Lea Valley, mainly during autumn. The greatest numbers occur when low water levels produce suitable feeding conditions, and the low rainfall from the end of the 1980s to late 1990s saw significant numbers at Abberton with internationally important counts in both 1995 and 1997. At Hanningfield, 25 on 23rd October 1997 was the peak. Exceptional numbers occurred at KGV during 2004 from 7th July–15th August, with a peak of 42 on 30th July. Elsewhere, occasional individuals have been noted, many of them flyovers. There were, however, nine at Coleman's on 6th November 1987. Inland records appear to peak earlier than on the coast, although this may simply be due to no regular August WeBS counts until recently. The double peaks are of note; do they point to the arrival of different populations?

GB 150 INT 700	70/71-74/75	75/76-79/80	80/81-84/85	85/86-89/90	90/91-94/95	95/96-99/00	00/01-04/05	Peak counts		Peak month
WeBS totals	780^	1,133	1,069	2,060	3,017	3,270	3,963^	Feb 01	4,939	*Oct*
Stour	642^	831	816	1,287	1,758	2,166	2,008^	Jan 96	3,848	*Jan*
Hamford Water	154^	441	414	451^	1,170	285	407^	Dec 90	2,025	Dec
Colne	0^	~	~	648	267	139	244^	Dec 88	1,400	Sep
Blackwater	20^	54	136	493	926	799	1,367^	Feb 01	2,094	Mar
Dengie	3^	0	0	1	34	4	1^	Dec 92	157	Oct
Crouch-Roach	0	0	0	0	96	212	239^	Mar 98	416	Jan
Thames	0	0	1	1	139	560	544^	Dec 03	1,503	Oct
Abberton	0	0	0	0	153*	50	0^	Dec 95	229	Oct

**Five-year average of peak WeBS counts (Dec-Mar)
of Black-tailed Godwits from 1970/71-2003/04**

There is no direct ringing evidence linking Essex with *limosa*. Indeed, there is no evidence of *limosa* from continental breeding populations occurring in Britain on passage (Migration Atlas); an Essex specimen, one of many ascribed to *limosa* in the British Museum of Natural History (Vernon 1963), was presumably from the small British population of this race.

There have, however, been sightings of colour-ringed *islandica* which have enabled a detailed pattern of this race's movements to be built up that have confirmed the importance of Essex not only for wintering but also spring and autumn passage birds. From late April–July, Black-tailed Godwits are on breeding grounds in Iceland. From July and August individuals begin to occur in Fife before moving south to The Wash in August, with some also reaching Essex by that month. Thereafter they disperse and sightings have come from Abberton and the Colne, Blackwater, Crouch, Stour and Thames Estuaries. Some of these individuals have continued south, and sightings in France suggest interchange between Britain and France, perhaps in response to the weather. It is possible that as winter progresses birds from further north drift south but there are no sightings in Essex to confirm this. The movements of some individuals have been tracked over a period of years and provide a fascinating insight into their lives. One bird, originally colour-ringed in Norfolk in August 1995, was seen at Abberton one month later and on the Thames two months thereafter. It was then sighted on the Stour in February 1996 and just two months later on the Blackwater. In August of that year it was back at Abberton. Another was ringed at Terrington, Norfolk, in July 1996, was in Cork Harbour, Eire, three months later, on the Swale, Kent, in the autumns of 1997 and 1998, The Wash, Norfolk/Lincolnshire, in the autumns of 1999 and 2000 and on the Blackwater in October 2000. These movements point to a far greater interchange between estuaries than is obvious from casual observations.

The Black-tailed Godwit has increased significantly over the last 20 years due to factors that operate principally outside the county. However, Essex clearly has a significant international responsibility to protect the species' feeding areas around the coast. Most of these are protected but, nonetheless, development proposals could seriously affect some of the major populations. As a breeding species, the Black-tailed Godwit remains so rare that there are few measures that could be taken to encourage the species other than perhaps large-scale habitat creation.

Bar-tailed Godwit   *Limosa lapponica*

Common passage migrant and winter visitor with a few usually present in summer   Amber List

The Bar-tailed Godwit breeds in a discontinuous belt through the high-arctic and subarctic zones from Norway east through European Russia and Asia and westernmost Alaska and replaces the Black-tailed Godwit ecologically in more northern areas where it occupies a wide variety of habitats generally above the tree-line (European Atlas). Two populations are distinguished, the nominate race *lapponica* that breeds from Lapland to the eastern Taimyr peninsula and *baueri*, which occurs in the remaining areas of the range. The European wintering population of 125,000 is far greater than the European breeding population of up to 15,000 pairs, suggesting that at least part of this population may include Asian breeding birds (European Atlas). Birds of European and western Siberian populations occur as passage migrants and winter visitors mainly in

GB 620 / INT 1,000	1970-1974	1975-1979	1980-1984	1985-1989	1990-1994	1995-1999	2000-2004	Peak counts		Peak month
WeBS totals	2,198*	2,094	3,340	2,937	5,252	3,377	5,152	*Nov 92*	10,222	*Oct*
Stour	13*	0	5	9	18	40	62	Nov 03	153	Nov
Hamford Water	64*	94^	193	110	203	263	495	Nov 03	<u>709</u>	Oct
Colne	10^	~	~	9	10	13	65	Sep 95	37	Sep
Blackwater	54*	100^	51	82	51	119	85	Oct 96	293	Nov
Dengie	178*	160	170	250	<u>665</u>	<u>861</u>	<u>902</u>	Oct 99	**3,000**	Oct
Crouch-Roach	7*	0	3	1	6	6	0	Nov 94	23	Nov
Thames	**2,003***	1,881	3,059	2,701	4,763	2,653	3,982	Nov 92	9,525	Sep

**Five-year average of peak WeBS counts (Sep-Nov)
of Bar-tailed Godwits from 1970-2004**

western Europe, including Britain, and northwest Africa. More eastern populations use western European wetlands as stopovers on their migration south to wintering areas in west Africa.

There is a 1547/48 reference to the Bar-tailed Godwit by its local, Essex name, 'Prine' or 'praynes', which meant an awl or bodkin, an allusion to the species' long, slightly curved bill (Lockwood 1993).

Christy considered the Bar-tailed Godwit to be a fairly common visitor to the coast, chiefly on migration in spring and autumn. Despite this assertion, he noted that the Maldon gunners considered the species to be "... one of the most abundant of our winter wildfowl". Glegg, however, considered the Bar-tailed Godwit "... an uncommon visitor to the Essex coast ... it would appear to have been commoner in the past than it is today", with just a few spring and autumn records from the Blackwater and Stour and occasional winter records from the Stour and Mersea Island. Neither writer referred to many inland reports, although Glegg mentioned a "... considerable passage..." over Theydon Bois in August or September 1916.

By the mid-1960s, the species' status as a passage migrant and winter visitor had been firmly established with small numbers present during summer (Hudson & Pyman). Only the advent of the monthly wildfowl and wader counts gave the first quantitative data available for the species, although a count of 3,000 off Foulness during September 1965 hinted at the prime importance of that area to the species. Cox noted that 81.5% of all Bar-tailed Godwits recorded in Essex during the BoEE (1972–75) were in this area, a situation that remains the same today. One of the species' most important food items are lugworms, which occur in abundance on the Foulness flats but only in small numbers elsewhere around the coast. Numbers at Foulness and indeed other sites have generally increased over the last two decades although, perhaps more than with any other wader, numbers vary significantly from year to year. This variability has been linked to predator levels on breeding grounds and perhaps also to weather conditions on the Continent. Bar-tailed Godwits are also highly mobile between wintering sites (Pollitt *et al.* 2000). Based on the period 2000/01–2004/05, Essex holds around 15% of the British and 7.4% of the European wintering populations of 61,590 and 125,000 respectively. However, the high count in January 1997 represented around 16% of the entire European population.

GB 620 INT 1,000	70/71-74/75	75/76-79/80	80/81-84/85	85/86-89/90	90/91-94/95	95/96-99/00	00/01-04/05	Peak counts		Peak month
WeBS totals	2,582^	4,471	8,831	4,029	6,876	10,013	9,205^	Jan 97	20,079	*Jan*
Stour	5^	3	1	8	53	148	339^	Jan 01	329	Feb
Hamford Water	125^	163	124	159^	379	694	668^	Jan 97	**1,380**	Jan
Colne	11^	~	~	24	21	56	46^	Feb 96	131	Feb
Blackwater	236^	184	80	209	205	92	299^	Feb 04	780	Jan
Dengie	400^	682^	391	374	1,096	2,030	2,826^	Feb 97	**5,500**	Feb
Crouch-Roach	38^	0	1	8	37	45	14^	Feb 95	154	Feb
Thames	2,176^	3,710	8,523	3,504	5,707	8,099	5,507^	Jan 85	**16,211**	Jan

**Five-year average of peak WeBS counts (Dec-Mar)
of Bar-tailed Godwits from 1970/71-2003/04**

Small numbers may arrive as early as July at which time they may be in moult; The Wash is the principal moulting site in Britain. By mid-August and September these early arrivals are probably joined by those individuals that have dispersed from The Wash, having completed their moult. It is possible that small numbers of non-moulting, short-billed, heavy individuals attributable to the west Siberian race may occur en route to west Africa (Taylor *et al.* 1999), although there are no Essex observations to confirm this. Autumn passage peaks during September, after which numbers decline before peaking markedly in January and February, as a result of dispersal from the Dutch Waddensee (Winter Atlas).

Numbers decline sharply in March but passage may be evident through spring as small flocks appear at localities where none has occurred during winter: again, some birds from more easterly populations may be involved.

Visible migration is rarely reported in Essex, the only records of note being 310 in off the sea at The Naze on the early morning of 1st June 1983, before heading northeast, and 220 past Southend-on-Sea in three hours on 3rd May 1974.

Although present all summer, numbers are usually very small in June, with most counts in single figures. There have, however, been two three-figure counts (apart from The Naze record above): 100 off Bradwell on 26th in 1960 and 191 off Foulness on 27th in 1965. Otherwise, the highest counts have been 75 at Goldhanger on 21st in 1955 and up to 54 at East Tilbury during 1991.

The Bar-tailed Godwit is less common inland than the Black-tailed Godwit with rarely more than a few records annually. In some years, however, significant overland movements have been noted, particularly from the Lea Valley, although it is in spring that both the largest totals and number of records have occurred. These movements coincide with an offshore easterly passage off Sussex and Kent, which probably involve birds that wintered in west Africa that are heading north to breeding grounds in Siberia (Migration Atlas). There have been three significant inland movements, the largest in 1980 when, following 28 over KGV on 26th April, 120 flew north over Walthamstow and 27 flew over Girling on 3rd May. In 1989, 35 flew over Hanningfield, with 20 over Thorndon CP on 6th May, whilst on 30th August 1992, 50 flew south over Girling, 30 passed in the same direction over KGV and 40 flew over Walthamstow. Other significant inland counts have been: 31 over Hanningfield, 6th May 1984; 40 over KGV, 10th September 1984; and 50 at Abberton, 10th November 1996 at a time of very low water levels. Many inland Bar-tailed Godwits have been following a north to northeasterly course in spring and the reverse in autumn, perhaps suggesting that some individuals take a direct overland route across southeast England from the English Channel to the North Sea (and *vice versa* in autumn). In this respect, 14 flying northeast over Hanningfield on 25th April 1985, 80 minutes after a similar number flew east over Staines Reservoir, Middlesex, some 65km to the west, lends support to this hypothesis.

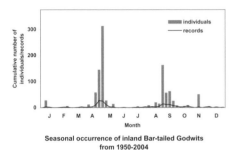

Seasonal occurrence of inland Bar-tailed Godwits from 1950-2004

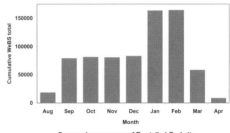

Seasonal occurrence of Bar-tailed Godwits from 1970-2004

There are a few ringing recoveries concerning Essex, all of which have referred to the nominate race. A colour-ringed individual moved from northeast England to Essex in the same autumn, whilst another showed onward movement to Hampshire in the same autumn. One ringed at East Tilbury in April 1961 was recovered in January 1964 at Thouars, Dous Sevres, France, whilst one ringed in the Netherlands in September 1972 was recovered 20 years later on Foulness, one of at least 210 Bar-tailed Godwits that were victims of the severe hailstorm of 18th September 1992 (Adcock 1993).

Given that the Bar-tailed Godwit is concentrated almost entirely in the Foulness/Dengie areas, disturbance in these parts of the county would have a significant impact on the Essex population. Proposals for Maplin and Cliffe airports and the use of mechanical shellfish harvesters have all threatened but fortunately never come to fruition; for now, the future of the species in Essex appears to be secure.

Whimbrel

Numenius phaeopus

Common passage migrant: occasional during winter

Amber List

The Whimbrel, a Holarctic wader, has its main breeding range within the boreal, subarctic and low-arctic zones of Eurasia and America, where it typically occurs in open, exposed habitats containing short vegetation. Within Europe the species' breeding range extends from Iceland and northern Britain in the west to the Urals in the east, and reaches as far north as 70° N in Norway and south to 50–55° N, east of the Volga. Four races are recognised (*HBW*) with Atlantic and northern European populations being of the nominate race *phaeopus*, whilst birds from eastern Eurasia are of the race *variegatus*. There appears to have been an overall increase in the European population, with that in Scotland increasing from around 200 pairs in 1969/70 to 530 pairs currently (Stone *et al.* 1997), more than 90% of which breed in the Shetland Islands (European Atlas). Birds from the European breeding population winter principally in west Africa. Important spring passage staging sites exist in Hungary and in the Low Countries, especially the Netherlands.

Christy gave the Whimbrel three local names, 'Titterel', 'May-bird' or 'Jack-Curlew'. With its distinctive seven-fold whistle, its similarity to its larger cousin the Curlew and the noticeable passage during May, these

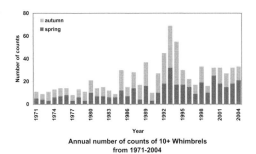

Annual number of counts of 10+ Whimbrels
from 1971-2004

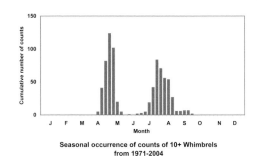

Seasonal occurrence of counts of 10+ Whimbrels
from 1971-2004

names are as appropriate today as they were over a century ago. He described the Whimbrel as "Common on the coast as a passing migrant in spring and autumn ... they are often seen until the end of May, and re-appear soon after the middle of July". He mentioned a "... very large flock of 40 or 50" on New England Island on 16th May 1836, suggesting that numbers were probably not dissimilar to those today, although he gives very little other quantitative data. Glegg described the Whimbrel as a double passage migrant that was more noticeable during autumn than spring. This generally remains the case today with, until the mid-1990s, more Whimbrels passing through during autumn than spring, although the very concentrated spring passage perhaps leads to the perception that more occurred in spring. Recently, numbers occurring in spring have outnumbered those in autumn.

Both Hudson & Pyman and Cox considered that the Whimbrel's status was similar to that described by previous writers, Cox noting that increased observer coverage had not produced evidence that the Whimbrel was any more numerous than previously supposed. Greater observer coverage has, almost certainly, been responsible for the increase in Whimbrels recorded since the mid-1980s.

Spring passage peaks during the last week of April and first two weeks of May. Autumn passage is more leisurely with most passing through between mid-July and the end of August.

As Whimbrel passage peaks outside the period of regular WeBS counts, comprehensive systematic counts are lacking. However, Whimbrels appear to migrate through Essex relatively quickly with flocks lingering for only a few days at any given site and thus monthly WeBS counts would probably under-record the species.

The lack of comprehensive counts makes it difficult to assess the Essex figures in a national or international context. However, in international terms the number of Whimbrels occurring in Britain is insignificant. The world breeding population has been estimated at 600,000–700,000 birds, giving a threshold of 6,500 for a site to qualify as being of international importance (Cranswick *et al.* 1995). The largest documented spring passage through Essex occurred in 2000, with over 500 present during the first week of May and a total spring passage of perhaps 1,200 Whimbrels, around 0.2% of the world population. Only slightly fewer occurred in the springs of 1993, 1998 and 2004, although the number of double-figure counts has not subsequently reached the levels seen in the early 1990s. Typically, spring passage numbers some 500–1,000 Whimbrels, although in some years numbers can be smaller. Weather conditions may influence the size of the passage, given the huge numbers that regularly pass through the Netherlands in spring.

Autumn numbers tend to be lower overall, with 500–750 typical, although perhaps 1,000 passed through in 1993.

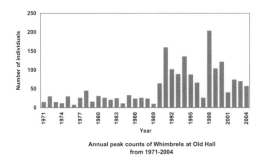

Annual peak counts of Whimbrels at Old Hall
from 1971-2004

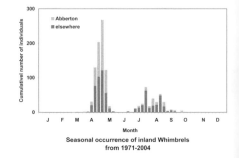

Seasonal occurrence of inland Whimbrels
from 1971-2004

The largest counts have been: 299 north over Bradwell in three hours, 9th May 2004; 200 on Bridgemarsh Island, 26th May 1951; 190 at East Mersea, 14th May 1952; 200 flying north over Fingringhoe Wick, 14th May 1971; and 204 at Old Hall, 24th April 1998. There have been a further 11 three-figure spring counts, including 160 at Old Hall in the first week of May 1991. There have been three three-figure counts in autumn: 116 at Canvey Point, 13th August 1970; 118 at Old Hall, 8th July 1994; and 100 at Bradwell, 5th August 2003. In addition 150 were counted along the Blackwater during the August WeBS count in 1981. Only at Old Hall does a comprehensive record exist of Whimbrel numbers. A record of 240 at Goldhanger on the late date of 10th September 1959 seems questionable given current knowledge.

Cox suggested that the increase in numbers of winter records of Whimbrels might have been due to increased observer coverage. Whilst this may well be a factor, increasing numbers of many wader species have been reported wintering in Britain since the 1930s, perhaps due to climatic change through global warming. The first Essex wintering record came from Langenhoe where one was noted twice in December 1967. Two in the 1970s followed, with ten in the 1980s (six of these in late 1981), 14 during the 1990s and six in the 2000s. The majority have occurred prior to the turn of the year suggesting that many have moved on by January. However, January and February records have increased during the 1990s, as have the numbers of March migrants.

Whimbrels have been recorded regularly inland, most often at Abberton but also frequently at Hanningfield and in the Lea Valley. Numbers vary from year to year, but the general pattern of occurrence is similar to that on the coast, although the proportion of spring to autumn records appears higher than on the coast.

Detailed records of inland Whimbrels are not available prior to the 1970s. However, numbers at Abberton appeared to have been greater in the 1960s and 1970s than today. Indeed, the count of 50 there on 9th May 1953 was not exceeded until 1st May 2004 when there were 57. A total of 41 flew north over Great Bentley on 16th May 1970 and 28 were over Sewardstone on 25th April 1957. The highest count at Hanningfield was 20 that flew over on 23rd August 1970.

A Whimbrel ringed in Belgium in July 1969 and found dead at Maldon in October 1972 is the only recovery involving Essex. The very few national recoveries have shown that birds passing through Britain are of the nominate race. Icelandic birds are thought to be most prevalent on the west coast with those occurring in southeast England being Continental breeders (Migration Atlas). An individual around Northey Island in October 2002 had an incomplete white rump suggestive of the eastern race *variegata*; unfortunately it was very elusive during its stay and its identity could not be confirmed.

(Eurasian) Curlew   *Numenius arquata*

Common passage migrant and winter visitor with small numbers present in summer   Amber List

The Curlew is a Palearctic species that occurs in the temperate and boreal climatic zones of Europe and Asia. In Europe the species is represented by the nominate race *arquata*, although this intergrades into the Asiatic race *orientalis* in southeast Europe and European Russia. Most Curlews now nest in rough marginal grassland, wet meadows, saltmarshes and even arable fields, but its traditional nesting locations are bogs and moorlands (European Atlas). In Britain, where the current population is estimated to be 100,000–125,000 pairs, it is principally an upland species, although small numbers are found in southern Britain on lowland heaths and bogs in counties such as Norfolk and Hampshire. European populations winter principally in western Europe, in the Mediterranean and many parts of Africa.

GB 1,500 / INT 3,500	1970 1974	1975- 1979	1980- 1984	1985- 1989	1990- 1994	1995- 1999	2000- 2004	Peak counts		Peak month
WeBS totals	6,526^	5,012	5,377	6,770	9,873	9,513	6,458	Sep 91	12,555	Sep
Stour	718^	~	699^	935	1,157	1,071	986	Nov 94	1,474	Oct
Hamford Water	651^	660^	1,152	989	2,205	1,803	1,146	Sep 92	**3,617**	Sep
Colne	1,855^	~	~	777	968	475	267	Sep 70	3,000	Sep
Blackwater	2,098^	1,675^	1,151	1,763	2,659	2,277	1,202	Sep 90	**3,514**	Oct
Dengie	684^	1,267^	594^	423^	577	565	470	Sep 75	2,500	Sep
Crouch-Roach	503^	~	317	410	504	407	389	Nov 91	612	Nov
Thames	2,042^	3,022	2,434	3,101	3,420	**3,839**	2,498	Sep 91	**5,640**	Sep

Five-year average of peak WeBs counts of Curlews (Sep-Nov) from 1970-2004

GB 1,500 / INT 3,500	70/71-74/75	75/76-79/80	80/81-84/85	85/86-89/90	90/91-94/95	95/96-99/00	00/01-04/05	Peak counts		Peak month
WeBS totals	6,386^	6,127	5,055	5,812	7,665	6,631	7,119^	Feb 80	11,240	Feb
Stour	635^	685	957	1,203	1,466	1,252	1,364^	Mar 85	2,395	Feb
Hamford Water	2,153^	1,784	676	407^	662	1,404	1,427^	Feb 80	4,800	Feb
Colne	1,231^	~	~	652	777	523	640^	Feb 72	2,100	Feb
Blackwater	1,267^	1,430	933	1,221	2,273	1,176	1,244^	Feb 71	3,300	Feb
Dengie	753^	502^	273	450	550	383	411^	May 92	1,030	Jan
Crouch-Roach	543*	439*	437	382	565	406	470^	Jan 94	830	Jan
Thames	1,845^	2,327	2,206	2,670	2,390	2,131	2,104^	Feb 87	3,908	Feb

Five-year average of peak WeBs counts (Dec-Mar) of Curlews from 1970/71-2003/0

A review of the literature has not revealed evidence of any breeding attempts by the Curlew in Essex, no doubt because the habitat is not ideal. However, the extensive estuarine mudflats provide a rich food source at others seasons with crabs, molluscs and ragworms especially favoured (Winter Atlas).

The species' status appears to have changed very little over the last two centuries or so. Christy described the Curlew as "... a very common bird of the mudbanks and saltings on the Essex coast". He gave little quantitative data but clearly large flocks occurred, as around the middle of the 19th century "... a gunner by the name of Frank Hope, of Maldon ... killed no less than seventy-five of these very wary birds at once". Glegg noted that the Curlew was "... abundant from the Thames to the Stour ...[and]... very numerous until about the middle of April ... The numbers increase again during August and the full winter status is achieved about October".

The largest counts known to Hudson & Pyman were 3,000 on 26th August 1956 and 2,000 on 18th September 1965 off Foulness. Subsequently, and based on the BoEE results (1972–75), Cox estimated that during winter Essex held an average of 7,000 Curlews, which represented some 7% of the British and 2% of the west European wintering populations.

Since then, winter numbers have been relatively constant, although there have been some signs of an increase in the 1990s, with numbers at least 15% higher than in the 1970s. Based on current British and European wintering populations of 147,100 (Rehfisch *et al.* 2003) and 250,000 (*HBW*) respectively, Essex currently holds around 4.8% of the British and 3% of the European populations. Despite stable numbers overall, there has been a redistribution of the population with declines since the 1970s in Hamford Water and along Dengie and a quite significant increase in the Stour, although numbers are variable at most sites.

Although significant numbers winter in Essex, the largest counts occur during autumn; counts increased significantly during the 1990s but have since fallen back to nearer the long-term average. As in winter, there has been a redistribution of the population, with the Thames now one of the most important sites in the country. It should be borne in mind that few estuaries are counted during July and August and it is possible that, particularly in August, numbers may well regularly exceed September WeBS peaks. A total of 4,000 (non-WeBS) was in the Fingringhoe Wick area on 1st October 1969 and 22nd August 1971 and along Dengie during October 1977. Other non-WeBS counts have included: 719 along the Crouch–Roach, July 1993; 804 at Old Hall, 3rd August 2004; 1,896 along the Stour, August 1989; and 3,650 along the Blackwater, July 1990.

An autumn passage population of around 9,500 represents around 5.5% of the British and 2.7% of the European populations. Nationally, the Curlew has increased by 22% over the last ten years and 69% over the last 30 (Pollitt *et al.* 2003).

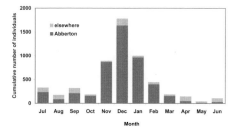

Seasonal occurrence of inland Curlews from 1971-2004

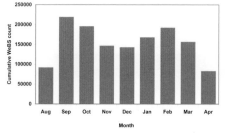

Seasonal occurrence of Curlews from 1970-2004

The Curlew can be found around the coast all year but numbers in May are generally small with returning birds occurring as early as June. It is likely that small numbers of probably first-year, non-breeding birds remain to summer, although separating these from late spring/early autumn migrants is difficult.

	Jan	Feb	Mar	Apr	May	Jun	Jul	Aug	Sep	Oct	Nov	Dec
Finland					1		2					
Norway												
Sweden						3	1					
Germany					1	1						
Netherlands				1	3	2		1				
Belgium				1	2	1						
Totals	*0*	*0*	*0*	*2*	*7*	*7*	*3*	*1*	*0*	*0*	*0*	*0*

Month of ringing and origin of Curlews ringed abroad and recovered in Essex

Inland, the Curlew is a regular visitor to the main reservoirs, with by far the largest numbers at Abberton, where flocks of 200 were recorded on 24th December 1992 and 19th July 1997, the latter a particularly early date for such numbers, and 165 on 2nd December 1998. At Hanningfield, peaks have been 34 on 16th September 1995 and 25 on 16th August 1980. Elsewhere, single birds and small parties have been recorded from time to time across Essex, particularly along the Lea Valley, including 21 flying northeast over KGV on 9th April 1988.

At Abberton, the largest numbers usually occur in winter when Curlews can be found feeding on the grassland adjacent to the reservoir. All other inland records show sharp peaks of occurrence in April and in late summer/early autumn.

Ringing recoveries in Britain have shown that the wintering population in southern England is composed primarily of birds breeding in western and central Europe and Scandinavia, with other populations moving through during migration (*BWP*, Prater 1981). Ringing recoveries from Essex are consistent with this general pattern.

The furthest movement involved one ringed at Tornio, Lappi, Finland, 2,044km to the northeast of East Mersea where its ring was read in January 1994, when it was ten years old. In addition, two birds colour-ringed in the Netherlands have occurred on the Blackwater and Crouch Estuaries. Curlews ringed in Essex have been recovered in Germany, Denmark (two) and Finland.

The Curlew is an adaptable and versatile wader that will utilise mudflats and saltings as well as arable grassland inside the seawall for feeding. An increasing amount of land is being farmed more sympathetically around the coast with cattle and sheep being used to graze grasslands that the species favours. This increase in suitable habitat inside the seawall may offset any losses of estuarine habitat caused by rising sea levels and thus ensure that the Curlew remains a common species around our coast.

Spotted Redshank   *Tringa erythropus*

Regular passage migrant: a few winter   Amber List

The Spotted Redshank is a monotypic wader that breeds in a rather narrow zone north of the taiga, along the north coasts of Sweden and Finland, Russia and Siberia. Birds from northern Europe and western Russia migrate through western Europe on their way south to wintering areas in western Africa, although small numbers remain in western Europe during winter. On passage, large numbers congregate at preferred staging posts, the nearest to Britain being the German-Dutch Waddensee and Dutch Delta region where up to 7,100 have been recorded (*BWP*).

Early observations suggest that the Spotted Redshank was a rare visitor with Christy and Glegg detailing just 12 records or so, from the first taken prior to 1832. All dated occurrences were in autumn, bar one, with the largest flock being 5-6 in Salcott Creek on 5th October 1927. It is difficult to know whether this was truly representative of the species' status during the 19th and early 20th centuries. In other counties, such as Norfolk, it was felt that the Spotted Redshank's early status might have been clouded by identification problems caused by the species' contrasting summer and winter plumages (Taylor *et al.* 1999). It is interesting to note that Christy commented: "... I only know of ... five or six ... though it is probably not very rare".

Both Hudson & Pyman and Cox considered the Spotted Redshank to be chiefly a passage migrant, although recorded in all months. Subsequently, the species' status has changed very little. Numbers vary considerably

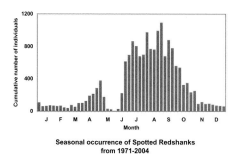

Seasonal occurrence of Spotted Redshanks
from 1971-2004

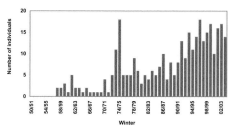

Annual totals of wintering Spotted Redshanks
from 1950/51-2003/04

from year to year and, although weather conditions at the time of migration are probably a factor, low water levels that expose large expanses of mud appear to affect significantly the number that pause in Essex on their way south. Following a study of Spotted Redshank movements through Abberton during autumn of 1998, Ekins (2000) estimated that 159 passed through: the highest individual day count was just 36. Although just one study, it points to the possibility that numbers passing through are substantially higher than random daily observation suggests.

Until 1968, the largest gatherings were at Abberton during periods of low water with counts of 20–40 regular during autumn with 50 in mid-October 1955, 53 on 23rd October 1964 and 60 on 15th October 1962. From 1968–81, the inner Blackwater and more particularly Mundon Stone Point, Chigborough Lakes and Heybridge GP, the latter regularly pumped for gravel extraction from 1968–85 (Ekins 2000), were favoured with 30–50 regular, the highest count being 61 at the latter on 13th October 1972.

By the early 1970s, increasing numbers were reported from the Geedon Saltings and Fingringhoe Wick on the Colne, and occasionally upriver at Rowhedge and The Hythe. Here numbers were generally similar to those at Abberton or on the Blackwater. However, there was an unprecedented count of 127 on 19th August 1972. Hamford Water held 70 during September 1968 and 73 on 25th August 1975, although generally counts of over 20 were exceptional there.

During the 1980s numbers were slightly lower, although counts of 70 were made on the Colne on 17th July and 14th August 1983 and 21st August 1988. In the 1990s low water levels saw high numbers at Abberton, peaking at 86 in September 1999. Along the Colne, numbers remained relatively constant and at times it has been apparent that higher numbers at Abberton have coincided with lower counts on the Colne, suggesting that the former is more attractive when water levels are low.

Since the mid-1980s, smaller numbers have also been noted along the Crouch and Roach, the highest counts being 29 along Barton Hall Creek on 22nd September 1992 and 24 there on 9th September 1992 and 22 at North Fambridge on 30th August 1998. Very few are reported from along the Thames Estuary with only Rainham recording the species with any regularity, the highest count being 15 on 27th August 1976.

Inland records away from Abberton occur annually but numbers are generally small with the majority coming from Hanningfield, where the species is reported in most years, with three double-figure counts, the highest being 15 on 3rd September 1956 when the filling of the reservoir produced suitable feeding conditions. In the Lea Valley, Spotted Redshanks are less than annual, the highest count being three. Otherwise the species has been reported from a further nine iland locations in generally small numbers, although there were eight at Romford SF on 1st–2nd September 1956.

Spring passage begins from late March and peaks markedly in the last week of April and first week of May before tailing off rapidly in mid-month. Numbers are generally small with just ten double-figure counts, the highest being: 21 at Fleet Head, 5th May 2000; 20 at Old Hall, 15th April 1996; and 17 flying northwest, 6.5km offshore Clacton-on-Sea, 26th April 1976.

Return passage begins very early with the first individuals arriving from early June with, in some years, up to 60 at Fingringhoe Wick by the end of that month, all of which are likely

	50-54	55-59	60-64	65-69	70-74	75-79	80-84	85-89	90-94	95-99	00-04
Hamford Water	1	1	1	70	16	73	19	9	5	7	3
Colne/Fingringhoe Wick	n/a	n/a	n/a	16	127	53	70	70	60	25	36
Old Hall	1	5	11	3	2	8	5	26	10	30	46
Inner Blackwater	n/a	n/a	24	50	61	12	45	18	30	1	3
Abberton	5	50	60	24	5	8	2	26	24	86	41
Hanningfield	~	15	10	n/a	8	6	4	4	1	3	6

Five- year peak counts of Spotted Redshanks at principal sites from 1950-2004

to be females. Like phalaropes, it is the male Spotted Redshanks that brood and raise the young. Males arrive in July and August with juveniles thereafter with passage peaking in late August/early September.

Small numbers continue to arrive through October, although some large counts have been made during the month. By early November numbers tail off.

Increasing numbers of Spotted Redshanks have been reported wintering in Essex, a trend that mirrors that in Britain and western Europe. Hudson & Pyman observed that 2-3 individuals wintered annually; Cox noted that 1–6 wintered with up to 11 occasionally and an estimated 18 in December 1974. During the 1990s, double-figure totals were noted in most winters with a peak of 18 in January 1997. Twelve at Old Hall on 7th December 1996 is the largest single count, although the Roach has generally been the most favoured location.

One Spotted Redshank ringed at Abberton in mid-October 1953 was recovered there on 15th July the following year, whilst another ringed at Abberton on 29th August 1963 was recovered in Sjaelland, Denmark, on 11th May 1967. Surprisingly there have been no national recoveries involving potential breeding areas in Scandinavia and eastwards with the only distant foreign recoveries involving birds presumably heading further south on migration.

Sponsored by Graham Ekins

(Common) Redshank   *Tringa totanus*

Resident, passage migrant and winter visitor   **Amber List**

The Redshank has an extensive Palearctic distribution, breeding from Iceland to eastern China, mainly in the temperate and boreal zones. In the west of its range, the species also breeds in sub-arctic and Mediterranean zones. Of the six currently recognised subspecies, the nominate *totanus* (Ireland to European Russia) and *robusta* occur in Europe (European Atlas). A seventh subspecies, *britannicus* from Britain and the Netherlands, may be valid (*HBW*). The Redshank's usual habitat is damp, but not wet, marshland and grassy fields generally without vegetation (First National Atlas). An estimated 31,000–44,000 pairs breed in Britain, the majority on saltmarshes. Inland, breeding has declined markedly in recent years, particularly in the lowlands of southern Britain. In Essex,

Atlas	Survey Area	% of 10km squares or tetrads in which	
		bred/probably bred	possibly bred or present
First National 10km	Essex	54.4	3.5
Second National 10km	Essex	45.6	14.0
First London Tetrad	Met. Essex	5.0	1.5
Second London Tetrad	Met. Essex	11.5	5.5
Essex Tetrad	Essex	12.6	3.2

Summary of results of Atlas surveys for Redshanks

Redshanks prefer stable marsh with little internal erosion, mid- to high saltmarsh, a mix of common saltmarsh grasses and Sea Purslane (Cook *et al.* 1994). British Redshanks are joined in winter by large numbers of Icelandic birds, together with a few from the Continent; far larger numbers of Continental birds occur on passage (Migration Atlas).

Christy considered that breeding Redshanks were restricted to the coast, although he noted that the species was found nesting as far up the Thames as Dagenham. It would seem that the species bred at quite a high density in suitable habitat along the coast, if some of the descriptions given by Christy can be relied on. In 1866, it was noted that "In the low pasture grounds of the south-eastern portion of this county, frequented by *Vanellus cristatus* [Lapwing] for breeding purposes …[it]… is to be found nesting in about equal numbers …[with]… a score of nests in a low pasture of a few acres …", whilst one observer noted that "… it breeds in such large numbers in the marshes along the coast that he has often found eight or ten nests in as many minutes in the grass shut up for hay".

Although it is possible that Redshanks bred inland prior to the Victorian drainage boom during the first 70 years of the 19th century which saw huge population and range contractions nationally (Batten *et al.* 1990), none of Christy's sources detailed any inland breeding records. However, drainage efficiency declined from around the 1880s and this saw inland populations recover both nationally and in Essex, leading Glegg to state that the species bred "… sparingly at several localities inland". From 10–15 pairs nested in marshy fields between Upminster and Langdon, the locality having been used for at least 20 years prior to 1929. He also noted that from 1909 a few pairs nested along the Roding between Abridge and Chigwell, and at Nazeingwood Common. On the Stour, Redshanks bred as far inland as Nayland where numbers were considered to be "… considerable". Breeding probably also occurred at Walthamstow SF. However, he noted that breeding ceased after 1908 in the Upper Colne Valley, at Felsted after 1910 and in the Chelmer Valley after 1926. Glegg's references to coastal breeding added little to Christy's narrative.

	1985		1993		1985-93
	No. of pairs	Density Pairs per km^2	No. of pairs	Density Pairs per km^2	% decrease in pairs
Colne Point	57	100.2	29	48.9	49
Ray Island, Mersea	12	38.5	3	8.8	75
Pewit Is., Hamford	22	73.8	17	58.8	23
Grange, Dengie	44	72.5	30	53.9	32
Totals	*135*		*79*		*59*

Redshank breeding densities (adapted from Cook *et al.* 1994)

GB 1,200p INT 1,500	1970- 1974	1975- 1979	1980- 1984	1985- 1989	1990- 1994	1995- 1999	2000- 2004	Peak counts		Peak month
WeBS totals	*11,780^*	*6,821*	*9,238*	*7,820*	*8,961*	*10,671*	*12,074*	*Sep 74*	*14,700*	*Oct*
Stour	**3,685^**	*1,454**	**2,696^**	1,216	1,431	**2,385**	**1,503**	Nov 73	**4,755**	Nov
Hamford Water	995^	1,210^	1,348	1,157	1,333	**2,512**	**1,962**	Sep 98	**3,648**	Oct
Colne	**2,155^**	~	~	847	1,107	1,263	1,175	Oct 70	**4,000**	Nov
Blackwater	**2,819***	1,246^	1,292	923	**1,927**	**2,414**	**2,794**	Feb 01	**4,199**	Oct
Dengie	627^	633^	515^	579^	475	601	646	Sep 89	1,460	Oct
Crouch-Roach	976^	~	1,305	651	854	568	648	Nov 84	**1,635**	Nov
Thames	**3,880^**	**4,559**	3,214	4,487	2,813	3,025	**4,698**	Sep 78	**8,367**	Oct

**Five-year average of peak WeBS counts (Sep-Nov)
of Redshanks from 1970-2004**

By the 1950s, the Redshank's status along the coast was described as "… quite common …" (Hudson & Pyman) suggesting that numbers may have declined, although there is no quantitative data with which to confirm this. However, inland the breeding range had contracted, although the construction of the main reservoirs helped maintain total inland breeding numbers with 41 pairs reported in 1957. In 1953 and 1957 Abberton held 20 pairs, although around ten pairs were more usual until the mid-1960s, whilst at Hanningfield up to 15 pairs bred during the late 1950s with around ten more usual during the 1960s. Up to five pairs bred in the Lea Valley during these two decades.

BoEE survey work produced an estimate of approximately 1,100 pairs in coastal regions (Cox). Based on the work of Cook *et al.* (1994) and results of the Essex Atlas survey, the Essex population was estimated at around 1,100–1,300 pairs in the late 1980s. Cook *et al.* (1994) noted that at four locations surveyed in 1985 and 1993 as part of a national survey (Allport *et al.* 1986), an average decline of 36% had occurred.

The 1993 study suggested that the BoEE figure was probably well below the true breeding population in 1972–73. Nationally, numbers declined markedly between 1973 and 1985 and there is nothing to suggest that this was not the case in Essex. Extrapolation back to 1985 produces a population of around 1,800 pairs. Assuming a similar rate of decline from 1973–85, the population in 1973 was perhaps in the region of 2,900 pairs, meaning that a decline of around 60% occurred from 1973–93. Since 1993, no further studies of Redshank numbers have been carried out. However, it is likely that overall Redshank numbers have remained constant with likely losses on salt marshes balanced by increasing numbers breeding on managed grasslands. A population of 1,200 pairs represents about 3% of the British population.

Various causes for the Redshank's decline have been suggested and include ongoing erosion, tidal inundation and consequent vegetation change, and winter mortality. Essex held around 8% (3,460ha) of British saltmarsh in 1993 (Cook *et al.* 1994), a 2% decline from the late 1980s attributed to erosion. Cook *et al.* (1994) found a correlation between the amount of erosion at a site and a decline in breeding densities; declines may also be linked to vegetation losses and changes in saltmarsh communities that are not totally due to erosion. Their estimate of 1,000 pairs equated to 28.9 pairs per km^2 and was based on a survey of 26% of Essex saltmarsh that located 371 pairs. Densities of 50 pairs per km^2 have been reported from 24 sites principally in East Anglia and northwest England. More recently, a combination of positive management and high rainfall allowed 124 pairs to breed at Old Hall in 2002, whilst 113 pairs were located on Horsey Island in 2002.

From the mid-1970s until the early 1990s, generally 10–15 pairs were reported from inland locations. During the Essex Atlas survey, numbers were generally higher, peaking at 22 pairs in 1992, suggesting that the species is probably under-recorded inland during the breeding season. In the latter half of the 1990s rarely more than ten pairs were reported annually, although there were at least 11 in 1999 and 13–15 in 2000. Most recent inland records have come from Metropolitan Essex, particularly along the Ingrebourne and Lea Valleys. At Abberton, breeding has not occurred since at least 1990 and since 1985 at Hanningfield. Allowing for a measure of under-recording, the current inland breeding population is probably around 15–20 pairs.

Outside the breeding season, the Redshank's status appears to have changed little since the 19th century, although the early writers left little useful data. Hudson & Pyman considered that coastal populations were "… very

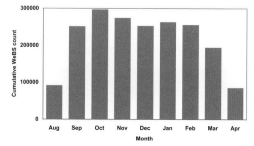

Seasonal occurrence of Redshanks from 1970-2004

GB 1,200w INT 1,500	70/71- 74/75	75/76- 79/80	80/81- 84/85	85/86- 89/90	90/91- 94/95	95/96- 99/00	00/01- 04/05	Peak counts		Peak month
WeBS totals	*9,663^*	*7,914*	*8,032*	*6,462*	*8,807*	*9,951*	*6,340^*	*Dec 94*	*14,224*	*Jan*
Stour	**2,932^**	**2,420**	**2,461**	1,097	**2,037**	**2,322**	**1,521^**	Feb 95	4,178	Jan
Hamford Water	1,269^	1,789	1,206	875^	1,344	2,078	1,993^	Dec 97	2,486	Jan
Colne	**2,168^**	~	~	1,074	2,012	1,471	1,399^	Jan 72	4,150	Jan
Blackwater	1,268^	1,296	1,168	900	**1,866**	**2,161**	**2,600^**	Feb 01	4,199	Feb
Dengie	458^	435^	314^	265	322	418	497^	Feb 02	751	Jan
Crouch-Roach	902^	922	1,220	630	849	688	449^	Dec 84	2,573	Feb
Thames	**2,227^**	**2,449**	**2,570**	**2,956**	**2,378**	**2,148**	**3,044^**	Jan 04	4,032	Jan

Five-year average of peak WeBS counts (Dec-Mar) of Redshanks from 1970/71-2003/04

considerably increased (by immigration)" and noted that, whilst the species did not generally form dense flocks, several of 1,000+ had been recorded, including one of 4,800 at Steeple on 27th January 1952.

Cox estimated that, based on the BoEE results, the regular winter population was around 12,000 birds. WeBS counts revealed a decline in wintering Redshanks from the late 1970s but numbers generally increased during the 1990s, peaking in the second half of the 1990s before declining in the first years of the 2000s. The Redshank's habit of feeding on the upper shore, which freezes more easily than elsewhere on the foreshore, makes the species especially vulnerable in severe weather, in fact more so than any other wader occurring in Essex. It was considered to have suffered badly in the winter of 1962/63, whilst in February 1986, 200 were found dead at Wrabness with 185 in Hamford Water in early March.

A winter population of 10,000 Redshanks represents around 8.5% of the British wintering population and about 6% of the European population.

Although winter numbers are considerable and of great importance internationally, it is in autumn that the largest numbers occur, with Redshanks from Iceland arriving to winter and large numbers of Continental birds moving through on their way south; close to 15,000 have occurred in Essex at this time with numbers typically 20% higher than the winter population; by the early 2000s passage numbers were at the highest level yet recorded.

Inland records of Redshanks during periods of migration have not been reported with any regularity. However, numbers are generally small with just three counts in excess of 50, all from Hanningfield: 80 on 15th and 100 on 17th April 1985, both flocks heading northeast; 150 north on 21st April 1995. From the limited data available, it would seem that passage numbers peak between August and October. Typically, most are reported from the two main reservoirs with smaller numbers regular through the Lea Valley.

Recoveries of Redshanks involving Essex are typical of the situation nationally. Redshanks trapped and ringed at East Tilbury during the spring of 1965 and winters of 1967, 1969 and 1971 showed plumage characteristics and biometrics of the Icelandic race *robusta*. Two that were ringed at East Tilbury have been recovered in Iceland: one ringed on 8th April 1964 was recovered on 10th July 1965 and another ringed on 13th April 1965 was recovered on 17th April 1967. Individuals ringed as chicks or breeding adults from a wide number of locations in Britain, including the Northern Isles of Scotland, have been recovered in Essex; all have followed the national pattern with Redshanks from all over Britain wintering in southeast England. Several Redshanks ringed in Essex during summer have been shot in west and northwest France in midwinter, suggesting that at least some locally bred birds move south for winter: birds from other east coast counties have been recovered in Iberia and northwest Africa. Redshanks ringed in Denmark (two), Germany, the Netherlands (six) and Belgium (two) have also been recovered in Essex. Of these, seven were recovered during winter, which, although a small sample, suggests that a fair proportion of wintering Redshanks in Essex may be of the nominate Continental race *totanus*.

The Redshank's future as a breeding species is threatened principally by rising sea levels which are slowly destroying its main breeding habitat, some 20% of Essex saltmarsh having been eroded between 1973 and 1988 (Burd 1992). Whether managed retreats will supply a suitable alternative habitat quickly enough and in large enough areas to benefit the species is unclear, those along the Blackwater at present replace only a few of the hundreds of hectares lost in the last 30 years. It is to be hoped, however, that the coastal grazing marshes may, with sensitive management, provide suitable alternative breeding areas and with much new land now coming under the control of conservation organisations, together with an increasing awareness that our farmland needs to be managed in a more environmentally sensitive way, there is a some hope that the Redshank may turn its fortunes around in the coming years.

Marsh Sandpiper

Tringa stagnatilis

Vagrant: nine records

The monotypic Marsh Sandpiper breeds mainly in the steppe-type areas of the former Soviet Union and winters principally in tropical Africa and the Indian subcontinent.

1956	The Naze	25th August	
1963	Rainham	26th–28th August	
1966	Chigwell SF	26th August	
1984	Holyfield Marsh	28th April	
1995	Old Hall	28th July and 8th August	
1999	Abberton	9th–20th August	Juvenile
2000	Vange Marsh	15th–16th August	Adult
2002	Old Hall	25th August	Adult
2004	Fobbing	28th July–14th August	Juvenile

The first record was the ninth for Britain. The 1963 individual was also noted at Swanscombe, Kent, just the other side of the Thames, between 18th August and 2nd September. The 1984 individual was also observed briefly at Broxbourne GP, Hertfordshire, the same day.

There had been 125 British records to the end of 2004 (BBRC 2005) with most occurring in East Anglia and the southeast. Whilst it was particularly rare as recently as 1970, national occurrences have increased in recent decades following the species' westward and northward expansion into Eastern Europe. Nationally, numbers peak in autumn but spring records are increasing. It is possible that with the westerly range expansion, increasing numbers are wintering in western Africa and these, when travelling northeast to their breeding grounds, are occasionally displaced by easterly winds (Cottridge & Vinicombe 1996).

(Common) Greenshank

Tringa nebularia

Common passage migrant; a few winter

The monotypic Greenshank breeds in the Palearctic boreal forests (taiga) north of the steppe and south of the tundra, from Britain in the west to the Kamchatka peninsula in the east, breeding in northern Europe from as far south as Latvia and in Russia between about 55° and 67° N. In Britain, where it is found mainly on the pool-dominated and boulder-strewn blanket bogs of the northwest and central Highlands of Scotland, the current population numbers 1,000–1,600 pairs, less than 1% of the estimated world population (Second National Atlas). The Greenshank is a long-distance migrant with north European populations generally wintering south and west of their ranges on inland and coastal wetlands in the Mediterranean and Africa. Increasing numbers winter in southern Britain.

Christy described the Greenshank as "A somewhat uncommon passage migrant in spring and autumn". The earliest documented record occurred prior to 1738, when one was "… shot … on the sandy bank of a river in Essex, and was not much used to the sight of men, it letting him come within ten yards of it before he fired at it". He listed few other observations with the largest flock being just five.

From Glegg's description that during autumn migration the Greenshank "… becomes fairly common without being abundant along the whole coast from the Stour to the Thames …", it appears that the species may have increased in the early 20th century, as it seems unlikely that it was ever overlooked, given its distinctive call note. Numbers were apparently small, although 50 were near Harwich in August 1890. Glegg considered the species "… by no means common during the spring …", with dated records all falling

GB ? IN ?	70/71- 74/75	75/76- 79/80	80/81- 84/85	85/86- 89/90	90/91- 94/95	95/96- 99/00	00/01- 04/05	Peak counts	
Stour	11^	5^	22	56	55	57	64^	Oct 88	142
Hamford Water	10^	32	54	29	44	83	52^	Sep 98	124
Colne	97^	39^	46	48	28	18	11^	Sep 74	143
Blackwater	73^	41	34	44	97	158	138^	Sep 95	209
Dengie	13^	20^	33^	24	10	24	28^	Aug 03	55
Crouch-Roach	14^	11^	25	18	28	28	20^	Aug 84	55
Thames	51^	107^	136	130	127	117	154^	Sep 02	223

**Five-year average of peak counts (combined)
of Greenshanks from 1971/72-2003/04**

during May. Glegg's assessment of its status does not seem to be too different from the present, giving due allowance to the today's much increased observer coverage. However, neither he nor Christy knew of any winter records.

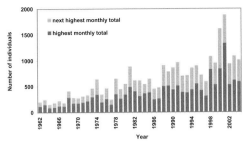

Annual totals of Greenshanks from 1962-2004

Over the last 50 years the Greenshank's status appears to have changed very little, except for the development of a small wintering population that may be made up of birds from the Scottish population (Winter Atlas).

The species is widespread around the coast in small numbers. However, three-figure counts are made only at its principal roost sites, the most favoured localities in recent years being: Cooper's Creek, at the western end of the Blackwater Estuary; and along Havengore and New England Creek on Foulness. Geedon Saltings, along the Colne Estuary, were favoured in the past.

Few estuaries in Britain regularly hold in excess of 100 Greenshanks and thus the Blackwater and Thames/Foulness are nationally important for the species. Numbers vary markedly from year to year, perhaps as a result of variable breeding success and weather at the time of migration. An accurate assessment of the total number occurring annually is difficult but, based on the assumption that in any one week 50% of Greenshanks present are new individuals rather than birds lingering from previous weeks, some 500–750 Greenshanks pass through in an average autumn. In peak years, such as 2001, perhaps 1,500 are involved, although this still represents a very small proportion of the world population. The annual number of Greenshanks reported has increased steadily, although passage was exceptionally heavy in 2000 and 2001.

A few birds are usually recorded throughout summer and, whilst it is possible that they are early/late migrants, they may be non-breeding first-year birds. Autumn passage begins towards the end of June or early July with numbers building rapidly through July, with a small peak at the end of the month perhaps signifying the arrival of the adult population, before numbers climb to another peak in mid-August as juveniles arrive.

Numbers remain relatively constant through to the last week of September, after which numbers decline rapidly.

Small but increasing numbers of Greenshanks winter in Essex, although numbers vary annually. Double-figure monthly counts have occurred during 12 winters, although 29 in December 1991, including 13 on Foulness on 8th December and 19 at Mundon on 9th December 1973, were exceptional. Most other winter records have involved just 1–2 birds, although there were 14 on Foulness on 14th January 1990, 12 in Hamford Water on 5th February 2004 and up to 11 roosted at Chigborough Lakes from January–March 2002. In Britain, the wintering distribution is predominantly western, the population being estimated at around 600 (Rehfisch *et al.* 2003).

Wintering numbers remain relatively stable until the end of February. However, numbers in March are lower than at any other time of year, suggesting that the wintering population has perhaps begun to move north. This supports the view that many of these birds are of Scottish origin, as they are known to arrive back on their breeding grounds around early April, a month earlier than their Scandinavian counterparts. Spring passage occurs from mid-April and peaks in the first half of May. Numbers in spring are generally small with few double-figure counts, 22 at Fingringhoe Wick on 13th May 1990 being the largest, although there were 27 along the Blackwater during the April 1998 WeBS count. A total

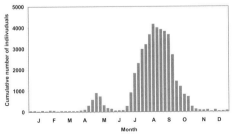

Seasonal occurrence of Greenshanks from 1971-2004

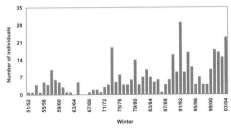

Annual totals of wintering Greenshanks from 1951/52-2003/04

of 93 occurred during the week commencing 7th May 2002, 86 during the week commencing 30th April 2000 and 83 during the week commencing 30th May 1999; otherwise rarely more than 50 pass through in any one week.

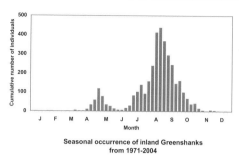

Seasonal occurrence of inland Greenshanks
from 1971-2004

Inland, Greenshanks are recorded mainly at the major reservoirs and along the Lea Valley where regular passage movements are evident. However, the species may turn up almost anywhere. Its pattern of occurrence is very similar to that on the coast, although inland winter records are scarce. Highest counts from the main sites have been: Abberton, 50, early September 1976; Hanningfield, 23, 10th September 1966; and KGV, 35, 26th August 2000.

Other than two local recoveries of Abberton-ringed birds several days after ringing, the only recovery involves one ringed at Abberton on 9th August 1962 and found dead on 24th March 1972 at Ravenna, Italy. Scottish-ringed birds have been recovered in southern Britain. However, many autumn arrivals coincide with the arrival of Spotted Redshanks and other breeding species from the Baltic and several national recoveries of Scandinavian Greenshanks suggest that, besides Scotland, the Baltic is the origin of many Greenshanks passing through Essex.

Sponsored by Martin Henry

Greater Yellowlegs   *Tringa melanoleuca*

Vagrant: two records

The monotypic Greater Yellowlegs breeds throughout the boreal zone of Alaska and Canada and winters from coastal southern USA south through South America.

1949	Abberton	28th–31st July	
1995	Holliwell Point	10th May	1st-summer

With just 30 British records, the last in 2002 (BBRC 2003), the species is far rarer than Lesser Yellowlegs. Quite why this is cannot easily be explained, although it is possible that, unlike its near cousin, it does not accumulate sufficient fat reserves to allow it to cross the Atlantic. Those that occur may therefore be larger individuals or perhaps arrive via a different route, perhaps from Hudson Bay, Canada, and across Greenland to Britain (Vinicombe & Cottridge 1996).

The 1949 individual was only the eighth British record. The 1995 individual was probably the same as that at Southwold, Suffolk, on 14th May and Breydon Water, Berney Marshes and Burgh Castle, Norfolk, on 15th–18th and 22nd–25th May, respectively. Both individuals probably arrived on the Continent during a previous autumn.

Lesser Yellowlegs   *Tringa flavipes*

Vagrant: nine records involving six individuals

The monotypic Lesser Yellowlegs breeds across much of Canada and into eastern Alaska and winters principally in the Caribbean and South America.

1921	West Mersea	8th August	Adult male shot
1950	Abberton	15th July	
1961	Foulness Point	13th May	
1998	Rainham	26th–27th August	Adult
	Fleet Head, Great Wakering	21st–24th September	Same as previous
	Abberton	26th October–6th November	Same as previous
1998/99	East Tilbury	27th December–21st March	Same as previous
2001	Manningtree	10th–11th October	Adult
2002	Old Hall	16th May	Adult

The 1921 individual was the sixth British record; the specimen is still in Southend-on-Sea Museum (Accession No. N80.20). A careful study of the plumage of the 1998/99 individuals confirmed that the same bird was responsible for all the records. For the latter part of its stay at East Tilbury, it spent some of the time across the Thames at Cliffe, Kent.

A total of 260 had been recorded in Britain to the end of 2004 (BBRC 2005), most occurring in September and October.

Solitary Sandpiper   *Tringa solitaria*

Vagrant: two records

The Solitary Sandpiper breeds in the conifer belt of northern North America and winters principally in South America. The nominate race *solitaria* breeds in the east of its range, whilst *cinnamomea* occurs in the west.

| 1967 | Roydon | 24th September–9th October |
| 1974 | Rainham | 1st–6th September |

The 1967 bird, the tenth British record, was found at Rye Meads, Hertfordshire, but crossed into Roydon parish on a number of occasions.

This is one of the rarer American waders to occur in Britain, with just 29 records, the last in 2003 (BBRC 2004). Numbers peak in September, although records have occurred between mid-July and October. The early autumn dates of both occurrences suggest that they may have made the transatlantic crossing in the same year as their occurrence.

Green Sandpiper   *Tringa ochropus*

Common passage migrant and recently increased winter visitor   Amber List

The monotypic Green Sandpiper is a trans-Palearctic species that breeds in the boreal zone, much of its range lying between the Arctic Circle in the north and the steppe zone in the south, from Scandinavia and the Baltic in the west to the Sea of Okhotsk in the east. It is a rare breeder in much of Eastern Europe. Green Sandpipers are common passage migrants throughout Britain, which is at the northern limit of the species' wintering range. Numbers wintering in Britain have increased over the last few decades. There are other small wintering areas in northwest Europe but the majority of Green Sandpipers winter in the Mzediterranean basin and in Africa south of the Sahara (Winter Atlas).

Christy described the Green Sandpiper as a "... mysterious bird..." perhaps on account of the general lack of knowledge of its breeding areas at that time. He considered the species to be at its most common in July and August, although not uncommon in May and September and detailed no satisfactory records for the period January–March. The earliest documented Essex record involved one shot at Epping in August 1832. One that was shot and injured near Epping in November 1840 was kept by Henry Doubleday and "... soon became very tame, running rapidly around the room, and feeding readily on small worms". Off the coast, they were regularly noted to "... fly aboard the dredgers at sea in August, and be knocked over by a stone". By Glegg's time, the Green Sandpiper had been recorded in every month of the year, although it is clear that there were still very few winter records. He considered the species much less numerous than Common Sandpiper, with autumn passage commencing in early July but not peaking until August and September.

The Green Sandpiper's status has changed very little to this day, save for the increase in wintering birds. The species is recorded regularly in all months of the year, although it is particularly rare in May, a month in which Christy

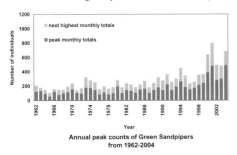

Annual peak counts of Green Sandpipers
from 1962-2004

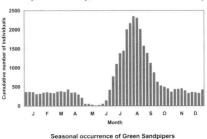

Seasonal occurrence of Green Sandpipers
from 1971-2004

considered it "... not uncommon...", perhaps suggesting that its pattern of occurrence has changed.

A small passage is evident in April, although in recent years this has been somewhat obscured by the presence of wintering birds. Returning autumn migrants begin to arrive as early as mid-June; it is the earliest returning of migrant waders, one parent, usually the female, leaving the breeding grounds as early as mid-May, with most leaving in early June (*BWP*). Whether any non-breeding birds summer in Essex is therefore impossible to ascertain. Passage peaks relatively early, during August, before declining fairly quickly through September.

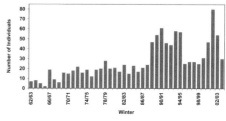

Annual totals of wintering Green Sandpipers from 1962/63-2003/04

Normally the Green Sandpiper frequents inland freshwater sites, rarely being found in intertidal habitats. In Essex, typical haunts include coastal grazing marshes, the muddy edges of lakes, gravel-pits and reservoirs as well as small ditches, temporarily flooded areas and wet silage clamps. Indeed, any body of freshwater, however small, may support individual birds, provided their principal prey, aquatic invertebrates (*BWP*), is available. The Green Sandpiper is a relatively inconspicuous species that rarely gathers into flocks of more than five. However, large areas of suitable habitat, particularly coastal grazing marshes, can hold significant numbers but obtaining accurate counts is often difficult due to the undulating topography of such sites; WeBS counts do not provide a representative assessment of numbers and generally miss the peak passage period. The largest counts have come from along the Thames. At Rainham, peak counts are normally in the range of 20–50, but there were 60 on 23rd July 1979, whilst at Bowers Gifford Marsh there were at least 70 on 7th August 1973 with 50 there in the subsequent two years (Cox). The number of sites holding 20–40 birds have increased steadily in recent years and many sites around the county may hold double figures.

Total numbers of Green Sandpipers passing through on migration vary considerably from year to year. In the region of 300–400 probably occur in an average year, although there may be 600–700 in peak years. It is, therefore, generally outnumbered by about 2:1 on migration by its close relative, the Common Sandpiper.

Until the late 1980s, rarely more than 20 Green Sandpipers wintered in Essex. However, numbers increased markedly after 1987/88 such that by the early to mid-1990s the wintering population stood at perhaps 50–60 birds. Although numbers were lower in the second half of the 1990s, they have subsequently increased again.

High winter populations have generally followed autumns with above-average passage numbers, although this is not always the case. A study of Green Sandpipers wintering at sewage farms (Munster 1989) suggested that the species shows strong site fidelity and that population changes correlate with the severity of the previous winter. Many winter records involve individual birds, with no single site holding more than eight.

Recoveries of moulting adults at Abberton, Pitsea and in the Lea Valley serve to illustrate the considerable site fidelity of the species even on passage. One ringed at Wangerooge-Ost, Germany, and recovered at Brentwood on 9th November 1970, illustrates a typical movement from the species' breeding areas further east. An adult ringed at Abberton on 20th July 1957 moved quickly south and was recovered at Cruilles, Gerona, Spain, on 4th August 1957. Two other Spanish recoveries of Abberton-ringed birds provide evidence as to the wintering location of some adult Green Sandpipers once they leave Essex after their late summer moult.

Wood Sandpiper   *Tringa glareola*

Scarce passage migrant   Amber List

The monotypic Wood Sandpiper is one of the most abundant and widespread *Tringa* waders and also one of the longest migrants. The species breeds right across the boreal and sub-arctic zones from Scotland in the west, where up to about ten pairs have bred since 1959, through Fennoscandia across to eastern Siberia. The European population of around 1,400,000 pairs (about 20% of the world's population (HBW)) winters mainly in sub-Saharan Africa, although it is scarcest on passage along the western seaboard of Europe. In Britain, it is principally an autumn migrant with small numbers passing through in spring.

Christy detailed four records, including the first documented, which was shot on New England Island on 24th July 1837, and one alleged to have been shot on the Stour at Nayland during December 1869. Glegg added one more record, from Paglesham in September 1898. Just two more were reported before 1950.

Hudson & Pyman suggested that Wood Sandpipers were probably overlooked in the past, as from 1950 the species was recorded annually; since then, the species' status has changed very little (Cox), although greater observer coverage has probably been responsible for the steady increase in records. Annual totals have generally been in the range of 10–50 individuals. However, exceptional numbers occurred from 2000–02, and in particular 2004 (including two flocks of 17 in mid-August), with numbers boosted by autumn totals some 50%

	Years with records	Years with counts of 5+	Years with counts of 10+	Peak counts	
Hythe	33	3	0	8	10th & 17th August 1963
Old Hall	27	5	1	17	11th August 2004
Rainham	46	12	1	10	16th August 1968
Abberton	50	13	3	21	16th August 1955
Hanningfield	44	10	1	10	21st August 1977

Principal sites for Wood Sandpipers from 1950-2004

higher than any previous peak. An exceptional national influx in 1952 did not appear to affect Essex (Nisbet 1956).

Most Wood Sandpipers migrate south via a route well to the east of Britain, and it is normally only when easterly winds displace a proportion of the population west that the larger influxes occur. However, low water levels also influence the number that stop over on their way south.

Being principally a freshwater species, few are seen on the estuaries and most records come from either the freshwater coastal marshes just inside seawalls or inland, around freshwater bodies such as reservoirs, gravel-pits and lakes. Annual totals have increased steadily over the last few decades, although a marked increase has occurred from the late 1990s, which may be due to greater observer coverage.

Other sites, in addition to those in the table, that have held more than six Wood Sandpipers have been: Holland Haven, 17, 17th August 2004 and nine, 21st August 2004; The Naze, eight, 25th July 1969; Vange, eight, 12th and 15th August 2000; and Romford SF, seven, 9th–10th August 1961.

Inland, away from Abberton and Hanningfield, numbers are generally small with the majority occurring along the Lea Valley.

Up until the late 1980s, numbers occurring in spring had generally been small but a noticeable increase has occurred since then. From 1988–91, far higher numbers than previously reported occurred. In 1990 a minimum of 24 was reported at 11 sites, and in 1991 there were 15 at eight sites. Records have subsequently fallen back but to a higher level than prior to the late 1980s. Most spring records have involved no more than 1–2 birds, but exceptions have been: six at Abberton, 27th May 1957; five at Chelmer Valley GP, 3rd May 1990; five at Old Hall, 16th May 2004; four at Old Hall, 4th May 1988; and four at The Hythe, 31st May–1st June 1991.

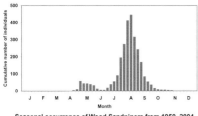

Seasonal occurrence of Wood Sandpipers from 1950–2004

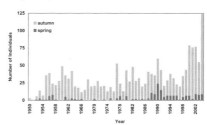

Annual totals of Wood Sandpipers from 1950-2004

Wood Sandpipers are not usually recorded until the very end of April, with passage peaking in May and continuing into June. The earliest was at East Tilbury on 9th April 2000, whilst there were two at The Hythe on 17th April 2002 and one at Fishers Green Goosefield on 18th April 2003. June individuals are difficult to ascribe to either passage movement. Single birds summered at Abberton in 1952 and 1953.

Autumn passage begins around the end of June, although it is not until August that Wood Sandpipers normally occur in any numbers. Records peak in late August/early September with most having departed by October. There have, however, been five November records: Abberton, 1st in 1959; Abberton, 4th in 1971; Romford SF, 6th in 1960; Old Hall, 11th in 1987; and Abberton, "mid-November" in 1953.

There are no ringing recoveries that involve Essex.

Terek Sandpiper   *Xenus cinereus*

Vagrant: three records

The monotypic Terek Sandpiper breeds principally from Russia east to Siberia and winters along the coasts of Africa, the Gulf, southern Asia and Australasia. Since the 1950s, a small population (numbering about 20 pairs in the 1990s) has existed in Finland (European Atlas).

1978	Old Hall	29th May	
1986	Colne Point	20th September	
2002	Blackwater,		
	off Heybridge GP	25th–29th August	Adult

Given the proximity of its breeding areas, the Terek Sandpiper is surprisingly rare in Britain, with just 63 records, the last in 2003 (BBRC 2004). However, as the species' range has spread westward, occurrences have increased and, since the late 1960s, it has been recorded almost annually.

Nationally, 1986 was one of the best years on record. Most occur in May and June as drift migrants, whilst a smaller peak occurs in August as birds disperse from breeding grounds (Cottridge & Vinicombe 1996). After two short-stayers, the first possibly being chased off by Ringed Plovers on territory (Mackenzie-Grieve 1979), the 2002 individual proved extremely popular (Neave 2003).

Sponsored by Russell Neave

Common Sandpiper *Actitis hypoleucos*

Common passage migrant – winters in small numbers

The monotypic Common Sandpiper is distributed across the whole Palearctic region except Iceland, and is replaced in the Nearctic region by the Spotted Sandpiper *A. macularius*. The main European population breeds above 55° N, from the northern half of Britain through Scandinavia and into Russia (European Atlas). The species breeds widely in the uplands of north and west Britain and Ireland but only sporadically in lowland Britain. Common Sandpipers are typical of upland lochs, reservoirs and streams. Recently, there have been signs of a decline at the edges of its range in Britain, where 12,000 pairs represent just 1.4% of the European population of 882,000 pairs, 96% of which breed in Fennoscandia (Second National Atlas). A few European birds winter, but most migrate in small flocks of no more than 5–10 to south of the Sahara.

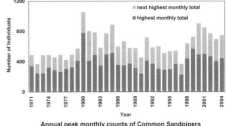

Annual peak monthly counts of Common Sandpipers from 1971-2004

Neither Christy nor Glegg could provide any satisfactory evidence of breeding. In fact the Common Sandpiper has been proved to breed just once in Essex, near Goldhanger in 1947 (*British Birds* 42: 93). An adult was seen "… in close attendance on a young bird about half its size" on 20th July. They allowed approach to within 10m. A second adult, presumed to be the mate of the other, was observed in the vicinity. Hudson & Pyman were unconvinced by the record on the grounds that the habitat was "… quite unsuitable …" and felt more supporting evidence was required. Cox followed the same line. However, there seems, with hindsight, to be no reason to doubt the record on the grounds of unsuitable habitat given that breeding has occurred several times in southern England, for instance in Norfolk (Taylor *et al.* 1999) and Surrey (Parr 1972), gravel-pits having been favoured in several instances. On the Continent, breeding also occurs irregularly in lowland environments in the Netherlands and Denmark and the species is a common nester at low levels around the Baltic. Nesting occurs at sea level (*BWP*) and has been known along the margins of lowland rivers (Population Trends). Occasionally birds have summered. In 1954, a male was noted displaying at Nazeingbury GPs on 5th June, whilst two summered at Ulting GP in 1977, although there was no evidence of breeding.

Outside the breeding season, the Common Sandpiper's status appears to have changed very little during the 19th and 20th centuries. Christy described the species as "Not uncommon as a passing migrant in spring and autumn…", whilst Glegg considered the Common Sandpiper a "… regular and common double passage migrant". Christy referred to "several" killed in February 1836 at Wenden, whilst Glegg added just two further winter records. Hudson & Pyman observed that the species was a "… not uncommon double passage migrant …" and that "… a very few winter", whilst Cox described it as a "… common passage migrant" with apparently increasing numbers in winter.

Spring passage begins in mid-April and peaks a month later. Numbers passing through in spring are relatively small with on average around 50–100 in total. However, numbers vary from year to year, presumably due to prevailing weather conditions at the time of migration, with easterly winds perhaps pushing some of the very large numbers of Fennoscandian migrants across the North Sea. Spring 2000 saw exceptional numbers with perhaps 250 involved, mostly in May. As at other times of year, it is the concrete edges of the main reservoirs that attract the largest numbers, although Common Sandpipers can be found in almost any damp or wet habitat both on the coast and inland. Counts of

GB ?		1971-	1976-	1980-	1985-	1990-	1995-	2000-	Peak counts	
IN ?		1975	1979	1984	1989	1994	1999	2004		
Rainham		32^	33	68	34	28	28	20	100	5th August 1982
Abberton		76^	67	119	96	69	91	57	185	9th August 1980
Hanningfield		34^	40	59	32	35	21	24	96	29th July 1981
Lea Valley Res*		33^	42	47	~	~	~	~	60	30th July 1978
KGV		~	~	~	14	24	14	20	40	16th August 2004
Girling		~	~	~	34	21	25	20	50	July 1989

* data not split between reservoirs until late 1980s

**Five-year average of peak counts (combined) (Sep-Mar)
of Common Sandpipers from 1971-2004**

more than 15 from any one location are rare: 16 at Hanningfield on both 3rd May 1970 and 10th May 1993; 17 along the Cam between Newport and Audley End, 18th April 1953 and at Abberton, 7th May 1979; 18 at Abberton, 14th May 1980 and 24th May 1991; 19 at Abberton, 9th May 2000; and 21 at Abberton, 14th May 1992.

By the third week in June, Common Sandpipers begin to return, although it is often difficult discerning the end of spring migration and the beginning of autumn passage. Many of the earliest birds are probably females; they begin to depart from nesting grounds in mid-June (European Atlas). Adults generally arrive first, followed by the juveniles, although there is much overlap in passage and no secondary peak of occurrence is evident to point to their arrival. Passage peaks at the end of July/early August, with numbers falling quickly towards the end of the month. As in spring, numbers vary markedly from year to year, breeding success being another important factor in determining numbers at this time. Following an apparent decline since the first half of the 1980s, a clear increase has occurred since the late 1990s; the British breeding population has been in slow decline since 1985.

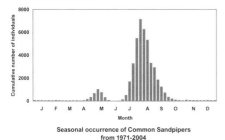

**Seasonal occurrence of Common Sandpipers
from 1971-2004**

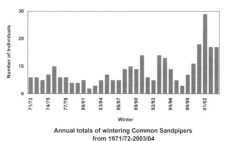

**Annual totals of wintering Common Sandpipers
from 1971/72-2003/04**

Although it is difficult to estimate the number passing through each autumn, on the basis of the data available since 1971 and assuming that 50% of all Common Sandpipers recorded in each week have moved on by the next, some 500–750 pass through in autumn and in good years perhaps in excess of 1,000. However, even these figures may be an underestimate: in 1957, 155 were ringed at Abberton when the maximum recorded was just 53. The largest counts have all come from Abberton and indeed all bar one of the three-figure counts have been from there. Counts of 100+ have occurred in nine years since the first in 1971, although the highest count of 185 is far greater than the next, 128 in August 1998. Five other sites have held 50 or more during autumn: Hanningfield; Rainham; Brandy Hole (56 on 1st September 1988); Lea Valley reservoirs; and Bradwell/Dengie.

Most migrant Common Sandpipers have departed by the end of October. However, since the 1950s the number of Common Sandpipers wintering has increased, albeit not at a consistent rate and with no apparent link to the number of autumn migrants. Over the last decade around 5–15 birds have wintered.

The inner Thames and Lea Valley have been the most favoured wintering localities. Up to six were present at Rainham during February, November and December 1991, whilst four were at Beckton in December 1994 and 1995. Further down river, six were at East Tilbury on 20th February 1955, and there were four at Walthamstow in December 1999 and six there on 22nd February 2003. Wintering individuals are also regular at Abberton and Hanningfield. Wintering Common Sandpipers are thought to originate from higher latitudes outside Britain but as yet there has been no ringing evidence to confirm this.

Abberton was one of the main locations for the ringing of Common Sandpipers outside the breeding season and recoveries abroad represent a significant proportion of the national total. Recoveries have confirmed that those passing through Essex come from two main areas: upland Britain, from where there are ringing recoveries linking Essex with Highland, Tayside, Cumbria and Yorkshire; and Fennoscandia. Recoveries in the

Netherlands, Belgium, France, Portugal, Spain and Morocco are typical of birds moving through Britain to/from wintering areas in Africa. There is one African ringing recovery involving Essex, an adult ringed at Abberton on 14th July 1964 and recovered at Sao Joao, Bolamo, Guinea-Bissau, 4,500 km to the south, on 15th September; this represents an average distance travelled of 71 km/day. This is the only British-ringed Common Sandpiper recovered south of the Sahara (Migration Atlas). This individual, like many at this season, would have used Essex as a staging post for feeding and fat deposition, enabling it to complete its onward journey in only a handful of further flights. During spring, Essex is used less as a staging post than in autumn, birds probably either overflying or passing further east on their return journey to Fennoscandia. One ringed in autumn at Pitsea was recovered in Germany in spring, whilst a Norwegian recovery involved one ringed at Abberton on 17th May 1950 and recovered four days later at Vestre Gausdal, Opland. One ringed at Abberton on 9th August 1950 and recovered at Zogno, Bergamo, Italy, on 17th May 1951 was unusually far to the east. Ringers at several Essex sites have provided evidence of site fidelity on migration by recapturing ringed birds in subsequent years. The sole recovery of a foreign-ringed bird involved one ringed in Belgium in May 1959, which was recovered at Bradwell on 17th August 1969. One adult ringed at Abberton on 16th July 1957 was found at Hovsherad, Rogaland, Norway, on 11th August 1981, making the individual at least 25 years old.

	Jan	Feb	Mar	Apr	May	Jun	Jul	Aug	Sep	Oct	Nov	Dec
Essex			1				1	2	1			
Scotland				1								
North England					4		1	1				
South England							2	1				
Norway					3		1	2				
Sweden							2	1				
Germany					1							
The Netherlands							1					
Belgium					1		2					
France				1	2			2				
Spain			1									
Portugal								1				
Morocco										1		
Italy					1							
Guinea Bissau									1			
Totals	0	0	2	2	12	0	10	10	2	1	0	0

Month and location of recovery of Common Sandpipers ringed in Essex

Spotted Sandpiper   *Actitis macularius*

Vagrant: four records

The monotypic Spotted Sandpiper breeds across northern North America and winters in the southern USA, Central America, the Caribbean and South America.

1978	Hanningfield	3rd–17th September	Adult
1983	Hanningfield	4th September	Adult
1989	KGV	25th September–6th October	Adult
2001	Hanningfield	30th December	1st-winter

The 1978 individual was the first adult in winter plumage to be identified in Britain (Smith 1979). The 2001 bird dived into the reservoir to escape from a Sparrowhawk.

Nationally, there were 134 records to the end of 2004 (BBRC 2005), 125 since 1970, the increase almost certainly due to greater observer awareness. Most occur in autumn, particularly in September and October.

Christy dismissed two records on the grounds of confusion of specimens or misidentification: one shot near 'Albins' in 1743 and another shot near Coggeshall in 1858.

(Ruddy) Turnstone   *Arenaria interpres*

Passage migrant and winter visitor: a few oversummer   Amber List

The Turnstone is one of the most northerly breeding landbirds in the world, breeding up to 83° N in Greenland and 80° N in Svalbard. The species' circumpolar Holarctic range also includes the boreal and temperate zones. The nominate race *interpres* occurs across all of the range except for northeast Alaska and most of arctic Canada (*HBW*). Almost the entire European population breeds in Norway, Finland and Sweden, with breeding occurring as far south as the Baltic. All populations are migratory, with those from Greenland/Canada and Scandinavia moving south

through Britain, although only the former population stays to winter in Britain and Ireland where they are found around the entire coastline.

The 'Stonerunner', to give the Turnstone one of its more descriptive 19th century local names, has clearly undergone a significant change in status over the last 150 years. Christy considered it to be "… a fairly common bird as a passing migrant in spring and autumn … sometimes met with in winter", although he gave just one winter record, one shot inland at Audley End on 18th January 1832. Glegg noted that it was "… chiefly an uncommon double passage migrant but it has been recorded in all months of the year except December, January and February". He considered it most common on the shingle stretches of the Colne and Stour and had personally never seen it between the Blackwater and Thames. Turnstones were generally considered to occur in small numbers, with the largest flock being just 20 at the mouth of the Thames in August, sometime between 1835 and 1842. There seems little doubt that the species was not very numerous even on migration and was unknown as a winter visitor, apart from occasional exceptional records, until at least the 1930s. Quite when it began to winter in any numbers is unclear but Hudson & Pyman stated that the Turnstone had increased over the previous 20–30 years, particularly during winter. The early *EBR*s mention three-figure wintering flocks, so it appears that the increase took place after 1930 and prior to 1950. Similar increases were noted in other counties e.g. Hampshire and Suffolk. Cox considered the species a passage migrant and winter visitor that was present in all months.

GB 500 INT 700	1970- 1974	1975- 1979	1980- 1984	1985- 1989	1990- 1994	1995- 1999	2000- 2004	Peak counts		Peak month
WeBS totals	*1,209^*	*1,219*	*1,387*	*1,700*	*1,996*	*1,933*	*1,889*	*Sep 92*	*2,594*	*Nov*
Stour	115^	141*	355^	489	551	**746**	576	Oct 98	**924**	Nov
Hamford Water	151^	130^	69	31	217	254	356	Nov 01	535	Nov
Colne	203*	~	~	386	319	182	97	Oct 89	625	Oct
Blackwater	434*	473^	391	340	293	498	471	Sep 00	696	Oct
Dengie	397^	461^	295	116	234	137	166	Sep 80	**860**	Sep
Crouch-Roach	9*	~	5	2	1	5	5	Nov 97	30	Nov
Thames	345*	489	369	583	697	450	445	Sep 92	**1,527**	Nov

**Five-year average of peak WeBS counts (Sep-Nov)
of Turnstones from 1970-2004**

Since the early 1980s, the average wintering population has increased, with total numbers currently only marginally lower than during autumn passage.

Although numbers have generally increased, the species' distribution around Essex has not altered with the Stour and Thames the county's principal sites at all seasons. Birds that winter in Essex probably show great site fidelity with movements over 10km rare; they may also return to the same stretch of coastline each winter (Metcalfe & Furness 1985).

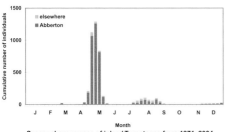

Seasonal occurrence of inland Turnstones from 1971–2004

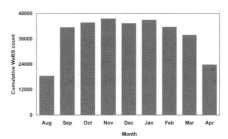

Seasonal occurrence of Turnstones from 1970-2004

The WeBS national Index has shown a continued downward trend since 1982/83. A preliminary analysis suggested a 36% decrease on sections counted by the 1984–85 Winter Shorebird Count and the 1998 NEWS survey, the largest declines being in Cornwall and parts of Scotland. Numbers in Essex have, however, increased by perhaps as much as 30% since the early 1980s. There is evidence to suggest that global warming may have shifted the Turnstone's distribution northeastward, although whether this is due to a redistribution of the existing population or a decline

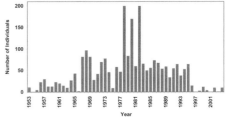

Maximum peak spring counts of Turnstones at Abberton
from 1953-2004

overall is unclear (Rehfisch 2002). A winter population of 1,800 Turnstones represents around 3.7% of the British population.

Returning Turnstones may occur from midsummer, with adults arriving during July and juveniles in strength from late August. Overall numbers remain fairly constant, although different populations are likely to be present in autumn and winter (see below).

Fewer Turnstones are usually recorded outside the main WeBS count period of September–March, although the occasional presence of large flocks suggests that passage is occurring. Indeed, the second largest WeBS count occurred in May 1975 when the total of 3,038 included 2,216 on Dengie. Small numbers are present through summer, possibly first-year non-breeders (Winter Atlas).

Inland, Abberton has attracted far more Turnstones than any other locality. Indeed, from the late 1960s until the mid-1990s numbers occurring in spring were quite exceptional for this type of habitat; the reasons for the marked increase and subsequent rapid decline are difficult to explain.

Migrants appear inland from early April with a marked peak in early to mid-May. Three-figure counts were noted at Abberton during May in three years: 200 on 2nd in 1978, 200 in mid-month in 1982; and 170 on 7th on 1980.

Small numbers pass through Abberton during autumn, eight being the maximum recorded at this time. Away from Abberton, very small numbers pass through Hanningfield during spring and autumn (maximum nine on 7th September 1997). Similar numbers occur along the Lea Valley, principally at the main reservoirs, with six at Girling on 28th July 1959 and eight at KGV on 6th May 2001 the highest counts. A very small number have occurred at other inland sites. Fennoscandian Turnstones that winter in Africa do not return through Britain in spring (Winter Atlas), so it is possible that those occurring inland during May are cutting across Britain and then migrating up the west coast to Greenland. Inland winter records are very rare and have come predominantly from Abberton, where ten on 3rd March 1985 was exceptional with three on 1st February 1965 the next highest inland winter count.

Ringing recoveries have confirmed the passage of the two principal Turnstone populations through Essex. It is generally accepted that it is the northwestern population from Greenland and Canada that winters in Essex, and has therefore increased over the last 75 years or altered its wintering areas, and that Fennoscandian populations are mainly migrants (*BWP*). There is no evidence to suggest that individuals from the tundra (Siberian) population have

GB 500 INT 700	70/71- 74/75	75/76- 79/80	80/81- 84/85	85/86- 89/90	90/91- 94/95	95/96- 99/00	00/01- 04/05	Peak counts		Peak month
WeBS totals	*1,236^*	*1,646*	*1,326*	*1,555*	*1,853*	*1,697*	*1,820^*	*Mar 78*	*3,344*	*Jan*
Stour	278^	295	420	440	550	536	558^	Dec 93	**799**	Jan
Hamford Water	117^	167	72	67^	295	294	356^	Jan 01	527	Jan
Colne	254^	~	~	371	330	159	152^	Mar 87	530	Jan
Blackwater	372^	437	351	296	360	464	308^	Jan 79	**730**	Jan
Dengie	293^	581	226	138	143	200	115^	Mar 78	**2,000**	Jan
Crouch-Roach	3^	2^	10	9	11	20	38^	Jan 04	110	Jan
Thames	205	360	468	591	659	363	529^	Dec 91	**1,297**	Dec

**Five-year average of peak WeBS counts (Dec-Mar)
of Turnstones from 1970/71-2003/04**

ever reached Essex, although there has been one national recovery (*BWP*). The movement of a Turnstone ringed along Dengie in August 1969 and recovered in Spain in October 1970 suggests that this individual was from the Fennoscandian population, whilst one ringed on its Greenland breeding grounds in June 1956 and recovered at Bradwell in August 1958 is likely to have wintered in Essex; the latter was the first national recovery of a Turnstone ringed on its breeding grounds. Other foreign-ringed Turnstones from Norway (three), Poland, the Netherlands (two) and Belgium have been recovered in Essex. One ringed as an adult on Canvey Island on 9th August 1980 was recovered in Belgium in April 1997 when it was at least 17 years old.

Sponsored by Heather Allman

Wilson's Phalarope   *Phalaropus tricolor*

Vagrant: six records involving five individuals

The monotypic Wilson's Phalarope breeds around the shallow marshy wetlands of the North American prairies and winters in South America, mainly on the Argentinean pampas (Hayman *et al.* 1986).

1977	Hanningfield	23rd October–2nd November	Immature
1980	Chigborough Lakes	6th-10th September	1st-winter
1988	Abberton	26th October	Age uncertain
1995	Old Hall	18th June–13th July	Adult female
2001	Old Hall	18th–19th May	Adult female
		23rd July–18th August	Same as previous

The 1977 occurrence was the 13th British record. Did the 1995 individual make a return visit in 2001?

The Wilson's Phalarope is a regular, almost annual transatlantic visitor with a total of 210 records nationally, the last in 2002 (BBRC 2003) and the first as recently as 1954. Numbers in the late 1970s and 1980s were generally higher than in the 1990s. Typically, occurrences peak in late August to early October and involve mainly first-winter/juvenile birds, so it is likely that the Abberton individual was this age. Spring and summer birds are almost invariably females, so the Old Hall individuals fall neatly into this pattern. This species shows sexual role reversal and this may explain why, unlike other summer vagrants, it is females and not males that tend to occur (Cottridge & Vinicombe 1996).

Red-necked Phalarope   *Phalaropus lobatus*

Scarce, less than annual passage migrant: around 78 individuals   Red List

The monotypic Red-necked Phalarope has a circumpolar breeding distribution with the nearest breeding colonies in Scotland, where there were just 19 breeding males in 2002 (RBBP 2004). The species winters at sea in the tropics and in the rest of Britain is a scarce spring and regular autumn passage migrant.

Christy cited five records from the first in August 1842 when "... one or two..." were at Southend-on-Sea and one "... in summer plumage, which was shot in the summer of 1850, whilst running between the rails near the station at Stratford". Glegg added just two more records, including one from the Kentish Knock Lightship on 30th September 1903. All the dated pre-1950 records occurred in late summer/early autumn with four from the coast and three inland.

Since 1950, a maximum of 72 has occurred in 33 years. The species has been recorded more regularly in recent years, probably due to increased observer coverage.

There have been just eight spring records, all involving singles, the earliest being at Hanningfield on 26th April 1967, some three weeks earlier than the next. The latest was also at Hanningfield on 23rd June 1977. The other

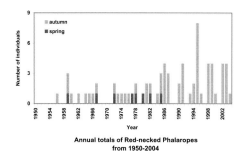

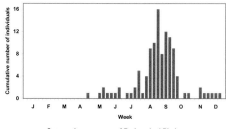

Annual totals of Red-necked Phalaropes
from 1950-2004

Seasonal occurrence of Red-necked Phalaropes
from 1950-2004

spring records were: Dengie, 25th May 1959; Chelmsford SF, 10th–15th June 1972; Rainham, 18th June 1978; Mundon, 17th May 1980; Heybridge GP, 28th May 1982; and Paglesham, 1st June 1985. The lack of a spring record for nearly 20 years is surprising. Of those sexed, all four were females.

Autumn passage commences in mid-July and lasts until late October, typically peaking between mid-August and mid-September. The earliest autumn arrival was an adult female at Old Hall from 6th–12th July 2000 and the latest was one on the Stour at Manningtree from 22nd November–17th December 1956.

Of the 72 individuals since 1950, 32 have occurred inland. A total of 12 has occurred at Hanningfield, including seven between 1959 and 1967 but none from 1978–90, and 12 at Abberton, where the first did not occur until 1982. In the Lea Valley, four have occurred at KGV and three at Girling with the remaining inland record coming from Chelmsford SF. Coastal sightings have come from scattered locations ranging from the Stour round to the Thames as far upstream as Rainham. However, the Blackwater Estuary, with a combined total of 15 individuals from several sites, has been particularly favoured, including Heybridge GP with seven and Old Hall six, the first in 1985. Five have also been reported from East Tilbury including three in 1987. All records have been of singles apart from two at: Foulness, adults, 27th July 1986; Limbourne Creek, Maldon, adults, 13th–19th August 1986; East Tilbury, immatures, 22nd August 1987; Abberton, juveniles, 29th–30th September and 5th October 1991, 2nd–3rd September 1995 and 15th September 1998; and Beaumont Quay, juveniles, 24th–27th September 1998.

Grey Phalarope   *Phalaropus fulicarius*

Scarce, less than annual passage migrant: about 89 records involving around 96 individuals - occasional in winter

The monotypic Grey Phalarope has a similar breeding range to Red-necked Phalarope but its nearest breeding grounds are in Iceland. The species winters at sea with western populations gathering off western and southern Africa.

Christy described the species as "An uncommon and irregular winter visitor when on migration in late autumn or early winter" and listed about 12 records from the first in 1838, when one was shot on the Blackwater and another was found "... in an exhausted state in the parish of Rayne", to the last in 1888, when one was "... killed by a stone from a catapult ..." on Wanstead Flats on 21st November. Christy added that the species was "common in Essex in winter and autumn after heavy northeast gales. Sometimes it is seen in the summer months, generally

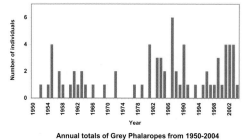

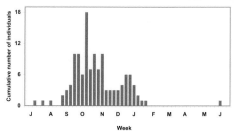

Annual totals of Grey Phalaropes from 1950-2004

Seasonal occurrence of Grey Phalaropes from 1950–2004

swimming inside the mouths of the estuaries". Glegg described the Grey Phalarope as an occasional straggler to Essex and added about 12 records, the latest being one shot near Manningtree about 14th November 1926. Of the total of around 24 records of 25 individuals (cf. Red-necked Phalarope), most of which were shot, 16 were dated: there were three in September, four in October, seven in November and singles in December and January. Just under half were recorded inland at Woodham Mortimer, Dunmow, Wanstead Park, North Weald, Debden, Stratford and Chingford in addition to those locations listed above.

Since 1950, there have been 65 records in 35 years involving a maximum of 71 individuals. There is no clear long-term trend in occurrence, greater observer coverage probably responsible for the apparent increase over the last few decades.

Small numbers occur from mid-July and probably refer to either non-breeders or failed breeders heading back south, the earliest being a moulting adult at Old Hall on 16th June 2002 (male) and a single at Hanningfield on 21st–22nd July 1984. It is possible that the former record may have involved a northward-bound spring migrant, rather than an autumn migrant, although spring records nationally are much rarer than winter records (Fraser *et al.* 1997). Occurrences in Essex are typically erratic but usually involve individuals forced inland after severe gale-force westerlies associated with the passage of vigorous Atlantic depressions. Indeed, numbers tend to peak at around the same time as the height of equinoctial autumn gales from late September to mid-November. Some also turn up after gale force northeasterlies and perhaps involve a very small number that pass through the North Sea, rather than the principal western seaboard migration route. The influx in 1987 occurred after the Great Storm of 16th–17th October. All occurred inland, apart from one at Rainham, with singles at Abberton and Hanningfield and three at KGV from 17th–23rd October (cf. Sabine's Gull).

Several individuals have occurred during winter: East Tilbury, 25th February 1950; Colne Point, tideline corpse, 5th January 1954; Abberton, 18th December 1977–15th January 1978, 21st October 1990–13th January 1991, with a second bird from 30th December–3rd February; KGV, 16th December 1990–11th January 1991; Old Hall, 17th November–28th December 1996; West Thurrock, 26th–28th December 1999; Dengie, a first-winter on 3rd December 2000; and Hanningfield, a first-winter, 1st January 2001. The increase in winter records during the 1990s is notable.

All records have been of singles apart from: the 1987 records above; three in Mucking Bay, 13th November 1955; two off Foulness, 3rd November 1985; and two at Abberton, 30th December 1990–13th January 1991.

Of the 71 individuals since 1950, 40 have occurred inland with the most favoured locations being: Abberton, 14; the Lea Valley reservoirs, 13 with ten at KGV, two at Walthamstow and one at Girling; and Hanningfield, nine. Singles have also been reported from: a farm pond at Stock, 30th September 1952; Wanstead Park lake, 14th November 1963; Audley End, September 9th–11th 1966 and 21st October 1983. The 31 recorded from the coast, which include one that occurred at both Vange and Hanningfield in 2004, show a wide geographical spread, although 17 have come from the Thames at Southend-on-Sea (two), Mucking (three), Canvey Island (five), Two Tree Island, Pitsea, Vange, Thurrock and Rainham (three). Away from the Thames, records come from Harwich (two), The Naze, offshore Clacton-on-Sea, Colne Point (two), West Mersea, Old Hall (three), Dengie (two) and Foulness (three).

Pomarine Skua   *Stercorarius pomarinus*

Late autumn passage migrant in variable numbers - scarce at other times

The monotypic Pomarine Skua has an almost circumpolar distribution, breeding on the tundra from the Kanin peninsula in Russia to Siberia, Alaska and arctic Canada. In the Western Palearctic the species breeds only in northern Russia and Novaya Zemlya. Nesting is sporadic in years when Lemmings, the species' principal prey, are scarce. The western breeding population is probably in the region of 1,000–10,000 pairs (European Atlas). Pomarine Skuas migrate from their breeding grounds to wintering quarters in the southeast Atlantic and Australasia usually by slow coastal progression. In Britain, the species is a regular inshore migrant, although numbers fluctuate annually. Few are recorded in spring apart from around the Western Isles but autumn numbers can be large. A small wintering population may be evident in some years.

The earliest documented Essex record involved one shot on Hackney Marshes prior to 1828 (Christy). Otherwise Christy and Glegg cited a further 11 records involving 12 birds, the last in 1922, all from the coast with records in

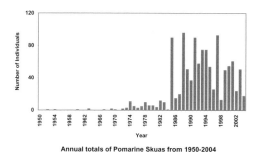

Annual totals of Pomarine Skuas from 1950-2004

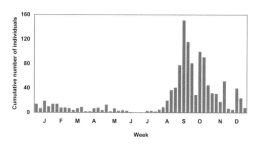

Seasonal occurrence of Pomarine Skuas from 1950–2004

August (two), September (three), October (two), November and December (three). At Harwich at the end of the 19th century Christy noted that "... a few are seen most autumns". Just how accurate these identifications were will never be known.

The next Essex record was not until 1952 when a dead individual was picked up at Frinton-on-Sea on 31st October. From then, until the late 1960s, there were just five further records (Hudson & Pyman).

From 1967, the presence of a birding orientated fisherman in Essex coastal waters saw small numbers reported with some regularity and by 1972 the species was being recorded annually. Numbers remained remarkably constant until the late 1980s at which time the increasing interest in seawatching and improvements in optical equipment established the species' true status. Currently an average year sees 50–75 recorded but larger influxes were noted in 1985 (90), 1988 (96), 1991 (90) and 1997 (93). The majority of recent records have come from the Thames Estuary, especially off Canvey Island. The 1985 influx, which occurred in December, saw 35 past Southend Pier on 15th with 11 on 22nd and ten off Shoebury on 17th. Amongst the 96 in 1988, there were 20 adults off East Tilbury on 25th September and 12 on 27th September off Maplin, whilst in November 13 immatures were off East Tilbury on 20th. The high numbers in 1991 were not the result of any major movements but a protracted passage. In 1997, there were 11 off Canvey Island on both 19th August and 12th October. The largest single-day count occurred in 1993 when 39 passed Canvey Island on 14th September. The only other double-figure counts have all come from the Thames Estuary: Southend Pier, 14 on 19th September 1987; Canvey Island, 18 on 9th September 1989, ten on 21st October 1990, 15 on 16th and 13 on 17th October 1994; East Tilbury, ten on 21st October 1990.

Most Pomarine Skuas occur from mid-September to October but influxes, presumably weather-induced, during November and December are not unusual; it is generally the latest of the skuas to occur off the Essex coast.

Since 1986 occasional wintering birds have been noted, primarily in the Thames Estuary. In 1986, following the previous autumn's influx, there were eight off Southend Pier on 1st February with 2–4 from January to the end of March, whilst in 1992, following the influx in late 1991, there were up to eight in the estuary, the peak count coming from East Tilbury on 20th January. In early 2000, another influx occurred despite small numbers in the previous autumn, with 4–5 present in January and February, up to seven in March and four in April. Unlike the previous influxes, most occurred from Dengie northwards during January–March but the majority of the April records came from the Thames.

A small spring passage is detectable in some years, although not on a scale in any way comparable with that along the English south coast, where peaks occur between 30th April and 14th May and perhaps involve Baltic breeding birds (*BWP*). Since 1990, usually 1–3 adults sporting their characteristic extended central tail feathers or 'spoons' have been reported annually although, in addition to April 2000 (see above), there were seven in 1994 with five at East Tilbury from 10th–18th April.

Only occasional individuals are reported after April with, until 2000, just one June and no July record. In 2000, however, following the high numbers present in winter and early spring, influxes occurred in mid-May, June and July in the Thames Estuary and it is possible that several immatures summered; most sightings coincided with a rising tide. Three first-years were off Canvey Island on 19th May, with two off East Tilbury on 4th June and three on 11th and 16th July, with odd birds on other dates.

Since 1950 there have been just five inland records: Hanningfield, five, 10th November 1985 and a first-winter bird, 28th December 1985–3rd January 1986; Walthamstow, a dark-phase adult, 28th November–4th December 1954; Girling, an immature, 11th–22nd December 1976; and KGV, an adult, 25th September 1988. Individuals have also been recorded as far up the Thames as Barking Bay and Rainham on a number of occasions and there were also singles at Heybridge GP on 23rd August 1981 and 5th May 2002 (an adult).

Arctic Skua

Stercorarius parasiticus

Autumn passage migrant - scarce at other times

The monotypic Arctic Skua is a circumpolar species that breeds on tundra and coastal moors. In Europe the species breeds near most coasts north of 59° and on inland tundra in Russia, Iceland, Svalbard, Norway and Sweden. The nearest breeding colonies are in Scotland where the population increased to 3,400 pairs during the 20th century (European Atlas), although more recently this has been nearer 2,100 pairs, around 7% of the world population (Mitchell *et al.* 2004). Arctic Skuas are long-distance migrants that winter off the southern coasts of Africa, South America and Australasia. Most migrate along coasts where they associate with and rob terns and small gulls of food. The species, however, regularly migrates overland.

The Arctic Skua declined, at least in Britain, during the 19th century due to intense persecution, although Christy described the species as "Fairly common on the coast as a passing migrant in spring and autumn". In all he listed around 11 records, from the first at "Sampford" in 1837: this may well be the same specimen as an alleged Long-tailed Skua shot at Sampford on 29th September 1837 and retained at Saffron Walden Museum (Accession No. 367D). Almost all the specimens were shot, either in autumn or winter and, in addition to the Sampford record, included one shot at High

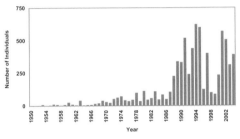

Annual totals of Arctic Skuas from 1950-2004

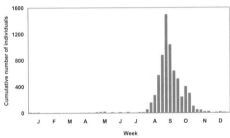

Seasonal occurrence of Arctic Skuas from 1950-2004

Ongar in the severe winter of 1837/38. At Harwich, at the end of the 19th century, Arctic Skuas were "rare". Glegg noted around 13 individuals, all bar one, at Bradwell on 10th June 1922, in autumn or winter. There were just two records between 1890 and 1929, suggesting a decline in occurrence. However, Glegg, commenting on observations made from the Kentish Knock Lightship in September and October 1903, and the fact that the species was annual along the Norfolk and Kent coasts, noted with some insight that "It would appear that after leaving the projecting Norfolk coast, the birds proceed directly southwards over the sea, thus missing the Essex coast".

Hudson & Pyman considered that the Arctic Skua was a "... regular autumn passage migrant in very small numbers ... though inshore numbers are small by the standard of other east coast counties". An influx of at least 40 in autumn 1963 was considered exceptional. However, the majority of records came from fishermen working the offshore waters; very few were seen from the coast. Nonetheless, numbers observed from the coast were increasing steadily and, although this may have been in part due to increases in the Scottish population, greater observer coverage was undoubtedly a factor.

Better understanding of the weather conditions in which Arctic Skuas were likely to occur and improvements in optics meant that by the early 1980s the Arctic Skua was confirmed as a regular autumn passage migrant with Cox noting "Observations in the last ten years have necessitated some revision of the status of the Arctic Skua". Much of the increase up to this time was due to concentrated seawatching in the outer Thames Estuary from Southend Pier to Foulness; at the latter, peak counts were 35 on 26th August 1978 and 40 on 30th August 1980.

Cox considered that northerly autumn gales produced the largest influxes, although good numbers have also occurred on strong easterlies and on calm days, particularly in late August/September; some have also occurred with influxes of Kittiwakes.

Between 1988 and 1990, SOG carried out an intensive campaign of seawatching in the outer Thames Estuary from Maplin Flats to Canvey Island (Saward 1991). This showed that weather-related movements of seabirds took

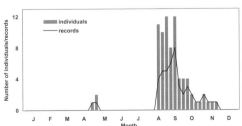

Seasonal occurrence of inland Arctic Skuas from 1950–2004

place annually along the Essex shore of the outer Thames and, given the right weather conditions, impressive movements could take place. Strong north to northeast winds are generally the most favourable, particularly during September and October when low pressure systems moving across the North Sea are not uncommon (Saward 1991). The largest influxes of Arctic Skuas have occurred on strong northeasterlies but small numbers appear to move through continually during autumn, not necessarily being restricted to days with a wind. The findings of this survey gave added impetus to seawatching in Essex and the number of Arctic Skuas reported has increased significantly, particularly from the Thames but also from other parts of the coast. Peak counts have been: 166 off Canvey Island, 7th September 2004; 79 off Southend Pier, 25th September 1988; and 72 off Canvey Island, 14th September 1994. More than 80% of the largest annual total of 623 birds in 1994 were reported from Canvey Island.

Arctic Skuas in the Thames often move through in flocks when they can be seen actively feeding and chasing groups of terns. The species will penetrate well up the Thames, being regular at East Tilbury where peak counts have been 60 on 5th September 1991 and a total of 95 on 9th and 10th September 1989. Indeed, whilst this site regularly shares in the influxes into the Thames, on several dates more Arctic Skuas have been recorded here than at sites nearer the mouth of the estuary. Whilst this may suggest that observers at the wider end of the estuary miss some Arctic Skuas, it is possible that others may be arriving from overland or are dropping down from high-level migration above the Thames when the 'bottleneck' becomes apparent to them at East Tilbury. Away from the Thames, counts of more than ten are rare with 20 off The Naze on the 19th September 1999 the highest north of Maplin in a very poor year for the species countywide.

In Essex, Arctic Skua passage begins in mid-July, although the presence offshore of what may be summering non-breeding individuals may mask the early movements to some degree. Passage peaks in mid-September and declines rapidly after the end of October. The southern movement of failed breeders and immatures starts in July with successful breeders leaving southern colonies such as the Shetland Islands between early August and September with birds from higher latitudes moving 1–2 weeks later; peak migration through Britain occurs in September (Furness 1987).

Small but increasing numbers of Arctic Skuas occur in Essex waters during winter, although numbers vary from year to year. Five were offshore from Clacton-on-Sea/St Osyth on 10th January 1974, and there were four off Foulness on 12th December 1982 and two off Wakering Stairs on the same day. In 1985 there was a late influx of Arctic Skuas towards the end of October and early November, after which above average numbers wintered in the Thames Estuary with 3–5 from November–January and 1–2 in February. Otherwise, the majority of winter records are of singles, mostly from the Thames Estuary, although records have come from all around the coast.

The number of Arctic Skuas in Essex decline through winter such that by the end of February and through to the end of March records are particularly rare. Furness (1987) noted that there were very few Northern Hemisphere records of Arctic Skua during February, suggesting that southern migration may continue until the end of February, when the first northbound birds start to return. It is therefore likely that those seen in Essex waters during winter are, perhaps, not wintering in the true sense of the word but drifting slowly south, taking advantage of good feeding conditions wherever available.

Spring passage through Essex is extremely light and apparently less than annual. The majority of records have involved single birds. However, there were nine off Canvey Island on 28th May 1988 and eight light-phase birds passed Colne Point on 19th May 1973. There were six off Southend Pier on 13th May 1974 out of a total of 13 between 13th and 24th May. The northern spring movement of Arctic Skuas is rapid, unlike the autumn movement, which is a far more leisurely affair (Olsen & Larsson 1997). It is interesting to note that quite a strong easterly passage is noted most years along the English Channel coast (e.g. Clarke & Eyre 1993) during late April–early May. That this is not detected in Essex suggests the movement occurs well offshore at this time of year.

Inland, there have been 45 records involving a total of 74 individuals at ten locations since 1950. The pattern of inland occurrences is generally similar to that on the coast. All records have occurred in autumn except for two at KGV: one on 23rd April 1977 and two there on 7th May 2000. Nearly 50% of the records have come from Hanningfield, where 21 records have involved 36 individuals, the largest flocks being six on 20th August 1988 and seven on 17th August 1990. At Abberton, five records involved eight birds. There have been four records each from Walthamstow, Girling and KGV involving in total 11, six and five birds, respectively, the largest inland flock being eight at Walthamstow on 30th August 1997. Inland records have also come from Friday Wood (two), Stansted Airport Lagoons, Ashdon, Dagnam Park (two) and Dagenham Chase. Records from the Lea Valley may well involve individuals that have been observed heading south inland from The Wash (Taylor *et al.* 1999).

There have been no ringing recoveries of Arctic Skuas affecting Essex. However, Shetland-ringed birds have been found dead in Norfolk, whilst Scandinavian-ringed nestlings have been recovered in Britain, suggesting that both populations may pass through eastern England.

Long-tailed Skua

Stercorarius longicaudus

Scarce autumn passage migrant: 147 individuals

The Long-tailed Skua has a circumpolar, largely Arctic, breeding distribution where the species breeds on tundra, although further south the species will nest on mountain plateaux. In Europe, where Long-tailed Skuas are of the nominate race *longicaudus*, the species nests in Norway, Sweden, Finland and Russia. Migration south to wintering areas in Antarctica and southern parts of Africa and South

America (Furness 1987) is generally pelagic, avoiding overland travel or coastlines (European Atlas).

Christy described the Long-tailed Skua as "A rare and occasional visitor when on migration" and listed five records. There is some considerable doubt over the alleged first, which was shot at "Sampford" on 29th September 1837, as there remains in Saffron Walden Museum an Arctic Skua (Accession No. 367D) shot at "Sampford" in 1837: Glegg quite rightly rejected the record and Hudson & Pyman concurred. Thus, the first Essex record was one at Southend-on-Sea in early 1842, although for some reason Glegg did not mention it. Christy recorded single specimens in each year from 1881–83, including one found emaciated at Wimbish on 20th October 1881.

Remarkably, it was another 90 years until the next record when one was seen from a fishing boat 10km off St Osyth on 28th September 1973, with the next (an immature) picked up moribund at Colne Point on 8th

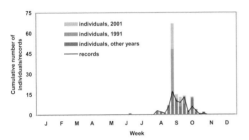

Seasonal occurrence of Long-tailed Skuas from 1973-2004

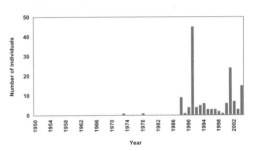

Annual totals of Long-tailed Skuas from 1950-2004

September 1978. It was a further ten years until the next, when nine occurred in 1988, since when it has been an annual migrant in small numbers with most of the records occurring in 1991 (31%) and 2001 (16%). Greater observer effort, better understanding of the species' identification and better optics have almost certainly been responsible for the increase with most occurring in the Thames Estuary, particularly off Southend Pier and Canvey Island.

Nationally, numbers recorded annually vary markedly, a pattern typical of many Arctic birds whose breeding success is so dependent on the Lemming cycle, although prevailing weather conditions at the time of migration probably also influence numbers. Those in 1991 were part of a huge influx, the largest ever recorded in Britain, following a very good breeding season.

There has been just one modern late spring/early summer record, an adult off Bradwell on 22nd June 2003. Autumn passage shows a marked peak during September.

The earliest reports, from Canvey Island on 8th August 1992 and 8th August 1995, involved adults, which migrate earlier than immatures; the latest record involved two juveniles off Canvey Island on 30th October 2000.

Since 1988 a total of 111 (76%) individuals has been recorded from the Thames Estuary, mostly from Canvey Island, with the largest counts being: 16 off Canvey Island on 8th September 2001, and ten off Southend Pier on 8th September 1991. The consistency of dates of the two largest influxes is remarkable. The remaining coastal records show a wide geographical spread, although no more than two have occurred at any location on any one day.

In addition to the 19th century record, there have been three inland occurrences: KGV, an immature, 23rd–28th September 1990; Girling, a juvenile, 8th–9th September 1993, which moved to KGV, 9th–23rd September; and Abberton, a juvenile, 12th–17th September 1996.

Great Skua

Stercorarius skua

Late autumn passage migrant: scarce at other times

Amber List

The monotypic Great Skua, or Bonxie, is endemic to Europe and has a restricted breeding distribution. Around 60% of the world population, a total of 9,600 breeding pairs (Mitchell *et al.* 2004), nest on the moorlands of the Scottish Northern Isles, with the remainder in Iceland (5,400 pairs) and the Faeroe Islands (275 pairs) and a few in Svalbard and Norway (European Atlas). After being reduced to virtual extinction in Scotland around 1900, protection from human persecution saw breeding numbers almost double in every decade until 1970. Subsequently, populations continued to increase at a slower rate but recent declines in Lesser Sandeel numbers, a principal prey item, have reduced numbers. The species is a regular, principally autumn, migrant around the coast of Britain and Ireland.

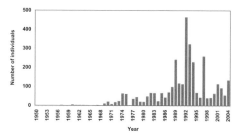

Annual totals of Great Skuas from 1950-2004

Christy considered the species "… a rare passing migrant, seen on the coast when migrating in spring and autumn". Of the five definite records he listed (a sixth Christy observed himself but he did not seem absolutely certain of its identification), the earliest documented was also the sole inland record, one shot at Elmdon around 1820. He listed several local names for the species, "Turd-bird", "Dung-bird" and "Dung-eater", which were some of the local names given by "… fishermen and others along the coast … which are expressive of one of its characteristic habits, rather than polite". Given the near-extinction of the main Scottish population by 1900, it is not surprising that Glegg could add just three further records, including one inland at Rayne in October 1913. Of the eight records prior to 1930, six were shot; all dated records occurred in autumn.

The Great Skua was still considered a very scarce, albeit probably regular autumn migrant in the 1960s (Hudson & Pyman). Until 1969 there had never been more than five in any single year. However, the same factors that saw increasing numbers of other seabirds recorded, revealed that more were passing down the coast than previously thought. Nonetheless, some 40% of Great Skuas recorded from 1972–82 were from fishing boats in offshore waters (Cox). Great Skuas are the most maritime of skuas, generally moving south over the continental shelf of western Europe, usually between 1–2 and 20–30km offshore (Furness 1987). Thus, in Essex at least, it is only in strong winds, usually with a northerly or easterly element, that any numbers are observed from the coast. It was not until 1989 that more than 100 were seen in a single year, at a time when intensive seawatching in the outer Thames by members of SOG was rewriting the seabird record book (Saward 1991).

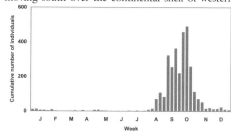

Seasonal occurrence of Great Skuas from 1950-2004

As with almost all other seabirds, the majority of records have come from the outer Thames. From 3rd–5th October 1992, a total of at least 240 flew past Canvey Island. This total included 185 on 4th which, along with 165 that passed Southend Pier on 14th October 1993 (151 passing Canvey Island the same day presumably involved the birds seen from the pier), are the county's only three-figure day counts. Given that counts in excess of 100 are not unusual off the north Norfolk coast but rare off east Norfolk (Taylor *et al.* 1999) and unknown in Suffolk (Piotrowski 2003), and that large numbers are regularly counted at south coast migration points, it seems that, like other seabirds, most move down the East Anglian coast out of sight of land, perhaps well beyond the sandbars that are a feature of the Essex coastline. Only in severe weather with moderate to strong onshore winds are large numbers pushed in view of the coast and even then high tides appear necessary to obscure the offshore sandbars. Comparison with the situation along the north Norfolk coast suggests that north Kent acts as a 'barrier' in severe weather with southerly migrating flocks diverting either east in to the English Channel or west into the Thames Estuary, depending on weather conditions and/or 'choice'.

The large numbers in 1992 occurred following moderate northeast winds, low cloud cover and sea fog. Some of those in the Thames may have been moving overland as flocks were seen descending from high altitude through the clouds above the river, circling or gathering on the water, and then climbing back into the clouds and striking off southwest into Kent. This behaviour has been seen in other years, too, but not necessarily in windy weather; movements have been noted on calm days (Saward 1991). Overland migration is common in skuas and, although

Great Skuas are more averse than most to land, migrating flocks of up to 80 of this species have been observed heading south inland from The Wash, Norfolk (Taylor *et al.* 1999).

Immatures leave the breeding sites in July, followed by failed breeders and early fledglings in August and finally the majority of adults and juveniles in September (Furness 1987). Passage through Essex peaks from mid-September to mid-October.

Occasional birds reported in midsummer might be wandering immatures (*BWP*) heading north. Juveniles tend to head south to winter off the coasts of southern France, the Iberian peninsula and north Africa. Adults from the Shetland Islands winter between Britain and Iberia (Furness 1987). The few midwinter Essex records are therefore likely to involve adults as they winter far closer to Essex than immatures. Most are single birds but off Southend Pier there have been: five on 10th February 1985 with three on 16th; three on 16th December 1985; and four on 7th December 2002.

Northward migration commences in March and April but few have been noted in Essex at this time, three at Bradwell on 3rd April 1983 being the highest count; a total of five was off Clacton-on-Sea between 16th and 30th April 1985. As in autumn, a strong spring migration is noted along the English Channel coast; the lack of Essex records at this time suggests that, like Arctic Skuas, they move rapidly north, well offshore.

Not surprisingly for such a maritime species, inland records are very rare. In addition to the two pre-1950 records there have been just ten, all since 1983, when there were ten at Hanningfield on 11th September following gale-force west to northwesterlies, which produced significant seabird movements off southwest England. Apart from six at KGV on 9th September 1989, which coincided with record coastal counts, the remaining eight records all involved singles: Girling/KGV, 22nd–23rd September 1984: Abberton, 20th November 1985; Hanningfield, 4th and 8th September 1985; Hanningfield, 25th August 1986; Abberton, 6th October 1992; Hanningfield, 16th September 1994; and KGV, 2nd September 1996. Interestingly, half of the records fall in the first two weeks in September, earlier than the peak on the coast. Movements through the Lea Valley may well be associated with apparent inland migration noted in The Wash, Norfolk (see above), almost due north. The bias towards Hanningfield is similar to the pattern seen with other skuas. It suggests that the Thames in some way influences the occurrence of skuas at Hanningfield, although just how is not clear.

There have been four ringing recoveries of Great Skua in Essex since 1950, all in autumn/winter, all tideline corpses and all from the Orkney or Shetland Islands. One from North Ronaldsay was recovered at West Mersea, whilst two from Foula were found at The Naze and East Tilbury with another from North Roe, Shetland Islands, found at West Mersea. These recoveries are typical of the national picture (Migration Atlas).

Mediterranean Gull   *Larus melanocephalus*

Increasing resident, passage migrant and winter visitor   Amber List

The monotypic Mediterranean Gull has a West Palearctic distribution, its main breeding grounds being the warm, dry north coast of the Black Sea. Having at one time been considered vulnerable and heading for extinction (Voous 1960), most populations have expanded and increased significantly since the 1950s (European Atlas). The current population numbers some 300,000–370,000 pairs, with 99% in the former USSR (*HBW*). The population increase has resulted in a westward range expansion through central and northwest Europe with around 2,100 pairs breeding in the Netherlands and 250–300 in Belgium (Olsen & Larsen 2004). Prior to the 1950s, the species was a very rare visitor to Britain with only four records prior to 1940. However, records began to increase as the species became more regular in northwest Europe, with breeding first occurring in 1968 in Hampshire, since when the population has risen slowly to 90–105 pairs in 2001 (Ogilvie *et al.* 2003), although there were only 63–75 in 2002. Increasing numbers are also wintering in northwest Europe.

The first British record involved an immature shot on the Thames at Barking Creek in January 1866 and identified by Saunders in 1871 from the specimen in the British Museum. It was not immediately accepted as a British bird, although some eminent ornithologists, such as Harting (1872), accepted the record as authentic. Seebohm (1883–85) stated that: "The only evidence for its admission to the British List is that of a specimen purchased for the British Museum from Mr Whitely, of Woolwich, who stated that it was shot in January, 1866, near Barking Creek. An accidental change of label, either at the British Museum or on Mr Whitely's part, is the probable explanation." It was only after the occurrence of a second one, shot quite by chance at Breydon Water, Norfolk, in December 1886 (Taylor *et al.* 1999) that the Barking record gained acceptance.

It was to be another 90 years before the next Essex record, when an adult made a protracted stay at The Naze from 28th July–25th October 1956. What was almost certainly the same bird returned to The Naze in the following five autumns. Single birds were subsequently recorded in five of the next ten years. After two in 1973, there was an increase

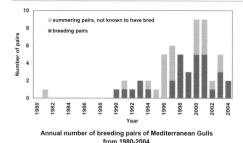

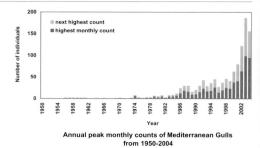

Annual number of breeding pairs of Mediterranean Gulls
from 1980-2004

Annual peak monthly counts of Mediterranean Gulls
from 1950-2004

to ten in 1974, six of which were found together on Foulness on 30th March, although one was dead. Thereafter there was a steady increase until the late 1990s since when numbers have increased sharply with the large number of confiding individuals around Southend Pier providing an excellent opportunity to observe the species at close quarters.

Arlow (2004) concluded that at least 160 different individuals had passed through the Southend-on-Sea area alone in 2003, a figure probably exceeded in 2004. The Thames has traditionally been the favoured locality of the species, particularly from Two Tree Island east to Shoebury. Initially, the cockle-sheds at Leigh-on-Sea and the refuse tip on Two Tree Island held the highest numbers with up to seven individuals during 1980. More recently, Canvey Island and Southend-on-Sea seafront, and particularly the Pier, have become the most regular sites. The largest single site counts have all come from Southend-on-Sea seafront between the pier and Westcliff-on-Sea with 86 on 19th August 2004, 73 on 14th August 2004, 66 on 3rd August 2004 and 65 on 1st July 2003. Away from the Thames, the Mediterranean Gull is regular around the entire coastline, although counts of more than three are rare. However, there were 11 at The Naze on 25th April 2003 and seven at: Dovercourt, 27th January 2002; East Mersea, 3rd April 2004; Old Hall, 26th May 2001; and Salcott, 6th May 2002.

A number of individuals have shown remarkable site fidelity. One that is at least 15 years old, and known locally as 'Limpy' on account of a damaged leg, has spent most of its life along the Blackwater between Maldon and Bradwell, having been seen at the latter location in the Black-headed Gull colony and strongly suspected to have bred there. 'Mike the Med' was also a regular around Southend Pier, whilst another has frequented the area around a well-known fast-food outlet in Basildon for the last few years.

Inland, Mediterranean Gulls are now reported with some regularity and, whilst the species can turn up almost anywhere, the Lea Valley has been particularly favoured, the highest inland count coming from Girling, with six on 1st March 1997. There were seven along the Lea Valley in early March 1995. Until recently, Mediterranean Gulls have been surprisingly scarce at Abberton.

Numbers of Mediterranean Gulls usually peak around March and again from July to September, suggesting that passage is probably occurring through Essex. In recent years there has been an increasing trend in the Southend-on-Sea area for numbers to peak very significantly from June to September, with a significant proportion being adults (Arlow 2004). Most of the west European breeding population is thought to gather at Le Portal, Pas-de-Calais, France, from late July to mid-August (Olsen & Larsson 2004); the autumn peak may therefore involve individuals moving to/from that locality. Otherwise, autumn and winter numbers are relatively constant, although whether this suggests that those that arrive in autumn remain to winter or move on and are replaced by later arriving winter birds is unclear. The fact that there is a strong spring passage supports the latter view that at least in part, many of the apparently 'new' individuals are adults that are perhaps heading back east to the near-Continent to breed.

Since the mid-1980s the number recorded summering has increased steadily, although as early as the 1970s occasional individuals had made extended stays. In 1970 a single adult was seen on three separate occasions in a Black-headed Gull colony in Hamford Water, although breeding was not suspected. In 1980 an adult was noted exhibiting breeding behaviour at Hanningfield. It was seen repeatedly carrying nesting material and then food to the same spot. However, no other adults were seen and it was suspected that it had paired with a Black-headed Gull, a not uncommon phenomenon, particularly for a newly arrived breeding species on the limit of its range. Hybrids of what were

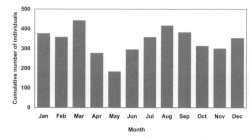

Seasonal occurrence of Mediterranean Gulls
from 1956-2004

thought to be Mediterranean x Black-headed Gulls have been seen on several occasions. It was not until 1990 that a pure Mediterranean Gull pair bred in Essex and breeding has been attempted or taken place in every year since.

Each breeding attempt has been within one of the large coastal Black-headed Gull colonies and most have been in the northeast. Breeding success has generally been low; the species is known to be extremely susceptible to disturbance and will only return to the nest after some time, which can result in heavy losses and desertion (HBW). In Hamford Water, the main cause has probably been due to high tides flooding out the nests (Simon Cox pers. comm.).

Information gained from a coordinated colour-ringing scheme across Europe has shown that most of the birds seen in Essex probably come from the near-Continent. Movements away from breeding areas can occur quite quickly. For instance a juvenile colour-ringed as a nestling at Bergen Op Zoom, Noord Brabant, the Netherlands, on 17th May 1990 was seen at Leigh-on-Sea on 21st July 1990. An individual ringed as a nestling in Hamford Water on 12th June 1992 was subsequently seen in Noord Brabant, the Netherlands, on 24th June 1997 indicating that movements occur both ways. Remarkably, all three individuals from one brood ringed in Hamford Water on 30th May 2001 have subsequently been sighted locally and in France, Devon and Cornwall. A nestling ringed at Leibes, Rostock, Germany, on 11th June 1983 was recovered at Pitsea on 8th February 1986, whilst three ringed/colour-ringed Mediterranean Gulls have occurred in the early 2000s. Remarkably, two of these ringed at the same former-Czechoslovakian site and bearing consecutive ring numbers have been observed around Southend-on-Sea. Birds from Hungary and the former Yugoslavia have been seen in Kent in recent years and it is likely that individuals from a range of Eastern European countries visit the county occasionally (Migration Atlas).

With numbers of this attractive gull continuing to increase nationally, there seems no reason for numbers breeding and wintering in Essex not to increase too. However, given that many gull colonies are regularly washed out by increasingly high tides and that predation at some sites, either by mammals or birds, is a problem, the species' particular susceptibility to disturbance suggests that any increases are liable to be very slow.

Laughing Gull $\qquad$ *Larus atricilla*

Vagrant: two records

The Laughing Gull breeds along the eastern seaboard of the USA, the Caribbean, Central America and northern South America, and generally winters south of its range from North Carolina to northern South America and on the Pacific coast from southern Mexico to Peru. The race *megalopterus* breeds in all areas, except the Caribbean, where the nominate race *atricilla* occurs.

1974	Holliwell Point	5th May	Adult summer
1999	Canvey Island	24th February	1st-winter

To the end of 2004, there had been 99 British records (BBRC 2005), with a marked increase in recent years, probably due to greater observer awareness. The 1974 occurrence was only the eighth British record. Unlike Ring-billed Gull, the species shows no westerly bias to records and no real pattern of occurrence except that many are seen at coastal locations (Cottridge & Vinicombe 1996).

A record of an adult in winter plumage at Abberton on 20th December 1957, which was belatedly accepted in 1968, has recently been removed from the official record by the BBRC as the bill and leg colour noted in the description were wrong (the late Mike Rogers pers. comm.).

Franklin's Gull $\qquad$ *Larus pipixcan*

Vagrant: two records possibly involving the same individual

The monotypic Franklin's Gull breeds in inland North America from British Columbia to Alberta and from Montana to Minnesota with scattered populations in the northern Rocky Mountains and Great Basin. Most winter off western South America, south as far as Chile.

2000	Barking Bay	13th–16th April	2nd-summer
	Southend Pier	29th December	Adult or 2nd-winter

The BBRC assumed this to be the same well-travelled individual that also visited Avon, Dorset and Somerset in 2000 (BBRC 2002). A total of 44 had been recorded in Britain to the end of 2004 (BBRC 2005). Although seen in Barking Bay, much of its time was spent in the Thamesmead area, thus ensuring that it was a first for Essex, Greater London and Kent.

Little Gull   *Larus minutus*

Regular passage migrant: scarce summer and winter visitor

The monotypic Little Gull occupies a huge breeding range stretching from the east and south coasts of the Baltic in the west to the Ob basin in the east, with the bulk of the population nesting in southwest Siberia and north Kazakhstan. However, the species will occasionally nest hundreds, even thousands of kilometres outside its normal range (European Atlas), and small numbers breed regularly in west and central Europe. There have been four confirmed breeding records in Britain, although all have failed at the egg stage (Messenger 2001). Little Gulls breed on inland marshes but winter in offshore waters, with West Palearctic populations dispersing west and south to winter offshore from the Baltic Sea, Britain and Ireland south to west Africa, and throughout the Mediterranean to the Black and Caspian Seas (European Atlas).

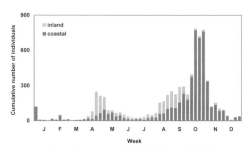

Seasonal occurrence of Little Gulls from 1971-2004

Christy described the Little Gull as "An irregular and uncommon winter visitor, of which about a dozen specimens, most of them in immature plumage, are recorded from Essex", the earliest documented being one "... shot at the mouth of a small river ..." prior to 1845. He also referred to several other occurrences where specimens were not obtained. Of the dated records, one was in spring, five in autumn and seven in winter. The sole inland record came from the Stort at Bishop's Stortford around 1870. Glegg detailed some 22 records, with 23 obtained, nine of which came from the Stour and seven from the Thames. Of the dated records, 11 fell between December and February, one in April (plus one in "spring") and six between August and October. Hudson & Pyman noted: " ... the Little Gull has appeared regularly since the last war (particularly so since 1956)." This increase occurred nationally at this time and became even more pronounced during the 1960s and 1970s with Cox noting that the Little Gull was "... much increased". It was considered probable that the rise was linked to an increase in the breeding population east of the Baltic (Hutchinson & Neath 1978). Since the 1980s, numbers have generally continued to rise. Total numbers recorded annually are greatly influenced by weather-related late autumn influxes along the coast.

Spring passage lasts from late April through to mid-June. The largest numbers tend to occur following overnight rain and strong winds from the east or southeast. Most occur inland. Usually full adults are the first to arrive, followed by first and second-year birds later in spring. In recent years, 25–50 have been recorded in an average spring. However, there have been several exceptional influxes. Thus, 67 at KGV on 16th April 2003 and 65 moving northeast there on 28th April 1995 are not only the largest individual spring counts, but also the largest from an inland location at any time of year. There was a total of around 160 Little Gulls during spring 1995, 150 in 2004 (including 102 on 1st May) and 144 in 2002. Other significant counts in excess of 20 at this time of year have all come from Hanningfield, except for 23 at Abberton on 1st May 2004: 40 (39 adults) on 22nd April 1987, 28 on 16th April 1996, 23 on 28th April 1995 and 20 on 21st April 1984. Few other spring day counts have reached double figures. Coastal passage is infrequently observed during spring with just one count exceeding ten: 62 off East Tilbury on 1st May 2004, 45 of which occurred further upriver the same day at Rainham.

A few individuals, mainly first-summer birds, have been noted summering. In 1989 a pair was noted displaying at Hanningfield. There has been no real increase in the number of summering birds in Essex

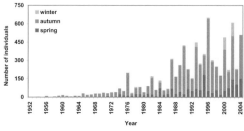

Annual totals of Little Gulls from 1952-2004

despite the significant increase in passage numbers. Nationally, Messenger (2001) concluded that an expansion of the breeding range of the Little Gull to Britain was "... extremely improbable in the foreseeable future".

Autumn passage may start as soon as early July. The pattern of occurrence in Essex at this time of year is interesting. Overall, numbers show a double peak with an early autumn inland peak, followed by a second larger coastal peak at the end of October. It has been suggested that Little Gulls undergo a two-stage dispersal from breeding grounds to enable them to undergo their autumn moult in relatively sheltered conditions (Hutchinson & Neath 1978). The first is a post-breeding dispersal to late summer quarters in sheltered bays, which allows the completion of the moult, and the second is a movement further out to sea for winter. It appears that the earlier inland peak may involve the first movement, with the second movement coinciding with the larger coastal numbers in October.

Autumnal peaks inland are generally small, although an exceptional influx occurred in the Lea Valley in September 1993 with at least 100 moving through Girling and KGV mid-month and maxima of 27 on 16th, 30 on 17th and 35 on 22nd. Otherwise, the highest counts have been: 36 at Walthamstow, 10th September 1989; 22 south over KGV/Walthamstow, 22nd October 2000; 20 at Hanningfield, 2nd September 1990; 13 at Fishers Green, 20th October 2000; 12 at Abberton, 20th November 1983; and 12 at Abberton, 18th September 1999.

Late autumn numbers vary considerably from year to year with the largest counts usually occurring along the coast after strong to gale-force north to northeasterlies, which presumably drive a proportion of the large numbers migrating through the southern North Sea much closer to shore than would be normal. The largest single influx was in October 1990 and followed a period of easterlies combined with poor visibility. A total of 176 was off Bradwell on 25th October, with 103 at Colne Point the same day assumed to have involved the same birds; there were still 88 off Colne Point two days later. The only other three-figure day count was 112 off The Naze on 8th October 2004. Other counts in excess of 50 off the coast have been: 70 offshore northeast coast, 4th October 1996 with 60 on 16th; 65 off Canvey Island, 24th October 1999; 61 off The Naze, 21st October 2000; and 60 off Colne Point, 18th October 1976.

Very small numbers of Little Gulls are present in most winters off the coast. Usually no more than 1–2 are reported. However, large numbers lingered in Essex waters well into December 2000 with 30 off The Naze on 1st and ten off Canvey Island on 24th-25th, whilst there were ten off East Tilbury on 7th December 2002. In early 2003 there was an exceptional passage along the Thames, peaking at 84 on 1st January off Southend Pier with double-figure counts at this time from Canvey Island and East Tilbury probably involving the same birds. After a period of very strong easterlies, 32 were off East Tilbury on 14th February 1994 and, following a period of severe weather in the North Sea, 13 were off Foulness on 29th January 1983.

Little Gulls have been recorded from all around the coast and from many inland sites. In recent years, observations offshore northeast coast have identified moderate numbers regularly present from autumn and throughout winter and it might be that, as these are recorded some distance from the coast, small numbers may use Essex offshore waters for moulting and wintering: periodic occurrences of small flocks close inshore after severe easterly winds, lend support to this theory. In recent years the Little Gull has also been most regularly recorded from Canvey Island and East Tilbury, although this is more likely due to regular seawatching than the species favouring the area over any other. Inland, Hanningfield generally holds the largest numbers of the species with counts at Abberton usually smaller and comparable with the prime site in the Lea Valley, KGV.

There is only one ringing recovery involving Essex, a bird ringed as a nestling at Suurlant, Kingisseppa, Estonia, in June 1983 and recovered at Old Hall on 2nd February 1984. This is an unusual midwinter record as most first-winter birds are thought to winter in the Atlantic. Nationally only two other recoveries have been reported of birds from the Baltic States.

Sabine's Gull   *Larus sabini*

Scarce, annual visitor, mainly in autumn: 113 individuals, 41 in 1987

The monotypic Sabine's Gull breeds on arctic tundra with bogs and small pools, often alongside Arctic Terns, and occurs mainly in arctic Canada and Russia, west to Taimyr, with small numbers in Greenland. The species is a long-distance, highly pelagic migrant wintering off the Atlantic coast of southern Africa and the Pacific coast of South America (Olsen & Larsson 2004).

Christy cited just one record, a juvenile shot on the Thames in early September 1862, near Bow Creek. The next occurrence was not until 1949, when a dead immature that appeared to have been shot, was found on Canvey Island on 5th November.

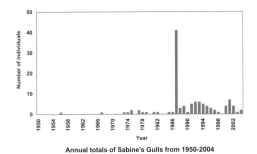

Annual totals of Sabine's Gulls from 1950-2004

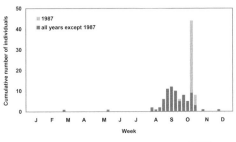

Seasonal occurrence of Sabine's Gulls from 1956-2004

From 1950 until the early 1970s only occasional individuals were reported, mostly by fishermen/birders off the Essex coast, but since then records have increased significantly—almost certainly as a result of greater observer coverage. Sabine's Gulls have been recorded annually since 1984, except in 1999.

Like Grey Phalaropes, Sabine's Gulls usually occur after the passage of autumn gales, with the majority passing down the western seaboard of Britain; these individuals are thought to be from the Nearctic breeding population. Most Essex records (1987 excepted) have involved juveniles; the majority off the western seaboard are adults.

The Great Storm of 1987 produced by far the largest influx of at least 41 individuals, 37% of the all-time Essex total. Virtually all records came from the Thames Estuary from East Tilbury westwards (24 adults and one juvenile) and on the Lea Valley reservoirs (nine adults and one juvenile). The first Sabine's Gulls appeared on 16th October, with an adult at KGV and two adults at Rainham. The next day there were 22 at six sites and on 18th there were 22 at four sites, including 12 adults in Barking Bay at dawn. Many were seen reorientating and heading back up the Thames. The only records away from the Thames/Lea Valley involved three juveniles on 22nd and two adults on 23rd off Clacton-on-Sea from where there was also an earlier September record.

Some 300 Sabine's Gulls were stranded across a narrow band of southeast England by the storm. It is likely that these birds originated in the late summer/early autumn feeding area in the Bay of Biscay and, once overtaken by the deepening depression, they moved with the eye of the storm

	16th	17th	18th	19th	20th	21st	22nd	23rd	24th
Offshore Clacton-on-Sea							3j	2a	
East Tilbury			5a						
West Thurrock		7a	3a						
Rainham	2a	2a 1j							
Barking		5a	12a	5a		2a			
Walthamstow		1a							
Girling		2a	2a	2a	2a 1j	3a 1j	2a	1a	1a
KGV	1a	4a							
Totals	3a	21a 1j	22a	7a	2a 1j	5a 1j	2a 3j	3a	1a

a = adult j = juvenile
Summary of Sabine's Gull influx of October 1987

until it made landfall in Dorset early on 16th. There they were overtaken by the violent southwesterly winds at the rear of the depression and were carried across central England on a path corresponding with the trajectory, not direction of the airflow (Elkins & Yesou 1998). Mainly adults were involved as the young had yet to reach the feeding area when the storm hit.

Inland, apart from 1987, there have been just five records of immatures: Abberton, 11th September 1995 and 15th–30th October 1996; Hanningfield, 9th–11th September 1961 and 29th October 1996; and Walthamstow, 10th September 1989.

All but two Sabine's Gulls have occurred during autumn and, whilst rare, spring records are part of a small, nationally recognised passage: off Foulness, 11th March 1956; a second-year bird 10km off Clacton-on-Sea, 26th May 1977. Although autumn records have occurred as early as 6th August, off Maplin Sands in 1982, the majority occur in September and October. The latest records involved an adult off Canvey Island on 6th November 2000, and a juvenile off Southend Pier on 9th December 1985.

Bonaparte's Gull *Larus philadelphia*

Vagrant: one record

The monotypic Bonaparte's Gull breeds in small colonies, often in trees, across the North American taiga up to the tree limit and winters on the Great Lakes and coastal USA, south to Mexico and the Caribbean.

1994	Hadleigh Marshes	27th August	Adult

A total of 130 had been recorded nationally up to the end of 2004 (BBRC 2005). The records are spread throughout the year, although a bias is shown towards the southwest in winter, suggesting either a movement out of America in severe weather or possibly individuals being swept across the Atlantic by fast-moving depressions (Cottridge & Vinicombe 1996). Found in a large high-tide roost of Black-headed Gulls, this individual flew off as the roost disbanded and was never seen again (Green 1995). This was one of five recorded nationally in 1994, an average year by recent standards.

Black-headed Gull
Larus ridibundus

Abundant resident, passage migrant and winter visitor: the commonest gull at all seasons Amber List

The monotypic Black-headed Gull breeds throughout the Palearctic from Kamchatka to the Atlantic, occurring mostly between 45° and 65° N and having the largest distribution of the 15 'hooded' gulls (European Atlas). In Europe, the largest populations are coastal and found

Atlas	Survey Area	% of 10km squares or tetrads in which	
		bred/probably bred	possibly bred or present
First National 10km	Essex	22.8	7.0
Second National 10km	Essex	21.1	0.0
First London Tetrad	Met. Essex	0.0	0.0
Second London Tetrad	Met. Essex	0.0	0.0
Essex Tetrad	Essex	1.8	1.0

Summary of results of Atlas surveys for Black-headed Gulls

in the Netherlands, Britain, Sweden, Germany, Denmark and the Baltic States. Typical breeding sites include both natural and artificial locations, usually in a wetland environment, but dry sites close to water may also be used. The European population has expanded since the late 19th century, probably due to a reduction in egg collecting and improved survival rates bought about by the species' exploitation of human activities. The British population stood at around 138,000 pairs in the late 1990s (Mitchell *et al.* 2004). Birds from Fennoscandia and the Baltic move south and west to western Europe in winter with other populations dispersive or partially migratory.

The Black-headed Gull has one of the longest recorded histories of any species in Essex with the first reference in the 17th century when Fuller (1662) referred to 'puits' on a 80ha island near Harwich, now known as Pewit Island in Hamford Water. Black-headed Gulls may also have bred on Foulness at this time. Many local Essex people were clearly familiar with its large gulleries suggesting that it was once a widespread coastal breeder. Thus, it has given its local name of 'Pewit' (now a common name for the Lapwing, but traditionally the local name for the Black-headed Gull) and 'Cob' to many locations, few of which were extant by Christy's time. Thus, in addition to the aforesaid Pewit Island, we have one near Mersea Island and Pewet Island off Bradwell (an estimated 10,000–12,000 eggs were taken annually from here in the 1830s), Great and Little Cob Islands in Tollesbury fleet, Cob Marsh Island in the Mersea Quarters and perhaps also Cobb's Farm near Goldhanger. Eggs were taken in considerable numbers until Christy's time and in the 17th century at least the young were considered a delicacy "Being [i.e. when] young, they consist only of bones, feathers, and lean flesh, which have a raw gust [i.e. taste] of the sea. But Poulterers take them then and feed them with Gravel and Curds … the one to scour, the other to fat them in a fortnight, and their flesh thus recruited is most delicious."

	Abberton	Hanningfield	Girling/KGV
1953	~	~	30,000
1963	~	15,000	24,000
1973	6,200	25,000	~
1983	~	~	55,000
1993	5,499	14,675	33,000
2004	2,006	3,851	24,600

Number of Black-headed Gulls located in Gull Roost Surveys

	No. of colonies	No. of pairs
1938	6	1,500-1,600
1958	7	4,262-4,500
1973	9	5,843-6,483
1996	13*	10,000+
2003	13*	9,000

*some adjacent colonies are amalgamated in this figure
Number of breeding pairs of Black-headed Gulls (adapted and updated from Cox and Essex Atlas)

By Christy's time, colonies were found only on Horsey Island in Hamford Water and possibly other sites nearby, probably on Pewet Island near Bradwell, "… in the vicinity of St Osyth", presumably meaning in the Colne Estuary, Old Hall and on Foulness, the only site at which it was then considered abundant. Although enclosure of marshlands may have affected the species, the available information suggests that it was uncontrolled egg-collecting that probably caused the decline during the 19th century, a similar situation to other parts of the country (Historical Atlas).

Glegg gave details of a number of colonies in Hamford Water totalling no more than 160–170 pairs, two along the Colne Estuary totalling some 160–200 pairs, at Pennyhole Bottom, Old Hall, where there were 80–100 pairs and 50–70 pairs on the north side of the Crouch; in all, the six gulleries totalled 450–540 pairs. These figures were probably far from complete and indeed the first full county census in 1938

		Peak counts					
		1950s	1960s	1970s	1980s	1990s	2000s
Hamford		2,000	2,500	3,500	3,910	6,935	11,000
Colne							
	Rat Island	2,000	2,000	3,000	1,500	2,000	2,300
	Langenhoe	~	~	"few"	~	1,500	~
	Cindery Island	~	~	~	~	~	200
Blackwater							
	Great Cob	158	100	130	198	272	324
	Bradwell/Pewit	100	26	~	~	650	200
Dengie							
	Tillingham	500	350	~	~	~	~
Foulness		~	102	1,000	586	574	88
Crouch							
	Bridgemarsh Is.	150	~	~	~	800	~
Abberton		1,000	100	~	~	~	~
Hanningfield		1	50	200	200	~	"few"

Summary of larger (200+ pairs) Black-headed Gull colonies since 1950 (figures given for each decade are the peak annual count)

suggested that three times that number bred. Subsequent censuses have revealed a steady increase over the last 60 years.

	1986	1988	1990	1992	1994	1996	1998	2000	2002	2003
No .of nests	2,596	4,473	6,060	7,533	4,926	5,368	6,935	11,000*	7,600	6,000

* estimate

Nest counts of Black-headed Gulls in Hamford Water from 1986-2003
(courtesy of K. Marsden & L. Woodrow)

The rather remote locations of several of the larger saltmarsh gulleries, plus their susceptibility to tidal flooding and in some cases to systematic egg collecting (which is known to have occurred in the fairly recent past), create difficulties in making really accurate counts, with the exception of the Hamford Water sites where biennial counts have been carried out since 1986. This rather spread out colony is now by far the largest in Essex.

Elsewhere, the colony on Rat Island in the Colne Estuary still holds some 1,500–2,000 pairs (2,000–2,300 in 2000) and there have recently been up to 650 pairs on Pewet Island, Bradwell, 800 on Bridgemarsh Island/Stow Creek on the Crouch and 600–1,000 pairs on Langenhoe Ranges. Numbers on Foulness have been much reduced recently and the artificially created Maplin Bank, which at its peak held 211 pairs, is no longer suitable, although several small colonies remain active in the area. Presumably in a response to more frequent flooding, some pairs are now shifting to inside the seawalls. At all colonies, the failure rate of nests is generally high and can often be 100% when high tides flood them out or predator pressure is particularly great. At Foulness, eggs were collected for several years for sale to the London specialist food markets, the last collection being made as recently as 1982 (Lewis 2000).

Smaller colonies have existed from time to time at several other coastal localities, many of them in the mouth of the Blackwater around Mersea Island, on many of the small islands including Packing Shed Island, Cob Marsh and Pewit Islands in Pyefleet Channel, whilst short-lived colonies have existed on the mainland saltings in one or two locations. At the west end of the Blackwater Estuary, a very small colony existed at Mundon Stone in the early 1950s, whilst more recently small colonies have been founded just inside the seawall at Heybridge GP (78 pairs in 1999), Lofts Farm GPs (65 pairs in 2004) and Chigborough Lakes (60 pairs in 1981), although only the first two remain in use; the islands at Chigborough have become overgrown. A colony of over 200 existed on The Strood, Mersea Island, in the early 1950s but was gone by 1953. A few also bred at Colne Point in the 1950s and 1960s (and unsuccessfully in 2004), although there were 60 pairs in 1962. Cindery Island in Brightlingsea Creek appears to be a new colony (200 pairs in 2004). Very small numbers have bred occasionally at Copperas Bay, Tollesbury Wick, West Wick and Paglesham Lagoon.

Inland colonies in Essex have always been small with numbers strongly influenced by low water levels and rates of vegetation growth. At Abberton, breeding took place from 1949–51 with 753 nests counted on the island in 1950, a year of low water levels. Some nested again in 1965, but midsummer water levels have not been sufficiently low for the island to reappear since then. Up to 200 pairs nested at Hanningfield from 1959–86 with the colony finally dying out as vegetation on the island became too dense. Small colonies have also existed or currently exist at Stanway, Boreham and in the Chelmer Valley, whilst single pairs bred in the Roman River Valley in 1969 and possibly once at Ardleigh and Walthamstow.

The current Essex population probably lies in the region of 13,000–15,000 pairs which represents 9–10% of the current British and 1% of the European population (Second National Atlas).

In winter the species is numerous and widespread, especially on or near the coast, but sizeable numbers are attracted to inland waters, refuse tips, playing fields, parks and arable land. Traditionally, the major reservoirs have held large mixed gull roosts and there was an exceptional count of

	Jan	Feb	Mar	Apr	May	Jun	Jul	Aug	Sep	Oct	Nov	Dec
Finland						18	7					
Norway						13	1	1				
Sweden					1	5	1			1		
Baltic States				5	9	77	6					
Poland			6		9	12	1					
Czech			1									
Denmark			3	2	7	17						
Germany			2		3	4	2					
The Netherlands	1	1		4	9	12	4		1	1	1	1
Belgium	8	6	3	1	4	1	2				1	8
Totals	9	7	15	12	42	159	24	1	1	2	2	9

Month of ringing and origin of Black-headed Gulls ringed abroad and recovered in Essex

150,000 Black-headed Gulls at Abberton in March 1978. Meadows (1961) published a series of roost counts from the Lea Valley, producing an average of 41,000 (peak 70,000) between November and February 1958–60. More recently, numbers have been lower although there were 38,000 at Girling on 10th January 1987. There have also been regular five-figure counts at Hanningfield, the highest being 25,000 in January 1973. The largest single coastal count was a roost gathering of 150,000 off Foulness in August 1978, but there may well have been many more than this amongst the 500,000 or so gulls drawn to Sprat shoals off the coast in January 1991. Recent counts from along the inner Thames have often been of the order of 10,000–25,000, although the more comprehensive 2004 national Winter Gull Roost Survey WiNGS located 43,600 along the inner Thames.

National Gull Roost surveys have produced the most comprehensive data for the Lea Valley reservoirs, although these are incomplete; countywide coverage has only been achieved in 2004, although large areas of the coast were not fully covered. The data point to an increase until the 1970s with a decline since.

More recently, Black-headed Gulls have been counted more accurately on WeBS counts and these together with WiNGS point to a current winter population of perhaps 70,000–90,000 with most being found along the Thames or in Metropolitan Essex.

Although the largest numbers of Black-headed Gulls are present during winter, there is some evidence for a passage through the county during July and August, although this may perhaps be no more than dispersal of locally bred birds from nearby English colonies.

Extensive ringing of both locally reared young and wintering birds, mainly caught by cannon-netting on the refuse tips at Pitsea and Rainham, has provided much insight into the species' movements to and from Essex. Many surviving chicks return to breed in their natal colonies, though there are examples of interchange between other British colonies, mainly in East Anglia and southeast England, whilst several have moved to colonies in the Netherlands. At the conclusion of the breeding season, the great majority of juveniles and some adults leave the county, with the most distant Essex-bred Black-headed Gulls occurring in Scotland, Wales and Ireland (a juvenile had reached there by 18th August in 1996), as well as in the Low Countries, France and Iberia and single recoveries from near Casablanca, Morocco, and Oran, Algeria. One ringed as a pullus in Hamford Water on 7th July 1999 was recovered at Vevey, Vaud, Switzerland on 9th December 1999; it was the first BTO-ringed Black-headed Gull to be recovered in Switzerland.

	Jan	Feb	Mar	Apr	May	Jun	Jul	Aug	Sep	Oct	Nov	Dec
Essex	29	27	36	28	32	78	92	46	31	22	14	22
Scotland					1	1						
North England	9	4	2	4	3	3	1	6	6	4	6	2
South England	63	78	40	26	16	29	29	30	27	26	59	59
Wales	2	1	2		1			2		2		
Ireland	1	4	1					1	1	1	2	2
Finland			3	27	29	34	21	8	3	2	1	
Norway					6	2	8	1	1			
Sweden	1		1	9	13	24	14	6	2			
Baltic States		1	2	13	15	8	5	1	1			
Russia					1	3	6		1			
Poland			4	3	1		1	2				
Czech					1	1						
Switzerland												1
Denmark	4	5	24	16	20	21	14	10	10	7	2	4
Germany	1		11	5	33	9	11	6	4	1		
The Netherlands	9	10	19	10	10	12	12	11	6	7	6	5
Belgium	1	3	3	1	2	2	4			1		1
France	5	2	2	1	2	1	1		1	2	3	5
Spain	4	2								1	3	4
Portugal											1	1
Algeria			1									
Morocco		1										
Totals	129	138	151	150	183	237	207	131	92	76	97	106

Month and location of recovery of Black-headed Gulls ringed in Essex

Immigrants from the breeding populations of Scandinavia, the Baltic States and Russia (some having travelled in excess of 2,500 km) begin arriving here from late July and returning mainly in February and March, although there have been recoveries of foreign-ringed individuals in Essex in every month. Thus the population of this abundant species is in a state of constant flux (Cox 1976).

Although Black-headed Gull numbers have increased steadily over the last 50 years, rising sea levels, predation and disturbance are significant threats to many of the colonies. The fact that most of the Essex population is found in Hamford Water, where increasingly regular high tides caused by sea level rises may have a significant detrimental impact on breeding success, suggests that the future is far from secure.

Sponsored in memory of Tariq Watson

Ring-billed Gull   *Larus delawarensis*

Rare passage migrant and winter visitor: 22 records including four returning wintering birds

The monotypic Ring-billed Gull breeds in North America around the prairies and the Great Lakes, east as far up as Newfoundland. It winters around the Great Lakes and southern coasts of the USA and Central America. Since the mid-1970s the species has become a regular vagrant to the Western Palearctic, especially Britain, where the records span all months of the year; a massive influx of more than 400 individuals in the first half of the 1980s has led to the species becoming virtually a resident in some coastal areas (*HBW*).

	One-off records		
1979	Rainham	25th February	First-winter
1985/86	Leigh-on-Sea/	13th–18th August and	Second-winter
	Southend-on-Sea Pier	20th February–29th March	
1985	Hanningfield	27th December	First-winter

1987	East Tilbury	22nd March	Adult
	Rainham	6th December	Second-winter
1990	Wakering Tip	1st December	Adult
1992	Hanningfield	4th February	Second-winter
1994	Wat Tyler CP	22nd December	Adult
1997	Rainham	8th February	Second-winter
	East Tilbury	4th October	Adult
1998	East Tilbury	31st January	First-winter
	Rainham	21st February	Possibly previous bird
1999/00	Beckton/Creekmouth	20th November–3rd January	Adult
1999	Barking Bay	20th December	Adult
2001	KGV	25th January	Near Adult
2002	Stanford Warren	5th January	Adult
	Stratford	18th March	Adult
2004	Linford	2nd January	Adult
	Returning birds		
1999/00	Shoebury	13th September–3rd April	Third-winter/adult
2000		27th November	Same as previous
2000	Westcliff-on-Sea	11th March–14th April	Adult
2000/01		17th September–27th March	Same as previous
2001/02		7th September–23rd March	Same as previous
2002/03		6th September–24th March	Same as previous
2003/04		23rd August–22nd March	Same as previous
2004/05		30th August into 2005	Same as previous
2001	Thames Barrier	during January	Adult
		17th December	Same as previous
2002		13th October	Same as previous
2003		January	Same as previous
2000	Colchester, Univ. of Essex	28th January–7th April	Near-adult
		15th-20th December	Same as previous

First recorded in Britain in 1973, the Ring-billed Gull was removed from the BBRC list just nine years later. This change in status cannot be due to increased observer coverage and identification skill alone, so the increase must be genuine. Most new arrivals in Britain seem to occur in mid- to late winter but the peak of occurrence is usually March and April when there is a regular passage though western areas that is thought to involve birds moving back north having wintered further south. Some may even be commuting regularly across the Atlantic (Cottridge & Vinicombe 1996). In Essex, the pattern of winter occurrence is evident with no records from May–July.

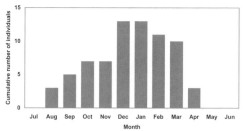

Seasonal occurrence of Ring-billed Gulls from 1979-2004

The majority of records have come from the Thames Estuary; birds at Hanningfield and the Lea Valley may have come from the Thames to bathe and roost with other gulls.

The regular returning Westcliff-on-Sea adult, popularly known locally as 'Rossi' as it frequents the area of the seafront around the Rossi Restaurant, has also been recorded on Canvey Island and in Gunners Park.

Common Gull (Mew Gull)   *Larus canus*

Common passage migrant and winter visitor with very small numbers in summer   Amber List

The Common Gull has an almost circumpolar distribution in the Northern Hemisphere. The nominate race *canus* is the most numerous subspecies, breeding from Iceland south to France and east to the White Sea, whilst *heinei* breeds from the Kanin peninsula, Dvina and Moscow region east to the Lena. Two further subspecies occur in eastern Asia and North America (European Atlas). The species is typically a coastal nester, although large numbers breed well inland in some locations. Almost 50% of the European population of 524,000 breeding pairs, which has increased significantly since the 1890s, is found in Norway and elsewhere in Scandinavia. The current British population of some 49,000 pairs represents nearly 10% of the European population and around 5% of the world population of one million pairs (Mitchell *et al.* 2004, Olsen & Larsson 2004).

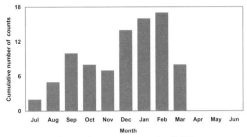

Seasonal occurrence of counts of 1,000+ Common Gulls from 1971-2004

The main breeding colonies in Britain are in the north and northwest, with perhaps 50% occurring at just two colonies in northeast Scotland (Second National Atlas). A few pairs have bred recently in Kent, Suffolk and Norfolk; these may derive from Continental birds that migrate to Britain in winter (Second National Atlas). The species is generally migratory with, as a general rule, northerly populations wintering north of southerly populations after migration (European Atlas).

There have been no definite breeding records of Common Gulls in Essex, despite recent reports from adjacent coastal counties. Christy regarded breeding records on the saltings at Peldon and Great Wigborough as a case of mistaken identity: "... I cannot help thinking that the 'Common Gull' they [Rev Atkinson and Yarrell] have met with was the Black-headed, which is certainly the common Gull of our coast". It is surprising that the apparent observations of someone so eminent as Yarrell (1845) should be considered incorrect but, despite the fact that "Rev. Canon J. C. Atkinson emphatically

	Abberton	Hanningfield	Girling/KGV
1953	~	~	4,000
1963	~	3,000	7,500
1973	~	~	~
1983	~	~	12,100
1993	1,975	4,421	4,550
2004	2,449	1,565	9,460

Number of Common Gulls located in Gull Roost Surveys

reiterated that his statement, that this species used to nest on the saltings at Wigborough and Peldon, was correct..." following the publication of Christy's book, Glegg also felt that "... there can be no doubt that this species was confused with the Black-headed Gull". With the benefit of hindsight, the very different appearance of the two species and recent breeding records from adjacent counties suggest that the Common Gull might have bred occasionally along the Blackwater. Today, very few are present from June–July, those remaining being principally immatures; by the end of July small numbers of migrant birds start to appear, many being adults.

To both Christy and Glegg, the Common Gull was a common winter visitor and, although neither author gave any specific data, Glegg noted that "At times its numbers rival those of the Black-headed, but generally it is considerably less numerous than this species". Hudson & Pyman considered that the species was always outnumbered by Black-headed Gulls and sometimes within the Thames Estuary by the Herring Gull as well. The largest numbers occurred on Girling and KGV, where in the late 1950s and early 1960s, there was an average of 10,500 but with a peak of 38,000 roosting there in March 1960 (Meadows 1961), the largest count yet made in Essex. Although coastal roosts had been identified, Hudson & Pyman concluded that "... very little is known of them yet".

Cox described the species in a similar vein and noted that 10,000–15,000 regularly flew out over BBO, heading for the Dengie roost during 1976 and 1980. However, all these counts were probably exceeded in January 1981 when hundreds of thousands of gulls gathered to feed around the Thames fishing fleet (Cox). More recently, numbers have been lower with the largest inland count since the early 1980s being 12,500 at Girling on 17th January 1987 and the peak on the coast being 7,000 off Harwich on 7th January 2000, which were probably attracted to the Sprat shoals in the area at that time. The once-a-decade Gull Roost Surveys have not covered the county comprehensively until the most recent one; the Lea Valley reservoirs have data back to the 1950s but even this is incomplete. However, the data point to numbers having been maintained over the last five decades.

Common Gulls can be found in some numbers all around the coast but may turn up almost anywhere inland on arable, short grassland (e.g. parks and playing fields) and refuse tips, as well as in some numbers in the offshore zone (Cox).

Although the largest numbers are invariably present in winter, particularly December and January, an influx during August/September and to a lesser extent in late February/March may be evident in most years. The late

	Jan	Feb	Mar	Apr	May	Jun	Jul	Aug	Sep	Oct	Nov	Dec
Essex	4	5	1			1	1	1	2		1	1
South England	3	4	1							1		
Finland					1	1	1	2	1	2		
Norway						2	3	2	5	2		
Sweden				1	2	2	2	2	1			
Baltic States							4	1	1			
Russia							1				1	
Denmark		1	2	1	3			2	2	1	2	
Germany		1	1		5	3	1				2	
The Netherlands	1	1	1				1			1		
Totals	1	10	14	8	18	12	14	8	5	6	1	1

Month and location of recovery of Common Gulls ringed in Essex

summer influx is particularly noticeable on Foulness where counts have included 3,423 in August 1996 and 3,334 in August 2000.

Surveys of the Dengie coast roosts in 1976 and 1980 found the greatest numbers present there between June and August, whilst at Leigh/Two Tree Island refuse tip in 1973 the peaks were from September–November and in January and at Great Wakering Tip there was a clear January peak (Cox).

	Jan	Feb	Mar	Apr	May	Jun	Jul	Aug	Sep	Oct	Nov	Dec
Finland						1	2					
Norway						4	4					
Sweden					1	1						
Baltic States					3	3						
Poland						1						
Denmark						1						
Germany				2		1	3					
The Netherlands						2	1			1		1
Belgium	1											
Totals	*1*	*0*	*0*	*2*	*4*	*14*	*10*	*0*	*0*	*1*	*0*	*1*

Month of ringing and origin of Common Gulls ringed abroad and recovered in Essex

Around 635,000 Common Gulls are thought to winter in Britain (Winter Atlas). The total of around 16,000 counted in the January 2004 WiNGS represents around 2.5% of the British wintering population, although it should be borne in mind that some areas of the coast were not covered.

Much is known about the movements of Common Gull in and out of Essex thanks to the large number ringed by the Pitsea Ringing Group at Rainham and Pitsea between 1980 and 1994. Numbers ringed during this project, which used cannon-nets, represented some 60% of the national ringing total of full-grown birds. The results showed that most birds that winter in Essex have come from breeding populations in the Low Countries, parts of Scandinavia and the Baltic States.

Very few birds from the British breeding population have occurred; most disperse well south and west from their breeding grounds in autumn (*BWP*). One ringed at Rainham in February 1976 was recovered in Archangel, Siberia, at almost 42° East and some 2,900km distant, in May 1980, whilst a colour-ringed bird from Schleswig-Holstein, Germany, was recorded in two consecutive winters (1995 and 1996) indicating some site fidelity. A bird ringed at Rainham on 31st January 1972 was recovered in the Netherlands on 17th August 1993 when it was at least 23 years old.

The Siberian race *heinei*, which is larger than the nominate race and has a darker mantle, normally disperses south-east from its breeding range to winter as far south as the Caspian Sea (*BWP*). However, a bird of this race was ringed at Pitsea on 18th February 1984 and was subsequently accepted as a first for Britain on the basis of biometrics: the wing length was far longer than that of the nominate race. There have been only three accepted records of this race in Britain, the last in 1987 (*Ibis* 136: 253-256). It is very difficult, perhaps impossible, to separate the two races in the field and indeed intergrades between *canus* and *heinei* are common in western Russia (Olsen & Larsson 2004); biometrics are considered the only safe way to separate the races. However, a number of individuals resembling this race have been claimed during the 1990s from Hanningfield, Leigh/Two Tree Island and Rainham. It should be borne in mind that the eastern-most recoveries in the ringing table from Russia and Estonia are within the western breeding range of *heinei*, so it is possible that odd individuals from this race may occur with some frequency in Essex.

Lesser Black-backed Gull   *Larus fuscus*

Common passage migrant but present all year and breeding in small but increasing numbers   AmberList

The Lesser Black-backed Gull breeds only in north and west Europe from the White Sea to Iceland, and south to the Iberian Peninsula. Populations from north Norway eastwards belong to the nominate race *fuscus*, whilst *graellsii* is found in Britain, Ireland, the Faeroe Islands and Iceland, and *intermedius* occurs in the rest of the range. Geographical variation is large and partly clinal in *graellsii* and *intermedius*, and these two races may represent just one clinal taxon, *graellsii* (Olsen & Larsson 2004).

The race *fuscus* has not been positively identified in Britain (Jonsson 1998) contra *EBR* 1999 and Hudson & Pyman. Overall, the population increased markedly in the 20th century, although *fuscus* has declined dramatically since the 1960s.

Atlas	Survey Area	% of 10km squares or tetrads in which	
		bred/probably bred	possibly bred or present
First National 10km	Essex	0.0	0.0
Second National 10km	Essex	5.3	0.0
First London Tetrad	Met. Essex	0.0	0.0
Second London Tetrad	Met. Essex	0.0	5.0
Essex Tetrad	Essex	0.5	0.1

Summary of results of Atlas surveys for Lesser Black-backed Gulls

The European population totals some 300,000–350,000 pairs, 114,000 of which breed in Britain (Mitchell *et al.* 2004), the majority in the north and west, although increasingly too in the south where roof nesting has become a common habit (European Atlas). Outside the breeding season, Lesser Black-backed Gulls move south with immatures moving further than adults. Birds from western Europe move southwest to the Iberian peninsula and northwest Africa with increasing numbers wintering in the North Sea and along the Bay of Biscay (European Atlas).

Christy described the Lesser Black-backed Gull as a common visitor to the coast from autumn to spring, occasionally being blown inland by storms. However, as Glegg pointed out, it is quite likely that some of the winter records may well have referred to the Great Black-backed Gull; the two species shared the same local names. Glegg considered that the species was only seen in any numbers whilst on passage with autumn migration peaking in August and a less obvious spring passage in April. Inland records were rare. By Hudson & Pymans' time, its status had changed; the species had bred in the county, was frequent inland and there was a small but increasing wintering population.

	Founded	Peak count	
		Pairs	Year
Hamford Water	1993	500	2001
Clacton Railway Station	1997	3+	1998
Rat Island	1990	45	2003
Langenhoe	1995	5	1999
Pewet Is. Bradwell	1994	12	2002
Foulness	1995	5	2002
Chelmsford Town Centre	2001	10	2003
Harlow	2001	4	2004
Walthamstow	1999	36	2003
Beckton SF	1997	109	2001

Principal Lesser Black-backed Gull breeding sites

The first documented Essex breeding record occurred in 1961 at Hanningfield when one pair reared three young on the island, shortly after the first breeding attempts at Havergate Island, Suffolk, but prior to the establishment of the Orfordness, Suffolk, colony. Breeding took place at the same location in 1962 but egg collectors raided the island before the eggs had hatched. However, despite the growth of the Orfordness colony to 5,000 pairs in 1984 (Piotrowski 2003), it was not until 1985 that there was another breeding attempt in Essex when three pairs nested on the Maplin Bank with unknown success. A failed breeding attempt at Bathside Bay on the Stour in 1988 was followed in 1990 by a single pair breeding unsuccessfully on Rat Island in the Colne, with perhaps the same pair breeding successfully in 1991 and 1992. A pair nested, probably unsuccessfully, in Hamford Water in 1993, since when the number of breeding pairs has risen rapidly both in Hamford Water, where there were 500 pairs in 2001, and also at several other sites, the largest of which at Beckton SF numbered 109 pairs in 2001. The colonisation of Essex appears to have taken place on two fronts: on the coast, principally in the northeast, presumably as a result of dispersal from the large Suffolk colonies; and along the inner Thames, presumably from the established inner London population.

Summering birds or nesting attempts have also occurred at: Hanningfield, where a pair held territory during May 1993; Essex Filter Beds, where a pair may have bred on nearby factories in 1994; Great Cob Island, Old Hall, one pair in 1997; and Colne Point, where one pair defended a territory in 1999.

It was originally thought that most breeding birds belonged to the British breeding race *graellsii*. However, a study in 1998 of those breeding along the Thames concluded that most pairs were made up of birds that closely resembled *intermedius* (Dennis 1998). The colonies in the northeast also appear to be close to the form *intermedius*; many of those at Orfordness are thought likely to be intergrades between the two races (Piotrowski 2003). Thus it would seem that the colonisation of Essex has taken place either from Orfordness or the large colonies found in the Low Countries; populations in the latter are sometimes considered to be intergrades between *intermedius* and *graellsii* (Olsen & Larsson 2004). It seems likely therefore that most of the Essex breeding population is of the intergrade form.

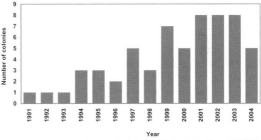

Annual number of Lesser Black-backed Gull colonies from 1991-2004

During summer, three-figure flocks of up to 500 mostly immature birds are now regular at a few mostly coastal sites around Essex.

There is a marked passage through Essex during autumn, with a lesser peak in late spring/early summer.

During the late 1950s comprehensive autumn counts of the Girling roost produced peaks of 8,000 in 1st September 1958, 7,600 on 20th August 1956 and 7,500 on 27th August 1959, which included birds from outside the county boundaries. During 1956 it was estimated that some 90% of the birds arrived at roost from between southeast and south-southeast from the Thames. There have been no comparable counts of this magnitude at this time of year since and it remains unclear as to why such large numbers were present at that time, although no recent comprehensive counts of the Lea Valley reservoirs have been made during autumn. Since 1960 four-figure counts have remained uncommon, with the highest autumn site counts being 1,640 at Barking Bay (most were considered to be *intermedius*) on 24th August 1999 and 2,167 at Rainham on 17th October 2004 (WeBS). Cox considered that the autumn population of Lesser Black-backed Gulls on the inner Thames was probably in excess of 2,000. There is nothing to suggest that there has been a significant change in numbers since.

Away from the inner Thames and Lea Valley, the largest autumn counts have come from Hanningfield where it is likely that many gulls originate from the Thames roost. Elsewhere, the largest autumn counts in excess of 300 have been: up to 450 in the Bradwell/Dengie area, September 1976; and 500 in the Bradwell area, 17th September 1980.

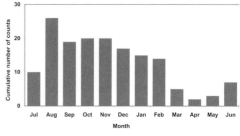

Seasonal occurrence of counts of 250+ Lesser Black-backed Gulls from 1950-2004

Historically the Lesser Black-backed Gull was a rare winter visitor. A survey of Lesser Black-backed Gulls in the winters of 1949/50 and 1950/51 resulted in a high count of just 17 in London and East Anglia (Barnes 1952). With the creation of many new refuse tips along the Thames, which provided attractive winter feeding for the species, numbers began to increase. Hudson & Pyman noted that "… the wintering population is increasing though still small and largely confined to Metropolitan Essex; no winter roost or other concentration has exceeded 500". Wintering began on Girling and KGV in 1954/55, where by January 1961 up to 500 were present. A total of 1,000 at Fairlop CP on 29th December 1968 was twice any previous midwinter count. Blindell (1977) estimated that some 1,600 frequented the Thames between Barking and Mucking from October–February. There were 1,010 on Girling/KGV in January 1993. More recently 1,000 were present at Rainham on 20th November 1999 and 30th December 2000, with 1,385 on 13th January 2001 and 1,703 on 11th February 2001. These figures do not appear significantly different from Blindell's estimate, suggesting a current inner Thames midwinter population of perhaps 1,500–2,000; the largest recent WeBS count was 1,763 in February 2001, whilst the January 2004 WiNGS found 1,898.

Away from the inner Thames and Lea Valley, the Lesser Black-backed Gull appears to be present only in relatively small numbers in winter. At Hanningfield, where some Thames birds may roost, winter counts have been noted of up to 650 (31st December 2001). Elsewhere, the highest winter counts have been 200 in Hamford Water during December 1976 and 140 at Abberton on 7th December 1991, although these appear to be exceptional with counts of up to 50 more typical.

Spring migration is probably more evident at Hanningfield than at any other locality—with peaks of 850 on 9th March 1994 and 600 on 27th March 1988—at a time when counts elsewhere are generally low. Smaller numbers are recorded from many other inland and coastal locations during the passage periods; 100 flying northeast over Chrishall Grange on 19th April 1992 being an example of overland migration.

Generally, *intermedius* seems to predominate at all seasons and it is only in spring and autumn that *graellsii* appears in any numbers. Their numbers also tend to peak earlier than *intermedius* with very few remaining in winter (Dennis 1998).

Essex has produced a number of significant recoveries of Lesser Black-backed Gulls, several involving birds ringed as pulli and thus of known origin. Several are from within the range of *intermedius*. Certain *graellsii* from, amongst other locations, the Firth of Forth and Skomer Island, Dyfed, have been recovered in Essex. One ringed at Pitsea

	Jan	Feb	Mar	Apr	May	Jun	Jul	Aug	Sep	Oct	Nov	Dec
North England				1		1						
South England					1	2	2				1	
Faeroe Islands							1					
Sweden						1						
Germany					1							
Totals	*0*	*0*	*0*	*1*	*2*	*4*	*3*	*0*	*0*	*0*	*1*	*0*

Month and location of recovery of Lesser Black-backed Gulls ringed in Essex

on 31st July 1986, was recovered at Hove, Suduroy, Faeroe Islands, and was presumably of the race *graellsii*.

Recoveries from the Netherlands may involve either race or intergrades. Colour-ringing at Orfordness has resulted in regular sightings from around Essex. One originally marked at Orfordness in July 1999 was subsequently seen in Portugal and Morocco in late 1999, Morocco again in early 2001 and then at Holyfield Lake in May 2001. Others have been noted in Spain. One marked in Bristol as a pullus in June 1997 was at Walthamstow Filter Beds in September 1999; the southeasterly orientation of the movement is unusual.

Lesser Black-backed Gull x Herring Gull hybrids have been recorded with increasing regularity in recent years, particularly at the Beckton colony where mixed breeding and possibly hybrid breeding has been noted.

The rise in the number of large gulls breeding on the Essex coast is likely to prove a difficult challenge for conservation organisations. Egg pricking now takes place annually in Hamford Water. The potential for predating waders and other sea birds is very great and, given the difficulties waders are already experiencing, continuing

	Jan	Feb	Mar	Apr	May	Jun	Jul	Aug	Sep	Oct	Nov	Dec
Norway						4	6	1				
Denmark							2					
The Netherlands							2					
Belgium							1					
Totals	*0*	*0*	*0*	*0*	*0*	*4*	*11*	*1*	*0*	*0*	*0*	*0*

Month of ringing and origin of Lesser Black-backed Gulls ringed abroad and recovered in Essex

control measures may prove necessary, although, unless these become particularly severe, there seems no reason to believe that the Lesser Black-backed Gull population is not going to continue to expand.

Yellow-legged Gull   *Larus michahellis*

Passage migrant and winter visitor

The Yellow-legged Gull breeds around the coasts of the Mediterranean, Aegean and Black Seas to Romania, in central Europe to around 52° N and along the Iberian Atlantic coastline (Olsen & Larsson 2004). Southwest European, Adriatic and eastern Mediterranean birds disperse north and west during July–October with some reaching north, west and central Europe. The nominate race *michahellis* occurs throughout much of the species' range.

Prior to the early 1970s, all claims of 'yellow-legged' Herring Gulls were referred to the race '*omissus*'; formerly found in the bogs of the east Baltic States and west Russia until the 1950s. This apparent morph of *argentatus* (*HBW*) was eventually hybridised to extinction when the pink-legged populations nearby expanded their ranges (Olsen & Larsson 2004). Ringing recoveries suggest that most of the early Essex 'yellow-legged gulls' were indeed from this population but some, however, may have referred to *michahellis*. Interestingly, the only published description (*EBR* 1953) of a suspected '*omissus*' (at Southend-on-Sea on 31st August 1953) noted that the bird "... had unmistakably yellow legs and a mantle a shade darker than that of a "normal" bird beside it ... this gull was too pale on the mantle for any Lesser Black-backed Gull ...". Perhaps it was an adult *michahellis*; typical '*omissus*' were considered to have pale yellow legs (Witherby *et al.* 1938–41).

In 1973 a gull survey at various refuse tips in the Rochford Hundred and at Chelmsford and Witham located 11 adult "yellow-legged Gulls". Although they were ascribed to *omissus*, these were probably the first Essex *michahellis* records; the species was regular in small numbers in Kent by this time (Taylor *et al.* 1981). A similar number, also ascribed to '*omissus*' were present, mostly along the Thames in 1974. A lack of records during the 1970s and early 1980s probably reflected a dearth of interest in gulls rather than an absence of the birds themselves. However, small numbers continued to be recorded into the 1980s.

In 1986 large numbers of Yellow-legged Gulls that regularly fed at the Stone refuse tip, Kent, began roosting along the foreshore at Thurrock and Mucking, a pattern that was to be repeated in subsequent years (Dennis 1998). Small numbers began to feed at Rainham and Mucking refuse tips but, with the closure of the Stone refuse tip in 1990, the majority of those birds shifted to feeding at Essex sites. Thus in August 1991 there were 220 at both Rainham and East Tilbury and in July 1993, 300 at East Tilbury. Totals of 450 at Mucking in August and September 1996 remain the largest individual site counts, probably the largest concentrations to be recorded in Britain. There were 394 at East Tilbury on 30th August 1999 and 389 on 8th September 2001

Away from these areas, numbers are generally small, although there were 60 at Aveley refuse tip in August 1994 and 50 at West Thurrock in August 1992. Away from the Thames, the only double-figure site count is 14 at Heybridge on 8th August 1994. The recent general increase in records from across Essex away from the Thames is probably largely due to greater observer awareness.

Numbers recorded during autumn vary markedly from year to year. However, the species is now being recorded regularly across Essex, both along the coast and inland at the main reservoirs. Most records have come from the Lea Valley and Hanningfield, not surprising given the apparent links that these two locations have with the Thames' gull populations. Many of the inland records relate to individuals associating with flocks of Lesser Black-backed Gulls on arable farmland in the southwest (Dennis 1998). Along the Blackwater, close to Heybridge GP, Yellow-legged Gulls almost invariably associate with Lesser Black-backed Gulls, even when Herring Gulls are present.

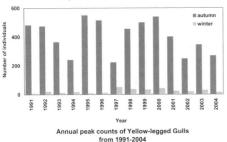

Annual peak counts of Yellow-legged Gulls from 1991-2004

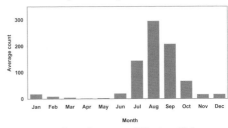

Seasonal occurrence of Yellow-legged Gulls from 1991-2004

Whilst there are birds present all year round, there are generally very few in late spring/early summer, although it is possible that this may be no more than recording bias in that until relatively recently immature birds, the ones most likely to remain all year, were not being identified. Along the Thames, birds return from their more southerly breeding sites as early as mid-June with numbers slowly increasing to a peak in August/early September, when adults are joined by immatures; the gatherings disperse through September and October.

Away from the Thames, along the Blackwater the pattern is generally the same although the first birds usually arrive in late June/early July, some 3–4 weeks prior to the first returning Herring Gulls.

Since the mid-1990s, small but increasing numbers, primarily adults (although immatures may simply be overlooked), have wintered in Essex with up to 12 at Rainham in 1997/98 from November–March with most dispersing in April (Dennis 1998). What is presumed to be the same adult has returned to winter on and around the west end of Northey Island in every winter since 1998/99, suggesting that wintering birds at least may show quite strong site fidelity. Returning birds have also occurred at The Strood, Mersea Island, and Brightlingsea.

The relationships between the various races of Herring Gull and Lesser Black-backed Gull and other large white-headed gulls is very complex and in recent years more has probably been written about this group in both the scientific and popular birding press than any other. The Yellow-legged Gull L. michahellis *and Armenian Gull L.* armenicus *have recently been split from Herring Gull but the taxonomic status of Caspian Gull* cachinnans *and American Herring Gull* smithsonianus *remain under review (Ibis 147: 821–826). They are currently considered to be races of Herring Gull and are treated accordingly below. Recent research into the genetic relationship amongst the different races of Herring, Yellow-legged and Lesser Black-backed Gulls suggests that the relationships may be more complicated than it already appears, with* cachinnans *possibly being the sister group to all the others (Collinson 2001).*

Herring Gull   *Larus argentatus*

Common winter visitor and passage migrant: breeds in small but increasing numbers   Amber List

The Herring Gull has a generally northern Holarctic range extending from northern Europe and central southern Europe across Eurasia and into North America. Several races exist, although these are often lumped into the 'northern' *argentatus*, the 'southern' *cachinnans* and American *smithsonianus* groups.

Herring Gull   *L. a. argenteus/argentatus*

Common winter visitor and passage migrant: breeds in small but increasing numbers   Amber List

The race *argenteus* occurs in the Netherlands, northern France, Britain and Ireland and North Atlantic islands with *argentatus* present across Fennoscandia, the Baltic and westernmost Russia. Around 114,000 pairs breed in Britain and Ireland.

Northerly populations of *argentatus* are the most migratory and winter around the southern North Sea (*BWP*) with more southerly birds generally more dispersive, whilst *argenteus* is generally sedentary.

Despite the founding of the colony at Orfordness, Suffolk, in the early 1960s, which had grown to

Atlas	Survey Area	% of 10km squares or tetrads in which	
		bred/probably bred	possibly bred or present
First National 10km	Essex	0.0	0.0
Second National 10km	Essex	5.3	0.0
First London Tetrad	Met. Essex	0.0	0.0
Second London Tetrad	Met. Essex	0.0	2.5
Essex Tetrad	Essex	0.2	0.4

Summary of results of Atlas surveys for Herring Gulls

several thousand pairs by the 1980s, and despite regular breeding in Kent for several decades, there were no records of Herring Gulls breeding in Essex until the 1990s. Prior to then, however, increasing numbers of mostly immature Herring Gulls were summering in the county; with them were a small number of adults. In 1992 a pair with three eggs was found on Foulness, although the outcome was unknown. The next records were in 1995 when single breeding pairs were located in Hamford Water, on Bridgemarsh Island, on Foulness and at Beckton. Breeding numbers have increased markedly since, although most are found in Hamford Water where they form a large mixed colony with Lesser Black-backed Gulls, which outnumber them. Presumably wanderers from the heavily predated Orfordness colony formed this. The small Beckton colony was probably founded by birds from colonies just the other side of the Thames in Kent.

In addition, during 2001 three pairs bred at Harwich and single pairs at Holland-on-Sea and Old Hall.

To Christy, the Herring Gull was a common winter visitor but only found inland after severe weather. He gave no quantitative data, although on 23rd and 25th December 1886 "… hundreds of thousands …"were seen near the Swin Lightship fishing for Sprats. Glegg's description of the species' status was similar to Christy's, although he noted that a few, mostly immatures, could be seen all year. Visits inland were still considered "... irregular ...", Glegg himself, a regular at the Lea Valley reservoirs, having seen on just one occasion a mixed party of ten adults and immatures on 20th March 1926.

	Founded	Peak counts		Comments
Hamford Water	1995	200	2001	No proper count since, but several 100 pairs
Clacton Railway Station	1995	about 30	1999	Declined?
Rat Island	1999?	4	2003	No count 2004 but bred
Packing Shed Is.	1997	16	1998	No count in 2002
Pewet Island	1997	10	2002	No count in 2003
Foulness	1992	24	2001	
Southend-on-Sea Hospital	1998	4	2001	
Beckton SF	1995	36	2001	No count in 2002 and 2003
Chelmsford	2000	5	2003	
Walthamstow	2001	4	2003	

Principal Herring Gull breeding colonies from 1995-2004

Hudson & Pyman noted a marked increase in inland occurrences which they considered a post-war phenomenon that "... may be a change of habit rather than a direct consequence of the undoubted increase in winter numbers". A total of 12,000 was counted roosting on Girling on 31st December 1955. Meadows (1961) detailed results of a census of the Lea Valley roosts over the period 1958–60 which showed that around 9,500 were usually present in midwinter, with an all-time peak of 15,600 in February 1960, a figure that has not been reached again anywhere in Essex, although it is possible that substantially more may have been present in offshore waters in January 1981, and perhaps at other times, when the Sprat shoals are particularly abundant. Totals of 9,000–11,000 were regularly recorded roosting on Girling and KGV in November and December 1961. Subsequently, the highest counts have been: 8,000 flying over Bradwell to roost on the offshore sandbanks, November 1976 (with 7,250 in December); 5,000 at roost (mostly) on Girling, 13th January 1963; 5,000 over Bradwell, 16th November 1974; 5,000 on Foulness, 27th August 1978; and 5,000 at Pitsea refuse tip, 26th August 2000.

Outside the breeding season, Herring Gulls are generally the commonest of the large gulls in Essex and four-figure congregations at the large refuse tips along the Thames are regular. Except for 2,500 feeding around fishing boats off East Mersea on 21st January 1992 and 1,165 in Hamford Water on 12th February 1978, there have been no four-figure counts of Herring Gulls north of Bradwell. Inland, the spread of refuse tips has allowed further expansion of the species' range such that Herring Gulls may be seen throughout Essex during winter and passage periods. Large numbers roost at Hanningfield, presumably a proportion of these from the Thames, with considerably smaller numbers roosting in the Lea Valley and at Abberton.

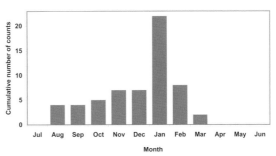

Sesaonal occurrence of counts of 1,000+ Herring Gulls from 1950-2004

By far the largest numbers are present from December–January, with most peak counts falling in the latter month. From the limited data available, there appears to be a late summer influx during August with a slight decline in numbers thereafter, before a further influx during October. Historically, the first peak, at Rainham at least, was during mid-September, but here too, mid-August is now typical (Dennis 1998). Two of the largest four-figure site counts have been in August. Spring passage is less obvious but small movements may be discernible on the coast and main reservoirs at this time.

WeBS count data are available from 1997. The small peak in October may be overemphasised by the lack of data for August and September. Thereafter, there is a build-up to a midwinter peak. Annual WeBS totals vary significantly; the presence of Sprat shoals off the coast and midwinter weather on the Continent are perhaps major influences on numbers. Insufficient data are available to comment further on movements other than that available from Foulness (Lewis 2000), where regular counts have shown that there is a decline in numbers during March and then a significant increase during April (no May data available). Return passage appears to begin in July, although it is not until the end of the month that any significant arrivals occur, with peak numbers from August to October. Numbers tail off during November and then increase significantly in December and January; numbers are, however, slightly lower than during the passage period.

A long-term ringing programme by the London Gull Study Group confirmed that many of the Herring Gulls wintering in southeast England are from colonies in Arctic Norway and Russia and attributable to the race *argentatus*.

	Jan	Feb	Mar	Apr	May	Jun	Jul	Aug	Sep	Oct	Nov	Dec
Norway								1				
Russia						1	3					
Denmark						1						
Germany						1						
The Netherlands						2	1			1		
Belgium	1	1	2	1				1				1
France						1	1					
Totals	*1*	*1*	*2*	*1*	*0*	*6*	*5*	*2*	*0*	*1*	*0*	*1*

Month of ringing and origin of Herring Gulls ringed abroad and recovered in Essex

Essex recoveries of *argentatus* go back to 1950; most were ringed as pulli and have come from as far to the northeast as Kharlov Island, Murmansk, Russia, some 2,727km distant. However, recoveries are more usually from colonies in the Norwegian Arctic. Pitsea Ringing Group cannon-netted several hundred from 1980-94. Several were subsequently recovered in the breeding season within the Arctic Circle in northern Norway and Finland, some 1,647–2,626km distant.

In addition, a number of Pitsea-ringed Herring Gulls have been reported in the breeding season within northeast Scotland (Grampian), east Scotland (Isle of May, Fife), the Farne Islands, Northumberland and Orfordness, Suffolk. Additionally, several have been recovered in the Netherlands. It is assumed that all of these birds were *argenteus*. There is, however, no evidence to suggest that birds from the west of Britain or Ireland have ever reached Essex. A few recoveries of Pitsea birds suggest that some individuals will move further south in particular winters to the south coast or to northwest France. The relative numbers of each race and the timings of occurrence of each in Essex have, rather surprisingly, never been investigated.

The increase in Herring Gull numbers has gone hand in hand with the increase in Lesser Black-backed Gull breeding numbers. The same conservation concerns apply equally to this species and careful observation on the impact of an increasing breeding population on other bird species will be necessary to assess whether control measures that have already been used in Hamford Water and in other counties are effective.

	Jan	Feb	Mar	Apr	May	Jun	Jul	Aug	Sep	Oct	Nov	Dec
Essex	1	1		1		2	2	2	2	2	3	1
Scotland					2	1	4	1	1			
North England	3			1	3	1	2	1	1			
South England		2	4		5	11	8	3	5	1	4	3
Wales					1							
Finland							1	1				
Norway				1	1	3		2	1			
Sweden							1					
Denmark						1				1		
Germany					1		1					
The Netherlands	2		2		2	2	8	7	4	1		1
Belgium						1						
France			1						1			
Totals	6	3	7	3	15	22	27	17	15	5	7	5

Month and location of recovery of Herring Gulls ringed in Essex

Caspian Gull   *L. a. cachinnans*

Very scarce passage migrant and rare winter visitor: first confirmed record in 1995

Caspian Gulls breed from east Germany and Poland to the Black Sea, east across the steppes of southern Russia and Kazakhstan to Xinjiang province, western China. They generally winter to the south of the breeding range from the east Mediterranean to the Persian Gulf and western India but are also recorded with increasing frequency in western Europe outside the breeding season.

During 1995 and 1996, many hours of study at Mucking Tip by a dedicated team of observers

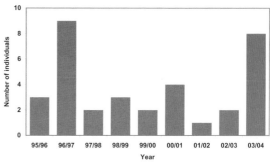

Annual totals of Caspian Gulls from 1995/96-2003/04

(Garner & Quinn 1997; Garner *et al.* 1997) resulted in the BOURC in 2003 accepting the record of an adult Caspian Gull on 16th August 1995 as a subspecies on the British List. In all, Garner *et al.* identified up to eight birds on 14th October 1996. From 1st January 2000 the BBRC no longer considered records of the race, although many prior claims remain outstanding. Caspian Gulls are proving to be very scarce autumn passage migrants and rare winter visitors to Essex with 1–3 occurring in the last few years. Increasing interest in the race will undoubtedly clarify the true status of Caspian Gulls over the next few years. Ringing recoveries dating back to 1953 from Denmark, Germany and France raise the question as to whether the species has been overlooked in the past, although there has been a westward range expansion in Europe in recent years (BBRC 2003). An adult that first arrived in the Royal Docks on 28th November 1998 has returned every winter since and has acquired the name 'Caspar' from its many admirers.

Iceland Gull   *Larus glaucoides*

Scarce winter visitor and passage migrant: 99 individuals

Iceland Gulls breed in Greenland and southern Baffin Island to northwestern Quebec, Canada. They winter in the North Atlantic and along the North American east coast. Although considered by some authorities (e.g. Olsen & Larsson 2004) to exist in two forms, the nominate *glaucoides* and *kumlieni* (Kumlien's Gull), others consider the taxonomic position of *kumlieni* unclear. Indeed, the BBRC no longer considers records of the race since, amongst other reasons, it is a highly variable taxon; no two birds are truly identical and are perhaps the result of hybridisation between *glaucoides* and Thayer's Gull *L. thayeri*.

Around 100–200 occur annually in Britain, although there is variation from year to year (Migration Atlas).

Christy detailed only one record, a second- or third-year bird shot on the Colne at Brightlingsea on 1st January 1887, to which Glegg added just two more, in 1892 and 1927. The next record was not until 1951, although it was not until the mid-1970s that increased scrutiny of gull flocks on refuse tips and at reservoir roosts revealed the species to be an annual visitor.

Records have generally increased in line with observer coverage in recent years, although there were fewer during the mid-1990s. The majority occur in Essex during January, with numbers tailing off through February, but with an increase in numbers again in mid-March to mid-April, presumably involving birds from further south moving back north through the county.

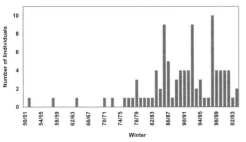

Annual totals of Iceland Gulls from 1950/51-2003/04

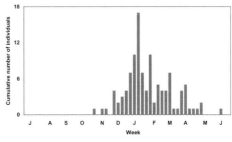

Seasonal occurrence of Iceland Gulls from 1950-2004

Apart from one off the Glebe Outfall, Dengie, on 13th June 1999, extreme dates have been 10th May: first-winter off Southend Pier in 1979; and 4th November, a sub-adult at Old Hall in 1985.

Almost 33% of the 96 that have occurred since 1950 has come from the Thames Estuary, where Rainham is the principal site (with 13), the remaining records coming from a wide spread of locations, and only Leigh/Two Tree Island (with four occurrences) recording more than three. A total of 23 from the Lea Valley includes 14 from Girling. Elsewhere, 14 have occurred at Hanningfield. Conceivably, some individuals noted at daytime feeding sites have also been recorded at roosts on the large reservoirs, thereby creating some duplication. Other records away from the aforementioned areas have come principally from the northeast with 12 records (13%), both offshore and along the coast. The remaining records have all been singles from widely scattered sites, apart from a total of four at Bradwell. There are no records from Abberton.

Remarkably, on only two occasions, at Pitsea from 13th–27th November 1927 and on Mersea Island from 20th–January-9th February 1991, has any Iceland Gull been seen for longer than ten days, although it is strongly suspected that birds seen irregularly at individual sites through a winter may be returning individuals. All records have involved singles apart from: two adults at Hanningfield, 21st January 1993; an adult and first-winter at Girling, 7th February 1993; and single first- and second-winters at Hallsford Bridge, Ongar, 24th January 1998.

Of those specifically aged, 33 were first-winters, 17 second-winters, one second-summer, two third-winter and 29 adults. Given that the majority of Iceland Gulls recorded in Europe are first-winters (Olsen & Larsson 2004), the high proportion of adults is surprising.

Two records have involved birds showing characteristics of *kumlieni*: at Rainham, an adult on 13th December 1997; and at Girling, a first-winter on 10th February 2003.

Glaucous Gull   *Larus hyperboreus*

Uncommon winter visitor and passage migrant

The Glaucous Gull is a circumpolar species and the large predatory gull of the Arctic. The nominate race *hyperboreus*, which breeds in northern Canada, Greenland, Iceland, the Arctic islands and the north coast of Russia, disperses south into the Atlantic in winter. The nearest population, in Iceland, numbers some 10,000–15,000 pairs (European Atlas) and increased by perhaps more than 50% during 1970–90; it is, however, mostly resident. Those occurring in Britain are probably from the northern European colonies (Spitzbergen, Novaya Zemlya) and perhaps northern Russia, and numbers occurring here depend on weather conditions in their normal, more northerly wintering areas. In Britain, the majority occur in northern Britain, particularly the Shetland Islands and Orkney Islands with relatively few in southern England (Second National Atlas).

The first Essex record involved an immature, probably a second-year, shot in Harwich Harbour on Christmas Day 1885; it was the only record Christy listed, although it was noted as "rare" at Harwich. Glegg added just two more records, and by the end of 1949 the total had increased to seven.

Following one in February 1951, the species has been reported in every winter since 1955/56, apart from 1958/59 and 1967/68.

Numbers have increased steadily over the last 30 years, probably largely due to increased observer coverage as monitoring of populations outside Iceland have not identified significant changes. Accurate census work is, however, difficult particularly in Svalbard (European Atlas). The particularly lean years during the mid-1990s may perhaps be attributable to a run of very mild winters but were followed by one of the largest influxes to date, a pattern generally mirrored in Suffolk (Piotrowski 2003).

Given the species' apparent high mobility, with few being reported with any regularity from individual sites other than for odd days, it is quite possible that the estimated number of birds is somewhat higher than the actual number present. Movements between the large refuse tips and the main reservoirs are probably common. Although it is very likely that birds return each winter to particular sites, there is no definite proof that any birds have done so (but see summering individual below) and indeed a stay numbered in weeks is exceptional. Immatures at Rainham from 28th November 1972–31st January 1973 and an adult at the same site from 19th October–15th December 1974 are the only definite long-stay records, with both occurrences perhaps involving the same bird.

A second-summer on the Colne Estuary from 11th April–25th July 1993 and a third-summer there on 22nd May–24th July 1994 may have involved the same individual; these are the only summering records, although a second-summer at Rainham on 14th June and 30th August 1997 may have summered locally. Additionally, there have been June records from: Leigh/Two Tree Island, an adult, 26th in 1980; Leigh/Two Tree Island, a first-summer, 2nd in 1979; and Rainham, a second-summer, 14th in 1997. The only other July record was a first-summer on Dengie on 9th July 1977. There have been four August records.

Usually, individuals begin to appear from September, although it is not until late December/early January that most occur. Although not obvious in the graph an early spring passage is discernible in some years. A few individuals are reported into May.

The majority of records have involved 1-2 individuals. However, there were up to three in the Holland Haven area from 1st–14th April 1979 and in the first half of January 1981, an adult and two immatures were attracted to the trawlers fishing in the Colne Estuary.

Glaucous Gulls have been recorded from right around the coast, although most of the records have come from the Thames where the large refuse tips are the obvious attraction with Rainham the most favoured locality. Reasonable numbers have been reported from the northeast, several from well offshore; here the attraction appears to be the trawlers that work out of the Colne.

Inland, Hanningfield and Girling have been the most favoured localities, although at the former it has been only in the last 25 years that the species has been regular; there were just three records up until 1974. At both sites birds often arrive on a bearing that suggests an origin along Thames-side. In winter, huge flocks of gulls assemble from midday onwards before dispersing throughout the afternoon prior to sunset. Surprisingly few have been recorded at Abberton;

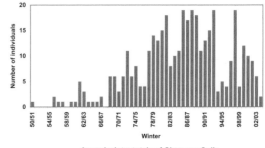

Annual winter totals of Glaucous Gulls from 1950/51-2003/04

this may be due to the difficulties in observing the roost flocks that fly in from the coast and settle in the most distant central areas of the reservoir, although few large gulls tend to visit the reservoir.

A Glaucous Gull recovered on Foulness on 1st March 1998 had been ringed as a nestling at Ternehaug, Flora, Norway, on 17th June 1997. It is one of only five foreign-ringed Glaucous Gulls recovered in Britain (Migration Atlas).

Hybridisation between Glaucous and Herring Gulls is not uncommon and several apparent hybrids have occurred in Essex.

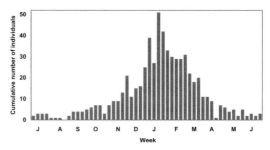

Seasonal occurrence of Glaucous Gulls
from 1950-2004

Great Black-backed Gull *Larus marinus*

Common winter visitor and passage migrant - small numbers present in summer

The monotypic Great Black-backed Gull, the largest of the European gulls, breeds on the coasts of the North Atlantic and Baltic Sea (European Atlas) and is more closely associated with the open sea than either Herring or Lesser Black-backed Gulls. Around 120,000 pairs breed in Europe, the majority in Norway, Iceland, Britain and Ireland with around 18,000 pairs in Britain (Mitchell *et al.* 2004), mostly in Scotland, where it typically breeds on islands and rocky stacks. The species is the least

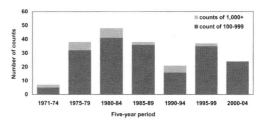

Number of counts of 100+ Great Black-backed Gull in
each five-year period from 1971-2004

common of the five breeding *Larus* gulls and, whilst it breeds around much of the north and west coasts, it is mostly absent from the east and south coasts between the Firth of Forth and Chichester Harbour (Second National Atlas). Only birds from the northernmost parts of the breeding range move far in winter, the rest dispersing shorter distances, generally southward (European Atlas). It is a very large and powerful bird; one at Dovercourt on 10th February 1987 killed an adult Brent Goose by repeatedly picking it up and dropping it to the ground.

The Dictionary of the Thames (Dickens 1887) stated that the species "... used formerly to breed in the marshes at the mouth of the Thames," which perhaps was quoting Yarrell (1845) who observed that in 1843 "On the flat shores of Kent and Essex at the mouth of the Thames, where this bird remains all year ... [it] is decidedly a marsh breeder". However, he described in some detail its nesting habits in Kent and Essex as if he had noted them personally. Given the Great Black-backed Gull's typical nesting habitat, the records do seem unusual. Nevertheless nesting on marshes has been noted in Hampshire (Clark & Eyre 1993) and several pairs have nested on Orfordness since 1999 (Piotrowski 2003), so there seems no clear reason to doubt that the species bred in Essex in the early 19th century. There have been no 20th century breeding attempts. However,

there has been a trend in recent years for very small numbers of mostly immature birds to summer in the county.

Outside the breeding season, the general status of the Great Black-backed Gull has not changed significantly since the 19th century, except for the general increase in numbers and inland records in particular. Christy considered the species "Common on the coast from autumn to spring ...", whilst Glegg noted that the species was found on the Essex coast "... chiefly

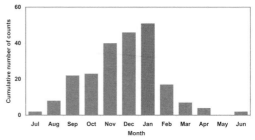

Seasonal occurrence of counts of 100+ Great Black-
backed Gulls from 1971-2004

during the autumn migration and throughout the winter". Neither author gave any quantitative data, although Glegg noted, "... generally single birds or very small parties, which rarely contain more than ten birds" were seen. With the increasing use of land adjacent to the Thames for landfill sites and the readiness of the species to exploit these for feeding, the numbers of Great Black-backed Gulls rose after WWII, a period that also saw an increase in inland records as the species began to use the main reservoirs for roosting.

Although never as numerous as Herring Gull, by the 1950s and early 1960s four-figure concentrations were being reported with regularity from the Thames-side refuse tips during winter. Numbers continued to increase until around the mid-1980s since when there has been an apparent decline, first commented upon in *EBR* 1995. The number of Great Black-backed Gulls breeding in Britain and northern Europe are considered to have remained relatively stable since the mid-1980s (Lloyd *et al.* 1991) but the national trend in recent years has been a general decline in maximum counts at the principal wintering sites (Pollitt *et al.* 2000). It should also be borne in mind that the species was undoubtedly under-recorded from the 1960s–80s and indeed was mentioned just once in the *EBR* Systematic List from 1963–87.

There were 5,000 in the county during the BoEE count of December 1973. The five largest site counts, all from Leigh/Two Tree Island refuse tip occurred in the late 1970s/early 1980s: 4,400, 14th January 1981; 3,000–3,500, 14th November 1977; 3,000, 7th November 1980; and 2,880, 1st December 1978. Away from Leigh/Two Tree Island, the only other significant four-figure coastal counts involved some 2,500 that flew east over Bradwell to roost on 16th November 1974, 2,500 on Two Tree Island on 14th December 1996 and 1,500 at Maldon refuse tip on 4th December 1984. However, it is likely that a five-figure total was present amongst the unprecedented influx of gulls to the outer Thames Estuary in January 1981. The most recent four-figure count came from Two Tree Island with 1,120 on 10th December 1999. Away from the Thames, where recent WeBS counts

	Jan	Feb	Mar	Apr	May	Jun	Jul	Aug	Sep	Oct	Nov	Dec
Essex									2			3
North England				1								
South England				1					1			1
Finland					1							
Norway					2	1	2	2				
Sweden							1					
Germany										1		
France										1		1
Totals	*0*	*0*	*0*	*2*	*3*	*1*	*3*	*2*	*3*	*2*	*0*	*5*

Month and location of recovery of Great Black-backed Gulls ringed in Essex

have confirmed that up to 80% of the wintering population may occur, coastal gatherings of more than 200 are rare. However, there were 550 on the Roach on 2nd January 1999 and 450 in Hamford Water on 12th October 1980.

There was a considerable increase in inland records after 1930; Glegg stated: "It rarely wanders inland..." but, by the late 1960s, up to 300 were roosting in the Lea Valley with a peak of 700 on Girling/KGV on 16th December 1961. Subsequently numbers at the various waters in the Lea Valley have rarely exceeded 300. Flight lines observed at the time suggested movements occurred from the west of the county out to the coast in the Blackwater area. The fact that there were no further inland counts in excess of 700 until the 1980s was probably due rather to lack of observer coverage than a genuine dearth of large inland flocks. However, it is only at Hanningfield that four-figure roost flocks have occurred and these were, with two exceptions, restricted to 1983/84 and 1984/85, the highest being 2,000 on 13th January 1985 and 1,750 on 22nd January 1983. The last four-figure count from here was 1,098 on 23rd January 1993. The largest count from Abberton was 420 on 22nd January 1983. Thus, inland data also suggest an apparent decline since the mid-1980s.

Spring and autumn passages, although undoubtedly regular, are more difficult to discern than for both Herring and Lesser Black-backed Gulls. No obvious inland movements have been noted and none of the four-figure counts has occurred before mid-October or after early February. Nationally, numbers show a September peak (Migration Atlas); recent WeBS counts have not detected this in Essex. The timing of all three-figure counts from Essex do not show an obvious autumn passage with an apparent steady build-up from August onwards, although regular counts from Foulness since the early 1970s do show a peak in August–September (Lewis 2000).

Spring passage is even less discernible than the autumn movement with very few three-figure counts after the end of February; indeed, most adults have left by the end of the month.

Several hundred Great Black-backed Gulls were caught by the Pitsea Ringing Group between 1980 and 1994 using cannon-netting methods, one of a very few British sites that have caught such significant numbers. Recoveries of Pitsea-ringed birds outside the winter period have come from the north end of the Baltic in northern Finland at Oja, Karleby, 1,898 km away and five north of the Arctic Circle on the Norwegian coast from 1,990–2,577km distant, the furthest at Mehamn.

In addition, ringed birds from the Orkney Islands, Denmark (one), Sweden, Norway (ten) and the Barent Sea coast of Russia (two) up to 2,585km distant (Great Ainov Island, Murmansk), have been recovered in Essex. The ringing evidence therefore suggests that a significant proportion of the county's wintering and passage populations is from the northern and eastern edge of the Great Black-backed Gull's main range. As yet there is no evidence of any Icelandic birds occurring nor any from the Irish and western populations of Britain, both of which are largely sedentary (Migration Atlas).

The Great Black-backed Gull has not made any serious attempt to nest in the county and it seems unlikely to do so in the future, although 1-2 pairs have taken to nesting on factory roofs in Felixstowe during the early 2000s (Piotrowski 2003). Indeed, perhaps because of changes in waste disposal management and a period of milder winters, the number visiting Essex appears to have declined over the last 10-15 years. However, overall it is not seriously threatened and is likely to remain a regular visitor to Essex for the foreseeable future.

(Black-legged) Kittiwake   *Rissa tridactyla*

Winter visitor and passage migrant: a few usually during summer   Amber List

The Kittiwake, by far the most abundant and oceanic of European gulls, breeds in the Arctic Ocean and the northern latitudes of the Pacific and Atlantic Oceans where it typically nests in vast colonies on the narrowest ledges of sea cliffs. The nominate race *tridactyla* occurs throughout its North Atlantic range. From 1900 until the mid-1970s, the species increased steadily, but since 1985 breeding success at several colonies has been very low, possibly due in part to over-fishing of Lesser Sandeels. In the Shetland Islands, where declines have been of the order of 70% since 1980, the primary cause

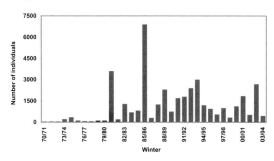

Annual winter totals of Kittiwakes from 1970/71-2003/04

has been predation by Great Skuas (Heubeck 2002). In Britain, most of the 380,000 or so pairs (17% of the European population) breed in Scotland and along the North Sea coasts, although there are a very few between Lincolnshire and Dorset. The nearest breeding colonies to Essex are at Lowestoft and Sizewell, Suffolk, where man-made structures are used (Piotrowski 2003). Outside the breeding season, European populations disperse from breeding areas and north of 40° N; flocks are common across the entire North Atlantic, often hundreds of kilometres from land (Winter Atlas).

Not surprisingly, due to a lack of natural habitat, the Kittiwake has never bred in Essex. However, in 1986 and echoing events in Suffolk, a pair was seen displaying on quay buildings at Harwich from 27th March but the birds had departed by mid-April.

Christy described the Kittiwake as "A fairly abundant winter visitor to the coast, and often driven inland by severe gales". The description of the species as "fairly abundant" may have perhaps exaggerated its status, as it was probably less common than it is now. Birds of the year were slaughtered in huge numbers not only for sport but also to fuel the fashionable millinery accessory trade (Historical Atlas). Even in Norfolk during the 19th century, it was felt that "… at no season can it be termed common" (Stevenson 1866–90). After receiving protection from the Bird Acts, Kittiwake numbers began to recover nationally, although Glegg could only describe the species as a "… scarce winter visitor". However, he noted that Kittiwakes occurred in considerable numbers at some distance from the coast, although a flock of 30 was the largest reported.

Apart from a report of 200 around fishing boats 8km off Brightlingsea during January 1964, which "… indicates how much more frequent the Kittiwake must be offshore", Hudson & Pyman considered double-figure counts rare. Since the 1970s increasing numbers have been observed from the coast, although it was not until the early 1980s that the increases became significant (Cox). Even allowing for greater observer coverage, the increase appears to be genuine (Winter Atlas).

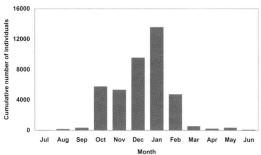

Seasonal occurrence of Kittiwakes from 1970-2004

Observations since the early 1980s have confirmed that numbers recorded in winter vary considerably from year to year and generally appear to be dependent mainly on the arrival of huge Sprat shoals in coastal waters or the prevalence of strong onshore winds: all the largest counts have coincided with the former. In 1981, following the arrival of exceptional numbers of Sprats in the southern North Sea, some 2,500 were off Foulness on 11th January, with several other flocks of up to 400 present around the coast; unsubstantiated reports from fishermen suggested

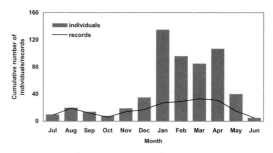

Seasonal occurrence of inland Kittiwakes from 1950-2004

that there were 10,000 off the coast (Cox). Despite high Sprat numbers in 1982, Kittiwake numbers were unexceptional. In December 1985, another significant influx occurred with 1,200 off Shoeburyness/Southend Pier on 15th and 5,000—the largest verified county day total—on 18th. Around 1,500 were off Southend Pier on 4th February 1994, whilst there were 1,100 off there on 1st January 2003. It is not clear whether these birds were from British colonies or from further afield, although it is likely that both were involved (Winter Atlas).

Kittiwakes do not migrate in the true sense of the word. After fledging, juveniles disperse from their breeding colonies as early as July and August, whilst adults may stay around the colony until as late as December and return as early as February. Many, particularly immatures, wander west as far as the Canadian coast, mostly by rounding northern Scotland, although some North Sea birds appear to move via the English Channel (*BWP*).

Prior to the 1980s autumn counts involved just double-figure flocks. Subsequently, three-figure counts have become regular. There have, however, been no four-figure counts during this period. This can be contrasted with the large movements regularly observed off the north Norfolk coast where four-figure counts are regular and five-figure movements occasional (Taylor *et al.* 1999). Likewise, in Suffolk several very large autumn movements have been noted (Piotrowski 2003). Like other seabirds it appears that, at least in autumn when weather conditions are less severe than in winter, large numbers move well offshore and out of view of land-based observers. The highest autumn counts, which have usually been weather-induced, were 940 off East Tilbury on 19th October 1991 and 800 passing Holland Haven in just two hours on 29th October 1988. In addition, there were 746 off East Tilbury on 8th October 1992 and 409 on 11th October 1988. Almost all the largest autumn movements have occurred along the Thames and particularly off East Tilbury, where all but two of the three-figure day counts during autumn have occurred. It appears that the bend of the Thames at East Tilbury acts as a bottleneck that results in the formation of large flocks.

Spring passage is generally very light with single-figure flocks usual. A relatively high proportion of records are from well up the main estuaries, suggesting a link with inland movements at this time of year. By far the largest spring count was 75 off West Thurrock on 28th April 1985 following strong northwesterlies, the only other counts in excess of 20 being: 29 at East Tilbury, 21st May 1995 and 28, 10th April 1994; and 25 in the Crouch Estuary, 9th May 1996.

Small numbers are normally reported offshore during summer, usually in ones and twos. Totals of 136, 1.5km off the northeast coast during June 1969 and 34 off The Naze at the same time were exceptional.

Most inland sightings have been at the large reservoirs, especially the Lea Valley complex (127 records involving 300 birds) of which KGV has been particularly favoured and Hanningfield (76 involving 292).The relatively small number of records from Abberton (26 involving 27 individuals) mirrors the pattern noted in other seabirds, the reasons for which remain unclear. Numbers are greatest in spring, a time when occasional Kitttiwakes are also recorded well up the main estuaries. Are these purposely migrating overland? It is possible that a proportion of those heading west up the Thames in spring turn north up the Lea Valley and continue north, perhaps heading for The Wash, Norfolk/Lincolnshire; more than 1,000 spiralled up and flew inland over Lynn Point, Norfolk, on 29th February 1988 during a northwesterly gale (Taylor *et al.* 1999). Fewer are recorded inland during the autumn movement. The highest counts have been: 100 at Hanningfield following a violent storm, 2nd January 1988; 52 at KGV, 22nd February 1959; 34 at KGV, 4th March 1956; 33 at Hanningfield, 29th April 1981 with 32 the day before; and 14 at KGV, 4th May 1985. At Abberton, all records have been of singles apart from two on 15th February 1957. Singles have been recorded at a further seven inland sites.

Given the Kittiwake's pelagic habitat, it is perhaps surprising that there have been three ringing recoveries involving Essex. Two birds ringed on the Farne Islands, one as a chick, were subsequently recovered in northeast Essex, whilst another, also ringed as a chick at Murmansk, on the Norwegian/Russian border, was recovered in Essex. National ringing data have confirmed that birds from the latter area are frequent visitors to British waters.

Bridled Tern

Onychoprion anaethetus

Vagrant: one record

The Bridled Tern breeds throughout the Tropics, the nearest breeding colonies being on the Banc d'Arguin, Mauretania in west Africa, where the race *melanoptera* occurs, whilst *recognita* occurs in the Caribbean.

1991	West Thurrock/Hanningfield	2nd June	Adult

There have been just 21 British records, the last in 2003 (BBRC 2005); several were corpses. This was the 14th and was also observed at Broadness, Kent, on the same day. Found whilst observers were looking for a White-winged Black Tern (Davies 1992), it subsequently flew upriver and out of sight, only to be relocated one hour later at Hanningfield (Smith 1992). Most recent records have been during summer, so this individual falls neatly into the pattern. Races from both the Caribbean and west Africa have been found dead in this country.

Christy and Glegg also referred to an adult taken on a lightship at the mouth of the Thames in September 1875. It was originally accepted as genuine, despite a number of eminent ornithologists having reservations. However, the record was subsequently rejected on the grounds that the condition of the moult did not agree with the declared date of capture (Witherby *et al.* 1938–41); the specimen remains in the Booth Museum, Brighton, Sussex, (Accession No. 208004).

Little Tern

Sternula albifrons

The Little Tern is found across much of the middle and southern latitudes of Eurasia, North America, Africa, Australia and eastern Asia. Up to ten races have been identified, although most authorities now split the taxon into three valid species, Little Tern *S. albifrons*, Least Tern *S. (a.) antillarum* and Saunder's Tern *S. (a.) saundersi*.

Little Tern

S. a. albifrons

Summer visitor and passage migrant   **Amber List**

The nominate race *albifrons* has a cosmopolitan range covering much of Eurasia, the Far East and Australasia. The largest European populations are in Italy, Spain and Britain where there are around 1,900 pairs (Mitchell *et al.* 2004), representing around 6% of the European and 2% of the world population (European Atlas). Typical nesting locations are on shell and shingle beaches, which are prone to human disturbance and predator pressure. Most European birds winter along the coasts of west Africa.

Christy referred to the Little Tern as "… a rare summer migrant which used to breed commonly on the Essex coast … I only know of a single breeding colony at this time". This colony was along the relatively undisturbed Harwich side of Hamford Water where birds from the "… shingle on the shore between Harwich and Walton-on-the Naze..." probably transferred to from Walton "… on account of the persecution to which they are subjected by the visitors from Walton, who kill a great many during the nesting season, notwithstanding the provisions of the Wild Bird Protection Act".

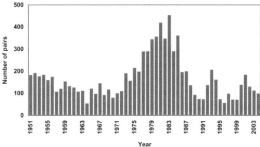

Annual totals of breeding Little Terns from 1951-2004

Although he gave no figures this colony was considered to consist of "… great numbers …". Historically, other breeding colonies existed "… on the eastern point of Osey [Osea] Island where there was a very large shingle-bank, but the colony was destroyed by the Maldon winkle-boys who took their eggs" and in the Paglesham district. Both Yarrell (1845) and Seebohm (1883–85) mentioned scattered colonies on the Essex coast but gave no localities. Christy's reference to the species formerly breeding commonly therefore suggests that the Little Tern declined markedly in Essex throughout the 19th century, a pattern repeated across much of its range in Britain at that time. The principal reasons for the decline were thought to be persecution for its feathers and eggs, disturbance and habitat destruction (Historical Atlas).

Presumably as a result of increased protection from the end of the 19th century, Glegg was able to confirm the existence of five colonies, the apparent increase being much in line with the national trend at that time. However, he noted: "All the colonies are small, are placed on a bank of shingle, and are probably decreasing owing to lack of protection". Because of the risk from egg-collectors he was, understandably, vague about their exact locations. Two colonies were located between Harwich and Walton, one between Walton and Mersea Island, one on the Blackwater and one along the Thames. The two Hamford Water colonies, both in use since 1890, had held up to six and 15 pairs respectively. The next site had 23 nests in 1912, no more than 15 in 1926 and fewer the following year. The Blackwater colony held 27 pairs prior to 1914 with 15 in 1928 whilst those in the Thames held just 3–4 pairs in 1923 and Glegg noted: "… its position is such that it is not likely to be occupied for much longer".

		Peak count in each decade					Year of	Comment
		1950s	1960s	1970s	1980s	1990s	2000s peak count	
Stour	Stour reserve	0	0	0	0	7	7	1994/2000	
Hamford**	Harwich-Lt. Oakley	20	73	50	36	32	18	1962	Mostly Lt. Oakley beach
	Horsey Is.	?	0	0	0	13	70	2000	
	Naze	25	25	53	63	75	7	1994	
Colne	Colne Point	70	36	40	77	30	47	1985	
	Jaywick	0	0	0	0	13	2	1999	also 7 pairs St Osyth Stone
	Fingringhoe Wick	0	0	0	0	0	2	2002	
	Langenhoe spit	1	0	2	16	9	3	1988	Offshoot of Colne colony?
Blackwater	Bradwell shellbanks/Pewet Is.	46	20	12	4	22	130	2001	Most now Pewet Is.
	Mersea Quarters*	8	6	4	9	41	0	1993	
	Tollesbury Wick	0	0	0	1	11	0	1999	
	Goldhanger	13	3	1	1	0	0	1952	Just three years after 1969
Thames	Foulness	77	95	285	360	53	0	1983	Recent data incomplete

Plus colonies in single years:

Pewit Is. (1997-23 pairs); St Osyth Stone (2003-3); Osea Is. (1962-2); Steeple Creek (1968-5); Maldon (1951-2); Mundon (1975-1); Heybridge GP (1969-1); Canvey Island (1951-1); Abberton (1965-10)

*Great Cob/Packing Shed/Company Shed and Cobmarsh Islands **total of 60-80 pairs combined in 2003

Summary of Little Tern colonies from 1950-2004

By 1950 there were about ten sites around the coast at which Little Terns bred, but only seven were used regularly. Foulness, with up to 95 pairs, was at the time one of the three largest colonies in Britain (Hudson & Pyman). From the 1960s until the mid-1980s, breeding numbers continued to increase along the coast, influenced principally by the colonisation of the Maplin Bank in 1975. The combined Foulness Point and Maplin Bank colonies numbered 360 pairs in 1983. Intensive wardening at other sites, particularly at Colne Point, The Naze and Little Oakley, meant that during the early 1980s Essex held around 20% of the British population. A current Essex population of 150 pairs represents around 8% of the British population.

In Essex, Little Terns typically breed on a variety of seashore habitats, usually on open sand and shingle beaches, with or without vegetation and normally close to or below spring high tideline. Nests are therefore vulnerable to high tides and adverse weather conditions. More recently artificial habitats have been used, such as the Maplin Bank off Foulness or beaches made from 'recharging' using dredgings from Harwich Harbour, in Hamford Water. Given the size of the human population of Essex and the Little Tern's specific habitat requirements, it is not surprising that human disturbance has increased over the last 50 years as recreational use of the coastline has risen. Egg collecting has, thankfully, become largely an historic problem but it is accidental disturbance, usually by holidaymakers, that has had catastrophic effects on nesting success. Natural predators have also caused significant damage to colonies: Kestrels have taken every nestling at Colne Point in some years. Other species known to have taken eggs or young include Foxes, 'wild' Dogs, feral Cats, Stoats, Weasels, Badgers (Foulness), Carrion Crows, Black-headed Gulls and possibly Brown Rats at The Naze. Not surprisingly, breeding success varies markedly from year to year and between colonies. Whilst fencing off colonies with wire and/or electric fences, wardening and predator control can be effective, none are a guarantee of success. Use of camouflaged shelters in Norfolk does, however, appear to be achieving notable success (Taylor *et al.* 1999) but this has yet to be ried in Essex.

The Little Oakley colony is almost certainly the same one referred to by Christy, making it the oldest still in existence. It originally consisted of a two main sub-colonies located some 2–3km apart along a shingle beach, both being below high spring tideline. The most favoured area, Middle Beach, used to hold up to 60 pairs but this declined due to severe human disturbance and the birds moved during the 1970s and 1980s to the relative quiet of Pewit Island. Currently, the beach that has been built up on the northeast corner of Horsey Island, holds most of Hamford Water's breeding Little Terns.

Much interchange occurs between the Little Oakley and The Naze colonies. At the latter, there were originally three sub-colonies on the narrow sand and shingle spit that heads northwest

Atlas	Survey	% of 10km squares or tetrads in which	
	Area	bred/probably bred	possibly bred or present
First National 10km	Essex	19.3	3.5
Second National 10km	Essex	14.0	0.0
First London Tetrad	Met. Essex	0.0	0.0
Second London Tetrad	Met. Essex	0.0	0.0
Essex Tetrad	Essex	1.7	2.1

Summary of results of Atlas surveys for Little Terns

towards Stone Point. In the 1970s, this was the best known and most actively wardened site in Essex and, whilst this was in place, the colony was relatively successful, peaking at 63 pairs in 1981. Soon afterwards, wardening ceased and the colony soon declined to extinction.

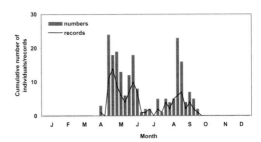

Seasonal occurrence of inland Little Terns
from 1971-2004

The colony at Colne Point was almost certainly one of those referred to by Glegg. Two sub-colonies used to exist there, one at Sandy Point towards Point Clear, which became extinct in the 1970s, and the surviving and principal sub-colony situated on the shingle beach/split just to the west of Leewick. During the 1950s, 50–70 pairs were present but numbers fell through the 1960s. However, a period of intensive wardening that included the erection of electric fencing around the colony, reversed the decline. Breeding numbers peaked at 77 pairs in 1985. However, numbers have subsequently declined due to less intensive wardening and particular difficulties with Kestrels against which fencing is ineffective. Perhaps some individuals from this colony moved the short distance northeast up the coast to Jaywick, where 5–12 pairs have been noted in the last 12 years, although breeding has not been annual.

Further up the Colne Estuary, odd pairs were noted at Langenhoe Spit in 1952 and 1973 with two pairs in 1970–71. However, expansion of the Colne Point colony possibly promoted increased use of the spit and since 1981 a colony has existed in most years, with peaks of 15 pairs in 1985 and 16 in 1988.

The islands and shingle spits in the Mersea Quarters have been used erratically since at least the early 1950s, most colonies appearing to utilise a particular site for only short periods. The locations of the colonies, with (in parenthesis) the peak number of pairs present followed by the number of years that Little Terns have bred at that site, are: Great Cob Island (41–6); Company Shed Island (6–3); Packing Shed Island (15–2); Cobmarsh Island (30–6); Tollesbury Wick (11–8); and "Mersea/Tollesbury" area (30–6).

Further up the Blackwater, the only colony of any size was at Lauriston Beach, Goldhanger, where there were 13 pairs in 1952, although by the 1960s only 1–3 bred with the colony effectively extinct by 1970; single pairs were present there in 1977, 1979 and 1986. Odd pairs have bred further west along the Blackwater, nearer to Maldon, in single years.

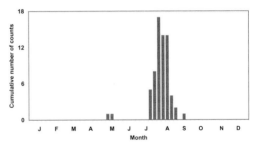

Seasonal occurrence of counts of 100+ Little Terns from
1971-2004 (excludes counts at breeding sites)

The Bradwell colonies have been reported since at least 1949, most pairs nesting on the Bradwell cockle spit until the mid-1960s. However, human disturbance and increasingly high tides caused a decline such that by 1974 the colony was extinct. Declines here, however, coincided with increases at Colne Point and Foulness, so some pairs may have relocated to these sites. From 1985, small numbers began nesting on Pewet Island, off Bradwell arapid growth saw a peak of about 130 pairs in 2001.

Little Terns were first recorded breeding on Foulness in 1951 at the Point, where the naturally deposited shell banks were used. Numbers here remained relatively stable through the 1950s–70s. However, from 1975 numbers increased markedly and peaked in 1983, although the most productive year was 1982 when 208 young were ringed. From 1984 a general decline set in with no breeding between 1987 and 1990 and, despite a small resurgence in numbers, none have bred at the Point since 1996. It is thought that the colony declined as a result of reshaping of the shell bank by natural forces, which allowed terrestrial predators greater access (Lewis 2000). Offshore from Foulness, the Maplin Trial Bank was colonised by Little Terns in 1975. Numbers built up rapidly to its most successful year in 1979 when 256 young were ringed. It continued to thrive until 1983 but subsequently a decline set in with the colony becoming extinct after 1993.

	Jan	Feb	Mar	Apr	May	Jun	Jul	Aug	Sep	Oct	Nov	Dec
Essex					4	2			1	1		
South England						3		1				
Germany						2						
The Netherlands					1	6	5					
Belgium					2							
France				1			2	2				
Spain									1			
Portugal								3	1			
Italy					1							
Senegal					1	1						1
Totals	0	0	0	2	9	13	7	6	3	1	0	1

Date and location of recovery of Little Terns ringed in Essex

In 1948 Little Terns bred at Abberton (Pyman 1948), with 20 pairs nesting on the island in 1949 and ten pairs there in 1965. These are the only known inland breeding attempts in Britain.

The earliest spring arrivals usually occur around the third week of April. However, there was one at Colne Point on 1st April 1956. During spring, definite passage movements along the coast are rarely detectable; even in autumn definite movements are uncommon. Most breeding birds, however, are usually back at breeding colonies by the second week in May.

In autumn, many of the large gatherings were considered to relate to post-breeding gatherings from the Foulness colony (Cox). However, it is clear that large numbers still occur in late summer, despite the demise of the colony, particularly around the Foulness area where three-figure counts are regular; this suggests that it is an important staging area for migrants from outside Essex at this time. The largest counts have been: 600 on Foulness, 29th July 1984; 510 in the Crouch Estuary, 5th August 1978; 444 on Foulness, 18th August 1996; 500 at Foulness/Wakering Stairs, 22nd August 1985; and 400+ at Wakering Stairs, 30th July 1989. Picking out definite southerly movements along the coast is difficult as Little Terns tend not to migrate in flocks like other terns but move southwards in a steady stream, often mixing with feeding local birds.

Numbers tend to peak in late July/early August with Little Terns generally rare after mid-September. Few are recorded in October with records in 18 years since 1960, the latest at Holland Haven on 28th in 1989. There has been just one November record, at Bradwell on 1st in 1959.

Inland, most records have traditionally come from Abberton, where its proximity to the Colne and Blackwater has meant that small feeding flocks have occurred with some regularity, mainly during July and August. The largest counts have been 50 on 25th July 1961 and 18th August 1985. Until the late 1980s, records were regular and counts of 10–20 not unusual. Since then, far fewer have been recorded. Elsewhere inland, the Little Tern is an annual visitor in small numbers. The Lea Valley and particularly KGV are favoured with smaller numbers reported from Hanningfield. Most are recorded in spring, with numbers/records peaking in late April and again in late May.

Most records have been of 1–4 but there were five at KGV on 9th May 1981 and six at: Hanningfield, 20th August 1996; KGV on 29th August 1990; KGV, 28th April 1995; and Walthamstow, 21st August 1966.

An intensive ringing campaign was carried out on Foulness from the 1970s–90s and recoveries of Little Terns ringed there illustrate the typical migration route of the species and dispersal of local birds. The Little Tern may show relatively low site fidelity (Migration Atlas), although many recoveries of returning Essex-ringed birds suggest that there is quite a high degree of fidelity to an area of coastline; this may explain why many colonies vary in size from year to year and from place to place. Some, however, leave their natal colonies to breed in the Netherlands, Belgium and Germany. Two nestlings ringed on Foulness and one from Colne Point have provided some of the most southerly recoveries of British Little Terns to date—in Senegal, west Africa. One ringed in June 1975, which was caught and released at Livorno, Italy, on 30th May 1977 was unusually far east; it was found dead just 11 weeks later near Calais, France. The speed of southerly movement can be rapid: one ringed at Bradwell on 21st August 1966 was recovered just six days later at Porto de Leixoes, Portugal; this movement represented an average speed of 230km per day. Two Little Terns ringed at Foulness were almost 21 years old when recovered, whilst another ringed there in June 1977 was breeding in a colony at Zeebrugge, Belgium, in 1994; this is the oldest British-ringed Little Tern to have been reported to the BTO.

The Little Tern has probably had more time and money put into its conservation than any other avian species in Essex. Results have shown that such expense can bring success with the colonies at The Naze and Colne Point in particular profiting from the efforts of conservation organisations. Once such protection is removed, declines are rapid. The future of the species in Essex will, therefore, rely heavily on conservation organisations' willingness to provide the necessary money and manpower. Innovations, such as the camouflaged chick shelters, used so effectively at Great Yarmouth, Norfolk, might, however, ensure that these efforts might not be quite so labour-intensive as they have been in the past.

Least Tern   *S. (a.) antillarum*

Vagrant: one record

S. a. antillarum is found in North and Central America and winters in Central America and northern South America.

1991	Colne Point	29th June–1st July

After many years of deliberation, this record has finally been accepted by the BBRC (BBRC 2005). This individual was the same one that was present at Rye Harbour, East Sussex, from 1983-92. Unfortunately, its presence was not widely publicised due to the potential for disturbing the Little Tern colony (Clifton 1992). It remains the only British record.

Gull-billed Tern

Gelochelidon nilotica

Vagrant: six records with a pair probably present in 1949; bred in 1950

The Gull-billed Tern has a fragmented breeding range throughout the Nearctic, South America and the Old World and winters in the tropics. European populations, which are represented by the nominate race *nilotica*, have been declining since the 1970s (European Atlas).

On 24th July 1949 a pair of large terns appeared amongst the Common Terns over the island at Abberton. Their behaviour suggested that they were breeding on the island. However, from the views obtained it was thought that they might have been Sandwich Terns, although the observers were unfamiliar with that species (Pyman & Wainwright 1952).

On 2nd July 1950 two terns were encountered in the same location and were immediately recognised as being the same species seen the previous year; they proved to be Gull-billed Terns. On 4th July a healthy chick was found on the island and ringed. It also appeared healthy on 6th July. On 10th July an adult was noted flying around some 200m from where the chick had been ringed. Three days later, the ringed chick was found dead; its identification was confirmed by Liverpool Museum where it was preserved and remains to this day (Accession No. 1983.778). No adult was seen after 10th July despite extensive searches.

This remains the only known nesting attempt in Britain and occurred when there used to be a small colony in the Netherlands and 400 pairs still bred in Denmark; only about 1–3 pairs remained in Denmark by 2003 (BBRC 2005).

The only other records are:

1901	Ashdon	21st May	One shot from five
1974	off Maplin Sands	5th September	
1997	Holland Haven	16th May	
2003	Shoebury East Beach	5th July	Adult

There had been 305 British records to the end of 2004 (BBRC 2005), although the species is far less common than formerly due to the declines on the Continent. However, a better understanding of its salient identification features and tightening of BBRC standards may have contributed to the apparent decline as well. Nationally, most occur from July–September.

Caspian Tern

Hydroprogne caspia

Vagrant: six records probably involving four individuals

The monotypic Caspian Tern has a fragmented worldwide breeding range with the nearest colonies in the Baltic and Black Seas, these populations wintering mainly in west Africa.

1959	Abberton	2nd August	Adult
1961	Walthamstow	9th July	Adult
	Abberton	6th August	Probably previous bird
	KGV	26th–27th August	Probably previous bird
1975	Colne Point/		
	Geedon Saltings	29th June–2nd July	Adult
1981	Heybridge GP	20th–22nd June	Adult

The Heybridge individual was considered the same as that at Minsmere RSPB, Suffolk, on 18th June and then again from 22nd June–13th July (BBRC 1982).

There were 273 British records to the end of 2004 (BBRC 2005), mainly involving individuals dispersing from their breeding colonies during July and August. The very few British ringing recoveries suggest an origin in the Baltic populations of Sweden and Finland, which have decreased significantly in recent years (European Atlas). It seems remarkable given the number of records from adjacent counties that the last Essex record was some 25 years ago.

Sponsored by Simon Cox

Whiskered Tern   *Chlidonias hybrida*

Vagrant: four records

The Whiskered Tern breeds throughout southern and eastern Europe, discontinuously through to China, as well as parts of Africa, India and Australia. In Europe, the species is represented by the nominate race *hybridus*. Western birds winter principally in Africa.

1967	Old Hall	4th June	Adult summer
1993	Abberton	3rd–6th July	Adult summer
1994	Abberton	3rd–12th May	Adult summer
1998	East Tilbury	26th July	Adult summer

There were 137 records nationally to the end of 2004 (BBRC 2005), most involving adults during May and June. Recently, there has been an increase nationally, although population trends are unclear on the Continent (European Atlas). The occurrence of Whiskered Terns is not always coincident with the other two *Chlidonias* marsh terns, which have easterly distributions, suggesting that vagrants from southern and eastern populations may be involved. Did the 1993 Abberton individual make a subsequent visit?

Black Tern   *Chlidonias niger*

Regular passage migrant in variable numbers

The Black Tern breeds across Europe, Asia and North America. The nominate race *niger* breeds from western Europe eastwards to the Yenisey in Asiatic Russia, whilst *surinamensis* breeds in North America. The species favours eutrophic natural freshwater marshes with stagnant shallow pools rich in floating aquatic vegetation (European Atlas). In Europe, where the population is thought to number 57,000–111,000 pairs, the largest colonies are found in the east. It is thought that almost the entire population spends 2–3 weeks moulting in the Dutch Ijseelmeer during autumn before migrating south to winter mainly along the west African coast. West European and Mediterranean populations are thought to have declined by 50% since the 1970s.

Christy considered that "It appears probable ... that it bred in Essex about fifty years ago, but drainage and cultivation have now quite banished it ..." Black Terns became extinct as regular breeders in the marshes of eastern England by about the middle of the 19th century (Historical Atlas). Unfortunately, Christy provided no evidence to back up his claim. Interestingly, three of the five pre-1860 Essex records came from the extreme northwest; the earliest documented record came from Shoebury in 1829. Was this due to observer coverage, proximity to relict breeding areas outside the county or was the species breeding on marshes in that area of Essex? The largest count detailed by Christy was six shot on Canvey Island on 12th August 1881.

	No. of counts 50+		No. of counts 100+	
	Spring	Autumn	Spring	Autumn
Thames	0	23	0	10
Abberton	8	5	0	3
Hanningfield	9	7	2	0
KGV	2	3	1	1

Principal sites for Black Terns from 1950-2004

Glegg considered the Black Tern "... an irregularly recorded double-passage migrant..." and that migration in spring was more extensive than in autumn, although his narrative actually suggests the opposite. A flock of ten at Bradfield on 21st April 1913 was the largest he detailed; others occurred on the Stour, at Paglesham, up the Thames as far as East Tilbury, Wanstead and in the Lea Valley.

Since 1950 Black Terns have been regular double passage migrants in numbers that vary considerably from year to year. Numbers occurring along the coast have increased, perhaps due to increased observer coverage.

The first Black Terns are normally reported during the third and fourth weeks of April, however, singles at Abberton on 9th in 1998 and Benfleet Creek on 9th in 1991 are the earliest. In 1980, there was a particularly early influx with singles at Hanningfield, Heybridge GP and along the Blackwater on 13th (possibly the last two records referring to the same bird), whilst in 1981 there was one at Bradwell on 13th and in 1998 there was one at KGV on 13th.

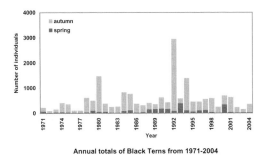

Annual totals of Black Terns from 1971-2004

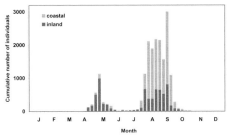

Seasonal occurrence of Black Terns from 1971-2004

Spring passage peaks around mid-May, with the majority occurring inland, usually at the main reservoirs and along the Lea Valley. Generally, Hanningfield appears to attract more Black Terns than Abberton in spring, with the situation reversed in autumn. Double-figure spring counts are regular, although flocks of 50+ are uncommon. Three-figure counts have been noted on just three occasions: 400 at Hanningfield, 2nd May 1958; 354 at Hanningfield, 13th May 1961; and 100+ at KGV, 23rd May 1959. In all, a total of 550 birds was recorded in spring 1958, the highest count yet at this season; a total of 430 occurred in spring 1961. All these counts occurred in the period 1958–61, when autumn counts were also above average. Spring counts of this magnitude have not been repeated subsequently, although a total of 391 passed through Essex in 1993 and 338 in 2000.

Spring passage continues until around mid-June, although it is impossible to identify when spring passage ends and autumn begins. Occasional birds have been seen displaying but none have stayed: there are no definite summering records.

Autumn passage begins by late June, peaks during late August/early September and is largely over by mid-October. However, stragglers have been noted into November, the latest at East Tilbury on 13th in 1984, whilst there was one off The Naze on 11th in 1975. Significantly more are recorded along the coast than inland during autumn. In Norfolk, generally larger numbers occur in spring than autumn (Taylor *et al.* 1999). Almost all of the largest autumn movements have occurred in the Thames Estuary with all the three-figure counts coming from here. The largest movement occurred from 6th–13th September 1992 when at least 1,500 birds passed through, including around 1,000 through the inner Thames on 6th; over the next few days around 500 more were noted around the coast and inland, albeit mainly along the Thames, including 459 that passed Canvey Island on 13th. This movement occurred following several days of strong southeasterly winds, heavy rain and poor visibility, which probably caused the displacement of birds migrating down the European coastline onto the eastern coast of England. This passage was also noted further north in Norfolk where birds were seen passing east along the north coast (Taylor *et al.* 1999). Such weather conditions, both in spring and autumn, typically result in influxes. On 17th August 1980 there were 600 off Foulness and Great Wakering with 300 off West Thurrock on 20th September and smaller numbers around the coast, contributing to a total just short of 1,000. Other three-figure coastal counts have been: 230 off Canvey Island, 31st August 1994; 200 off Foulness, 5th August 1978; 200 off Tilbury Power Station, 30th August 1990; and a further six counts off up to 200. Away from the Thames, the highest counts have been 99 off Bradwell on 12th September 1995 and 90 off Colne Point on 21st August 1991.

Inland records during autumn, although fewer in number than coastal records, generally outnumber spring inland records. The largest autumn three-figure counts have all come from Abberton: 300, 18th August 1955; 270, 4th August 1984; and 120, 11th September 1992. There were 100 at KGV on 15th September 1994.

White-winged Black Tern (White-winged Tern)   *Chlidonias leucopterus*

Rare passage migrant: 45 records involving 51 individuals

The monotypic White-winged Black Tern is an Old World species typical of natural extensive freshwater marshes, which occurs from east-central Europe east to central Asia and to north China and Ussuriland (European Atlas). The species is an annual migrant to Britain with 836 records to the end of 2004 (BBRC 2005). European populations winter in Africa south of the Sahara.

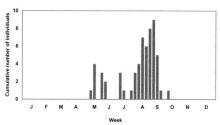

Seasonal occurrence of White-winged Black Terns
from 1912-2004

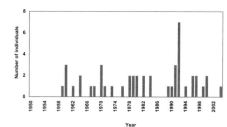

Annual totals of White-winged Black Terns
from 1950-2004

1912	Burnham-on-Crouch	28th May	Four
1949	Abberton	24th–31st July	Adult
1959	Hanningfield	5th–20th September	Immature
1960	Parkeston	13th May	Adult
	Hanningfield	20th May	Adult
	Abberton	19th August	Adult
1962	Abberton	6th–9th September	Juvenile
1964	Abberton	16th–30th August	Immature
	Hanningfield	20th–22nd August	Juvenile
1967	Thames Haven	13th–14th and 27th August	Adult
1968	Thames Haven	18th August	
1970	Abberton	14th–31st August	Immature
		22nd August	Adult
	Crouch Estuary	15th August	Immature
1971	Abberton	10th–11th August	Adult
1973	Walthamstow	27th August	Immature
1976	Hanningfield	22nd–24th August	Immature
1978	Abberton	4th–9th August	Adult
	Bradwell	8th September	Adult
	Foulness	9th September	Same as previous
1979	Abberton	31st August–5th September	Immature
	West Thurrock	9th–13th September	Immature
1980	Abberton	4th–5th August	Immature
	West Thurrock	16th September	Immature
1982	Abberton	5th–6th October	Immature
	West Thurrock	7th August	Immature
1984	Chelmer Valley	8th June	Two
1989	Abberton	2nd July	Adult
1990	West Thurrock/Tilbury	27th August-6th September	Juvenile
1991	Cattawade	2nd–4th June	Two adults
	West Thurrock	2nd June	Adult
1992	Abberton	29th July	1st-summer
		24th–31st August	Juvenile
	Hanningfield	18th May	Two adults, one sub-adult
	Canvey Island	11th September	Juvenile
	Girling	13th–14th September	Juvenile
1994	Hanningfield	31st July	Adult
1996	Silvertown	4th–5th July	Adult
	Abberton	6th–11th August	Juvenile
1997	Hanningfield	3rd–4th September	Juvenile
	Abberton	7th September	Juvenile
1999	Heybridge GP	30th August–3rd September	Immature
2000	Hanningfield	7th July	Adult

	Barking Bay	14th July	Adult
2004	Abberton	17th–19th August	Juvenile

Just under 38% of the records have come from Abberton. Generally, numbers have increased during the period, although in line with the national trend there were several lean years in the 1980s. The slight increase in the frequency of records is likely to be due to increased observer coverage but appearances remain erratic and are usually linked with weather conditions causing a westerly displacement. The 1992 influx, which involved 49 nationally, was such an incursion and coincided with influxes of other eastern species (cf. Red-footed Falcon). Over 1,000 stayed to breed in Poland, the possible source of autumn records that year.

White-winged Black Terns usually associate with flocks of Black Terns, which pass through principally in May–June and August–September. The majority of Essex occurrences are during August and early September; in Suffolk the species is predominantly a spring migrant (Piotrowski 2003).

Sponsored by David Bradnum

Sandwich Tern   *Sterna sandvicensis*

Local and erratic summer visitor - common passage migrant   Amber List

The nominate race of the Sandwich Tern, *sandvicensis*, breeds along the Atlantic coasts of Europe, the western Mediterranean, Black Sea, Sea of Azov and Caspian Sea. A further two sub-species are found along the eastern coasts of North and South America (European Atlas). In Europe, most colonies are situated in low-lying areas on coasts, sometimes in exposed locations. Islands are preferred but mainland spits and dunes are also used. Generally the European population increased during the 20th century. In Britain and Ireland, the increase was dramatic, rising from about 6,000 pairs in 1962 to 18,400 by 1987 (Lloyd *et al.* 1991), but declining recently to 13,000 (Mitchell *et al.* 2004). The nearest substantial colonies are

Atlas	Survey Area	% of 10km squares or tetrads in which	
		bred/probably bred	possibly bred or present
First National 10km	Essex	5.3	0.0
Second National 10km	Essex	1.8	0.0
First London Tetrad	Met. Essex	0.0	0.0
Second London Tetrad	Met. Essex	0.0	0.0
Essex Tetrad	Essex	0.1	0.4

Summary of results of Atlas surveys for Sandwich Terns

Havergate Island, Suffolk, where around 300 pairs breed annually (Piotrowski 2003) and in Norfolk at Blakeney Point and Scolt Head where variable numbers breed, although the annual combined total of both sites is around 3,000–4,000 pairs (Taylor *et al.* 1999). West European populations of Sandwich Terns migrate south along the west coast of Africa to winter between Mauritania and South Africa (Cape of Good Hope).

Remains attributed to Sandwich Terns have been found in the 300,000-year-old 'elephant bone beds' at East Mersea (Urquhart 2000).

One figured by Albin (1731–38) was the earliest documented Essex record.

The status of the Sandwich Tern as an Essex breeding species has, it would appear, always been erratic. During the first half of the 19th century, eggs were collected and sold, like Lapwings' eggs, in the London markets (Historical Atlas) and it is possible that this was responsible for the eradication of colonies along the Blackwater Estuary by 1850. Christy noted: "It used to breed on the Essex coast, but does so, I believe, no longer". The earliest evidence for its breeding was provided by Christopher Parsons who noted in 1834: "I have had the pleasure of bringing home the beautiful eggs of this fine bird from some salterns at the mouth of the River Blackwater ...". The species may have also bred in Essex at the mouth of the Thames in 1865, whilst "... one pair or more used ... to breed annually on Colne Beach" up until the late 1880s.

There were no more breeding records until the early 1960s when, following a series of midsummer sightings around Hamford Water, a chick and an addled egg were found in the Black-headed Gull colony on Hedge End Island on 30th June 1963. Although perhaps not an isolated instance, no further nesting attempts were confirmed in Hamford Water at the time. However, with numbers increasing nationally it was not to be long before the next

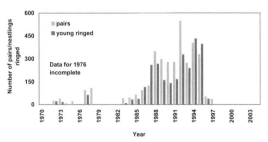

Number of breeding pairs of Sandwich Terns and nestlings ringed on Foulness and Maplin Bank from 1970-2004 (adapted from Lewis 2000)

335

breeding attempt, this time on Foulness, where in 1969 several pairs attempted to nest, although the high tides washed away the eggs. In the same year at least three pairs appeared to be present around Hamford Water and one individual was observed carrying food. Breeding may have occurred on Rat Island in 1970 and 1971. In 1972, 27 nests were found at Foulness Point. Numbers increased to 95 pairs in 1977, when 64 young were ringed, and peaked in 1978 at 110 pairs, although they failed to hatch any young, possibly due to adverse weather conditions. No breeding occurred here for the next four years (Lewis 2000).

In the early 1970s a trial hydrological shingle bank was constructed on the MoD restricted area of Maplin Sands, about 4km south of Wakering Stairs. This work was undertaken by the Maplin Airport Development Authority, prior to plans being abandoned for the area becoming the site for London's third airport. Maplin Bank, although rather exposed to the elements, was relatively free from disturbance and ground predators. It was first colonised by Common and Little Terns but Sandwich Terns followed in 1983 with 42 nests found that year. Numbers continued to increase until 1988 after which they were lower for the next three years. In 1992 the colony peaked at 548 nests. In 1996 numbers declined markedly, probably as a result of erosion of the Maplin Bank due to increasingly high tides. The residual colony of some 36 pairs was probably destroyed in 1997 when a boat crew made an illegal landing and lit a barbecue in the middle of the colony (Lewis 2000). In an attempt to entice terns back, Maplin Bank was enlarged in early 1999. However, it was left with a ridge upon it and it is possible that this did not prove attractive to Sandwich Terns since there were too few flat areas left for the birds to nest tightly together (the late Maurice Adcock pers. comm.). The ridge has now been flattened and it is hoped that this fickle breeder will eventually recolonise.

Elsewhere, and despite the occasional presence of summering Sandwich Terns, it was not until 1999—when four pairs laid eggs in Hamford Water but were flooded out—that breeding occurred away from Foulness for the first time since 1963. It is possible, however, that odd pairs nest undetected amongst the Black-headed Gull colonies in Hamford Water or the Colne Estuary.

The Sandwich Tern is generally the earliest of the terns to return in spring. The majority arrive around the end of April and early May, but March records are not uncommon. The earliest county records have both been inland, one at Hanningfield on 16th March 2002 and two over Walthamstow on 17th March 1991. On the coast, the earliest records have been 18th March 1992 at East Tilbury and 19th March, two at Fingringhoe Wick in 1970 and one at Colne Point in 1977. Spring passage is generally light with counts of more than ten uncommon. A total of 151 that flew north in two hours at The Naze on 5th April 1967 is more than double any other spring count.

Returning birds start to appear from mid-July with numbers peaking during September. Until the founding of the Foulness breeding colony, counts of 50+ were rare (Cox). Indeed, unlike other terns, the species rarely appears in large numbers or shows significant passage movements. All of the largest counts came from the Thames, although 300 off Canvey Island on 4th September 1955 and 500 at Mucking/Shellhaven on 24th August 1963 were far in excess of any others. With the growth of the Foulness colony reasonably large counts were made in the Thames Estuary, although sur-

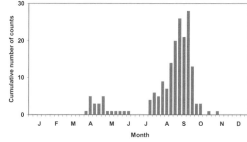

Seasonal occurrence of counts of 10+ Sandwich Terns from 1971-2004

prisingly, given the number of birds possibly present at the colony's peak (1,000–1,500 birds), the highest counts were somewhat lower: 300 on 7th and 250 on 27th August 1995 off Canvey Island; 200 off Canvey Island, 29th August 1997; 160 off Shoebury, 30th July 1994; and 150+ off Southend Pier, 9th September 1989. Despite the demise of the Foulness colony, numbers on the Thames have generally been maintained with regular passage movements noted: 350 on 25th August 2003, 250 on 31st August 2002, 225 on 29th September 2001, 200 on 21st August 2004 and 130 on 20th September 1999—all off Canvey Island—are the largest. It is interesting to speculate on the origin of the large numbers noted off Canvey Island in 1955 and Mucking in 1963 as the dates of the counts are similar to those when the Foulness colony was in existence, but 3–4 weeks earlier than most recent passage movements: were Sandwich Terns breeding somewhere on/near Foulness at this time?

Away from the Thames, passage numbers are generally small and rarely reach double figures. There have only been three counts of 70+, all in September: 70 off The Naze, 11th in 1983; 70 off Bradwell, 22nd in 1991; and 126 off Dengie, 23rd in 1983.

Very small numbers of Sandwich Tern occur into November, although 11 off Dengie on 6th in 1982 was exceptional. There have been three December records in addition to the wintering record below: 17th in 1978 off Foulness; 9th in 1979 in Hamford Water; and mid-month in 1999 in Hamford Water; also, one was at Tollesbury on 1st January 1999. During the winter of 2002/03 one was seen in the area of the Blackwater/Dengie 12 times during November–January.

Inland, Sandwich Terns have been recorded annually since 1954 with most occurring at Hanningfield and in the Lea Valley, particularly at KGV. The number of individual records vary considerably from year to year.

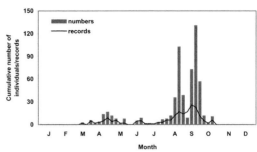

Seasonal occurrence of inland Sandwich Terns from 1950-2004

There have been 12 double-figure counts only one of which was away from the main reservoirs: 33 over Woodham Mortimer on 25th September 1980. Inland, Sandwich Tern records show an unusual pattern of occurrence: there is a peak in late April, which coincides with peak passage on the coast, and then a secondary peak in late June/early July. The latter peak appears to coincide with post-fledging dispersal of British Sandwich Terns in late June (Smith 1975). In autumn, records peak in mid-August and then again in mid-September before declining sharply in October, with the latest inland record being two at Hanningfield on 18th October 1987.

A programme of ringing on Foulness has produced a large number of recoveries. The majority of the African recoveries involved birds caught by man, either inadvertently by offshore fishermen or inshore by children for whom the activity is a sport, although up to 25% of those caught were released

	Years with records	Total numbers	No. of double-figure counts	Peak counts
Abberton	18	92	1	50 17th September 1974
Hanningfield	36	222	6	36 7th September 1990
KGV	28	135	2	27 20th September 2000
Girling	16	78	1	35 23rd August 1967
Walthamstow	22	76	1	20 18th-26th August 1966
Other sites	30	87	1	33 25th September 1980

Summary of inland Sandwich Tern records from 1950-2004

unharmed with the ring removed (Mead 1978). Although clearly fortuitous for the bird, this has not helped ringing studies. The recoveries of Maplin birds have shown that the favoured wintering area for Essex Sandwich Terns is the west African coast from Senegal south to South Africa, the principal wintering area for British and Dutch birds (*BWP*). The migration route can be traced down the European and then African coast in the table. Post-fledging migration can be rapid: a juvenile ringed on 16th June 1995 reached Senegal by 18th September that year. The recoveries suggest that there is a continued southerly movement towards the end of the year but that adults are already heading north by February. The presence of immature birds off the west African coast in summer is typical (*BWP*). There have been no records of first-summer individuals in Essex, although there are a very few records from, for example,

Norfolk (Taylor *et al.* 1999). Studies at Continental colonies have confirmed that Essex Sandwich Terns may move to other colonies to breed, whilst studies in Norfolk have confirmed that mass failure early in the breeding season may cause large numbers of birds in a colony to move.

Only one large Sandwich Tern colony has existed in Essex in the last 50 years, ironically on an artificial site that fortunately did not become the planned offshore airport. Only time will tell whether the Maplin Bank will be recolonised. It is unlikely that there are, at present, any other sites suitable for the species. Further artificial sites may

	Jan	Feb	Mar	Apr	May	Jun	Jul	Aug	Sep	Oct	Nov	Dec
North England								1				
South England						2			2	2		
Germany									1			
The Netherlands				1	3		3					
Belgium					1		1					
France							1	1	2			
Spain										1		
Morocco								1				
Senegal	1	3	3		1				4	3	2	1
Gambia			1									
Guinea Bissau			1						1			
Guinea	1											
Sierra Leone	1											1
Liberia		1										
Ivory Coast								1		1	2	
Ghana		1	1									1
Benin	1											
Nigeria					1							
Gabon										1		
South Africa												1
Totals	4	5	6	2	5	2	5	6	9	5	6	4

Month and location of recovery of Sandwich Terns ringed in Essex

perhaps lure the species back to breed in some numbers, but the resources required to construct another Maplin Bank are unlikely to be forthcoming, unless as a consequence of sea defence works which, given increasing sea levels, may not be entirely out of the question. The EC Council Directive on Wild Birds classifies the species as a cause of some concern, the primary threat at present being persecution in wintering and first-summer quarters off the west coast of Africa.

Forster's Tern   *Sterna forsteri*

Vagrant: one long-staying individual

The monotypic Forster's Tern breeds in the interior of North America and on the east and Gulf coasts and winters along the coast of the southern states into Central America.

1998	West Mersea	16th November	1st-winter
	Tollesbury Creek	22nd December	1st-winter
1999/2000	Hamford Water and	18th February 1999-	1st-winter then
	Blackwater Estuary	1st September 2000	2nd-summer/winter

Following the two initial sightings, this individual relocated to Hamford Water where it remained for several weeks before returning to the Blackwater. During the course of its stay there it was seen as far upriver as Goldhanger and also at Bradwell. It apparently went missing for long periods, although it may have simply been overlooked along what is one of the longest coastlines of any British county. However, a Forster's Tern present on Terschelling, the Netherlands, from 13th–14th November 1999 may have been the same bird.

This was the 16th British record and only the second on the English east coast, the majority occurring in southwest Britain and Ireland. The first British record was as recent as 1980, coinciding with an apparent increase and range expansion on the eastern seaboard of North America; there have been 20 nationally, the last in 2003 (BBRC 2004). Winter records are typical, with many remaining for long periods. Summering is almost unique, although given that in the west and particularly Ireland what seem to be the same individuals reappear in successive winters, it seems that they may simply be overlooked in summer, given their similarity to Common Terns at this time of year.

Common Tern   *Sterna hirundo*

Summer resident and passage migrant

The Common Tern is the most widespread of the *Sterna* terns, and occurs widely from the Arctic fringe south through the boreal and temperate zones (European Atlas), the nominate race *hirundo* breeding throughout Britain and Europe. Although typically a coastal species, where it usually nests colonially in association with Arctic

Atlas	Survey Area	% of 10km squares or tetrads in which	
		bred/probably bred	possibly bred or present
First National 10km	Essex	24.6	10.5
Second National 10km	Essex	38.6	0.0
First London Tetrad	Met. Essex	2.0	0.5
Second London Tetrad	Met. Essex	8.0	12.0
Essex Tetrad	Essex	3.7	3.8

Summary of results of Atlas surveys for Common Terns

Terns and Black-headed Gulls, Common Terns regularly breed inland where they may inhabit inland marshes, gravel-pits, specially provided rafts and even rooftops. In Britain it is the third most common breeding tern after Arctic and Sandwich, numbering some 12,000 pairs (Mitchell *et al.* 2004), although it is far more widespread than the former. The British population overall appears to be relatively stable: declines in coastal colonies in England and Ireland have been offset by an increase in Scotland. Western European birds winter principally off the west coast of Africa, with first-year birds generally remaining in winter quarters (European Atlas).

The earliest documented Essex record involved one shot at Wrabness on 9th May 1821. Christy described the Common Tern as "An uncommon summer visitor, which used to breed on our coast but does not do so now". At some time during the 1830s it apparently nested not uncommonly on the saltings at Peldon and Wigborough, and nests were also found on "Shingle Hill" (possibly now known as Shinglehead Point, Tollesbury Wick) in later years. During the 1880s the species was considered common in the Colchester and Paglesham districts, but it was

	Year founded	Peak count in each decade						Comment
		1950s	1960s	1970s	1980s	1990s	2000s	
Hamford								
Horsey Is	pre-1951	120	30	31	10	25	6	
Colne								
Rat Island	pre-1951	12	3	11	4	0	0	Driven off by breeding large gulls and high tides?
Blackwater								
Pewet Is	1978/2001	0	0	15	0	0	110	
Great Cob	pre-1951	70	60	40	80	58	21	Transferred to Pewet Island 2001?
Heybridge GP	1968		13	17	35	35	41	
Foulness								
Point	1954	2	1	160	108*	1	0	
Maplin Bank	1979	0	0	0	238*	206	0	Artificial shell bank
New England	1991	0	0	0	0	148	83	On rafts
Abberton	pre-1949	40	25	1	30	35	40	Originally on island; raft from 1980
Hanningfield	1959	10	30	25	2	26	15	Originally on island; raft from 1989
Walthamstow	1983	0	0	0	10	40	42	On rafts
* chicks ringed								

Summary of principal Common Tern breeding colonies from 1950-2004

never known to have bred in either. In the late 1880s Essex was the only coastal county between Lincolnshire and Sussex that did not have breeding Common Terns (Historical Atlas). However, probably as a result of protection and perhaps range expansion, the species began to increase generally throughout England at the end of the 19th century (Historical Atlas) and thus Glegg was able to note that "... it breeds annually, although in limited numbers". However, he was aware of just two colonies, both along the Colne Estuary. One colony, founded prior to 1909, numbered 51 nests in 1909 with about 20 in 1913 and 20–30 pairs in 1926. On the opposite side of the Colne a small colony, perhaps founded prior to 1894, numbered 15 pairs in 1927.

Over the next 20 years, numbers continued to increase, but a decline appears to have set in after WWII as a consequence of increased disturbance around the coast (Hudson & Pyman). Since then, however, the pattern has been one of general increase although three factors have influenced annual totals: the founding of a large colony on the Maplin Bank and its subsequent demise; the increased use of inland nesting sites; and increased observer coverage.

In addition to the principal coastal sites mentioned in the table, there were 8–10 pairs on The Strood, Mersea Island, in 1951 but none since. Periodically, short-lived colonies have existed on Cobmarsh Island and around the Mersea Quarters, although rarely recently. There were 30–40 pairs in 1953 and 22 in 1997. At West Mersea there were 12–15 pairs in 1979. Along the Crouch, 27–30 pairs were on Bridgemarsh Island in 1954, but few have been recorded since and there were up to 11 pairs at Stow Creek, North Fambridge, in the early/mid-1990s.

Disturbance by humans or predators, periodic high tides and poor weather all mean that annual success at individual colonies varies markedly from year to year. The largest former Essex colony, on Maplin Bank, was founded in 1979, with numbers peaking at 206 pairs in 1992, although 1987 was the most productive year when 239 young were ringed (Lewis 2000). As Maplin Bank was increasingly eroded by high tides, so numbers declined with none breeding there by 1999. At least part of the colony, however, transferred to a pontoon anchored in the middle of New England Creek. It is possible that some of the colony moved northwards where, on Pewet Island, off Bradwell Marina, the county's largest colony now exists amongst the Black-headed Gull colony, numbers rising rapidly to 110 pairs in 2002. Until 2001, Great Cob Island, off Old Hall, was the oldest known surviving colony. However, the founding of the nearby Pewet Island colony appears to have caused its abandonment. Numbers in Hamford Water are considerably lower than in the past, probably due to increased flooding of the older saltmarsh sites (Simon Cox pers. comm.). Up to five pairs have bred in the Royal Docks, London, in the last decade.

Historically, most inland breeding records came from Abberton and Hanningfield, with nesting away from these two sites not being confirmed until 1968 when a pair bred at a central Essex gravel-pit. Since then, inland breeding has continued to increase as the species has taken advantage of the increase in gravel extraction sites across the county.

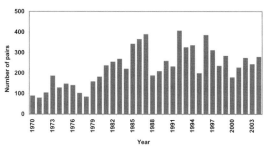

Annual totals of breeding pairs of Common Terns from 1970–2004

The Lea Valley in particular has seen notable increases, with all sites along the valley currently holding up to 50 pairs in recent years, the majority at Walthamstow where a colony has used a raft since 1983. Similar rafts have also been used successfully at Abberton since 1980 and Hanningfield since 1989. Breeding success of raft-based colonies has, in general, been greater than at traditional sites. Use of man-made gravel-pits can be transient as bare gravel banks and islands become overgrown with vegetation. Thus, although the Common Tern bred at both the Chelmer Valley Pits and Chigborough Lakes, neither site is now suitable for the species. At other sites, variable water levels mean that numbers in a colony may vary considerably from year to year; at Heybridge GP numbers have fluctuated annually in the last ten years or so from 6–40 pairs.

The Common Tern is the most numerous member of the family to pass through the county. Coastal movements are common with many birds also using the sand and shell banks both offshore and close to the coast as temporary roost sites. Inland passage is noticeable, particularly during spring when passage numbers sometimes exceed those on the coast.

The first spring arrivals usually occur around the first ten days of April. Apart from one at KGV on 11th February 1933, the earliest record remains that of a party of about a dozen at Walthamstow on 9th March 1924. More recently there was one at Fingringhoe Wick on 18th March 1963 and in Hamford Water on 23rd March 1967, although during the last 25 years the earliest record was at Abberton on 27th March 1981. Passage peaks during early May.

In spring, numbers recorded on passage along the coast are generally low with, in the last decade or so, 1–2 three-figure counts at most. A total of 550 at Foulness on 13th May 1978 was exceptional. Other high counts have been: 340 off Gunners Park, Shoebury, 19th April 2000 and 300 there on 22nd April 2004; 205 at Canvey Point, 23rd April 1994; 200 off Wakering Stairs, early May 1987; and 200 off Canvey Island, 30th April 2001. A record of 200 'Commic' terns at East Tilbury on 21st April 1996 presumably referred to predominantly Common Terns.

Coastal passage begins again by the end of July and peaks in late August/early September and may, on occasions, involve quite significant numbers; conversely, inland passage at this time of year is far less noticeable. An estimated 3,000 Common and Arctic Terns, almost all of which were presumably Common, roosted at Canvey Point on 4th September 1955, whilst the only other four-figure counts involved 1,400 that passed Foulness on 10th September 1978 and 1,150 off Canvey Island on 12th August 2001 with 600 off the latter on 19th. Over the last two decades, increased coverage along the Thames has shown that there is a significant passage upriver on a regular basis to East Tilbury, Thurrock and beyond: 410 were in Barking Bay on 5th September 1998. The highest counts have been: 750 at East Tilbury,

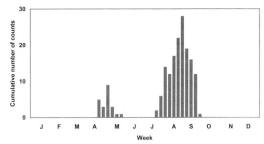

Seasonal occurrence of counts of 100+ Common Terns from 1971-2004

22nd August 1987 and 662 upriver at the same location on 26th August 1989; a flock of 700 'Commic' terns in the mouth of the Thames, 4th September 1988; 600 off Canvey Island, 19th September 2001; and 500 off Canvey Island, 8th September 1996. Excepting those in 2001, counts have generally been lower since the decline of the Foulness colony. Observations in the 1950s showed that birds do not necessarily pass upstream on a rising tide and in fact some of the largest westward movements occurred on a falling tide. Away from the Thames, counts have generally been much lower and rarely in excess of 100, 350 off Colne Point on 3rd September 1990 and 250 from Holland Haven on 23rd August 1996 being the largest recently.

Most Common Terns have left the county by mid-October, although stragglers may be recorded into November. A bird lingered around St Osyth boating lake from the summer of 1966 and was found dead on 2nd January 1967. Also, one at Old Hall on 8th January 1999 may have been attempting to winter in the area, one passed Southend Pier on 1st December 1977 and a 'Commic' tern was noted off Holland Haven on 5th December 1982.

Inland records follow the trend of many terns, in that spring passage tends to be more noticeable than the autumn movement. Three-figure counts have come from Abberton on a number of occasions with a peak of 300 on 2nd May 1971. A total of 250 at Abberton on 31st May 1955 may have come inland to feed; the date is late for large numbers of migrants. Movement between Abberton and Great Cob Island was noted on 24th May 1959.

Smaller numbers generally pass through Hanningfield and the Lea Valley. Fewer pass through during autumn with counts rarely exceeding 100. Thus, 400 at KGV on 30th August 1992 was unprecedented.

Large numbers of Common Terns from Scandinavia, the Baltic States and the Low Countries move west along the English Channel in August and September (*BWP*). Thus, the recoveries of German and Dutch-ringed birds in Essex are typical. Common Terns ringed as nestlings in Essex have been recovered primarily from west African countries.

	Jan	Feb	Mar	Apr	May	Jun	Jul	Aug	Sep	Oct	Nov	Dec
Essex			1				3			1		
North England							2	1				
South England					1	2	2					
The Netherlands							1					
France					1							
Spain									1			
Portugal									1			
Senegal	1	1	1			1			1			2
Guinea Bissau						1						
Sierra Leone	1	2										1
Liberia					1							
Ivory Coast										1		
Ghana							1			1	1	1
Nigeria		1	1									
Totals	*2*	*4*	*3*	*0*	*3*	*5*	*8*	*1*	*3*	*4*	*1*	*4*

Month and location of recovery of Common Terns ringed in Essex

Those recovered in Guinea Bissau and Senegal during June are first-year birds (see below) presumably summering off the African coast. Birds move very quickly south with September and October records in Senegal, Ghana and the Ivory Coast. The most distant recovery involved one ringed at Foulness on 4th July 1979 as a nestling and recovered near Ayiforo village, Nigeria, around 5,079km to the south. Common Terns are generally more site-faithful than, for instance, Little Terns. Thus, one caught on the raft at Hanningfield on 23rd June 1993 having been ringed as a chick in the Netherlands in June 1988 and two Foulness individuals subsequently found on Merseyside in July and presumably nesting locally, are noteworthy.

Most first-year birds remain in their winter quarters and are therefore generally rare in Britain. The only Essex records all occurred in 1992. At West Thurrock, there was one from 14th–18th and three on 19th July and two on 29th August, whilst there were singles (at least two birds being involved) at KGV on 17th, 19th and 22nd August. It is likely that, despite being rare, these first-summer birds are overlooked.

Traditional coastal sites are coming under increasing pressure from rising sea levels, extreme weather conditions, predators and general disturbance. It seems likely, therefore, that the provision of artificial nest sites will be needed on both the coast and inland if Common Tern numbers are to remain stable or increase. It is possible, however, that recharging of shingle beaches, whereby large volumes of shingle are mechanically moved onto existing beaches or offshore sandbanks to assist in sea defence works, may add scope for breeding Common Terns, although any colonies are likely to be short-lived. Inland breeding sites can soon become unsuitable due to habitat succession, so management will be required for these to remain attractive to Common Terns.

Roseate Tern   *Sterna dougallii*

Rare passage migrant: 28 records involving 39 individuals

The Roseate Tern is a widespread species found throughout many coastal areas in the Southern Hemisphere. The few Northern Hemisphere populations, which are of the nominate race *dougallii*, are severely threatened. In northwest Europe, the largest populations are in Ireland and Brittany. Severe declines since the 1970s, due to loss of breeding habitat and high mortality in their wintering areas, have seen the British population reduce from 600 pairs in 1970 to just 73–74 pairs at eight sites by 2002 (RBBP 2004), making it one of the rarest breeding seabirds in Britain. European populations winter predominantly off west Africa, particularly around the Gulf of Guinea.

1973	Mistley	22nd May	
1975	Southend Pier	15th September	
1977	Foulness Point	22nd May	Three
	Bradwell	27th August	Three adults flew south
1978	The Naze	7th May	
	Bradwell	12th May	Two
	Foulness	13th August	
		9th September	

		10th September	Three
		23rd September	
		24th September	Two
1979	The Naze	11th May	
	Bradwell	12th August	Immature
		25th August	Two adults
1980	Pitsea	11th May	
	Bradwell	14th September	
1981	Foulness	20th September	
1983	Dengie	23rd September	
1986	Canvey Island	13th August	
1988	West Thurrock	20th–23rd August	Moulting adult
1990	Old Hall	12th August	Adult
1991	Wakering Stairs	27th July	Adult in heavy moult
1993	Bradwell	15th August	Adult
1994	Canvey Island	31st August	Adult
1997	Deal Hall, Dengie	27th July	
1999	The Naze	29th August	Two juveniles
2001	Barking Bay	18th September	Adult
2002	Lea/Thames confluence	14th May	Two adults

The fact that there were no Essex records until 1973 suggests that Roseate Terns were probably overlooked. Indeed, the series of records from Foulness prior to the catastrophic decline in the British breeding population suggests that they were probably regular in small numbers off the coast. Roseate Terns remain regular in very small numbers in Norfolk and Suffolk with breeding having been attempted, albeit unsuccessfully, in Norfolk from 1996–99 (Taylor *et al.* 1999).

All spring records have occurred in May and most during autumn occur in late August/early September.

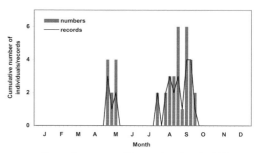

Seasonal occurrence of Roseate Terns from 1973-2004

Arctic Tern

Sterna paradisaea

Regular passage migrant: one pair bred in 1959 and 1960

Amber List

The monotypic Arctic Tern has an extensive circumpolar range. It is the most northerly breeding of all terns, occurring extensively in the boreal zone north of the tree line. In Europe, Arctic Terns breed in Iceland (which holds 60% of the European population), Britain and Ireland, Scandinavia, the Netherlands, north Germany and the Baltic States (European Atlas). Following recent significant declines in the Northern Isles, Scotland, the species' stronghold, the current British population stands at 53,000 pairs, around 8% of the European total (Mitchell *et al.* 2004). Away from the Northern Isles much of the rest of the population is found in northwest Scotland and Ireland (Second National Atlas). A few pairs nest most years in north Norfolk (Taylor *et al.* 1999) and rarely in Suffolk (Piotrowski 2003). Arctic Terns winter in the Antarctic and have the longest known of all avian migration routes.

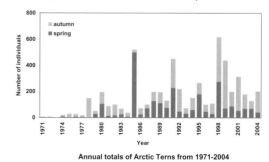

Annual totals of Arctic Terns from 1971-2004

The Arctic Tern breeds in very small numbers in southern England, with inland records away from the marine environment particularly rare. Following an exceptional influx of up to 30 Arctic Terns at Hanningfield in mid-August 1958, a pair bred successfully in 1959 and raised at least two young. The nest was amongst small numbers of Common Terns and was under observation from 30th May, with the chicks hatching around 17th July. It is assumed that the same pair returned and bred in 1960. These are the only breeding records.

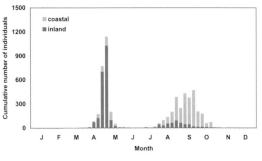

Seasonal occurrence of Arctic Terns from 1971-2004

Confusion with the very similar Common Tern has almost certainly meant that Arctic Terns were—and probably continued to be—under-recorded and mis-identified. As recently as the 1980s, it was not unusual for migrating flocks of terns to be described as "Commic" without specific identification attempted.

Christy described the species as an uncommon passage migrant both in spring and autumn but gave only four records, all of birds shot. Glegg, noting the difficulties of identification, added just two further records. All these early records were from the coast. Hudson & Pyman again mentioned the problem of 'Commic' tern identification but noted, "Probably most flocks [of Commic terns] include some of the present species". However, their assertion that perhaps 30% of a flock of 3,000 terns at Canvey Point on 4th September 1955 were Arctic Terns should now be viewed with caution given current knowledge. Today, much of the inland passage is probably reported, but along the coast it is probably to a large extent still overlooked.

Cox noted that greater expertise in identification had clarified the extent to which Arctic Terns migrated through Essex. However, it was only in 1980 that it was first suggested that Essex received the inland passage which had been observed at the west London and Hertfordshire reservoirs, when on 26th April 80–100 passed through KGV. Subsequent observations have shown that spring passage is typified by far larger numbers passing inland than on the coast; the extent to which this is affected by observer bias is unclear.

There are two March records: 28th at Old Hall in 1999; and 31st at Hanningfield in 1998. Otherwise the earliest, all singles, have occurred during the first week of April: 1st, KGV in 1983; 3rd, Sewardstone in 1983; 6th, Hanningfield in 1988 (four); 6th, KGV in 1991; and 7th, Nazeing in 1993. Usually the first arrivals occur during the second and third weeks of April. Inland spring passage peaks very markedly at the end of April/early May with all of the counts of more than 50 falling in a seven-day period (except for one record of 60 possible Arctic Terns at Hanningfield on 17th April 1987).

At the end of April/early May 1985, following an influx across central and southeast England, the largest inland movement yet recorded occurred with some 500 passing through, most of them at Hanningfield and KGV on 2nd May, with 250 at the former and 110 at the latter. These two sites have recorded all the large movements; numbers at Abberton rarely reach double figures at this time. There were at least 100 at Hanningfield on 30th April 1991 in a year when about 300 passed inland during spring, whilst in 1990 there were 60+ at Hanningfield. On 2nd May 1998 there were 80 at KGV on 1st and 68+ at Walthamstow on 2nd, with perhaps 250 moving through during 1st–4th May, at a time of very strong northerlies; record numbers passed north over Welney, Norfolk, at this time (Taylor *et al.* 1999). Such influxes are thought to be due to poor flying conditions at high altitude over land or at sea (Kramer 1995).

Invariably, spring flocks do not stay at the reservoirs long: many tend to leave high to the north on the same day that they arrive. The flocks tend to keep to themselves and can draw attention by their apparently excited state as they fly around the reservoirs in a relatively tight group.

Numbers along the coast in spring are generally small with few double-figure counts and the highest by some way—78 reported as most probably Arctic Terns off Southend Pier on 10th May 1979—seeming so exceptional as to call into question the identification.

Aside from the breeding birds mentioned above, a few individuals have been noted during midsummer, mainly at the reservoirs; these are difficult to ascribe to either migration period.

Autumn passage is usually evident from late July but in general numbers reported are lower than in the spring with relatively more seen from coastal vantage points. It is thought that the bulk of the southerly movement of Arctic Terns occurs further offshore (Migration Atlas). In most years, there are a few double-figure counts reported from around the coast, although most of the larger autumn counts have come from locations along the Thames Estuary. The only three-figure count involved 245 off Canvey Island on 19th September 1999 at a time of heavy tern passage (Jeff Saward pers. obs.). Otherwise the highest counts have been: 75 off Canvey Island, 7th September 2004; 64 at West Thurrock, 23rd August 1980; 45 at Foulness, 10th September 1978; and 45 off Canvey Island, 2nd October 1998. A total of 42 off Bradwell on 25th September 1982 is the highest count away from the Thames.

Autumn counts inland are generally small and, apart from the influx prior to breeding at Hanningfield in the late 1950s, there has been just one double-figure count: 35 at Fishers Green on 24th August 1985. Passage peaks around late August/early September on the coast (at about the same time as Common Tern), but during August inland. As autumn progresses and Common Tern numbers dwindle, the relative proportion of Arctic to Common Terns increases, although Arctics are generally in the minority. Most have departed by the end of October. However, there have been six November records, all involving singles: Canvey Island, 2nd in 1989; Old Hall, 5th in 2003; Abberton, 7th in 1953; Tollesbury, 7th in 1999; Southend Pier, 9th in 1991; and Canvey Island, 20th in 1996.

Other than a female that was ringed on the Farne Islands, Northumberland, and found offshore somewhere between Southwold, Suffolk, and Shoeburyness, there have been no ringing recoveries affecting Essex. Birds controlled in August and September in Fife by the Tay Ringing Group over several years have been from Scandinavian and Baltic populations, rather than from the Icelandic or Shetland Island ones. Thus it seems likely that many of the birds on passage through Essex are from these areas. However, what is unclear is the destination of those birds heading north through Essex in spring. Do they continue north before hitting the coast in Norfolk and then head east to the Baltic or do they continue north to northern Scotland and Iceland?

(Common) Guillemot   *Uria aalge*

Passage migrant and winter visitor   Amber List

The Guillemot is the most widespread of all auks, having a circumpolar breeding distribution on northern boreal and low-arctic coasts of the Atlantic and Pacific Oceans. Around 41% of the total European population of 2.0–2.5 million pairs is found in Britain and Ireland, with most in northwest Scotland (Mitchell *et al.* 2004). The species is a colonial nester and requires ledges on sheer cliffs, isolated sea stacks or islands free from predators. Three subspecies occur in Europe: the nominate race *aalge* breeds in eastern North America, Greenland, Iceland, through the Faeroe Islands to Scotland to south Norway and Baltic Sea; *albionis* occurs in southern Britain and Ireland, Brittany, western Iberia and Helgoland; and *hyperborea* breeds from Svalbard through north Norway and Murmansk to Novaya Zemlya. Most populations disperse south to winter in offshore waters.

Christy considered the Guillemot to be "Common at sea from spring to autumn", one of his correspondents noting that they "... come south in August ... when they skim over the water it is considered a sign of foul weather coming". He provided very little other information regarding the species, although he noted that the 'ringed' or bridled form was recorded occasionally. Glegg's description of the Guillemot as "...

recorded only occasionally from the proximity of the Essex coast" suggested a reduction in numbers over the previous 40 years, although he noted "It is probably more numerous farther from the coast", observations from the Kentish Knock Lightship during September and October 1903 showing the species to be not uncommon off the sandbanks. Glegg made the first reference to oiled birds, two that he picked up at Colne Point on 10th April 1925, an occurrence that was unfortunately to become increasingly familiar during the following decades.

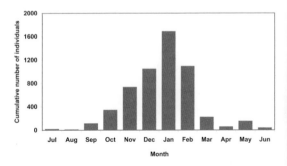

Seasonal occurrence of Guillemots from 1971-2004

By the mid-1960s the Guillemot was still considered to be "A scarce visitor so far as inshore waters are concerned" (Hudson & Pyman). Although the most frequent of the auks, a total of 35, many of which were picked up oiled during early 1963, was exceptional with annual totals of ten or more unusual.

Invariably, the majority of records during the period from 1950–80 involved oiled individuals. However, in the last two decades of the 20th century the incidence of oiled birds appears to have reduced.

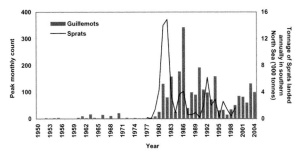

Estimated annual totals of Guillemots (1950-2004) and annual catches of Sprat in the southern North Sea (1977-97)
(adapted from Cox and updated with data from MAFF Fisheries Statistics Division)

Until 1980 counts of live birds were relatively small, 20 offshore from Clacton-on-Sea/St Osyth during January 1970 being the highest single count reported. From 1980, however, there were several significant influxes, the largest being in 1985/86 when unprecedented numbers were reported from the Thames Estuary during December and January. A total of 120 flew upriver past Southend Pier on the morning of 23rd December, with 156 on 3rd January; numbers increased markedly to 314 on 6th, with 260 on 25th, 220 on 1st February and 310 on 8th February. Slightly further upriver there were 100 off Canvey Island on 5th February. Apart from 150 off Southend Pier on 4th November 1990, 105 on 6th January 1991 and 112 on 12th February 1994, the only recent treble-figure count was 112 off the northeast coast on 17th January 2003.

Cox suggested that "... the sudden increase can perhaps be linked with recent changes in the distribution of sprats in the North Sea"; the species' winter distribution is largely determined by concentrations of schooling fish (*HBW*). Whilst the link with Sprat numbers appears to have contributed to the increase in the early 1980s, the apparent correlation is less obvious in subsequent years, suggesting that other factors are at play, weather conditions perhaps being the most significant.

Although most of the largest counts of Guillemots have occurred in the Thames Estuary, double-figure counts are now regular from most parts of the coast, although the northeast is particularly favoured. Indeed, prior to the 'discovery' of the Thames Estuary's importance for seabirds, the majority of Guillemot records came from this area, albeit that many were from fishermen working the offshore waters. The highest counts have been: 60 off the northeast coast, 24th November 2001; 56 off Walton Pier, 4th January 1981; and 50 off the northeast coast, December 1981 and 20th January 1994. Small numbers are recorded with some regularity well up the estuaries and some of these may linger.

There have been just six inland records, all of singles: Abberton, 7th November 1965; Chingford, 3rd December 1982; Brentwood, 21st February 1983; Theydon Bois GC, 25th October 1983; Woodham Mortimer, 14th February 1986; and Essex Filter Beds, one flew over, 30th October 1993.

Numbers of Guillemots generally peak in the first two months of the year, coincident with the presence of Sprat shoals in inshore waters. Outside the period November to March, numbers are very small with, until 2003, 14 off Bradwell on 22nd May 1980 and nine off Wakering Stairs on 3rd June 2001 being exceptional. In 2003 there were 19 off the northeast coast on 14th May and 55 (but possibly 70) in the outer Thames on 15th May. A juvenile off The Naze on 22nd July 1965 had partially developed primary feathering. August records are particularly rare.

There have been three ringing recoveries involving Essex that suggest that most Guillemots originate from northern British colonies. Indeed there have been relatively few national recoveries of birds from foreign colonies. One ringed at Cruden Bay, Northumberland, on 6th July 1976 was recovered oiled at The Naze on 10th February 1985. Another ringed on Canna, Inner Hebrides, on 7th July 1985 was found long dead in Kirby Creek on 17th March 1986 and another from there ringed on 6th July 1976 had its ring read at Walton on 10th November 1985. Another ringed as fully-grown at Ijmuiden, the Netherlands, on 2nd October 1985, which had probably originated from one of the northern colonies, was found ill at Frinton-on-Sea on 8th January 1989, suggesting fidelity to the southern North Sea for wintering. Both *albionis* and *aalge* have been reported from Essex. However, the proportions of each population involved are unknown.

Razorbill

Alca torda

Uncommon passage migrant and winter visitor

Amber List

The Razorbill is endemic to the North Atlantic and associated seas, the nominate race *torda* occurring in North America, Greenland, Scandinavia and the Baltic region and *islandica* in Iceland, Faeroe Islands, Britain and Ireland and northwestern Europe. Around 126,000 pairs breed in Britain and Ireland (Mitchell *et al.* 2004), about 21% of the European population, nesting on rocky cliffs right around the coastline, apart from between Flamborough Head, Yorkshire, and the Isle of Wight; numbers have increased in recent decades. Scottish

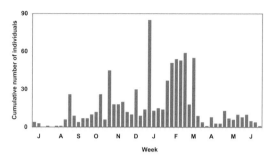

Seasonal occurrence of Razorbills from 1950/51–2003/04

first-year birds and some 2–4 year-olds move south through the North Sea and Straits of Dover and winter in the Bay of Biscay and as far south as Morocco, whilst adults tend to winter mainly in the North Sea and English Channel (Lloyd *et al.* 1991). More northern and easterly populations sometimes also disperse into the North Sea.

Christy's assertion that the species was "Common on the seas round our coast from autumn to spring" was based on very few observations, but Razorbill breeding numbers may have been higher at the end of the 19th and early 20th century than at any time since (Lloyd *et al.* 1991). Glegg described the species as "... seen ... only on rare occasions and out of the breeding season" and detailed just seven observations between 1840 and 1927. However, he believed the Razorbill was fairly common further from the coast. Indeed, Dr Eagle Clarke, in his month-long sojourn on the Kentish Knock Lightship in September/October 1903, stated that "... it was not uncommon off the edge of the sand". Between 1928 and 1950 there were four inland records from: Knighton Lake, Epping Forest, 18th September 1937; Lea Valley reservoirs, 11th November 1934–4th May 1935 when found dead, 6th February 1937 and 5th October 1948 (four).

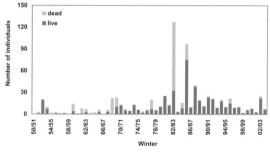

Annual totals of Razorbills from 1950/51-2003/04

Razorbills have been recorded in all but one (1966/67) winter since 1951/52. Numbers vary markedly from winter to winter but the greatest occur following wrecks when corpses make up the majority of the records. The largest influx, in 1983, involved 127 individuals, including 95 corpses recovered over a five-week period. There were also ten live birds off Southend Pier on 8th February, 20 the next day and 25 on 12th, which—apart from an exceptional count of 50 offshore from the Thames Estuary on 5th January 1986—have not been repeated. The 1983 wreck occurred at a time when adults were probably returning to breeding grounds, which they reoccupy from late February. Caught up in severe weather in the North Sea that severely interrupted their ability to feed, they were weakened and became wrecked along the coast. The only other double-figure counts have been 20, some 5km off the southeast coast on 29th August 1952 and 12 off Southend Pier on 1st March 2003, with ten the next day and ten off Bradwell on 6th February 1994. Other earlier wrecks appeared to have been due to oil pollution at sea. For example, 22 oiled corpses were found between Dovercourt and Dengie in early 1969. More rigid pollution controls have seen a significant decline in such occurrences. Influxes do not always coincide with those of Guillemots and vice versa. There were, for example, very few Razorbills noted in the significant Guillemot influx in January 1991. The general increase over the last few decades has probably been due to increased observer coverage, although it is possible that increases in the Scottish population (Mead 2000) may also be a factor.

Although Razorbills occur most regularly in the Thames, reports have come from around the entire coast. Since the late 1980s Razorbills have also been noted as far up the Thames as East Tilbury, with records in five years since 1988, the largest count being five on 4th November 1990. One was off Rainham Marshes on 20th February 1996.

Since 1950 there have been just two inland records involving singletons: Walthamstow, dead, on 11th September 1961; and Fairlop CP, 10th–13th December 1988, when found dead.

Peak numbers occur during late winter/early spring as birds begin to move back north from their more southerly wintering grounds. A second, smaller peak during late April and May perhaps involves individuals of different populations or ages from the main movement; it coincides with peak movements along the English Channel coast.

In August/September 1967 an adult and chick were 13km off Clacton-on-Sea, the nearest breeding colony on the east coast being at Flamborough Head, Yorkshire. Whilst there have been a few recoveries of Razorbills ringed at Irish Sea colonies in East Anglia, it is likely that the majority occurring in Essex are from the north and east coast colonies. Indeed, four individuals recovered in Essex had been ringed at colonies on Handa Island, Sutherland (two), Isle of May, Fife, and Foula, Shetland Islands. It is possible that individuals from the Norwegian and Swedish populations occur, although to date there have been no recoveries to confirm this.

Black Guillemot   *Cepphus grylle*

Vagrant: nine records   Amber List

The Black Guillemot has a Holarctic breeding distribution along Arctic and North Atlantic coasts, with by far the largest colonies in the Arctic. The subspecies *arcticus* breeds in Britain, where strongholds are the rocky north and west coasts of Scotland, although colonies occur as far south as North Wales on the west coast and Aberdeen on the east coast. This race also occurs in parts of North America, Greenland and Scandinavia with other races occurring in North America, Iceland, Faeroe Islands and Baltic. This is the rarest of the four common breeding auks in Britain and, despite apparent increases in the 20th century, remains extremely rare in the southern North Sea.

1869	Mersea Island	December	Female shot
1885	Mucking Light	28th August	Immature shot
1912	Southend Pier	February	Adult summer shot
1953	Blackwater Estuary	28th November	1st-year shot
1980/81	Hamford Water	27th December then intermittently to end of 1981	
1981	Bradwell	11th–16th December	
1982	Wakering Stairs	13th March	
1991	off Clacton-on-Sea	22nd October	
1995	Bradwell	2nd November	

By far the rarest of all auks to occur in Essex, Black Guillemots are generally extremely sedentary, many spending their entire lives close to their natal colony. The 1953 individual had been ringed on 31st July 1953 as a chick on Fair Isle, Shetland Islands, and supports the view that individuals recorded in Essex probably originate from colonies from the east of Scotland, namely the Firth of Forth north to the Shetland Islands. Ringing recoveries of Black Guillemots are extremely rare (Migration Atlas).

Little Auk   *Alle alle*

Normally scarce winter visitor and passage migrant but subject to periodic influxes

The Little Auk is the most northerly and probably the most abundant Atlantic alcid, totalling about 12 million pairs, 10 million of which occur in the Thule region of northwest Greenland (*HBW*). The nominate race *alle* occurs through much of the species' range. Many winter off southwest Greenland but periodically numbers move further south, with many exhausted birds being wrecked ashore often following gales, although overpopulation and food supply failure may also be factors. There is some evidence to suggest that, being a plankton feeder, severe

347

weather may affect Little Auks; prolonged gales cause the plankton to descend beyond reach and weakened birds then drift downwind further south than normal and become wrecked when they meet a leeward coastline in a continuing storm (*BWP*). Numbers occurring in Britain are typically greatest in the north, but in some years large influxes occur well to the south.

Although the size of influxes has increased significantly in the last 10–15 years, presumably because of the considerable increase in observer coverage, its general status has changed very little since Christy and Gleggs' time. The first documented Essex records involved one seen in a collection at Colchester in 1832, which had been obtained nearby and another shot at The Naze in 1832 (Christy). Little Auks were recorded in 21 years between 1832 and 1930, with a surprising proportion inland. A major influx along the east coast in 1878/79 produced two Essex records, whilst in 1895 eight were "taken" and others seen. Another influx in 1912 saw five reported (Glegg) and in 1930, 8–9 were off West Mersea (*British Birds* 24: 29). Not surprisingly, some managed to appear in unusual locations: "... in a gentleman's garden in Witham..." in 1837/38, whilst during a severe northeasterly gale on 9th November 1873 one was "... taken alive among the pigeons on a farm near Walton."

The first records following the formation of the EBS in 1949 were in 1955, since when the Little Auk has occurred in all but seven winters with a total of 1,108 reported.

North to northeasterly gales are now known to produce large movements into the North Sea and if persistent, particularly during November, are likely to cause influxes into Essex waters. Whilst numbers tend to peak in November, Little Auks have occurred from September to March. The three September records came from: Holland Haven, 16th in 1984; Heybridge, 23rd in 1956; and off The Naze, 26th in 1999. Since 1950 Little Auks have only occurred after December in 13 years, with the largest influx of 18 occurring in late January and February 1983. There were also 11 off Bradwell on 14th January 1990. The two March records came from: Southend Pier, 24th in 1988; and The Naze, dead, 9th in 1969.

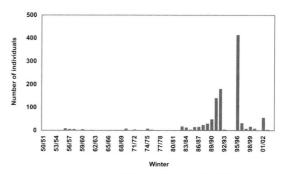

Annual totals of Little Auks from 1950/51-2003/04

The 1995 influx produced almost as many individuals as recorded in the previous 45 years. The total of over 400 included by far the largest day count with 254 off Canvey Island and 62 off Bradwell on 2nd November. In 1990 there were 27 off Shoebury on 11th December, at least 30 off Colne Point and 22 off East Tilbury on 13th December and four other double-figure counts. In 1991 there were 30 off Colne Point, 27 off Southend Pier and 24 off East Tilbury and three other double-figure counts on 20th October. Birds very rarely stay any length of time.

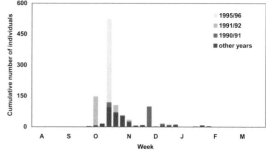

Seasonal occurrence of Little Auks from 1950-2004

Inland records have come from 15 widely scattered localities since 1950. Unfortunately, if not dead when found, many soon succumb, although benevolent finders have returned a few successfully to the sea where they have flown off strongly. Remarkably, a total of 15 has been found at Abberton, including ten between 1983 and 1991, all singles apart from two on 3rd November 1990. Five singles have occurred at KGV and four at Hanningfield with others inland at: Borley; Chelmsford (twice); Wix; High Roding; Great Leighs; Hatfield Heath; Canning Town; Manuden; Highwood; Walthamstow; Girling; and Langham.

(Atlantic) Puffin   *Fratercula arctica*

Very scarce winter visitor and passage migrant   **Amber List**

The monotypic Puffin is an exclusively marine species that breeds on rocky coasts and offshore islands in the northern Atlantic and Arctic. In Britain there are around 621,000 pairs (Mitchell *et al.* 2004). The species is largely pelagic in winter, generally staying far from land, where its diet consists of small fish augmented by pelagic worms and crustaceans. Few appear to reach the southernmost North Sea except during severe weather.

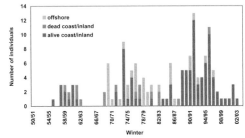

Annual totals of Puffins from 1950/51-2003/04

Christy considered that the Puffin could be "... met with on the seas around our coast during autumn, winter and spring, but not common", whilst Glegg observed that the species was an "... occasional wanderer to Essex". Between them they listed just ten records, six from the coast and four inland, the first being shot at Southend-on-Sea in 1842 and the last in 1925, captured at Ongar.

The next record was not until 1955 and from then until the winter of 2003/04 there had been 97 in all but eight winters, with influxes in 1973/74, 1991/92 and 1995/96 with the largest numbers occurring at times of other sea bird movements. Many records prior to 1980 came from one fisherman–birdwatcher in the offshore zone.

Whilst increased observer coverage and awareness may account for the greater numbers reported since the 1970s, recent increases in breeding numbers at east coast breeding colonies such as the Isle of May, Fife, may also be a factor. Most records refer to singles. However, there have been seven records of two and three records of three individuals. There were six together 10km off Clacton-on-Sea on 18th January 1970 and at Bradwell on 24th November 1973, whilst seven passed Canvey Island on 2nd November 1995. Puffins are surprisingly sedentary and the first ringing recovery from the northeast populations outside the North Sea was not made until December 1995 (out of 106 recoveries). However, other recoveries suggest that Norwegian birds reach our shores (Migration Atlas), so some Essex records may relate to these. The number of birds picked up as tideline corpses have declined recently; Piotrowski (2003) suggested that this may be due to the decline of the East Anglian fishing fleet as Puffins were often caught in Sprat and Herring nets and thrown overboard.

Like other auks, most occur in the period October–November, with smaller numbers in winter and then a small spring passage.

Although records have come from all around the coast, many of the recent occurrences have been in the Thames Estuary, particularly off Southend Pier or

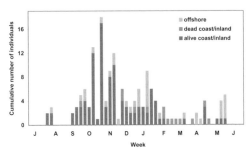

Seasonal occurence of Puffins from 1950-2004

Canvey Island, although Puffins are recorded with some regularity as far upriver as East Tilbury.

The species is occasionally recorded inland, usually after gales, although just seven have occurred since 1950, the last in 1984. One of these, a juvenile picked up at Plaistow in mid-January 1959, had been ringed on Fair Isle, Shetland Islands, the previous July. The other records are: Saffron Walden, one dead, January 1978; Harlow, February 1984; Clavering/Manuden, one dead, 16th January 1977; KGV, dead juvenile, 11th August 1958; Navestock, one picked up exhausted, 21st October 1960; and Blackmore, immature picked up, 23rd February 1978.

Pallas's Sandgrouse

Syrrhaptes paradoxus

Vagrant: influxes in 1863, 1888 and 1908 involving around 120 individuals

The monotypic Pallas's Sandgrouse breeds from Kazakhstan and Uzbekistan through to China and Mongolia. It is a partial migrant, although the extent of its movements varies, and on occasions it is extremely irruptive.

1863/64	At least 11 were obtained and a similar number observed between May and July 1863, with one in 1864. In 1863, one was shot at Forest Gate in June; a male and two females were shot on Mersea Island on May(?) 29th; a female was shot at Peldon; three were shot near Terling; "a good many" were shot at Seward's End, "the cottagers and others making "pigeon pies" of them ...", although a male and female shot on 7th June were preserved; and on Foulness, one of seven was shot. The following year, one was shot on Wanstead Flats in July 1864, presumably a survivor from the previous year.
1888/89	At least 80 individuals were observed or taken: 12 or 13 at Ardleigh on 30th May; nine on Foulness on either 28th May or 4th June, with seven still present on 30th June and some remaining on 8th September; 16 on 4th June, with two males subsequently shot, at Barkingside; near Harwich there were five towards the end of May with 15 or 16 on 23rd June; at Stratford there were about 12 on 10th June; at Audley End there were about 12 during the summer; at Walton-on-the-Naze two were shot on 18th October and two more present; near Colchester one was shot in November; at Fingringhoe one was shot on 4th February 1889; and at Barkingside and Fairlop Plain about 12 present during July 1889 may have been survivors from the previous year.
1908	Two near Southend-on-Sea during June; one shot at South Ockendon on 1st September; and 13 on Peewit Island, Hamford Water, on 7th September.

It seems remarkable that a short-range migrant from some of the most inaccessible areas of central Asia should occur (and breed as it did in 1888/89) in Britain at all. Periodic difficulties in finding food during severe weather, such as heavy snow or drought, seems a more likely explanation than, for example, cyclical variations in population size, as may be seen in some grouse (*HBW*). Irruptions into Britain were noted in 12 different years between 1859 and 1909, the largest being in 1863 and 1888. There have only been six national records since 1909, the last in the Shetland Islands in 1990 (BBRC 1991).

Rock Dove/Feral Pigeon (Rock Pigeon)

Columba livia

Common and widespread resident

The natural range of the Rock Dove is probably now limited to the most isolated Atlantic coasts of Scotland and Ireland. Elsewhere the natural range probably covered much of the Western Palearctic, northern Africa and Indian subcontinent, although the presence of domesticated birds means that the exact limits are unclear. The original Rock Doves of Europe were of the nominate race *livia*.

The Rock Dove was domesticated in the Mediterranean some 5,000–10,000 years ago and is the earliest of all avian domestications (*HBW*). Bronze Age peat deposits in England have revealed Rock Dove remains, almost certainly domesticated (Fisher 1966), as have Roman sites, whilst Feral Pigeons have been a feature of London's bird life since at least the 14th century (Homes 1957).

Although Christy was informed that a truly wild Rock Dove had been obtained at The Naze, he was of the opinion that all Essex records were either of the Stock Dove or domestic pigeon, as he called it.

Unfortunately, little is known about the history of Essex birds, a fact deplored by Hudson & Pyman; even Cox relegated the species to the appendices. Numbers increased significantly across Essex between the two National Atlas surveys and in Metropolitan Essex between the two London Atlas surveys but the Feral Pigeon was not mentioned in *EBRs* until 1988 and until the Essex Atlas survey its detailed distribution was not known; although it is true to say that the species was probably widely distributed across rural areas and most urban areas had their resident colonies.

Historically, it is likely that the Feral Pigeon was more of a rural species with many being kept in dovecotes constructed either within buildings or as separate structures. However, with the decline in the keeping of pigeons for food and the reduction in seed and spilt grain available in the countryside caused by modern farming methods, the Feral Pigeon has become a predominantly urban creature. Here, the year round supply of food provided by both man's fast-food culture and his desire to feed birds has allowed the species to flourish.

Atlas	Survey Area	% of 10km squares or tetrads in which	
		bred/probably bred	possibly bred or present
First National 10km	Essex	40.4	14.0
Second National 10km	Essex	66.7	22.8
First London Tetrad	Met. Essex	19.5	15.0
Second London Tetrad	Met. Essex	59.0	31.5
Essex Tetrad	Essex	26.2	26.6

Summary of results of Atlas surveys for Feral Pigeons

The Essex Atlas survey found the species in almost 53% of tetrads with breeding confirmed in over 26%. There was a definite bias to the south, where urban development is at its greatest, with few in the predominantly arable areas of east, central and northern Essex. Breeding numbers reported in recent *EBRs* are almost certainly unrepresentative.

Feral Pigeons live and nest colonially and will utilise almost any man-made structure that provides a suitable nesting ledge which in urban areas usually means older, more traditionally constructed buildings and in the countryside derelict farm buildings and church towers. Breeding may take place all year round if there is a regular food source, and consequently numbers can increase at a significant rate and cause problems as their droppings are not only a health risk due to the potential for the spread of diseases such as salmonellosis, tuberculosis and ornithosis, but also because their acid content stains and erodes stonework. Many buildings now bristle with protective spikes and nettings to prevent colonies establishing.

More detailed recording in recent years, particularly in Metropolitan areas, gives some idea of the numbers present in urban areas, although it is likely that the counts are on the low side: a cull of birds in a church tower in northeast Essex in the late 1990s totalled over 250 birds, but only 70–80 were present at any one time. The largest counts have been: Hainault Forest CP, 1,500, 17th October 1992 and 1,000, 27th September 1997; East Tilbury, 1,000, 4th December 1990; Corbets Tey, 1,000, 24th and 29th August 1993; Fairlop CP, 1,000, 23rd October 1994; Walthamstow, 1,000, 31st May 1997; and Collier Row, 1,000, 1st September 1995. Three-figure flocks are reported regularly from across the county, although there is, not surprisingly, a bias to Metropolitan Essex.

The urban Feral Pigeon, whilst giving pleasure to many, also causes major problems for others and control of existing populations has proved a necessity. Unfortunately, culling is only a short-term solution as other Feral Pigeons quickly take the vacant sites. Regularly unsettling the colonies by using trained raptors is a longer-term solution, although the only completely effective method would be to remove their food supplies which in a modern urban environment is quite impossible.

Stock Dove (Stock Pigeon)   *Columba oenas*

Common resident and very scarce passage migrant   Amber List

The Stock Dove's breeding range extends over the west and central Palearctic, with the nominate race *oenas* breeding from the Atlantic coast to western Siberia and from the Mediterranean to the Caspian Sea and northern Kazakhstan. The species breeds right across Britain, where

Atlas	Survey Area	% of 10km squares or tetrads in which	
		bred/probably bred	possibly bred or present
First National 10km	Essex	86.0	7.0
Second National 10km	Essex	86.0	8.8
First London Tetrad	Met. Essex	20.0	14.5
Second London Tetrad	Met. Essex	50.5	27.5
Essex Tetrad	Essex	41.0	18.5

Summary of results of Atlas surveys for Stock Doves

the population has increased rapidly to 309,000 pairs, 50% of the European population. The Stock Dove is a species of parkland, forest edge and wooded farmland where it nests mainly in holes in trees. Two factors determine its local abundance: the availability of food and the existence of sufficient nest holes. Populations in Britain, western Europe and the Mediterranean are largely resident, whilst those from northeast and central Europe winter in the Mediterranean.

It was not until the latter years of the 18th century that the Stock Dove was separated from the Rock Dove and even by the mid-19th century its distribution was poorly understood (Historical Atlas). Yarrell (1845) was only aware of breeding in Norfolk and Suffolk but, according to Christy, the species was common around Sudbury in 1838, bred in Epping Forest in 1840 and around Saffron Walden in 1845, although it was not very common. Stock Doves apparently increased their range and numbers across Essex in the 19th century; Christy commented that he believed the species to be common and increasing across Essex. This increase has been correlated to the expansion of arable farming across the country (O'Connor & Shrubb 1986), although it is also possible that this was also due simply to a better understanding of its status and not entirely a real increase in numbers (Historical Atlas). Reduced competition from traditionally maintained dovecote pigeons may have also been a factor. Glegg observed: "The Stock-Dove is a fairly common resident, although somewhat local …"

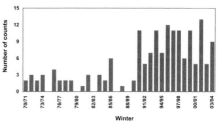

Annual number of counts of 100+ Stock Doves from 1970/71-2003/04

Hudson & Pyman agreed closely with Glegg's description of the species' status, suggesting little change in population or range during the first half of the 20th century. However, from the late 1950s there was a considerable decline across Essex, although the then less intensively farmed northwest was less affected. This decline was linked to the use of pesticides, particularly organochlorine seed dressings during the 1950s, which caused a halving of breeding success from 1950–59 compared to the period 1942–49 (Population Trends). Nationally, a ten-fold decline in numbers between 1951 and 1961 was indicated by indices based on annual ringing totals and nest-record cards. The only quantitative local data during the period came from the Writtle area, where in 1963 just two known breeding sites were occupied and all the eggs proved infertile, compared with 32 in previous years. During 1964, three pairs bred and again the eggs were infertile. By 1965 the species was extinct in the area. However, four pairs were breeding again by 1969. This appeared to be the situation over much of the country, Essex probably being hit harder than many other counties (First National Atlas): just four breeding pairs were reported countywide in 1965.

A recovery was well underway by the 1970s with, in the Writtle area, numbers recovering their pre-1960s levels by 1972. By the time of the First National Atlas survey, breeding was confirmed in 86% of 10km squares with a presence in a further 7%. The CBC/BBS (England) Index showed a 44% increase from 1977–2002, whilst from 1981–94 the local CBC Index for Essex and surrounding counties showed an 80% increase, equating to about 4% per annum. In 1982 the Stock Dove was removed from the list of legal quarry species.

The Second National Atlas survey revealed an almost identical distribution to the First Atlas, whilst the Essex Atlas survey confirmed a presence in 59.5% of tetrads with breeding confirmed in just under 70% of these. The species was most thinly distributed in the southeast, where in general there are fewer trees and parkland and agriculture is more intensive. Stock Doves were also absent from the built-up area in the extreme southwest. However, numbers breeding in Metropolitan Essex increased significantly between the two London Atlas surveys. Since the late 1990s there has been a marked increase in the number of breeding pairs reported in the *EBR*, which seems too great to be solely due to increased observer coverage. BBS (England) data for the period 1994–2003 suggest a continuing increase with the Index rising by some 11%, although local BBS data suggest a generally stable situation.

Whether numbers have returned to those prior to the crash in the 1960s is not possible to ascertain. However, increased agricultural intensification together with a loss of suitable nesting trees, particularly Elms following the Dutch Elm disease epidemic and the Great Storm of 1987, may mean that there are fewer suitable nesting sites than 50 years ago. However, Stock Doves will, where there are no suitable nest sites, adapt and use alternative structures. On Dengie, Foulness and Old Hall, nesting has been observed in rabbit burrows, on derelict farm buildings, RAF control towers, pillboxes, haystacks and nest boxes. Glegg also noted nesting on Colchester and Hedingham castles, on a boathouse in the middle of Navestock Lake and in a high level stone window at White Notley church.

It is unclear whether movements of Stock Doves have been overlooked in the past. However, despite increased observer coverage there remain just two reports referring to what may have been migrants: 100 high west over the Blackwater at Bradwell on 14th November 1954 with a second similar flock from the south-southwest; and 200 in off the sea at Colne Point on 10th November 1998. However, it is quite likely that these were British birds coasting (Murton & Ridpath 1962) rather than Continental immigrants. Large autumn coastal movements have been noted at Landguard Point, Suffolk (Piotrowski 2003).

Large flocks gather in winter, many in coastal areas where breeding numbers are low. Whilst it is possible that this bias to the coast could be due to the disproportionate observer coverage of these areas, it appears that local dispersal to the coast occurs and is apparently not a new phenomenon as Glegg noted that "… throughout the year [the Stock Dove] evinces a partiality for the marshes in the vicinity of the coast …". As populations have recovered, so the number of large flocks have increased, perhaps confirming that local birds do indeed move towards the coast in winter. The size and number of these winter flocks perhaps provide an indicator as to Essex population trends.

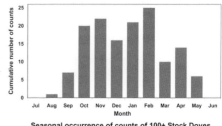

Seasonal occurrence of counts of 100+ Stock Doves from 1971-2004

Hudson & Pyman cited a flock of 300 at East Tilbury on 2nd January 1965 as the highest yet recorded in Essex. Peak counts have continued to increase with 600 at Holliwell Point on 6th December 1981, 610 at East Tilbury on 9th January 2000 and 1,000 between Jaywick and Colne Point on 26th October 2000. Other counts of 500 or more have been: 500 at Holliwell Point, 26th December 1991; 500 at South Woodham Ferrers, February 1992; and 517 at the same site on 17th February 1991. In typical winters, several flocks of 50 or more are common.

The number of large flocks peak in February, with a rapid decline thereafter, although an apparent peak in April points to some form of movement through Essex at that time.

There have been nine ringing recoveries involving Essex. Five were movements within the county, whilst two moved from Essex to Kent and singles from Kent and Soham, Cambridgeshire (the longest movement of 96km). Such recoveries suggest that there is movement between Essex and neighbouring counties and confirm that some Stock Doves may move from their breeding areas to the coast in winter. Nationally, there have been movements recorded between Britain and France, Spain, Finland, the Netherlands and Belgium, which suggest that some Continental individuals may winter in Essex. A very high proportion of all ringing recoveries, however, reveals that movements are short and local.

Over the last 30 years, the Stock Dove has adapted well to modern farming practices and numbers would seem to be stable or increasing. Their willingness to use nest boxes is, however, unlikely to cover the total loss of nest sites due to Dutch Elm disease, severe weather and the tidying up of woodland and grubbing out of hedgerows and removal of old farm buildings. Additionally, with autumn sowing now the norm and pesticides still in use, there remain threats to its future. It is still regarded as a pest species of farmland.

Woodpigeon (Common Wood Pigeon) *Columba palumbus*

Abundant resident, passage migrant and winter visitor

The Woodpigeon is a Palearctic species that has a predominantly European distribution, breeding in all but the highest latitudes. The nominate race *palumbus* occurs across much of the range. Originally a woodland species, Woodpigeons can now only maintain high population levels by close association with arable farming. It has also adapted to life in towns and cities. The British population of around 2.6–3.2 million pairs is largely resident, but those in Fennoscandia and Eastern Europe are mainly migratory moving southwest in autumn. These populations appear reluctant to cross wide areas of water and are readily deflected along the Continental coastline. Irregular occurrences in Britain have been attributed to drift movements in overcast conditions over the North Sea (Murton & Ridpath 1962) but more recent systematic observations along the east coast have revealed variable but annual movements during late autumn (Taylor *et al.* 1999, Piotrowski 2003).

The Woodpigeon's preference for lowland habitat of woodland fringe and well-vegetated open spaces means that the species is abundant

Atlas	Survey Area	\% of 10km squares or tetrads in which bred/probably bred	possibly bred or present
First National 10km	Essex	100.0	0.0
Second National 10km	Essex	100.0	0.0
First London Tetrad	Met. Essex	69.5	11.5
Second London Tetrad	Met. Essex	99.0	1.0
Essex Tetrad	Essex	98.9	0.6

Summary of results of Atlas surveys for Woodpigeons

all the year round in Essex where it is the principal avian pest (Winter Atlas); due to persecution it is a wary rural species. In contrast it is relatively tame in the urban/suburban environment.

Christy described the Woodpigeon as "A far too abundant resident, especially in the well-wooded districts. They are unquestionably very injurious to the farmer". He, however, provided no quantitative data. According to a Reverend Atkinson (Christy) "It was a common belief in Essex that, if you touch—still more, if you breathe on—the Ring Dove's eggs she will forsake them. It is, however, totally without foundation; for I remember when a school-boy testing its truth". Glegg also referred to the Woodpigeon as a very common resident and made reference to breeding in towns. Across the country, it was only during the last quarter of the 19th century that the species spread from wooded and enclosed areas into more open habitats and by 1900 it could be found in parks and gardens (Historical Atlas). The destruction of raptors and corvids and the spread of arable farming accelerated the progressive increase. An organised shooting campaign in the early 1940s to increase crop yield and perhaps to supplement wartime rations was only a temporary check on the population; Hudson & Pymans' description of the species as "… an all too familiar agricultural pest", suggests little real change since the 19th century.

Woodpigeons seemed less affected than other farmland birds by the use of chlorinated hydrocarbons as seed dressings during the 1960s. More serious was the loss of grass and clover leys to cereal production and, despite the withdrawal of the cartridge subsidy in 1965 (Potts 1981), populations only began to recover in the mid-1970s when the introduction of Oil-seed Rape provided valuable year round feeding for Woodpigeons (Inglis *et al.* 1990).

Anecdotal evidence suggests that since the 1980s numbers have remained relatively stable despite continuing to sustain heavy shooting losses.

The ubiquity of the Woodpigeon is apparent in all the Atlas surveys of the last four decades with a 100% or almost 100% presence in every 10km square or tetrad. Small increases in more recent surveys have been attributed to improved coverage rather than local increases. Actual data on breeding numbers are rarely received. Recently up to 35 pairs have bred in Hainault Forest CP and up to 15 pairs on the relatively treeless Rainham Marshes. Cox noted breeding densities of around 750 pairs in the parishes of Writtle, Roxwell and Highwood in 1962, whilst in 1992 48 nests were found in the Writtle area, including 11 in one churchyard. Although typically a tree-nester, Woodpigeons were noted nesting on Dengie seawall in 1954, 1958 and 1973 and periodically on salt marshes in Hamford Water. Nesting in a woodshed at Tillingham in 1981 appears to be the only record of the species using a man-made structure in Essex.

Glegg considered that the "... native population is very much increased by the arrival of immigrants ... the numbers which arrive are apparently governed by food-supply ... a good beech-mast year usually sees very large gatherings in suitable woodlands". Today, there is no evidence to suggest a link to the Beech mast crop and indeed it is likely that, although still exploited, this food source is of less importance now than in the past.

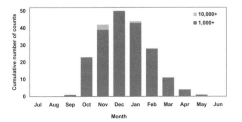

Seasonal occurrence of counts of 1,000+ and 10,000+ Woodpigeons from 1971-2004

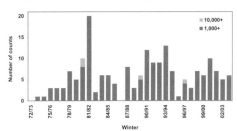

Annual totals of counts of 1,000+ and 10,000+ Woodpigeons from 1972/73-2003/04

From late September through December, but particularly in late October and early November, large movements of Woodpigeons have been noted, principally inland but also on the coast. Ideal conditions are bright and clear days with a light northeasterly. Birds probably begin to move before first light with little subsequent movement after the first 2–3 hours of daylight. Similar observations at Landguard Point, Suffolk, perhaps indicate direct passage from Scandinavia (Piotrowski 2003). The largest reported movements have been around 10,000 flying north over Strethall/Audley End/Saffron Walden districts on 23rd November 1955 and the same number west over Collier Row on 6th November 1989. Over the period 4th–9th November 1991 a total of 10,000 flew south at Holland Haven, whilst in 2000 14,000 flew south over West Bergholt between the 2nd and 5th November. The largest single flock reported in Essex, some 20,000 at Little Oakley on 7th–8th November 1996, almost certainly involved immigrants and occurred at the same time as several other large counts along the coast including 7,300 at Holland Haven and 4,000 at Holland-on-Sea. At this time both northern and central Europe were experiencing freezing conditions with snow, rain and strong southeasterly winds. Such drift conditions have resulted in records of 100–700 noted flying in off the sea in the northeast. A resident of Danbury, who has lived all his 67 years there, confirms that almost annually in early November, early morning movements totalling "many thousands of pigeons" occur from northeast to southwest. Recently, most of these movements have coincided with large movements at Landguard Point, Suffolk. Some 10,000 flying north over South Woodham Ferrers on 17th January 1981 was outside the typical migration period and was perhaps a movement caused by food shortage and/or severe weather (Murton & Ridpath 1962).

Once winter sets in, feeding flocks will form on arable land. Whilst Oil-seed Rape is particularly favoured, flocks will also descend on Peas, corn stubble and miscellaneous root crops as well as coastal salt marshes. Woodpigeons will also exploit their original food sources such as Beech mast and acorns. In recent years, however, there has been just one record of a substantial flock feeding in this way: 10,000 at Mill Green/Margaretting on 18th November 1980 were feeding on acorns and, given the date, may have been immigrants.

The number of four- and five-figure counts vary considerably from winter to winter, although apparent influxes do not necessarily coincide with severe weather here or on the Continent. Whilst the largest winter flocks are generally not as substantial as the peak autumn counts, the greatest number of Woodpigeons are probably present during December with numbers tailing off thereafter and a significant drop in numbers after February: Woodpigeons being early nesters, flocks are probably dispersing rapidly at this time.

Few large flocks have been reported during spring, although there is evidence of migration from the coast at this time, the only four-figure flocks being: 1,000 that flew southeast and out to sea at The Naze, 31st March 1962; 1,620 at Foulness, 21st April 1985; and 1,500 at Colne Point, 4th April 1988.

Just eight foreign-ringed Woodpigeons have been recovered in Britain (Migration Atlas). One of these involved a nestling ringed in the Netherlands in July 1962 and recovered at Tillingham on 3rd February 1963, a suspected cold weather movement triggered by the severe weather of early 1963. Recoveries of Essex-ringed birds suggest that few move long distances: 82% have been found still within the county boundaries with the remainder in southern England.

Having adapted so well to modern agricultural practice, there seem to be no obvious threats to the Woodpigeon's future. More regular mild winters and increased areas of winter feeding have probably virtually eliminated winter starvation and despite increased predation by corvids, each pair on average produces 2.1 young per annum (Inglis *et al.* 1990), more than sufficient to maintain populations at current levels.

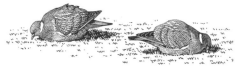

(Eurasian) Collared Dove *Streptopelia decaocto*

Common resident

The Collared Dove is found throughout much of Europe, Middle East, Asia Minor, India, China, Korea and Japan. The nominate race *decaocto* originally came from northern India but has spread west then northwest from the Balkans and Europe at the rate of 44km per year (Hengeveld & van den Bosch 1991). The remarkable colonisation of Europe has been well documented (Fisher 1953). At the turn of the 20th century the species barely had a toehold in Europe, being restricted to Turkey and the Balkans. However, by 1949 Collared Doves had reached the southern edge of the North Sea and first bred in Britain in Norfolk in 1955 (Taylor *et al.* 1999) after which a rapid colonisation of the country took place. The initial population growth was staggering. From four individuals in 1955, just nine years later there were 18,855 and by 1970 some 15–25,000 pairs (Hudson 1972). By the time of the Second National Atlas, all of Britain had been colonised and there are now around 298,000 pairs. In Britain, the species has adapted to all habitats bar high mountain and moorland. Their abundance is probably at its greatest in suburban areas, whilst high numbers are also found within villages, towns and even city centres. They can also be found in farmyards, parks and orchards and particularly around flourmills, maltings and docks where spilt grain is a strong attraction. Unlike their congener, the Turtle Dove, they do not favour open arable land, although in some areas large numbers will gather to feed on spilt grain in fields of cereal stubble.

The first occurrence of the species in Essex was at Tollesbury in 1957, the name of the location being withheld by the *EBR* editors until the 1958 edition. Here, a male was present from late May, being joined by a second male on 22nd September. By 24th November, there

Atlas	Survey Area	% of 10km squares or tetrads in which	
		bred/probably bred	possibly bred or present
First National 10km	Essex	96.5	1.8
Second National 10km	Essex	96.5	3.5
First London Tetrad	Met. Essex	29.0	11.5
Second London Tetrad	Met. Essex	84.5	12.5
Essex Tetrad	Essex	84.3	7.9

Summary of results of Atlas surveys for Collared Doves

were six, which remained until the year's end. There were no other Essex records, perhaps suggesting that Collared Doves had bred in the area in 1957. Numbers declined to three on 16th February 1958 with just one by 13th April, which stayed until 22nd September, although an immature bird of unknown origin was nearby at Salcott on 29th July. Just one individual was recorded in 1959, at The Naze on 25th September.

Following the arrival of several birds in the Clacton-on-Sea area in spring 1960, breeding was finally confirmed with two pairs raising at least seven young. One pair nested three times (Felstead 1961). This colony grew rapidly. In 1961, 20 adults and six juveniles were ringed and the species spread to Walton and Frinton-on-Sea. At the latter, in 1962 there were 50 on 10th October and 72 on 26th November. Breeding also took place at Thorpe Bay in 1961 where numbers increased to 40 on 13th November 1962. The species finally gained more than a foothold in Essex during 1963, with the first inland records and the first inland breeding from Shenfield/Hutton where two pairs bred. By 1964, Collared Doves were common along the northeast coast between Walton and Clacton-on-Sea with feeding flocks of up to 200 and breeding at Mistley (two pairs) and Harwich (at least eight pairs). Several pairs bred at Bradwell and in the southeast, the Thorpe Bay colony spread to the Rochford Hundred, with 50 at Great Wakering in September, and inland to Rayleigh. The species spread up the Thames Estuary and reached Grays, but it remained very scarce in central and western Essex, where apart from Shenfield/Hutton it was resident only at Ilford and Buckhurst Hill (Hudson 1965). By the end of the

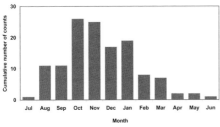

Seasonal occurrence of counts of 100+ Collared Doves
from 1971-2004

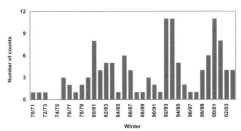

Annual number of counts of 100+ Collared Doves
from 1970/71-2003/04

1960s it was "... extremely common in most coastal localities although the impetus of the initial colonisation seems to have slowed down". It was, however, still rare in the far north and also in the parishes north of Braintree.

The First National Atlas recorded Collared Doves in all but one 10km square, around Hatfield Broad Oak and The Rodings. In 1970 the Essex Recording Committee withdrew its request for detailed notes on observations and thereafter the ongoing colonisation was not monitored closely. The more recent surveys have confirmed its ubiquity. The Essex Atlas survey located Collared Doves in 92.2% of tetrads, the main gaps in distribution being in a few inland areas, as well as on Dengie and Canvey Island. Beckton, an inner Metropolitan district, was without records during the Essex survey but has since been colonised (*EBR* 1997). Apart from this expansion, little further has been reported on the breeding distribution during the latter part of the 1990s but it seems safe to suggest on the evidence available that the population has remained relatively stable. That said, there appear to have been local declines in some areas. It is possible that this may be due to increased pressure from Sparrowhawks that are particularly successful at taking immature birds, but another factor may be the increased protection now being given to grain stores; it has been calculated that a flock of 800 birds on a Sussex farm was taking the equivalent of 18.25 tonnes a year (O'Connor & Shrubb 1986).

Collared Doves are gregarious outside the breeding season and flocks of up to 300 are not exceptional, the largest reported being: 500 at The Naze, 2nd February 1971; 420 at Highwood, 3rd January 1984; 410 at South Hall Farm, Paglesham, 9th September 2000; 370 at Highwood, 2nd January 1987; and 350 at Fingringhoe Mill, 13th February 1977. In addition, it was estimated that some 350 were resident in Boreham during October-December 1994, based on capture-recapture data estimates. During 1972/73 750 were shot on a single farm in the Great Holland area. The pattern of occurrence of the largest flocks is of note, as it suggests some movement or dispersal through Essex during autumn with a peak in October, a decline thereafter and then an increase to a secondary peak in January, caused perhaps by smaller flocks coalescing in the search for ever diminishing winter food sources. The number of three-figure counts vary markedly from year to year; factors such as breeding success and severity of winter weather probably all playing a part in overall population levels.

A Collared Dove ringed in the Netherlands was recovered in Essex in 1964 and birds of Belgian origin were recovered here in 1965 and 1972. Individuals ringed in Essex between 1963 and 1966 were subsequently reported at some distance in France, Wales, Ireland, North Yorkshire and Redruth, Cornwall (13 years and eight months after it was ringed in November 1965 at Bradwell). More recently, several hundred have been ringed but only local recoveries have resulted. This pattern of ringing recoveries is the same across the country. When the species arrived the population was very mobile with birds apparently 'programmed' to continue on a northwesterly heading. Once breeding numbers in Britain peaked and levelled off, the number of long-distance movements declined, perhaps because the balance of 'selective advantage' had now changed; individuals now had a better chance of entering the breeding population by staying put in an area familiar to them rather than moving on somewhere else that was almost invariably fully occupied (*BWP*).

The Collared Dove has shown itself to be an exceptionally adaptable species. It thrives alongside humans, being readily prepared to exploit food sources ranging from bird tables to spilt grain, including rice at Rainham. Whilst it is possible that some reductions have occurred in the more open countryside due to the apparently relentless desire to tidy everything up, there are few threats to the continuing success of the species in Essex.

(European) Turtle Dove   *Streptopelia turtur*

Declining summer resident and passage migrant   Red List

This, the only long-distance migrant pigeon, has a world range that covers most of Europe, north Africa, Transcaspia east to the Near East, the western Altai and Sinkiang. The nominate race *turtur* is largely confined to Europe. The

Turtle Dove is a lowland species requiring open countryside for feeding and thus largely confined to the fertile south and east of Britain; in all, some 44,000 pairs currently remain. Its main source of food is the seeds and fruits of weeds (*BWP*). A significant decline has occurred in the British population since the 1980s, which may be at least partly due to current farming practices (Jarry 1995) with breeding success in East Anglia declining by almost 50% in 30 years (Aebischer *et al.* 2001). However, almost as important is the apparent deterioration of winter habitat through droughts in the Sahel and to a lesser extent hunting in the Mediterranean (Jarry 1994). Western populations winter principally through the Sahel and adjacent savannah regions of west–central Africa.

Christy described the Turtle Dove as "A common summer visitant ... I believe it is becoming more common than formerly...". This increase, at least in the last quarter of the 19th century, was noted nationally (Historical Atlas). Glegg considered the species to be "...

Atlas	Survey Area	% of 10km squares or tetrads in which	
		bred/probably bred	possibly bred or present
First National 10km	Essex	96.5	3.5
Second National 10km	Essex	93.0	3.5
First London Tetrad	Met. Essex	43.0	11.5
Second London Tetrad	Met. Essex	45.5	19.5
Essex Tetrad	Essex	71.6	3.8

Summary of results of Atlas surveys for Turtle Doves

a very common summer resident, which breeds freely throughout the county, with the exception of Epping Forest district where it is scarce". He went on: "It is, taking the county as a whole, the most numerous pigeon during the breeding season, and at times may be seen in the field in flocks". He referred to a count of 300 in one field at Bradfield on 21st May 1913.

Hudson & Pyman considered the Turtle Dove a common summer resident and passage migrant, which on balance was maintaining its numbers. National CBC data showed a steady increase in the Index until about 1972 at which point it was thought that the population was at an all time high (Population Trends). Subsequently the CBC/BBS (England) Index fell by 78% between 1977 and 2002 with the BBS (England) Index declining by 44% between 1994 and 2003; local trends have mirrored the national ones. There was a significant range contraction evident between the two National Atlas surveys, which mainly affected Wales, and southwest England, with the species' stronghold becoming Lincolnshire, East Anglia and Kent.

In Essex, the Turtle Dove's distribution remained virtually unchanged between the two National Atlas surveys, numbers probably continuing to increase until at least the early 1980s. The Essex Atlas survey confirmed the species' presence in 75.4% of all tetrads and in all but two 10km squares, both in east London. In Metropolitan Essex, there was little overall change between the two London Atlas surveys. Thus, despite reported declines elsewhere, the species remained fairly widespread throughout Essex until the 1990s since when the evidence points to an overall population decline. The reduction in numbers has been particularly noticeable in the southwest where several tetrads have been abandoned; it no longer breeds in Hainault Forest CP where up to six pairs bred during the Essex Atlas survey. Recent *EBR*s confirm the generally eastern bias to the Turtle Dove's current distribution. Breeding pairs reported in recent *EBR*s have shown a steady increase but this is surely due to increased observer interest in the species prompted by its conservation status and requests for information in *EBR*s. However, the 152 territories reported in the 2003 *EBR* were more than double any previous year; 186 were reported in 2004. The 28 territories located on Foulness during 2004 illustrate that, in suitable habitat in the east of the county, Turtle Doves remain fairly common.

Essex CBC data from 1980–99 revealed a relatively slow decline until about the mid-1990s and then a more noticeable one, although some sites had seen declines from the early to mid-1980s. Breeding numbers at each CBC site varied considerably from year to year: at Weeleyhall Wood from 1980–86 these varied from five pairs in 1982 to 22 in 1986, the latter equating to a breeding density of 69 pairs per km², far higher than any other Essex CBC site.

Turtle Doves can form significant feeding flocks, particularly as they move through during May and June and again as they depart in July and August. The size and number of flocks have generally varied greatly from year to year. A combination of feeding and migrating birds at Colne Point totalled some 1,000 on 5th June 1977. A flock of 600 was present in a field at Rayleigh on 20th May 1971, whilst 400 were at Layer-de-la-Haye on 15th May 1973; there are a further three spring counts of 300+. In autumn, flock sizes are generally smaller, the largest being 380 at Colne Point on 18th August 1976, whilst there were 350 on St Osyth Marsh on 26th August 1977 and 300 at Maldon on 30th July 1978. Visible migration is rarely recorded, indeed Turtle Doves are generally considered to be night migrants (Jarry 1995) with any small diurnal movements likely to involve juveniles.

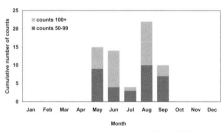

Seasonal occurrence of counts of 50+ and 100+ Turtle Doves from 1971-2004

The number of large flocks have declined significantly since the early 1990s. There have been no counts in excess of 300 since 1978, only one three-figure count since 1995 (150 at Old Hall on 14th August 1996) and no flocks of 50+ since 1999.

Whilst most Turtle Doves arrive during May and early June, the first usually appear during mid-April. However, there have been several March records: South House Farm, Maldon, 9th in 2003, which may have been an early migrant, although one was present in Chelmsford on 26th January;

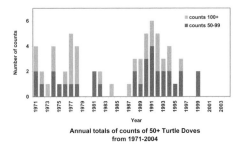

Annual totals of counts of 50+ Turtle Doves from 1971-2004

Billericay, 24th in 1967 was probably a genuine arrival; Battlesbridge, 29th in 1975 had possibly wintered; and North Fambridge, 26th in 1989 may also have been a genuine arrival, although it too could have wintered undetected with the local Collared Dove flock.

Apart from these, the next earliest arrival date has been 9th April at: High Ongar in 1955; Great Horkesley in 1970; and East Tilbury in 1977.

Numbers passing through Essex peak in August with most having departed by the end of September. Very few used to be

	Jan	Feb	Mar	Apr	May	Jun	Jul	Aug	Sep	Oct	Nov	Dec
Essex					3	4	2	1	2			
South England						1						
France					8			3	8	1		
Spain					3		1		7	2	1	
Portugal									3	1		
Mali				1								
Totals	*0*	*0*	*0*	*1*	*14*	*4*	*4*	*4*	*20*	*4*	*1*	*0*

Month and location of recovery of Turtle Doves ringed in Essex

recorded in October and beyond. However, since the late 1960s there have been a number of records involving late migrants or wintering individuals, several of which have associated with Collared Doves around grain storage facilities, with five records during November and in December at: Clacton-on-Sea, 1st in 1968; Woodham Ferrers, 19th–21st in 1974 and presumably the same bird at Althorne on 13th January 1975 (and possibly Battlesbridge on 29th March 1975); The Hythe, 8th in 1981; Great Wigborough, 25th in 1983 with Collared Doves; and West Bergholt, 26th in 1996–20th January 1997.

Many Turtle Doves were ringed in Essex during the 1950s and 1960s, sadly with the majority subsequently trapped or shot in southern Europe. In all, 39 Essex-ringed Turtle Doves have been recovered abroad. The recovery from Mali (near Bamako during April 1964, 4,422km to the south of Abberton where it was ringed in July 1963), is one of only three from the BTO ringing scheme (Migration Atlas). This individual was probably moving north at the time as most winter further south; its reporting was likely to have been delayed. Peak passage through Iberia is from mid-August to the end of September (Migration Atlas), so the July and November individuals were respectively early and late. One shot in Gers, France, on 19th September 1974 had been ringed 11 years earlier at Tiptree; it is the oldest British-ringed Turtle Dove to have been reported to the BTO. The only recoveries in Essex of Turtle Doves from elsewhere involve one ringed near Peterborough, Cambridgeshire, and recovered at Waltham Abbey and another ringed on Great Saltee, County Wexford, Eire, in July 1963 that was recovered at Ashdon in July 1966. Such a southeast orientation is unusual.

Although the causes of the recent declines in Turtle Doves in both Britain and Essex are not absolutely clear, the increasing tidying up of the countryside and the use of herbicides and fertilisers have undoubtedly reduced the diversity and quantity of 'weeds' and their seeds in arable fields and so removed the species' main source of food. Pressure to change the way that modern farming methods affect the countryside will, hopefully, overcome this problem. As to hunting pressures in southern Europe and droughts in the Sahel, there is little that can be done directly within the county to ameliorate these threats.

Sponsored by John Clark

Ring-necked Parakeet (Rose-ringed Parakeet)   *Psittacula krameri*

Uncommon introduced resident and visitor: occasional breeding suspected but not confirmed until 2004

The Ring-necked Parakeet is widespread throughout the Afrotropical and Oriental regions, where four races occur, and has established naturalised populations in Germany, Belgium, the Netherlands and Britain, which supports the largest population. The British population continues to increase, although it remains centred on west London, where a considerable roost at Esher Rugby Club, Surrey, has at times numbered over 4,000 birds.

There is an intriguing reference in the EFC Report of 1932 to "paraquets at Loughton" in the autumn of 1930. Originally six were present, but by 1932 there was just one. Whilst other species cannot be ruled out, it seems highly likely that Ring-necked Parakeets were involved. Together wih a series of records that included breeding in Norfolk in 1855 and the possibility that the species was present south of the Thames during the 1890s (Chandler 2003), these records may represent some of the earliest feral records of the species (Hudson 1974).

Hudson (1974) published details from Woodford Green/Highams Park area back to at least 1971 of flocks of up to 22, by far the largest yet to be recorded in Essex.

Records have only been published in the *EBR* since 1976; the species was added to the Category C of the British List in 1977. Since then numbers have remained remarkably stable with only a very slow increase.

Ring-necked Parakeets are long-lived birds and those breeding in the wild in Britain are remarkably sedentary; both factors may well explain why numbers have remained so constant in Essex over the years with perhaps rarely more than 6–10 annually. Indeed, several of those present from year to year are known to be long-staying individuals that wander around a 'home range'. For example, eight records in the Hanningfield/Billericay area between 1996 and 2002 are likely to have involved the same bird and several in Metropolitan Essex in recent years likewise wandered widely.

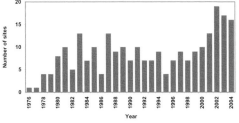

Number of sites annually recording Ring-necked Parakeets from 1976-2004

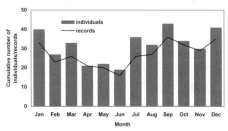

Seasonal occurrence of Ring-necked Parakeets from 1976-2004

Given the significant increase in the size of the west London colonies, it seems remarkable that the species has not increased in Essex. Breeding has been suspected, but never proven at: South Woodford/Highams Park (1973); Rainham (1987); Chadwell Heath (1988); Havering area (1990); Pygro Park, Havering (1991); and Epping Forest/South Woodford (two pairs in 1994). In 2004, a pair raised two young at Corbets Tey, the only confirmed county breeding record. One present at Dagenham Chase in the late 1990s was bonded with a Woodpigeon. It has been suggested in the past that the very slightly cooler winters to the east of London were a bar to range expansion. However, there is an apparently thriving sub-population around Margate and Ramsgate, Kent.

Periodically larger flocks are reported, although whether these originate from the feral population or are new escapes is unknown. The largest flocks, apart from the records from Woodford/Highams Park in 1971 are: six at Leigh/Two Tree Island, 9th August 2004; five at Hadleigh Downs, January-March 1977; five at Earls Colne, 18th July 1996 with the same flock at Old Hall on 2nd August and Maldon on 3rd; four at Pitsea, 15th July 1995; and four at Grays, 13th June 2000. The 1996 records illustrate how some Ring-necked Parakeets move over large distances, quite contrary to the apparently sedentary nature of the feral population.

Interestingly, there does appear to be a seasonal pattern of occurrence in Essex with the fewest records/parakeets in summer and an increase during autumn. Although difficult to confirm, the data suggest that there may be some limited post-breeding dispersal from the main London/Kent colonies.

(Common) Cuckoo   *Cuculus canorus*

Summer resident and passage migrant, possibly declining   **Amber List**

The Cuckoo's extensive breeding range covers all of Europe and much of Asia from the Arctic tree-limit south as far as northwest Africa and east across Russia to China and Japan. North and central European forms are represented by the nominate race *canorus*. Cuckoos are brood parasites and their distribution and abundance are therefore influenced by their two main requirements: nests of potential host species and a supply of hairy caterpillars, the main prey (European Atlas). In Britain, the Cuckoo ranges over a wide variety of habitats including woodland and scrub, open country with scattered trees and hedgerows, farmland of various types, wetlands with reed beds and rough grassland. Western populations winter in Africa south of the Sahara, although their exact winter range is poorly known.

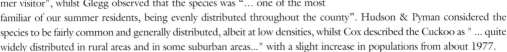

The distinctive 'cu-coo' call of the male is familiar to many people, whether birdwatchers or not. Thus, its arrival in Essex every spring has been well documented. When life was far more precarious and the rural economy, and hence people's existence, were more directly related to the seasons, the harbinger of spring was vitally important. Even today, we look forward to the first Cuckoo and *The Times* continues to print its 'first-Cuckoo' letters (Greenoak 1981).

Christy considered the Cuckoo to be "A common and very familiar summer visitor", whilst Glegg observed that the species was "... one of the most familiar of our summer residents, being evenly distributed throughout the county". Hudson & Pyman considered the species to be fairly common and generally distributed, albeit at low densities, whilst Cox described the Cuckoo as " ... quite widely distributed in rural areas and in some suburban areas..." with a slight increase in populations from about 1977.

Anecdotal evidence from across Essex suggested a marked population decline prior to the 1950s and indeed one observer in the northeast considered that by 1967 the population had decreased by 80% since WWII. By the early 1960s "... considerable declines..." (*EBR* 1962) had been noted in the northeast, northwest and parts of south and central Essex. These declines were reported nationally from about 1950, but their extent was difficult to assess (Population Trends). However, despite reported declines in areas where it was still represented, such as the Danbury/Little Baddow/Woodham Walter area, the species nonetheless remained fairly well represented, particularly along the Chelmer Valley water meadows.

The Cuckoo was present in almost every 10km square during the two National Atlas surveys; the increase noted by Cox that began around 1977 continued until at least the mid-1980s. Subsequently, there has been some evidence to suggest a steady and sustained decline, although Cuckoo numbers appear to fluctuate quite markedly from year to year. This trend has generally been borne out by the CBC (England) since 1972, although this scheme is not good for monitoring Cuckoos. Nonetheless, the Index fell by 56% between 1977 and 2002 with the recent BBS (England) highlighting a 48% reduction from 1994–2003. Local indices have also identified a significant decline. Apart from a possible link to a fall in Meadow Pipit numbers, other factors such as habitat loss and annually fluctuating abundance of caterpillars caused by extreme weather conditions may be responsible for the decline (First National Atlas), although negative factors at play in their winter quarters are, as yet, unresearched possibilities.

The Essex Atlas survey revealed the Cuckoo to be widely distributed throughout, breeding being noted in 42.6% of tetrads with a presence in a further 32.5%. The Cuckoo was particularly well represented in the coastal fringe, excepting urban areas, where populations of Meadow Pipits and Reed Warblers are also high. Few breed in inner Metropolitan Essex or other built-up locations and areas of more intensive farming, particularly in the northwest, hold few pairs.

No modern research has been carried out in Essex into host species. However, during an unspecified period prior to 1926, around Felsted

Atlas	Survey Area	% of 10km squares or tetrads in which	
		bred/probably bred	possibly bred or present
First National 10km	Essex	96.5	3.5
Second National 10km	Essex	86.0	12.3
First London Tetrad	Met. Essex	36.0	16.5
Second London Tetrad	Met. Essex	54.5	25.5
Essex Tetrad	Essex	42.6	32.5

Summary of results of Atlas surveys for Cuckoos

and district some 400 victims were identified, which suggests an abundance far greater than seen today. The victims included: 225 Dunnocks; 53 Pied Wagtails; 35 Sedge Warblers; 24 Robins; and single Linnet, Whitethroat, Reed Bunting, Wren, Reed Warbler, Greenfinch, Song Thrush, Blackbird, Lesser Whitethroat, Tree Pipit, Yellowhammer, Goldfinch, Bullfinch, Chaffinch, Goldcrest and Spotted Flycatcher. The instance of a Goldcrest being used as a host seems quite remarkable; indeed the record, from a garden in Great Dunmow in 1911, was probably the first British record (Glegg). Glegg noted that Meadow Pipit and Reed Warbler were commonly chosen on the coast, whilst other hosts were Red-backed Shrike and Chiffchaff. Today, Reed Warbler, then Meadow Pipit and Dunnock are the most favoured of around 50 host species (First National Atlas).

In Essex, Cuckoos usually arrive during the first and second weeks of April with most arriving during late April and early May. There have, however, been 11 March records: 17th at Birchanger in 1953; 18th at Billericay in 1967 and East Mersea in 1990, the latter occurring at about the same time as two in Suffolk (*Suffolk Bird Report* 1991); 21st at Stansted in 1924; 26th at Pitsea in 1993; 27th at Blackmore in 1981 and East Ham in 2000; 30th at Rainham town in 2004; and 31st at an unnamed locality in 1903, Saffron Walden in 1954 and Hornchurch CP in 2004. Numbers noted on spring migration are generally greater than in autumn, although double-figure counts from the coast are rare. Ten at Foulness on 25th April 2004, 12 at Langenhoe on 28th May 1989 and up to 15 on Foulness in late May/early June 1991 were either migrants or local breeders—or more likely a combination of both.

Adults begin to disperse from breeding grounds and head south as early as late June with most having left by mid-July; fledglings disperse away from breeding areas from July and begin their southerly migration from early August (*BWP*). There is clearly some onward passage through Essex, although very few are seen on active migration and those that are generally move through in ones and twos. Twelve through Bradwell on 27th August 1978 and 12 at St Osyth/Colne Point on 7th July 1950 are therefore notable. Generally, few are left by mid-September. However, there are two November records: one killed at the Swin Middle Lightship on 26th in 1885, and one shot at West Thurrock mid-month (year unknown, late 19th century). In addition, there have been ten October records, all except two, at Saffron Walden on 12th in 1957 and at Bradwell on 10th in 1976, falling within the first seven days of the month.

A total of around 30 rufous colour phase or 'hepatic morph' females has been noted, the majority occurring in the last 15 years and including at least three in 1993 and four in 1995. Increased observer coverage is the most likely explanation for this trend; the proportion of this morph within the population has never been researched but is likely to be small (*BWP*).

Fully-grown Cuckoos are difficult to trap and hence ring, as they tend to fly high and fast even when on territory. Hence very few have been ringed in Essex. Two ringed at Pitsea, an adult and a juvenile, were re-trapped in subsequent years suggesting significant site fidelity which has also been noted at national level (*BWP*). A very early ringing recovery dating back to 1910 involving a Yorkshire-ringed nestling found five weeks later at Southend-on-Sea, and a more recent recovery of a juvenile ringed at Saffron Walden in July 1989 and recovered at Lydd, Kent, in August 1989 both tie in well with the species' southeast migration out of the country in autumn.

Within Essex, the principal threats to Cuckoo populations are continuing loss of suitable habitat of host species, either by direct human interference or indirectly (e.g. rising sea levels may reduce areas of *Phragmites* for Reed Warblers), and reductions in the amount of available food through indiscriminate pesticide use and general air pollution.

Barn Owl   *Tyto alba*

The Barn Owl is essentially a subtropical and tropical species, although it is found on every continent except Antarctica. In Europe, the species is found everywhere apart from Fennoscandia and Iceland; those in Scotland are the most northerly in the world. Of the 35 recognised subspecies (European Atlas), six occur in Europe, two are widespread and four are island races. The species is largely sedentary.

Barn Owl   *T. a. alba*

Locally common resident: very rare migrant   Amber List

The nominate race is generally found to the west of the January 3°C isotherm in southern and western Europe. Throughout much of its range the species favours rank open grassland and is basically sedentary (European Atlas). The species has declined markedly over much of Britain and western Europe during the 20th century. Currently there are around 4,000 pairs in Britain (Toms 1999).

The earliest reference to the species was at Waltham Abbey prior to 1838. Christy knew the Barn Owl well, considering it a "… fairly common resident, breeding in old hollow trees, church towers, dove-cotes, &c". However, he made it clear that the loss of many of the pollarded trees that abounded in the countryside during the early decades of the 19th century (see also Rackham 1986) had affected the species' numbers: "Fifty years ago, before scientific farming came in, and before a cheap, abundant supply of coal was obtainable in Essex, numerous large old pollarded trees stood in the hedge-rows in all parts of the county, and afforded logs for the winter fires … These were I think invaluable to the farmers as … nesting places of numerous Owls. Most of these have now gone, and with them have disappeared the Owls to a great extent. Formerly rats were rarely found in the fields; but now, from the destruction of Owls and other so-called vermin, they abound, and may be found in almost every hedge … The destruction … of pollards has, in my opinion, resulted in great injury to the county generally". Christy declared: "No bird more richly deserves protection than this". Just how numerous the Barn Owl was during the late 18th and early 19th century is now impossible to guess. In many parts of the country it was considered the commonest owl (Historical Atlas) and there is no reason to believe that this was not the case in Essex.

Glegg described the Barn Owl as a fairly common resident. He considered the species typical of "… deserted buildings and sheds on the outlying marshes … it is seen not infrequently hunting during the day … searching systematically the sea-wall to which locality it is partial". He noted, however, that the Barn Owl was "… probably a declining species" and referred to reductions in the Epping district, at Sible Hedingham and Felsted. He felt that the increase in Little Owl numbers might have been at least part of the cause of the decline, although he based this solely on observations from Thames-side.

By the mid-1960s, the species had declined markedly "… especially during the last ten years or so, although there are signs that this trend may have halted, at least temporarily" (Hudson & Pyman). The first national survey, carried out in 1932, indicated an Essex population of

Atlas	Survey Area	% of 10km squares or tetrads in which	
		bred/probably bred	possibly bred or present
First National 10km	Essex	77.2	15.8
Second National 10km	Essex	31.6	22.8
First London Tetrad	Met. Essex	9.0	11.5
Second London Tetrad	Met. Essex	8.5	12.5
Essex Tetrad	Essex	5.4	6.0

Summary of results of Atlas surveys for Barn Owls

around 500 pairs, the overall density of some 13 pairs per 10km square being the highest of any English county (Blaker 1934). Hudson & Pyman considered the population in the mid-1960s to be no more than 30% of this figure and, although still widespread, it was very thinly distributed. Cox suggested that by the early 1980s the Essex population was perhaps no more than 100 pairs. His estimate was based upon general reports of continuing decreases across Essex, an average of two pairs per 10km square within Metropolitan Essex during 1968–72, together with observations from the Dengie Hundred where there were ten pairs in an area of no more than 1.5 10km squares, a density probably not exceeded elsewhere in the county. Cox cited the main causes for the declines to be: loss of nesting sites; reduction in grassland so important for the species' rodent prey; increasing mortality due to road traffic (today the majority of ringing recoveries come from this source); and the use of chlorinated hydrocarbons in agriculture. However, the latter factor was becoming less marked at this time with residues of hydrocarbons found in owls and raptors from Essex apparently in decline.

Between 1981 and 1985, the Hawk and Owl Trust undertook a nationwide Barn Owl survey. The long census period was necessary as it was known that Barn Owl numbers fluctuate markedly every three to four years in response to cyclical changes in the Field Vole population (Love 1997), the species' major source of food in mainland Britain. The results, as they related to Essex, were published in the 1987 *EBR* (Shawyer 1988). Detailed analysis of the data suggested an overall Essex population of 120 pairs, equivalent to 3.4 pairs per 10km square, a decline of 75% over 50 years greater than the 69% decrease over England and Wales as a whole. Shawyer considered the major factor for the decline to be the serious worsening of the winter climate since the 1940s with the number of days with snow cover increasing from five days in any winter at the beginning of the 20th century to over 20 days by the mid-1970s. However, major agricultural changes since the 1940s compounded the problem with the loss of rickyards and stabling areas where rodents swarmed depriving the Barn Owl of a source of food during even the most severe winter weather.

The Essex Atlas survey located birds in 11.4% of tetrads with breeding confirmed in just 5.4%. Although not directly comparable, it is interesting to note that during the Hawk and Owl Trust survey period (1983–85), a total of 62 nest records was confirmed, slightly higher than the 58 in the Essex survey. However, it should be borne in mind that Shawyer's survey, and indeed Blaker's, was questionnaire-based, whilst the Essex survey was carried out by individual observers who, unlike respondents of the survey questionnaire such as farmers and landowners, may not have been aware of all Barn Owl records (Essex Atlas). The species may have therefore been underestimated and indeed a survey of Dengie in 1995 east of Latchingdon and Althorne produced an estimate of some 20–25 pairs (Robert Harvey pers. comm.), very similar to Shawyer's results for the same area. In contrast, the Essex Atlas survey of the area located just 4–8 pairs, all along the most regularly watched coastal region. Whether or not the survey coincided with a good or bad vole year is unknown. A follow-up survey in 1996, which surveyed Dengie east of Steeple and north of Southminster, produced 13 definite breeding pairs (with almost certainly two further nests), seven of which were using nest boxes (Robert Harvey pers. comm.). Comparison of the two London Atlases suggested a relatively stable population. However, a marked decline was apparent across Essex between the two National Atlas surveys.

Despite the run of exceptionally mild, snow-free winters, there has been little sign of a positive increase in Barn Owls, although many experienced observers consider that the species is making a steady comeback from a low point during the 1970s, helped in many areas by the provision of nest boxes and areas of rough set-aside grassland. The

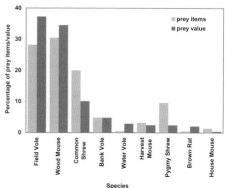

Graph showing a) percentage of commonest mammals found in pellet analysis b) prey value (i.e. importance of the prey item taking into account such factors as body weight, seasonal variations, etc.) of each item.
(Adapted from Love (1997))

species' stronghold therefore remains in the low-lying coastal areas with some penetration up river valleys. To what extent any apparent increase in the population has been assisted by reintroduced birds is unclear; Essex probably saw more Barn Owls released than any other county (Second London Atlas).

An analysis of some 4,733 Barn Owl pellets collected in the Dengie Hundred between November 1994 and May 1997 identified some 17,352 individual prey items, 98.7% of which were small mammals, 1.2% bird prey and the remaining 0.1% were reptile and amphibian prey. A total of 14 species of mammal was recorded, although three species accounted for 78.6% of the total: Field Vole, Wood Mouse and Common Shrew (Love 1997).

British Barn Owls are very sedentary; 60% of Essex-ringed Barn Owls had moved less than 10km when recovered, with a further 36% having moved between 10km and 99km. The four most distant recoveries involved singles ringed at Fingringhoe Wick and found at South Wootton and Burnham Overy Staithe, both Norfolk; one ringed on Foulness and found dead in Gabbet Park, Sussex; and one ringed as a pullus at St Osyth in June 2000 and found dead as a road casualty at South Witham, Lincolnshire, in September 2000. Several British-ringed Barn Owls have occurred in Essex, one ringed as a nestling in Lancashire and found dead at The Hythe in November of the same year having moved the greatest distance by far. There has been just one record of a foreign-ringed Barn Owl recovered in Essex, a Belgian-ringed owlet recovered at Stock in 1974. This was the first foreign-ringed Barn Owl to be recovered in Britain. It is not clear whether this individual showed any characteristics of *guttata*.

Although road-kills may be having an impact on Barn Owl populations, the current move towards more sustainable and environmentally friendly farming point towards a more promising future for the Barn Owl than has been the case for many decades and, if global warming does result in warmer winters, the species may benefit further.

Dark-breasted Barn Owl   *T. a. guttata*

Very rare winter visitor: ten records

The Dark-breasted Barn Owl is general found in central Europe, generally to the east of the 3°C January isotherm, from Germany east to the Ukraine and Bulgaria (Migration Atlas).

about 1843	Epping Forest		Shot
1864	Epping Forest	December	Shot
1949	Abberton	2nd December	
1960	Foulness	20th February	
1963	Horsey	16th August	
1977	The Naze	4th September	
1982	Northey Island	18th January	
1991	Colne Point	6th October	Dead
1997	Bradwell Rescue Centre	21st February	Injured
2002	The Naze/Old Walton Hall	29th–30th November and 20th December	

The origin of the 1997 individual is not known but was most likely to have been within Essex. The first two records pre-date the first accepted British record of one in Kent in 1937 (Palmer 2000). The 1843 report is therefore, potentially, a British first. It was recorded by Henry Doubleday who noted that the Barn Owl had "… the whole of the underside parts, legs, &c., of deep ochre-yellow, with a few black spots. The face alone was white". One observed at the Tongue Lightship (37km east of Shoeburyness) on 20th October 1885 may have been of this form.

Sponsored by Steve and Kim Norrell

(Eurasian) Scops Owl   *Otus scops*

Vagrant: two 19th century records

The Scops Owl breeds across mid and south Europe and north Africa as far east as Lake Baikal and is represented in central and eastern Europe by the nominate race *scops* with at least three other races occurring in southern Europe and the Mediterranean. Most of the European population winters south of the Sahara.

| about 1821 | Audley End | Undated | Two shot |
| 1888 | Littlebury, Howe Wood | 11th June | Male shot |

Glegg also referred to a Mr Fitch's annotated copy of Christy's *Birds of Essex* that noted that two were shot at Audley End in 1847. Glegg raised the possibility that this and the 1821 record were one and the same, given the similarity of both. Recent enquiries at Saffron Walden Museum have found no further evidence to confirm or disprove this theory; the similarity is so great, however, and clearly based on hearsay, that the record is treated here as an error.

The second record refers to an individual that had been present in the wood for some time; the person who shot it was sure a second bird was present. The cry of the bird(s) was described "… as somewhat resembling the loud croak of a frog, and the village boys tried to imitate it by crying "*chalk, chalk*". Its dismal cry was kept up the greater part of the night, and could be heard more than half a mile off. The country people got quite superstitious about the bird and regarded it as an evil spirit…" Littlebury is a short distance from Audley End.

Christy also mentioned one that was present for several weeks in 1854 in a Privet hedge at Paglesham, although Glegg, without explanation, considered the record unacceptable. Birds heard in a plantation at Heydon from 1886–89 which were thought to have been Scops Owls were more likely to have been young Long-eared Owls (Christy).

Nationally, the species has become increasingly rare in recent years as its breeding range has contracted on the Continent. There were only 31 records in the period 1958–2004 (BBRC 2005), with 56 before then. Most occurred between late March and late June.

Snowy Owl   *Bubo scandiacus*

Vagrant: one record

The monotypic Snowy Owl breeds throughout the Arctic Circle and bred on Fetlar in the Shetland Islands between 1967 and 1975 with individuals summering in the Cairngorms, Highland, in recent years. Otherwise, the species is a vagrant, subject to periodic influxes, usually to the north of Scotland, with a national total of 159 records since 1958 (BBRC 2005).

| 1963 | Sewardstonebury | 2nd –28th March | Adult female |

The possibility of an escape was raised at the time of the record. However, it appeared at the beginning of a period when singletons turned up in southern England. The winter of 1962/63 was one of the most severe for many years with sub-zero conditions lasting for almost the first three months of 1963.

Christy noted that it was "… seen on the borders of Essex at Christmas time". He also referred to one seen at Paglesham in the winter of 1883/84, but Glegg, without reason, felt that no Essex records were acceptable.

An escape was at Corringham on 29th May 2000.

Little Owl   *Athene noctua*

Fairly common and widespread resident

The Little Owl has a trans-Palearctic distribution, occurring throughout Europe south as far as the Mediterranean Basin and east to China. It also occurs in the Afrotropical region in Ethiopia and south of the Gulf of Arabia (European Atlas). Up to 13 races are recognised (*HBW*) with *vidalii* occurring in west and northern Europe, east to northwest Russia and the nominate race *noctua* present in central Europe south to Sardinia and Sicily and east to Romania. Although Little Owls may have been present in England during the Pleistocene (Lambrecht 1917), the species became extinct during the subsequent glaciation. Only in the 19th century, following several attempts, was it successfully introduced into Britain where it has subsequently become widespread. It is typical of a wide range of open agricultural landscapes and is generally sedentary. There are currently around 7,000 pairs in the UK (Toms *et al.* 2000).

Apart from an unconfirmed occurrence of "… a curious little Owl, no bigger than a Starling which had just been knocked down in the county of Essex" on 18th October 1836, the first confirmed record was reported by Christy who noted: "Mr Edwin Ward records that on January 2nd 1865, whilst out shooting, [he] found an adult female in perfect plumage and quite fresh, lying dead beneath a tree in a small fir-plantation at Chigwell. It had apparently killed itself by flying against a tree, as the skull and atlas-bone were fractured and there was extravasated blood in the throat." This was at the time about the 23rd British record (Harting 1901) and was probably of natural origin, although the earliest attempt at introduction took place in Yorkshire in 1843. There were many other attempts to introduce the species into England during the 19th century but only those in Kent during the 1870s and in Northamptonshire during the 1880s are thought to have led to the successful colonisation of Britain (Historical Atlas). However, it was not until 1899 that the next Essex record occurred when one was caught in a Rabbit trap at Harlow about the middle of October (Glegg). Occasional records occurred thereafter, helped no doubt by the release of ten around Loughton during 1905 and five at Rettendon in 1908.

The first confirmed Essex breeding record occurred in 1910 when a pair reared 4–5 young in Easton Park (Glegg). By 1914, Glegg considered that it had spread right across the county and that it then "... multiplied with great rapidity ...", presumably helped by the lack of gamekeepers during WWI, such that by 1919 he considered it "... a really common bird everywhere ...". The extent to which it increased seems remarkable as, for example, in mid-Essex within the space of the five years 1914–19, it had changed from a new arrival to occurring in such numbers as to be a nuisance. In one part of Essex, 59 were shot in three years, whilst on some 'beats' more than 100 were killed a year. The 1922 *Felsted School Scientific Society Report* considered that the decline in the Tree Pipit was due to the Little Owl and that Red-backed Shrikes were also targeted. In 1926, 72 were killed on one Essex poultry farm. Such apparent densities have never been reached since. The species was considered a pest and a "... wholesale slaughterer of pheasants, partridge and poultry chicks". One observer noted, "... a neighbour missed thirty-six chickens, and on the coops being watched the bird was traced to its nest, where the remains of the chickens were found inside" (Glegg). The British Fields Sport Society published a pamphlet urging the authorities to remove the species from the list of protected birds. Indeed by 1936, 15 counties had done so, with the approval of the Home Office (Dark 1936). To address the allegations, a detailed study of the Little Owl's feeding habits was instigated by the BTO. Alice Hibbert-Ware, who had already carried out a study of the gizzards of Little Owls in Essex (Hibbert-Ware 1922), led the two-year enquiry, which vindicated the Little Owl, demonstrating that it fed primarily on rodents and insects, although it was thought that 'rogue' birds might be responsible for occasionally taking gamebirds (Hibbert-Ware 1938).

Hudson & Pyman considered the species a "Resident, fairly common; apparently sedentary". However, they observed that there had been "... a noticeable reduction in numbers

| | Atlas | Survey Area | % of 10km squares or tetrads in which | |
			bred/probably bred	possibly bred or present
First National 10km		Essex	87.7	8.8
Second National 10km		Essex	59.6	29.8
First London Tetrad		Met. Essex	19.5	13.0
Second London Tetrad		Met. Essex	30.0	16.0
Essex Tetrad		Essex	25.3	21.0

Summary of results of Atlas surveys for Little Owls

since about 1960 ... ", the decline subsequently attributed to the use of pesticides, although changes in land use and a number of severe winters in the late 1950s and early 1960s may have been contributory factors. There is little detailed information in the early *EBRs* but in the Writtle/Roxwell/Highwood area 28 pairs in 1950 had declined to just two by 1963. However, as early as the mid-1960s there were signs of a recovery at least in this area with ten pairs noted there in 1966, 20 in 1968 and 28 in 1973.

Cox described the Little Owl as "... common over much of the County", although populations in the northeast had perhaps never regained their pre-1960 level. During the 1970s, relatively high breeding densities were noted around Mountnessing, Ingatestone and Margaretting where there were about 40 pairs in TL 60 and the northern half of TQ69 (equating to 2–3 pairs per 10km square), 25 pairs around Dengie villages from Bradwell south to Burnham-on-Crouch and ten pairs at Braxted. Since 1980, there appears to have been a general decline with reductions of around 50% in the areas mentioned above and decreases reported from many other areas (Essex Atlas). It is probable that the declines have resulted from the substantial changes to farming practices during the last three decades of the 20th century. The change from spring to autumn sown Wheat and Barley, the reduction in acreage of pastureland and removal of hedgerows have all combined to reduce the ideal habitat for the species' principal prey items.

However, the Essex Atlas survey revealed that the species was still widespread over much of the county, being absent only from the most built-up areas and from more intensively farmed arable land. The CBC/BBS Index suggested a 6% increase during the period 1977–2002, although as the species is difficult to detect the data may be unreliable. In recent years, the largest concentrations have been up to ten pairs in the Great Clacton/St Osyth area and seven at each of Terling, Ingatestone, Weald CP, Navestock and South Woodham Ferrers.

Little change in distribution was apparent between the two London Atlases, although recent countywide trends remain unclear, with declines noted in many parts of Metropolitan Essex but reverses of the declines or general stability elsewhere. Such inconsistent observations should always be viewed in the light of the species' 3–5 year cyclical pattern of abundance, which is tied to the availability of small mammals, which in turn also exhibit a similar pattern of occurrence. Nationally, the BBS has suggested a 6% increase during the period 1994–2003.

Little Owls are very sedentary with the majority of recoveries nationally occurring within 10km of the ringing location. Recoveries from Essex follow broadly the same pattern with the oldest record, one ringed as a nestling at Bishop's Stortford on 28th May 1927 and recovered at Elsenham in June 1928, being typical. Two recoveries have, however, involved longer than usual movements. One ringed as a nestling at Cardington, Bedfordshire, on 22nd June 1983 was found dead at Tawney Common, Toot Hill, on 4th January 1987, some 63km to the southeast, whilst another also ringed as a nestling, at East Tilbury on 2nd June 1957, was found dead near Tonbridge, Kent, 43km to the southeast on 10th July 1959.

The continuing loss of hedgerows, individual trees and orchards and the decay and destruction of old farm buildings are likely to continue to reduce nest site availability despite a short-term increase in suitable hunting habitat created by various environmental improvement schemes and agricultural set-aside programmes. The Little Owl's future in Essex may require a substantial change in farming practice that must go hand in hand with a more sympathetic and understanding approach to the countryside in general, perhaps through what is so aptly described in the Essex Atlas as a policy of "controlled untidiness".

Sponsored by Martin Henry

Tawny Owl   *Strix aluco*

Common resident

The Tawny Owl is widely distributed throughout Britain and mainland Europe where it is the commonest owl. The species' Palearctic range extends from Portugal in the west to Korea in the east. Around 11 races are recognised, the nominate *aluco* occurring in northern and eastern Europe, east into Russia and south to the Alps and Black Sea and *sylvatica* in Britain, France and Iberia and the Mediterranean (*HBW*). The species is generally sedentary.

Like all other owls and birds of prey, the Tawny Owl undoubtedly suffered during the 19th century at the hands of gamekeepers. Thus Christy noted that it was "A resident in the county, but locally distributed ... becoming rarer with us and now nowhere common." He knew of breeding only at Birch, Danbury, Birdbrook and Epping. The earliest documented Essex record referred to the species being common in the Rochford Hundred around 1832 at which time it was also known at Southminster and Lexden. In 1838, the Tawny Owl was described as common at Sudbury but by 1876 it was "now very seldom heard", whilst it was also rare around Saffron Walden by Christy's time. The species was described as not uncommon in Epping Forest and Birch Hall, the woods around Danbury, Boreham Park and Tofts (Little Baddow), fairly common at Harwich and common in the Colchester and Paglesham districts. Although shot occasionally in the Orsett district, Tawny Owls were not known to breed. By Glegg's time, it appeared that the Tawny Owl had increased its range as he described it as "... a common resident throughout the county and evidently very sedentary". He noted that it persisted even quite close to towns, having nested annually at Walthamstow town and Colchester and that it was increasing in some districts, with Felsted and Sible Hedingham mentioned. In Epping Forest, it was described as, "a really common bird".

The Tawny Owl was not mentioned in the Systematic List of the *EBR* until 1965. However, Hudson & Pyman described the species as fairly evenly distributed in moderate numbers in all but the most sparsely timbered parts of Essex. It was not obviously affected by the use of organochlorine pesticides in the 1950s and 1960s, although at least in the southeast of England, data from the BTO Nest Record Cards and the Ringing Scheme showed that there has subsequently been a slight improvement in the survival rate of young owls probably because of a reduction in pesticide residues (First National Atlas).

Atlas	Survey Area	% of 10km squares or tetrads in which	
		bred/probably bred	possibly bred or present
First National 10km	Essex	91.2	8.8
Second National 10km	Essex	66.7	22.8
First London Tetrad	Met. Essex	29.0	15.0
Second London Tetrad	Met. Essex	48.5	14.0
Essex Tetrad	Essex	31.2	23.0

Summary of results of Atlas surveys for Tawny Owls

The first detailed survey of at least part of Essex, the First London Atlas, revealed the species' presence in 44% of Metropolitan Essex tetrads suggesting that it was more widespread than the Little Owl in this area. Comparison with the Second London Atlas suggested an increase, although this may simply have been due to increased observer coverage.

The First National Atlas recorded Tawny Owls in almost all 10km squares in Essex; the Second confirmed an absence from seven, suggesting a decline. The Essex Atlas survey recorded the Tawny Owl in around 7.9% more tetrads than the Little Owl; whilst coverage was the best achieved across Essex to date, the species was almost certainly under-recorded. Likewise, the number of reports detailed within *EBRs* each year probably bear little comparison to numbers actually present within Essex.

In Britain, where there are around 20,000 pairs (Stone *et al.* 1997), although primarily a woodland species, Tawny Owls are also found commonly in farmland and gardens where there are enough trees to provide secure nest and roost sites (Second National Atlas). The BTO Tawny Owl Survey (Percival 1990) showed that the amount of woodland within an area is more important in determining the number of Tawny Owls it supports than the geographical location of the square. Tawny Owls frequent richly structured habitat with lookout posts, woodland with clearings, avenues, cemeteries, hedges and gardens with mature trees.

However, there is certainly some dynamism in the Essex population as changes in range have been noted during the 1990s. A range expansion has occurred into the less well-wooded areas around our coastline where it appears to utilise coastal thickets and shelterbelts. Thus, there have been an increasing number of records from along the Stour, Colne, Blackwater and Crouch Estuaries, as well as from the northeast coast around St Osyth and Little Clacton and Dengie. Expansion has also occurred into the Lea Valley, probably aided by the provision of nest boxes (*EBR* 1993). In contrast, a decline, first noted in the early 1990s in the Upminster/Collier Row area, has resulted in the disappearance of the species from the area, with no reports since 1994; however, the species has spread onto nearby Cranham Marshes in recent years. Circumstantial evidence suggests that there have also been reductions at many traditional sites from the late 1990s, though this might simply reflect a reduced level of reporting since the conclusion of the Atlas survey work. Alternatively, these traditionally favoured areas may no longer be capable of supporting previous densities so that juveniles have been forced to explore marginal habitats. Research on this matter is required. National CBC (England) data for the period 1977–2002 suggested a slight population decline, with recent BBS (England) figures showing a 1% decline from 1994–2003.

Tawny Owl populations are regulated through the medium of territorial behaviour (Population Trends). The comparative stability until recently of Tawny Owl populations compared with those of other British owls can probably be attributed to their longer lifespan, their ability to cope better with severe winter weather and their broader diet. Despite being generally sedentary, at least in Essex, they have shown an ability to expand into previously uninhabited territory. However, the availability of habitat into which juveniles can disperse is the most important factor regulating the increase and spread of the species. Juveniles, which cannot set up territories soon after they disperse in August, tend not to survive.

An individual of the uncommon 'grey phase' was noted at Great Braxted on 18th November 1994. Grey birds become increasingly common further east through the Palearctic.

The Tawny Owl is one of our most sedentary species, almost all national recoveries being found within 10km of the ringing location; only 4–5 movements of more than 50km are reported annually (Toms & Clark 1999). Southern (1954) suggested that as the species survives because of its intimate knowledge of its habitat any movements away would likely result in starvation and death. Essex recoveries are typical with a total of 11 Essex-ringed individuals being found up to five years after ringing, the furthest just 13km from the place of ringing.

There are no immediate threats to the survival of the Tawny Owl in Essex provided there is no significant change in the amount of suitable habitat. The species readily takes to nest boxes and this has allowed it to expand into areas where few natural nesting sites occur. The break-up of large gardens and parkland may, however, present a threat to the species in less rural areas. As early as the mid-1960s, declines were noted in Saffron Walden for this reason (*EBR* 1965). The move into coastal areas may have an effect on Long-eared Owl populations as it is in these areas that most of the small Essex population breeds; Tawny Owls will not tolerate Long-eared Owls in their territories.

Long-eared Owl   *Asio otus*

Uncommon resident, fairly common passage migrant and winter visitor

The Long-eared Owl is a circumpolar Holarctic species that breeds over much of the boreal, temperate and wooded Mediterranean and steppe zones (European Atlas). The species breeds across Eurasia, south to Morocco and the Canaries, the Levant and Japan. Four races are recognised, the nominate *otus* occurring across much of its Old World range. It is primarily a nocturnal species and easily overlooked. In Britain Long-eared Owls have a widespread, if scattered, distribution but appear to have declined in Britain since about 1930, perhaps due to intraspecific competition with the Tawny Owl, which increased during the early years of the 20th century (Historical Atlas). In the north of its range the population is migratory.

Christy considered the Long-eared Owl a "... rather uncommon winter visitor ... It seems once to have been much more common than it is now". He knew of just one breeding record, from around Harwich where the species was considered common. Most of the documented records, from the first at Newport in 1829, involved 1–2 birds invariably shot. However, at Alresford prior to 1880 about 15 were noted roosting in a fir tree "... which when tapped noiselessly fly away, but return again when it is all quiet". In 1831, the species was considered "... not uncommon in the wooded districts of Hadleigh and Hockley..." whilst in

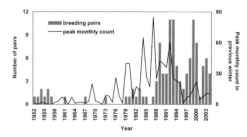

Breeding pairs of Long-eared Owls and peak monthly counts in previous winter from 1952-2004

the late 19th century it was "not rare" at Danbury and in Epping Forest it "... had been obtained several times and would multiply rapidly if it were not so frequently destroyed by gamekeepers". Long-eared Owls are well known for their unusual calls; one of Christy's correspondents noted that prior to the mid-1860s "... the screams of one of these birds caused the country people to regard as haunted a certain wood at Hockley". As the species is generally quiet outside the breeding season, nesting may have occurred at this location.

Glegg described the Long-eared Owl as "... the least common of the five owls which breed in Essex, where it is a scarce bird ... whose numbers are increased by winter arrivals". He noted definite breeding records from: Langdon Hills, 1890; Littlebury, 1893; Little Baddow, 1897; Felsted district, 1915, 1916 and 1918; Tolleshunt D'Arcy, 1925; and two pairs on a marsh north of the Blackwater in 1926. Rather vague references were also made to breeding at Harwich, Alresford and Birch.

Since 1950, the increase in observer coverage has steadily improved our knowledge of the status of this extremely secretive species in Essex. However, it almost certainly remains under-recorded, at least as a breeding species. Long-eared

Atlas	Survey Area	% of 10km squares or tetrads in which	
		bred/probably bred	possibly bred or present
First National 10km	Essex	10.5	10.5
Second National 10km	Essex	12.3	3.5
First London Tetrad	Met. Essex	0.0	0.5
Second London Tetrad	Met. Essex	1.5	2.5
Essex Tetrad	Essex	1.2	0.7

Summary of results of Atlas surveys for Long-eared Owls

Owls show a preference for conifer plantations, very few of which have been planted in Essex. Hudson & Pyman mentioned several records of 1–2 pairs nesting at Tiptree and Great Horkesley around 1930 and 1–2 pairs near Tollesbury in the 1930s and 1940s. They also list single pairs at Canewdon between 1950 and 1960 (until the site was bulldozed), Althorne between 1957 and 1963 and in the Hockley/Althorne area in 1961 and perhaps other years around this time. An unsuccessful breeding attempt took place at Fingringhoe Wick in 1959, the female being accidentally shot off the nest during a crow shoot.

Cox added just two further confirmed breeding records prior to 1980, at Creaksea in 1967 and East Tilbury in 1973. Additionally, a pair was found at a site in west Essex on 11th June 1970; one was noted carrying food at Hanningfield on 9th June 1979; and eight were present at another site in August 1979. Subsequently, it was learnt that a pair bred on Horsey Island from 1979–84 at least. From around 1980 breeding appeared to become annual, with the number of confirmed records climbing steadily through the 1980s to peak at a minimum of 11 pairs in 1992 and 1993. These peak years coincided with the Essex Atlas survey period and suggested that a fairly representative breeding population would have been around 8–12 pairs (Essex Atlas) and probably remains at that level, or perhaps slightly higher to this day. Breeding numbers declined slightly after 1993, but once again rose to a peak of 11 pairs in 1999, five in Metropolitan Essex and four at one small area of inland grazing marsh. Almost all of the breeding sites are along the coast or close to water with some being in the vicinity of the large winter roosts. There does not,

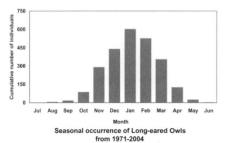

Seasonal occurrence of Long-eared Owls from 1971-2004

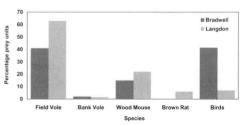

Summary in % prey units of two studies of Long-eared Owl pellets (Smith 1980, Ekins & Steward 1994)

however, appear to be a clear correlation between the number of breeding pairs and peak monthly counts during the previous winter. Indeed, breeding densities are determined by the abundance of rodents (Mikkola 1983) and so suitable habitat and thus prey availability are probably the main factors affecting the overall population level.

Long-eared and Tawny Owls are known to have similar ecological requirements and thus competition between the two seems probable (Mikkola 1983); this may explain the fact that many Long-eared Owl breeding records come from areas in which Tawny Owls are generally absent.

Hudson & Pyman recorded a maximum annual count of five, in 1958, three being autumn migrants. From 1970, wintering and passage numbers increased, although to what extent greater observer coverage had to play in this trend is unclear. Periodically, numbers of Long-eared Owls invade the country during winter, such influxes being attributed to crashes in the number of microtine rodents on the Continental breeding grounds (Winter Atlas). These influxes tend to follow a 3–5 year cycle that follows rodent population levels and this is evident in the numbers recorded annually. Long-eared Owls are well known for their communal roosting activities and will use the same location over a number of winters. The majority of roosts have been found in dense hedgerows or thickets with plenty of undergrowth, although some have been in conifer plantations (Cox).

The former roost sites at Clacton-on-Sea and Colchester are now, respectively, under a housing estate and a sports complex (Cox). Many of the roosts are close to or near the coast, although large roosts have occurred well inland. It may be that the smaller numbers noted inland are simply due to less extensive observer coverage than on the coast.

Long-eared Owl numbers build up to a mid-winter peak after which they decline steadily, with few left by the end of March.

Two studies have analysed the contents of Long-eared Owl pellets at sites in Essex, at a Bradwell roost in early 1977 and early 1979 (Smith 1980) and Langdon Hills in 1992/93 (Ekins & Steward 1994). Comparisons of the results of each survey revealed a considerable difference in the proportion of bird prey taken at each site. At Bradwell, the main bird prey species were: House Sparrow (5–13%); Reed Bunting (0–5%); Skylark (5–7%); and Greenfinch (5%). More unusual species included Brambling and Tree Sparrow. Some bird remains still retained the rings that the first author had placed on them in earlier years. At Langdon, House Sparrow (3.3%) was the most common bird, followed by Song Thrush/Redwing (1.6%). The proportion of birds at Langdon was at the time the lowest of any British studies analysed (Ekins & Steward 1994), whilst those at Bradwell were similar to two other coastal sites in Kent and Yorkshire.

Populations of Long-eared Owls breeding above 50° N are largely migratory with the proportion decreasing further south and west within the breeding range (BWP). National recoveries have shown that the majority that reach Britain are from Scandinavia and the Low Countries, whilst most local breeding birds remain in the natal area during winter. Three Essex recoveries illustrate this pattern with singles from Norway and Denmark recovered at Little Sampford on 5th November 1975 and Bowers Gifford in January 1987; another ringed in a Wickford garden in January 1990 was killed by a car in Germany in April 1991. Single birds ringed in Cambridgeshire, Suffolk (two) and Kent have also been recovered in Essex. A measure of site fidelity is shown by the species: five birds trapped on Foulness in early 1992 had been ringed there in previous years.

Long-eared Owls appear to have increased as an Essex breeding species over the last two decades or so. It is, however, likely to remain a very scarce breeding species as Tawny Owls, which remain widespread throughout Essex, would limit numbers where they came into direct competition. It is possible that the increase in rough areas of grassland in coastal areas as a result of various environmental improvement schemes may increase the availability of prey and boost the species' chances of spreading further into these areas where the Tawny Owl is generally scarce. Whether the apparently recent spread of the Tawny Owl into such areas is going to affect the Long-eared Owl remains to be seen.

	Peak count	Winter
Harwich	27	1983/84
Parkeston	19	1991/92
Langenhoe	16	1991/92
Colchester	15	1975/76
Pitsea	15	1983/84
Dunton	15	1992/93
Principal Long-eared Owl roosts		

Short-eared Owl

Asio flammeus

Locally common migrant and winter visitor: rare breeder

Amber List

The monotypic Short-eared Owl is principally a Holarctic species with a circumpolar range. In Europe, it is found chiefly in tundra, boreal and temperate zones as well as some northern mountain regions (European Atlas). The majority of the

European populations occur in northern latitudes. Central European populations have declined during the 20th century probably due to drainage of wet grasslands and marshland. In Britain, most are found in Wales or upland areas from Staffordshire northwards with small pockets in south and southeast England (Second National Atlas). Population levels vary dramatically from year to year across the species' range in response to food supply resulting in periodic invasions further south every 3–5 years in line with the vole population cycle (*BWP*). Northernmost birds are generally migratory.

The Short-eared Owl has one of the earliest written references of any Essex bird: Holinshed in his *Chronicles* (1587) noted "About Hallowtide last past [1580], in the marshes of Danesey Hundred, in a place called Southminster, in the countie of Essex, a strange thing happened; there sodainlie appeared an infinite multitude of mice, which, overwhelming the whole earth in the said marshes, did sheare and knaw the grasse by the rootes, spoyling and tainting the same with their venimous tetth, in such sort that the cattell which grazed thereon were smitten with a murreine, and died thereof; whoch vermine by policie of man could not be destroyed till at the last it came to passe that there flocked together all about the same marishes such a number of Owles as all the shire was not able to yeeld; whereby the marsh-holders were shortly delivered from the vexation of the said mice". Fuller (1662) described a similar invasion of Rochford and Foulness Hundreds in 1648 and there was another at Southminster in 1660 (Childrey 1662).

Short-eared Owls appear to have always been scarce breeders in Essex, despite Christy's assertion, made without any clear evidence, that the species probably formerly bred abundantly. He gave just one breeding

Atlas	Survey Area	% of 10km squares or tetrads in which	
		bred/probably bred	possibly bred or present
First National 10km	Essex	7.0	7.0
Second National 10km	Essex	3.5	7.0
First London Tetrad	Met. Essex	0.0	0.0
Second London Tetrad	Met. Essex	0.5	1.5
Essex Tetrad	Essex	0.4	1.0

Summary of results of Atlas surveys for Short-eared Owls

record, on "Walton Marshes" in 1889 where it may have bred also in 1884. Otherwise, he detailed several winter records, many from the northwest including 13 at Great Chesterford on 27th November 1879, 12 at Littlebury and seven at Rickling on January 18th 1881. No large counts were noted along the coast, although at Harwich "It was especially numerous there during the week ending Nov. 4th 1876, when a great many were shot". Glegg described the species in a similar vein but added a few further breeding records. The Walton birds continued to breed until 1897 when the sea encroached on the breeding site, whilst single pairs nested at: Bradwell (1898); Northey Island (1896); Mundon (1910); Burnham-on-Crouch (1921); and Langenhoe (1926).

Since 1950, instances of breeding have become more regular, although no more than three pairs (in 1965 and 1968) have been confirmed breeding in any one year with 0–1 typical, and there have been no definite breeding records since 1994. Short-eared Owls require extensive areas of open ground, substantial populations of animal prey and freedom from persistent disturbance by ground predators including man (Second National Atlas). Most breeding records have, therefore, come from coastal locations, typically in areas of rank grassland or grazing marsh (Essex Atlas). There is no apparent correlation between the slight increase in breeding numbers and the increase in autumn/winter visitors seen since the 1970s. Breeding success is linked to high vole populations with breeding unlikely to occur in poor vole years. Foulness and adjacent islands have been the only regular breeding sites for Short-eared Owls. Here access restrictions and the elusive nature of the species when breeding means that perhaps only a fraction of nesting attempts is recorded. A total of three confirmed breeding attempts in 1968 (two successfully and one destroyed) is the most in any one year. Otherwise, single pairs have been confirmed breeding, although not always successfully, in 15 years since 1950. Hamford Water has occasionally held the odd successful pair (three in 1965 and two in 1989). Confirmed breeding has also been noted at Fingringhoe Wick, Bradwell and Burnham-on-Crouch.

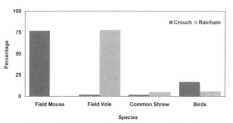

Summary showing percentage of various species found in two studies of Short-eared Owl pellets (Smith 1981, Dennis 1986)

Annual numbers of confirmed breeding pairs (1954-2004) of Short-eared Owls and peak monthly counts from the previous winter (1970/71-2003/04)

Total annual numbers of autumn/winter visitors varies significantly in response to rodent population levels and peak monthly counts since 1971 illustrate the cyclical nature of Short-eared Owl numbers occurring in Essex. In winter, Short-eared Owls are highly nomadic and individuals may traverse several 10km squares in the course of a winter (Winter Atlas). Thus the total number recorded in any one season is difficult to estimate.

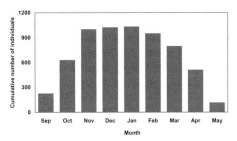

Seasonal occurrence of Short-eared Owls from 1971-2004

Short-eared Owls begin to arrive as early as August; possibly many are locally dispersing breeders. In some years numbers recorded in autumn (and spring) exceed those present in winter, suggesting that regular passage occurs.

After the autumn passage numbers usually build to a peak during December and January. In general, the highest winter numbers occur after a strong autumn passage. After January, numbers generally decline, although it is not unusual for March numbers to exceed those in February as passage birds return through Essex to their breeding grounds.

In winter, Short-eared Owls are found principally in estuarine locations where there is plenty of rank grass. They are opportunist feeders, taking whatever prey is easily available. Thus, whilst their chief food item is known to be the Field Vole, which was found to be the case at Rainham (Dennis 1986), a study of pellets collected along the Crouch Estuary during early 1980 showed that the principal prey item there was the Wood Mouse (Smith 1981), perhaps selected here because of the nearby railway embankment over which the species was most regularly observed. More unusual prey species found in the Crouch pellets were Dunlin and Bullfinch.

When populations of rodents become extremely high (as in the 'plagues' of old), owls will gather to exploit this temporary abundance (Winter Atlas). Thus counts of ten or more have been noted in some years with regularity from its most favoured localities: Hamford Water; Langenhoe; East Mersea; the northern side of the Blackwater from Goldhanger eastward; Dengie; Foulness; and Rainham. The largest single counts have been 19 at Tollesbury Wick on 26th November 2002 and 18 in the Langenhoe/East Mersea area during December 1991. In addition, there were 17 on Dengie on 13th December 1970 and 16 at Old Hall on 31st December 1981. The number of double-figure counts peak in November and December, suggesting that as areas of abundant prey become exhausted, individuals disperse to other areas to hunt.

Although found to use communal roosts in other nearby counties, Short-eared Owl roosts have not been reported from Essex.

Inland records are regular and normally involve 1–2 individuals at any locality. However, there were 8–10 at Walthamstow in early November 1982.

There have been just three ringing recoveries involving Essex, although two were reported just weeks after ringing, a few kilometres distant. The only distant movement involved a nestling ringed on Foulness on 4th June 1961 and recovered on 25th December 1961 at Handzame, West-vlaanderen, Belgium, an atypical movement for a British-bred bird, most of which exhibit south to southwesterly movements in autumn (Migration Atlas). Observations of birds from fishing boats and arriving off the sea in autumn are strongly suggestive of a foreign origin of some Short-eared Owls, a fact confirmed nationally by the recovery of individuals ringed in Scandinavia and the Low Countries.

The Short-eared Owl is a very rare and localised breeder in Essex. Fortunately, much of its favoured breeding and wintering habitat is already managed sympathetically by conservation organisations. It is possible that the area of such land may increase in forthcoming years as greater emphasis is placed on 'greener' farming methods. Significant breeding population increases are, however, unlikely and the Short-eared Owl is likely to remain one of the county's rarest breeding species.

Sponsored by Tony Moverley

Tengmalm's Owl   *Aegolius funereus*

Vagrant: one 19th century record

Tengmalm's Owls breed throughout the conifer zone of the northern Hemisphere. In Europe, where the species is represented by the nominate race *funereus*, populations extend as far south as the mountains of southern Europe. The nearest populations to Britain are in Belgium. Northern populations are occasionally eruptive.

| 1877 | Barking Road, Poplar | End of January | One killed |

Christy recounted that "... some boys noticed a bird in a tree near the iron bridge in the Barking Road, Poplar, which on being disturbed was soon killed ... The sex was not ascertained". Glegg considered that one shot in 1910 near Clare, Suffolk, but just in Essex was "... almost certainly..." a Little Owl and not a Tengmalm's Owl.

Nationally, this owl was recorded 49 times up to 1958 but only seven times since and five of those were on the Orkney Islands (Cottridge & Vinicombe 1996), the last in 1986.

(European) Nightjar   *Caprimulgus europaeus*

Rare passage migrant and summer visitor   **Red List**

The Nightjar is a Palearctic species that breeds from Britain east to China and Mongolia. Its range includes much of Continental Europe, although it is absent from large areas of northern Europe as well as mountain ranges and intensively farmed areas. The nominate race *europaeus* occurs in north and central Europe, east through north-central Asia to Lake Baikal (*HBW*). Declines that have probably been due to habitat change were first noted in Britain in the early 1900s but became more pronounced during the 1950s: the population had fallen to just 2,000 males by 1981, but has subsequently increased to 4,500. Only about 50% of the species' original pre-1970s range has, however, been re-colonised, the species' stronghold now being southern and southeast England and East Anglia. West European populations winter in Africa south of the Sahara.

Atlas	Survey Area	% of 10km squares or tetrads in which	
		bred/probably bred	possibly bred or present
First National 10km	Essex	7.0	10.5
Second National 10km	Essex	1.8	3.5
First London Tetrad	Met. Essex	1.5	2.0
Second London Tetrad	Met. Essex	0.0	0.0
Essex Tetrad	Essex	0.2	0.1

Summary of results of Atlas surveys for Nightjars

The earliest documented Essex record dates back to the early 18th century when Albin (1731–38) observed "I have seen them in Epping Forest and divers other places". Christy described the species as a "... regular summer visitor, but very sparingly distributed, except in a few spots which are peculiarly suited to its habits such as Epping Forest, Ongar Park Wood and the woods and commons around Danbury, Tiptree, Warley and elsewhere". Nightjars were said to abound amongst the heaths and commons around Danbury and Little Baddow and on Tiptree Heath. Other locations he mentioned included Sudbury where it was "rather rare"; Harwich, "fairly common and breeds"; Orsett, "not common"; Colchester and Paglesham, "common"; Saffron Walden, "uncommon"; Chesterford, "breeds commonly"; and Hazeleigh Woods and Littlebury, "breeds every year". To Glegg, the Nightjar nested "... not commonly, and locally, throughout the county", with Epping Forest perhaps its stronghold. Declines had been noted in Wanstead Park, Stanway and the Forest of Waltham, perhaps the first signs of a general decline across Essex as heathland habitats declined.

In the early 1950s, a countywide survey revealed no more than 18 pairs, located mainly from Epping Forest northeast to Danbury Common, with small outlying populations in the Hadleigh area in the south, the Roman River Valley in the northeast and Strethall/ Littlebury in the northwest. Cox suggested that the population at this time was in the region of 20–25 pairs. The *EBR* 1954 remarked that the species "... has obviously decreased to a marked extent over the last 10–20 years". The decline through the 1950s and 1960s was rapid with almost complete extinction as a breeding species by the early 1970s. A minor revival in fortune in the late 1970s and the early 1980s saw 1–2 pairs present but the recovery was short-lived and,

	1950s	1960s	1970s	1980s	1990s	2000s
Tiptree/Birch/Layers	3	1	0	1	1	0
Hadleigh area	2	0	0	0	0	0
Danbury/Lt Baddow	2	3	1	0	0	0
Ingatestone/Mill Gn/Margaretting	6	2	1	0	0	0
N. Weald/Ongar	3	2	2	2	0	0
Brentwood/Warley CP/Thorndon CP	6	2	0	0	0	0
Northwest Essex	2	0	0	0	0	0
Epping area	3	1	2	0	0	0
Metropolitan Essex*	0	0	0	0	1	0
*Localities withheld	0	0	0	0	1	0

Summary of highest counts of breeding/churring male Nightjars from principal breeding areas from 1950-2004

other than single pairs present in 1989, 1991 and 1996, the Nightjar has been lost as an Essex breeding species. Since 1950, breeding has been confirmed on just 13 occasions, all but two prior to 1989. However, proof of breeding is difficult to obtain and it is likely that many more of the pairs known to be present bred successfully. Rarely, single birds continue to be recorded in suitable breeding habitat, although two at different sites in 2004 was the highest since the 1980s, the species being a less than annual visitor through the 1990s.

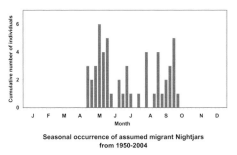

Seasonal occurrence of assumed migrant Nightjars
from 1950-2004

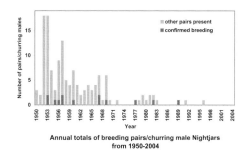

Annual totals of breeding pairs/churring male Nightjars
from 1950-2004

In Britain, Nightjars use heathland and other unimproved ground for nesting, although more recently many clear-felled conifer plantations have also been utilised. Unfortunately, due to destruction and scrub encroachment there are very few remaining areas of heathland in Essex, nor are there any substantial areas of conifer plantation. However, given the recent increases in Nightjar populations in southern England it is possible that breeding may occur again, although any population will be small given the habitat limitations. Positive management strategies for many of the relict heathlands in Essex that have been put in hand to check and grub out invasive Birch scrub, for example Tiptree, Danbury and Galleywood Commons, may entice the odd pair back, although local opposition to 'woodland destruction' has occurred.

Given its crepuscular behaviour, it is not surprising that few are noted on migration. Individuals considered to be migrants were noted in most years up to 1970 and included many churring males noted at sites for one date during April and May; documentation of migrants during the 1950s was probably incomplete. Up to four have been reported in any one year, all singles apart from a remarkable record of three together at Orsett on 27th September 1986.

Nightjars have a habit of turning up in rather unusual locations such as on a fishing boat 10km off Clacton-on-Sea on 17th September 1969, on a postal sorting office ledge at Canning Town on 19th June 1979 and in the Colne Point Little Tern colony in broad daylight on 30th May 1983. The majority of recent records have come from the northeast, although there is no particular bias to coastal localities. Extreme dates since 1950 have been 23rd April, in both Epping Forest in 1970 (one also on 2nd April 1926) and Fuller Street in 2004, and 1st October at Althorne in 1968. Christy mentioned one in a wood at Roxwell during the winter of 1881/82.

Sponsored in memory of Tariq Watson

White-throated Needletail   *Hirundapus caudacutus*

Vagrant: one 19th century record

The White-throated Needletail breeds mainly in southern Siberia and central Asia, with the highly migratory nominate race *caudacutus* breeding in central and eastern Siberia, northern Mongolia and China and wintering in Australia.

1846	Great Horkesley	6th–8th July, when shot

This was the first British record of this long-distance migrant. Christy recounted that "It was shot about 9p.m. on the 8th of this month [July 1846] by a farmer's son … in the parish of Great Horkesley, about four miles from Colchester. He saw it first on the evening of the 6th. He tells me it occasionally flew to a great height, [and] was principally engaged in hawking for flies over a small wood and neighbouring trees. Being only wounded, it cried very much as it fell, and when he took it up, clung so tightly to some clover … as to draw some stalks from the ground." Messrs Newman, Yarrell, E. Doubleday and W. R. Fisher examined the specimen. After passing into the private collection of the Catchpool family, it was donated to the Chelmsford and Essex Museum by the family in 1919, where it remains on prominent display (Accession No. D7003). Christy referred to another possible specimen apparently preserved by a bird-stuffer from Leyton; nothing further was known about it, however.

There have only been seven subsequent records nationally, all occurring between late May and late July, with five of these since 1983, four from the Orkney or Shetland Islands (Cottridge & Vinicombe 1996).

(Common) Swift

Apus apus

Common summer resident and passage migrant

The Swift is widely distributed throughout the Palearctic from northern Africa, right across Europe and east to Mongolia and northern China, occurring as far as 70°N in Norway. The species is represented in Europe by the nominate race *apus*. In Britain, Swifts are widely distributed, although it is commonest in the warmer and drier south and east (Second National Atlas). All populations winter in Africa, mostly south of the Equator (European Atlas).

The status of the Swift in Essex has probably changed very little over the last 150 years or so. Christy observed that the Swift was "A common summer visitor in all parts of the county, breeding wherever there are suitable nest holes in either ancient or modern buildings". Glegg, Hudson & Pyman and Cox all described the species in much the same way, as a common summer visitor and passage migrant. None of the authors were able to provide any quantitative or qualitative data and even today, both locally and nationally, little is available that have allowed population trends to be monitored.

Originally, nesting locations would have been in crevices found in trees, cliffs and caves but natural nest sites have never been reported in Essex. All nesting locations are in buildings where there is a preference for those where the nest holes are 5m or more above the ground. Thus, the species' breeding distribution across Essex is tied entirely to the built environment. In many areas it is often only the ancient parish church that provides suitable nesting localities, provided the construction at the eaves of the roofs allows entry to the top of the very wide masonry walls. However, the design of most Essex church towers provides few breeding opportunities.

Swifts disappeared from the centre of London by the early 20th century, perhaps as a result of air pollution, but after WWII the species returned to breed, possibly helped by the positive effects of the Clean Air Acts (Historical Atlas), although this may be an oversimplification as Swifts feed many kilometres from their

Atlas	Survey Area	% of 10km squares or tetrads in which	
		bred/probably bred	possibly bred or present
First National 10km	Essex	91.2	7.0
Second National 10km	Essex	87.7	12.3
First London Tetrad	Met. Essex	28.5	35.5
Second London Tetrad	Met. Essex	49.0	49.5
Essex Tetrad	Essex	27.5	42.2

Summary of results of Atlas surveys for Swifts

nest sites. The First London Atlas survey located the species in 64% of Essex tetrads, but breeding was confirmed in only 28.5%. The Second London Atlas found Swifts in 98.5% of tetrads with breeding confirmed in 49% and suggested an increase along the Thames. Little change in distribution occurred between the two National Atlases. The Essex Atlas survey found the species to be widespread with records in 69.7% of all tetrads but with breeding in just 27.5%. The distribution not surprisingly showed a marked bias to Metropolitan Essex and other built-up areas.

Subsequent random observations during the 1990s have suggested declines in some areas but a sustained study of a large population would be required to confirm trends, although the BBS (England) Index declined by 29% between 1994 and 2003. Swifts are extremely difficult to census and, as they may not breed until four years old (Perrins 1971), the presence of screaming flocks, which may contain non-breeders, is not a good indicator of the breeding population. Only in Chelmsford and surroundings during 1955–57 was an attempt to estimate Swift populations made, with a total of 242 pairs noted in Chelmsford and ten surrounding parishes (180 in Chelmsford Borough). Swifts may use nesting sites for many years. Thus colonies at Collier Row and Writtle are known to have existed for at least 50 years.

Exceptionally large gatherings have been recorded from time to time at Abberton and Hanningfield. Such gatherings often occur during cool weather when insect numbers, away from large water bodies, may be very low. Flocks of up to 10,000 have been recorded regularly with 16 reported in excess of this figure. At Abberton the largest counts have been: around 50,000 on 21st May 1987, 12th May 1995 and 22nd June 1996; and 20,000 on 9th May 1968 and 26th July 1981. At Hanningfield, peak counts have been: 80,000, an Essex record, on 24th May 1978; 60,000 on 18th June 1991; 50,000 on 12th May 1995; and 30,000 on 26th May 1979 and 11th June 1991. Many of the May flocks probably involve migrants. However, some counts occurred at the height of the breeding season and flocks of several thousand are a regular mid-summer feature at Abberton and Hanningfield. Such gatherings must involve birds that have travelled considerable distances from breeding colonies to feed (Cox), although many may be wandering non-breeders. However, it is also known that Swifts will make large weather movements in Europe during the breeding season, involving thousands or even tens of thousands of birds (*BWP*). Swifts will often move around a depression to avoid rain, with birds flying into the wind to get to the warm sector in the least time. Thus, large numbers may appear quite suddenly at the main reservoirs and, once the cold front passes, they move off; perhaps European breeders are involved in the large mid-summer influxes.

Away from Abberton and Hanningfield, coastal movements are regularly noted throughout summer and early autumn; the largest involved 8,000 that flew west over Bradwell on 26th July 1981. Autumn movements of Swifts through Britain are generally in a south to southwesterly direction

The rapid onset of unseasonably cold weather can cause Swifts great difficulty in finding food and maintaining sufficient energy to remain in flight. Glegg noted that at the end of June 1835 "... on a cold wet day a number of Swifts stupefied by the cold clung to the cliffs at The Naze ... In some places they were settled one upon another, four or five deep, and we literally took them up in handfuls, five or six together. So numerous were they, we could have probably caught some hundreds". Likewise at the same time at Harwich "A large cluster [was] seen hanging to the waterspout of Harwich church. Some boys were able, with poles, to knock them down, and many were caught". In recent years, cold weather at Abberton has been observed to cause Swifts to fly very low over the causeways and collisions have occurred with the wire fencing and even moving vehicles.

Cox noted that only a small minority of Swifts appear before the end of April. Since the mid-1980s, however, April records have occurred with increasing regularity. An exceptionally early individual was at The Naze from 3rd–8th February 1967, at a time of unusually mild weather. Otherwise, the earliest was at Leigh-on-Sea on 2nd April 1992, whilst singles were at Abberton and KGV on 9th April 1994.

Most British Swifts have departed for their winter quarters by the end of August. Indeed, many are in northern Afrotropical regions by mid-August (*BWP*). Thus October records are exceptional and November records particularly rare and are normally associated with a warm southerly airflow. Glegg noted the first in November: "... two from Essex on 6th November 1912" and this remained the latest Essex record for 64 years. Other November records have been: 1st, Clacton in 1976; 2nd, Foulness in 1975 and Chalkwell in 2004; 3rd, Frinton-on-Sea in 1961 (present for a week) and The Naze in 1981; 5th, The Naze in 1975; 6th, Abberton in 1979; 7th, Black Notley in 1976; 8th, Eight Ash Green in 1991; 11th, Bradwell in 1984 and Wrabness in 1988; 15th, Black Notley in 1986; and 19th, Thundersley in 1986. The latest county record, however, was one at Bradwell on the quite exceptional date of 4th December 1994.

Swifts are long-lived birds, the British longevity record being 16 years. An adult ringed at Chigwell Row on 17th June 1967 was recovered at Wakefield, West Yorkshire, on 27th May 1976 making it at least ten years old. Swifts are also known to display site fidelity, but only one old Essex record illustrates this, one ringed as an adult at Shenfield on 26th June 1927 being caught on the same nest on 14th May 1928. Two caught at St Osyth boating lake on 9th July 1955 were reported from north Suffolk and Norfolk later in the same month, illustrating the distances travelled even during the breeding season, although both may have been non-breeders. Three trapped at the same location in July 1956 were noted at Falkirk, Stirlingshire, in May 1958, Water Orton, West Midlands, in May 1963 and Boston, Lincolnshire, in July 1963. The only Essex-ringed Swift to be recovered abroad was ringed at Epping as a nestling on 15th July 1984 and found at Marrakech, Morocco, on 21st October 1987.

Aberrant Swifts have been reported from time to time, some looking remarkably similar to vagrant swift species. Individuals with various combinations of white throat crescents, white upper breast and white rumps have all been noted.

At 2200hrs on 9th May 1965 at Kirby-le-Soken a Swift was caught, which was clutching the breast of a Starling. The Starling was unharmed apart from losing a few feathers and the Swift flew off strongly after release the next day.

Probably the biggest single threat to Swifts is the loss of suitable breeding locations. The increased interest in the conservation of ancient buildings, particularly churches, and the modernisation of the ageing housing stock have seen many colonies destroyed by insensitive repair works. However, the Concern for Swifts group has been trying to influence architects and surveyors involved in the repair of such buildings. At St John's Church, Great Clacton, an adapted version of the group's Swift box design has had some success in retaining a breeding population despite major roof repairs during the late 1990s. Increased public awareness and the willingness to tolerate 'birds in the roof space' will be vital in ensuring that further sites are not lost.

Pallid Swift   *Apus pallidus*

Vagrant: one record

The Pallid Swift has a predominantly Western Palearctic breeding range, which also extends to west Asia and the Middle East. The nominate race *pallidus* occurs throughout the Western Palearctic. The species winters mainly in Africa.

2001	Cudmore Grove CP	18th October

There were just ten British records prior to 1998, but major influxes in 1999 and 2001 took the total to 45 by 2004 (BBRC 2005). The increase is probably due to greater observer awareness. Many of the records have been particularly late or early in the year for swifts and some previous February/March and October/November records assigned to Common Swifts may perhaps have referred to this species. Typically, this individual was a short-stayer (Thompson 2003).

Alpine Swift   *Apus melba*

Very rare passage migrant: 17 records

The Alpine Swift is an Old World species with a scattered distribution across southern and east Africa and Madagascar, to the Mediterranean, across the northern edge of the Alps and east through Asia Minor to the Himalayas, India and Sri Lanka. In Europe, the species is represented by the nominate race *melba,* which winters in west and east Africa.

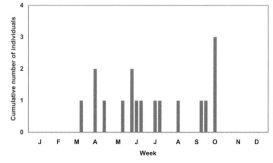

1871	near Colchester	8th June	
1930	Dovercourt	17th–19th August	
1955	St Osyth	9th June	
1961	The Naze	24th September	
1970	Great Maplestead	25th May	Picked up dead
1976	The Naze	9th October	
1977	The Naze	9th October	
1980	Walthamstow	21st June	
1985	Colne Point	10th April	
1990	Gunners Park	22nd March	
1991	Dovercourt	11th July	
1993	Fingringhoe Wick	13th June	
	Bradwell	19th September	Adult, freshly dead
1995	Roman River Valley	10th April	
2001	Hooks Marsh	13th October	
2002	Mundon	20th July	
2003	Fairlop CP	27th April	

In addition, Christy referred to one that was said to have occurred at Romford prior to 1833 but the reference is extremely vague. The Alpine Swift is an annual visitor to Britain with 565 records to the end of 2004 (BBRC 2005), averaging 10–15 individuals per annum. All bar one of the Essex records have been brief fly-over records; a long-stayer appears well overdue. The increase in recent years is probably due to greater observer coverage, although there has been a range extension along its northern limits in France (European Atlas). Nationally, most occur from April–June, with a few throughout summer and a second peak in late September–early October; Essex records fall neatly into this pattern.

Spring records probably relate to northward migrating birds overshooting their breeding grounds, whilst those in autumn are presumably dispersing adults and juveniles.

Seasonal occurrence of Alpine Swifts from 1871-2004

(Common) Kingfisher

Alcedo atthis

Resident and passage migrant

Amber List

The Kingfisher is an extremely widespread species that is found throughout the Palearctic from the Atlantic coast to Japan, including northern Africa, the entire Indo-Malayan region and Papua New Guinea. In Europe, it is absent only from Iceland and some Mediterranean islands. Of the seven races, two occur in Europe: *ispida* throughout much of north and central Europe and the nominate race *atthis* in south and east Spain, east to Bulgaria (*HBW*). Kingfishers require relatively shallow and slow-moving freshwater with thriving populations of small fish and vertical banks of fairly soft material in which to excavate their nest burrows (Second National Atlas). In Essex, the species breeds in the banks of rivers and streams, but readily takes to a range

Atlas	Survey Area	% of 10km squares or tetrads in which	
		bred/probably bred	possibly bred or present
First National 10km	Essex	77.2	15.8
Second National 10km	Essex	56.1	19.3
First London Tetrad	Met. Essex	11.5	8.0
Second London Tetrad	Met. Essex	23.5	26.0
Essex Tetrad	Essex	14.6	20.0

Summary of results of Atlas surveys for Kingfishers

of man-made structures, including ponds and gravel-pits. Outside the breeding season it ranges more widely to other water bodies and particularly to the coast, which provides a final refuge during severe winters. Northernmost populations are generally migratory.

Christy considered the Kingfisher "A resident throughout the county … though nowhere common". Nationally the species was in decline from around the 1860s due to intense hunting pressure, both because of its perceived threat to fish stocks and high demand from bird stuffers: every schoolboy attempted to kill one for his collection (Historical Atlas). However, by the 1890s a general recovery had begun, perhaps aided by the Wild Bird Protection Acts. This increase would appear to have occurred in Essex too, as Glegg described the species as "… a common resident throughout the county". Two records, if representative, suggest that Kingfisher numbers were higher in historical times than they are today, a fact noted in other counties such as Norfolk (Taylor *et al.* 1999). During the severe weather of December 1890 to January 1891, many were killed around Colchester and just one taxidermist received no fewer than 50 to preserve in one week, whilst in August 1911, 22 were caught by a collector using a 'kingfisher-net' on a short stretch of the Chingbrook, near Woodford (now developed). Interestingly, every one was heading in a southerly direction.

Kingfisher populations can suffer badly in severe winters as sub-zero temperatures lead to the icing-up of water bodies: being unable to feed, the species rapidly succumbs to the cold. However, the ability to rear up to four broods and seven young means that population recovery can be quite rapid, given a run of mild winters (Morgan & Glue 1977). The earliest *EBR*s documented the recovery of the Essex population from the 1946/47 winter and by 1950/51 it was reckoned to have reached its pre-1946/47 status in most areas. The 1962/63 winter affected this species more than any other in Britain (Dobinson & Richards 1964), with populations reduced by 90% in some areas of the country. In Essex, the population could not even find refuge on the coast as the sea iced over. Consequently, single breeding pairs, at Coggeshall during 1963 and Roxwell in 1964, were the only ones located in the whole county during those two years. The subsequent recovery appeared to be slow, particularly when compared to the rate of recovery after the 1946/47 winter. In southwest Essex and Hertfordshire this slow recovery was linked to high numbers of fish-kills caused by pollutants in streams with low dry-weather flow rates. The relatively low rainfall in Essex meant that pollutants were not being diluted and so apparently ideal nesting and feeding sites were actually unsuitable (Meadows 1972b). Survey work along the Lea from 1967–72 and 1975 located a total of 38 nests, of which 66% were in natural stream banks and 24% in gravel-pits; drainpipes, the bank of a dry road quarry and a hole in a pollarded Oak were also used (Meadows 1972b). The winter of 1978/79 appeared to have had less affect on the population than was expected (*EBR* 1979).

Cox considered that the Kingfisher was a "Recently declined resident", that during the period of the First National Atlas survey perhaps numbered 100 pairs but that "Reports in 1982 … suggest that the current total is much lower". The period 1988–94 saw, in addition to the local and national atlas surveys, two others that provided data on Kingfishers, the NRA river corridor birds surveys and an EWT survey. The NRA survey involved visits in April, May and June to all rivers in Essex east of the Roding. Unfortunately, the severe freeze of February 1991 occurred when only about 30% of the rivers had been surveyed and consequently fewer Kingfishers were recorded on those surveyed after 1991 than before. The EWT survey located a total of 91 breeding/summering pairs with a further 200 reports during summer. Almost 70% were located along rivers, whilst a further 15 (16.5%) were on ponds with the remaining locations used being, in order of importance, gravel-pits, reservoirs, streams and fleets.

The Essex Atlas, which combined the results of the county atlas survey work, the EWT and NRA surveys, showed that the species was widespread throughout Essex, but generally scarce in Tendring district, Dengie, and in the extreme southeast and northwest. At this time the Essex population was considered to be around 200 pairs (Dennis 1990), suggesting a doubling of the population since the 1970s, although increased observer coverage may have been a significant factor in this increase. In Metropolitan Essex, the number of tetrads in which the species were reported rose from 19.5 to 49.5% between the two London Atlas surveys. This increase was probably due to a combination of the population recovering from the effects of the 1962/63 winter and also the cleaning up of the smaller rivers within the London area. However, the two National Atlas surveys confirmed a decline in 10km squares occupied with losses in the south and extreme northwest of Essex.

No comprehensive survey work has been carried out since the end of the Essex Atlas survey period in 1994. Numbers reported annually in the *EBR*s vary considerably from year to year which simply reflects observer coverage with no real trends obvious. Recent BBS (England) data for the period 1994–2003 have suggested a 37% increase in Kingfisher numbers, albeit that the sample population size is small (Raven & Noble 2003). Because of its unfavourable conservation status in Europe, the Kingfisher was been included on the 'Amber List' in the Birds of Conservation Concern in 1996.

In Essex, Kingfishers are found mainly in the upper reaches of the rivers (Dennis 1990); their absence further down could be due to pollution, a lack of suitable habitat or general disturbance. The apparent declines since the early 20th century and the more recent decreases have probably been caused by unsympathetic management and pollution of watercourses, although disturbance due to habitat destruction and river-dredging (e.g. in the construction of the M11 and M25) have also affected populations locally in Essex (Cox). Pollution, which kills fish along long stretches of river, drives out Kingfishers until the fish return or man restocks the stretch affected. More recently, low water levels caused by ever increasing water abstraction and low rainfall, particularly during the late 1980s and early 1990s, have made some areas unsuitable for its principal prey items. Also, some rivers, particularly in the northwest chalk areas, may dry up completely. Leaching of fertilisers and subsequent eutrophication of the watercourses often encourage vegetation growth and this can make fishing difficult for the Kingfisher. More recently, however, pollution control has been improved and more thought has been given to bank-side management. In addition, the trend towards re-instating 'natural' river features such as meanders and ox-bow lakes to slow water flow rates

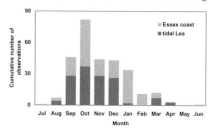

Monthly Kingfisher sightings along the tidal Lea from 1964-72 and the coast (Hamford Water-Mucking Flats) from 1962-70
[adapted from Cox]

and reduce flooding has increased the amount of suitable habitat and these factors may explain why, nationally at least, Kingfisher numbers appear to be increasing.

Few counts have been made along Essex river systems during winter, the only record of note being 22 individuals along an 8km stretch of the Cam between Newport and Great Chesterford in February 1953.

British Kingfishers are generally very sedentary with most recoveries being less than 9km from the nest site. Longer movements occur in autumn when juveniles disperse from breeding areas. Adults will generally remain on territory throughout winter, unless moved on by ice (Winter Atlas). Christy considered that the Kingfisher increased along the coast from September onwards, whilst Glegg noted that local movements affected the species; increases on the coast were, however, not mirrored by decreases inland.

Ringing in Essex has revealed that surprising numbers appear to make local movements along our watercourses, perhaps involving individuals searching for optimum breeding habitat or feeding territories. In autumn 1968, seven were trapped at Abberton, six of them juveniles. None were, however, re-trapped and only two were present at any one time. At Epping Forest SF, 31 were ringed in 1976 and 16 in 1977, whilst 18 were ringed in a garden at Stock in 1981. Nearly 50 ringing recoveries involve Essex, several having been picked up dead during cold weather in December and January. Most have been short-distance movements, although one ringed at Stock in August 1972 was found dead in Lincolnshire, 193km to the northwest, in June 1973.

The most significant recovery, however, related to one ringed at Suttrup, Germany, on 8th June 1990 and found dead on 26th October 1990 at Walthamstow, 581km to the

	Jan	Feb	Mar	Apr	May	Jun	Jul	Aug	Sep	Oct	Nov	Dec
Essex				1		1	5	5	5	1	1	
South England						3	5	2	3		1	
Totals	0	0	0	1	0	4	10	7	8	1	2	0

Month of ringing and origin of Kingfishers ringed in Britain and recovered in Essex

west. This was the first movement to/from Britain involving Germany and is one of very few movements to/from the Continent, the British population being considered almost isolated (Morgan & Glue 1977). Cox had, however, hinted that such a movement from the Continent during October might be expected as

	Jan	Feb	Mar	Apr	May	Jun	Jul	Aug	Sep	Oct	Nov	Dec
Essex	4		2		2		4	3	2		1	1
North England						1						
South England		1		1	1			2	1	2	1	
Totals	4	1	2	1	3	1	4	5	3	2	2	1

Month and location of recovery of Kingfishers ringed in Essex

numbers on the Lea and the coast both peaked in that month. Glegg also mentioned one killed on the Kentish Knock Lightship on 20th March 1904.

The future of the Kingfisher in Essex will depend on the ability of the responsible statutory agencies to ensure correct and sensitive management of our watercourses and the prevention of pollution.

(European) Bee-eater   *Merops apiaster*

Very rare summer visitor and passage migrant: 18 records involving at least 43 individuals

The monotypic Bee-eater breeds throughout southwest, central and eastern Europe, east-central Asia and Asia Minor and northwest Africa and winters in west, east and southern Africa.

1854	Feering Parish	About 21st June	Shot
1954	Felsted	16th August	
1960	Stanford-le-Hope	20th April	Two
1979	Thorndon CP	24th–25th April	Four
1986	Foulness/Bradwell	20th–21st September	Immature
1987	The Naze	5th–6th July	Two adults
	Paglesham	26th–31st August	Two juveniles
1990	Barling	14th July	
1991	Horsey Wade	2nd July	Four
	Bradwell	5th July	Two
	Old Hall	11th July	Five
1992	Holland Haven	15th May	
1996	The Naze	18th August	
1997	Great Maplestead	17th May	
	Great Holland	22nd August	12–15
	Bradwell	24th August	
	Holland Haven	6th September	
2001	The Naze	31st May	

Regrettably, what seems likely to have been a genuine record of a family party of seven at a south Essex gravel-pit between mid-July and 3rd September 1973 was never formally submitted (Cox).

There has been a significant increase in national records since 1973, resulting in the species being dropped from the BBRC Rarities List in 1990. Whilst undoubtedly weather plays a part in displacing Bee-eaters, the species has expanded and spread northward in France since the 1930s and has bred regularly as close as Paris since 1968 and in England twice since 2002. There were 71 nationally in 1991 with 132 in 1997 (Fraser & Rogers 2004). The majority of British records occur in spring and involve overshooting migrants from south European populations, so it is interesting to note the occurrence pattern in Essex.

The three peaks of occurrence probably involve: spring migrants overshooting their breeding areas; failed breeders dispersing from breeding areas; successful breeders and young birds dispersing away from natal areas.

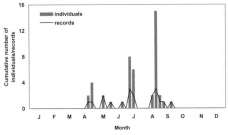

Seasonal occurrence of Bee-eaters from 1854-2004

379

(European) Roller

Coracias garrulus

Vagrant: four records

The Roller breeds from Iberia and North Africa to northwest Iran and southwest Siberia and eastwards to Kashmir and northern Turkmenistan. It is represented in Europe by the nominate race *garrulus*. The species' main distribution lies in Europe west of the Urals. Rollers declined markedly in north and central Europe during the 19th and early 20th centuries and, since the 1970s, this decline has accelerated over much of the rest of its European range (European Atlas). Rollers winter predominantly in the savannah region of east Africa.

1865	Chesterford Park	14th June	Shot
1921	Ramsey	17th June	Hit wires and died later
1968	Great Holland	24th October–18th November	Adult
1976	Beaumont	16th–26th June	

Although there have been 230 British records, the last in 2002 (BBRC 2003), the species has become particularly rare over the last 20 years, currently averaging fewer than two per annum, presumably due to the marked decline in the remaining European populations. Many records have come from east coast counties, suggesting that the individuals reaching Essex are probably from the east, rather than the south. Most occur in late spring and summer. The consistency of the three June dates is remarkable. The individual at Great Holland is one of the latest recorded in the country. Nationally, 1968 and 1976 were two of the best years on record for the species.

The Chesterford individual remains in the Saffron Walden Museum (Accession No. NB208).

Hoopoe

Upupa epops

Scarce passage migrant: at least 194 individuals with 137 since 1950

The Hoopoe is a breeding bird of the temperate and sub-tropical zones from the Canary Islands in the west to the Pacific coast of China and Siberia in the east, as well as much of Africa. In Europe, where the species is represented by the nominate race *epops*, it is predominantly found to the south and southeast with the northern breeding limit being south of a line through northern France to northern Germany and Estonia. In the last it is typically a lowland species, preferring low-intensity farmland and open woodland and woodland edges (European Atlas). Most European Hoopoes winter south of the Sahara.

Merret's statement, "in the New Forrest in Hampshire and in Essexia, sed raro invenitur" in his *Pinax Rerum Naturaluum Britannicarum* of 1667, perhaps suggests that Hoopoes might have been slightly more regular at this time, given the very small number of observers. Albin figured a male, shot at Woodford, in his *Natural History of Birds* (1731–38).

Christy observed that the Hoopoe was "An uncommon, though, it may almost be said, a regular, passing migrant in both spring and autumn". Glegg, however, noted that "The visits of the Hoopoe … are apparently decreasing". His subsequent paper in *Ibis* (1942: 390–434) on the species' national status confirmed that records had declined over the period 1839–1938. In all, Christy and Glegg detailed around 56 records, many of which were shot, 48 between 1821 and 1890 and just eight between 1890 and 1928. Of the dated records, two were in March, 24 in April and May, 13 in August and September and one in October, a similar pattern to today except for the

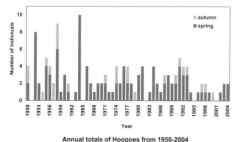

Annual totals of Hoopoes from 1950-2004

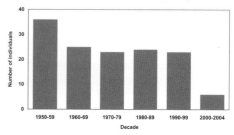

Ten-year totals of Hoopoes from 1950-2004

proportionally larger numbers during autumn, suggesting that, currently, fewer young birds occur than in the past. Three of the records involved two birds together. Between 1929 and 1949, there were just two more records, including an unusual mid-winter occurrence of three at Westcliff-on-Sea on 2nd January 1947.

Since 1950, Hoopoes have been recorded in all but seven years up to 2004, with the largest influx involving ten in 1964. The total of 137 individuals averages 2–3 birds per annum. Both nationally and locally, numbers have remained remarkably constant over the last 30 years suggesting that, as observer coverage has increased, the true incidence has probably declined.

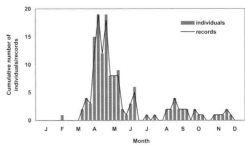

Seasonal occurrence of Hoopoes from 1950-2004

Almost all the records since 1950 have involved single birds. However, there have been four records involving two Hoopoes and up to four may have been present at Leigh/Two Tree Island on 11th April 1964.

The main passage period is April–May, with a smaller peak in August and September. Spring records involve overshooting migrants, heading north through Europe, whilst those in autumn probably relate to those dispersing from breeding grounds.

There have been two winter records since 1950, both of singles at: Westcliff-on-Sea/Leigh-on-Sea, 12th February 1960; Mersea Island, 10th November–7th December 1998.

Records show a wide geographical spread with no site particularly favoured; only around 40% have come from truly coastal sites.

(Eurasian) Wryneck   *Jynx torquila*

Uncommon passage migrant, 396 individuals since 1950: last bred in 1950   **Red List**

The Wryneck inhabits the boreal, temperate and sub-tropical zones in Europe and most of Asia, east to Sakhalin Island and Hokkaido, Japan, where typically it is found in warm and sunny deciduous woodlands and margins and low-intensity farmland. The nominate race *torquila* occurs through much of Eurasia. Dramatic declines have occurred in northwest Europe that have been attributed mainly to long-term variations in temperature and rainfall, but detrimental habitat changes may have also been factors (European Atlas). From probable high numbers in the mid-19th century, the British population declined to effective extinction by the mid-1980s. In most of its breeding range, it is fully migratory, wintering mostly south of the Sahara in Africa.

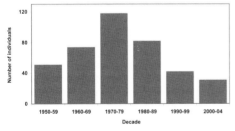

Ten-year totals of Wrynecks from 1950-2004

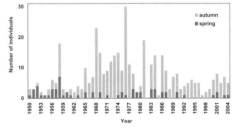

Annual totals of Wrynecks from 1950-2004

The early writers left little evidence as to the Wryneck's status in Essex, presumably because it was considered too common to merit much attention. Christy described the species as a fairly common summer resident albeit scarce in some years; Glegg considered the Wryneck to be no more than a scarce summer resident some 40 years later.

As early as 1832, a decline had been noted in Epping Forest by Henry Doubleday (Christy) who stated: "This bird, which used to be heard a few years since in all directions, is now so scarce that I have not heard more than three or four in the neighbourhoods", whilst in 1833 he observed: "This bird appears to decrease in number every year in the neighbourhood". Around Epping, the Wryneck was recorded annually from 1828–45 and at Southchurch from 1837–46, with the exception of 1840 and 1844, whilst migrants were recorded annually at Wrabness from 1818–1829. During the 1880s and 1890s the species was still breeding around Birdbrook, Maldon, Rayleigh and Orsett (Glegg).

Glegg observed that the species was an annual visitor at Bradfield from 1898–1911, after which it became irregular and less frequent. In the Sible Hedingham area, Wrynecks became scarce from about 1906, prior to which they had been common. At Stanway, the last nesting attempt was in 1925, whilst the species bred annually at Felsted from 1907–12, and again in 1922, prior to which it had been fairly common. A pair nested annually at Wanstead from 1891–1910 and at Loughton in 1891 and 1902 but apparently not at all in Epping Forest. Single pairs bred at Hazeleigh Hall in 1897, Pitsea in 1901, Brentwood in 1904, Hockley in 1909 and Loughton in 1927.

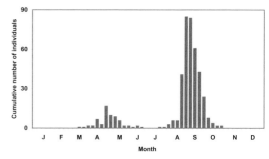

Seasonal occurrence of Wrynecks from 1950-2004

By 1929, Wrynecks were extremely scarce and local and by 1937, only in Rochford Hundred were there a few breeding pairs (Hudson & Pyman). One pair may have bred at Loughton in 1949, whilst in 1950 two pairs bred in the Rochford Hundred, but the following year none bred and the Wryneck became extinct as a breeding bird in Essex, although occasional summering individuals were reported in Rochford Hundred up until 1961, including three in 1958, one of which was observed inspecting a prospective nest hole. In 1978, individuals were seen at Bicknacre and North Fambridge during July. The last definite breeding in Kent was in 1968 (Taylor *et al.* 1981) and in Suffolk in 1972 (Piotrowski 2003). Nationally, no more than one definite breeding record per annum has occurred in the last 15 years with 2001 being the first year ever without a breeding season record (RBBP 2003).

As a migrant, it is reported in both spring and autumn, although autumn records predominate. Numbers of migrants vary considerably from year to year, dependent primarily on autumn weather conditions, which, when suitable, drift southward-bound Scandinavian birds across the North Sea. Overall, the number of migrants has declined from a peak during the 1970s, despite increased observer coverage, although there have been signs of a slight recovery in numbers in the 2000s; numbers have declined in Fennoscandia (European Atlas).

Peak numbers occur during late August and early September. Small numbers occur in spring, although there have only been six since 1990. There have been three March records: Epping Forest, 13th in 1965; Mistley, 23rd in 1958; and Hainault Forest CP, 28th in 1976.

Of several October records, the latest were at Gunners Park on 27th in 2003, and on the Dengie coast on 24th in 1976. There were two at Berechurch on 12th October 1950.

Records have shown a wide geographical spread, with around 45% of all occurrences being inland, although recently the proportion of inland records has declined. Currently, The Naze is the most favoured Wryneck site in Essex; given the dense cover others may go undetected there.

Green Woodpecker   *Picus viridis*

Fairly common resident   Amber List

This, the largest of the three species of breeding woodpeckers, is generally restricted to the boreal, temperate and Mediterranean climatic zones of the western Palearctic. Populations in central Europe, northwards to Britain and southern Fennoscandia are represented by the nominate race *viridis* (European Atlas). In Britain, where there are about 24,000 pairs, the Green Woodpecker is most abundant in well wooded areas of southern England and Wales, although there was a northerly range expansion during the 20th century into the Lake District and central and eastern Scotland.

Several local names particular to Essex and Hertfordshire have been given to the Green Woodpecker. The most well known is 'Yaffle', from the species' call, but others include 'Rainbird' and 'Whetile' (wet-tail) from the belief that its appearance meant rain. In Essex, the species is found in open, deciduous woodland interspersed with areas of grassland, parkland, heaths and commons where it feeds mainly on the ground, principally on adult and larval ants, making it the most specialised of western Palearctic woodpeckers.

Christy described the Green Woodpecker as "A fairly-common resident, especially in parks and thickly-timbered districts, as round Danbury, Epping, Maldon, &c", whilst Glegg considered the species "... a common resident ... and more generally distributed throughout

Atlas	Survey Area	% of 10km squares or tetrads in which	
		bred/probably bred	possibly bred or present
First National 10km	Essex	73.7	17.5
Second National 10km	Essex	71.9	19.3
First London Tetrad	Met. Essex	12.5	11.5
Second London Tetrad	Met. Essex	51.0	15.0
Essex Tetrad	Essex	35.8	16.8

Summary of results of Atlas surveys for Green Woodpeckers

the county than the other two breeding Woodpeckers ... It is certainly our most numerous Woodpecker". Glegg believed that there had been no overall change in numbers since Christy's time, although around Epping Forest it had become less common as Starlings took over nest holes. Hudson & Pyman also considered the species to be a "Fairly common resident ... throughout the county, though becoming scarce in built-up areas and in exposed coastal districts". However, they considered that, although until quite recently the commonest Woodpecker, its numbers were now equalled or exceeded by the much-increased Great Spotted Woodpecker, particularly following the severe weather of early 1963: the species being a ground-feeder, the long period of frozen snow cover made feeding extremely difficult. Unfortunately, the species was not mentioned in the *EBR* Systematic List until 1965, so direct comparison with numbers prior to 1963 is not possible. The recovery was, however, considered to have been slow with, for example, no breeding season records from a previous stronghold in Hockley Woods by 1967 and no records at all from Mersea Island. Indeed evidence suggested a continuing decline until the early 1970s. By 1970, Green Woodpeckers had virtually disappeared from the area immediately west and southwest of Chelmsford, was unrecorded between Epping and Ongar, much diminished in Corringham area, local and uncommon around Harlow and scarce with no signs of recovery in Epping Forest. Only in the Danbury/Little Baddow area did the population recover quickly. Subsequently, numbers recovered steadily through the 1970s, such that by the 1980s it was once more widespread in wooded areas throughout the county.

Despite the increase, Cox concluded that the Green Woodpecker "... has undoubtedly declined over the last two or three decades..." as a result of the loss of large areas of grassland, the removal of old timber and the effects of prolonged periods of severe winter weather. He considered it to be reduced in parts of central and southern Essex although in areas that retained abundant Wood Ant populations, such as the Danbury/Little Baddow areas, the species' numbers had been maintained. Cox also noted that the extensive drainage of coastal marshes and conversion to cereal growing had robbed the species of the many anthills which were a popular feeding target until the 1950s. Other factors that may have had negative affects on the population included the reduction in sheep husbandry and perhaps also a decrease in rabbit grazing following deliberate introductions of the myxomatosis virus: the feeding activities of both Rabbits and Sheep produce ideal conditions for large and diverse ant populations (Population Trends).

Little change in distribution was observable between the two National Atlases; there were, however, notable increases in Metropolitan Essex between the two London Atlases. The Essex Atlas survey revealed the Green Woodpecker to be widespread throughout Essex with breeding confirmed in 35.8% of tetrads and sight records from a further 16.8%. The species was generally absent only from urban areas, along much of the coastal strip and inland in scattered pockets of arable 'prairie-land'. Its absence from the valleys of the Colne, Blackwater, Crouch and Roach can probably be explained by the lack of suitable feeding.

Since the end of the Essex Atlas survey period, an apparent increase in both numbers and range has been noted, particularly in the south and southwest; regularly surveyed sites, such as Hainault Forest CP, have seen steady increases in recent years. Although remaining uncommon in the coastal belt, increases have been noted, particularly in the numbers feeding on ants on grazing marshes such as at Old Hall. BBS (England) data suggest a 36% increase during 1994–2003, whilst local CBC/BBS Indices point to significant increases since 1980. It is possible that the reduction in Starling numbers has reduced pressure for suitable nesting sites.

Since 1990 the following sites have held ten or more pairs: Danbury/Little Baddow; Hainault Forest CP; Langdon Hills; Wanstead Park; and Writtle.

The species is very sedentary, although post-juvenile dispersal does occur. Of the eight recoveries involving Essex, seven were ringed and recovered in Essex no further than 16km from the ringing site. One ringed at Landguard Point, Suffolk, on 1st August 1990 was found dead at Wormingford on 21st May 1991, 34km to the west; individual movements of over 20km are unusual (Migration Atlas). The Winter Atlas revealed that during winter there appears to be a range contraction within Essex, which suggests that local birds may make seasonal, short distance movements.

The type of short, dense, unimproved grassland upon which the Green Woodpecker depends for its principal food sources has declined over the last few decades but recently many areas of coastal grazing marsh have come into the ownership of conservation organisations and thus there is hope that some lost habitat will be recreated for this and other species; recent population increases suggest that the Green Woodpecker may already be benefiting.

Great Spotted Woodpecker

Dendrocopos major

Common resident and scarce passage migrant

The Great Spotted Woodpecker is distributed throughout the trans-Palearctic coniferous and broad-leaved forests between the northern taiga zone and the Mediterranean. Some ten subspecies occur throughout Europe, with the nominate race *major* found in Scandinavia and western Siberia east to the Urals and south to Poland and northern Ukraine, whilst *pinetorum* occurs across Britain, France and central Europe east to the Volga and south to Italy and east to the Caucasus (*HBW*). It is the commonest European woodpecker. In Britain, the species is generally distributed throughout England and Wales, being absent only from the treeless areas of the fens and uplands (Second National Atlas). The species seems to have increased nationally during most of the 20th century. The Great Spotted Woodpecker is now the most widespread and numerous woodpecker across Britain, having a population of 37,000–44,000 pairs. Whilst most populations are sedentary, the boreal and eastern populations are short-distance irruptive migrants (European Atlas), with individuals of the northern race *major* observed in Britain in some years.

The status of the Great Spotted Woodpecker appears to have changed markedly since Christy's time. For most of the 19th century, its scarcity meant that even in the most wooded parts it was relatively rarely seen. Christy observed that the species was "A resident, though very sparsely distributed over the county. I have seldom seen the bird". Henry Doubleday writing in 1832 (Christy), following the "procurement" of two eggs, noted: "The bird is scarce here, and I never saw the nest before". Of very few other references given by Christy, only at Upminster was it considered common. Glegg described the Great Spotted Woodpecker as a "... somewhat uncommon and local resident ... " but added that it was "... increasing generally throughout the county". The records he detailed suggested that the increase began around the last decade of the 19th century and was continuing during the 1920s. It was possible that a decline in intensive woodland management at about this time (e.g. coppicing) allowed the species, which prefers mature woodland, to increase (Historical Atlas). It was, however, still less common than the Green Woodpecker. Hudson & Pyman confirmed that "... this increase continues still" and that the species was "... now as common as the Green Woodpecker, which, in places, it even exceeds in numbers". The *EBR*s recorded large increases in the early 1950s including in sparsely wooded areas and these increases continued during 1970s.

By 1982 the Great Spotted Woodpecker was considered widespread throughout the county but there were few areas "...where it can be described as really common" (*EBR* 1982). This was perhaps due to the fact that only 2% of Essex is covered by ancient, semi-natural woodland. Although the species nests in conifers, only 4% of nest record cards come from such trees and only 1.7% of nests were found in pure coniferous stands (Glue & Boswell 1994). Cox considered that that the increases documented by previous writers had now halted and that in some areas, for example around Ingatestone and in the Dengie Hundred, a decrease had been noted.

The *EBR*s through the 1980s and 1990s document an apparently relatively stable population. However, more detailed, long-term surveys in Hainault Forest CP revealed notable increases from 1980 to the mid-1990s (Essex Atlas), paralleling the big national increases. However, the number of territories in The Mores Wood, near Brentwood, remained remarkably constant at 1–2 pairs from 1981–98 (Gibbs 2000), whilst comparison of the two London Atlases confirmed a continuing increase in Metropolitan Essex, even in areas lacking extensive woodland. This illustrates that this species is not an easy one to assess without detailed territory mapping. Point counts and other ad hoc visits by birdwatchers will underestimate the species, which remains under-studied (Glue 2000). The Essex Atlas survey recorded the species in 60.9% of all tetrads, by which time it had become a familiar bird of park and woodland. National CBC/BBS (England) data for the period 1977–2002 showed a 61% increase, with an 81% rise in the BBS (England) Index between 1994 and 2003; locally the trend has been similar.

The large increase in the population is probably due to a number of factors. Firstly, it has managed to colonise town centres and farmland along linear tree features rather than relying on woodland blocks. Secondly, it has been a beneficiary of supplementary feeding in winter with its use of garden bird tables having doubled since 1970, and 43% of sites in the BTO's Garden Bird Feeding Survey are regularly visited (Glue 2000). Thirdly, it has almost certainly increased as a result of Dutch Elm disease, which created very large numbers of dying and decaying trees full of suitable insect food. Finally, underlying all this there has been a massive increase in the coverage of Birch in

Atlas	Survey Area	% of 10km squares or tetrads in which	
		bred/probably bred	possibly bred or present
First National 10km	Essex	78.9	17.5
Second National 10km	Essex	71.9	19.3
First London Tetrad	Met. Essex	23.0	8.0
Second London Tetrad	Met. Essex	61.5	11.5
Essex Tetrad	Essex	42.6	18.3

Summary of results of Atlas surveys for Great Spotted Woodpeckers

384

woodlands across Essex during the 20th century, which could explain much of the species' expansion. The Great Spotted Woodpecker has a preference for Birch (Glue & Boswell 1994) and particularly for decaying Birch of more than 28cm diameter at breast height (Smith 1997). For example, in Epping Forest Birch has gone from being a relatively uncommon tree in the 19th century to a common one in the 1920s, with an estimated population of 20,000 (Paulson 1926), to the most numerous (> 250,000) of all tree species (Forest Projects C.P.A. 1985). Now, nearly 100 years on, a large cohort of Birch trees in Essex is over-mature and decaying. The species shows an even stronger selection for dead trees generally (Smith 1997), and the presence or absence of the right sort of dead tree may be an important limiting factor in some woodlands. For example, in some parts of Epping Forest, even though there are high densities of dead standing Beech and Oak, Smith found (pers. comm.) that the density of Great Spotted Woodpeckers was relatively low: compared to an average of 8 pairs per km^2 in other woodlands (Smith in press), the density was 6.6 in Bury Wood, Chingford, and only 5.8 in Great Monk Wood. Interestingly, the woodpeckers may adapt to this limiting factor. In the southeast Hertfordshire woodlands studied by Smith (1997), the birds re-used their nest holes significantly more than usual compared with other studies of woodpeckers across Europe. Such re-use was also observed many years ago by J. Ross in Epping Forest (Glegg) who found that a site had been re-used over a period of at least seven years. Since 1980 CBC sites across Essex have recorded densities of 1–18 pairs per km^2 in all habitats.

The Great Spotted Woodpecker's population is predominantly rural, but it has become increasingly common in towns and gardens and can now be encountered more or less anywhere where there are trees. This move into the suburbs and rural gardens seems to have begun in the 1950s (Glue & Boswell 1994) on the back of its increasing national population and the increasing sprawl of the suburbs themselves. Great Spotted Woodpeckers generally require at least 2–3 ha of woodland for breeding, with 77% of all recorded nests in this habitat, whereas only 2% of nests were recorded in gardens (Glue & Boswell 1994). Although better able to cope with woodland fragmentation than the Nuthatch (Bellamy *et al.* 1996), its reliance on substantial woodland blocks still makes woodland coverage a limiting factor for this species. Thus, the southwest of Essex is likely to remain its stronghold.

Church spires covered in wooden shingles have regularly been holed by Great Spotted Woodpeckers; clearly the woodpecker sees a spire as just another tree. However, it is unclear whether the birds are hunting for food or whether they are using the hollow spire structure as a huge sounding board that amplifies the drumming. Spires at Great Henny and Copford have been holed badly; in these two cases the wooden shingles on the spires have been renewed in Oak. At Copford, thin stainless steel sheet was introduced behind the timber to try to deter the birds; whether it will work remains to be seen.

Although the Great Spotted Woodpecker is considered to be a very scarce passage migrant, it was—apart from 1957—not until 2002 that any migrant activity was reported in the *EBR*; then, perhaps 33 migrants were noted during September and October at The Naze, including a total of six moving north with flocks of Skylarks on 13th October. Although these records may simply involve just short-distance movements by locally bred individuals, some may refer to the northern race. An individual, shot on Foulness in September 1903, coincided with an influx of northern birds into Britain.

Eleven Essex-ringed Great Spotted Woodpeckers and three ringed outside the county have all been recovered in Essex; None were more than 99km from the ringing site.

Given our current knowledge, it is seems that the Great Spotted Woodpecker should maintain its numbers over the next few decades. However, in the longer term the Great Spotted Woodpecker's continued success will depend on how the new broad-leaved woodlands, which have been encouraged by recent schemes and grants, are managed and exploited. Woodpeckers are a very important part of a woodland's ecology and a great symbol of the importance of dead standing trees. Making the case for their continued conservation will protect much more than the birds themselves. Ironically, a return to a greater role for coppicing may adversely affect the species' numbers through Essex.

Lesser Spotted Woodpecker   *Dendrocopos minor*

Uncommon resident - significant declines during the 1990s   **Red List**

The Lesser Spotted Woodpecker is the smallest of the European woodpeckers. It breeds in deciduous, mixed deciduous and coniferous forests across the Palearctic from Portugal in the west to Kamchatka in the east (European Atlas). Eleven races are recognised, the nominate *minor*, occurring in northern Europe east to the Urals, *hortorum* from France east through central Europe and *comminutus* in south and central Britain. Due to its small size and habit of feeding high in the canopy and nesting within smaller branches rather than on the trunk, it can be difficult to observe and may go undetected in areas where its presence had not been previously suspected (European Atlas). British populations increased significantly during the 1970s and 1980s but declined dramatically thereafter. Although the species is generally sedentary, migratory and irruptive movements of northern populations occur (Winkler *et al.* 1995).

Christy described the species as "A rare resident though it occurs from time to time and is occasionally found breeding in most parts of the county and is even common around Danbury". However, it appears that it was particularly rare in the early part of the 19th century, suggesting that the species had increased in the county in subsequent decades. The earliest documented record came from Saffron Walden, the home to several well-known naturalist collectors, on 2nd March 1830. Just two more were recorded up to 1852, with the only subsequent record, in 1882, referring to breeding. In 1832 Henry Doubleday noted: "I have seen it here [Epping] once or twice", whilst in 1840 he wrote: "it is, as far as my observations go, very rare [round London] ... a solitary, straggling individual or two, is all I have ever heard of anywhere around us". Given Doubleday's intimate knowledge of the area, it was clearly very rare. However, by 1885 Buxton described it rather quaintly as "not very uncommon" around Epping Forest. Other locations mentioned by Christy were Great Braxted, Stanford Rivers, Tiptree, Wix, Ramsey, Marks Hall at Upminster ("common"), Colchester, Wixoe and Maldon. However, only the records from Great Braxted were prior to 1870 and even then the eminent local naturalist Dr Bree felt its occurrence at Tiptree in April 1870 to be of sufficient rarity to record it in the pages of *The Field*.

Glegg considered the Lesser Spotted Woodpecker to be the least common of the three breeding woodpeckers, although resident throughout Essex and apparently sedentary. Based on Christy's evidence, he believed that the species had increased markedly in the previous 50 years and, although not common in any part of the county, was evenly, though sparingly, distributed throughout. He considered that increases were still occurring in some districts.

Hudson & Pyman felt that the species' status had changed very little since Glegg's time, although there had been signs of a spread eastwards towards the coast since the early 1950s.

Over the next 20 years or so, however, the Lesser Spotted Woodpecker increased markedly, in fact so much so that Cox observed that in some areas the species was considered to be the most numerous of the three woodpeckers. This marked change in status was almost certainly due to the abundance of invertebrate foods caused by the spread of Dutch Elm disease, which left much dead wood in the countryside (European Atlas). The availability of decaying or easily worked wood is probably more essential than tree species or height to the Lesser Spotted Woodpecker (*BWP*). Thus, it increased throughout wooded areas and at the same time over-spilled onto farmland where growing numbers of infected and moribund hedgerow Elms provided good feeding (Osborne 1982). Up to four pairs between Bradwell and Southminster from 1978–82 were a good example of this adaptability. Large gardens and pollarded willows in marshy areas were also utilised for breeding (Cox). During the early 1980s the largest populations were: 5–10 pairs, Danbury/Little Baddow area; 5–10 pairs, Margaretting, Highwood, Blackmore, Mill Green area; 5–7 pairs, Thorndon CP; four pairs, Hainault Forest CP; and 3–4 pairs, Langdon Hills. There were 5–8 pairs in Copperas Wood during 1986.

Quite why the Lesser Spotted Woodpecker should have benefited to a greater extent than its two cousins is unclear. However, the increase did not continue and, as the amount of infected timber lessened, the species went into decline. The decrease may have been exacerbated by the destruction of a lot of the dead wood in the name of 'tidying up'. Pinpointing exactly when the decline began in Essex is difficult as very few records were reported in the *EBRs* in the 1980s and the species was not mentioned in the Systematic List from 1983–87. However, on the assumption that this followed a similar pattern to that seen nationally numbers peaked in the early 1980s and went into fairly steep decline after 1985, about the time that the Dutch Elm disease epidemic began to subside (Population Trends).

Nationally, the gains made since the early 1970s had been lost by 1988. It was hoped that the Great Storm of October 1987, which toppled tens of thousands of trees across Essex, might have revived its fortunes but over-zealous and over tidy-minded landowners and councils cleared away the felled timber before it could rot (Essex Atlas). This tidying up would have included any remaining dead Elms as well. The BTO Nest Record data showed that before the epidemic, Elms were one of

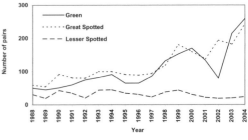

Annual totals of reported breeding woodpeckers from 1988-2004

the most important nesting trees for the species and their loss was probably a further factor in the decline (Second National Atlas); interaction with the increasingly common Great Spotted Woodpecker may have reduced numbers (Fuller *et al.* 2005). The decline has continued to this day and appears to have accelerated in the late 1990s, although it is possible that it has merely been overlooked following completion of survey work for the Essex Atlas. However, national CBC data highlighted a severe population decline with a decrease of more than 50% evident between 1988 and 1998; thus the population doubled during the 1970s and declined by 75% between 1979 and 1996. The species is now so scarce that BBS monitoring is not possible.

Populations of individual sites have not, except in Hainault Forest CP and The Mores Wood, near Brentwood, been monitored on a regular basis. In the former, numbers slowly increased from the mid-1970s, peaked in the first half of the 1990s and have now returned to the level seen in the 1970s; at the latter site there was no trend evident between 1981 and 1998 with single territories in four random years (Gibbs 2000). Totals of five pairs in Wanstead Park in 2000 and 2002 were the largest counts made away from Hainault Forest CP since 1982.

The First National Atlas survey recorded confirmed or probable breeding in 59.6% of 10km squares in Essex just prior to the outbreak of Dutch Elm disease. Survey work for the Second National Atlas was carried out as populations began to decline again after the

Atlas	Survey Area	% of 10km squares or tetrads in which	
		bred/probably bred	possibly bred or present
First National 10km	Essex	59.6	15.8
Second National 10km	Essex	56.1	26.3
First London Tetrad	Met. Essex	10.0	4.5
Second London Tetrad	Met. Essex	36.5	17.5
Essex Tetrad	Essex	17.2	11.9

Summary of results of Atlas surveys for Lesser Spotted Woodpecker

passing of the epidemic. Whilst the overall number of 10km squares in which it was recorded were about the same there were gains in coastal areas, from Dengie northwards and in southwest Essex, whereas there were apparent losses in the far southeast and a few inland 10km squares. The abundance map in the Second National Atlas showed central and southwest Essex to be particularly important in a national context. Both National Atlases confirmed that the Lesser Spotted Woodpecker was the least numerous of its family.

During the Essex Atlas survey, Lesser Spotted Woodpeckers were reported from 29.1% of tetrads, with breeding confirmed in 17.2%; again it was the least common of the woodpeckers. The highest concentrations occurred in the woodlands of southwest and Metropolitan Essex. There were also smaller populations in adjacent areas of west, south and central Essex. Otherwise, it was only sparingly distributed throughout Essex and even then the species tended to occur in isolated pockets with large areas of countryside both inland and on the coast apparently devoid of the species. Since completion of the Essex Atlas, numbers reported annually in *EBRs* have shown a general downward trend.

Lesser Spotted Woodpeckers are generally very sedentary and to date there have been no recoveries of foreign-ringed individuals in Britain or British ones abroad. A very small number have been ringed in Essex with four recovered, the furthest having travelled just 7km (this individual, which was at least seven years old when found dead, is the oldest British-ringed Lesser Spotted Woodpecker to have been reported to the BTO). Short-distance local movements may be undertaken and this may account for sightings of individuals in unusual locations such as along seawalls or on coastal marshes.

The Lesser Spotted Woodpecker has a history of population rises and falls. The reasons for the significant and continuing decreases in recent years are not clear, although the general tidying up of the countryside, whereby dead trees are taken out before they rot well and provide suitable feeding for the species, must be a factor. However, there is sufficient woodland within Essex to ensure an adequate supply of deadwood and there seems to be no reason for concern for its immediate future.

(Greater) Short-toed Lark   *Calandrella brachydactyla*

Vagrant: three records

The Short-toed Lark breeds locally in France, through Iberia and the Mediterranean region, North Africa and east as far as China, where it is found in arid grasslands in the steppe and semi-desert zones. The nominate race *brachydactyla* occurs throughout most of its European range. Western birds winter mainly in northern Africa.

1965	Hanningfield	20th May
1997	Wallasea Island	8th June
1999	Deal Hall	22nd October

Increased observer coverage is probably the reason for the growth in national records in recent years, which led to it being removed from the BBRC List in 1993. On average, 27 were recorded annually in Britain during the 1990s (Fraser & Rogers 2004), although the majority occured in the Shetland Islands or Isles of Scilly. Most records occur in May and September–October. The dearth of county records is difficult to explain; there have been 14 in Suffolk (*Suffolk Bird Report 2003*) and it is annual in very small numbers in Norfolk (Taylor *et al.* 1999). The two spring Essex records are likely to be of the nominate southern race, which tends to have a redder crown than the eastern races; the latter are generally greyer overall and are thought to predominate in autumn (Dymond *et al.* 1989).

Woodlark (Wood Lark) *Lullula arborea*

Uncommon, but increasing passage migrant - sporadic breeder **Red List**

The Woodlark is predominantly a European bird that occurs mostly below 60°N. The nominate race *arborea* occupies most of Europe, with *pallida* inhabiting southern Spain, most of Italy, the Mediterranean islands, southern Balkans, Crimea and Caucasus (European Atlas). The British population has increased in recent years and currently numbers around 1,500 pairs, the majority in Norfolk, Suffolk and Surrey. Northernmost populations are largely migratory.

Christy observed that the Woodlark was "Formerly a rare and local resident in the Epping Forest and Saffron Walden districts, but it seems of late years to have … disappeared from those localities, and I have not heard of the occurrence of more than a single specimen in the county for years". In 1832, the Woodlark had "… become very rare…", but in 1839 the species was rapidly increasing and in April 1840 it was noted that there were "… a great many Wood Larks". Numbers declined again prior to 1859, whilst a severe frost in that year appears to have wiped out the species (Glegg), although in 1880 his correspondent included the species in the list of residents of Epping Forest. Around 1845 the species was "… rarely seen…" around Saffron Walden, although Woodlarks had once been fairly common there.

By the latter half of the 19th century, the species had become very rare with the only record involving one shot at Danbury on 21st January 1889. Glegg noted that: "The Woodlark is so rare in Essex that on its present status it would not be entitled to a place in the list of Essex birds". He referred to just one contemporary record, a singing male in Epping Forest on 5th November 1905.

There were very few subsequent records and no evidence of breeding until 1943, when a pair nested near Colchester (Hudson & Pyman). A considerable upsurge in breeding numbers occurred thereafter with nesting occurring at about 25 widely scattered locations between 1949 and 1961. Around 26+ pairs were perhaps present between 1949 and 1952 (Goodey 2001), although this could have been as high as 30–40 (Cox); however, 10–12 pairs and three singing males in 1952

Atlas	Survey Area	% of 10km squares or tetrads in which bred/probably bred	% of 10km squares or tetrads in which possibly bred or present
First National 10km	Essex	1.8	1.8
Second National 10km	Essex	1.8	1.0
First London Tetrad	Met. Essex	0.0	0.0
Second London Tetrad	Met. Essex	0.0	0.0
Essex Tetrad	Essex	0.1	0.0

Summary of results of Atlas surveys for Woodlarks

were the most actually reported in the *EBR* in any one year. Indeed, the numbers reported annually at this time rarely came from more than a handful of the known breeding areas, probably as a result of poor observer coverage. Favoured localities were: several areas just south of Colchester, including Berechurch, Layer-de-la-Haye and Friday Wood; Little Baddow/Woodham Walter; Hainault Forest CP; and Epping Forest.

There was a marked decline from the late 1950s, although as early as 1955, when the *EBR* listed the second highest annual number of breeding pairs, it was suggested that the species was declining. By 1961 there was just one breeding attempt, in Epping Forest, and none thereafter until 1990 when a pair fledged at least one young in Writtle Forest. Subsequently, there have been a number of records of birds in suitable habitat during spring or summer but for never more than a single day.

Numbers throughout Europe appear to fluctuate markedly as a result of rapid changes in habitat availability and harsh weather conditions in the main wintering area in southwest Europe (European Atlas). Since the early 1980s numbers in Norfolk and Suffolk have increased significantly due to more clear-felling in Forestry Commission land and the Great Storm of 1987; both created large areas of suitable habitat which the Woodlark quickly colonised. Elsewhere, increases have been smaller but the species has shown signs of using alternative habitats.

After 1961, the Woodlark became a very rare passage migrant through Essex, although with the increases in the Norfolk and Suffolk populations records have increased markedly over the last ten years. The majority of records occur in spring and autumn. Between mid-March and May most British-breeding birds are back on

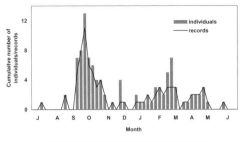

Seasonal occurrence of Woodlarks from 1950-2004

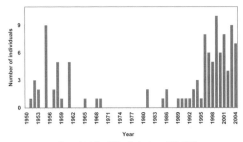

Annual totals of Woodlarks from 1950-2004

territory (Migration Atlas), so the small secondary spring peak may involve some Continental birds; just over 50% have occurred on the coast.

Metropolitan Essex has also recorded the Woodlark regularly on passage. Between 1961 and 1989, all except one record came from inland.

Wintering records in Essex are rare; British Woodlarks are partially migratory with some, particularly in the south, wintering close to breeding areas and others, particularly from the Brecklands, Norfolk/Suffolk, moving long distances (Migration Atlas). Of the few winter records, by far the longest-stayer was an individual at Walthamstow town from 14th January–22nd February 1985.

Skylark (Sky Lark)   *Alauda arvensis*

Common but recently declined resident, passage migrant and winter visitor   Red List - Essex BAP

The Skylark breeds throughout the Palearctic region, from around 35°–65°N in both oceanic and continental climate zones, and is absent only from Iceland. Six subspecies occur in Europe with *arvensis* occurring in northern Europe east to the Urals, England and Wales, and *scotica* breeding in Ireland, Scotland and the Faeroes (European Atlas). Skylarks occur throughout the British Isles being most common in the lowlands of eastern Britain (Second National Atlas): significant declines occurred nationally during the last quarter of the 20th century. Skylarks are totally migratory in north and eastern Europe, moving generally south and west to winter in Britain, Ireland, the Low Countries, France, Iberia and perhaps northern Africa. In the southern part of its range and in temperate western Europe, the species generally makes no more than local movements (European Atlas).

The general status of the Skylark has changed very little since the early 19th century. To Christy, the species was "An abundant and well-known resident, though partially migratory", whilst Glegg stated that it was "… a very abundant resident". Hudson & Pyman described the Skylark as a "Common resident, winter visitor and passage migrant" but noted that numbers had declined markedly since 1960, a trend attributed to the use of organopesticides. However, the severe winters of 1961/62 and 1962/63 were more likely to have been the main cause of this decline (Population Trends). Particularly during the winter of 1962/63 mortality was high: 43 corpses were found at East Tilbury on 27th January 1963, a remarkably large number given that small passerines dying of natural causes are rarely recovered. Nationally, the recovery was rapid and apparently complete by 1965 (Population Trends). Unfortunately being such a common species, little was published in *EBR*s regarding breeding numbers until 1985. However, Cox noted that on an 85ha CBC plot at Little Waltham there was a pro-

Atlas	Survey Area	% of 10km squares or tetrads in which	
		bred/probably bred	possibly bred or present
First National 10km	Essex	100.0	0.0
Second National 10km	Essex	96.5	3.5
First London Tetrad	Met. Essex	67.0	7.5
Second London Tetrad	Met. Essex	86.0	7.5
Essex Tetrad	Essex	95.8	1.7

Summary of results of Atlas surveys for Skylarks

gressive increase in the number of territories from 20 to 42 between 1965 and 1971 and that the mean density of Skylarks on Essex farmland plots was 33 pairs per km².

Following the recovery, numbers in Essex appeared to remain stable for a while, although circumstantial evidence pointed to declines in some areas. Payn (1978) considered that there had been considerable declines in the 'prairie farming' areas of Suffolk. By the mid-1980s, however, observers were once again reporting declines. Two of the longest running CBC plots, at Ongar/Newney Green and Sawyers Hall, observed this trend with numbers declining after the mid/late 1980s at both sites. At the former, peaks of 23 territories in 1985 and 1990 fell to just nine by 1999, and at the latter 14 in 1987 had declined to four by 1999. From 1977–2002, CBC (England) data had shown a 61% decline, whilst BBS (England) data for the period 1994–2003 recorded a 20% reduction. Circumstantial evidence suggests that in Essex the declines may have been halted by the late 1990s but there are, as yet, few obvious signs of a recovery. Indeed local BBS data suggest that the decline is ongoing.

Populations of many birds breeding on agricultural land have declined over many parts of Europe (Pain & Pienkowski 1997). Over the last four decades, agriculture has undergone some significant changes and it is species that could best be described as farmland specialists, such as the Skylark, which have suffered most (Siriwardena *et al.* 1998). Such changes have included the enlargement of field sizes by the removal of hedges, specialisation on individual farms such that the traditional patchwork of land uses has largely disappeared, a switch to predominantly autumn-sown crops and the extensive use of fertilisers and pesticides (Sotherton 1998). Cutting of set-aside in the breeding season has been shown to destroy many Skylarks' nests (Poulson & Sotherton 1993). Thus such areas may act as population sinks (Mason & MacDonald 2000a) exacerbating local declines. Mason & MacDonald (2000a) in studies on the Tendring peninsula found that more than half of all territories were in autumn-sown cereals but densities were higher in set-aside and spring-sown crops with conservation grassland cut for hay in late July holding the highest densities.

Breeding densities in the mid/late 1980s at Ongar/Newney Green were around 20–25 pairs per km², around Sawyers Hall 20 pairs per km² and at Greenstead 20–25 pairs per km², all significantly lower than that mentioned by Cox for the period 1965–71. At Ongar, the breeding density has now dropped to around ten pairs per km² and at Sawyers Hall, five pairs per km². There was a slight change in distribution between the two National Atlases, whilst the Essex Atlas recorded the Skylark in 97.5% of all tetrads, being absent only from the inner Metropolitan areas and the larger urban areas across Essex. Slight declines were noted in Metropolitan Essex between the two London Atlases.

Despite these declines, the species remains a widespread breeding bird throughout Essex, being found not only in open fields but also on grazing marshes, saltings, seawalls and even neglected wastelands sometimes well within the urban environment (Essex Atlas). There were 265 pairs at Old Hall in 1998, 176 singing males on Foulness in 2001, 112 pairs at Tollesbury Wick in 1999 and 91 pairs at Rainham in 1998. Even in fairly built-up areas reasonable numbers may occur, for example 45 pairs along the Ingrebourne Valley in 2004, 29 pairs at Dagenham Chase in 2001 and 21 pairs at Barking in 1999. Seven pairs were present at Silvertown in 1997.

The Skylark is one of the most obvious diurnal migrants. During passage periods, movements may last from dawn until dusk, unlike those of many other passerines, which tend to tail off by mid-morning. Christy said very little about the Skylark's movements, whilst Glegg observed that "... the autumn immigration of Skylarks from Central Europe is perhaps more remarkable than that of any other British species. This movement ... is said to have the Essex coast and the mouth of the Thames as its centre, many of the immigrants passing inland by the Thames, and dispersing over the eastern, southern and midland counties". He gave details of several movements seen in Essex from mid-October, but merely noted "... considerable numbers ..." or "... thousands of Rooks, Hooded Crows, Jackdaws, Starlings and Skylarks coming in from the sea ...".

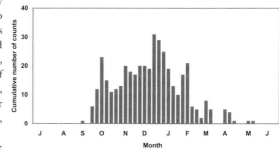

Seasonal occurrence of counts of 100+ Skylarks from 1971-2004

Such movements continue to this day and are most obvious during autumn and winter when arrivals of typically hundreds, but occasionally thousands have been witnessed along the coast and sometimes inland. The arrivals are generally from between southeast and northeast (Cox) but, on occasions, passage at coastal locations such as at The Naze appears to be from the south, perhaps suggesting that individuals are arriving further south along the coast and then reorientating and heading north. From the estuaries, these movements possibly proceed west and inland and account for large-scale movements noted in the Lea Valley and in the far northwest of Essex. The largest autumnal movement occurred on the 18th October 1958 when 2,480 flew in off the sea at The Naze and 2,000 headed north at St Osyth. Most other four-figure autumn counts have come from Dengie, the largest involving at least 3,000 between the Observatory and Howe Outfall on 16th November 1975, although there were "several thousand" on fields between Bradwell Waterside and the fields near the Observatory on 9th October 1976. Inland, a total of 2,200 flew northwest over the Lea Valley on 12th November 1959. The last four-figure autumn counts were in 1989 at Holland Haven and Colne Point on 28th–29th September when 1,000–1,500 were estimated during sporadic watches.

Overall, Skylark numbers are at their greatest during winter and particularly in times of severe weather when significant gatherings will form wherever there is a readily available food source, many apparently coinciding with large-scale, long-distance movements, perhaps from the Continent. On 1st January 1962, an estimated 15,000 gathered on 3–4km^2 of agricultural land around Little Clacton and were joined by a further 5,000 that flew in from the northeast during the course of the day. At the same time 2,000–3,000 an hour passed over Foulness over a three-hour period. During the severe weather of early 1979, an exceptional movement occurred along the Blackwater with 10,000 noted at Mersea Island and 15,000 at Goldhanger on 18th February; elsewhere 3,000 had passed over Hadleigh the previous day. Another massive hard-weather movement occurred in early 1985 when 10,000 were noted heading southwest in just 2.5 hours after sunrise at Tollesbury on 5th January. There has been just one four-figure count since 1990, 4,000 at Colne Point on 13th–14th February 1991. Although densities were low, Skylarks remained the most abundant species on a study area in the Tendring district during October–December 1997 and October–December 1998 (Mason & Macdonald 1999c).

Movements in spring are generally small and usually go undetected. The small numbers that have been observed have usually been in a northeasterly direction, often over inland locations (Cox).

There has been a total of 18 recoveries of Essex-ringed birds, all but three being found within the county and only one abroad: one ringed at Romford SF on 6th February 1966 and recovered in the Gironde, France, on 9th November 1967. The only other recoveries of note involved: one ringed at Romford SF in the winter of 1961/62 and recovered in Jersey, Channel Islands, on 4th January 1962, a southwesterly movement to avoid the severe weather; and another ringed at Lound, Nottingham, on 26th March 1985 and found dead in Hamford Water on 13th January 1990.

The national Skylark population has declined by some 1–2 million pairs since the early 1970s, a loss equivalent to almost 100 pairs per day. Winter survival may be a crucial factor in the decline in Skylark populations; modern farming techniques have virtually eradicated weedy stubble fields that appear vital to the species (Gillings & Fuller 2001). Reversing the loss of stubble will therefore be critical in turning around the trends of the last 30 years and the slow introduction of more environmentally friendly farming schemes is a positive step forward. On their own, though, these schemes would seem to be insufficient to stem the decline; only a complete and wholesale national change in farmland management is likely to do that.

Shore Lark (Horned Lark) *Eremophila alpestris*

Uncommon winter visitor and passage migrant

The Shore Lark is widely distributed across the Holarctic with the race *flava* breeding along the Arctic coast westward from the Kolyma River and also the Fennoscandian mountains; three other races occur in southeastern Europe. Fennoscandian populations have declined significantly since the 1950s but eastern populations may well have increased (European Atlas). Regular wintering along the east coast of Britain dates only from about 1870 (*BWP*): British wintering Shorelarks probably originate from the western edge of the breeding range in Scandinavia or western Russia (Migration Atlas).

Christy cited just seven records, from the first at Maldon on 29th November 1862 and described the Shore Lark as a "… rare and irregular straggler to our coast during winter", although he considered that "… other occurrences have probably passed unrecorded". A record of 35 shot from "… a large flight of Shore-Larks" at Harwich at the end of 1882 has only recently been exceeded in terms of flock size. Glegg considered the species an irregular winter visitor, although occurring in numbers in some winters, the last being 1890/91. Thereafter, he mentioned just two records, the last at Bradfield from 30th–31st October 1902.

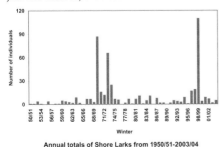

Annual totals of Shore Larks from 1950/51-2003/04

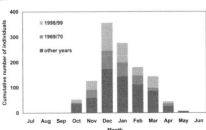

Seasonal occurrence of Shore Larks from 1950-2004

The next record was not until 1950 when one was along the Crouch on 2nd December. Since then, Shore Larks have been recorded in all but six winters. The underlying increase is almost certainly linked to increased observer coverage. Generally, however, numbers have been very small apart from the periods 1969/70–1973/74 and 1996/97–1998/99, a pattern mirrored nationally. Fluctuations in numbers are probably closely tied to breeding success, although prevailing weather conditions during autumn migration are perhaps also a factor.

During the winter of 1969/70 there was a peak of 60 at Bradwell on 6th December with 28 at Colne Point on 25th January and 17 at Mundon Stone on 2nd February; in all, around 85 were present. In 1972/73, about 65 occurred although the flocks were smaller and more widely distributed than in 1969/70 with peaks of 13 at The Naze on 29th December, 22 at Colne Point during January and February and 40 at Bradwell on 4th February.

After very low numbers from the mid-1970s to mid-1990s, larger numbers in 1996/97 and 1997/98, which included up to 13 at Colne Point from January–April 1998, were the prelude to a substantial influx during 1998/99 with around 110 being reported, including a flock of 64 on Foulness on 27th December 1998, the largest gathering recorded in Essex. Other counts included a peak of 28 in the St Osyth/Point Clear/Brightlingsea area on 5th December 1998 and 12 at Bradwell from 18th October 1998 into 1999. A peak of 18 at East Mersea from 22nd–24th November 1998 almost certainly involved the St Osyth flock.

Shore Larks feed on exposed salt marsh at low tide, mainly on the seeds of *Salicornia*. At high tide they retreat to the sandier upper shore were there is an abundance of wind- and water-borne seeds (*BWP*). In Essex, therefore, Shore Larks tend to prefer the area around the mouth of the Colne-Blackwater Estuaries and Foulness where there is a suitable combination of salt marsh and relatively undisturbed sandy beaches. The species is known to be very mobile and may forage over several kilometres of suitable coastline (Winter Atlas) and this has been apparent in Essex with flocks recorded moving between Colne Point, Mersea Island and Bradwell. Other favoured areas have been The Naze/Hamford Water and Foulness. Along the Thames, records are uncommon and have come mainly from Canvey Point.

There have been nine inland records: near Cavalry Barracks, Colchester, 1880/81; Walthamstow, October 1881; Abberton, 16th–23rd October 1953, 29th November 1991, 21st–22nd October 1994, 9th–10th November 1996 and 4th November–31st December 2004; and Hanningfield, two, 28th–31st October 1994 and one, 1st November 1997. In addition singles, unless stated otherwise, have occurred at: Heybridge GP, 11th March 1972 and two, 28th February–7th March 1982; Maldon refuse tip, 1st December 1988; South Woodham Ferrers, 27th November 1995; and Rainham, 7th November 1998.

Most birds arrive in November and December, with the largest flocks occurring in December, after which some dispersal seems to occur. In early 1998, however, ten were still present at Colne Point on 24th April and there were 24 at Brightlingsea on 8th March 1999.

One at Holland Haven on 7th–8th October 1979 is the earliest returning migrant, whilst a flock of 12 at Bradwell from 18th October 1998 is exceptionally early for such large numbers. The latest to depart was at Colne Point on 9th May 1973, although there were two on Mersea Island until 5th May 1988 and four at Colne Point until 4th May 1998.

It is likely that many of the earlier arriving individuals are passage birds; occasional individuals appear briefly at well-watched coastal sites at this time. Indeed, one found dead at Brightlingsea on 30th November 1962 had been ringed at Walberswick, Suffolk, on the 1st of that month, the first national ringing recovery of a Shore Lark.

Sand Martin   *Riparia riparia*

Locally common summer visitor and passage migrant   Amber List

The Sand Martin is a widespread and common lowland breeding bird across much of Europe, Asia to northern India and southeast China, the Pacific coastal islands and much of North America. The nominate race *riparia* breeds throughout much of North America, Europe and locally in North Africa and parts of the Near East and western Russia. In Britain, the species is widespread but patchily distributed over the whole country, although generally absent from large areas of south and east England where chalk and limestone predominate. As Sand

Martins are largely dependent on sandy riverbanks or gravel-pits for nesting sites, their distribution is in part constrained by geology (Second National Atlas). Apart from eastern populations, European breeders winter in the Sahel zone, just south of the Sahara.

Atlas	Survey Area	% of 10km squares or tetrads in which bred/probably bred	possibly bred or present
First National 10km	Essex	75.4	10.5
Second National 10km	Essex	47.4	26.3
First London Tetrad	Met. Essex	11.5	7.0
Second London Tetrad	Met. Essex	15.5	14.0
Essex Tetrad	Essex	6.5	12.3

Summary of results of Atlas surveys for Sand Martins

Both Christy and Glegg described the Sand Martin as a common summer visitor, although localised due to its specialised habitat requirements. Christy noted that it was most numerous in "... a ballast-pit at Fingringhoe ...", quite possibly what is now the EWT reserve. In addition, several pairs were noted "... carrying nesting-materials into holes in the stone walls of Colchester castle on May 25th, 1878". Glegg mentioned colonies in the cliffs between Clacton-on-Sea and Frinton-on-Sea, The Naze and Wrabness. Additionally, 12 pairs nested in trenches used for army training purposes at Gidea Park from April to June 1918.

No widespread population changes were noted nationally in the 19th (Historical Atlas) or the first half of the 20th centuries but since 1950, numbers have fluctuated markedly. After WWII, the growth of the sand and gravel industry increased the availability of suitable breeding habitat both nationally and in Essex. It is not clear whether a genuine increase in the population occurred or rather that the population simply redistributed from less suitable habitat in the north and west, where numbers had declined during the same period (Parslow 1973): indeed, data from Europe suggested that high Sand Martin breeding densities were only recorded from 1965 (Kuhnen 1975).

Requests for information within the *EBRs* from 1955–57 produced an estimated population of about 2,000 pairs at 48 sites, 41 in sand/gravel-pits (mostly active), two each in drainage pipes, earth banks and sea cliffs and one in a river bank. There were 400 pairs at Rowhedge and 200 at both Fingringhoe in 1955 and Alresford in 1957. During 1962 there were at least 220 pairs in three colonies at Fingringhoe Wick, whilst 366 nests were counted at Sandon GP in 1966 with 300 in 1967.

A survey in 1968, although considered incomplete, located 2,260 pairs at just 16 sites. Whether this represented an increase since 1955–57 is uncertain, as both surveys were incomplete. However, the *EBR* 1968 noted that it might well have been so, given the growth of the gravel industry in Essex. A total of 2,260 pairs at 16 sites in 1968 included about 500 pairs at Marsh Farm, Brightlingsea, 400 at Wivenhoe, 300 at Moverons, Brightlingsea, 250 at Southminster and 220 at Sible Hedingham. In all, some 60% were located in gravel-workings to the east of the Colne.

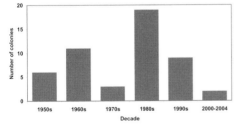

Number of colonies of 100+ Sand Martins reported in each decade from 1950

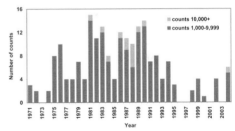

Annual totals of counts of 1,000+ Sand Martins from 1971-2004

The spring of 1969 saw Sand Martins return late and in much reduced numbers right across Britain. This catastrophic crash has been attributed to drought in the Sahel region of Africa (Winstanley *et al.* 1974). Numbers have to this day not returned to pre-1969 levels. The population recovered slowly throughout the 1970s, such that several Essex colonies in excess of 100 were being reported by 1979, when there were at least 324 pairs at Sandon GP. A further population crash in 1983/84, again attributed to droughts in the wintering quarters, left the national population at around 10% of that prior to 1968 (Mead 1984): just 345 pairs were reported from 13 colonies across Essex in 1985, although a rapid increase saw 1,760 pairs in 1987 including 525 at Holyfield. The year 1985 was the nadir of the Sand Martin in Britain and Europe (Population Trends) and, although the population recovered soon after, numbers once again appear to have declined; nationally, the WBS for 1978–2002 recorded an 8% decline and the BBS (England) a 29% decline over the period 1994–2003.

Essex Atlas survey work revealed the Sand Martin to be present in 18.8% of tetrads, although breeding was only confirmed in 6.5%. Numbers in Metropolitan Essex showed an overall increase between the two London Atlases, particularly in southern Essex. Although the general trend over the last decade or so has been a decline, numbers vary from year to year and, ironically, the largest colony reported from Essex occurred at a time of very low populations: 650 active holes in Fingringhoe GP in 2000; also, there were 540 at Stanway GP in 1995. Breeding densities are influenced by weather during the breeding season. In good years, two broods may be raised but, if spring is cold and wet, just one will result (Second National Atlas). The run of cold and wet springs during the 1990s and 2000s is, therefore, likely to have kept populations depressed.

The location of many nest sites means that colony size varies markedly from year to year with some sites becoming unsuitable and abandoned. The majority are within artificial sand and gravel-pits and thus concentrated within the former flood plains of the rivers Colne, Thames, Lea and Stort, although chalk quarries in the south of Essex have also been used. Occasionally, colonies are reported from other artificial nest sites. Relief channel drain holes at the Lea Valley reservoirs have been used since 1918 (Nau 1961), with around 100 pairs in 1955 but 25–50 more recently, whilst ten pairs nested in a similar locality at Stratford Marsh in 2000–02. A few pairs used the drainpipes underneath the promenade and over the beach at Frinton-on-Sea during the 1950s and four pairs used the crumbling concrete wall of Royal Albert Docks in 1997 with seven pairs in 2001.

Its natural breeding habitat is sand banks along rivers and sea cliffs, neither of which is, nor has been, particularly widespread in Essex. The sandy cliffs at The Naze continue to be used, numbers varying considerably from year to year, the peak count being 60 pairs in 1962 but 20–30 pairs more recently. Very small numbers occasionally nest in the remnants of the sea cliffs between The Naze and Clacton-on-Sea. Two or three pairs nested in the low sea cliffs at East Mersea in 1956. However, in 1999 Sand Martins recolonised the cliffs with 80 holes noted, 200 in 2002 but only 55 in 2004. Nests in river cliffs have been noted just twice: at Little Chesterford in 1955 when a number nested in the 2m-tall bank of the Cam; and at Walthamstow, where nine pairs nested in the banks of the Lea in 1967 and 1968.

Sand Martins are one of the earliest spring migrants and generally the earliest of the hirundines with the first individuals usually noted from mid-March. However, between 1989 and 2002 there were nine arrivals on or before 10th March, the earliest being at Walthamstow on 1st in 1992, where there was also one on 3rd in 1994. Numbers passing through Essex, however, generally peak from mid-April to mid-May. Gatherings in spring are generally small in comparison to those in autumn and most high counts are in three figures. Only Hanningfield attracted any great numbers, although the estimated 10,000 that arrived during a storm and left immediately after it had passed on 2nd May 1981 were exceptional. Otherwise, there were 1,000 there on 4th May 1979 and 2,500 on 26th May 1979. There were 1,000 at Abberton on 3rd–4th May 2004.

Small return movements are often noted during the first half of July but it is not until the end of the month that any large gatherings occur, with numbers peaking during August and early September. Since 1950 there has been an apparent increase in the size of autumn influxes to the main reservoirs. This may, however, be simply due to increased observer coverage. During the 1950s the largest gatherings were 5,000–7,000 at Abberton on 29th July 1953 and 5,000 there on 24th August 1958. In the 1960s the highest count was 10,000 at Abberton on 17th August 1968, with 5,000 at Hanningfield on 19th August 1968. Few large gatherings were noted during the 1970s and it was not until the mid-1970s that substantial counts were made, although all were either roost counts or pre-roost gatherings: at Layer-de-la-Haye there were 7,000–8,000 on 13th August 1978, 8,000 on 24th August 1975 and 7,000 on 25th August 1974; and at Southminster there were 3,000–5,000 during August 1978. Reed beds are typically used for roosting, although fields of cereals and Oil-seed Rape have also been used in Essex.

Substantially larger counts were noted during the 1980s and into the mid-1990s. An estimated 50,000 were at Hanningfield on 4th September 1983 and 40,000 at Abberton on 4th September 1984. Other five-figure counts in the 1980s included 15,000 at Hanningfield on both 25th August 1986 and 21st August 1988 with 10,000 there on 29th August 1988; there were also 10,000 at Paglesham on 18th August 1988 and 20,000 at Abberton from 2nd–3rd September 1989. After an excellent breeding season in 1990 at least 50,000—and possibly as many as 100,000—were at Abberton on 18th August, with 15,000 at Hanningfield on the previous day and 25,000 on 17th September. An estimated 100,000 moved through Abberton during the 25 days commencing 15th August 1992, with a peak of 10,000 on 15th. The last five-figure count in the 1990s was 25,000 at Abberton on 29th August

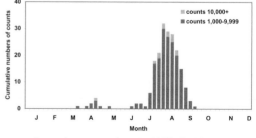

Seasonal occurrence of counts of 1,000+ Sand Martins
from 1971-2004

1994. Autumn gatherings since 1995 have been significantly smaller with the highest being 8,000 at Abberton on 21st August 1999 and 10,000 there on 29th August 2004; the significant decline in large counts has mirrored the national population decline.

Away from the main reservoirs, few spring movements have been noted. However, it is not unusual for large numbers to be seen during autumn. Throughout the 1950s, Romford ringing station reported heavy passage down the Beam that regularly totalled four figures, with 3,500–4,000 on 29th August 1958. Otherwise, southerly movements of up to 2,000 have been reported from the coast with some regularity. Exceptionally, some 10,000 birds moved south in just one hour at Great Wakering during the evening of 7th August 1987 and 8,000–10,000 moved south past Clacton-on-Sea/Holland-on-Sea between 0930hrs and 1130hrs on 1st September 1955.

The Sand Martin is the earliest of the hirundines to leave the country and most have departed by mid-October. However, 15 have been noted in Essex in November, 11 in the first two weeks of the month but with singles at; Fingringhoe, 15th in 1970; Shoebury, 18th in 1865(2); Abberton, 18th in 1960; Foulness, 28th in 2004. The latest, by almost three weeks, was at Walthamstow on 8th December 1959. In addition, Christy referred to Sand Martins having been seen during Christmas week but gave no further details.

	Jan	Feb	Mar	Apr	May	Jun	Jul	Aug	Sep	Oct	Nov	Dec
Essex					10	9	8	5	2			
Scotland						1	2	3				
North England						4	5					
South England				1	10	19	39	34	14	1		
France					2		1	1				
Spain					1							
Morocco									1			
Tunisia					1							
Algeria	1				1							
Senegal			1									2
Totals	*1*	*0*	*1*	*6*	*21*	*32*	*55*	*43*	*17*	*1*	*0*	*2*

Month and location of recovery of Sand Martins ringed in Essex

Nearly 200 Essex-ringed Sand Martins have been recovered with over 75% in Essex or southern England. However, a number have been recovered in northern England and Scotland, suggesting that the late summer gatherings may be made up of Sand Martins from across Britain. Additionally, there have been several recoveries abroad, including three from Parc National du Djoudj, Fleuve, Senegal, the species' main wintering area in Africa. The recovery in January in Algeria is unusually far north for the time of year.

Two foreign-ringed Sand Martins have been recovered in Essex, one from France and the other that was recovered at Shrub End, Colchester, on 11th August 1981, had been ringed at Lac Aougoundou, Mali, on 2nd April 1981.

Pure albinos have been noted in Essex on five occasions: 11th August 1952 for five weeks at Abberton; 13th September 1955 at Hanningfield; 1st September 1956 at Hanningfield; 19th–26th August 1971 at Layer-de-la-Haye; and 8th September 1992 at Abberton. An almost pure albino, apart from a brown crown, was noted in the Chelmer Valley on 4th October 1958, whilst leucistic individuals were at The Naze on 31st August 1996 and 26th August 1998, Abberton on 5th August 2002 and Wat Tyler CP on 16th August 2004.

There is little direct conservation action that can be taken across Essex to encourage the species. Experience has shown that purpose-made Sand Martin banks may not necessarily be accepted by the species. Encouraging quarry operators to leave areas of pits undisturbed is probably the most positive action that could be taken. Recently, however, fewer steep banks have been left, rather they have been graded to gentle slopes, perhaps in response to more stringent health and safety requirements. This is likely to have a negative affect on breeding numbers. That said, it is the impact of changes in land use and climate in the species' winter quarters which may ultimately determine the Sand Martin's future in Essex.

(Barn) Swallow   *Hirundo rustica*

Common summer visitor and passage migrant   Amber List

The Swallow is a Holarctic species and the most widespread of its family. The species breeds throughout much of Europe, apart from Iceland and Norway, where it is represented by the nominate race *rustica* (European Atlas). The Swallow is a semi-colonial species that builds its nests in any permanently open buildings and is well distributed throughout the whole of Britain, being absent from only a few areas, mostly in northwest Scotland, Shetland Islands and the Outer Hebrides. Northern populations 'leapfrog' those from southern Europe to winter in southern Africa.

Christy described the Swallow as an abundant summer visitor, although he provided no quantitative data. Glegg considered the species to be "… a numerous summer resident … Some recorders hold the view that it has decreased and others that it has increased". There is little evidence to suggest that national Swallow populations fluctuated significantly in the 19th and 20th centuries (Historical Atlas).

Being so common, few data have been published; the Swallow was not mentioned in the Systematic List of the *EBR* between 1959 and 1969 and it was not until 1989 that specific reference was made to breeding numbers. Hudson & Pyman described the Swallow as a common summer resident, being most numerous in rural areas and scarce in urban areas. No change in distribution was noted between the two National Atlases, the Swallow being found in every 10km square, whilst the two London Atlases, which covered similar survey periods, noted an increase in Metropolitan Essex. The Essex Atlas survey found Swallows breeding in 85.3% of tetrads and present in a further 11.5%, the only absences being predominantly in urban centres.

Since around 1992, many observers consider that the Swallow has been becoming scarcer in Essex, although the species is under-recorded. The national CBC Index for the period 1962–73 showed generally stable numbers. In 1974, however, there was a notable decline, but the CBC/BBS Index for the period 1977–2002 showed only a marginal 2% fall whilst the BBS (England) Index showed a small increase of 4% from 1994–2003. The local CBC/BBS Indices increased during the 1990s but have shown a marginal decline recently.

Such data appear contrary to the apparent declines noted by experienced observers. Fluctuations on a local scale appear to be typical of the species and it may be these differences that are normally noted by people who lose their Swallows. Improved farm hygiene, intensive stock rearing, modern buildings and the use of pesticides reduce both food and nesting sites and so make farms less suitable for Swallows (Second National Atlas) and this may have caused some declines in the south and east of England. However, droughts in southern Africa, where British Swallows winter, will have reduced winter food supplies and may have had more influence on numbers than farming change in Britain (Population Trends). This may lead not only to higher winter mortality but also birds in poorer condition that can raise fewer young (Møller 1989). Cold, wet autumn weather, particularly at high altitude, can cause serious losses to migrating populations.

Swallows have long associated with man, perhaps from Neolithic times, and natural breeding sites are now rare. Farmland is the most important habitat and breeding densities increase with the area of farm buildings (Møller 1983). Most Swallows nest in barns and outhouses as well as in, for example, porches and garages but alternative nest sites in Essex over the years have included WWII pill boxes where up to 150 pairs have bred along Dengie, the frames of derelict aircraft on Foulness, flood-damaged caravans, chalets and boats at St Osyth following the 1953 flood and old Blackwater barge hulks laid up amongst the saltings at Maldon. The majority of adults return to the same site in successive years (males being more site-faithful than females) and they often stay with the same mate. First-year birds often return to within three and usually within 30km of their birth site, although 70–80% die before they get the chance to breed (Turner & Rose 1989). In 1957, a female attempted to incubate two nests at the same time at Daws Heath: one fledged young resulted.

The first Swallows normally arrive during the first week of April with passage peaking in late April and early May. Records during the last week of March are, however, not uncommon but these usually involve single birds, ten at Abberton on 24th in 1985 being exceptional. There have been just nine records prior to 20th March, the earliest at Wivenhoe on 2nd in 2000, with another at Stanford-le-Hope on 3rd in 2002. Spring passage is generally inconspicuous, most records involving no more than three-figure counts. The majority of the larger counts have come from the main reservoirs with the largest from Hanningfield: 1,000, 7th and 9th May 1979; 5,000, 26th May 1979; 1,000, 5th May 1984; "many thousands", 21st April 1988; and 1,000, 28th April 2002. The only four-figure spring counts from Abberton were 2,000 on 7th May 1979 and 1,200 on 3rd May 2004. Coasting movements in spring are more obvious than those of the two martins: 7,500 moving north at Bradwell on 11th May 1975 was, however, exceptional.

Autumn passage begins in late July with the southward movement and dispersal of juveniles, although this is probably masked in part by the presence of local populations. By mid-August, however, large numbers move

Atlas	Survey Area	% of 10km squares or tetrads in which	
		bred/probably bred	possibly bred or present
First National 10km	Essex	100.0	0.0
Second National 10km	Essex	100.0	0.0
First London Tetrad	Met. Essex	49.0	17.5
Second London Tetrad	Met. Essex	87.0	10.5
Essex Tetrad	Essex	85.3	11.5

Summary of results of Atlas surveys for Swallows

through Essex with the highest counts generally occurring in September and early October. Passage is on a broad front and large movements are noted inland as well as from the coast. During the early 1950s, autumn observations along various river valleys showed these to be minor flight lines (Pyman 1953) and a flock of hirundines, apparently all Swallows, estimated at about 10,000 birds was noted passing at a height of about 30m down the Chelmer into the Blackwater at Maldon on 20th September 1952. About 3,000 moved south over Colchester in two hours on 5th October 1985.

Coastal movements are particularly conspicuous and protracted. Most individuals appear to follow the coast from The Naze to Colne Point, then strike out over the sea to Bradwell or Mersea Island. Quite large numbers appear to move up the Blackwater Estuary: for example, 5,000 moved west in about four hours on 28th August 1954 before moving south across Dengie, and coasting birds regularly pass over Dengie. Although some pass south directly over the Thames, many appear to move west along the north shore before striking out south.

Day counts of 1,000–2,000 are regular at individual coastal sites although numbers vary considerably from year to year, and as well as being influenced by breeding success, weather conditions prevailing at the time of migration must also influence passage. In some years exceptional passage has occurred through Essex, although attempts at determining the possible source of such influxes have proved inconclusive (Lawton 2000). Thus, following a series of very poor years between 1995 and 1997, a huge movement was noted across Essex during the autumn of 1999. This movement included 17,000 southwest at The Naze on 26th September and 16,000 through Colne Point on the same day. Many sites inland also recorded a strong passage around this time and the total number of birds was perhaps of the order of 50,000–100,000. This unprecedented movement was also noted in Norfolk (>100,000 birds) but not in Suffolk (Piotrowski 2003). The highest single site count recorded in Essex came from Colne Point in 1981, when about 20,000 flew west on 13th August. There were 8,500 there on 4th September 1994, whilst around 5,500 flew southwest over Abberton in 2.5 hours on 12th September 1992.

Swallows, like Sand Martins, will form large roosts in autumn, usually in *Phragmites* reed beds around the edges of various water bodies. Roosts of 1,000–2,000 are not uncommon. However, by far the largest gatherings were at Pitsea, where in 1986 a total of 100,000 was estimated to have used the reed bed between August and early October, and in 1988 perhaps 150,000 were involved, of which 2,500 were ringed. Maximum counts of 5,000 were also noted there in 1985 and 1987. A total of 10,000 at Abberton on the evening of 13th September 1993 is likely to have roosted locally. At Bocking, a roost that averaged 3,000 birds between 23rd September and 10th October 1977 peaked at 4,000–5,000 on 7th October, and about 3,250 roosted at Berwick Ponds on 21st August 1983. About 2,000 roosted in a bed of Great Reedmace in a pond at the entrance to Colchester General Hospital during September 1992.

Swallows are recorded with some regularity well into November, sometimes in small flocks. Since 1950, there have been 16 December records, all involving singles apart from 3–4 at Colne Point on 2nd in 1953, two at Steeple on 16th in 1960, and two at Braintree on 4th in 1994. Seven of the records occurred in the first week of December with four in the second, three in the third and two during the last week. The latest were at South Benfleet on 24th in 1958 and Hanningfield on 24th in 1983. Christy also mentioned one that lived through to January in the winter of 1876/77 in the parish of Little Waltham and another that lived through a winter [undated] in a church at Epping. Dr Bree also recounted to Christy that he had "... a nest and eggs taken while the old bird was sitting on them in the middle of December [1866] at Walton-on-the-Naze". One was seen at Colchester on 23rd December 1868. One at Abberton on 28th January 2002 may have been an exceptionally early migrant.

Around 260 Essex-ringed Swallows have subsequently been recovered, 85% of them in Essex and southern England. The majority of the remainder have been recovered in their wintering grounds with surprisingly few along the migration route, particularly in Europe. In addition, two have been recovered in the mid-North Sea in spring. Swallows probably overfly the Sahara/Sahel zones and first stop to refuel in western Africa in October before moving on to the wintering quarters from December through to February (*HBW*). The most southerly recovery involved one ringed as a nestling at Braintree on 22nd August 1951 and recovered on 15th January 1952 some 9,807km to the south in East London, South Africa, one of the longest migrations of any passerine. One ringed in central Essex on 10th August 1968 was recovered 106 days later in Transvaal, South Africa, an average journey

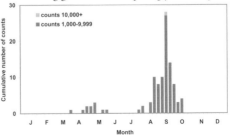

Seasonal occurrence of counts of 1000+ Swallows from 1971-2004

time of over 85km/day. The recovery off Norway and those in the North Sea suggest that Continental Swallows may well occur in Essex on passage. No foreign-ringed Swallows have been recovered in Essex.

Aberrant plumaged individuals are recorded with some regularity, the majority being apparent albinos. A blind albino was hand-reared at West Bergholt in 1953 but subsequently died. A juvenile with a pinky-buff rump at Hanningfield on 8th

	Jan	Feb	Mar	Apr	May	Jun	Jul	Aug	Sep	Oct	Nov	Dec
Essex			1	6	33	27	30	31	27	2		
Scotland						1						
North England					1		2	3	1			
South England				1	10	4	6	15	24	2		
Norway					1							
Germany				1	1							
Belgium					1							
France				1	3				1	2		
Spain					1							
Algeria						1						
Nigeria										1	1	
Zaire											1	
Namibia	1		1									
South Africa	4	1									2	3
Totals	*5*	*1*	*2*	*9*	*51*	*33*	*38*	*49*	*53*	*7*	*4*	*3*

Month and location of recovery of Swallows ringed in Essex

September 1956 and felt by the observers to have been confusable with a Red-rumped Swallow may have been a Swallow/House Martin hybrid of which there has been one definite Essex record, one found in a mist-net at Holland Haven on 31st August 1992 (Cox 1993).

One with darker reddish-buff underparts that was present at Seventy Acres Lake on 29th April 2004 was almost certainly an aberrant individual and most unlikely to have been of the Palestinian race *transitiva* (Angela Turner pers. comm.).

Despite both BBS and CBC data suggesting that the Swallow has increased during the 1990s, anecdotal evidence appears to point to a decline over the last two decades or so. Numbers recorded on passage do not appear to have declined, indeed the contrary may have occurred, although greater observer coverage may be partly responsible for this trend. It is possible that the loss of cattle from large areas of Essex, together with the grubbing out of hundreds of kilometres of hedges, have resulted in declines in insect availability, which in turn has affected the Swallow. Thus, whilst still fairly common, the long-term future of the Swallow in Essex remains uncertain; a return to more traditional farming methods that produce a patchwork of habitat across the countryside would undoubtedly benefit the species.

Sponsored by Martin Henry in memory of Stan Hudgell

House Martin *Delichon urbicum*

Common summer resident and passage migrant Amber List

The House Martin breeds across almost the entire Palearctic from Britain and Ireland east to Japan and China, with the nominate subspecies *urbica* breeding in Europe, where it is absent only from Iceland, the Faeroe Islands and Svalbard. Its distribution in Britain is very similar to that of the Swallow where there appears to have been a slow long-term decline in numbers (Population Trends). Three factors seem to govern its distribution: suitable nest sites; warmth, sunshine and very moderate rain and winds for easy availability and exploitation of aerial insects (Bryant 1975); the locality should have a sufficient supply of insects for nesting success. House Martins are closer ecologically to Swifts than Swallows in being high-flying feeders. House Martins also share Swifts' ability to nest in towns (Tatner 1978). In some ways, therefore, they are the Swallow's urban counterparts. Their principal food items also differ, with House Martins taking mostly aphids, midges and similar-sized flying insects, whilst Swallows concentrate on larger flies such as Bluebottles (Turner & Rose 1989).

Christy described the House Martin as an abundant summer visitor and observed: "They would be very much commoner than they are ... were it not for the Sparrows taking possession of their nests", one of his correspondents noting that at Stubbers near North Ockendon "... useful and ornamental Martins are being steadily exterminated by the injurious and obnoxious Sparrows". Every sparrow was subsequently shot and from just seven House Martin nests in 1870, numbers increased to 110 by 1877 and 237 by 1885. More recently, no single colony has approached this size, suggesting perhaps that numbers are not as great as they were a century ago. At Harwich, the species was declining in each year towards the end of the 19th century; Christy concluded that: "I am inclined

Atlas	Survey Area	% of 10km squares or tetrads in which bred/probably bred	possibly bred or present
First National 10km	Essex	100.0	0.0
Second National 10km	Essex	100.0	0.0
First London Tetrad	Met. Essex	56.5	12.5
Second London Tetrad	Met. Essex	79.0	17.5
Essex Tetrad	Essex	50.0	33.5

Summary of results of Atlas surveys for House Martins

to think that the same remark applies to the whole county".

Glegg, Hudson & Pyman and Cox all considered the House Martin to be a common summer resident throughout Essex. Overall, therefore, the species' status appeared to change very little during the first 75 years of the 20th century. However, Hudson & Pyman noted that: "... its numbers are doubtfully as high as they were a decade ago". Despite its preference for urban areas, they considered the species rare in built-up areas and absent from most London suburbs.

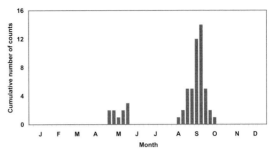

Seasonal occurrence of counts of 1000+ House Martins from 1971-2004

The House Martin was originally a cliff- and cave-nesting species using both coastal and inland sites (Clark & McNeil 1980), but no such locations have been used in Essex in recorded times, although a few pairs have used old Sand Martins' nest-holes at Stanway GP and East Tilbury, a near-natural nesting location. The typical nesting site is under the eaves of houses. Additionally, up to 300–400 scattered pairs nested on oil storage tanks in the East Tilbury/Shellhaven area in the 1980s (Cox) with 47 around the refinery tanks at Harwich in 1987. Aircraft hangers at Stansted Airport, railway signal boxes at Parkeston Quay and the towers on the dam at Hanningfield have also supported small colonies.

Like the Swallow, the House Martin has only been mentioned regularly in the Systematic List of the *EBR* since the 1980s. In 1983 there were 48 nests on one semi-detached house at Boxted and the same number at Bradwell juxta Braintree, whilst in 1988 it was noted that "... a decline has been apparent in recent years".

The Essex Atlas survey confirmed the species' presence in 83.5% of all tetrads, whilst the two National Atlases confirmed that House Martins, like Swallows, were breeding in every 10km square. However, although there was little change in distribution between the two London Atlases, if anything there appeared to have been an increase along the Thames, there was concern that this apparent stability masked an underlying decline (Second London Atlas). The species increased in central areas of London in the 1960s and 1970s, possibly as a result of a reduction in pollution following the Clean Air Acts, which lead to an increase in flying insects (Cramp & Gooders 1967). In addition, modern town planning has promoted increased areas of urban 'countryside' within built-up areas, which has encouraged insect numbers (Turner 1982). More recently, however, air pollution caused mainly by traffic fumes again appears to be increasing and this, together with other factors such as climate change, may have once again reduced air quality. In Metropolitan Essex, the Essex Atlas referred to significant population declines, particularly since the late 1980s. This apparent reduction has continued to be recorded in *EBRs* almost to the present day, not only in Metropolitan Essex but also in most other parts of the county. In the Romford and Hornchurch area, declines between 1997 and 2000 may have been as high as 80% but almost every regularly observed site in Essex has seen apparent, sometimes quite marked, decreases since the early 1990s, although signs of numbers stabilising have been evident since 2000. These apparent trends are largely subjective and not based on quantitative data, and counts at individual colonies are an unreliable guide to population trends over a wider area. National surveys have not detected any significant declines in the population, which appears to be either stable or in a slow long-term decline (Population Trends). Although the CBC/BBS (England) Index for the period 1977–2002 suggested a 69% decline, the BBS (England) Index for the period 1994–2003 has shown a small increase of 3%. It has been suggested that nesting has become more dispersed with larger colonies replaced with smaller ones, which are less likely to be recorded (Second National Atlas). If reductions are occurring, it is probably a combination of factors that are involved. In addition to air pollution, the use of insecticides in modern agriculture and gardens is likely, over time, to result in the reduction in availability of insect prey, whilst droughts are likely to reduce the availability of mud required for nest building. Droughts in the wintering grounds are less likely to affect the House Martin as its highly aerial and nomadic lifestyle probably mitigate the effects that have influenced Swallow and Sand Martin populations.

On both spring and autumn migration, numbers reported are rarely as high as either Sand Martins or Swallows. Like the Swallow, the first arrivals tend to occur around the first week of April, but in general the main arrival is later, during May. In February 2004, there was a remarkably early arrival of House Martins with two at Copford on 7th and one at Dagenham Chase on 9th; these are the only February records. March records have occurred in 18 years since 1950, with four in each of the 1950s and 1980s, six in the 1990s and four in the 2000s; there were none in the 1970s. The earliest March arrival involved two at Berwick Ponds on 13th in 1993 with the next at

Dagenham Chase on 16th in 2004. Small movements involving three-figure counts are reported regularly from the coast where House Martins often move through with Swallows. A total of 750–1,000 moving south at Bradwell on 4th June 1989 was unusual. Most of the largest spring counts have come from inland waters, and Hanningfield has been particularly favoured with seven four-figure counts noted, the highest being 2,500 on 26th May 1979, whilst gatherings of 2,000 were noted there on: 2nd May 1981; 5th May 1984; 28th May 1994; and 13th May 1995. Away from Hanningfield, the only four-figure counts have come from Abberton: 1,500 on 29th May 1984; and East Tilbury, 1,000 on 28th May 1994.

Return migration, often in the company of Swallows, commences in late July with numbers (like those of Swallows) peaking in mid-September. In the first two decades of the 20th century it was observed that many House Martins were moving west through Essex along the estuaries. Many thousands, sometimes passing at a rate of more than 100 a minute, were noted moving west along the Thames on 20th September 1914. Glegg noted a similar westerly route along the Stour on 22nd September 1924. Eagle Clarke (1912) noted the east–west flight of House Martins on his stay on the Kentish Knock Lightship and suggested that the westerly migrations noted in Essex may have involved Continental birds. Today, much the same movements are noted and, like other species, there is an apparent northerly movement through The Naze during autumn, which presumably is a local phenomenon, individuals then striking out west and south around the back of The Naze.

Like Swallows, House Martins appear to move on a broad front through Essex. Inland, an exceptional movement of 6,000+ over Ongar on 29th September 1971 occurred with many exhausted birds crowding rooftops around the observer's house. Other large counts have come from: Oliver's, 3,000 south in two hours, 5th October 1985; Essex Filter Beds, 2,500 south, 6th October 1995; West Bergholt, 2,000–3,000 high southwest, 28th August 1985; Newport, 1,800 southwest in two hours, 30th August 2002; and Bradwell, 1,500 south, 16th September 1993. The main reservoirs attract significant numbers with the largest count being 5,000–10,000 at Hanningfield on 29th September 1974, the next highest count there being 4,000 on 14th September 1986. The highest counts from Abberton have been 5,000 on 18th August 1990, 23rd September 1993 and 11th September 1994. In the Lea Valley, there were 2,000 on 23rd September 1990, 1,500 on 3rd August 2000, 1,000 on 29th September 1995 at KGV and 1,000 at Walthamstow on 18th September 1999. Four-figure totals from coastal sites are regular, the highest being 4,000 south at Bradwell on 24th August 1975, an early date for such a large number. At Colne Point about 2,500 flew south in just 30 minutes on 25th September 1980 whilst 4,200 moved through on 22nd September 1999. There were 3,000 at Rainham on both 1st October 1989 and 16th September 1990.

The House Martin is a relatively late-nesting species and this, together with its extended fledging period of up to 30 days, means that it is not unusual to find second broods still in the nest in early October. In 1979, young were still being fed at Silver End on 22nd October and at Halstead on 4th November. Not surprisingly small flocks are regularly recorded into early November. A flock of 30 at Layer-de-la-Haye on 10th in 1976 (15 still on 11th), ten at Weeleyhall Wood on 16th in 1977 with eight there on 19th, six around Southend Pier on 22nd in 1976 and six at both Chalkwell on 30th in 1985 and Foulness on 20th in 2004 are exceptional. There have been 14 December records, all singles apart from three at Fingringhoe Wick on 1st in 1982, two at West Mersea on 8th in 1951 and two at Southend-on-Sea on 1st in 1987. Of the 14, eight were in the first week of the month with four in the second week at: West Mersea (see above); Dovercourt, 11th in 1986; Abberton, 11th in 2001; and Stansted, 14th in 1986. The latest were at Danbury on 19th in 1960 and Colchester on 23rd in 1869.

Fewer aberrant individuals are noted than is the case for the Swallow with just over ten records of pure/partial albino or leucistic birds. For details of a Swallow x House Martin hybrid, refer to Swallow.

Unlike Sand Martins and Swallows, House Martins tend not to roost colonially and hence fewer have been ringed. In all, there have been 44 recoveries of Essex-ringed House Martins, all bar three coming from England: two have been found in France, whilst another that was ringed at Leigh-on-Sea on 1st September 1976 was recovered on Sicily, Italy, 1,805km to the south-southeast on 10th November 1976. The latter was particularly far to the east of the regular migration route that British House Martins take through France and eastern Spain; perhaps it was a Continental bird reorientating itself as these populations tend to migrate through central Europe? Nationally, out of 290,000 House Martins ringed in Britain, just one has been recovered south of the Sahara (Migration Atlas). Nearly 20 House Martins ringed in England have been recovered in Essex including singles from North Yorkshire and Greater Manchester.

Much of the available evidence regarding House Martin populations appears contradictory and it is therefore difficult to predict the species' future in Essex. However, reducing pollution and pesticide levels should ensure that insect populations remain healthy. In addition, the provision of artificial nest-sites and greater tolerance by the public of what can be a somewhat messy addition to any building would probably benefit the House Martin. House Sparrows, which some authors considered a threat to the House Martin, are in serious decline so direct competition for nest sites has at least decreased for the time being.

Sponsored by Steve Grimwade

Red-rumped Swallow   *Cecropis daurica*

Very rare passage migrant: 16 records involving 19 individuals

The Red-rumped Swallow breeds through Iberia and Morocco, locally in the western and central Mediterranean and east through the Balkans as far as Japan. European populations belong to the race *rufula*. Western populations are assumed to winter in the savannah of the African tropics, although they are inseparable from local races.

1969	Chigborough Lakes	26th April	
1975	Wanstead Park	4th–5th June	
1980	Abberton	6th–11th May	
1990	Gunners Park	11th May	
	Belfairs Park	2nd November	
	Layer-de-la-Haye	11th–17th November	
1992	Hainault Forest CP	23rd May	
1993	East Tilbury	26th September	
1994	Barling	23rd May–3rd June	
1997	Hanningfield	29th April	
1999	The Naze	2nd April	
2002	Stort/Hollingsons Mead	28th–29th May	
2003	Hanningfield	28th April	
	Ardleigh village	2nd May	Three
2004	Abberton	18th April	
	Hanningfield	29th April	Two

There were only seven British records prior to 1958, but this species has become annual since 1964 and there had been 484 by the end of 2004 (BBRC 2005). Red-rumped Swallows have shown a marked increase nationally since the late 1980s. This may be partly due to increased observer coverage and perhaps atypical weather patterns but is principally due to the spread of the species through Iberia and into southern France over recent decades, as well as expansion northward into the Balkans since the 1970s (European Atlas). It is likely that Britain receives migrants from both the east and south. The species usually occurs as a spring overshoot with smaller numbers occurring from October to early November. Ironically, the largest national influx, involving 64 birds in October and November 1987 (BBRC 1989), failed to produce one Essex record. It is quite possible that four birds were present at Ardleigh village (Lansdown 2004).

Richard's Pipit   *Anthus richardi*

Very rare passage migrant: 21 records

The monotypic Richard's Pipit breeds across southern Siberia, Mongolia and eastern China and winters in southern Asia (Alström *et al.* 2003). The species' occurrence in Europe has increased markedly since the 1960s.

1968	Holliwell Point	19th October
1973	Latton Common, Harlow	25th October
1987	Fairlop CP	20th September
	Two Tree Island	29th September

	Old Hall	3rd October
1988	Stanford Warren	20th September
	Holland Haven	25th September–1st October
	The Naze	1st October
	Maldon	21st–28th October
1989	Dagnam Park	2nd–3rd October
	Kirby-le-Soken	18th–23rd October
1991	Gunners Park	10th May
1992	Fairlop CP	15th May
	Holland Haven	1st–2nd October
1996	Barking	4th–5th October
1998	Chingford Plain	23rd October–1st November
2000	Old Hall	19th October
	Colne Point	24th October
2001	The Naze	28th October
2003	Walton Channel	19th October
2004	Colne Point	28th September

In addition, one was on the Kentish Knock Lightship, 43km off Holliwell Point, on 25th September 1903. Nationally, only about seven were recorded annually until 1965. However, since then numbers have increased markedly with an average of over 130 per annum during the 1990s (Fraser & Rogers 2004). The increase is undoubtedly due, at least in part, to greater observer awareness and coverage, but it seems that increasing numbers are occurring well west of their normal range. The first major influx in 1968 saw 141 nationally and produced the first Essex record. Other significant national influxes occurred in 1994 (352), 1995 (159) and 2001 (175) (Fraser & Rogers 2004), so the numbers recorded in Essex seem particularly low; there had been 53 Suffolk records to the end of 2004 (*Suffolk Bird Report* 2004).

Most occur from mid-September to November. A few occur in spring, presumably birds that have wintered further south. The double autumn peak of occurrence is marked, although this trend has not been noticed outside Essex.

The number of inland records suggest that Richard's Pipits may migrate on a broad front through Essex, rather than simply occurring as coastal vagrants pushed off course by vagaries of the weather. With this in mind, it is interesting to note that the species may have established wintering quarters in the western Palearctic as up to 15 have been counted at Oued Massa in Morocco, 29 at Villafáfila, Spain, and 33 in Sardinia in recent winters (Grussu & Biondi 2004).

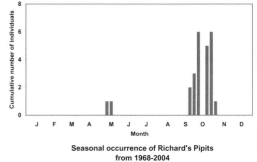

Seasonal occurrence of Richard's Pipits from 1968-2004

Sponsored by Moss Taylor

Tawny Pipit   *Anthus campestris*

Very rare passage migrant: 14 records

The Tawny Pipit breeds right across Continental Europe and North Africa, east to China and Mongolia. The nominate race *campestris* occurs across the western Palearctic. It is a species of dry, open countryside and has declined markedly over much of west and central Europe since the mid-1960s, due to habitat loss and perhaps also climatic change (European Atlas). Western populations winter south of the Sahara.

1951	Colne Point	31st August
1955	Goldhanger	12th July
1960	Frinton-on-Sea	13th–14th and 16th September
1969	Holliwell Point	7th November

1970	Colne Point	13th–16th September	
1976	Colne Point	18th September	
1981	Colne Point	12th September	
1984	East Tilbury	4th–5th November	
1987	East Mersea	29th–30th September	
1990	The Naze	7th May	
1991	Colne Point	30th May	
1992	East Tilbury	31st August	
1995	Harwich	9th September	1st-winter
1996	Abberton	25th August	

The species has decreased significantly on the near-Continent and national records have fallen from 36 per annum during the 1980s to only 12 in the 2000s (Fraser & Rogers 2004). Despite this, and presumably due to increased observer coverage, the number of sightings in Essex increased during the 1980s and early 1990s, since when it has become very rare. Small numbers, presumably northward-bound migrants overshooting their breeding range, occur in spring but the majority occur from late August to mid-October and probably involve birds dispersing from their breeding grounds. The two November records are particularly late, whilst the July record is early, but not unprecedented.

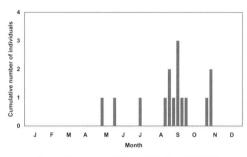

Seasonal occurrence of Tawny Pipits from 1951-2004

Olive-backed Pipit

Anthus hodgsoni

Vagrant: two records

The Olive-backed Pipit breeds in the taiga belt across Siberia, Mongolia, China and Japan and winters in southern Asia; the race *yunnanensi* occurs over much of the species' range.

| 1992 | Woodford Green | 23rd–26th October | |
| 1994 | Wat Tyler CP | 13th January–2nd April | Ringed on 19th February |

This is another Siberian vagrant that appears to have shown a genuine increase in occurrence nationally. Up to 1979 there had been just 14 records but by the end of 2004 this had increased to 274 (BBRC 2005), with significant influxes in several years, including 35 in autumn 1993, when presumably the Wat Tyler individual arrived. Possible reasons for the increase may include a change in distribution or migratory patterns resulting from deforestation in its range (Cottridge & Vinicombe 1996). Most occur in October, but a wintering individual is not unprecedented. Note that neither record was from a traditional coastal migration site.

Tree Pipit

Anthus trivialis

Uncommon and decreasing summer visitor and passage migrant　　　　　　　　Amber List

The Tree Pipit breeds throughout most of Europe, although it is absent from Iceland, southern Iberia and most Mediterranean islands and is generally scarce in Portugal and Ireland. Its breeding range extends east through Siberia as far as Yakutskaya and south to the Caspian and the Himalayas. The nominate race *trivialis* breeds throughout Europe (European Atlas). In Britain, the Tree Pipit is widespread, although most are found in upland regions and the species is relatively scarce in central and eastern England (Second National Atlas). It is a long-distance migrant, the nominate race wintering mainly in sub-Saharan Africa and the Indian subcontinent and in smaller numbers in the Middle East, on Crete and the Aegean islands (European Atlas).

It seems that, from the very limited evidence presented by Christy, the Tree Pipit was far more common during the 19th century than at any time since. Nationally, the Tree Pipit was a common bird over much of England, Wales and southern Scotland at that time, although the species was uncommon in parts of the east (Historical Atlas). Christy described the species as "A fairly common summer visitor" and, like other birds that were well known and common to him, he gave little further detail other than noting that at Epping it was "… frequent about the borders of the wood" and that 1–2 nested in the Maldon area. Glegg considered the Tree Pipit "… a not uncommon summer resident throughout the county…It may be decreasing in some areas". To what extent any suggested declines were genuine or linked simply to habitat change is unclear. Tree Pipits require open lowland woods, wooded borders, heaths and parklands with scattered trees and hedges and young conifer plantations up to thicket stage with areas of trees that have been felled or burnt approaching the ideal habitat (Simms 1971). Such habitat is typically transitional, as natural vegetation regeneration/succession will render previously suitable areas unusable relatively quickly.

Atlas	Survey Area	% of 10km squares or tetrads in which	
		bred/probably bred	possibly bred or present
First National 10km	Essex	45.6	5.3
Second National 10km	Essex	12.3	7.0
First London Tetrad	Met. Essex	14.0	0.5
Second London Tetrad	Met. Essex	6.5	3.0
Essex Tetrad	Essex	2.2	1.1

Summary of results of Atlas surveys for Tree Pipits

During the last 50 years, the majority of Tree Pipit breeding sites have been in the generally well-wooded area that runs from Epping Forest in the southwest to Colchester in the northeast, although in the 1950s and 1960s breeding records came from many parts of Essex. The larger populations have tended to be found in either young conifer or Silver Birch plantations with others occupying clearings in mature woodlands or in parks or on commons. During the 1950s the species seems to have remained widespread, although it was probably not common. At least 30 pairs were noted in an area of around 8ha at Danbury in 1952 (although there were just 2–3 pairs the following year) and 12 pairs in the Stansted/Spellbrook/Hallingbury area in 1952 (with just one pair in 1953). Four pairs also bred around the refuse tips at Rainham in 1955. Tree Pipits apparently made use of railway embankments, which in the age of steam trains were kept clear of trees by regular fires, and there is evidence from Essex that the running down of the railway services during the 1950s and 1960s reduced Tree Pipit numbers. For instance, a small colony on the Bishop's Stortford/Braintree line became extinct in 1953 after the trains were withdrawn. Hudson & Pyman observed "… it has decreased markedly in the last decade and can no longer be regarded as numerous anywhere". However, a lack of data makes assessment of such statements difficult. Nationally there was a general consensus that the Tree Pipit had by the 1950s and 1960s become less common and widespread in the lowlands of southeastern Britain, despite benefiting locally from new conifer plantings (Population Trends). Nonetheless, the species appears to have still been relatively widespread in Essex during the 1960s and 1970s. For example, in 1968 there were up to nine pairs in Chalkney Woods, Earls Colne, and a similar number in High Wood, Chishill, and a small population existed in the Harlow area. Many of these 'outer' populations disappeared during the 1970s such that by the end of the decade the broad distribution approximated to that seen today.

Essex population estimates up until the time of the First National and London Atlas surveys during 1968–72 were little more than guess work. The First London Atlas found confirmed or probable breeding in 14% of tetrads in Metropolitan Essex, traditionally the species' county stronghold, including perhaps 40–50 pairs in the Coopersale area in 1970. Cox estimated that the Essex population at this time was in the region of 140 pairs. However, given that the numbers noted at Coopersale appeared to have been exceptional in 1970 and that the survey occurred over five years, it is possible that a more typical Essex breeding population at this time was nearer to 100 pairs.

The ongoing decline continued through the 1970s such that within five years of the first National Atlas survey the population had halved, although reduced observer coverage following the end of the survey period may have been a factor in this trend. Despite a slight improvement in numbers in the early 1980s, the general steady reduction continued, although the rate of decrease accelerated during the 1990s, the Second National Atlas confirming significant losses across Essex. The Second London Atlas confirmed a decline of over 50% in confirmed breeding records in Metropolitan Essex over the 20 years since the First Atlas. With reductions continuing, the Tree Pipit is apparently moving inexorably towards extinction during the first decade of the 21st century: by 2004 the species was largely restricted to Epping Forest. The pattern of decline has not been straightforward. Thus, whilst numbers were declining elsewhere during the early 1970s, at Hainault Forest CP a rapid increase occurred peaking at ten pairs in 1973 (Essex Atlas), after which 7–10 pairs bred in an area of deciduous plantation until the mid-1980s. A large population was discovered in the Ingatestone area in the early 1990s and at the time accounted for some 50% of the Essex population; it was extinct by 2000. Other formerly healthy populations have also disappeared and, whilst it is possible that maturing of plantations may have been the cause of some declines (e.g. Hainault Forest CP, Dagnam

Park and Ingatestone), the widespread nature of the decline suggests other factors may be at work. Tree Pipits were not affected by the Sahel drought as they generally winter in wooded areas to the south of this region, but there may be other unknown factors at work in their winter quarters (Population Trends). Locally it is perhaps a number of factors, in addition to maturing plantations, such as scrub removal, loss of woodland, the conversion of many areas of rough land to farming, increasing urbanisation and the generally 'tidying up' of the landscape that have all contributed to the decline.

The Tree Pipit is one of the earlier returning summer migrants with records from the end of March not unusual. In 1993, however, and in common with several other summer migrants the species was reported exceptionally early with one at Walthamstow on 12th–13th March and at Abberton on 13th. Numbers

	1970-74	1975-1979	1980-84	1985-89	1990-94	1995-99	2000-04
Brentwood area including Weald CP, Thorndon CP, Warley CP etc	10	10	8	8	2	2	1
Writtle area including Ingatestone, Blackmore, Highwood & Fryerning	15	22	10	9	27	15	3
Hainault Forest CP	10	8	7	5	1	0	0
Epping Forest area including Ongar Park and North Weald	40	14	24	30	9	4	7
Dagnam Park/Maylands GC	10	9	10	6	5	4	0
Peak Essex annual total	49	55	60	57	47	16	12

Principal Tree Pipit breeding sites from 1971-2004 (peak counts in each decade)

in spring are, however, generally small with almost all records involving just 1–2 birds passing through during any one day, although there were three at The Naze on both 20th April 1981 and 2nd May 2004 and at Weald CP (a former breeding site) on 3rd May 2004. Five at Great Braxted on 24th April 1983 were described as migrants (*EBR* 1983) but were close to a known breeding area. Peak spring passage occurs from mid-April to early May.

By the end of July, Tree Pipits are beginning to move back through Essex, with most records coming from the coast. Passage peaks from mid-August through to mid-September and generally involves small numbers. The majority tend to be fly-over records; Tree Pipits have a very distinctive, strained, rasping call-note. Rarely are more than 1–3 reported from individual sites. The largest single day count involved 19 at Colne Point on 17th September 1993 at a time of a significant Meadow Pipit movement. In addition, there was a total of ten at The Naze between 5th and 8th September 1958 and seven passed over East Tilbury on 18th August 1984. Most Tree Pipits have left Essex by the end of September, although records during early October are not exceptional. The latest county record involved one at Leigh/Two Tree Island on 5th November 1981, some two weeks later than the next, at Colne Point on 22nd October 1990.

There are no ringing recoveries involving Essex. However, nationally it is thought likely that a significant proportion of the Tree Pipits occurring along the east coast of Britain in spring and autumn are from Continental breeding populations (Migration Atlas).

The status of the Tree Pipit as an Essex breeding species hangs very much in the balance. Only with some positive management of suitable moderate to large areas of woodlands, involving perhaps large scale coppicing or felling of mature plantations and replanting with new young trees, is the current trend likely to be reversed. Few areas lend themselves to this treatment apart from one of its last strongholds, Epping Forest, and perhaps Forestry Commission land at Pods Wood, Tiptree. If external factors allow, the large-scale planting along the Thames corridor may also provide some suitable habitat in the near future, as might areas of planting currently taking place around Essex as part of various environmental improvement schemes. The Tree Pipit population

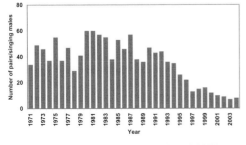

Annual totals of breeding Tree Pipits from 1971-2004

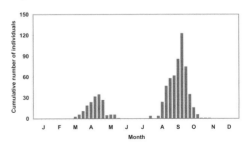

Seasonal occurrence of migrant Tree Pipits away from breeding sites from 1971-2004

405

is known to fluctuate quite markedly from year to year and it is possible that longer-term fluctuations may also be at work. However, at the current rate of decline the species will have been lost as a breeding species by 2010.

Meadow Pipit   *Anthus pratensis*

Resident, passage migrant and winter visitor   Amber List

The Meadow Pipit is almost exclusively European, being a common breeder in most open habitats in central and northern Europe. Its range extends from eastern Greenland in the west, across northern Europe to the mountains of central and northernmost southern Europe and to the lowlands of the River Ob east of the Urals (European Atlas). The nominate race *pratensis* occurs over much of the species' range, with *whistleri* occurring in Ireland and western Scotland. The species is found throughout Britain but is most abundant in upland areas, although it can be locally abundant in some lowland areas, too. In western Europe the species is generally sedentary. Northernmost populations, however, migrate annually, whilst other populations will move as short-distance migrants only when the weather becomes severe. Most migrants move to central, west and southern Europe with the largest numbers congregating in the western Mediterranean.

The Meadow Pipit's overall status has changed very little since Christy's time, although the instances of inland breeding appear to have increased in recent years. Christy observed that the species was "A common resident in some parts of the county, though not in others; especially abundant on the marshes and the saltings near the coast; rarer inland, where it is seldom met with except during winter". Glegg described a similar distribution, again noting that the species was "... a scarce bird inland ..." during the breeding

Atlas	Survey Area	% of 10km squares or tetrads in which	
		bred/probably bred	possibly bred or present
First National 10km	Essex	63.2	15.8
Second National 10km	Essex	54.4	21.1
First London Tetrad	Met. Essex	12.5	7.0
Second London Tetrad	Met. Essex	25.5	15.0
Essex Tetrad	Essex	21.5	6.0

Summary of results of Atlas surveys for Meadow Pipits

season, adding "... summer inland Meadow Pipits are so restricted in numbers as not to permit of consideration". These statements are contrary to the Essex Atlas, which suggested that it was not uncommon inland in Christy's day and declined markedly between then and Glegg's time of writing. The species appears therefore never to have been common inland, at least not since the mid-19th century. Neither writer gave any quantitative data for breeding numbers and indeed over 75% of Glegg's wnarration dealt with the species' migration.

Hudson & Pyman confirmed that, as a breeding species, Meadow Pipits were confined to the coast and estuaries. They were aware of just eight inland breeding records between 1950 and 1966. On the coast and the estuaries, Cox described the Meadow Pipit as "... well represented ..." with breeding occurring regularly up the Thames as far as Barking, whilst both National Atlases confirmed the preference for coastal areas and recorded a slight range contraction, principally from inland sites, although the two London Atlas surveys revealed a general increase in Metropolitan Essex, particularly along Thames-side. The Essex Atlas survey confirmed the mainly coastal distribution with the only gaps being in built-up areas. Coastal populations were believed to be stable, although declines were noted in parts of Dengie where, for instance, a population of 25–30 pairs between Sales Point and Glebe Outfall during the 1960s had declined to just five pairs in 1991. These declines may have been the result of more intensive grazing of seawalls and adjacent grasslands and perhaps also over-zealous grass-cutting regimes in such areas. Since the Essex Atlas survey, there has been no regular detailed census work carried out other than at a few sites such as Rainham. There, cessation of grazing on

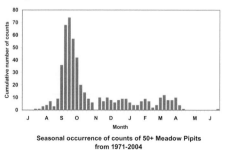

Seasonal occurrence of counts of 50+ Meadow Pipits
from 1971-2004

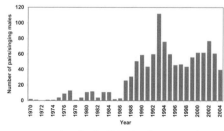

Annual totals of inland breeding/singing male
Meadow Pipits from 1970-2004

the former MoD land and general habitat loss led to a decline from a peak of 115 pairs in 1993 to 47 in 1998 but with a slight increase since. A total of 89 pairs was present at Tollesbury Wick in 2000, 50 pairs on Foulness in 2000 and around 30–40 pairs in Barking Bay around the turn of the 21st century.

Inland breeding records have tended to show a steady increase since the 1970s, despite the losses apparent between the two National Atlases. Cox noted breeding at Abberton, Ardleigh and Hanningfield, as well as in the Lea Valley and other smaller inland waters, sewage farms and also in drier areas such as airfields, "waste ground", allotments and within the chalky boulder clay region of northwest Essex. The number of inland records remained relatively small, however, until the early 1980s since when the inland population increased to around 50–80 pairs, although there were some 112 pairs at 17 sites in 1993. Breeding populations show large annual fluctuations, attributable, at least in part, to the severity of weather in wintering quarters and during spring migration (European Atlas) and these factors, together with inconsistent r ecording effort, may explain the variable numbers noted breeding inland from year to year.

Almost the entire inland population is found in Metropolitan Essex, with only occasional breeding reported away from there, although the species is undoubtedly under-recorded. Recently there have been up to 32 pairs in the Ingrebourne Valley and 19 at Dagenham Chase. Meadow Pipits have increasingly made use of old gravel-pits and airfields (Essex Atlas) as well as long-term set-aside, golf courses and local country parks where less intensive grass management, either as the result of enlightened conservation measures or economic necessity resulting in less mowing, has seen an increase in rough grassland that the species favours.

The Meadow Pipit is a regular passage migrant through Essex, sometimes in considerable numbers, whilst in winter birds appear to move into the county from elsewhere. Outside the breeding season, the species may be found almost anywhere inland, becoming quite numerous in suitable habitat.

Spring passage is not nearly as marked as autumn passage, the opposite of the situation in Norfolk (Taylor *et al.* 1999). Return passage appears to take place from late February through to mid-April and counts are generally small. The largest spring movement involved 1,250 that arrived along Dengie during four hours on 30th March 1980, whilst 700 were in a field at Althorne on 16th April 1963. In addition, 135 counted in off the sea along Dengie on 26th March 1978 was perhaps just 10% of the entire front of birds noted moving at that time. Three-figure counts are generally scarce at this time of year; those that have occurred have usually been noted at reservoirs or sewage farms.

Autumn passage begins around early August and peaks in late September and early October. Four-figure counts have been noted on several occasions with the largest single movement occurring on 30th September 1996 when over 2,500 moved in off the sea at Bradwell. In 1999 some 2,000 were at Deal Hall, Dengie, on 21st September, with 500 there the next day. Part of this movement was also noted at Colne Point with 300 on 21st. Other four-figure counts have been: at least 1,000 at The Naze, 19th September 1965; 1,000 along Dengie, 17th September 1988; 1,100 at Colne Point, 22nd September 1993; 1,205 at St Osyth beach, 19th October 1998; and 1,000 at Bradwell, 22nd September 2002. On the coast the general direction of movement tends to be to the west or southwest. However, at The Naze (and in common with other passerines) strong northerly movements are noted regularly. Although large movements are most often reported from the coast, three-figure counts have been recorded from many inland areas, mainly in October/early November, and have included 900 moving northwest along the Lea Valley on 1st November 1959. In the early

	Jan	Feb	Mar	Apr	May	Jun	Jul	Aug	Sep	Oct	Nov	Dec
Essex	4	1	1				1	1		1		1
North England					1							
South England	4			1							1	1
Faeroe Islands						1						
France										3		3
Spain	2	1								2	1	
Portugal	1	1									2	1
Totals	*11*	*3*	*1*	*1*	*1*	*1*	*1*	*1*	*0*	*6*	*4*	*6*

Month and location of recovery of Meadow Pipits ringed in Essex

1950s and from the late 1990s observations in the northwest of Essex have revealed the presence of various flyways, which although predominantly southwesterly in direction, were nonetheless variable, with autumn movements also occurring in any direction from east through south to west and very occasionally northwest. Once the large movements have tailed off, those remaining in Essex tend to disperse through the favoured habitat with gatherings of any great size rarely recorded during winter.

Glegg suggested that coastal breeding birds left Essex in autumn, whilst birds that occurred in winter at inland sites may have been of Continental origin; modern ringing recoveries have generally confirmed this suggestion. Nearly 40 Essex-ringed Meadow Pipits have subsequently been recovered, around 50% in England and with most of the remainder in France and Iberia.

Although most British Meadow Pipits are known to winter in Spain and Portugal, many remain within Britain all year (Migration Atlas). An individual recovered on the Faeroe Islands was probably from either the Faeroe Islands or Icelandic breeding populations, both of which occur in Britain during winter. The only foreign Meadow Pipit recovered in Essex was ringed in Belgium in October 1984 and found dead at Hatfield Peverel in January 1985.

With more of the coastline being managed for the benefit of wildlife and increasing areas inland of rough grassland around reservoirs, old gravel-workings and in country parks, it is to be hoped that the Meadow Pipit can exploit the expansion of its favoured habitat and perhaps become more widespread on both the coast and inland in the coming years.

Sponsored by the late Mike Dennis

Red-throated Pipit   *Anthus cervinus*

Vagrant: five records

The monotypic Red-throated Pipit breeds almost entirely within the Arctic Circle across much of Eurasia, making it one of the most northerly breeding passerines, It winters in Africa as far west as Gambia and Morocco.

1982	Rainham	1st May	Summer plumage
1993	Bradwell	17th September	
	Rainham	19th September	
	Bradwell	5th October	
1994	Gunners Park	21st–22nd May	Summer plumage

The Red-throated Pipit is an annual vagrant to Britain with 424 records to the end of 2004 (BBRC 2005). The species is mainly recorded from the Northern Isles, along the east coast and on the Isles of Scilly with almost equal numbers in both spring and autumn. The increase in records, both nationally and in Essex in the 1990s, is probably due to greater observer coverage. The three individuals in 1993 all occurred at times of particularly heavy Meadow Pipit passage.

Rock Pipit   *Anthus petrosus*

Locally common winter visitor and passage migrant

The Rock Pipit breeds only in Europe where three races occur: *petrosus* in Britain and Ireland, the Channel Islands and north and northwest France; *littoralis* in Fennoscandia and the Baltic States; and *kleinschmidti* in the Faeroe Islands, Shetland, Orkney, and St Kilda (European Atlas). During the breeding season, it is a bird of rocky coasts and in Britain is absent from the east coast between Lincolnshire and Essex (Second National Atlas). The nominate race *petrosus* is generally very sedentary but northern populations of *littoralis* move south during autumn and occur around much of the British coast.

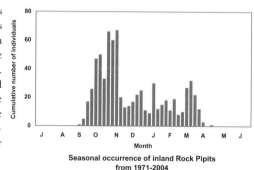

Seasonal occurrence of inland Rock Pipits
from 1971-2004

Christy described the Rock Pipit as a "... common bird on the marshes and saltings on or near our coast from autumn to spring". He considered that alleged breeding records along the coast from The Naze to the Blackwater actually involved Meadow Pipits. Glegg described the species as a regular winter visitor in some numbers but strictly confined to the saltings and their immediate vicinity. He added that it is "... only when the tide is well up, the creeks and rills full and the Pipit driven from its hiding places that a fair estimate can be made of the numbers present". He dismissed a record of breeding at East Mersea in 1892; it was based on the assumption that the excitement of two birds when approached meant that a nest was nearby. Given that the record was in summer, mistaken identity seemed more likely. He concluded his species' summary with the prophetic statement: "Although no inland records exist, it is quite possible, especially during migration, that occasional birds may occur, and the Pipits at such places as reservoirs, where there are stony facings, should be watched"; the origins of the wintering population were not known.

Both Hudson & Pyman and Cox described the Rock Pipit as a winter visitor and passage migrant that was quite common and well distributed around the coastline, principally between October and March with small numbers recorded inland, mainly from the principal reservoirs, on passage and to a lesser extent in winter. The same can be said of its status today with little apparent change in numbers over the last few decades.

Mud and saltings are the species' preferred habitat with few occurring on sand and shingle. They feed in the numerous creeks and gullies that cross the saltings and also pick their way through tideline debris. The main food supply is found within the inter-tidal zone (Winter Atlas). As Glegg observed, it is very difficult estimating numbers unless they are pushed off saltings by high tides. They do not tend to form flocks but some idea of the numbers present can be gained from total counts of 100 on The Naze on 11th November 1962, 80 in Hamford Water on 13th December 1981, up to 75 along Dengie in the early months of 1977 and 70 there on 19th March 1980. However, it is most likely that the real numbers present are far higher than suggested by these random counts (Taylor *et al.* 1999).

All the estuaries and the open coast have varying sized populations and small numbers occur even along the predominantly sand/shingle stretch of coastline between The Naze and Colne Point. Rock Pipits are regular up the Thames as far as Rainham where a reasonable-sized winter population has been maintained, despite increasing disturbance (Dennis 1989), the maximum count from here being 32 during November 1998. There are very few parts of the coast that do not hold Rock Pipits and, as they appear to tolerate quite heavy disturbance, they can be found feeding within quite built-up areas (Dennis 1989). From 1995 small numbers have been noted as far up the Thames as Beckton and Barking Bay, with numbers at the former reaching 12 on 12th December 1999 and 12 at the latter on 7th November 1998. Numbers on the inner Thames have increased in recent years, which perhaps is due to the generally cleaner condition of the river. Less typical winter habitat includes the sludge lagoons at The Hythe, Colchester.

Remarkably, *EBR*s have never documented any significant visible migration at coastal sites, although occasional individuals are noted annually, apparently moving through either on their own or with flocks of Meadow Pipits and Chaffinches. Whether this lack of observations is due to the fact that the species generally does not form flocks but rather migrates in ones and twos or simply because it is overlooked is not clear. That migration takes place through Essex is suggested by many peak counts occurring in spring and autumn, with numbers peaking inland at these times; small numbers also occur inland throughout winter.

Most inland records have come from the main reservoirs and usually involve 1–5 individuals. There have, however, been seven double-figure counts, six of them from Abberton: 20 on both 18th October 1968 and 30th October 1974; 15 on 20th December 1957; 13 during November 1980; 12 on 14th March 1962; and ten on 19th March 1996; the other double-figure count was ten at Walthamstow on 10th October 1967.

The first passage individuals are generally noted during early October, although records during the second half of September are not unusual. The earliest record involved one at East Tilbury on the exceptionally early date of 1st August 1981, whilst another was there on 21st August 1953. Otherwise there were singles at Bradwell on 5th September 1982 and East Tilbury on 6th September 1998. The majority have usually left the county by mid-April with occasional stragglers until the end of the month. There have been five May records, the latest being one at The Naze on 27th in 1984, with singles noted at: South Woodham Ferrers, 18th in 2003; Leigh/Two Tree Island, 16th in 1976; Bradwell, 6th in 1957; and The Naze, 1st in 1976.

In Essex, all individuals have been considered to be of the Scandinavian subspecies *littoralis*; there has never been any conclusive evidence to suggest that *petrosus* has occurred, although there have been a very few reports of individuals considered to show characteristics of this race, the most recent at Hanningfield on 30th December 1990. However, subspecific identification in both winter and summer is exceptionally difficult, with most summer individuals not safely assignable to a subspecies, whilst in winter the subspecies are indistinguishable (Alstrom *et al.* 2003).

The only ringing recoveries involving Essex have involved individuals from within the range of *littoralis*: one ringed in Sweden was recovered at Southminster in November 1949; another ringed near Onsala, Halland, Sweden, on 16th March 1983 was recovered on Barling Marshes on 5th February 1984; and one ringed at The Hythe on 30th December 1981 was recovered at Zalivnoye, Kaliningrad, Russia (1,359km to the east), on 6th October 1984. The last record is one of very few foreign recoveries of British-ringed Rock Pipits (Migration Atlas) and was at the eastern edge of the species' range.

The species' tolerance of disturbance and the relative abundance of suitable habitat along the Essex coast mean that, apart from rising sea levels, there are no immediate threats to the future of the Rock Pipit within the county.

Water Pipit

Anthus spinoletta

Uncommon winter visitor and passage migrant

The Water Pipit is very closely related to the Rock and Buff-bellied Pipits (*A. rubescens*) from which it was separated in 1988 (Knox 1988). The species breeds in mountainous regions across southern and central Europe, Asia Minor, the Caucasus, Iran and central Asia. In Europe, where the species is represented by the nominate race *spinoletta*, its typical habitat is mountain or alpine pasture and high mountain meadows (European Atlas). In winter, many birds leave the mountains for the valleys below, and others moving to larger lakes and rivers and the coasts of the North Sea, Atlantic and Mediterranean. In Britain, the Water Pipit is a winter visitor and passage migrant in small numbers, principally to southern and central England where its preferred habitats in order of preference are Water Cress beds, coastal freshwater/brackish pools or marshes, inland freshwater marshes or rivers and sewage farms (Johnson 1970).

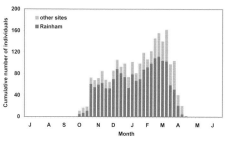

Seasonal occurrence of Water Pipits from 1950-2004

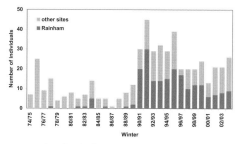

Annual totals of Water Pipits from 1974/75-2003/04

The early history of the species in Essex is undoubtedly clouded by its close similarity to Rock Pipit and perhaps also under-recording due to, until recently, its status as a subspecies of Rock Pipit; it has undoubtedly received greater attention since its elevation to full species' status, although improved optics and understanding of its identification features have probably influenced reporting levels. The earliest claimed record relates to one "… in a muddy creek, near Leigh, on 27th November 1923". Although at the time accepted by *British Birds*, it is unlikely that "… the eye-stripe, showing up against the greyish brown ear-coverts, being considered sufficient for identification" (Glegg) would be considered an acceptable description by the present EBS Identification Panel.

Hudson & Pyman noted 40 Essex records involving 46 individuals, 21 in March. They added that "Probably a number of these (though certainly not all) were actually *littoralis*, for few observers appreciate their similarity". Cox added a similar rider to his summary, although he referred to several undoubted records of individuals examined in the hand at Bishop's Stortford SF.

Since the mid-1980s, numbers reported have increased noticeably. This increase has been principally due to the discovery of a nationally significant (Dennis 1992a) wintering flock at Rainham, but small numbers are now reported from many locations throughout Essex in winter. The numbers of sites at which individuals occur generally increases every year, although the majority are in southern or Metropolitan Essex. Clearly there has been a significant change in the status of the Water Pipit at Rainham over the last 20 years. Prior to 1971, there had been no records from the site. However, six were reported there on 20th March 1971, with 12 five days later. Apparent occasional migrants and wintering individuals were recorded in the 1970s and 1980s but, since the winter of 1989/90, Water Pipits became an annual winter visitor with numbers increasing to a peak of 30 on 7th March 1992. More typically 12–17 were present with a reduction to 5–10 in the last few years. Dennis (1992a) considered that the increase in numbers at Rainham may have been a consequence of the drought in southeast England which resulted in many of the cress beds, the species' favoured habitat in Britain, becoming dry and some going out of business altogether. Additionally, many small streams had dried out and the on-going changes in sewage treatment resulted in a reduction in suitable habitat in the country. The habitat at Rainham provided a suitable alternative and perhaps the slightly higher temperatures along the Thames ensured continuing use when inland areas froze. The species is known to show high site fidelity (*BWP*), which may explain the continuing use of the site. The recent return to wetter winters has seen a decline in the wintering population.

In Essex, the favoured winter habitat is brackish or freshwater pools adjacent to tidal rivers, man-made sludge lagoons, rivers, sewage farms and damp areas of low but dense vegetation. On passage, the species occurs in a wider range of habitats that includes reservoirs, coastal saltings and marshes. At Rainham they are normally found on the small freshwater pools and wet areas on the man-made lagoons. Until the late 1970s the species frequented the small brackish pools inside the river wall but these were filled with rubbish or dried up after the wall was raised. In severe weather the foreshore may also be used. Water Pipits regularly mix with Rock Pipits at this site, affording observers excellent opportunities to compare the species. At The Hythe, the sludge lagoons created by dumping of dredgings from the adjacent Colne have attracted small numbers since the 1960s. Up to six (early 2004) have occurred recently around the Splodge Pool near Cattawade Marshes, an area of damp grazing land.

On migration, Water Pipits are recorded regularly from all of the main reservoirs with occasional records elsewhere. Highest counts generally occur in March or early April, even at regular wintering sites. Johnson (1970) suggested that this may be due to the development of the distinctive summer plumage and the increasing tendency to flock in late winter giving the impression of a false increase: at wintering sites the higher numbers had been present all winter but a percentage was simply overlooked. Some migration does undoubtedly occur through Essex at this time, however, as small numbers in full summer plumage are recorded with regularity away from the usual wintering sites at well-watched sites such as the large reservoirs. The latest county record by almost a month was one at Stansted Airport Lagoons on 26th May 1997; there was one at Heybridge GP on 28th April 1974. There appears to be little sign of an obvious passage through Essex during autumn, although very small numbers pass through some of the reservoirs at this time. The earliest records involve singles at Dovercourt on 28th September 1965 and Hanningfield on 29th September 1992. Most autumn records, at least over the last decade, are of individuals already back at the wintering sites.

If correctly identified as a Water Pipit, one ringed near Fraena, More Og Romsdal, Norway, on 14th September 1989 and recovered in Kirby Creek on 19th February 1991, was unusually far north when originally trapped. It is assumed that all county records refer to the nominate race *spinoletta*; the race *coutellii* occurs in extreme southeast Europe and the Middle East and Arabia.

Yellow Wagtail   *Motacilla flava*

The Yellow Wagtail is a widespread species found across almost the entire Palearctic region, from western Europe to Kamchatka and across the Bering Sea into Alaska. Some 13 subspecies are recognised worldwide (Alström *et al.* 2003). The complexity of races, with varying degrees of intergradation, has led to a number of different theories on just how many species exist, various authors having divided the races into 2–7 different 'groups'/species.

Yellow Wagtail   *M. f. flavissima*

Common summer visitor and passage migrant   Amber List

The race *flavissima* breeds in Britain north to southern Scotland and along the coast of Europe from Brittany north to Norway and winters in tropical west Africa. It is a lowland race inhabiting level or gently sloping land and preferring moist grassy areas (European Atlas). In Britain, *flavissima* has been in long-term decline since at least the 1920s (Historical Atlas), although the rate of decline has increased with the BBS recording a 15% reduction in the period 1994–2003. The subspecies' range has generally contracted to the south and east,

with breeding Yellow Wagtails now virtually absent from west Wales, southwest England and Ireland and only breeding sparsely in southern Scotland (Second National Atlas). Breeding birds are invariably associated with water, although not necessarily running water—damp water meadows and marshy

Atlas	Survey Area	% of 10km squares or tetrads in which	
		bred/probably bred	possibly bred or present
First National 10km	Essex	77.2	8.8
Second National 10km	Essex	86.0	7.0
First London Tetrad	Met. Essex	22.5	6.5
Second London Tetrad	Met. Essex	46.0	9.5
Essex Tetrad	Essex	37.8	12.9

Summary of results of Atlas surveys for Yellow Wagtails

fields along river valleys and freshwater marshes on the coast are favoured. Similar conditions also occur at sewage farms, flooded gravel-pits and along reservoir margins, with market gardens and industrial waste sites providing drier, suburban habitat (First National Atlas).

Christy described the Yellow Wagtail as a regular and common summer migrant, although he "... had never seen it, except occasionally during the times of its migration in autumn and spring, or known it to nest (though it seems formerly to have done so in Epping Forest) in the inland parts of the county; but it breeds very commonly on the marshes and lowlands along the whole of our coastline, placing its nest in the sides of the mud walls". Christy considered that it was common around Orsett, Harwich, Maldon, South Shoebury and present in the Colchester and Paglesham districts. At Maldon it was observed that Yellow Wagtails nested "… in the foot-marks left by cattle at the sides of the marsh-ditches".

Glegg considered the Yellow Wagtail a regular summer resident with a limited breeding distribution, its chief haunts being the cattle-frequented meadows along the coast and the estuaries and Lea Valley reservoirs, breeding being first noted at the latter in 1911. Indeed, he considered the Yellow Wagtail to be commoner at the Lea Valley reservoirs than on the coast, and by 1926 had noted a range expansion into the Wanstead Basin area. Nowhere, however, did he consider it abundant and throughout the remainder of Essex he described it as rare. Around Tollesbury, he attributed declines to the cessation of cultivation and the subsequent growth of long grasses.

It is possible that the Yellow Wagtail was under-recorded inland prior to the 1950s as a three-year EBS enquiry (1952–54) revealed that it occurred by most watercourses and reservoirs (in some considerable numbers by the larger reservoirs) and at a number of sewage farms. It is, however, possible that the large-scale construction of sewage farms, reservoirs and gravel-pits provided the Yellow Wagtail with habitats that enabled it to spread throughout inland Essex between the 1920s and 1950s. The survey revealed that only in the extreme northwest, where there was a lack of suitable habitat, was the species absent. Inland counts included up to 200 pairs at Abberton in both 1952 and 1953, whilst in the Lea Valley the numbers present during the enquiry period were variously described as, "many", "large" and "substantial". On the coast, notable counts included 110 pairs on Mersea Island, a density of some six pairs per km², without subtracting for unsuitable habitat (Cox). "Moderate" numbers bred as far up the Thames as the Ripple Level, Barking, with a few breeding as close to Inner London as the Lea between Old Ford and Stratford.

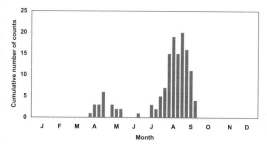

Seasonal occurrence of counts of 100+ Yellow Wagtails from 1971-2004

Hudson & Pyman described the Yellow Wagtail as rather rare inland, suggesting that some declines may have taken place between the early 1950s and late 1960s. Unfortunately, being relatively common, the species was not particularly well recorded in the *EBR* from the late 1950s until the late 1970s, but it was not until the early 1990s that concerns over the apparent decline of the Yellow Wagtail were first expressed. During the 1970s and early 1980s, healthy populations were confined to coastal sites such as Dengie, where the 150 pairs in 1977 (about three pairs per km²) were marginally lower than the early 1970s, and Hamford Water, where the species could still be described as "numerous". The species was scarce along the north Blackwater, declined to just four pairs on Foulness and had disappeared from a former stronghold, Fobbing Marshes, by 1977. Inland, healthy populations still existed at Abberton, where there were 50–100 pairs in 1981, albeit only 50% of the population of 30 years previous, and the Lea Valley where there were "many pairs" in 1982. Otherwise, inland records had become few and far between, even along the river valleys.

Survey work for the Essex Atlas from 1988–94 revealed the Yellow Wagtail to be present in 50.7% of all Essex tetrads and distributed right around the coast and along the main river valleys with a virtual absence north and west of Colchester. The range is surprisingly similar to that revealed by the enquiry in the early 1950s, although numbers breeding at each locality had declined. The Second National Atlas appeared to suggest that a range expansion had occurred since the First National Atlas as there were apparent increases in the north and northwest and decreases in Metropolitan Essex with confirmed or probable breeding in 77.2% of 10km squares in the First Atlas but 86% in the latter. In national terms, the Essex coastal population reached a peak of abundance (Second National Atlas). Comparison of the two London Atlases also suggested an increase in range in Metropolitan Essex, but again numbers nesting at individual sites had declined.

Since the end of the Essex Atlas survey period, *EBR*s have continued to document the Yellow Wagtail's decline with range contractions noted particularly in the north, southwest and inland areas, although observers consider that coastal populations have also suffered recently. For example, at Rainham the population has fallen from 20 pairs in the mid-1980s to four by 2000. Here it has been forced onto atypical habitat adjacent to the refuse tip. There were still 21 pairs at Abberton in 1994, just 10–20% of the population in the early 1950s, although there were 84–94 pairs there in 1993. No recent population figures for Abberton are available but the Yellow Wagtail appears to have declined; cutting of the adjacent fields right up to the fence line has destroyed much of the potential habitat. Along part of the Stour regularly surveyed for the WBS, breeding pairs fell from seven in 1987 to two in 1995 along a 4.5-km stretch.

Unlike many other migrants, there is no good evidence to suggest that the species has suffered from the droughts in Africa (Population Trends). However, the increasing width of the Sahara Desert may have increased mortality amongst migrants (European Atlas). Not being a truly riparian species, the Yellow Wagtail has not been affected by modern river management. Declines have been noted where there is large-scale conversion of grass to arable land, something that has happened in Essex over the last 50 years. In addition, many crops that were previously autumn sown are now replaced by spring tillage, which tends to reduce the amount of available prey (O'Connor & Shrubb 1986). The BSE crisis is likely to have reduced further the keeping of cattle across Essex and therefore habitat availability. The CBC/BBS (England) Index detected a 64% decline across the UK over the period 1977–2002, whilst the WBS confirmed a 92% decline from 1975–2002. The BBS (England) Index fell by 15% between 1994 and 2003.

In Essex, Yellow Wagtails are associated with open farmland, mostly damp grassland, close to water, whilst nesting also occurs in arable crops. Thus in Essex they are characteristic of the seawall/borrow dyke zone around the coast and the grasslands surrounding the principal reservoirs (Essex Atlas). The Yellow Wagtail can be an opportunist breeder (Burton 1972) and it is therefore not unusual for artificial nesting sites to be used. Nesting in built-up areas is also not unusual and, even with numbers declining, pairs will use suitable habitat if available, such as the two pairs that bred in the Thames Barrier area of Silvertown in 1998. Yellow Wagtails, however, can often be absent from seemingly suitable areas (First National Atlas). The concrete banks of reservoirs have been used for many years, those in the Lea Valley being colonised in the early years of the 20th century. At Rainham, the drying mud pumped onto the marshes by the Port of London Authority was colonised quickly (Simms 1992). In 1955, a pair reared young in a Rhubarb field on Whalebone Lane North, Chadwell Heath, some distance from the nearest water.

Yellow Wagtails are one of the earlier migrants to return in spring with late March records regular. Males usually precede females by at least two weeks (Simms 1992). The earliest Essex record is of one at South Benfleet on 8th March 1961; the next earliest, singles on 13th at Wakering Stairs in 1983 and off Foulness in 1991 and on 14th from Abberton in 1971 and 1992. Spring passage is noticeable mainly at the principal reservoirs, although small numbers may be noted coasting at this time of year. Three-figure spring counts are generally uncommon with around 17 counts of 100+ since 1950, all except five coming from Abberton, where the peak count was 500–600 on 1st May 1964, This was exceptional, the next highest count being 200 on both 29th April 1983 and 15th April 1996. Away from Abberton, the highest count came from The Naze, where following a storm approximately 140 were grounded for a few hours on 2nd April 1980, in itself a high count for such an early date. Other three-figure counts have come from Hanningfield (twice), the highest being 120 on 27th April 1981, and Holland Haven (twice) where the highest count was 120 on 29th April 1992.

Autumn passage begins in late summer as juveniles begin to disperse from breeding areas and peaks in late August and September. In autumn, sizeable numbers roost in reed beds, the largest noted in Essex being some 2,000 at Great Wakering on 12th September 1991, an extremely large roost by British standards. About 1,000 roosted in a reed bed at Rainham from 4th–18th August 1956. Other regularly used roosts include: Flag Creek, St Osyth, where up to 1,000 were estimated to have passed through in the autumn of 1976; Pitsea, where there were at least 1,000 in the autumns of 1986 and 1988, with 3,000 in 1987; and Old Hall, which had peaks of 812 on 23rd August 1989 and 756 on 16th September 1986.

	Jan	Feb	Mar	Apr	May	Jun	Jul	Aug	Sep	Oct	Nov	Dec
Essex					8	7	2	7				
North England								1				
South England					1		2	7	4			
France				1					1			
Spain			2	5					2	2		
Portugal									5	7		
Morocco			1	1	1				1	1	1	
Algeria				1								
Senegal				1								
Totals	*0*	*0*	*3*	*9*	*10*	*7*	*4*	*15*	*13*	*10*	*1*	*0*

Month and location of recovery of Yellow Wagtails ringed in Essex

Aside from roost counts, three-figure flocks are relatively common during autumn, typically at the principal reservoirs, but numbers also pass along the coast. A total of 1,000 around Abberton on 7th August 1970 was exceptional, the next largest count being 300–350 there on 7th–10th August 1976. The only other count over 300 was 350 south over Hanningfield by 0900 hrs on 29th July 1985. Most Yellow Wagtails have left the county by the middle of October but stragglers are recorded fairly regularly into November, there being about 14 records from that month. There have been six records during December, three of them in 1985, although it is difficult to know whether they relate to exceptionally late migrants or individuals attempting to over-winter: Cattawade, 3rd in 1993; Abberton, 8th in 1981; Abberton, 9th in 1984; Old Hall, 15th in 1985; Abberton, 28th in 1985; and Girling, 27th-29th in 1985. There have also been two records after the turn of the year, one at Southminster SF on 1st and 15th January 1978 and another at Wivenhoe GP from 20th January to early February 1988. Nationally, winter records are not exceptional, survey work for the Winter Atlas noting records from 14 10km squares.

Large-scale ringing has been carried out at autumn roost sites at St Osyth, Abberton, Pitsea and Bradwell. A total of 73 Yellow Wagtails ringed in Essex has subsequently been recovered outside the county, in addition to which 20 ringed in southern England have been recovered in Essex. The recoveries are typical, with many occurring along the Yellow Wagtail's migration route through Iberia and Morocco; the recoveries suggest a more easterly return through Europe in spring with no records in Portugal at this time. Senegal is within the known winter range of the subspecies, although limited ringing in *flavissima*'s assumed wintering range means there are few recoveries of British-ringed birds.

Continued loss of suitable breeding habitat both through agricultural conversion and loss of cattle herds is a very real threat to the future of the species in Essex, although in coastal areas where wet grassland still occurs and conservation organisations continue to graze with cattle, the Yellow Wagtail is just holding its own. Recently, small numbers have taken to breeding in areas of agricultural set-aside suggesting that a switch to less intensive farming may bring the Yellow Wagtail some benefit in the future.

Alström et al. *(2003) advocated that great care should be taken when identifying different subspecies in the field as the occurrence of aberrant individuals and interbreeding appear to result in individuals looking like a third taxon. This should, therefore, be borne in mind when considering the races detailed below.*

Blue-headed Wagtail   *M. f. flava*

Uncommon passage migrant

The Blue-headed Wagtail breeds in north and central Europe, east to the Urals and north to Sweden and Leningrad; it winters in Africa between 10° W and 50° E, south to South Africa and the Cape.

The first British record of the commonest Continental race of Yellow Wagtail to reach Britain, came from Essex: "On the 3rd of October [1834], walking with two friends on the top of the cliffs at Walton-on-the Naze, I had the pleasure of seeing two individuals of the Grey-headed Yellow Wagtail ... one of which (a male) I fortunately shot, thus proving this bird occasionally at least, visits this country" (Yarrell 1845). Grey-headed Wagtail was the name that Blue-headed Wagtails were known by at this time.

The majority of Essex records occur in spring, probably because the race is more distinctive in breeding plumage, with fewer in summer and only c.20 during autumn. Females are almost inseparable from other races in the field and few have been claimed. The upsurge in records since 1979 is striking. The reason for this increase is unclear but the continuing decline of *flavissima* and the general increase in observers have perhaps meant that Yellow Wagtails are scrutinised more now; the recent decline in records is difficult to interpret. The earliest arrival was at Abberton on 30th March 1981 and the latest at Rainham on 27th September 1986.

Most records have come from the coast or the main reservoirs.

Blue-headed Wagtails are occasionally recorded during summer, and breeding has taken place on a number of occasions between apparent pure pairings and also with *flavissima* individuals. Glegg's reference to possible breeding

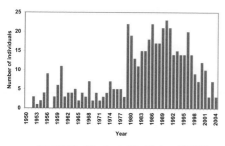

Annual totals of Blue-headed Wagtails from 1950-2004

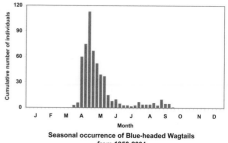

**Seasonal occurrence of Blue-headed Wagtails
from 1950-2004**

at Southminster, based on the presence of six individuals on 12th September 1909, should be dismissed. Since the first record of breeding in Essex, a pair at St Osyth in 1947, there have been a further seven records: 1962, Hanningfield; 1979, Abberton, a male carrying food in July; 1980, Little Oakley, a pair raised four young; 1983, Rainham; 1992, Mersea Island; 1993, Bradwell, a pair summered and a male was noted feeding young; and 1994, Colne Point.

Grey-headed Wagtail   *M. f. thunbergi*

Very rare passage migrant: 14 records

The race *thunbergi* breeds from Norway east to northern Siberia and south to 60° S; it winters in sub-Saharan Africa, south to the Cape (Simms 1992).

1954	Abberton	2nd June	Male, ringed
1957	Abberton	14th August	Male, ringed
1973	Heybridge GP	19th May	Male
1980	Dengie	5th May	Two
	Hanningfield	11th May	
1981	Rainham	9th May	
1983	Hanningfield	2nd–8th May	Male
1984	The Naze	18th May	
1986	Hanningfield	16th September	Moulting male
1988	Holland Haven	22nd September	
1993	The Naze	10th and 18th May	
1994	Heybridge GP	16th May	
	Hanningfield	19th September	

Glegg also made vague reference to an undated record of one at Southend-on-Sea. Note the pattern of arrival, with all spring records in May and June, some 1–2 weeks later on average than the peak passage of *flavissima*: Being a more northerly breeding race, passage to the breeding grounds is later.

Ashy-headed Wagtail   *M. f. cinereocapilla*

Vagrant: six records

The Ashy-headed Wagtail breeds in Italy, Sicily and Sardinia and winters in tropical west Africa, east to Cameroon.

1959	The Hythe	7th–8th April	Male
1979	KGV	20th–22nd April	Male
1980	Girling	3rd May	
1983	Rainham	19th–21st April	Male
1991	KGV	7th May	
2001	Holland Haven	28th–30th April	Male

Northward-bound individuals of this race, which is most similar to Grey-headed Wagtail, perhaps overshoot their normal breeding ranges and continue moving north with *flava* and *flavissima*.

[Sykes's Wagtail]   *M. f. beema*

Sykes's Wagtail breeds in Russia along the Lower Volga, south to Lake Baikal, to 60° N and south to the Altai mountains; it winters in Chad and Sudan, south to the Cape, and in India (Simms 1992).

A total of around 25 records of this race has been claimed in Essex, apparently making it the second most common non-breeding race to occur in Essex after *flava*. This seems surprising given the fact that it is one of the more distant races from Britain and its migration route does not lend itself to regular vagrancy to the country. A small population of *beema*-like birds ('Channel Wagtail') breeding in northwest France is thought to be intergrades between *flavissima* and *flava* (Dubois 2001), although further studies are needed to confirm this (Alström *et al.* 2003). In fact, it is generally accepted that the incidence of variations in populations of the more common races is so high that it would be impossible to detect natural vagrancy of *beema*, even if it did occur (Milne 1959). Thus many, if not all, Essex records probably involve hybrids of the commoner races or extreme plumage variants within the population. This would probably account for a few summering and breeding records including a series of breeding records from Wivenhoe GP from 1973–75 at least, where a male *beema*-type wagtail bred with a female *flavissima,* and the presence of a male in the Lea Valley in the summers of 1999 and 2000 and at Upminster in 2001.

[Black-headed Wagtail]   *M. f. feldegg*

The Black-headed Wagtail breeds from the Balkans east to the Caspian Sea and Afghanistan and winters principally in east Africa.

Van den Berg & Oreel (1985) confirmed the existence of a black-headed variant of *thunbergi*, although the extent to which this occurs in the population has been contested (Svenson 1988a, 1988b). However, BBRC has subsequently reassessed all previous British records and rejected many (BBRC 1994): there are just nine accepted British records. Unfortunately, one at East Tilbury on 13th May 1981 was never submitted to the BBRC. One at Maylandsea from 24th May–24th June 1999, which showed a thin supercilium in front of and behind the eye, was considered most likely to have been an intergrade between *feldegg* and another form of Yellow Wagtail rather than a pure *feldegg* (Rowlands 2003).

[White-headed Wagtail]   *M. f. leucocephala*

The White-headed Wagtail breeds in northwest Mongolia and China and winters in northwest India.

This subspecies is not on the British List but one showing the characteristics of this race was at St Lawrence on 8th May 1989. Individuals with plumage similar to *leucocephala* have been found breeding in France and are thought to be the result of intergradation between *flava* and *flavissima* (Dubois 2001).

[Spanish Wagtail]   *M. f. iberiae*

The Spanish Wagtail breeds in southwest France, Iberia and northwest Africa and winters in tropical Africa, east to Chad.

Another race that is not on the British list, although one showing characteristics of this subspecies was at Abberton on 13th May 1981.

Sponsored by Katie Norrell

Citrine Wagtail   *Motacilla citreola*

Vagrant: two records

The Citrine Wagtail breeds over much of central northern Asia, west into Eastern Europe, the nominate race *citreola* occurring throughout most of the range except for the Himalayas and Tibet. Most winter in India but small numbers occur in southeast Asia.

1976	Hamford Water	4th–24th July	Adult male
1994	KGV	22nd August	Immature

There were 173 British records to the end of 2004 (BBRC 2005), the first as recent as 1954. The species has averaged about seven records per annum in recent years with most arriving along the east coast and on the Isles of Scilly, although—unlike most other eastern vagrants—the species normally occurs in early autumn. In recent years, its European range has expanded west and southwest (European Atlas) and this, along with greater observer coverage, probably explains its increased incidence.

The 1976 record remains unique. On 4th July, a male was found carrying food to a nest, situated in an area of Common Salt-marsh Grass, containing four young wagtails about one week old. The male was observed on eight further occasions, until 24th July, for at least 16 hours and the fledged young were observed being fed by the male on 18th and 24th. At no stage was an adult female seen to positively associate with the male, although on 11th a female Yellow Wagtail briefly alighted near the nest but flew off after inspecting the area. It subsequently returned, only to be chased off by the male Citrine Wagtail. Although it was thought likely that the young were Citrine x Yellow Wagtail hybrids, this could not be confirmed conclusively (Cox & Inskipp 1978).

Sponsored by Simon Cox

Grey Wagtail
Motacilla cinerea

A local resident, passage migrant and winter visitor

Amber List

The Grey Wagtail has a widespread but discontinuous range across the Palearctic. Western populations occur throughout Europe, with the exception of northern latitudes, and also in northwest Africa. The eastern population extends from the

Atlas	Survey Area	% of 10km squares or tetrads in which	
		bred/probably bred	possibly bred or present
First National 10km	Essex	14.0	15.8
Second National 10km	Essex	40.4	12.3
First London Tetrad	Met. Essex	1.0	2.5
Second London Tetrad	Met. Essex	15.0	7.0
Essex Tetrad	Essex	5.6	4.7

Summary of results of Atlas surveys for Grey Wagtails

western Urals and Afghanistan into eastern Asia. The nominate race *cinerea* occurs across almost the species' entire range. In Britain, it is most abundant in the north and west, particularly in upland areas where it has a preference for feeding by fast-flowing watercourses (with rocks, riffles and areas of shingle) bordered by broad-leaved trees (Second National Atlas). It is absent from much of central and eastern England. Populations of northern and eastern Europe are migratory, with central European and Atlantic populations partially so and British, French, Belgian, Iberian and Mediterranean populations mainly resident or locally dispersive (European Atlas).

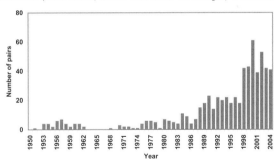

Annual totals of breeding/summering pairs of Grey Wagtails from 1950-2004

Christy considered the Grey Wagtail an uncommon autumn and winter visitor. He had "... no knowledge of its having ever bred with us". In the first half of the 19th century, the species was a winter visitor to Epping, although rare, and to Sudbury, whilst in the latter half of the 19th century it was recorded at Saffron Walden, Epping, along the Roding, Orsett ("uncommon"), Colchester and Paglesham districts, Dedham and Maldon.

Glegg considered the Grey Wagtail a winter visitor in small numbers and a passage migrant, although parties of more than 2–3 were unknown. Almost a ll the records came from inland freshwaters. Hudson & Pyman described the Grey Wagtail similarly, except that the species had begun to breed in Essex with the first record coming from Gosfield Lake in 1951, although it is possible that two pairs bred the year before at Fordstreet on the Colne. For the next ten years, up to five pairs bred at a wide number of sites across Essex but these were all apparently wiped out by the severe winter weather of early 1963. Breeding was not confirmed again until 1970 when single pairs bred in the

Colne and Lea Valleys, although a pair may have bred close to the Essex border at Bishop's Stortford in 1968. Since then, numbers have continued to increase, particularly since the 1980s, although the severe winters of 1978/79, 1985/86 and 1990/91 checked numbers.

Nationally, the spread into east and central England began around 1950 (Population Trends). At the time of the First National Atlas, the species was recorded as breeding or probably breeding in 14% of 10km squares, which had increased to 40.4% by the time of the Second National Atlas. In Metropolitan Essex, numbers

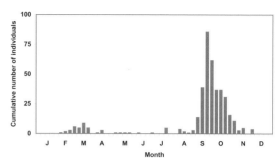

Seasonal occurrence of assumed migrant Grey Wagtails at coastal sites from 1971-2004

increased significantly between the two London Atlas surveys; Dennis (1994) attributed this to improved water quality and a succession of relatively mild winters. Trends nationally are contradictory: WBS data suggested a 12% decline between 1977 and 2002 but the BBS (England) Index for the period 1994–2003 has shown a 60% increase. In Essex, over the same period, there has clearly been an increase through the 1980s with numbers stable during most of the 1990s. The marked increase from 1988 may be attributable to increased observer coverage during Essex Atlas fieldwork. Recent sharp increases since 1998 have coincided with a period of wetter climatic conditions following the lean years of rainfall during the late 1980s and much of the 1990s.

The distribution in 1988–94 generally followed the river valleys but with an absence in the Dengie and Tendring Hundreds, presumably reflecting a lack of suitable artificial habitat (Essex Atlas). Typical nesting locations in Essex have generally mimicked their more usual upland stream habitats. Thus, most nests are situated where there is a combination of shallow, rapidly flowing water and masonry structures, the former providing suitable feeding and the latter nest sites. Locations such as mills and millraces, weirs, dams, lock gates and reservoir intakes/overflows have all been used at one time or other. Indeed, modern river management, that has had such a negative effect on most riparian species, may have actually assisted the Grey Wagtail's spread through Essex: it is in built-up areas where such management is at its greatest that the highest breeding numbers occur. Individuals may be found hunting for their invertebrate prey almost anywhere that the Pied Wagtail is found.

Outside the breeding season, passage through Essex begins in late July, presumably as juveniles disperse away from breeding areas; numbers peak during late September. Small numbers are recorded throughout the autumn passage period from the main reservoirs and along the coast. Inland passage has been particularly noticeable along the Lea Valley, where up to 12 have been recorded at Walthamstow (in November 2001 and on 7th September 2002) with perhaps as many as 38 passing through in September and October 2002; 12 were in Valentines Park, Ilford, on 11th October 2003. Elsewhere, at Newport a total of 29 flew over between 9th September and 5th October 2002 with 24 logged between 3rd and 21st September 2003; ten on 29th August 2000, with 12 at Newport SF on 26th August 2003. There were 12 at Rainham on 2nd October 2002 and 12 at both Black Notley and Becton SW on 28th October 2003.

Until recently, numbers along the coast were low and usually involved single birds moving through either on their own or with flocks of Meadow Pipits during late September and October. However, numbers have increased steadily over the last decade, and since 1998 there have been three double-figure counts from The Naze: 11 on 10th October 1998; 11 on 10th October 1999; and 18 on 22nd September 2002.

Wintering numbers have increased in line with the breeding population, suggesting that most of our wintering birds are local individuals. Indeed, in the Writtle area, birds are often seen in winter close to nesting sites (Essex Atlas).

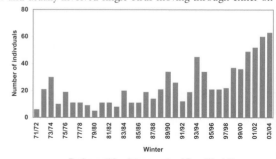

Peak monthly winter counts of Grey Wagtails from 1971/72-2003/04

418

Generally, numbers are small but in particularly favoured habitats such as sewage farms and around slurry pits and dung heaps small gatherings occur from time to time. There have, however, been just seven double-figure winter counts: 20 roosting at Harold Wood SF, January 1999 and 14 on 26th January 1997; 17, Walthamstow during January 2003; 15, Bishop's Stortford SF, 18th November 1960; 14, Royal Docks/Beckton/Barking area during December 2000; 13, Nag's Head SF, Brentwood, during February 2003; and 12, Bishop's Stortford SF, 17th February 1956.

Spring passage is rarely discernible, although odd individuals may be observed moving along the coast.

There are ten ringing recoveries involving Essex, although only two had moved further than 100km. The first involved an adult female ringed at Great Hallingbury on 21st July 1973 and found in Oxfordshire some 11 weeks later, and the other was trapped at Epping during January 1980 and recovered in Greater Manchester in October 1981. Birds from northern Britain are known to move south during autumn and these, together with possible Scandinavian migrants, may account for autumn passage. Occasionally, individuals have been observed flying in off the sea during autumn.

With the continuing efforts to increase the water quality of the river system and the generally improved awareness of managing our rivers with conservation in mind, the future of the Grey Wagtail in Essex seems assured for the immediate future.

White Wagtail   *Motacilla alba*

The White Wagtail is a widespread species found in southeast Greenland, northwest Africa, Europe, and most of northern, central and southeast Asia east to the extreme northwest of Alaska (Alström *et al.* 2003). Nine subspecies are recognised.

Pied Wagtail   *M. a. yarrellii*

Common resident and passage migrant

The Pied Wagtail breeds in Britain and Ireland and coastal parts of Denmark, the Netherlands, Belgium and northern France: this race is partially migratory.

This, the most familiar of all wagtails to occur in Essex, has a widespread distribution

Atlas	Survey Area	% of 10km squares or tetrads in which	
		bred/probably bred	possibly bred or present
First National 10km	Essex	94.7	5.3
Second National 10km	Essex	91.2	8.8
First London Tetrad	Met. Essex	43.5	21.0
Second London Tetrad	Met. Essex	68.0	20.5
Essex Tetrad	Essex	37.7	23.9

Summary of results of Atlas surveys for Pied Wagtails

throughout the whole of Britain and occurs in a wide range of urban and rural habitats, where it will often breed in close proximity to man. Decreases have been noted in southern England, perhaps due to changing agricultural practices.

Christy described the Pied Wagtail as a common resident and, interestingly, considered that most local birds left the county in winter. Familiarity with the Pied Wagtail meant that many local names evolved, two that Christy mentioned being "Nanny Wagtail" and "Dishwasher", the latter perhaps coming from the similarity of the species' bobbing movement to the action of washing clothes by the waterside (Greenoak 1981). Glegg considered the Pied Wagtail a resident that was evenly distributed throughout the county during the breeding season. Like Christy, he noted the apparent decrease in winter, but considered that the decrease might not indicate an actual reduction in numbers, because the size of winter roosting flocks "... probably balance the general reduction". Little change had occurred by the time of Hudson & Pyman who felt that there were few, if any, districts from which it was absent. A big decline was noted in the Writtle area from the early 1950s, at about which time hay and corn stacks were no longer constructed. Further declines were noted where plastic apple crates replaced wooden ones on

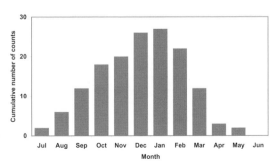

Seasonal occurrence of counts of 100+ Pied Wagtails from 1971-2004

orchards. In both cases, it was the loss of nest sites that caused the decline, suggesting that population levels, at least in part are controlled by the availability of nest sites (Essex Atlas). Cox considered that the move from mixed to predominantly arable farming might have been responsible for some long-term population declines but these were and remain unquantifiable. Nonetheless, the Pied Wagtail remained common and widespread.

The species being so common, few breeding data have ever been published in the *EBRs*. There was virtually no change in range between the two National Atlas surveys, whilst a notable increase occurred in the 20 years between the two London Atlases. The Essex Atlas recorded the Pied Wagtail in 61.6% of tetrads, it being absent only from predominantly wooded areas and areas of intensive cereal cultivation, although even here occasional pairs may be found breeding around buildings. Winter weather appears to have the strongest influence on population size (Population Trends). Nationally, the winter of 1962/63 had a severe impact on the population, which declined by 55% on farmland CBC sites (Winter Atlas) and it took some 12 years for the national CBC Index to return to its pre-1963 level (Population Trends). Between 1977 and 2002, there was a decline on both CBC/BBS (England) plots (–6%) and WBS (–41%) plots: the BBS (England) for the period 1994–2003 has, however, identified a 36% increase. Local CBC/BBS data based on a rather smaller sample have shown, despite being rather erratic, a general increase since the late 1980s, following a run of cold winters and a return to a wetter climate in the last few years.

In Essex, most breeding sites seem to be away from the typical habitat of ponds and streams. Indeed, virtually no breeding Pied Wagtails were found during the NRA river corridor surveys from 1990–92. Certainly in Essex, the preferred habitat appears to be around farm buildings, stables and sewage farms. In the Writtle area, most breeding sites utilised human artefacts such as greenhouses, disused trailers and farm machinery, outhouses and walls (Essex Atlas). Single pairs regularly raise 1–2 broods in a busy builder's yard at Danbury, although the nesting site moves from building to building each year. Information on nesting sites in urban areas is generally lacking but, given that feeding birds may be seen regularly in such areas as car parks, school playing fields and upon large flat roofs, many nesting sites in urban locations appear to go largely unnoticed.

Juveniles begin to disperse from their breeding grounds in July and small movements can be detected across Essex from then until late October/early November. Numbers moving along the coast are generally small with few flocks of any size occurring, most movements usually involving ones and twos moving through with Meadow Pipits. Rarely are more than 100 reported from any one locality. Ringing has shown that there is an exodus of British birds during winter and many of those passing through Essex during autumn presumably come from further north. Spring passage is generally light and often only noticeable at the larger reservoirs.

It is the species' habit of forming communal roosts, especially in winter, that has

	Jan	Feb	Mar	Apr	May	Jun	Jul	Aug	Sep	Oct	Nov	Dec
Essex	19	9	4	5	10	5	9	6	4	0	2	6
South England	6	4	1	2	1	1	2	1	0	5	2	3
France							1			4		
Spain									2			1
Portugal	3	1	1	1						2	3	2
Morocco	1											
Totals	*29*	*14*	*6*	*8*	*11*	*7*	*11*	*7*	*4*	*13*	*7*	*12*

Month and location of recovery of Pied Wagtails ringed in Essex

drawn the most attention and this has been well documented in *EBRs*. Many different localities have been used from reed beds, *leylandii* hedges, laurel bushes, sewage farms, commercial greenhouses, lone trees in an otherwise urban environment, factory roofs and even the turbine room at the Bradwell Power Station. In recent years there appears to have been an increasing tendency for the species to form pre-roost assemblies on the roofs of large supermarket buildings (e.g. Maldon and Ilford) before moving off to a roost site. Some of these roosts are transient in nature but many are used throughout winter. Roosts may form as early as August and be used through until April, although numbers at most roosts peak between October and February. Most birds feed within 12km of the roost site (Winter Atlas). Few counts have exceeded 500: 1,500 in 1967 at Thorndon CP; 630 in trees outside Chelmsford Civic Centre on 5th February 1989; 520 in Bradwell Power Station in December 1978; and 500 outside Chelmsford Civic Centre at the end of 1988. Otherwise three-figure roosts counts are not uncommon. However, in the late 1990s these declined.

Pied Wagtails, particularly juveniles, from southern Britain move south to winter within Britain and Ireland, along the Atlantic coast of France, in the Iberian peninsula and in northwest Africa (Migration Atlas): recoveries of Essex-ringed birds conform to this pattern. The most distant recovery involved one ringed at Abberton on 2nd October 1953 and found dead at Port Lyauten, Morocco, around 15th January 1954 some 2,032km to the southsouthwest. Some wintering individuals may well have originated from further north; recoveries of birds involving Essex in Leicestershire, Derbyshire and Selkirk lend support to this.

The Pied Wagtail has adapted well to the modern environment and copes well with human disturbance and should continue to do well in ever-changing urban and rural habitats.

White Wagtail

M. a. alba

Fairly common passage migrant

Christy observed: "It occurs, without doubt, occasionally in Essex" and referred to two records, one of which involved apparent breeding at Saffron Walden. Here, it was said to breed occasionally and specific reference was made to a brood of five raised at Wenden in 1836. Glegg described the White Wagtail as having been recorded in Essex on several occasions and added ten records: one in February, two in March, five in April, one in May, and one in August. The last, a male *alba* seen feeding young at Lawford on 20th, he did not consider to be conclusive proof of breeding.

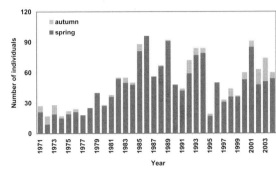

Annual totals of White Wagtails from 1971-2004

Both Hudson & Pyman and Cox considered White Wagtails regular passage migrants, both suggesting that the bias to spring records was probably due to the difficulty of distinguishing juveniles and some females from *yarrellii*. There have been no recent records of *alba* breeding in Essex, although a male was apparently paired with a female *yarrellii* at Hanningfield during late May and June 1974 when nest-building was observed, whilst an adult *alba* was noted feeding fledged young at Colchester on 25th May 1988.

Annual numbers have generally increased since the 1970s, presumably due to greater observer coverage. There have been 12 double-figure counts, the highest being 21 at Abberton on 26th April 1989, 20 at Abberton on 6th April 1986 and 19 at Essex Filter Beds on the very early date of 4th March 1999. In autumn, counts rarely exceed two. There were, however, six at both Romford SF on 16th September 1961 and Abberton on 17th September 1998.

Spring passage through Essex peaks during mid-April, although individuals may occur as early as the end of February and throughout summer. The earliest were at Abberton on 22nd February 1985 and Hornchurch CP on 23rd February 2002.

Autumn passage commences in early August and peaks during mid-September, although in some years there are no records; surely White Wagtails are significantly under-recorded at this time of year? The latest individual was at Abberton on 19th November 1964: Hudson & Pyman and Cox referred to the later date of 30th November (year not specified) but no such record could be located. Additionally, there have been two winter records: The Hythe, 22nd January 1962; and Hanningfield, 6th January 1968.

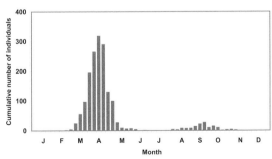

Seasonal occurrence of White Wagtails from 1971-2004

[Moroccan Wagtail]

M. a. subpersonata

This race is found entirely within Morocco and is resident

An individual showing characteristics of the race was at Abberton from 8th–23rd August 1990. This race is not on the British List.

(Bohemian) Waxwing

Bombycilla garrulus

Rare winter visitor and passage migrant, subject to influxes

The Waxwing is a typical species of the boreal forests of Eurasia and has a Holarctic distribution, the nominate race *garrulus* occurring in Europe. During winter, the species' principal food is the Rowan berry and, when the crop is good, the species stays in the north, close to its breeding grounds. In years of crop failure, large-scale irruptions to the south and west into Europe occur (*European Atlas*).

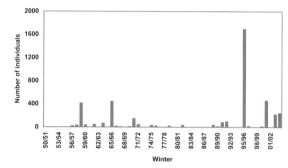

Annual total of Waxwings from 1950/51-2003/04

Christy and Glegg cited records in just 23 winters, from the first shot from a flock at Saffron Walden during August 1835 (Yarrell 1845), a year in which an influx occurred nationally, to the latest in 1929. Most of the records involved shot birds and apart from references to "flocks", no more than two were reported from any locality. Few were reported from 1929–49, but there was a sizeable influx of approximately 180–200 individuals during 1946/47 including a flock of around 60 at Langdon Hills on 30th January.

Since 1950, Waxwings have been recorded in all but 12 winters with major influxes in 1958/59, 1965/66, 1995/96 and 2000/01.

Although it is thought that large-scale irruptions may be caused by an acute imbalance between population size and food supply in Fennoscandia, they do not necessarily coincide with movements of other irruptive species and are not directly attributable to severe winters. There is some evidence of a ten-year cycle to these events, although the reasons for this are unclear (*BWP*); the ten-year cycle is not obvious from the species' occurrence in Essex and indeed the invasions appear to be becoming more frequent.

The four major invasions into Essex coincided with substantial influxes nationally. Around 10,000 were estimated to have occurred nationally in both 1965/66 and 1995/96, and the latter influx into Essex made up a significant proportion of the national total.

There have been six flocks of 100+, all but one in 1996: Romford, 215 on 20th March 1996; Pitsea/Basildon, 150 on 8th March 1996; Colchester, Mersea Road, 134 on 1st March 1996; Colchester, Greenstead, 125 on 28th February 1996; and Thundersley, 100+ on 25th January–1st February 1959. In addition, the aggregate of several flocks in Little Baddow/Danbury area in January 1959 was 200 birds.

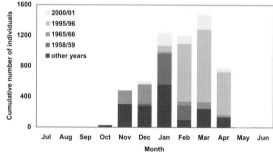

Seasonal occurrence of Waxwings from 1950-2004

Waxwings appear to arrive in the northeast of Essex and then filter steadily southwest; in 1996 many of the larger flocks were in the southwest. Numbers tend to peak in late winter, presumably as flocks coalesce as they search for the diminishing supplies of berries (Wood 1998). The advent of urban landscaping and in particular the widespread planting of bushes such as *Cotoneaster* and *Pyracanthus*, has meant that the largest flocks are most often found in built-up areas. Although berries are their principal food item, late-staying flocks may take advantage of warmer spring days to feed like flycatchers on emerging insects from suitable vantage points.

Most Waxwings arrive between November and February, although timings of the main influxes are variable: in 1965/66 the main arrival was in October and November, with a gradual withdrawal during January–March, whilst in the 1995/96 influx the earliest arrivals were not until mid-January and numbers peaked in late February/early March, with large numbers still present in mid-April with three still present at Colchester on 3rd May. The latest Essex record, however, involved 12 at Leigh-on-Sea on 4th–5th May 2001. Apart from the August 1835 record mentioned previously, the earliest occurrence involved 4–5 at Kirby Cross on 3rd October 1966.

One Waxwing, ringed at Ipswich on 21st January 1960, was found dead at Cressing four weeks later and follows the pattern of a southwesterly drift through winter.

(White-throated) Dipper
Cinclus cinclus

Vagrant: 11–13 records involving 12–15 individuals

The Dipper is a Palearctic species found throughout much of Europe, north Africa, Lebanon, Asia Minor and central Asia, from the Urals to western Siberia. Although found throughout a diverse range of habitats, it breeds alongside and feeds almost exclusively in well-oxygenated waters of fast-flowing streams or rivers. In Britain, where it is represented by the race *gularis*, it breeds almost entirely in the upland areas of the north and west. The nominate race *cinclus*, often referred to as Black-bellied Dipper is, unlike the British race, migratory. It occurs through Fennoscandia, Denmark, central France, western Iberia, Corsica and Sardinia and a few are recorded from eastern Britain each winter. A further race, *aquaticus*, is found throughout much of the rest of Continental Europe (European Atlas).

undated	Stour near Sudbury	Undated	Two
			gularis/aquaticus
1830	Audley End	Undated	Shot
1835	St Osyth	Early autumn	Shot
	"within 16 miles		
	of Colchester"	Undated	Shot
1880/81	near Colchester	Undated	Shot
1887	Wrabness	Undated	
1889	Leigh Ray	Early September	Shot
1948	St Osyth	29th February	
		18th December	
1950	Colne at Fordstreet/		
	Chappel	10th November–31st December	*cinclus*
1956	Beaumont Quay	28th December	
1964/65	Stour at Langham	Early November two,	At least one
		with one on 10th–3rd January	*cinclus*
1976	Walthamstow	1st January	

The first record came from "… the Stour above Sudbury" (Christy); depending exactly where this was, it may be either a Suffolk record or a joint Essex/Suffolk one as the Stour forms the county boundary in some areas around Sudbury. It seems likely that the two records in 1835 related to one and the same specimen, although neither Christy nor Glegg made the link. The race *gularis* is very similar to *aquaticus*, and given the former's extremely sedentary nature records referred to *gularis* may in fact involve *aquaticus*, although there has as yet been no evidence to suggest that the latter has occurred in Britain (Migration Atlas). Most Essex records, however, probably involved *cinclus*, but the one killed at Audley End may have also have been *gularis/aquaticus* if it was the same specimen still present in Saffron Walden Museum in the 1920s (Glegg). Apart from the Leigh Ray and Walthamstow records, all have occurred in the north or northeast of the county, where at least some suitable habitat occurs. Within Essex, locations approximating to its typical habitat have been used such as seawalls, reservoir edges and the few stony stretches that do exist on Essex rivers.

(Winter) Wren
Troglodytes troglodytes

Abundant and widespread resident

The Wren is a Holarctic species, breeding across the Palearctic region and into continental North America. It is almost unique in being a North American passerine that has successfully invaded Asia, Europe and north Africa (European Atlas). In Britain, where the mainland populations are represented by the nominate race *troglodytes* in the north and *indigenus* in central and southern England, the species is one of the most widespread breeding birds and is probably one of the most numerous too, albeit subject to considerable variation from year to year (Second National Atlas).

The 'Tiddy' or 'Tiddley Wren', to give two of its old Essex names, has readily adapted to the ever-changing environment. Christy recounted a gruesome example of this adaptability in his description of a pair at Lexden: "About the year 1886 a keeper at Lexden shot a Hooded Crow and hung it up to a tree by a piece of wire to swing

423

in the wind as a warning to its fellows. In the spring of 1888, a pair of Wrens built their nest of oak leaves within its hollow carcase, and therein safely reared a brood". The Wren's preferred habitat is woodland and waterside vegetation (Population Trends) but a wide variety of habitats is occupied from gardens to reed beds, coastal scrub, *Suaeda* and hedgerows; it can breed successfully in very small areas of suitable habitat.

All previous Essex writers considered the Wren to be an abundant or very common resident. Hudson & Pyman stated that the species was "… scarce or absent from heavily built-up areas" and "… inclined to suffer badly in severe winters…" However, the Wren's ubiquity has meant that in general it has been overlooked; the species was mentioned in the Systematic List of just five *EBRs* prior to 1988. Cox quoted mean densities on Essex census plots of 110 pairs per km² in woodland and 14 pairs per km² on farmland. Data since 1981 have produced mean densities of 144 pairs per km² in woodland (range 106–195) and 22 pairs per km² in farmland (range 3–33). The Essex Atlas survey revealed the Wren to be present in 96.6% of tetrads: only in the heavily built-up areas of Metropolitan Essex and the sparsely vegetated areas of Dengie, Rochford Hundred and exposed coastal areas was it scarce. However, the Second London Atlas survey appeared to suggest that increases occurred in some of the most densely populated areas of Metropolitan Essex between the late 1960s and late 1980s/early 1990s.

Few species suffer in severe winter weather more than the Wren. Being so small, it chills very rapidly and has little potential for storing fat. Extensive periods of low temperature cause many fatalities, although the Wren is able to feed and

Atlas	Survey Area	% of 10km squares or tetrads in which	
		bred/probably bred	possibly bred or present
First National 10km	Essex	100.0	0.0
Second National 10km	Essex	98.2	1.8
First London Tetrad	Met. Essex	67.0	9.5
Second London Tetrad	Met. Essex	98.5	1.5
Essex Tetrad	Essex	96.3	0.3

Summary of results of Atlas surveys for Wrens

roost under snow, eking out an existence by being able to penetrate into feeding areas which are difficult for larger species to reach (Winter Atlas). The species' numbers vary more from year to year than any other species monitored by the CBC/BBS (Winter Atlas), although national trends over the last 25 years suggest a steadily increasing population. Following the severe winter of 1962/63, the *EBR* 1963 noted that none could be found in many areas during the first half of the year. However, its resilience is such that by the following year a marked recovery had already occurred. Nationally, however, it was reckoned that it took until 1967 or 1968 before the population had recovered to pre-1963 levels (Population Trends). Similarly, the 1979 winter resulted in heavy mortality with decreases of 70% noted at Blake's Wood, Little Baddow, 68% at Weeleyhall Wood and 40% at Hainault Forest CP. Numbers in the Hornchurch and Romford area were considered to be only slightly lower. It is interesting to note that populations close to or within urban areas suffered less than the rural ones and it may be that they were able to find warmer roosting sites and unfrozen food. Evidence of recovery was forthcoming in subsequent years.

Sharp annual variations in the CBC/BBS Index have continued despite a recent run of mild winters, suggesting that, although obvious decreases occur after hard winters, other, perhaps more local, factors may be involved in determining population levels.

Nationally some upland breeding areas are vacated during winter and farmland hedgerows are also empty with birds moving to other habitats, such as reed beds (Lack 1986). Communal roosting during winter is well known and often occurs during severe weather when counts of up to 30 have been noted. The choice of roost sites can sometimes be as bizarre as some breeding sites, for example 14 in an old tractor tyre in a shed at Writtle in 1992.

The Wren's year round presence in most coastal habitats makes passage difficult to assess, although there is some evidence to suggest it. Glegg described the species as "… apparently sedentary" but remarked that from 1881–86 "… considerable movements had been observed at the lights off the Essex coast" from mid-August to the end of October. He could not, however, find any evidence of spring movements. More recently, above average numbers were recorded in a large southerly movement of passerines along the Essex coast in the late autumn of 1951. Moreover, singles were reported on boats offshore from The Naze and Clacton-on-Sea on 10th and 18th October 1974, whilst 60 were present at Bradwell on 6th October 1974.

Of the few ringing recoveries involving Essex, None have seen movements of more than 200km either into or out of the county. A number of the recoveries do, however, hint at migration rather than local dispersal. These include one ringed at Gibraltar Point, Lincolnshire, on 10th October 1971 and recovered at Westcliff-on-Sea on 7th March 1972, and a first-winter ringed at Spurn Point, East Yorkshire, on 24th September 1994 and found in a Barn Owl pellet at Tillingham in January 1995; there have been two other recoveries of Wrens ringed at Spurn in September/October. Perhaps less typical was the northerly movement of one ringed at Abberton in January 1959 to East Harling, Norfolk, in May 1959. Also of interest were two ringed on the same morning (14th October

1987) at Holland Haven: one was recovered at Deal, Kent, on 5th November 1988 and the other at Newbury, Buckinghamshire, on 26th July 1988. Most coastal migrants are undoubtedly British birds that are dispersing or moving southwards or coastward for winter, although ringing recoveries outside Essex suggest that at least some of the movements involve immigrants or passage migrants from the Continent (Migration Atlas).

While it seems certain that the Wren has suffered due to the continual destruction of marginal habitats, it has also exploited newly created ones. The planting of large numbers of trees, such as those along the Thames corridor and similar landscape enhancements schemes throughout Essex, together with moves towards creating more diverse farmland and open countryside, should all encourage Wren populations. There appears to be no obvious reason to suppose that it will continue to be anything but a common and widespread species across Essex for the foreseeable future.

Northern Mockingbird   *Mimus polyglottos*

Vagrant: one record

The Northern Mockingbird is a generally sedentary species throughout much of its range, which is much of the USA and south into parts of Central America and the Caribbean. It has been expanding its range northwards in recent years. These populations have tended to be more migratory than the southern ones (Cottridge & Vinicombe 1996). Three races are recognised, the nominate *polygottos* occurring in the east of its range.

| 1988 | Horsey Island | 17th–23rd May | Probably 1st-summer |

This is one of only two accepted British records, the other being of one at Saltash, Cornwall, on 30th August 1982; two further records are in Category D. With Britain's largest port at Felixstowe, Suffolk, close by, it seems likely that this was a ship-assisted individual. The only other European record also occurred in 1988 from 16th-23rd October in the Netherlands.

Dunnock (Hedge Sparrow)   *Prunella modularis*

Abundant resident and passage migrant   **Amber List**

The Dunnock is principally a European bird, breeding from the high-arctic areas of Fennoscandia and Russia south to parts of the Mediterranean and the Caucasus (European Atlas). Several races are recognised, the nominate form *modularis* occurring over much of central and northern Europe and *occidentalis* across much of Britain, where the species is somewhat more catholic in habitat requirements than on the Continent. In Britain it is found throughout the country apart from in the mountainous areas and Flow country of northern Scotland (Second National Atlas). Originally a montane and coniferous forest species, the Dunnock moved into other habitats during the 17th century (Montagu 1831). In central Europe its preferred habitat remains scrubby vegetation not far below the tree line. Since the 1970s the British population has been in decline (Population Trends), the CBC/BBS (England) recording a 33% decrease over the period 1977–2002.

Christy referred to the Dunnock with, amongst others, the local names 'Hedge-bet' and 'Hedge-moke' and described the species as "... an abundant resident everywhere ... It is sometimes styled the Hedge Accentor ... as it is not nearly related to our mischievous enemy the House Sparrow". The Dunnock's status has subsequently changed very little. Glegg considered the species a very common resident throughout the county "... which being so much under cultivation and possessing so many hedgerows is highly suitable to the habits of the species". Hudson & Pyman described the Dunnock as very common or abundant resident. Their statement that it was "... amongst the more numerous and ubiquitous of Essex birds, being absent only from the most densely built-over areas", remains true today. The fact the species has always been common has meant that it has received little attention, with just six mentions in the *EBR* Systematic List prior to 1988 and only one of these referring indirectly to breeding numbers. Consequently, the various breeding atlases have been the only source of data available with which to assess any local trends. Dunnocks declined

Atlas	Survey Area	% of 10km squares or tetrads in which	
		bred/probably bred	possibly bred or present
First National 10km	Essex	100.0	0.0
Second National 10km	Essex	100.0	0.0
First London Tetrad	Met. Essex	67.5	11.5
Second London Tetrad	Met. Essex	99.0	1.0
Essex Tetrad	Essex	97.8	0.2

Summary of results of Atlas surveys for Dunnocks

through the period 1977–2002 according to CBC/BBS (England) data but more recent BBS (England) data have suggested a 13% increase. Local indices point to a generally stable population.

In Essex, as elsewhere in the country, the Dunnock favours the thickest of cover and is therefore numerous in woodland edges and coppices, farm hedgerows, parks, gardens and suitable areas of 'waste ground', whilst on the coast a few pairs will breed in the extensive tracts of Shrubby Seablite (Cox), such as at Colne Point, although this habit appears to have only been recognised as recently as 1952 (*EBR* 1952). Both National Atlas surveys confirmed breeding in every 10km square, whilst the Essex Atlas survey located Dunnocks in 96.8% of all tetrads, in almost all of which breeding was confirmed. The species was absent from just a few coastal tetrads in southeast Essex, parts of Dengie and the most built-up areas of the extreme southwest. Numbers increased slightly in Metropolitan Essex between the two London Atlases, particularly along Thames-side, suggesting that the species had moved into and exploited urban gardens and brown-field sites.

Cox noted that woodland CBC plots in Essex averaged 82 pairs per km^2 (range 37–126) and though less numerous on farmland with a mean density of 27 pairs per km^2 (range 6–91), densities were behind only Blackbirds and Skylarks in terms of abundance. More recent local CBC data suggest an average of 62 pairs per km^2 (range 44–102 on five plots) in woodland and 16 pairs per km^2 (range 9–21 on seven plots) on farmland; downward trends have occurred on farmland CBC plots in Essex, although some plots have continued to report steady populations, whilst trends on woodland plots are more stable, suggesting that changes to agricultural practice may be affecting the species.

Dunnocks are affected by hard winters with declines occurring after the 1962/63 and 1981/82 winters, but numbers appear to have recovered quickly. For instance, after the 1962/63 winter the population appeared to have fully recovered by the end of the 1964 breeding season according to national CBC data. Glegg noted losses of 50–80% in Essex after the severe winter of 1916/17.

During autumn and to a lesser extent in spring, influxes are occasionally noted along the coast, although at some localities (e.g. The Naze) differentiating between migrants and residents is not easy. Most of the time, passage at The Naze is suggested by relative increases in numbers, but occasionally small groups may assemble on the top of prominent bushes, call excitedly and then head off skyward. Distinct movements are noted regularly at Landguard Point, Suffolk, just to the north (Piotrowski 2003). Whilst it seems likely that most individuals are of the British race *occidentalis*, which, although generally sedentary, may undertake southward movements outside the breeding season, individuals of the Continental nominate race *modularis* probably also occur, although there are no Essex recoveries to confirm this. Recently, three-figure counts have been almost annual at The Naze, with the largest Essex count being 150 on 12th October 2002, the same day as an arrival of Robins and Goldcrests and a record count of 32 Firecrests. Other large counts of Dunnocks at other coastal sites have coincided with similar arrivals of migrants and perhaps lend support to a Scandinavian origin for some individuals.

Many Dunnocks have been ringed in Essex but few have been recovered. The fact that juveniles disperse away from natal areas is supported by recoveries of juveniles ringed at Walberswick, Suffolk, in June 1976 and found dead at Frinton-on-Sea five months later; another ringed at Layer Breton on 26th June 1988 and re-trapped at Sevenoaks, Kent, on 2nd December 1988; and a third ringed at Copped Hall, Epping, on 12th August 1983 and trapped on St Albans Head, Purbeck, Dorset, on 22nd October 1983. That some British Dunnocks move south in winter is suggested by one ringed at Gibraltar Point, Lincolnshire, on 28th August 1961 and found dead at Colchester on 27th November 1961.

The Dunnock remains an abundant resident throughout much of Essex and in general appears to be adapting well to the modern environment and townscape. Increased tree planting and provision of landscaped areas in built-up areas should also benefit the species. In the wider countryside, re-planting of hedges and increasing the areas of permanent set-aside will all provide replacement habitat for the wider losses across Essex.

Alpine Accentor   *Prunella collaris*

Vagrant: one 19th century record

The Alpine Accentor breeds through the mountain ranges of southern Europe and Morocco, east through Asia Minor as far as eastern Asia and Japan. The nominate race *collaris* occurs in northwest Africa through west and central Europe to Romania, whilst *subalpina* occurs in southeast Europe and west Turkey. The species is a partial migrant, which makes regular, seasonal altitudinal movements.

| 1817 | Forest House, Epping Forest | August | Shot |

This was the first British record and one of very few inland occurrences. Christy detailed the history provided by Mr James Pamplin who shot it: "A few years since I shot a small bird in a garden on the borders of Epping Forest, which I did not know, nor could anyone tell me what it was, till within a fortnight a gentleman requested me to allow him to take it to London. He accordingly went to Mr. Gould, Naturalist...who sends me an account of its being *Accentor alpinus*, or Alpine Warbler, the only one known to have been killed in England ...". Subsequent investigations revealed that it was shot in August 1817 in the garden of Forest House from amongst a number of Chaffinches which flew up from one of the flowerbeds.

It is a very rare vagrant to Britain with just 45 records to the end of 2004 (BBRC 2003) and only 15 of those since 1958. Most recent occurrences have been from the south or east coast in spring, although earlier records fell predominantly in the period August–January.

(European) Robin   *Erithacus rubecula*

Abundant resident, passage migrant and winter visitor

The Robin breeds over much of Europe, its range extending to northwest Africa, Turkey, Iran and east of the Urals to 88° E. The nominate race *rubecula* occurs through much of western Europe but intergrades with *melophilus*, which is found in Ireland and Britain, in southeast England and a broad coastal zone from northern Portugal to Denmark (European Atlas). In Britain and some other areas in western Europe, the Robin tends to associate far more closely with humans than in other parts of its range. The species is found throughout Britain but is most abundant south of a line from Chester northeast to York. The majority of Scandinavian, central and eastern European populations migrate to winter in western Europe and around the Mediterranean.

The Robin has always been a familiar bird in Essex, perhaps not surprisingly given its very close association with man. Thus, Christy described the Robin or 'Red-breast' as "An abundant and very familiar resident" and Glegg "... a very common resident, being one of the most noticeable birds which occur in the county". Christy also mentioned a piece of Essex folklore regarding the Robin, namely that it was unlucky to destroy a Robin's nest,

> The Robin and the Redbreast,
>
> The Robin and the Wren,
>
> If ye take out of their nest,
>
> Ye'll never thrive again.

Amongst the more unusual nesting locations that Christy mentioned were underneath the Bible in the reading desk in Blackmore Church and above a clock inside an occupied house at Stanford Rivers. One Robin became so tame that "During the winter a year or two back ... he entered my bedroom every day and fought himself in the looking-glass".

To Hudson & Pyman the Robin was "... a very common resident [and] regular passage-migrant", whilst Cox's description of the species as an "Abundant resident, passage migrant and winter visitor" suggests a level of abundance that appears to have remained remarkably stable from the 19th to the 21st century. Both National Atlases recorded the Robin breeding in every 10km square, whilst the Essex Atlas survey located Robins in 95.3% of all tetrads, the only large areas from which it was absent being parts of Dengie and Potton and Wallasea Islands, presumably due to lack of suitable nesting sites. A range expansion, mainly along the Thames, was noted in Metropolitan Essex between the two London Atlases. Since the Essex Atlas, the general stability of the population appears to have continued. Possible losses in farmland areas appear to have been offset by colonisation of the increasing number of new gardens created by the housing boom in Essex. Nationally, there has been a steady increase in the CBC/BBS Index over the last three decades with a 25% increase recorded by the BBS (England) Index between 1994 and 2003.

Cox observed that whilst the Robin was a familiar garden bird, the species was in fact one of our most common woodland birds, the mean densities on Essex CBC plots being 120 pairs per km^2 (range 62–172). It was also ever present on county farmland plots with an average of around 14 pairs per km^2, presumably concentrated in hedgerows, spinneys, scrub and farmyards. More recently, densities in woodland have averaged 143 pairs per km^2 (range 92–223 on five plots) and on farmland 27 pairs per km^2 (range 7–57 on seven plots). Trends on the longer-running

Atlas	Survey Area	% of 10km squares or tetrads in which	
		bred/probably bred	possibly bred or present
First National 10km	Essex	100.0	0.0
Second National 10km	Essex	100.0	0.0
First London Tetrad	Met. Essex	70.0	10.0
Second London Tetrad	Met. Essex	99.5	0.5
Essex Tetrad	Essex	95.2	0.1

Summary of results of Atlas surveys for Robins

woodland plots (two) have been downward but those on farmland have generally shown increases; the reasons for such trends are unclear but in recent years many woodland birds have been declining with woodland bird populations having fallen 20% in 20 years.

Annual fluctuations in breeding numbers have been closely linked to the severity of winters. At The Mores Wood, near Brentwood, the lowest populations were noted after the winters of 1981/82 and 1985/86 (Gibbs 2000), a trend closely mirrored by the CBC regional Indices. Being double and sometimes treble-brooded, Robin populations quickly recover from such crashes.

Movements through Essex are normally only detected at regularly watched coastal sites where there are usually few resident Robins. During spring, the numbers of migrants appear to be very small: indeed there have been just two double-figure coastal counts: 30+ at Bradwell, 22nd March 1969; and 25 at The Naze, 25th March 2003. One flew aboard a fishing boat several kilometres off Foulness on 23rd April 1982.

Autumn movements are more pronounced with double-figure counts regular, although until recently, counts of more than 50 at any location were rare. Continental *rubecula* Robins tend to be less confiding and more skulking than the British race and the 'ticking' contact call of many Robins from the depths of bushes after a period of easterly winds is often an indicator of Continental migrants.

Three-figure counts have occurred in just five years: 1976, 220 between Bradwell and The Naze, 125 of them at Bradwell, 25th September; 1988, an unprecedented arrival on 16th and 17th October with at least 1,500 along the coast, including around 1,000 along Dengie, the main point of arrival, and smaller numbers noted north and south of there; 1998, 200 at The Naze, 10th October; 1999, 105 at The Naze, 26th September; and 2000, 131 at The Naze, 8th October. Increased observer coverage at The Naze is likely to be responsible for the upsurge in large counts rather than a genuine increase in arrivals.

National ringing recoveries have revealed that many Robins arrive on our shores in autumn from Scandinavia and east as far as Poland, but very rarely from further east, as although large numbers have been ringed in Latvia, Lithuania and western Russia, very few have been recovered in Britain (Migration Atlas). Two Swedish and one Norwegian-ringed birds have been recovered in Essex, whilst Robins from the Low Countries and around also occur as migrants with recoveries in Essex of Belgian,

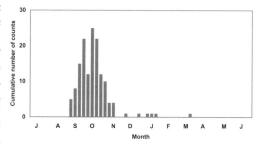

Seasonal occurrence of counts of 10+ Robins from coastal sites from 1971-2004

German and Dutch-ringed individuals. During the huge fall in 1988, a bird that had been ringed in the Netherlands on 14th October was controlled the next day at Great Wakering. In addition, single birds ringed in Essex have been recovered in Norway and Sweden. Few of the migrants controlled in Essex appear to move any further south than the Iberian peninsula where most appear to winter; one controlled in Spain is a typical example. The few winter recoveries suggest that few Continental birds winter in Britain. Nonetheless Cox noted the occurrence of two *rubecula* in January and February near Leigh-on-Sea suggesting that, whilst unusual, small numbers may well winter in Essex. The majority of the hundreds of recoveries involving Robins ringed in Essex have occurred less than 40km from their ringing location, most being "found where ringed". However, individuals have been recovered subsequently as far north as Lincolnshire, North Yorkshire and Durham.

The Robin is an adaptable species that thrives in and around human habitation and it seems likely that, as semi-urbanisation creeps across Essex, the species will benefit. This should offset any losses that may occur in the wider countryside.

(Common) Nightingale *Luscinia megarhynchos*

Fairly common summer resident and passage migrant Amber List

The Nightingale is distributed widely throughout the Mediterranean, warm and temperate zones of the southwest Palearctic, the nominate race *megarhynchos* occupying most of Europe and northernmost Africa (European Atlas). In Britain, the species is restricted to the southeast of England with Kent (26.6%), Suffolk (19.7%), Sussex (15.4%) and Essex (9.1%) holding over 70% of the population (Wilson 2000). The species has been in long-term decline in England since the beginning of the 20th century, although numbers in many areas increased in the 1930s, only to fall dramatically thereafter (Historical Atlas). Climatic change, both in this country and on the African wintering quarters (Wilson 2000), may be the cause of this decline, indicated by a retreat towards the southeast and the fact that many areas of suitable

Atlas	Survey Area	% of 10km squares or tetrads in which	
		bred/probably bred	possibly bred or present
First National 10km	Essex	77.2	5.3
Second National 10km	Essex	40.4	19.3
First London Tetrad	Met. Essex	6.0	2.5
Second London Tetrad	Met. Essex	8.5	4.5
Essex Tetrad	Essex	9.5	2.5

Summary of results of Atlas surveys for Nightingales

habitat still exist from where the species has now withdrawn. Nightingales are generally regarded as a pioneer scrub and woodland species, with coppice being particularly favoured. Here they will seek out the densest cover for their territories, favouring an almost impenetrable thicket of coppice poles with some leaf-cover down to ground level. They do not use stands of less than three years old, nor of more than 8–10. Sweet Chestnut coppice, which is common in Essex, is not generally suitable, except along rides or where other tree species are present and managed on short rotation (Bayes *et al.* 1988).

Morant (1768) in his *History of Essex* provided the earliest reference to the Nightingale when, in describing Havering he noted that it was " … an ancient retiring-place of some of our Saxon kings, particularly of that simple saint, Edward the Confessor, who took great delight in it as being woody and solitary, fit for his private devotions. The legend says it abounded with warbling nightingales; that they disturbed him at his prayers; and he earnestly desired of God their absence. Since which time, as the credulous neighbouring swains believe, never nightingale was heard to sing in the park, but [as] many without the pales as in other places". Christy described the Nightingale as "… a common summer visitor, especially abundant, I think, in the Epping Forest and Saffron Walden districts". One of Christy's correspondents noted: "In the spring of 1858, an old Leytonstone bird-catcher caught 34 about the avenues". Glegg also described the species as a common summer resident throughout, considering it most numerous on Danbury Common. Specifically, he noted breeding at the Walthamstow end of the Lea Valley reservoirs, Felsted and at Bradfield. Hudson & Pyman observed that the Nightingale had "Undoubtedly decreased markedly during the last decade and has deserted some traditional sites". No numerical data were available to back up this assertion but the *EBR* 1953 noted a marked decline from 1952 in the Saffron Walden/Bishop's Stortford and Danbury/Little Baddow/Woodham Walter areas: in the latter as many as 90 singing males may have been present immediately after WWII (*EBR* 1976). Wooded haunts north and west of Chelmsford and in the Rochford Hundred were abandoned in the 1960s. By the early 1970s, the Nightingale was rare in the northwest and many seasoned observers considered that the species had declined markedly across Essex since the end of WWII.

Between the two National Atlases the Nightingale's range contracted to the east, with breeding confirmed in 77.2% of tetrads in the First Atlas but in only 40.4% in the Second.

The first comprehensive county survey occurred in 1976 when the first BTO Nightingale survey was carried out, although coverage was almost certainly incomplete. This revealed that most Nightingales were concentrated into a few areas, most noticeably around the Colne Estuary and in the Danbury Ridge and Ingatestone areas. Peak counts included 27 singing males on Danbury Ridge, 18 pairs at Fingringhoe Wick, ten pairs at both Copperas Wood and in the Mill Green/Fryerning area. In all, a total of 130 breeding pairs or singing males was located, which at the time represented 4% of the national population.

Subsequent national surveys in 1980 and 1999 have meant that the species has one of the best-known distributions of any Essex breeding passerine. The surveys confirmed a general pattern of losses in the south and west of Essex, which have been more than offset by increases in the northeast, whilst there has been an increase in the number of scattered sites holding 1–4 singing males. There has also been a definite move away from woodland/coppice into scrub, a trend also seen nationally (Wilson 2000). For example, at Abberton the scrub around the visitor centre has been colonised in recent years, whilst a significant number now occur along the Chelmer Valley. Grazing of coppice by Fallow and Muntjac Deer, which restricts regrowth, may have had an impact on woodland populations: even if deer are excluded long enough for the coppice stools to regrow, it is possible that deer will get in at a later date and graze the dense vegetation that the Nightingale requires close to the ground (Bayes *et al.* 1988). The future impact of deer on Nightingale populations is uncertain.

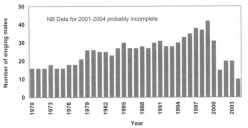

Annual totals of singing male Nightingales at Fingringhoe Wick from 1970-2004

(Source EWT records)

The most important site in Essex is Fingringhoe Wick, where numbers increased from 16 pairs in 1970 to 42 in 1999 (10% of the Essex and 1% of the national population). The population increase since 1995 has made the assessment of exact numbers increasingly difficult (retired warden, Laurie Forsyth pers. comm.). The low number in 2001 was due to access difficulties caused by FMD

Year	Copperas Wood	Thorrington Hall	East Donyland	Friday Wood	Fingringhoe Wick	Lt. Baddow & Danbury	Mill Green	Hatfield Forest	Dunton & Langdon
1976	10	5	5	2	18	44	13	4	7
1980	6	8	12	18	26	26	1	11	17
1999	13	10	15	14	42	27	0	4	1

(including those heard on one visit only)

Year	Singing males	Population change 1976-1980	Population change 1980-99	Population change 1976-99	Proportion of National Population
1976	129	~	~	~	4.00%
1980	263	204%	~	~	5.50%
1999	403	~	153%	312%	9.10%

Summary of the results of national Nightingale surveys in 1976, 1980 and 1999

restrictions. It is thought that Fingringhoe Wick is particularly attractive to Nightingales because, firstly, the 1987 Great Storm created a network of small patches of young thick scrub around the reserve and, secondly, management has focused on enlarging rabbit-grazed glades, which provide good feeding areas (Laurie Forsyth pers. comm.). A population of around 40 pairs represents a breeding density of about 30 pairs per km^2 at this site.

Christy observed that the Nightingale was normally first heard around 15th April, and mentioned an early bird at West Bergholt on 7th April 1879. The earliest Essex record involved one at Layer Breton on the exceptionally early date of 20th March 1953. The only other March records involved singles at: Great Holland, 29th in 1981; Fishers Green, 29th in 2002; Two Tree Island, 30th in 1986; and Berwick Ponds, 30th in 2000. Arrivals peak from mid-April to mid-May with most records involving singing males back at breeding sites, although individuals may be found singing for a few days from almost any suitable patch of cover.

The warning croaks of adults with young can be heard on the breeding sites until early July but, thereafter, the species is hardly in evidence with just over 20 records since 1970 of presumed migrants away from known breeding sites. Occurrences are less than annual and usually between mid-July and early September, and they are typically at coastal localities where it is possible that some may be Continental drift migrants.

Records after mid-September are exceptional with the latest being singles at: Hockley, 4th October 1957; Romford SF, 2nd October 1955; Pitsea, 28th September 1986; and The Naze, 26th September 1976. In addition, an injured individual was at Bures on the Essex/Suffolk border on 12th November 1873 (Payn 1962).

There is a total of five ringing recoveries involving Essex, the furthest movement being just 59km from Church Wood, Canterbury, Kent, on 19th May 1986, north to Layer Breton on 3rd August 1986; this suggests that not all Nightingales back at known breeding sites during spring have completed their migration. One ringed at Langdon Hills in June 1964 and recovered at Billericay in May 1965 and another retrapped at St Osyth on 5th August 1989 after it was ringed there as a first-year bird on 12th August 1987 suggest an element of site-faithfulness. There are very few national ringing recoveries (Migration Atlas).

The Nightingale has experienced a moderate population decline over the last 25 years. In Essex, the shift to scrubland means that this habitat requires conservation, although ironically such habitat is probably undervalued and can often be perceived as wasteland of little significance (Wilson 2000). The reintroduction of coppicing may have some influence on numbers, although its importance seems to have declined in recent years; pressures on migration and in wintering quarters may also be influencing numbers (Fuller *et al.* 2005). Although climate change may have some effect on numbers in Essex in the future, the results of the recent survey show that numbers in the county appear to be increasing and thus the immediate future of the Nightingale seems assured.

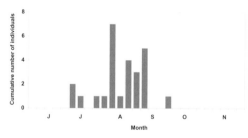

Seasonal occurrence of assumed migrant Nightingales during autumn from 1971-2004

Bluethroat

Luscinia svecica

Very rare passage migrant: 48 records involving 12 White-spotted, eight Red-spotted and 28 not ascribed to race

Amber List

The Bluethroat breeds widely across the Palearctic from Spain and Norway to Kashmir, northern China and the Bering Sea in easternmost Siberia (*BWP*). The nominate Red-spotted Bluethroat *svecica* breeds mainly north of the Baltic through Scandinavia and across Russia to Alaska, whilst the White-spotted Bluethroat *cyanecula* breeds from Spain and the Netherlands eastward to the Ukraine and Baltic States, patchily across western and central Europe (Migration Atlas). Being a more southern-breeding race than *svecica*, White-spotted Bluethroats return earlier to their breeding grounds and hence occur earlier in Britain. Western populations of Bluethroats winter mainly in eastern Africa. Spring males are easy to separate racially but many females and first-winters are inseparable; hence a high proportion of autumn Bluethroats are not racially identified.

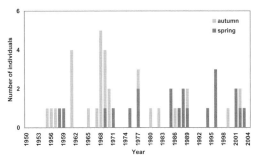

Annual totals of Bluethroats from 1950-2004

Christy included the species on the basis of one stated to have occurred near Harwich in the late 19th century. Glegg did not accept it; the record is vague and may even relate to a Suffolk occurrence. The first documented Essex record is therefore from Walthamstow on 19th–20th September 1936 but there were no further occurrences until 1955 when one was seen at Dagenham GP on 3rd September. Since 1955, Bluethroats have been recorded in 27 years with the most in any one year being five in 1968, none of which were, racially identified. Surprisingly few have been found in Essex compared with Suffolk, where there have been over 150 since 1950 (Piotrowski 2003) and in Norfolk, where in spring 1985 alone there were 54 (Taylor *et al.* 1999).

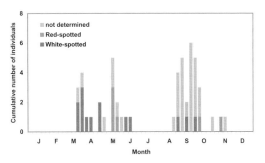

Seasonal occurrence of Bluethroats from 1950-2004

Although most autumn records are of indeterminate race, it is likely that many involve *svecica*, as their departure from breeding grounds in late August (BWP) correlates with the Essex peak from early September. In recent years, there has been an increasing tendency for more to occur in spring than autumn with numbers in autumn generally lower than previously, a pattern noted nationally. Quite why this should be is not clear. Increased observer coverage and increases in *cyanecula* on the near-Continent since the 1970s (Migration Atlas) could account for the increase in spring, but it may be that the declines seen in autumn records since the 1960s are linked to declines in the Scandinavian *svecica* population due to droughts in the Sahel wintering grounds and perhaps an eastward shift in the migratory route. Nationally, an average of 186 Bluethroats occurred annually during the 1980s but this fell to 116 in the 1990s and just 92 in the 2000s (Fraser & Rogers 2004).

The earliest arriving Bluethroats are all White-spotted (see below). The earliest definite Red-spotted was at Abberton on 16th May 1971, whilst the latest was a Red-spotted at Cudmore Grove CP on 15th–16th November 2002.

Generally, Bluethroats have made only short stays, although their extremely skulking nature may count against them being re-found once discovered. Only one *svecica* has stayed for more than two days, a first-winter male on Foulness from 2nd–9th September 1961.

The 12 definite records of White-spotted Bluethroat are:

1958	Colne Point	28th–29th March	Male
1970	Berwick Ponds	30th August	Male
1977	Leigh/Two Tree Island	14th–17th September	Male
1980	South Woodham Ferrers	28th September	Male
1988	The Naze	1st April	Male
1989	East Tilbury/Mucking	9th–15th June	Singing male
1994	Rainham	26th April	Singing male
1996	Cornmill Meadows	3rd–5th April	
	Bradwell	8th-14th April	
2001	Gunners Park	19th–27th March	Singing male
	Two Tree Island	24th March	Male
2002	Holland Haven	27th April	Male

In addition, it is quite likely that individuals at Bishop's Stortford SF on 31st March 1959 and at Bradwell on 22nd March 1969 were *cyanecula* given the early arrival dates.

A first-year male *svecica* ringed at Korkar, Kymi, Finland, on 22nd September 1995 had its ring read in the field at The Naze on 18th May 1999; it was the first recorded movement of the species from Finland and one of only a handful of British recoveries.

Black Redstart   *Phoenicurus ochruros*

Uncommon summer visitor and passage migrant: occasionally winters   **Amber List**

The Black Redstart has an extensive Palearctic breeding range, extending from northwest Africa through most European countries eastward through the Caucasus, Asia Minor, Iran, north to central Asia and east to western China (European Atlas). The race *gibraltariensis* occurs over much of the species' European range with *aterrimus* present in Iberia. The Black Redstart favours habitat where plant communities are scarce and typically possess much exposed rock, pebbles and boulders. The species has spread across much of northwest Europe since the 1850s and has bred in England since 1923 when a few pairs used natural cliff sites. From 1926–42 breeding occurred on the site of the National Exhibition at Wembley with a spread into London from 1942. Consolidation of the London population probably occurred only as a result of exploitation of nesting sites created by aerial bombing of urban areas during WWII, combined with the favourable city environment microclimate (Williamson 1975).

The first documented Essex record occurred in 1879, when one was shot at Ramsey on 14th April (Christy) with a further 11 prior to 1930. National records were rare in the first half of the 19th century but from around 1860, records increased and from about 1880 the species was recorded annually (Historical Atlas).

Since 1941, the Black Redstart has occurred regularly in Essex with the first breeding occurring in 1949 when a pair bred at Shellhaven, although birds were heard there, but not located in 1948. Breeding continued until 1954, with numbers peaking in 1951 when four pairs reared at least one brood each. All located nests were in recesses in brickwork built around oil tanks during WWII. Breeding was not confirmed again until 1960 when one pair bred in Colchester; another pair almost certainly bred in Dagenham docks. Breeding has occurred annually since 1966, although numbers vary considerably from year to year, a pattern typical of a species on the northwest limit of its breeding range. However, irregular coverage and perhaps redevelopment of breeding sites may also be factors.

Generally, numbers were relatively stable through the 1970s and 1980s, but declined through the early and mid-1990s, only to recover thereafter. Being on the edge of its range means that the Black Redstart is a less prolific breeder than in its core range and it is possible that breeding populations in Britain are not self-sustaining (Glue 1994). Indeed, the Essex population has not increased significantly in the last 50 years and perhaps, therefore, has to rely on continuing recruitment of new birds for its survival.

A number of key features appear to be required for a potential breeding location to be suitable for Black Redstarts (Frith *et al.* 2000): tracts of largely undisturbed, sparsely vegetated and rocky terrain; a good selection of complex structures; herbaceous vegetation, which attracts insects and provides seeds especially during the late period of the breeding season; water; a poor or absent shrub layer. These requirements are most readily met in large, urban built-up areas and almost all breeding records

Atlas	Survey Area	% of 10km squares or tetrads in which	
		bred/probably bred	possibly bred or present
First National 10km	Essex	14.0	5.3
Second National 10km	Essex	14.0	7.0
First London Tetrad	Met. Essex	6.0	1.0
Second London Tetrad	Met. Essex	7.0	4.0
Essex Tetrad	Essex	1.2	1.1

Summary of results of Atlas surveys for Black Redstarts

have come from along the Thames between the City and the large oil refineries at Coryton or up the Lea Valley as far as KGV. Like other breeding areas in southeast England, nesting sites tend to be located particularly in industrial areas, in use or derelict, where the variety of buildings best mimic their traditional habitat requirements. Thus docks, power stations, oil refineries, railway goods yards, gas works, cement factories, building sites and derelict buildings have all been used as breeding sites.

Breeding Black Redstarts have used many different sites but confirmation of breeding is often difficult, and at many locations singing males observed on occasional days may be the only indication of a local breeding pair; many sites have intermittent records over a period of years. An interesting trend has been for increasing numbers to be recorded in the Docklands area of London; these 'new' Black Redstarts were probably always present in the area but only with the coming of local housing and commercial developments and the increasing presence of local resident birders been the population been observed. Given the amount of available habitat throughout east London and the access difficulties and unattractiveness of many locations to birders, it is very likely that some pairs are overlooked. The largest populations have been found at West Thurrock (four pairs in 1986), Beckton Gas Works (five pairs in 1975 and 1981) and Silvertown (six pairs in 1998), whilst up to three pairs have been present at Rainham and Coryton.

Only in a few instances has breeding occurred away from Thames-side/Metropolitan Essex, all involving single pairs: Parkeston (1969, 1974, 1976); Harwich (1988); The Hythe (1975–77); Essex University, Colchester (1960 and in the 1980s); Stanway (1975); and Harlow (1969). In addition, singing males and/or females have occasionally been noted at these and a few other sites since 1950. All records typically involved breeding around large buildings or structures except for the 1975 record from Stanway where a pair nested successfully in a Sand Martin hole within the cliff face of the gravel-pit.

The general increase in breeding numbers has been paralleled by an increase in migrants, although the two

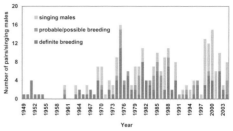

Annual numbers of breeding Black Redstarts from 1949-2004

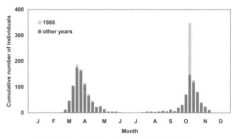

Seasonal occurrence of migrant Black Redstarts away from breeding areas from 1971-2004

should perhaps not be linked as the species continues to spread northwest in Europe and the increase may be due to changing migration patterns. Numbers occurring in spring and autumn vary considerably from year to year, probably in response to the weather prevailing at the time. Black Redstarts are one of the earliest spring and latest autumn migrants with spring numbers slightly higher than those in autumn. Spring migration starts in early March and peaks at the end of March/early April and is largely complete by the end of April. Although numbers overall are generally higher than in autumn, there have only been two double-figure counts: 18 along Dengie, 29th March 1998, and ten at Colne Point, 10th April 1987. A total of 61 in 1987 is the largest spring total, 10–30 being more typical.

Occasional individuals are recorded throughout summer, sometimes from coastal watch points, and perhaps involving wandering non-breeders. Movements of what are presumably relatively local birds occur throughout August and September, but it is not until October that numbers increase and peak at the end of the month and into early November. Autumn totals of 10–30 are the norm but on 16th–17th October 1988 there was an unprecedented arrival of at least 200 that coincided with a huge arrival of Robins (q.v.). Counts included 17 on Foulness on 16th, although elsewhere numbers were not exceptional. By the next day, however, there were 28 at The Naze, 50+ between Burnham-on-Crouch and Howe Outfall, Dengie, and 60 along the Dengie coast. On 18th and 19th, the area inland from Holliwell Point had 1–2 in every field, with numbers estimated to be in three figures. The arrival was localised as

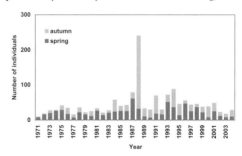

Annual totals of migrant Black Redstarts from 1971-2004

numbers were not significant in Norfolk and 17 at Felixstowe was the largest count from Suffolk (Piotrowski 2003). There have been no other autumn double-figure counts.

Occasional individuals have wintered in Essex, although this occurs less than annually and usually at or very close to known breeding sites. All mid-winter records have involved 1–2, although there were 3–4 at KGV in December 1995, 1998 and 1999.

The Black Redstart is one of Britain's rarest breeding birds with an estimated 30–93 pairs (RBBP 2004) and in theory one of the most protected, yet some conservation organisations appear to treat it with marked indifference (Frith *et al.* 2001). Little attempt has been made to protect its urban habitat when faced with destruction, and planning authorities have largely been ignorant of its presence. The current trend towards massive redevelopment of large areas east of London is, therefore, a significant threat to the species. Its future in Essex largely depends on raising overall awareness of the species so that its requirements are taken into account in future redevelopment of existing breeding sites. Two pioneering schemes, albeit just outside the county, at Deptford and Wandsworth, may lead the way in this respect (Frith *et al.* 2001).

Sponsored by John Fitzpatrick

(Common) Redstart   *Phoenicurus phoenicurus*

Regular passage migrant in small numbers: bred in small numbers until 1993   Amber List

The Redstart breeds widely across Europe and through Siberia as far east as Lake Baikal. In Europe, it is absent from much of Ireland, Greece and southern Spain and absent from Iceland and Svalbard, Corsica and Sardinia. The species winters in sub-Saharan Africa in areas of savannah and scrub (European Atlas). The nominate race *phoenicurus* breeds throughout Europe and Siberia and northwest Africa, whilst *samamisicus* breeds around the Caspian and Black Seas and northern Middle East (*BWP*). In Britain, the species is most common in the south and west and shows a particular preference for Oak woods, but is uncommon or absent across much of lowland Britain. The species appears to be increasing in those parts of its range where it is more abundant, whilst decreasing at the periphery of its range (Second National Atlas). Nationally, the CBC recorded a 160% increase over the period 1975–2000, with the BBS for the period 1994–2002 noting a 133% increase.

Christy described the Redstart as "A regular summer visitor, though rather uncommon, at least in the inland parts of the county ... It breeds sparingly in all parts of the county ...". The species had clearly declined quite significantly prior to Christy's time. For example, at Epping Forest in 1832, Henry Doubleday noted: "The Redstart has arrived this year in immense numbers. I have never seen so many before", whilst a little latter, he described it as "... more abundant than I ever knew it before. The forest literally swarms with them". It continued to be "frequent in summer" in the Forest until at least 1885. It remained common around Saffron Walden and Sudbury during the 1840s, whilst at South Shoebury around 1865, the Redstart was described as "... very plentiful around here, frequenting particularly those parts where the pollard willows most abound ... I never saw them so plentiful in any part of England, and most probably it is on account of the number of trees, which line the ditches in the marshy districts that are so common here". Christy described a rather unusual nesting site at Saffron Walden in 1878: "After the excavation of the supposed Saxon cemetery ... when nearly two hundred skeletons were discovered, a Redstart made its nest and reared four young in one of the skulls during the time that it remained exposed. Access to the interior was through the eye orbit".

Glegg considered that, on Christy's evidence, the Redstart was formerly "... more general in its distribution than it is today". He concluded that the Redstart's chief haunts were Epping, Hatfield and Hainault Forests with smaller numbers

Atlas	Survey Area	% of 10km squares or tetrads in which	
		bred/probably bred	possibly bred or present
First National 10km	Essex	14.0	10.5
Second National 10km	Essex	7.0	12.3
First London Tetrad	Met. Essex	8.0	2.5
Second London Tetrad	Met. Essex	1.0	1.5
Essex Tetrad	Essex	0.6	0.8

Summary of results of Atlas surveys for Redstarts

in the woods around Brentwood and Laindon, Gosfield and intermittently at other rather scattered sites. Around "Stubbers", North Ockendon, the Redstart was considered "... as numerous ... as ... anywhere" in 1885, whilst in 1900 it was still "... one of ... [the] ... commonest birds", with five occupied nest boxes, each no more than 40m apart. The species remained common around Sible Hedingham and Gosfield at the turn of the 19th century. By 1912, it had decreased near Chelmsford and at Mistley it was at one time a common nester but by Glegg's time had decreased.

Nationally, Redstarts were declining throughout lowland Britain in the 19th century. Whilst the decreases are largely unexplained, there is some evidence to suggest that it may have been related in part to the removal of dead and dying trees, which deprived the species of its nest holes (Historical Atlas). From the available evidence, a marked decline took place in Essex between 1890 and 1910, which ties in with declines noted elsewhere in lowland Britain. Nationally, the declines had been fully recovered by 1967/68, only for a crash to occur in 1973 (Population Trends), the cause being attributed to severe drought conditions in the wintering area, the Sahel, Africa. Since then numbers have returned to pre-1973 levels.

Since 1950, annual numbers of breeding pairs/singing males in Essex have varied considerably. However, the general trend has been one of decline, such that by the last decade of the 20th century the Redstart was effectively lost as an Essex breeding species. During the 1960s and early 1970s, the population was fairly stable. However, there was a marked decline in 1973, in line with the national trend, but the Essex breeding population has never recovered, although the Great Storm of 1987 opened up areas of Epping Forest, which were adopted by up to six pairs in 1988.

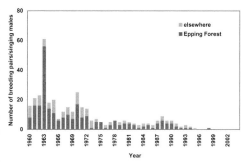

Annual totals of breeding Redstarts from 1960-2004

Since 1950, most breeding records have come from five main areas: Epping Forest; Writtle/Blackmore/Margaretting/Ingatestone; Brentwood/Shenfield/Warley CP/Weald CP; Hainault Forest CP; and Danbury/Little Baddow/Woodham Walter.

Counts from Epping Forest have varied more from year to year than at any other site, probably due to variable observer coverage over such a large area. The largest numbers reported after 1950 were 56 singing males, of which at least 30 were paired, during 1963, although this was exceptional and perhaps linked to very low population levels of resident species following the severe winter of 1962/63 (Cox). The second largest count, in 1957, which was based on three transects radiating from High Beech, out to Wake Arms Public House, Chingford and Robin Hood Public House, located 11 confirmed breeding pairs, ten further pairs and ten singing males. Numbers crashed in the early 1970s from at least 17 singing males in 1970, the last double-figure breeding count from the Forest, to just a single singing male in 1973. The population recovered to a maximum of six singing males in 1978, but thereafter no more than four pairs/singing males were located until 1988, when a total of six pairs bred in two areas opened up by the Great Storm. However, numbers thereafter declined and the last confirmed Essex breeding record came in 1993, when a single pair bred in the northern part of the Forest. Apart from a pair present in 1994, the only subsequent record involved a singing male at Long Running in 1998.

During the 1950s, up to five pairs/singing males (one breeding pair and four singing males in 1957) were reported regularly from Hainault Forest CP with breeding confirmed three times, single pairs in 1957 and 1959 and two in 1969. Subsequently, there have been just three records of singing males in 1970, 1984 and 1991.

Around the Brentwood area, the species' stronghold was Thorndon CP, with occasional records coming from Weald CP, Hart's Wood, Barrack Wood and Childerditch. The last records that may be attributed to breeding involved a male and a female at Thorndon CP in 1982, with three individuals observed in July. The population peaked in the late 1950s when around six pairs/singing males were noted, with similar numbers in 1965 and 1970, although after 1974 counts were very much lower with records in just five years involving no more than a single pair or two singing males.

The Writtle area population, like others, appeared to peak in the late 1950s, with seven pairs and a singing male in 1957 and seven pairs and four singing males in 1958. Thereafter numbers declined markedly and after 1963, no more than a single pair or singing male were noted, breeding last being confirmed in 1977 when a pair bred in a hollow rubber owl previously used as a bird-scarer in a garden at Margaretting. The species was last reported from the area in 1990 when a pair was noted in Highwood.

The small Danbury population consisted of single pairs or up to two singing males, although four pairs were present on Woodham Walter Common in 1960 and a total of three singing males was noted at two locations in 1971. Since 1974, there have been just two records of singing males in the area, both in 1991, although neither appeared to stay.

In Hatfield Forest no more than two pairs/singing males were noted intermittently during the 1950s; breeding was never confirmed. The last breeding season record involved two singing males in 1965. At Weeleyhall Wood, a pair was noted in 1979, with 1–2 pairs possibly breeding most years until 1989, whilst at Friday Wood, a singing male was present in 1988 and then from 1990–95, although a female was never seen. At Gosfield, the species was reckoned to breed until around 1930, whilst at Strethall Woods it was described as "… still present although numbers have declined" in the *EBR* 1965.

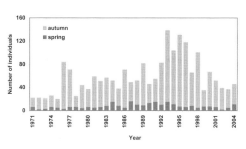

Annual totals of migrant Redstarts from 1971-2004

Away from these locations, there have been very few breeding season records with confirmed breeding coming only from Mistley in 1961. Many records of singing males in suitable habitat may simply relate to migrants passing through the county.

Spring passage through Essex is generally very light and it is rare for more than ten to be recorded annually, although there were 18 in 1993 and 16 in 1987. The earliest arrival involved one at Dagnam Park on 12th March 1992, whilst there was one at Dovercourt on 16th March 1964. Otherwise, there have been eight further March records, all in the last eight days of the month. Spring passage peaks around late April/early May. All records since 1966 have involved 1–2 individuals, except for three in Gunners Park on 7th May 1990.

Autumn passage begins during late July, presumably involving juveniles dispersing from breeding areas. Numbers of migrants peak during late September, with few occurring after mid-October. In all, there have been nine November records, the latest at Rainham on 22nd in 1981 and Halstead on 27th in 1959.

The Redstart is a classic drift migrant, although Essex has generally missed the largest falls that have been noted in Norfolk (Taylor *et al.* 1999) and Suffolk (Piotrowski 2003). With numbers occurring in autumn largely dependent on a suitable easterly airflow, it is not surprising that totals vary markedly from year to year. However, following an apparent increase during the 1990s, totals have been lower since 1999. The largest influx occurred in mid-September 1995 when around 100 arrived, coinciding with a large fall along the East Anglian coast, including 5,000 in Norfolk alone (Taylor *et al.* 1999). The highest counts were ten at both The Naze and Foulness on 23rd September. The largest count from a single site in Essex was 22 at The Naze on 21st September 1957, whilst counts of 20 have come from: Bradwell, 2nd September 1956; North Weald airfield, 27th August 1968 (the only double-figure count outside September); The Naze, 22nd September 1968; Bradwell/Dengie, 25th September 1976; Foulness, 24th September 1977; and Foulness, 6th September 1981. In

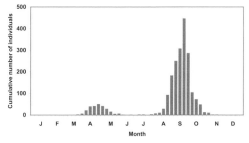

Seasonal occurrence of migrant Redstarts from 1971-2004

addition, there have been a further 13 double-figure counts, five from The Naze, four from Foulness, three from Bradwell/Dengie and one from Shoebury.

Relatively few Redstarts have been ringed in Essex. However, Redstarts from both British and northern European populations have been recovered within the county. One ringed in Gloucestershire was recovered at Waltham Abbey on 5th May 1968, a Finnish bird was found at Hadleigh on 24th October 1976 five weeks after it was ringed, and one recovered at Stock on 3rd October 1981 had been ringed three weeks previously on Helgoland, Germany.

The Essex Atlas survey noted somewhat prophetically that the Redstart might be lost as a breeding species by the end of the 20th century. Whilst conditions within the species' wintering quarters and on passage may have been factors in its decline in Essex, local habitat change through the removal of old trees and cessation of traditional woodland management techniques such as pollarding have perhaps had a greater impact. Resumption of such management in the species' old haunts where habitat otherwise looks suitable, combined with the provision of nest boxes may assist the re-establishment of the Redstart within Essex (Essex Atlas), particularly as it is thriving in its existing strongholds in western Britain.

There have been two records of males showing white wing patches characteristic of the eastern race *samamisicus*: The Naze, 13th October 1992; and Holland Haven, 13th October 2001.

Whinchat   *Saxicola rubetra*

Fairly common passage migrant; very scarce summer visitor that last bred in 1999

The monotypic Whinchat is primarily a meadow-breeding bird of the Palearctic, inhabiting the temperate, boreal, steppe and mountain regions of Europe and central parts of western Asia. Eastwards, its range is further south, the northern limit being influenced by the extended spring frosts, whilst it is local in the Mediterranean (Urquhart 2002). In Britain, the Whinchat has been in decline since at least the 1930s (Population Trends) and is now principally an upland species of the west and north where it frequents open grassland and areas of mixed low vegetation such as Gorse, Heather and Bracken. Only small numbers now breed in eastern England. Whinchats are long-distance trans-Saharan migrants with a winter distribution not dissimilar to that of Wheatears.

Christy described the Whinchat as "A regular, though rather local, summer visitor, coming to us about the middle of April, and leaving again in October. It is most commonly seen at the times of its migration, but is fairly abundant during summer on some of our furze-covered commons, and nests, not very rarely in meadows and cultivated fields throughout the county." According to Doubleday, the Whinchat was numerous in Epping Forest in 1831, although in 1839 he observed that the species had become "... so remarkably scarce ..." and, in 1843: "Although in former years one of our most abundant visitors, for the last two or three seasons [it] has been very scarce". However, the Whinchat was still breeding in the area in 1888, being "... a summer visitor breeding in the furze-bushes". Around Saffron Walden, the species bred until at least 1845, whilst in the Sudbury area in 1838 it was common. In the late 19th century it was scarce, though still breeding around Harwich and uncommon in the Orsett area. Yarrell (1845) considered the Whinchat to be widespread in England, a situation that had changed little by the end of the 19th century (Historical Atlas).

By the 1920s, the Whinchat appeared to have declined, Glegg noting that the species was "... a somewhat uncommon and certainly local summer resident". He felt that a decline was underway, although he only cited the fact that it now bred rarely in Epping Forest to back up his statement. The national breeding distribution detailed in Witherby *et al.* (1938–41) was very similar to that recorded by the 19th century authors and was confirmed by Alexander & Lack (1944).

Since the 1950s the decline has continued. Hudson & Pyman considered the Whinchat a decreasing summer visitor, although the species was reported fairly widely until the mid-1950s with inland breeding reported from Abberton (ten pairs in 1952), the Chelmer Valley between Chelmsford and Little Baddow (ten pairs in 1953) and around Romford SF (four pairs in 1955 and 1956), together with a wide scattering of records, principally from the south and west of the county. On the coast, the species was still fairly well distributed, although the largest numbers were along Thames-side, where there were ten pairs at Rainham in 1955, eight at Vange Marsh in 1955, four at Shoeburyness in 1956 and three at Fobbing in 1955. Away from Thames-side, there were mostly odd pairs, although at Colne Point/St Osyth, there were 6–7 pairs from 1954–56.

A noticeable decline seemed to have begun around the mid-1950s. Inland, none was ever to be recorded breeding again at Abberton after 1955 and, by the end of the decade, the species had also disappeared from the Chelmer Valley and Romford SF. Breeding became sporadic elsewhere.

From 1965, inland breeding was reported from just four sites: Hanningfield, 1–2 pairs until 1967; Roman River Valley, one pair, 1968; Great Parndon, one pair, 1970; Hornchurch airfield, up to two pairs, 1967–71. Since then, the only inland records have come from: Donyland Wood, singing male, 1977 and 1978; and Fairlop CP, one pair may have bred, 1984. On the coast, breeding was more or less confined to just two areas by the mid-1960s: Thames-side and the Colne Estuary. Even at these, however, numbers continued to decline with a peak of 15–16 singing males at Thames-side in 1974 reduced to occasional odd pairs/singing males during the 1990s and from peaks of seven pairs in 1983 and 1987 at Langenhoe Marshes there have been only singing males since the mid-1990s, except for 1999 when a pair bred, the last year that breeding was confirmed in Essex.

The decline of the species nationally and in Essex since the late 1950s is graphically illustrated by the two National Atlases, although in Metropolitan Essex numbers appeared to have remained stable until the 1990s; greater observer coverage may have been a significant factor in this trend. The Essex Atlas concluded with the sadly prophetic statement that "... the current survey may present the final days of the Whinchat as a breeding bird of Essex".

Whinchats feed on insects in low-level field vegetation, especially from umbellifers, and often nest in mown grass. Following an increase in this type of habitat in the 1920s and 1930s caused by the agricultural depression, post-war farming destroyed this habitat. Added to this, many alternative breeding areas disappeared under dense scrub following the myxamotosis outbreak in the mid-1950s and the increased use of herbicides, the switch from haymaking to silage and the modern management of roadside verges all significantly impacted on the species' habi-tat (O'Connor & Shrubb 1986). In Essex, the decline of the Whinchat has, at least in the last 20 years, coincided with the increase in Stonechats, particularly along Thames-side. Whilst this may be no more than coincidence, studies of interactions

Atlas	Survey Area	% of 10km squares or tetrads in which	
		bred/probably bred	possibly bred or present
First National 10km	Essex	24.6	7.0
Second National 10km	Essex	7.0	10.5
First London Tetrad	Met. Essex	4.0	0.5
Second London Tetrad	Met. Essex	2.0	7.5
Essex Tetrad	Essex	0.5	0.9

Summary of results of Atlas surveys for Whinchats

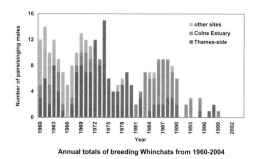

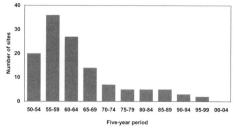

Annual totals of breeding Whinchats from 1960-2004

No of sites in each five-year period at which Whinchats bred/probably bred from 1950-2004

between the two have noted that Stonechats are generally more aggressive than Whinchats, which they tend to dislodge from suitable breeding sites (Second National Atlas).

In most years the first Whinchats do not normally arrive back in Essex until the second half of April. However, there have been three March records, the earliest being two at East Tilbury on 28th in 1977 with two at South Hanningfield on 30th in 1957 and one at Colne Point on 31st in 1958. Passage through the county peaks around the very end of April and early May with apparent stragglers occurring until mid-June. Numbers are generally small: since 1971, it has been rare for more than 30 to be recorded in any spring. However, there were 65–70 in 1991, including nine at The Naze and eight in Gunners Park on 21st May, the only counts of more than five since 1971, prior to which published records of migrants were scant.

With juveniles dispersing from breeding grounds from mid-July onwards, the first returning migrants begin to arrive in Essex. Indeed, some of the earliest arrivals may involve family parties. Numbers build steadily to a peak from late August to mid-September with numbers declining quickly after the third week of the month. A few stragglers are regularly recorded through October, although almost all have left Essex by the last week of that month. There have been nine November and two December records: 4th at Tollesbury Wick in 1999, and 27th at Rainham in 2000. Numbers recorded on passage vary considerably from year to year with easterly winds perhaps causing periodic influxes of Continental birds. There does, however, appear to have been a decline in total migrant numbers since the mid-1990s.

There have been 13 site counts of 50 or more, the largest being: about 100 on Foulness, 7th September 1958; 60 on Foulness, 31st August 1980; 60 at Bradwell/Dengie, 6th September 1980; about 70 at The Naze, 18th–19th September 1982; 80 on Foulness, 26th August and 100, 2nd September 1984; 60 on Foulness, 26th August 1990.

Whinchats at Leigh/Two Tree Island on 25th January 1976 and Walthamstow on 9th January 1983 may have been attempting to winter in Essex.

There have been just three recoveries of birds ringed on passage in Essex. Singles recovered in Morocco in April and Spain in December are typical of birds on migration from/to Africa, whilst one recovered in June near Nysatra, Enkoping, Sweden, hints at the origin of some of the Whinchats occurring in Essex during autumn. Nationally, the recovery rate of ringed Whinchats is low (Migration Atlas) and relatively little is known about movements once they leave Britain.

Despite the fact that large areas of coast are now owned and managed as nature reserves, there have been no signs of a recolonisation of Essex by Whinchats. In the Netherlands, increases have been noted since the 1980s on damp nature reserves (European Atlas). Although reasons for the historic decline have been attributed to local

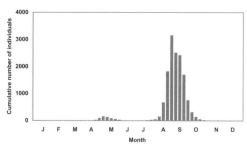

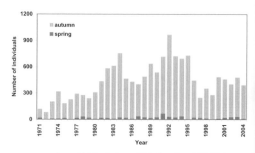

Seasonal occurrence of migrant Whinchats from 1971-2004

Annual totals of migrant Whinchats from 1971-2004

habitat loss and degradation, it is possible that problems in the species' Sahel wintering area are suppressing numbers sufficiently to count against the re-establishment of the population in lowland Britain.

Stonechat   *Saxicola torquata*

The Stonechat's range extends across Europe, Asia and Africa, from the Arctic Circle to the very tip of South Africa and as far east as Japan. Its taxonomy is complex with perhaps as many as 25 subspecies recognised, although some authorities (e.g. Urquhart 2002) have suggested that the 'Common' Stonechat should be considered as three separate species, European Stonechat *S. rubicola*, Siberian Stonechat *S. maura* and African Stonechat *S. torquata*. The BOURC does not yet support this split.

(European) Stonechat   *S. t. hibernans/torquata*

Small coastal breeding population, common passage migrant and winter visitor   Amber List

The Stonechat is widely distributed through the temperate and boreal zones, breeding over most of Eurasia, from Norway, Finland and southern Denmark in the north, west through Britain, France, Spain and Portugal, on the larger Mediterranean islands and in northern Africa and east across northern Europe to southern Poland, Ukraine and Belarus and in southern Europe east to Turkey and Transcaucasia (Urquhart 2002). The subspecies *hibernans* is found in Britain, Ireland, western France and western Iberia with the race *torquata* occurring over the much of its European range. Intergradation occurs between theses two races, which are generally very similar, although the former tends to be generally darker than the latter. In Britain, the species is principally found in the more temperate western areas where winters are generally less severe. British Stonechats are generally sedentary but *torquata* is migratory in the northern part of its range, moving south to winter in the southern parts of its range.

Christy described the Stonechat as "Chiefly a summer visitor, though partially resident, as some remain throughout winter. It breeds commonly on Lingwood, Danbury, Mill Green, Fryerning, and other furze-covered commons through out the county". The earliest documented Essex record dates back to 1831 when Doubleday (Christy) noted that the species "used to abound on the furze bushes by the sides of the forest [Epping], but, what is very singular, it has within the last three years totally disappeared". However, by the 1860s, the Stonechat was described as "... much more common than the Whinchat ..." At Orsett in the late 19th century, the

Atlas	Survey Area	% of 10km squares or tetrads in which	
		bred/probably bred	possibly bred or present
First National 10km	Essex	12.3	3.5
Second National 10km	Essex	12.3	5.3
First London Tetrad	Met. Essex	1.0	0.5
Second London Tetrad	Met. Essex	7.0	3.0
Essex Tetrad	Essex	2.1	0.7

Summary of results of Atlas surveys for Stonechats

species was likewise described as "... far more abundant than the Whinchat, especially in furze-covered districts such as Mucking Heath and Orsett Heath, where it resides". It was also common and bred at Harwich during the late 19th century and bred at Saffron Walden occasionally to at least 1845. It remained a widespread breeding species throughout the British Isles at the end of the 19th century (Historical Atlas).

Glegg considered the Stonechat a local resident and described its main breeding haunts as the "... less-frequented parts of the coast". He attributed the lack of inland breeding to the absence of Gorse-clad, heathy commons and even where the species did remain it was not common. A decline seems, therefore, to have occurred over the preceding 40 years. Ongoing agricultural change and a series of severe winters especially during the 1940s caused declines in eastern England (Historical Atlas).

The decline continued in Essex and, by the 1950s, the Stonechat was no more than an occasional breeding species (Hudson & Pyman). The only confirmed 1950s' breeding records came from: Chrishall, one pair, 1950; Rainham, one pair, 1952. Thereafter, there were just single breeding records in three years until 1962. Stonechats are adversely affected by severe winter weather and, following the winter of 1962/63, there were no further breeding season records until 1969 when a pair nested at Rainham. This heralded the slow recolonisation of Essex, although almost all records have subsequently occurred along Thames-side and the Lea Valley, with Rainham accounting for a significant proportion of the annual total of breeding pairs. The habitat here is clearly different from the 'typical' Stonechat habitat of Gorse, Heather and Bracken interspersed with close-cropped grass (*BWP*).

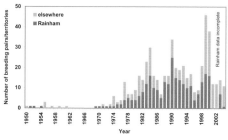

Anual totals of breeding Stonechats from 1950-2004

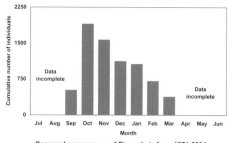

Seasonal occcurrence of Stonechats from 1971-2004

Indeed, the habitat along Thames-side seems almost more typical of Continental populations (European Atlas): perhaps the *rubicola* population of northwest Europe actually intergrades with *hibernans* in southeast England (Walker 2001, Dally 2001).

Since the 1980s, the number of reported pairs have varied between seven in 1987 and 46 in 1990, although totals vary considerably from year to year. At Rainham, numbers generally increased through the 1980s to peak in 1990 when a full survey located 25 territories. Subsequently, numbers declined to a low of just four pairs in 1996 and seven in 1997, possibly due to disturbance caused by the road building works, but recovered quickly following completion of the new A13 to 17 pairs in 1998 but have declined again since. It has been suggested that the reason for the species doing so well at Rainham has been its ability to utilise unfrozen areas in and around the dump (which generates heat) for feeding during severe weather. Rainham appears to have acted as a nucleus for the spread along Thames-side (Dennis 1986).

In recent years, breeding has regularly been reported from East Tilbury (maximum six pairs in 1999), West Tilbury (six pairs in 1999), West Thurrock (maximum four pairs), Fobbing/Pitsea area (maximum 2–3 pairs), Canvey Island (1–3 pairs) and 1–2 pairs at Mucking, Barking, Hornchurch area, Stanford-le-Hope, Coryton, Two Tree Island, Benfleet Creek, Hadleigh CP, Wakering Stairs and the Lea Valley.

Away from Thames-side, around the Colne Estuary, one pair may have bred near Colne Point in 1978, a pair bred on Langenhoe in 1990 and a pair bred successfully at Colne Point in 1998 and perhaps in 1999. Elsewhere, a male carrying food was observed at Bradwell in 2002, whilst a pair bred successfully at Heybridge GP in 2003 and 2004; two juveniles at Holland Haven in June 1993 suggested that breeding might have occurred nearby. The recent upsurge in breeding records away from Thames-side suggest that the Stonechat is expanding and consolidating its range in Essex.

Nationally, there was a decline between the two National Atlases but in recent years the BBS (England) Index increased by 34% between 1994 and 2003. Whilst the species was probably not monitored sufficiently to record trends accurately, it seems likely that the increases are probably the result of the run of exceptionally mild winters during the last 15–20 years.

Both juveniles and adults may disperse from breeding locations from late July but it is not until September that significant numbers are recorded in Essex with passage peaking in October. Most occur at coastal localities, although inland records are regular. The origin of these individuals is unclear. Many are probably British-bred Stonechats and, although it is possible that some are immigrants, to date there have been no foreign-ringing recoveries within Essex to confirm this. The highest autumn counts have come from Bradwell, where there were 20 on 21st October 1972 with 30 both there and on Foulness on 24th October 1976 and 20 on Foulness on 4th November 2001, whilst at Rainham there were 25 from October-December 1990, 27 on 17th October 2004 and 26 on 14th November 2004. Although overall numbers decline through winter, it is not clear whether autumn arrivals move on through the county or stay to winter or whether our breeding population remains or departs for winter. Although studies at Rainham from the mid-1980s to mid-1990s suggested that most of the breeding population moved out in late autumn and returned in March to breed (Essex Atlas), currently this does not appear to be the situation with up to 15 (December 2002) present during winter. Elsewhere, there were 18 at Old Hall on 15th December

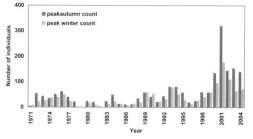

Peak monthly autumn and winter counts of Stonechats
from 1971-2004

2001. A strong autumn passage has tended to be followed by a high wintering population, although many of the highest autumn and winter counts have also coincided with high population levels and so the situation is rather unclear. Given the large number and size of Stonechat broods, it is quite possible for a population of 20 pairs to produce an early autumn population of 100–150 given that most pairs are triple brooded, an average of five eggs are laid (*BWP*) and allowing a survival rate of 50%. Perhaps increases in breeding and wintering numbers in Essex are due to the run of milder winters: Stonechats that adopt a sedentary lifestyle are favoured over those that leave the county.

There is no marked return movement through the county in spring, although from late February individuals may occur at coastal locations, where none have wintered, for short periods before moving on.

There are just two movements of ringed Stonechats involving Essex and both were ringed in Essex and moved no more than 50km. Nationally, ringing has shown that a proportion of the British Stonechat population moves south to winter in France and Iberia.

Despite the decline at Ranham, a small population exists along Thames-side which should act as a nucleus for expansion into the ever-changing environment in this area. Away from Thames-side, there is potential for the species to continue to breed sporadically around the coast and indeed with the increase in reserves around our coastline there is the potential for numbers to increase. Inland, however, suitable Gorse and Heather commons, typical of the species' usual breeding requirements, is almost completely lacking and despite restoration work such as that being carried out by the National Trust on Danbury Common, there is little hope of recolonisation. Overall, the future of the species in Essex seems assured and whilst the population is very small in a national context, the species is an important part of the county's biodiversity.

Siberian Stonechat   *S. t. maura/stejnegeri*

Vagrant: three records

The Siberian Stonechat breeds from the White Sea east through Siberia and winters south of the mouth of the Ural River, along the Caspian Sea to the eastern Caucasus.

1984	Holland Haven	14th October	Female/immature
1986/87	Hanningfield	6th December–10th January	Female/immature
1992	Hanningfield	4th October	Female/immature

The 1986/87 individual may have been present since 29th September. The Siberian Stonechat is a rare but annual vagrant to Britain with 315 records to the end of 2004 (BBRC 2005). Although typically an autumn vagrant, wintering individuals are not unknown.

Sponsored by the late Mike Dennis

(Northern) Wheatear   *Oenanthe oenanthe*

The Wheatear is the most numerous and widespread of its genus, found throughout much of Europe from the Mediterranean Islands, north to Iceland, the Faeroe Islands, Svalbard and North Cape, Norway. Its world range extends across much of the central and northern Eurasian land mass and across into parts of northwest and north-east Canada and also Greenland. Four races are recognised, the nominate race *oenanthe*, *leucorhoa*, *libanotica* and *seebohmi*. It is a typical species of open plains, meadows and rolling, short-sward grassy areas and tundra (European Atlas). Almost the entire world population winters in Africa, south of the Sahara.

Wheatear   *O. o. oenanthe*

Common passage migrant – occasionally breeds

The Wheatear breeds throughout much of Europe, central and northern Asia. In Britain, it is chiefly found in western and northern areas, with the majority breeding above 300m (Second National Atlas). In lowland Britain, where the

Wheatear was far more common prior to 1900, it is scarce and primarily found in coastal areas apart from concentrations on Dartmoor, Devon, and in the Brecklands of Norfolk/Suffolk. Habitat change and the myxamotosis outbreak during the 1950s, which further reduced the habitat provided

Atlas	Survey Area	% of 10km squares or tetrads in which	
		bred/probably bred	possibly bred or present
First National 10km	Essex	5.3	15.8
Second National 10km	Essex	8.8	22.8
First London Tetrad	Met. Essex	0.0	0.0
Second London Tetrad	Met. Essex	1.0	6.0
Essex Tetrad	Essex	0.3	1.7

Summary of results of Atlas surveys for Wheatears

by rabbit grazing and burrowing, are likely causes for the decline, which continued into the early 1990s at least (National Atlases). Recent BBS figures show no clear trend for either lowland or upland populations.

Christy stated that the Wheatear was "Best known ... as a passing migrant in spring and autumn (especially the former), though it breeds commonly along our sea-coast at Maldon, Burnham-on-Crouch, Brightlingsea, Walton, Shoebury and elsewhere. I have never known it breed in the inland parts of the county, except occasionally near Saffron Walden, where the hilly and chalky country is exactly suited to its habits". One of his correspondents writing in 1865 from South Shoebury noted: "This handsome bird is very plentiful [here], frequenting the flat wastes and uncultivated lands. They build here in the holes between dry sods or in deserted rabbit burrows. The young birds of the year are very plentiful on the marshes in August, and may be seen in all directions, perched on some stone or clod, bowing and cocking their tails".

Glegg was rather hesitant in agreeing with Christy's statements regarding breeding because of the long period in which passage birds occurred in the county. However, there seems no reason to doubt Christy's assertions, indeed the description of their breeding habitat at Shoebury is quite normal of the species. Glegg added a few other breeding records, noting that "... a lot of young Wheatears scarcely able to fly and evidently just out of the nest" were on Little Wakering marshes on 10th June 1841. The Wheatear also used to nest "... in some numbers" on Old Hall, three eggs being taken in the spring of 1890, but Glegg knew of only one record there after WWI. Breeding probably took place at Bradfield in 1913, when a young bird was observed being fed. In Essex, therefore, the Wheatear appears to have declined markedly as a breeding species around the early years of the 20th century, mirroring the national trend.

Hudson & Pyman felt that early breeding records "... lacked conviction ..." and there have been surprisingly few confirmed breeding records since 1950. A single pair nested at Colne Point in 1964 and 1965 and may have done so in the next three years. Indeed, the species may have bred there regularly prior to 1950 (Cox). The next record was not until 1978 when a pair bred in allotments at Beckton, with breeding there in 1979 and possibly in 1980 and 1981. Single pairs bred at Colne Point in 1986 and 1987, along Dengie in 1993, Old Hall in 1998, the first time there since prior to 1929, and Holland Haven in 2001. Whilst it is possible that some of the juveniles recorded in early July with regularity from such locations as Colne Point and Old Hall are locally bred, it should be borne in mind that dispersal from breeding areas can begin as early as late June.

The Wheatear is one of the more conspicuous passage migrants and, whilst the largest numbers are reported from the coast, it is commonly found inland as well. Numbers appear to have changed little over the last 30 years; as observer coverage has increased over the same period, numbers in real terms would appear therefore to have declined. Spring passage usually begins around mid-March and continues until late May/early June. The earliest report, aside from one taken on the Swin Middle Lightship on 4th February 1885, was from Foulness on 2nd March 1997, with singles at The Naze on 3rd March 1982 and Beckton on 3rd March 1994. Numbers passing through Essex peak in early April and again in early May. It is likely that the earlier peak comprises Wheatears of the nominate race, whilst the later involves mostly Greenland Wheatears (see below). Numbers occurring in spring vary markedly from year to year. At least 100 at Little Oakley on 18th April 1970 is an exceptional count: the vast major-ity of peak spring counts are in the region of 10–30 birds. However, there were 50 at Rainham on 8th May 1982 and a total of 50 across 25km^2 of the northwest chalk on 10th May 1964. Inland, other double-figure spring counts have included: 23, Foxearth, 20th April 1983; 27, Walthamstow, 3rd April 1986; 25, KGV, 25th April 1989; 24, KGV, 28th March 1998; and 35, Walthamstow, 22nd April 1998.

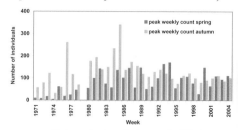

Peak annual spring and autumn counts of Wheatears from 1971-2004

Return passage begins in early July with numbers build-ing to a peak in late August/early September, the majority having passed through by the end of September, although small numbers are usually present throughout October with stragglers occurring into November. An influx of at least 100 in the first week of October 1998 was exceptional. Many later individuals probably involve Greenland Wheatears (see below). There have been four December records, the latest being two at Tollesbury on 14th in 1983, with singles on Foulness on 2nd and 10th in 2000, Bradwell on 1st in 1998 and Stansted Mountfitchet on 1st in 1956.

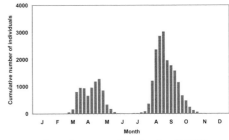

Seasonal occurrence of Wheatears from 1971-2004

Counts of up to 50 from individual sites are not unusual and there have been several three-figure counts, the largest of which was 500–600 on Foulness on 7th September 1958 with 300 there on 24th August 1958. There were 230 along the Dengie coast on 14th August 1976 and 160 on 7th August 1976, 150 at Bradwell on 9th September 1972, at least 100 at Colne Point on 6th September 1968, 100 along the Dengie coast on 26th August 1973 and 100 at Pitsea in late August 1985.

There has been just one ringing recovery involving Essex: one ringed at East Tilbury on 15th April 1961 was found dead near Cadiz, Spain, at the end of March 1962, presumably on migration.

The Wheatear is likely to remain a very rare Essex breeding bird, as typical breeding habitat is scarce and likely to remain so across Essex for the foreseeable future.

Greenland Wheatear   *O. o. leucorhoa*

Locally common passage migrant

The Greenland Wheatear breeds from Labrador and eastern arctic Canada to Greenland and Iceland and has the longest transoceanic migration of any passerine (Migration Atlas). This race is distinctly larger and the plumage brighter than the nominate race.

It has traditionally been thought that small numbers of *leucorhoa* occur in Essex during spring. However, ringing in Norfolk has confirmed that birds on passage in March are almost entirely *oenanthe*, those ringed in April are divided evenly between the two races and most occurring in May are *leucorhoa* (Middleton 1996). There is some historic Essex evidence to support this, and analysis of Essex records confirms that there are two spring peaks that are suggestive of the earlier arrival of *oenanthe* and the later *leucorhoa*. Thus prior estimates of numbers of Greenland Wheatears passing through Essex were probably low and it is likely that regular influxes of 50–100 in late April and May involve mainly this subspecies. These birds take an overland, northwesterly route through Europe and Britain to their breeding grounds and many of the largest inland counts have occurred in late April and early May.

In autumn, a later secondary peak is not discernible, possibly because *leucorhoa* takes a more westerly route at this time (Migration Atlas), but it is likely that most Essex records from late September involve Greenland Wheatears.

Black-eared Wheatear   *Oenanthe hispanica*

Vagrant: two records

The Black-eared Wheatear breeds throughout the Mediterranean east to Asia Minor, Iran and Turkestan. Two subspecies occur, the nominate *hispanica*, which generally occurs in the west of its range, and *melanoleuca* from southern Italy eastwards. The species winters in Africa, immediately south of the Sahara.

1989	Jaywick GP	26th May	Male
1997	Writtle	3rd May	Male

The Black-eared Wheatear is surprisingly rare in Britain for a long-distance migrant that breeds as close as southern France; there are just 58 records, the last in 2003 (BBRC 2004). Most occur as overshooting spring migrants along the south and east coasts, the majority being of the western race. Although originally ascribed to *melanoleuca*

(Atkins 1990), the first record is now considered to have involved a bird of indeterminate race (BBRC 2003). Inland records are rare but not unprecedented. Typical of spring records, both were short-stayers.

Desert Wheatear   *Oenanthe deserti*

Vagrant: two records

The Desert Wheatear breeds across northern Africa and the Middle East to the Caspian Sea, and east as far as Mongolia. The nearest populations are of the nominate race *deserti*, which occurs in the Levant, and *homochroa* in north Africa. The species winters in Africa south of the Sahara, the Middle East and parts of the Indian subcontinent.

1958	East Mersea	12th–13th January and 3rd February	Immature male
1987	The Naze	12th October	Female

The Desert Wheatear is the commonest of the vagrant wheatears to occur in Britain with a total of 87 up to the end of 2003 (BBRC 2004); 17 occurred in an exceptional influx in 1997. There is a distinct eastern bias to national records. This species is one of the latest-arriving autumn vagrants with records typically falling in the period late October–December. Autumn records probably involve the eastern race *deserti* (the record at The Naze occurred at the same time as a Paddyfield Warbler there), whilst the somewhat fewer spring records probably involve overshooting individuals of the north African race *homochroa* (Cottridge & Vinicombe 1996).

The 1958 record is one of only four examples of attempted wintering in the country and constituted the 12th British record. Despite regular searches, it was only observed on three occasions (Barton 1958).

White's Thrush   *Zoothera dauma*

Vagrant: one 19th century record

The White's Thrush breeds as far west as the Urals but its main range is across Siberia to Japan and Korea. The race *aurea*, the most migratory of the four recognised subspecies, occurs from western Siberia in the southern Urals across to the Pacific coast. The species winters throughout India and southeast Asia.

1894	Langley, High Wood	January	Shot

There were 64 British records to the end of 2004 (BBRC 2005), but only 33 since 1958 and these have generally been from remote locations. Older records showed a far wider geographical spread. Most occur between late September and November but there have been a few winter occurrences. The Essex individual was obtained by a member of a shooting party and was initially mistaken for a Woodcock and, although badly shot, was successfully preserved. The sex was not noted. The record was overlooked at a national level until recognised by the BBRC in 1999 (BBRC 1999).

Hermit Thrush   *Catharus guttatus*

Vagrant: one record

The Hermit Thrush breeds across northern North America and through the mountains of the west. Eight subspecies are recognised (Clement & Hathway 2000). The species winters in the southern and western states and as far south as El Salvador.

1994	Chipping Ongar	28th October–3rd November	Probably 1st-winter

There have been just seven British records up to the end of 2004, the last of which was in 2000 (BBRC 2001). The other records have come from the Isles of Scilly (three), Fair Isle (two) and Shetland Islands (one). All bar two have occurred in October. Although not unprecedented as far as Nearctic land birds are concerned, this was nonetheless a quite remarkable occurrence. It was found exhausted, taken into care and released on 2nd November (Pepper 1996).

Ring Ouzel   *Turdus torquatus*

Fairly common passage migrant   **Red List**

The breeding range of the Ring Ouzel, a bird of both upland and tundra, is almost completely restricted to the Western Palearctic with populations of the nominate race *torquatus* occurring in Britain and Scandinavia, *alpestris* in the Pyrenees and central Europe and *armoricum* in eastern Turkey through to northern Iran. The northern race winters in southern Spain and northwest Africa. In Britain, a marked range contraction occurred between the two National Atlas surveys, although declines had been noted as early as the 1950s (Baxter & Rintoul 1953). Surveys from 1988-91 and in 1999 revealed a 58% decline.

Although Christy accepted a breeding record, Glegg quite rightly felt there was something suspicious about it and rejected it: "... A Mr C. E. Bishop of Wickham found a nest with four eggs, almost upon the ground, about a foot from the edge of the Blackwater in that parish on May 10th 1879. The hen only was seen and she was sitting"; probably an aberrant female Blackbird was involved. Yarrell (1845) quoted a breeding record from Saffron Walden based upon the shooting of a bird there in early August 1836. Although this was probably an early migrant, it is possible that a few pairs bred up on the northwest chalk, given that breeding had occurred on and off in East Anglia until the mid-19th century (Historical Atlas).

In 1831, Henry Doubleday noted that at Epping the Ring Ouzel "... is only seen now and again in spring and autumn". Christy and Glegg considered the species to be a less than annual spring and autumn passage migrant, with Glegg noting that of the 30 or so records, well over half came from inland locations. Of spring records, all were

in April and May except for two in March, in 1907 on 23rd at an unnamed location and at Felsted in 1913 on 27th. A female was noted at the same location on 29th February 1924. In autumn, observations were made from August to November, but principally in October.

Hudson & Pyman concluded that there had been a considerable reduction in numbers over the previous 100 years, basing their assumption on the significant reduction in inland records during that time. However, since the mid-1960s records have increased, despite declines in the British population, and have continued to do so. The increase is probably due, in part, to increased observer coverage, although ring-

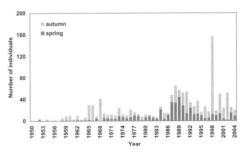

Annual totals of Ring Ouzels from 1950-2004

ing recoveries have confirmed that individuals from the Scandinavian population occur in Britain and it is possible that recent changes in weather patterns have increased the number occurring as drift migrants.

The substantial influx in autumn 1998 involved about 150 individuals and was part of an unprecedented arrival that saw a peak of 2,100 in Kent on 17th October (*Birdwatch* December 1998) and several hundred in Suffolk. The first arrival in Essex was on 2nd October with a female in Gunners Park. The next day there were 35 in the county, including 23 at The Naze. Numbers peaked on 5th when at least 50 were present at Deal Hall. Other double-figure counts during the influx were 14 at The Naze on 4th with 13 still on 9th and 12 at Holland Haven on 6th. The only

other double-figure counts have been: 15–20 at The Naze, 16th September 1968; 16 at The Naze, 16th October 2002; 14 on Foulness, 29th September 1991; and 12 at Little Oakley, 16th September 1968. In spring, fewer large flocks are noted, with counts of more than five being exceptional. Eight at Gunners Park on 23rd April 1989 was the largest flock, with six there one week earlier. There were also seven at The Naze on 25th April 1978, five at Holland Haven on 26th April 1987, and five on Foulness on 17th April 1987.

British Ring Ouzels take a more westerly migration route in spring than autumn and most records during

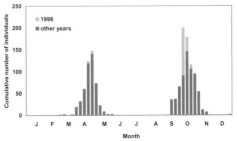

Seasonal occurrence of Ring Ouzels from 1950-2004

March and early April are probably British birds as many are back on territory by the end of March (*BWP*). The larger numbers recorded from mid-April probably involve Scandinavian birds and hence numbers vary considerably from year to year depending on weather conditions. The earliest spring record came from Benfleet on 20th–27th February 1996 with what was possibly the same bird at Rayleigh from 2nd–3rd March, whilst there was one at Felsted on 29th February 1924 and a male on Two Tree Island on 4th March 1975. Could these perhaps be early migrants from the British population that is perhaps the source of a small wintering population in north-central France? Numbers peak around late April/early May with odd individuals noted throughout May. Late spring birds have involved two at Holland Haven on 1st and one on 2nd June 1991 and a female at Nazeing on 31st May 1965.

Returning individuals usually begin to appear from mid-September and probably involve mainly British breeders until October when Scandinavian migrants occur. A remarkably early individual was at Holland Haven on 10th August 1995, some three weeks prior to the next earliest, a male at Southend-on-Sea on 2nd September 1981. Autumn passage peaks around early/mid October with individuals noted through to mid-November. One remained at Girling/KGV Reservoirs from 17th November 1987–1st January 1988, whilst one fed on fallen apples in a garden at Frinton-on-Sea from 28th–30th December 1968. One was at Bradwell on 23rd January 2000.

Until the 1990s it was usual for spring inland records to outnumber those in autumn: only in 1959, 1964 and 1966 was it not the case. However, in the last ten years, autumn inland records have been in the majority in 60% of years.

The larger inland totals have generally coincided with influxes on the coast. A total of 16 in 1992, three in spring and 13 in autumn, is the largest annual inland total with the largest individual site count being four at Fishers Green on 22nd April 1992, although five different individuals passed through Dagnam Park in both spring and autumn 1988.

A female at Hanningfield on 9th April 1989 showed characteristics of the race *alpestris*, although not officially recognised on the British List, vagrancy to Sweden has been confirmed (Clement & Hathway 2000).

Blackbird   *Turdus merula*

Abundant resident, passage migrant and winter visitor

This Palearctic thrush breeds in all but the most northerly areas of Europe. Worldwide, its distribution stretches from north Africa and central Asia through to southeast China with introduced populations in Australia. It is found in most habitats except open steppe, marsh, fen and tundra. The Blackbird is found throughout Britain except for bare moorland and mountain areas in Scotland (Second National Atlas). Fifteen races are recognised, with the nominate race occurring over much of Europe from Britain and Iceland east  to the Urals. Originally a bird of deciduous habitats, the species has adapted well to areas of human habitation and colonised most European towns from the 1850s (European Atlas). The change of behaviour seems to have occurred quickly as Bewick noted in 1804 that the Blackbird was "... a solitary bird, frequenting woodlands and thickets" but one which, by the mid-19th century, was being described by many writers as not only nesting in woodland but also frequenting the neighbourhood of houses and even coming into towns in winter (Snow 1958).

Blackbirds appear to have been hunted in Hatfield Forest in the early 17th century (Rackham 1989). Both Christy and Glegg made little comment concerning the species other than to confirm that it was an "abundant resident" or a "very common resident". Christy noted an unusual breeding record, detailed in the *Essex Chronicle* of 1st May 1877: "There is a break-van at Mistley station, which is used for the purpose of 'breaking down' trucks to the quay, a distance of half-a-mile. This is used two or three times a day, and is frequently left on the quay two hours before being brought back to the siding in the yard. On the framework underneath the van, a Blackbird and his mate have built their nest, and the latter is now sitting upon four eggs, regardless of the frequent journeys to and fro". Around the turn of the 19th century the Blackbird was actually less common than the Song Thrush but its range increased along with its numbers in the warmer climatic period between 1890 and 1950 (Population Trends).

Hudson and Pyman stated that "Very likely this is now THE most numerous Essex breeding bird", a description that Cox agreed with. Although impossible to confirm, the species probably remains one of, if not the, commonest of Essex breeding birds. Both National Atlases recorded Blackbirds breeding in every 10km square, the Essex Atlas confirmed breeding in 98.6% of all tetrads with the only absences being in the estuarine areas of the Roach and Crouch in the Rochford Hundred, and breeding occurred in all Metropolitan Essex tetrads during the Second London Atlas survey, a noticeable increase from the first.

Atlas	Survey Area	% of 10km squares or tetrads in which	
		bred/probably bred	possibly bred or present
First National 10km	Essex	100.0	0.0
Second National 10km	Essex	100.0	0.0
First London Tetrad	Met. Essex	81.5	5.0
Second London Tetrad	Met. Essex	100.0	0.0
Essex Tetrad	Essex	98.6	0.0

Summary of results of Atlas surveys for Blackbird

Nationally, CBC (England) data suggested a shallow decline of around 12% for the period 1977–2002, which is revealed in the local CBC Index for the same period. More recently, the BBS (England) noted a 17% increase from 1994–2003 suggesting that the initial decline, which may be at least in part linked to agricultural intensification (Fuller *et al.* 1995), may have now been reversed; recent local BBS results also confirm this trend. Since 1980, local CBC sites have recorded densities that averaged 99 pairs per km^2 in woodland (range 39–186) and 29 pairs per km^2 on farmland (range 8–54), both figures lower than those quoted by Cox (117 and 43 pairs per km^2). In the urban environment, which is not covered by BBS/CBC surveys, Mason (2003) showed that Blackbird territory density within Harwich, Dovercourt, Parkeston, Ramsey and Little Oakley was related to the proportion of gardens, open space and housing density within individual developments. Overall, densities in these areas were higher than in farmland or woodland plots with an overall density of 169 territories per km^2, although densities ranged from just 43 territories per km^2 in areas of historic/Victorian terraces to 361 territories per km^2 in more recent housing developments.

The earliest documented reference to Blackbirds in Essex mentioned an influx on New England Island in October 1836 when "… almost every hedge was full of them for a week or two". Glegg noted that a large immigration was observed from lightships off the Essex coast from mid-October to mid-November and again during March. An "immense" influx occurred between 27th and 31st October 1910, whilst Blackbirds were unusually abundant in southeast Essex in the winter of 1921/22, 80–90% being males.

Typically, Blackbird immigration occurs at night, the large autumn influxes being evident by the presence of feeding flocks in coastal hedges and scrub at dawn. A significant influx occurred in mid-October 1958, although

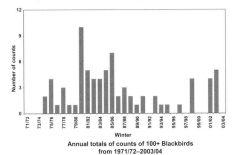

Annual totals of counts of 100+ Blackbirds from 1971/72–2003/04

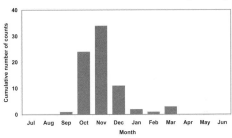

Seasonal occurrence of counts of 100+ Blackbirds from 1971-2004

unfortunately no counts were made: the residents of Foulness noted very large numbers, the concentration being likened to Starling flocks. Elsewhere there was a "heavy landfall" at St Osyth and "considerable numbers" at Bradwell. However, a quite exceptional daytime movement occurred in 1961 involving some 10,000 that passed over Foulness on 5th November, with similar numbers the same day at The Naze. No significant flocks were figure counts were not until 1977 with "thousands" around Colne Point from 17th–18th November and 1,500 at Bradwell on 19th November. No other four-figure counts have been reported, although three-figure counts of the order of 100–200 are almost annual and recently there were 500 at The Naze on 7th November 1998 and 850 on 30th October 2002.

Spring migration generally goes unnoticed, although in 1964 birds were observed arriving off the sea in an exhausted state on 25th March. The largest spring gatherings have been: 40 at The Naze, 22nd March 1982; 40 at The Naze, 28th April 1994; 45 on Foulness, 19th March 1995; and 150 on Foulness, 10th March 1984. An example of the hazards faced by migrants was that of a male Blackbird that was knocked into the sea off Walton by a Great Black-backed Gull and then eaten, on 2nd November 1990.

The number of large counts appear to have declined over the last decade suggesting that the number of immigrant Blackbirds reaching our shores each winter may be declining; milder winters across Europe may mean that populations of Blackbirds that normally migrate west are not moving so far to winter. The apparent increase recently may well be due to greater observer coverage at The Naze, where many of the largest counts have been made.

Over 2,000 Blackbirds ringed in Essex have been controlled in the county, with 90% within 10km of the ringing site, confirming that most local Blackbirds are generally sedentary. Some birds may move south and southwest, to Wales and Ireland, for instance, perhaps in response to severe weather. The vast majority of national recoveries confirm a considerable movement

	Jan	Feb	Mar	Apr	May	Jun	Jul	Aug	Sep	Oct	Nov	Dec
Essex	120	163	265	246	268	270	194	96	76	51	64	75
Scotland	1		1									1
North England	1		1	1						2	1	
South England	22	10	12	11	11	12	8	7	5	4	6	4
Wales			1	1						1	1	
Ireland	4	1									1	
Finland			1	3					1	3		
Norway			1	2	1			1			1	1
Sweden	1		3	2	2	4	2	2				
Baltic States								1				
Russia					1	1						
Denmark		2	5	3		2				1	5	2
Germany	1	2	11	8	9	8	1	1	2		1	
The Netherlands			1	3	6	1		1	1		2	
Belgium	3		1	1		1		1		1		
France	4	4					1			2	5	5
Spain	3									1		
Totals	*160*	*183*	*305*	*285*	*293*	*297*	*208*	*109*	*84*	*65*	*88*	*88*

Month and location of recovery of Blackbirds ringed in Essex

from the Continent in autumn, a situation mirrored in Essex. Those Blackbirds recovered in France and Spain suggest that some may continue south after passing through Essex. Thus immigrant Blackbirds ringed in Essex belong to both the wholly migratory northern populations and the partially migratory populations of the Netherlands, Germany and southern Scandinavia (Migration Atlas). The most distant recovery of a Blackbird ringed in Essex was found dead in October 1970 at Mikkeli, Finland, 1,851km to the northeast of its ringing locality. An adult female ringed on Helgoland, Germany, on 10th March 1991 was found dead at Maldon on 13th March 1997, making the individual at least seven years old, a respectable age for a small passerine. In addition to the recoveries in the table, foreign-ringed birds controlled in Essex have originated from Norway (three), Sweden (three), Denmark (three), Germany (seven), the Netherlands (eight) and Belgium (three).

Blackbirds are one of the most regularly reported species to exhibit albinism and partial albinos are reported fairly regularly within Essex. Glegg mentioned that at Warley Place partial albinos were reported in the gardens for some 30 years. Pure albinos are rare, although pure white birds with just the odd dark feather have been noted on occasions. Recently an albino was reported near St Botolph's Priory, Colchester, in December 1993, a near-albino at Maldon in December 1998 and an albino was resident around Eves Corner, Danbury, for around six months over the winter of 1999/2000.

The Blackbird has adapted well to the modern environment and, following declines through the 1970s and 1980s, appears to be prospering again. The species may actually benefit from the conversion of farmland to housing, provided semi-natural habitats are retained as far as possible, housing densities do not exceed 25 dwellings per hectare and areas of open space are created (Mason 2003).

Sponsored in memory of Tariq Watson

Dusky Thrush   *Turdus naumanni*

The Dusky Thrush breeds through central and east Siberia, south to Mongolia and east to the Pacific coast and winters principally in Ussiriland, north Korea, China, southeast Tibet and northeast India. Northerly populations are generally of the race *eunomus* (Dusky Thrush) and southerly ones of the nominate race *naumanni* (Naumann's Thrush).

Naumann's Thrush   *T. n. naumanni*

Vagrant: two records

The Naumann's Thrush breeds in central and eastern Siberia and winters in northeast China, Korea, Taiwan and less commonly Japan.

1990	Woodford Green, Chingford	19th January–9th March	1st-winter male
1997	South Woodford	6th–11th January	1st-winter

These constitute the only two British records of the nominate race, although there have been a further eight records of Dusky Thrush (BBRC 1998). All occurrences have been in late autumn and winter. The locations of both records are remarkable, and their proximity is a striking coincidence. The 1990 individual frequented back gardens where it appears to have been taken by a Sparrowhawk (Murray 1991), whilst the 1997 individual's identity was pieced together over several days; it was very elusive (Whitfield & Whitfield 1998).

Some authorities treat each race as a distinct species, although there is much interbreeding where their respective ranges overlap (Clement & Hathway 2000).

Dark-throated Thrush   *Turdus ruficollis*

The Dark-throated Thrush breeds in west and central Siberia, western Mongolia and northwest China and winters from Iran to Kazakhstan to southern China and northern Burma (Clement & Hathway 2000). Two subspecies are recognised, the more westerly race *atrogularis* (Black-throated Thrush) and the nominate, easterly race *ruficollis*, the Red-throated Thrush.

Red-throated Thrush   *T. r. ruficollis*

Vagrant: one record

The Red-throated Thrush breeds in the central and northern Urals, east across southwest Siberia and eastern Kazakhstan and winters from Iraq east to northern India and east through the Himalayan foothills to Bhutan.

1994	The Naze	29th September–7th October	1st-winter male

This is the sole British record of Red-throated Thrush. The remaining 53 British records of Dark-throated Thrush have all involved the Black-throated Thrush (BBRC 2005). Some authorities consider the races to be distinct species but, given the considerable range of overlap of the two races and the number of intermediates/hybrids in this area, they are currently treated as one species (Clement & Hathway 2000). Most have occurred in late autumn and winter and there has been an increase, particularly of wintering individuals, in recent years.

This individual occurred around the same time as an arrival of other Asiatic vagrants in Britain, including Siberian Thrush and a handful of Pechora Pipits, Paddyfield Warblers, Pallas's Grasshopper Warblers and Lanceolated Warblers. Most of these arrived around ten days or so prior to this bird being found making it possible that it remained undetected for some time after its arrival. Not surprisingly it caused one of the largest twitches to be seen in Essex. Initially faithful to the undercliff area of The Naze, it ranged widely towards the end of its stay and was observed up to 500m away (Smith *et al.* 1999).

Fieldfare   *Turdus pilaris*

**Common winter visitor and passage migrant in variable numbers: one pair bred
in 1980 but unsuccessfully**   Amber List

The monotypic Fieldfare is a Palearctic species, which breeds from southeast France, the Low Countries, Denmark and Norway in the west to the Upper Yenisey and Amur Rivers in the east. It is typical of farmland and other culti-vated landscapes where it breeds in orchards, forest edges and hedgerows and is also found in deciduous and mixed forests. It is one of the most abundant breeding birds of northern Europe (European Atlas). Britain was colonised in the 1960s but little progress has since been made with just 2–6 pairs reported in the late 1990s/early 2000s,

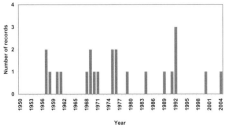

Annual totals of June and July records of Fieldfares from
1950-2004 (excludes 1980/81 breeding attempts)

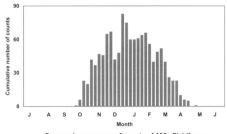

Seasonal occurrence of counts of 100+ Fieldfares
from 1971-2004

mainly from Scotland and northern England. In autumn many Fieldfares move south and west from their breeding grounds. Around 1 million birds winter in Britain (Migration Atlas).

Remains attributed to Fieldfares have been found in the 300,000-year-old 'elephant bone beds' at East Mersea (Urquhart 2000).

In 1980 a pair of Fieldfares built a nest and laid eggs in Barking Park; unfortunately the nest was predated by Carrion Crows (*per* H. Vaughan). In 1981 the pair returned and built a nest in the same tree but did not breed. There have been no other proven Essex breeding records. A "well attested and proved case" of Fieldfares nesting and rearing young in the grounds of the Rectory at Alresford in 1869 was described by Christy, but he considered it to be lacking corroborative evidence.

Occasional midsummer records, sufficient for the species to be included in the appendix of additional species in the Essex Atlas, and breeding in Kent in 1991 suggests that the species could breed again. Further analysis of the 21 June/July records (involving 25 individuals but excluding the 1980 and 1981 records above) show periods of occurrence by very small numbers interspersed with apparent absence. Six at South Woodham Ferrers on 27th July 1998 and three at Rainham on 26th July 2004 are presumed to have been exceptionally early migrants and are not included in the table. There has been no particular geographical concentration of summer records, with occurrences from The Naze in the northeast to Shellhaven and Epping in the south. Of the records, only five could be described as summering: 1957, Wormingford, all summer until 18th August; 1961, Shellhaven, 4th–25th June (ringed); 1976, Old Hall, 7th June, 25th July and 8th August are assumed to refer to the same individual; 1979, The Naze, one all summer; and 1992, Fishers Green, one with Mistle Thrushes until 29th June. In addition, a presumed pair stayed at The Naze until 3rd June 1969, and two flew east over Burnham-on-Crouch on 22nd June 1992. It appears that the occurrence of summering records is not linked to abundance either later in the preceding winter or spring passage numbers, with the inevitable conclusion that even if breeding were to occur again, it is likely under current circumstances to be a random event.

As a winter visitor and passage migrant, the status of the Fieldfare in Essex has changed little over the years, with both Christy and Glegg reporting the species as a common winter resident, numbers varying from year to year depending on the severity of the weather. Glegg suggested that the adequacy of food supply was a factor affecting its abundance, whilst Cox also referred to concentrations where food was available, for example in orchards, parks or grassy areas. Its status remains much the same today.

The chacking call of flocks of Fieldfares is an evocative sound and, as most migration is undertaken at fairly low level, the species is one of the most familiar migrants. It is a common passage migrant both on the coast and inland with three-figure flocks a regular feature in October and November. Though wintering in variable numbers, return passage can often be obvious in spring. The Fieldfare is a nocturnal migrant, although many movements and arrivals are also undertaken by day. The latter are mostly onward or local nomadic movements or dawn arrivals of large numbers of birds (Clement & Hathway 2000).

Timing of arrivals and departures has also remained quite consistent with Glegg noting "It commences to arrive from the middle of October, and is observed until the middle of April—in some years to the end of the first week in May". This remains very much the case today, though Cox considered occurrences in late August exceptional.

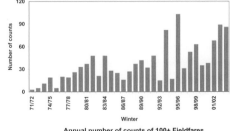

Annual number of counts of 100+ Fieldfares
from 1971/72-2003/04

Since 1980, however, the frequency of August arrivals has increased with singles unless otherwise stated occurring in: 1980 at The Naze, 16th; 1981 on Horsey Island, 31st; 1983 at Colne Point, one, 20th–28th and two, 26th and another at Holland Haven on 31st; 1987 at Norsey Wood, Billericay, seven, 26th (this exceptionally early movement was also noted in Norfolk and Suffolk); 1988 at Blackmore, 28th; 1990 at Broomfield, 9th; and 1994 at Dagenham Chase, 10th. Autumn arrivals consistently show a pattern of odd birds arriving early, followed by more substantial numbers later at any time from mid-October to late November. Dates of first arrivals are inconsistent and patterns difficult to find. Thus, whilst in some years there are very early records, in others there may be none until October; the earliest arrivals in 1995 were not until 2nd November.

Most arrivals follow post-breeding flocking or local movements on the Continent (Clement & Hathway 2000), leading to some very large numbers being reported, particularly on the coast from time to time. Two thousand roosted on the saltings at Little Oakley on 20th November 1955, whilst 5,000 over Foulness on 5th November 1961 were accompanied by reports of good numbers elsewhere at the same time, including "large numbers" at The Naze. There were 3,500 at Fingringhoe in early November 1962, and several thousand flew over The Naze on 22nd October 1973. At Bradwell, there were 1,500 on 23rd October 1955, whilst around 1,200 flew in off the sea on 27th November 1993. Inland passage is noted regularly, often coinciding with that observed on the coast. On 5th November 1961 1,000 passed over Bishop's Stortford SF in 4.5 hours, 1,200 flew over Sewardstonebury on 20th November 1968 and 1,000 passed south over Romford on 14th November 1995. A total of 1,500 at Ulting on 20th November 2001 was the largest autumn count since the 1960s.

Midwinter numbers vary from year to year and the species shows little site fidelity, a trait noted throughout its wintering range in Europe (*BWP*). Some substantial counts have been made at this time, with four-figure flocks a regular feature, although 5,000 roosting at Fingringhoe Wick on 19th December 1971 was exceptional given that it could not be linked to severe weather at the time. "Thousands" were present in both the Lea Valley and Abberton/Tollesbury/Salcott areas in January 1984, around 4,500 were in the Langenhoe/Abberton area on 28th January 1996, whilst gatherings of 3,000 have been observed at East Tilbury on 25th January 1959, Shotgate on 1st February 1972 and Boxted during the winter of 1979/80, where they were attracted to rotting apples in an orchard.

The onset of very cold weather can produce some spectacular movements, the largest of which have been 4,000 flying south over Salcott/Tollesbury on 7th January 1967 and 9,000 south at The Naze on 28th December 1968. As noted by Cox, these hard weather movements may reflect either fresh arrivals from Europe or departures from the county, as when two ringed in Stock in January 1963 were

	Jan	Feb	Mar	Apr	May	Jun	Jul	Aug	Sep	Oct	Nov	Dec
Essex	2	5	6	1			1					1
North England		1										
South England	1	1	1									
Ireland	1											
Finland				1	1	3						
Norway				1	2	1	1	1	1			
Sweden					1	1	1					
Russia					1		1					
Denmark	1											
France	3	2					1			2	3	2
Spain											1	
Italy		1	1								2	1
Romania		1										
Totals	*8*	*11*	*8*	*3*	*5*	*5*	*5*	*1*	*1*	*2*	*6*	*4*

Month and location of recovery of Fieldfares ringed in Essex

recovered in France later that same month. It does seem, however, that there is no consistent link between high numbers and hard weather so far as Essex is concerned, and such conditions—either here or abroad—do not necessarily herald any such movement or influx. Availability of wild fruit crops is probably the principal factor that affects the number of migrants and winter visitors to the county.

Spring passage is also prolonged, lasting typically from mid-February through to April, with small numbers sometimes present/moving through during May. Numbers in spring are consistently lower than in autumn, though three-figure flocks are not uncommon: 1,000 at each of Abberton on 14th March 1971, Roydon on 1st March 1992 and on Hunsdon Meads during the first week of April 1969 are the only four-figure counts in March and April, the latter being quite exceptional. There have, however, been no recent records to compare with Henry Doubleday's comments that: "I saw vast flocks on 10th and 11th May [1834]" and in addition that they, "... remained in vast flocks until the third week in May [1835]", although there were 100 at Hainault Forest CP on 9th May 1980.

Moderate numbers of Fieldfares have been trapped and ringed in Essex, with 60 subsequently being re-trapped, around 25% in Essex. The recoveries confirm that many of the Fieldfares occurring in Essex on passage and wintering are from the Scandinavian breeding populations with some originating even further east in Russia. Some

Fieldfares appear to continue south and southwest as shown by the recoveries in Ireland, France and Spain. The recovery of five Fieldfares ringed in Essex in Italy and one in Romania in subsequent winters illustrates just how widely the species, and particularly first-winter birds (Migration Atlas), may wander outside the breeding season. The most distant recovery involved one ringed at Stock on 18th January 1966 and found at Aleksandrov, Vladimir, Russia, 2,568km east-northeast on 22nd May 1966. In addition, there have been a total of three ringing recoveries of birds ringed in southern England and three foreign-ringed Fieldfares from Belgium, the Netherlands and Finland. One ringed at Clacton-on-Sea on 11th November 1963 as an adult was found dead at Hame, Finland, on 15th July 1972 making it at least ten years old.

As it is difficult to forecast if and when breeding might occur again in Essex, there are no conservation measures that can be taken to encourage the Fieldfare to do so. As a migrant and winter visitor, annual numbers are impossible to predict and at least in Essex are not clearly linked to severe weather or food supplies. Whilst it is possible that there has been a reduction in food availability in the county due to the grubbing out of hedges, this has probably been offset by new planting around built-up areas and more recently with hedge and woodland planting in the countryside. Any likely affects of global warming are unclear but for the foreseeable future at least, the Fieldfare's status as a visitor to the county appears secure.

Song Thrush   *Turdus philomelos*

Common resident, passage migrant and winter visitor   Red List ~ Essex BAP

The Song Thrush, a widespread species throughout the Palearctic, is found throughout of western Europe eastwards into Russia and beyond as far as Lake Baikal, and from the mountains of southern Spain and Iran north into northern Scandinavia and Siberia. The nominate

Atlas	Survey Area	% of 10km squares or tetrads in which	
		bred/probably bred	possibly bred or present
First National 10km	Essex	100.0	0.0
Second National 10km	Essex	100.0	0.0
First London Tetrad	Met. Essex	75.0	10.0
Second London Tetrad	Met. Essex	98.0	2.0
Essex Tetrad	Essex	93.3	0.7

Summary of results of Atlas surveys for Song Thrushes

race *philomelos* occurs over much of the species' range, with *clarkei* occurring throughout Britain, except on the Outer Hebrides and the Isle of Skye, where the race *hebridensis* occurs. Song Thrushes can be found over most of Britain except for much of the Shetland Islands and the mountains and moorlands of northern Scotland. The species will breed in almost any habitat as long as bushes or trees are present (Second National Atlas). Despite being more common than Blackbird at the beginning of the 20th century (Second National Atlas), numbers have been in decline from at least the 1940s when the Blackbird became the commoner of the two (Simms 1978). Northern and eastern European populations of the nominate race are migratory and winter in southwest Europe, whilst *clarkei* is largely resident.

Bones attributed to Song Thrushes have been found in the 300,000-year-old 'elephant bone beds' at East Mersea (Urquhart 2000).

The earliest mention of the Song Thrush in Essex was in John Ray's *Philosophical Letters* of 1676 where it was noted that locally thrushes were called 'Mevisses'. Christy described the Song Thrush as an "... abundant resident". He gave few specific examples but considered the species to be "abundant in autumn, but almost absent in mid-winter" in Epping Forest. He also described how a pair nested in one of the "break-vans" that was shunted around on the quay close to Mistley station (cf. Blackbird). At Woodford from 1904–11, a total of 97 Song Thrush nests was found against 94 Blackbirds (Homes 1957). However, after WWI the

	Song Thrush		Mistle Thrush		Blackbird	
	No.	Density (/km²)	No.	Density (/km²)	No.	Density (/km²)
Rural	39	1.9	17	0.8	298	14.8
Urban	46	7.3	11	1.8	528	84.3
Territory registrations (%) and density (/km²)	%	Density (/km²)	%	Density (/km²)	%	Density (/km²)
Rural						
Farmland	0.0	0.0	36.1	11.1	12.0	2.0
Arable	~	~	11.1	0.3	5.4	1.0
Grass	~	~	25.0	4.0	5.6	7.6
Set-aside	~	~	0.0	~	1.0	17.6
Woodland	31.8	13.0	16.7	5.6	20.3	56.5
Scrub	15.9	25.0	0.0	~	7.0	75.0
Built environment	52.3	25.0	47.2	18.5	60.8	198.9
Urban						
Woodland and scrub	35.8	55.9	14.3	5.9	6.8	105.8
Built environment	64.1	5.5	85.7	2.0	93.2	84.0

Number and density (per km²) of thrushes in urban and rural parts of Tendring study area and distribution of territory registrations, with densities (per km²) within habitats [adapted from Mason 2000]

same authors found that Blackbirds were five times as common as Song Thrushes, due purely to decreases in Song Thrush numbers and not increases in Blackbirds. Thus, a substantial decline had taken place very quickly, possibly due to the severe winters in the second decade of the 20th century; the species appears to fare badly in such conditions (Historical Atlas).

Glegg, however, made no reference to any declines, merely noting that the Song Thrush was "… a very common resident throughout the county, but during the winter months there is a marked reduction in its numbers". The early years of the EBS saw little attention given to the species: within the first 22 *EBRs* (i.e. 1949–70) the Song Thrush was mentioned just twice and it was only from 1984 that the species' status was summarised annually. Neither Hudson & Pyman nor Cox referred to population trends. Indeed, it is only since 1991 that it was first suggested in the *EBR* that declines were in progress. Signs of a decline were not evident in the two National Atlas surveys nor London Atlas surveys. The Essex Atlas confirmed breeding in almost all of the 94% of tetrads in which it was found, when it was described as widespread and common throughout the county. However, local CBC data recorded a steady decline through the 1980s with a marked acceleration of the decline from 1991, such that by 1999 the Index stood at just 36% of its 1981 level. Nationally, losses have been particularly severe in farmland. Indeed in the Tendring peninsula the Song Thrush is now largely restricted to the woodland, where woodland edge is favoured (Mason 2001), and particularly the built environment (Mason 1998, 2000).

The decline appears to have been driven by the reduced survival of birds during their first winter and perhaps also whilst fledging (Robinson *et al.* 2004), whilst a lack of invertebrates caused by drainage appears to be important (Peach *et al.* 2004). Drying out of woodlands and changes to the woodland under-storey may also be factors (Fuller *et al.* 2005). Nationally, the CBC/BBS Index for the period 1977–2002 showed a decline of 38%, although the more recent BBS (England) Index has pointed to a 15% increase

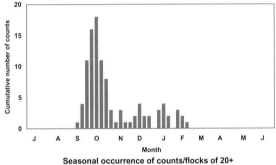

Seasonal occurrence of counts/flocks of 20+ Song Thrushes from 1950-2004

from 1994–2003, a trend also observed in local BBS data; perhaps an end of the periods of dry weather in the mid-1990s is benefiting the species?

Essex CBC plots during the 1980s recorded average densities of 26 pairs per km^2 (range 25–77) in woodland and four pairs per km^2 (range 2–8) on farmland, compared to those noted by Cox of 48 (range 12–87) and 18 (range 3–43), respectively.

Tabor (2004) found that there was no significant change in the number of contacts with Song Thrushes in Shadwell Wood during a study from 1989–2000, although there was a quite marked seasonal variation with most in summer but none from August–October. In general, less rain meant more Song Thrushes occurring in Shadwell Wood; perhaps woods offer a stable habitat?

Although the local race *clarkei* is considered to be resident, there is ringing evidence to suggest that individuals move out of the county, particularly in severe weather. It is interesting to note that both Christy and Glegg considered that there was a marked reduction in numbers during winter, at a time when winters were generally more severe.

Small influxes at coastal locations in early autumn signal the arrival of nominate race Song Thrushes from Continental Europe. In general, numbers appear to be low: indeed Song Thrushes seem to be the least numerous of the common migrant winter thrushes. A total of only 14 three-figure counts/flocks involving assumed migrants has occurred since 1950, including seven since 1998 at The Naze where the increase has probably been due to greater

	Jan	Feb	Mar	Apr	May	Jun	Jul	Aug	Sep	Oct	Nov	Dec
Essex	33	41	66	49	82	76	57	33	19	12	9	24
South England	11	8	10	5	12	10	8		4	2	2	3
Wales					1							
Germany								1				
The Netherlands			1	1		1						
Belgium						1						
France	10	2		1						1	1	3
Spain	3			1						1		2
Portugal		1										
Totals	*57*	*52*	*77*	*57*	*95*	*88*	*65*	*34*	*23*	*16*	*12*	*32*

Month and location of recovery of Song Thrushes ringed in Essex

observer coverage. The largest count was 500 on Pitsea Marsh on 14th November 1982, whilst there were 350 at The Naze on 20th October 2004 (170 still present the next day), 300 on Foulness on 6th October 1984 and 200 at The Naze on 16th October 2002. Numbers arriving in Essex generally peak around the first half of October making it the earliest migrant thrush to arrive.

Severe weather may cause further movements of either locals or individuals from elsewhere, the most obvious example being 300 that coasted into the Blackwater Estuary on 14th December 1975. Eighty at Pitsea on 18th January 1982 and 70 along the Crouch on 12th January 1982 were probably also weather-related gatherings.

Large numbers of Song Thrushes have been trapped and ringed in Essex, with just under 600 subsequently recovered, almost 90% of them within Essex. This suggests that most are site-faithful, both in and outside the breeding season. Of the remainder, many have been shot in France and Iberia and probably involve both locally-bred *clarkei* and migrant *philomelos*, which are known to pass through Britain on their way south from breeding grounds in Fennoscandia. Recoveries of Song Thrushes ringed during winter in Essex, at breeding grounds in Germany, Belgium and the Netherlands, are typical, with populations from these countries apparently regularly wintering in Britain (Migration Atlas). In addition, more than 80 Song Thrushes ringed in England have been recovered in Essex, all except one from southern England. One Belgian-ringed Song Thrush has also been recovered in Essex.

Whilst populations appear to have declined markedly on farmland and to a lesser extent in woodland, suburban and urban populations appear to be holding their own. Any subsequent recovery may therefore rely on expansion of the existing urban population into the wider landscape. The conversion of green-field farmland to housing over the next two decades is an opportunity to ensure that suitable habitats are both retained and created within new developments for the benefit of both wildlife and human inhabitants (Mason 2000).

Sponsored by Martin Henry

Redwing *Turdus iliacus*

The Redwing has an extensive Palearctic breeding range, stretching from Iceland to eastern Siberia, mainly in the boreal taiga, but also the subarctic and alpine zones. Two very similar races are recognised, the nominate race *iliacus* and *coburni*, the 'Icelandic Redwing'. The species breeds in a mosaic of essentially forest habitats, utilising anything from thickets and forest edges to parks and gardens. Almost the entire population leaves the breeding grounds in winter and moves between west and south to most of Europe, and south to parts of northern Africa and around the Black Sea, the Caucasus, northwest Iran and Caspian (Clement & Hathway 2000).

Redwing *T. i. iliacus*

Common winter visitor and passage migrant Amber List

The nominate race occurs throughout the species' range from Britain in the west then east through Scandinavia and Russia to eastern Siberia. It winters throughout Europe from Britain south into North Africa and east to Poland and central Europe and into the Middle East. Britain was first colonised in 1925, with numbers peaking in the late 1960s and early 1970s at around 300 pairs in 1971 and 1972 (Batten *et al.* 1990). However, during the 1990s no more than 38 pairs have been reported in any year, almost all in northern Scotland and just a handful of breeding records from southern England. Scrub near water seems to be favoured habitat in Britain (Second National Atlas).

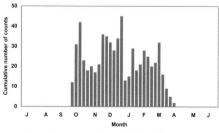

Seasonal occurrence of counts/flocks of 100+ Redwings
from 1950-2004

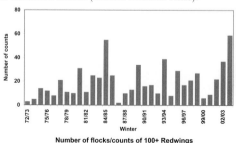

Number of flocks/counts of 100+ Redwings
from 1972/73-2003/04

Redwings have never been reported summering in Essex, although singing individuals are reported from time to time whilst on passage. Whether one at Leigh-on-Sea on 19th July 2004 had summered or was an early or late migrant is a matter of conjecture. Given that breeding has occurred in Kent, any late-staying individuals, and particularly those in full song, are worth investigating.

The Redwing's status appears to have changed little since the 19th century. Christy described the species as "A common winter visitor, especially abundant in severe winters", but by Glegg's time this was further expanded to include reference to spring and autumn movements, recording, for example, two large arrivals down the whole east coast in mid-October and mid-November 1885, a pattern not unusual over a century later. Glegg also detailed reports from the Kentish Knock Lightship, with a comment that "The species generally arrives in the county about the middle of October and remains to the first week in April", a statement that is as accurate now as it was then, although early and late dates have become more extreme in recent years. Today, it is as a winter visitor and passage migrant that it is known best, its lisping calls from overhead a familiar feature of anticyclonic nights in late autumn. Three-figure counts are regular from autumn to spring, with several four-figure gatherings/movements also noted.

Numbers vary dramatically from year to year, even within the same season, depending mostly on weather conditions. However, the species appears to be somewhat irruptive in nature and both within and between winter movements are not entirely understood; cold weather movements within the wintering range can give the appearance of nomadism (Second National Atlas). Marked fluctuations in breeding numbers also occur, with significant declines in the population in Finland reported after severe winters in Europe in the late 1970s and early 1980s (European Atlas). Interestingly, the number of counts of 100+ reported each winter in Essex appear to peak every ten years or so.

In autumn, October is the peak month of arrival, although September records are not unusual. The earliest report involved one at The Naze on 21st August 1977 with two other August records: one at The Naze on 22nd in 1978, and two at Little Baddow on 26th in 1981.

A total of eleven four-figure movements has been noted since 1950. The largest involved about 6,000 that came in off the sea at Bradwell in flocks of up to 200, mainly between 1000hrs and 1100hrs on 23rd October 1955. The same day 2,000 headed north over Littlebury. About 3,700 flew west over West Bergholt between dawn and 1100hrs on 12th October 1997, the same day that 2,000 flew west over Hatfield Forest. On 21st October 1995, a total of 2,000 flew southwest over Hainault Forest CP in just one hour, and 2,000 gathered at Sewardstonebury on 1st November 1968. The most recent four-figure counts have come from: Colchester, 1,500 on 16th October 2002; The Naze, 1,700 on 30th October 2002; and Wivenhoe, 2,000 (including 1,250 that flew northwest in 1.25 hours) on 8th October 2004. These observations show that the larger movements are just as likely to be observed inland as on the coast. Autumn arrivals invariably coincide with those of Fieldfares, flocks of both regularly arriving together and frequenting the same fields and hedgerows. The Redwing's habitat preferences differ slightly from the Fieldfare's and, later in winter, flocks where one or other dominates may be more common. Influxes of one species, however, do not necessarily coincide with those of the other.

	Jan	Feb	Mar	Apr	May	Jun	Jul	Aug	Sep	Oct	Nov	Dec
Essex	4	6	7	2								1
South England	2	1		1					1			
Finland					1		1	1				
Russia											2	
Denmark		1										
Belgium			1								1	
France	2	1									2	1
Spain	4											1
Portugal		1								1		
Italy												1
Sardinia		1										
Greece		1										
Totals	12	12	8	3	1	0	1	1	1	1	5	4

Month and location of recovery of Redwings ringed in Essex

Not surprisingly for a species that is affected by severe conditions, hard weather movements are regularly reported. During the most severe winter of the 20th century, in 1962/63, many individuals took to extreme behaviour to survive. During January 1963, 30 sought food beneath the stalls at Chelmsford market and 60 fed in the gutters of Southend-on-Sea High Street. The largest cold-weather movement occurred on 7th–8th January 1967 when 1,500–2,000 flew south over the Salcott/Tollesbury area, whilst 1,000 flew south along the Lea Valley and over Hockley. At The Naze, 1,000 flew in off the sea, suggesting a Continental origin for the influx rather than from elsewhere in the country. A similar movement occurred around 1st–5th January 1985, with 1,500 over The Naze, 2,000 at Abberton and 1,000 northwest over Tollesbury. A total of 2,000 at Vange on 4th December 1993 was followed the next day by 1,400 at Dagenham Chase. Around 1,000 were at Hanningfield on 23rd January 1999. The largest numbers occur on grassland, particularly close-cut horse paddocks, for instance, hedges with berries and orchards, and woodland clearings. Gardens will also be used during severe weather.

Occasionally, large roosts are found during winter. However, one at Little Parndon is by far the largest to be reported in Essex: 1,200 on 29th November had increased to a remarkable 5,660 on 4th December 1985, then declining to 500 by 8th January but increasing again to 850 on 12th March. It was located in Blackthorn and Hawthorn scrub adjacent to a small brook (Alan Harris pers. comm.). Other four-figure roosts have been 1,600 at Dagnam Park on 25th November 1984 and about 1,000 in Chalkney Woods on 27th November 1983.

The return movement in spring can sometimes be heavier than the arrival during the previous autumn as birds from further south and west head back through the county, although overall numbers are never as great as in autumn with just two four-figure counts: 1,000–1,250 at Thorndon CP on 19th February 1978, and 1,000 at Fryerning on 7th March 1978. Numbers tend to decrease more quickly than with Fieldfare and most have gone by early April. Occasional birds, however, linger into May, the latest being singles at: The Naze, 22nd in 1960; Holliwell Point, 20th–28th in 1990; The Naze, 27th in 1995; Writtle, 30th in 1984; and Dagenham Chase, 30th in 1994.

Around 50 Essex-ringed Redwings have subsequently been controlled, around 40% of them within Essex.

It is thought likely that the majority of Redwings wintering in Britain are from Finland and populations further east in Russia (Migration Atlas). Onward movement of some of these birds is apparent by the number of recoveries in France and Iberia after the turn of the year. Small numbers of British-ringed Redwings have also been recovered further east in subsequent winters in the eastern Mediterranean and as far east as Iran, suggesting a link in some winters between eastern breeding areas and Britain. In addition, one Finnish and two Belgian-ringed Redwings have been recovered in Essex.

The Redwing is never likely to be more than a 'one-off' breeder in Essex and thus any conservation measures can only aim to encourage the provision of suitable feeding and habitat. Losses of farmland hedgerows and the conversion of much of the county's grazing land to arable may have had a short-term effect on the number of Redwings that winter within the county, but in the longer term its status appears to be assured.

Icelandic Redwing   *T. i. coburni*

Vagrant: four records of five individuals

The Icelandic Redwing breeds throughout Iceland and The Faeroe Islands, and winters mainly in Scotland, Ireland, western France and Iberia (Migration Atlas).

1940	Halstead	20th November	Female, "Obtained"
1955	Havering	20th February	Two trapped and ringed
1960	Bradwell	30th October	Trapped and ringed
1963	Witham	3rd January	Dead

The 1963 individual is in Colchester Museum (Accession No. 1998.31.196). The two at Havering had wing-lengths of 123mm and 124mm respectively, which are typical of *coburni* (*BWP*). The Halstead individual had a wing length of 119.5mm (Bulletin BOC 62:18) and is potentially referable to either race. According to the Migration Atlas, there are no ringing recoveries of *coburni* in England and Wales, although there are records from the Netherlands and Denmark (Clement & Hathway 2000).

Mistle Thrush   *Turdus viscivorus*

A common resident but scarce passage migrant and winter visitor   Amber List

The Mistle Thrush is a large, stocky thrush that breeds throughout Europe, western Asia and much of Asia Minor, with small populations in central Asia and the western Himalayas (Clement & Hathway 2000). The nominate race *viscivorus* breeds across west and central Europe and east through west and central Russia. The species prefers to nest in large trees, feeding in nearby grazed or mown grassland, cultivated soil and woodland glades. The Mistle Thrush's occurrence in suburban parks and gardens is a relatively recent phenomenon (European Atlas). The species is more arboreal than the Song Thrush, hence its rather more restricted range. In Britain, Mistle Thrushes are widespread throughout the country, having increased dramatically during the 18th and 19th centuries, although the reasons for this expansion are unclear (Historical Atlas). Northerly populations tend to be more migratory than southern ones.

Christy said very little about the species, other than that it was a common resident in all districts. Glegg considered the Mistle Thrush to be common throughout, although not so common as the Song Thrush, whilst Hudson & Pyman observed "… it breeds throughout the county and occurs in most habitats (though notably scarce in built-up areas except in parks)…". Cox considered the Mistle Thrush to be locally common, but much the least common of the resident thrushes being particularly scarce in "… the cereal desert areas that are now such a feature of the Essex landscape". Its status remains very similar to this day.

Atlas	Survey Area	% of 10km squares or tetrads in which	
		bred/probably bred	possibly bred or present
First National 10km	Essex	94.7	3.5
Second National 10km	Essex	96.5	3.5
First London Tetrad	Met. Essex	48.0	17.0
Second London Tetrad	Met. Essex	84.0	14.0
Essex Tetrad	Essex	67.2	19.1

Summary of results of Atlas surveys for Mistle Thrushes

Atlas surveys have confirmed that the Mistle Thrush is widespread with breeding recorded in almost every 10km square during each National Atlas survey and in 67.2% of tetrads during the Essex Atlas survey with the species absent mainly from Dengie, Foulness, and the south side of the Crouch where there was probably a lack of suitable nesting sites and feeding areas. However, the species occurs at the lowest densities of all the thrushes with local CBC plots since 1980 recording in woodland average densities of ten pairs per km^2 (range 5.2–18) and on farmland just one pair per km^2, very similar to the figures quoted by Cox. Parks and gardens, in which the Mistle Thrush is most common, are not covered by the CBC/BBS surveys but Mason (2000) found densities of up to 18 pairs per km^2 in the built environment.

The species is particularly susceptible to hard winters and the national CBC figures showed a severe decline after the 1962/63 winter with a fairly rapid recovery thereafter and stable numbers until 1981. Since then numbers appear to have declined in both farmland and woodland with an overall 41% decline in the CBC/BBS (England) Indices over the period 1977–2002; more recent BBS surveys suggest a 9% decline from 1994–2003. Local CBC/BBS data suggested a decline from 1984–87 with a subsequent recovery but a further ongoing decline since the mid-1990s.

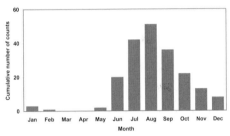

Seasonal occurrence of counts/flocks of 10+ Mistle Thrushes from 1971-2004

From late June and into early September post-breeding flocks may form, predominantly of juveniles. Glegg referred to flocks of 200–300 recorded regularly from Felsted during July, which suggests higher population levels than today, although after the harsh winter of 1916–17 fewer than 20–30 were noted. No recent flocks have approached such numbers, although counts of 20–40 are not uncommon and the largest have been: 70+ at Newport, 1st September 2002; 60 at Springfield, 24th July 1984; and 60 at Margaretting Tye, 7th July 1998. Most large counts in recent years have occurred in late summer/early autumn.

There is evidence from elsewhere (e.g. Piotrowski 2003) that numbers of migrant Mistle Thrushes may formerly have been greater. The largest movements noted in Essex involved migrating flocks of 200 on 31st October 1959 and 285 on 7th November 1959 over the Lea Valley; interestingly, exceptional numbers were recorded at Cape Clear, West Cork, Eire, in late October 1959 (Sharrock 1973) so perhaps the Lea Valley birds were correctly identified and not in fact Fieldfares? Subsequently, the largest counts have been 100 on 20th November 1968 in the Lea Valley and 60+ that flew in off the sea at The Naze on 6th November 1969. Small numbers of apparent migrants are reported regularly from the coast, some flying in off the sea during most autumns. English birds are partially migratory, at least in their first year, as there is no evidence for long-distance movements in later winters. The very few ringing recoveries of individuals that have crossed the North Sea have involved young birds, although none has involved Essex.

By winter, any post-breeding flocks have broken up and flocks are generally small with adult Mistle Thrushes vigorously defending trees and bushes that are laden with sufficient fruit to last through to the following spring (Snow & Snow 1984). Young birds will move on to find their own food supply, the distance they travel varying from a few to several hundred kilometres (Winter Atlas).

Of the 65 recoveries of Mistle Thrushes ringed in Essex, all but one were in the county and just seven had travelled further than 10km. Mistle Thrushes ringed in Hampshire, Lincolnshire and Kent have been recovered in Essex.

Mistle Thrush populations have not declined in counties dominated by pasture and sheep farming; where declines have taken place it they have been in cereal-dominated areas. The population trends produced by different farming practices are reflected in the breeding statistics. In cereal-growing eastern England, the average clutch size is 2.9, whereas in areas pasture predominates it is 4.5. Clutch size and fledging success rise steeply with the amount of mown grass available for feeding sites (Population Trends). Only a change from current agricultural practice in Essex, where cereal growing now dominates, is likely to reverse the Mistle Thrush's fortunes.

Cetti's Warbler

Cettia cetti

Scarce but increasing resident

The Cetti's Warbler breeds almost continuously from Spain to Turkestan and the borders with Mongolia, north to southern England and the Netherlands and south (but avoiding much of central and eastern Europe) to north Africa, the Near East to the Persian Gulf and northern Baluchistan. The nominate race *cetti* occurs generally across the west of the species' range with *albiventris* present in Iran, Afghanistan and central Asia. Typical breeding habitat is thick, damp or wet scrub and low vegetation where as residents they depend on the marginally warmer microclimate of such habitat to sustain their insect prey through winter. After a northward expansion in western Europe from about the 1920s, breeding first occurred in Britain in Kent in 1972. Since then it has colonised southern England with the current stronghold in the southwest, although large populations exist farther north, for instance in the Yare Valley, Norfolk. Numbers can be drastically reduced by severe winter weather. There were at least 850 singing males in England and Wales in 2002 (RBBP 2004).

The first Essex record occurred in 1976 when perhaps two singing males were located at Berwick Ponds, Rainham, during April. Both stayed into June. Later in 1976 one was ringed at Pitsea Marsh on 10th October and retrapped on 21st November and 26th December. Between

Atlas	Survey Area	% of 10km squares or tetrads in which bred/probably bred	possibly bred or present
First National 10km	Essex	0.0	0.0
Second National 10km	Essex	3.5	1.8
First London Tetrad	Met. Essex	0.0	0.0
Second London Tetrad	Met. Essex	1.5	2.0
Essex Tetrad	Essex	0.3	0.2

Summary of results of Atlas surveys for Cetti's Warblers

1977 and 1979 further singing males were located at Berwick Ponds, Walthamstow (where a second bird was also present with the singing male), Fishers Green, Fingringhoe Wick and a few scattered sites along the Thames. Many, however, were present at the particular site for one year only. The severe winter weather of 1978/79 did not seem to affect the species, which is surprising given its susceptibility to the cold: there were six singing males in 1979. The first confirmed breeding record was not until 1981 when single pairs bred at: St Osyth, where two adults and three juveniles were ringed; Pitsea Marsh; and probably Silver End GP. Pairs bred successfully at St Osyth from 1982–83 and probably also in 1984. However, particularly cold winter weather in the mid-1980s severely reduced the Essex population and no further breeding records were received until 1990 when a second wave of colonisation occurred with birds at three sites in the Lea Valley and at Berwick Ponds. At the latter site, there were up to four singing males in 1991–92 with 2–3 in the Lea Valley. In 1993, all the sites were abandoned, the last possibly due to the partial cutting of reed banks at the request of anglers. Breeding did not occur again until 1999 when a pair bred in south Essex. In 2000 and 2001, singing males were present at three sites but from 2002 numbers increased markedly, although all except the traditional St Osyth colony were found along Thames-side or in Metropolitan Essex, where favoured localities have been Stanford Warren (four territories in 2004), the Ingrebourne Valley, (three), Wat Tyler CP (three) and Vange (three). With numbers increasing rapidly elsewhere in England, further increases are to be expected if the run of mild winters continues. Breeding is difficult to prove and has been confirmed just 13 times in Essex.

Most records outside the breeding season come from suspected or known breeding sites, although, particularly during autumn and to a lesser extent in winter, there is a tendency for occasional wandering individuals to occur at sites away from breeding areas, suggesting some local dispersal, presumably of young. Again, most records come from Thames-side but a slow spread up the Lea Valley and to other coastal sites is taking place.

Although a number of Cetti's Warblers have been ringed in Essex, the majority at Pitsea, all except one have been retrapped very close by. The exception was a bird of the year originally ringed at Pitsea on 27th July 2002, which was

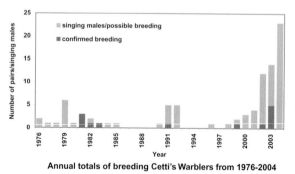

Annual totals of breeding Cetti's Warblers from 1976-2004

last retrapped there on 10th August 2002 and subsequently trapped at Flatford Mill, Suffolk, on 10th April 2003. It is thought that juvenile Cetti's Warblers are far more prone to disperse than adults and are therefore likely to be responsible for the founding of new colonies (Migration Atlas). In addition, an adult ringed at Filsham, Sussex, on 21st September 2003 was controlled at Pitsea on 8th June 2004.

(Common) Grasshopper Warbler   *Locustella naevia*

Scarce summer resident and passage migrant   **Red List**

The Grasshopper Warbler breeds patchily across central and northern Europe, being mostly absent from Mediterranean regions. Its range extends eastwards as far as southeastern Siberia. The nominate race *naevia* occurs over much of the species' European range. Nesting is typically in both damp and dry habitats, the necessary criterion being thick, low-lying vegetation containing several prominent features, usually bushes, for song perches (European Atlas). In Britain, Grasshopper Warblers are widespread but thinly distributed, almost exclusively below 300m (Second National Atlas). Grasshopper Warblers are more prone than most summer visitors to annual fluctuations in numbers and are erratic in their occupation of some breeding sites (Parslow 1973). It is a surprisingly poorly known species and it was only as recently as 1993 that two ringing recoveries in Britain of birds ringed in winter in Senegal confirmed at least part of the species' wintering range.

Christy described the Grasshopper Warbler as "A summer visitor to all parts of the county, I believe, but decidedly uncommon, and always

Atlas	Survey Area	% of 10km squares or tetrads in which	
		bred/probably bred	possibly bred or present
First National 10km	Essex	77.2	5.3
Second National 10km	Essex	15.8	21.1
First London Tetrad	Met. Essex	7.0	1.5
Second London Tetrad	Met. Essex	8.0	5.5
Essex Tetrad	Essex	3.7	3.6

Summary of results of Atlas surveys for Grasshopper Warblers

far more often heard than seen". The earliest documented record was in 1819 at Wrabness on 1st May. In 1832, Doubleday observed that only one pair occurred in the Epping Forest area, although 50 years later the species was described as common throughout the district (Buxton 1885). At Chignal, Christy considered Grasshopper Warblers to be "... not uncommon among the standing corn". Breeding was also noted around Harwich and Maldon in the late 19th century. Glegg, in considering the Grasshopper Warbler an "... unusual straggler to Essex ..." accepted just two breeding records at Loughton Plain in 1894 and Felsted in 1928, although the species probably bred at Gosfield in 1928. Apparently he dismissed or perhaps overlooked Christy's own record. It would seem from the scant evidence available that the Grasshopper Warbler had declined by the late 1920s.

Hudson & Pyman considered that the Grasshopper Warbler was an uncommon passage migrant that had formerly bred and may have done so regularly. They added just two breeding records – Great Hallingbury in 1956 and Rochford in 1966—but added that "Bearing in mind how difficult a species this is to track down, it is thought likely, on the evidence available, that a pair or two nest in the county most years". Breeding was suspected in the Rochford Hundred in the 1930s and Stort Valley in the 1940s. Recently uncovered correspondence between Pyman and Glegg (Pyman 1938a), suggested that Grasshopper Warblers also bred regularly in Belfairs Park until the late 1930s, but ceased following housing encroachment.

From around 1964, the status of the species changed remarkably over the course of just a few years, with a period of comparative abundance that peaked in 1970 when reeling individuals were reported from 45 sites. However, by 1975 numbers had again declined to the level of the early 1960s, only to be followed by another increase around the late 1980s and early 1990s. However, higher population levels appeared to coincide with Atlas survey work during the late 1960s and early 1970s and the late 1980s and early 1990s, pointing to at least part of the observed increases being due to greater observer coverage.

An approximately ten-year cycle of peak abundance is apparent for the period 1950–90. The CBC Index for all habitats showed a peak around the early 1970s, followed by a crash during 1972–74, improvements between 1979 and 1981 and then a further decline, such that by 1985 the Index was barely 20% of the average level of the late 1960s (Population Trends). Possible causes for the decline since the early 1970s are unknown, although the Sahelian

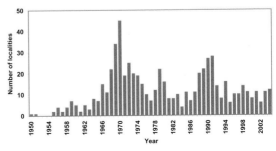

Number of localities with reeling Grasshopper Warblers from 1950-2004

drought has been implicated. It has, however, been suggested that the current situation is the typical population level, following a temporary rise to higher numbers in the 1960s, the reasons for which remain unknown (Riddiford 1983). Recent BBS data have shown little change since 1994.

The Second National Atlas recorded the fall from peak numbers in the early 1970s, although the London Atlas recorded only a marginal decline. The Essex Atlas confirmed breeding in 21 10km squares with breeding proved in 3.7% of tetrads; the number occurring in any one year was almost certainly smaller. Records were clustered around certain areas: the Lea Valley, Rainham and the Ingrebourne Valley, Hanningfield, Danbury Ridge and Chelmer Valley, Shoeburyness and Wakering Stairs, Weald CP and Dagnam Park. These locations provide typical "damp" habitats along river valleys and around sewage farms, reservoirs and gravel-pits. In 1970, the species was far more widespread, albeit with fewer in the southeast and northwest, perhaps due to poor observer coverage at the time. A significant proportion was in young conifer plantations or dry heathland in northern Essex including around Newport/Strethall/Chrishall, Harlow, Earls Colne/Halstead, Berechurch/Donyland and Birch/Tiptree/Tolleshunt Knights (Cox). Few now occur in this habitat.

Not surprisingly, it is spring that most migrants are noted when reeling birds temporarily take up residence at sites across Essex with small falls having been noted in some years, such as at Pitsea on 26th April 1970 when ten were reeling in one area, but not subsequently. The earliest arrival was at Bradwell on 31st March 1957, but it is more usual for the first to occur from mid-April onwards. Records of reeling birds peak in May, after which there is a marked decline. This may be due either to individuals moving on or the males having paired up successfully.

Autumn records are generally few with none recorded in Essex after July in some years. Greater observer coverage has resulted in more being identified at coastal localities but even then the best years for migrants—1992 and 1993—saw only five recorded in each, including in the former year one killed by a Cat at Braxted on 15th August. Most have passed through by mid-September but there have been five October records, all involving singles, at: Little Baddow, 4th in 1979; Foulness, 6th in 1985; Bradwell, 6th in 1991; Hanningfield, 8th in 1972; and Bradwell, 13th in 1970.

The only Essex ringing recovery involved one ringed at East Tilbury on 27th June 1976 and controlled at Flint Cross, Cambridgeshire, on 25th May 1978.

In national terms the Essex population is a small proportion of the British population of 10,500 pairs (Second National Atlas). The marked fluctuations from year to year and the general lack of site fidelity is likely to mean that a small, but variable-sized population will survive in Essex for the foreseeable future.

Savi's Warbler *Locustella luscinioides*

Vagrant: three records Red List

The Savi's Warbler has a scattered and patchy distribution in west, central and eastern Europe, with a separate population from the west Caspian to southwest Siberia. The nominate race *luscinioides* occurs throughout much of Europe. In west and central Europe the species is largely restricted to extensive stands of reeds and bulrushes. Although it is likely that overall numbers are stable in Europe, declines have been noted on the western edge of its range (European Atlas). Savi's Warblers winter in sub-Saharan Africa, especially in southern Sudan.

1981	Pitsea Marsh	16th May	Adult ringed
	Pitsea Marsh	31st July	Juvenile ringed
1983	Hanningfield	16th–23rd May	Singing male

It is tempting to think that breeding may have taken place in 1981, but given the size of the reed bed this could not be proven.

Christy considered that "It is very probable that it used to nest in Essex when the marshes were entirely undrained …", although he presented no evidence on which to base his statement. A nest was supposed to have been found at Dagenham on 14th May 1850, but Christy dismissed the record, as the finder was a known dealer in rare bird skins.

The Savi's Warbler has a very chequered history as a British breeding bird. It bred in small numbers in East Anglia until about 1856 after which it became extinct. However, from 1960–80 a small population built up, principally in southeast England and East Anglia, which peaked around 1978–80 when some 28–30 pairs were recorded. The species was removed from the BBRC List after 31st December 1982 (Grant 1982). However, the species subsequently declined and was therefore readmitted onto the BBRC List on 1st January 1999 (Bradshaw 1999). In 2000, there were 0–6 pairs breeding nationally (RBBP 2004).

Aquatic Warbler   *Acrocephalus paludicola*

Vagrant: eight records   **Red List**

The monotypic Aquatic Warbler breeds from Germany east to the River Ob in western Siberia, although its eastern and southern breeding limits are poorly known. The species' preferred habitat is open, eutrophic marshes where sedge and mosses predominate. It has declined drastically since 1875 and is now one of the rarest breeding migratory passerines in Europe. It is thought western populations move to west Africa, although its winter quarters are poorly known (European Atlas).

1957	Hanningfield	11th August	
1966	Brookend, near Chelmsford	13th August	Trapped and ringed
1973	Two Tree Island	23rd September	
1976	Bradwell	29th–30th August	Trapped and ringed
1977	Fingringhoe Wick	21st August	
1981	Rainham	12th August	
1998	The Naze	12th September	
2004	Rainham	24th August	Juvenile

The Aquatic Warbler has an intriguing migration strategy, moving west out of its breeding areas, passing mainly through Belgium and northwest France then into Iberia and south. This may explain why it is so rare on the east coast of Britain (Cottridge & Vinicombe 1996) but regular in south and southwest Britain, where ringing in reed beds, the means by which most individuals are reported, has produced annual totals of up to 102 (in 1976), although this was exceptional (Fraser & Rogers 2004). Nationally, numbers typically peak in mid-August but records span the period late July to early November.

Sponsored by Howard Vaughan

Sedge Warbler   *Acrocephalus schoenobaenus*

Common summer resident and passage migrant

The monotypic Sedge Warbler is a common breeding species throughout much of Europe. The species' range extends from the high-arctic of northern Fennoscandia to Greece and Turkey in the south and from Ireland across to central Siberia. The species seemingly prefers lowland marsh and waterside habitats for breeding, although frequently utilises drier habitats including hedges, scrub, young conifers and arable crops (European Atlas). In Britain, it is a widespread species particularly in lowland eastern England, where Essex is considered important for the species (Second National Atlas). Western populations migrate south to winter in western Africa (Dowsett *et al.* 1988).

All the early writers considered the Sedge Warbler to be a common or very common summer resident that was, because of its more catholic breeding requirements, more widespread and plentiful than the Reed Warbler. It is typically found along the coast and along river

Atlas	Survey Area	% of 10km squares or tetrads in which	
		bred/probably bred	possibly bred or present
First National 10km	Essex	100.0	0.0
Second National 10km	Essex	96.5	3.5
First London Tetrad	Met. Essex	44.5	8.5
Second London Tetrad	Met. Essex	81.5	11.0
Essex Tetrad	Essex	61.5	23.0

Summary of results of Atlas surveys for Sedge Warblers

valleys but anywhere that reed beds and marshy areas occur are likely to hold the species, whilst more recently some territories have been established in Oil-seed Rape and cereal crops. Its status in general has changed very little to this day, although regular recording has revealed annual fluctuations over the last few decades. The British population remained remarkably stable until the late 1960s, but following exceptional numbers during 1968 the population crashed in 1969 and a further decline occurred during the 1970s (Population Trends). BTO Nest record cards confirmed that this was not due to a decline in nesting success but as a result of a series of severe droughts in its west African wintering quarters, which killed many adults (Peach *et al.* 1991). In 1983, following one particularly severe drought, fewer than 5% of adult Sedge Warblers were estimated to have returned to England to breed. However, recent research in Russia suggests that spring temperatures in northern Europe can influence breeding numbers. Thus in cold springs many simply do not push as far north as usual and so breed further south than they would otherwise.

Unfortunately, the Sedge Warbler received scant attention in *EBR*s until the early 1980s. There is therefore little local data on which to assess trends until then, except for that provided by WBS surveys: Sedge Warblers do not occur on many CBC/BBS plots, although where they do there has been little change since 1977. CES and national WBS plots have, however, recorded declines of the order of at least 20% since the mid-1970s. Local WBS plots showed an average of 1.5 pairs per km with a maximum of 34 pairs along 5.2km of the Stort in 1975. More recent (post-1980) WBS data have shown an average of about two pairs per km (range 0–6.3) and a maximum of 39 pairs along a 6.2-km stretch of the River Lea in 2000. Cox made no specific mention of trends except to suggest that any local decrease due to loss of habitat had probably been counter-balanced by the creation of new habitat around gravel-pits and reservoirs. At those sites where there has been regular monitoring since the 1980s, there appears to have been a steady increase in numbers overall during the 1990s. Local populations can be very high with close to 90 singing males noted at Rainham and 60+ on Langenhoe Ranges, Old Hall and Heybridge GP during the last decade.

The Sedge Warbler's distribution across the county was similar in both National Atlas surveys, with breeding confirmed in every 10km square in the First and all but two in the northwest in the Second, suggesting that the population had substantially recovered from the losses of the previous 20 years. In London, numbers apparently increased, although there had been losses in the north of Metropolitan Essex and gains along Thames-side. The Essex Atlas revealed the Sedge Warbler to be widespread with breeding confirmed in 61.5% of tetrads and, like many other species, apparently absent only from the extreme northwest.

Very little has been written concerning the Sedge Warbler's migration through Essex. In spring, most arrive in the latter half of April, although there have been six March records, the earliest being one on Foulness on 19th in 1961 with singles at Heybridge GP on 25th in 2000 and Barling GP on 28th in 1989. Few migrants are seen at coastal sites.

Many adults probably leave breeding areas in July/early August when they have deposited sufficient fat to make the trip to sub-Saharan Africa in one flight (Bibby & Green 1981). Juveniles move through Essex later in August and early September and probably utilise the very same reed beds that breeding birds use. Many British Sedge Warblers use the reed beds of southern England to fatten up for the trip south; those beds with high densities of Plum-reed Aphids, a somewhat ephemeral food source, are favoured. Few migrants are reported from the coast; Sedge Warblers typically head south of southwest on migration, which takes them away from the traditional migration watchpoints. Most have departed by the end of September, although stragglers are regularly recorded into October. There are, however, four November records, the latest being one at Cattawade on 19th in 1960, with other late singles reported from Fingringhoe Wick on 4th in 1972, Sewardstone on 4th in 1974 and Sawbridgeworth on 3rd in 1985.

Many Sedge Warblers have been ringed in Essex and around 120 have subsequently been recovered, about 25% in Essex and 50% in southern England. The relatively high number of recoveries in France during autumn suggests that in some years at least Sedge Warblers do not manage to attain the full weight for the final trip south whilst in southern England. The two recoveries in Belgium, just days after ringing in Essex, suggest that not all Sedge Warblers take a southwesterly route, a fact reinforced by one trapped at Bishop's Stortford SF on 28th April 1970 that had been ringed in Malta just 24 days earlier which provided the first indication of a northwesterly route into Britain (Cox). There have also been two recoveries of birds ringed in France whilst on migration.

Despite local losses, the Sedge Warbler appears to be adaptable. Provided existing sites are protected, it is likely that other habitats will continue to be created to offset those lost through habitat change and destruction. However,

	Jan	Feb	Mar	Apr	May	Jun	Jul	Aug	Sep	Oct	Nov	Dec
Essex				2	10	4	4	6	2			
Scotland						1						
North England					2		1	1				
South England				1	9	7	15	21	7			
Wales								1				
Ireland								1				
Belgium								2				
France			1	1	1			9	3			
Spain				1					1			
Portugal									1	1		
Morocco			1									
Totals	*0*	*0*	*2*	*5*	*22*	*12*	*20*	*41*	*14*	*1*	*0*	*0*

Month and location of recovery of Sedge Warblers ringed in Essex

given that population levels and survival rates are governed by factors outside Essex, its long-term survival in the county is unlikely to be influenced significantly by any local conservation measures.

Paddyfield Warbler   *Acrocephalus agricola*

Vagrant: two records

The Paddyfield Warbler breeds in Romania and Bulgaria and just north of the Caspian Sea then east as far as western China, as well as Afghanistan and Iran. In Europe it is represented by the race *septima*. Paddyfield Warblers are typical of forest-steppe and semi-desert zones and inhabit reed beds and bushes around shallow water bodies (European Atlas). The species winters in the Indian subcontinent.

1987	The Naze	11th October	
1999	Seventy Acres Lake	26th–28th October	1st-winter

There were 56 British records to the end of 2004 (BBRC 2005), the majority since 1980, this increase possibly linked to a slow increase in the European population (European Atlas). The 1987 record was the 15th nationally and only the third from the southeast of England.

A truly remarkable find, the Lea Valley individual was the third inland record nationally, following those at Tring Reservoirs, Hertfordshire, on 9th November 1981 and Thatcham, Berkshire, on 7th September 1998. Most occur in late September and October in the Northern Isles and down the east coast.

Blyth's Reed Warbler   *Acrocephalus dumetorum*

Vagrant: one record

The monotypic Blyth's Reed Warbler has a central Palearctic range covering the warmer boreal to cooler temperature zones, from southern Finland, Estonia and Latvia eastward to Lake Baikal. The species winters in India and Nepal to Burma (European Atlas).

2003	Fishers Green Goose-field	16th June	Singing male

This was the 58th British record (BBRC 2004), although the species has been recorded with increasing regularity in recent years; there have been 28 since 2000. A range expansion in Europe is part of the reason for the increase but far greater observer awareness must also be a significant factor.

Although this individual's identity was suspected at the time, it was only after the bird had left that its identity was confirmed from 11 minutes of recorded song.

Marsh Warbler   *Acrocephalus palustris*

Very rare migrant and summer visitor. Has bred   Red List

The monotypic Marsh Warbler is largely restricted to the cool temperate latitudes of the western Palearctic, where it inhabits mainly lowlands, from central and eastern Europe and east to beyond the Urals. The species is generally absent from the Mediterranean. It is typically found in stands of tall herbage, such as Nettle, Meadowsweet and Willowherb, characteristic of moist or seasonally flooded soils, which are somewhat transient and unstable in nature (European Atlas). Its range has increased markedly in Europe since 1900, mainly at its northern limits. The small British population is at the extreme western edge of its distribution and has been in decline during the last few decades of the 20th century: there were just 0–14 breeding pairs nationally in 2002 (RBBP 2004).

The Marsh Warbler has probably the most chequered history of any species on the Essex list. Although Christy mentioned one record and considered that the species might well occur in Essex, he did not feel confident enough to accept the record as it involved a 30 year-old, rather faded, specimen shot at Wendens Ambo and deposited at Saffron Walden Museum which, although labelled as a Reed Warbler, was considered by one of his correspondents to be a Marsh Warbler. Glegg referred to a breeding record involving a clutch of four eggs taken at Tillingham on 6th June 1892, although there is an air of uncertainty about the record. Witherby *et al.* (1938–41) mentioned the record as "… possibly … but not certain …". In 1934, three nests were found in the Lea Valley at Edmonton Marsh, now the site of Girling Reservoir. Witherby *et al.* accepted these in the supplement to the *Handbook*.

Between 1955 and 1962, there was a series of records centred mainly on the Chelmer Valley east of Chelmsford, but with others from sites in northeast Essex and Nazeing GP. All were properly claimed by observers and accepted by the Essex Recording Committee. However, by 1962 doubts were raised about certain field identification criteria relevant to habitat selection and powers of mimicry. The eventual result, following further intensive research in the field was the clarification of Marsh Warbler identification features (Davis *et al.* 1965), which led to the removal of every Marsh Warbler record on the Essex list (Hudson & Pyman).

The Marsh Warbler was finally reinstated on the Essex List in 1983 when one was at Bradwell from 5th–11th June at least. It was trapped and ringed and responded to the recording of a Marsh Warbler's song. Barrett (1998) summarised all records to which the most recent have been added.

1983	Bradwell	5th–11th June at least	Trapped and ringed
1984	Hanningfield	22nd–24th June	
1994	Wat Tyler CP	28th May	Trapped and ringed
1996	Barking Marsh	One pair fledged three young	
	Mucking	One pair bred but eggs deserted	
1997	Barking Marsh	3rd–13th June	1–2 birds present
	Ingrebourne Valley	One pair	Assumed to have bred
	Lea Valley	Late July/early August	Singing male
1998	Ingrebourne Valley	14th–24th May	Singing male
1999	Fingringhoe Wick	12th–17th June	Pair present, male singing
2000	Roding, Barking	9th June	Singing male
2001	Rainham	One pair bred	
	Walthamstow Marsh	One pair bred	
2002	Rainham	One pair bred	
2004	Barking Bay	Late May	Singing male

All territorial Essex birds have been found close to river valleys on disused ground with depressions and nearby banks that probably influence the ground vegetation (Barrett 1998).

The British breeding population peaked at 100–120 pairs between 1920 and 1940 during a settled climatic period that saw the continued northerly expansion of the species (Voous 1960). At that time and until the early 1980s, the lush sheltered valleys of the Avon and Severn supported most of the population. The national population has continued to decline with the West Midlands' population now extinct. The decline was linked to a succession of poor summers and isolation of the population (Kelsey 1989). However, very small numbers now breed in southern England, although the Kent population of 21 singing males in 1995 had declined to just six in 2002 (RBBP 2004). In national terms therefore, Essex held around 10–15% of the national population of this, the rarest regular breeding passerine in Britain. There have been no Essex ringing recoveries. However, a juvenile ringed near Maidstone, Kent, on 23rd July 1991 was controlled as a territorial singing male on 22nd May 1993, at Rye Meads, Hertfordshire, and may indicate the source of the Thames-side birds. Ringing studies have shown that Marsh Warblers show low site fidelity, which along the edge of its range is likely to mean that any colonisation may 'ebb and flow', which appears to be the case in Essex at present.

There is little in the way of positive conservation action that can be carried out to encourage the species to colonise and it is likely to remain a very rare Essex bird. Ironically, almost all of the sites that the Marsh Warbler has chosen to date have been what are known as 'brown-field' sites; many are about to be, or already have been built upon.

(Eurasian) Reed Warbler

Acrocephalus scirpaceus

Common summer resident and passage migrant

The Reed Warbler breeds in the mid-latitude lowlands of the west and central Palearctic and is strongly associated with reed beds, particularly of Common Reeds. The nominate race *scirpaceus* breeds throughout Europe from the Volga west through the Ukraine to the Iberian coast, its

Atlas	Survey Area	% of 10km squares or tetrads in which bred/probably bred	possibly bred or present
First National 10km	Essex	82.5	3.5
Second National 10km	Essex	80.7	8.8
First London Tetrad	Met. Essex	16.5	2.5
Second London Tetrad	Met. Essex	30.0	8.0
Essex Tetrad	Essex	30.8	3.9

Summary of results of Atlas surveys for Reed Warblers

northern range extending to central Fennoscandia and the southern to coastal northwest Africa. The eastern race *fuscus* breeds from Asia Minor through Iran to Kazakhstan. The Reed Warbler has extended its range northward even faster than Marsh Warbler (European Atlas). In Britain, Reed Warblers occur mainly in lowland Britain, south of a line from south Yorkshire to Lancashire, and are particularly abundant in East Anglia and on the east coast (Second National Atlas). West, central and northern European populations migrate southwestward and winter mainly in the Sudan-Zambezi region.

Christy described the Reed Warbler as a "… regular summer visitor, though rather uncommon except on our coast, and decidedly local … I have never met with it in the central parts of our county". None of his correspondents knew of any inland breeding records, apart from around Sudbury where it "… abounds in the reeds on the banks of the Stour, and in the ditches communicating with the river". Doubleday mentioned a single specimen shot near Epping in 1835. Thus the Reed Warbler appears to have been less widespread across Essex than it is today with an apparent lack of records from any of the principal rivers such as the Chelmer, Lea, Stort etc., where suitable habitat must have existed. Around the coast it was observed in reed beds and fleets at Orsett, where it was known as the 'Reedchat', Harwich, Little Oakley, Maldon and South Shoebury.

Glegg's description of the Reed Warbler's range was fairly similar to Christy's. However, the species was now present right along the Stour, rather than just around Sudbury and had colonised the Lea Valley in 1912 and was increasing. Reed Warblers had also been noted breeding on a pond at Birch Hall, Theydon Bois, along the Roding at Abridge, around Navestock Lake, along the Blackwater between Kelvedon and Coggeshall, near Great Dunmow and at Sible Hedingham. The range therefore appeared to have expanded since Christy's time but there were still surprising omissions from its range that are not easily explained by observer coverage alone.

Hudson & Pyman described the species as a locally common summer visitor and passage migrant. Whilst noting that the largest numbers were to be found on the coast, the Chelmer Valley was readily favoured, the first time that it had been mentioned in any literature. Abandoned gravel-pits along the Colne, Lea and Stort flood plains were also being used. Whilst it is possible that the number of gravel-workings had increased the areas of suitable habitat, it is unclear as to whether the apparent increase in population was due to this or factors external to the county, as there appeared to be much suitable but unused habitat in the county prior to 1960.

The Reed Warbler's particular affinity for reed beds gives it a patchier distribution across Essex than the Sedge Warbler, a fact confirmed by the two National Atlases; the range remained virtually unchanged over the two decades between the atlases. Although there has been no significant overall change to the national population, some evidence from CBC studies suggests an increase, although the species is notoriously difficult to census accurately (Second National Atlas). The WBS measured a 60% population increase from 1981–2002, whilst more recent BBS figures for England suggested a 6% increase from 1994–2003. However, CES sites probably provide the most accurate measure of trends; these showed a 20% decline from 1984–2002, with an 8% decline from 1997–2002. The Essex Atlas survey confirmed breeding in 30.8% of tetrads with a high proportion near the coast, with most of the remainder along the principal river valleys where instead of reed beds, damp areas in such vegetation as Meadowsweet, Willowherb and even bushes may be used (Population Trends). Numbers in Metropolitan Essex increased significantly between the two London Atlases as the species colonised gravel-workings along Thames-side and areas created by the building of the M11. Annual numbers do not seem to vary as much as Sedge Warblers', perhaps because they are relatively unaffected by the droughts in the Sahel.

Reed Warblers can be far more abundant than Sedge Warblers in optimum habitat. Ringing data from several sites provide evidence for this relative abundance.

In many of the coastal borrow dykes it can be very common. On Dengie, a survey in the early 1980s located some 400 pairs (Cox), whilst peaks at other principal sites have been: 172 singing males at Old Hall, 1986; 200 pairs at Pitsea, 1987; 254 pairs at Rainham in an RSPB survey, 2003; 132 pairs at Berwick Ponds/

Ingrebourne Valley, 2000; 109 pairs at Langenhoe, 1990. No other Essex sites have recorded three-figure breeding populations, but there are many sites holding double-figure populations. Dennis (1991) using Essex Atlas and National River Authority (Anglian Region) surveys estimated a minimum population of 1,700 pairs in Essex. Today, this would seem to be an underestimate; its accuracy would depend on whether or not any visits coincided with peak song periods (Bell *et al.* 1968). As populations within the county appear to have been fairly stable over the last 20 years, apparently significant variations at individual sites may simply be due to observer coverage. Based on the peak counts from each individual site mentioned over the last decade in the *EBRs*, the Essex population is perhaps of the order of 2,500–3,000 pairs which represents a 3.0–7.5% of the British population of 40,000–80,000 pairs (European Atlas).

Reed Warblers normally begin to arrive from around the third week in April, somewhat later than the Sedge Warbler, with the majority arriving in early May. The earliest arrivals were at East Tilbury on 22nd March 2002 and 26th March 2000, with the next almost two weeks later on 6th April at Seventy Acres Lake in 1989 (Howard Vaughan pers. obs.). Almost all spring records involve birds back at breeding sites; there have been very few records of apparent migrants at this time.

Unlike Sedge Warblers, Reed Warblers undertake their journey south in a series of short 'hops'. It is therefore not until mid-July that

	Jan	Feb	Mar	Apr	May	Jun	Jul	Aug	Sep	Oct	Nov	Dec
Essex				3	21	25	41	32	14	1		
South England				1	16	11	46	76	26	2	1	1
Belgium						1		1	1	2		
The Netherlands				1								
France				1	3	2		2		3		1
Spain					2				6	1		
Portugal								2	7	3	3	
Morocco				1	3	1			2			
Mauretania												1
Senegal			1									
Gambia	1											
At sea, west of Angola										1		
Totals	*1*	*0*	*1*	*7*	*45*	*40*	*87*	*113*	*56*	*13*	*4*	*3*

Month and location of recovery of Reed Warblers ringed in Essex

the species begins to leave its breeding grounds with adults preceding juveniles. Peak movement along the southern coast of Britain is during the last ten days of August but passage, including Continental drift-migrants, continues into October (*BWP*). It is likely that September passage involves mainly juveniles: at Flag Creek, St Osyth, the proportion of adults dropped to well under 10% by early September (Simon Cox pers. obs.). Because there are large populations around the coast, it is very difficult distinguishing migrants from local birds and there have in fact been no obvious influxes that could clearly be attributed to migrants, although they undoubtedly occur.

There have been four November records, the latest being one at Old Hall on 26th in 1994 with other late singles at Layer GP on 13th in 1990, East Tilbury on 5th in 1987 and The Naze on 3rd in 1982.

Many thousands of Reed Warblers have been trapped and ringed in Essex, more than 14,500 of them at Pitsea since 1974. Over 350 have subsequently been controlled, nearly 40% in Essex and 50% in southern England. The remaining recoveries confirm the species' southerly migration route through France, Iberia and northern Africa and on to wintering grounds in western Africa. The most remarkable recovery was of an individual ringed at Pitsea on 12th August 2000 and found freshly dead on a ship at sea on 2nd October 2000, 2,000km west of Luanda, Angola, and 2,000km south of Abidjan, Ivory Coast, some 2,000km west of its normal wintering area; presumably severe weather had displaced it. Another ringed at Pitsea on 29th August 1998 was found dead in the Pyrenees-Atlantique, France, on 21st February 1999: it is very unusual for Reed Warblers to winter north of the Sahara—was it an exceptionally early migrant? In addition, over 150 British-ringed Reed Warblers have been controlled in Essex, mostly from southern England with small numbers from northern England and one from Scotland, whilst foreign-ringed birds have been recovered originating from France (four) and Belgium (one). At Pitsea, retraps form around 10% of the annual catch (Brian Manton pers. obs.) and confirm a fairly strong degree of site fidelity. This included one ringed at Kergalan, Finisterre, France, on 25th August 1982 and retrapped at Pitsea on 4th June 1983 and 28th July 1984.

Reed-bed habitat is vulnerable to encroachment by Willow and Alder scrub as part of the natural succession without conservation management (Population Trends). Likewise, sensitive river management is necessary for maintaining Reed Warbler populations inland. Raven (1986) described how construction of a channel along part of the Roding allowed Reed Warblers to breed only three years after completion, much more quickly than the case after dredging. Most of the Essex population are in coastal borrow dykes just behind the seawall. In the short-term

	Pitsea	Flag Creek St Osyth	Holland Haven	Bradwell
Period	1974-2004	1976-93	1987-98	2002-04
Reed Warbler	16,424	3,084	586	216
Sedge Warbler	4,667	1,233	259	36

Data courtesy of Pitsea Ringing Group, Simon Cox, Chris Harris

Cumulative ringing totals of Reed and Sedge Warblers at selected localities from 1974-2004

these populations are secure but any rapid rises in sea level may increase the salinity in these watercourses and kill off the reed stands.

Great Reed Warbler   *Acrocephalus arundinaceus*

Vagrant: three records

This, the largest *Acrocephalus* warbler, breeds throughout much of Continental Europe and North Africa, east through Asia to the Pacific. The species inhabits reed beds with the tallest and strongest Common Reed and Lesser Bulrush. The nominate *arundinaceus* occurs throughout Europe as far as central Asia with *zarudnyi* further east. Western populations winter in tropical Africa.

1965	Hanningfield	6th June	
1984	Pitsea	28th July	Trapped and ringed
2004	Abberton	17th–30th May	Singing male

Although there were 219 British records to the end of 2004 (BBRC 2005), averaging 4-5 per annum, it has not increased in recent years, despite increased observer coverage. This may be due to declines in recent years in west, central and southern Europe, although eastern populations appear stable (European Atlas). Great Reed Warblers occur predominantly as spring overshoots, with a smaller peak in late August and early September as individuals disperse from their breeding grounds.

A record of two at North Fambridge from 28th–29th August 1959 has recently been reviewed and rejected on the grounds that the record was inadequately documented (BBRC 2000). Christy mentioned, but rejected, a record of one caught at Dagenham on 16th June 1853, on the grounds that the finder was a dealer, who was also responsible for the rejected Savi's Warbler record from about this time.

Icterine Warbler   *Hippolais icterina*

Very rare passage migrant: 25 records

The monotypic Icterine Warbler breeds across mid, southern and parts of northern Europe from northern Norway to southern France, east to Russia and Kazakhstan, where it occurs in lightly forested areas, forest margins and a variety of wet habitats. The species winters in southeast and south-central Africa and follows a generally easterly migration route in autumn but in spring returns more to the west (European Atlas).

1962	Bradwell	3rd September	
1963	The Naze	30th August	
1968	Brightlingsea	15th July	Trapped and ringed
1973	Hanningfield	23rd September	
1974	Holliwell Point	1st September	
1975	The Naze	27th August	
1976	Bradwell	21st September	Trapped and ringed
1977	Pitsea	14th August	
	Leigh/Two Tree Island	22nd August	
	Foulness	24th September	
1979	Benfleet Downs	4th June	
1980	Colne Point	23rd September	Trapped and ringed
	Holland Haven	21st–22nd October	
1982	Leigh/Two Tree Island	8th–9th September	
1984	The Naze	14th October	
1985	Holland Haven	31st August	
1986	Holland Haven	22nd September	
	Tillingham	25th September	

	The Naze	29th September
1989	Holliwell Point	17th September
1992	Coate Outfall, Dengie	20th August
	Bradwell	23rd August
	Sales Point, Dengie	11th September
1995	Colne Point	20th-21st August
2003	The Naze	14th September

Additionally, one was on the Kentish Knock Lightship on 22nd September 1903. Numbers reported in Essex are but a fraction of those reported in Suffolk and Kent, and the absence of one that has stayed longer than two days is remarkable. Despite being extremely common on the near-Continent it is only a scarce migrant in Britain, with the greatest numbers occurring in autumn. The 1990s saw an average of 138 recorded annually (Fraser & Rogers 2004). Nationally, there has been an increase in records recently (except for 2000 and 2001, which were the worst years on record), particularly in spring; this is probably due to a combination of greater observer coverage, coupled with increasing populations in Sweden and possibly in the Netherlands and Finland. However, numbers vary considerably from year to year, perhaps on account of weather conditions. Nonetheless, the marked decrease in the number of Essex records since 1990 is difficult to explain.

Nationally, 1992 was one of the best years on record with 277 recorded, although more than 180 of them were in spring, one of very few years in which numbers in spring have exceeded those in autumn (Fraser & Rogers 2002). The species occurs in Britain from mid-May to early June and again from August to mid-October. Essex records peak in late August/early September and then again in late September. Although the sample is small, there appears to be a double peak of occurrence that could be the result of either the arrival of adults and juveniles birds at different times or individuals from different populations.

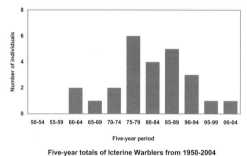

Five-year period

Five-year totals of Icterine Warblers from 1950-2004

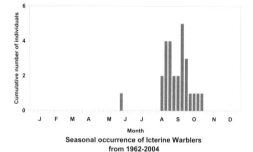

Month

Seasonal occurrence of Icterine Warblers from 1962-2004

Melodious Warbler   *Hippolais polyglotta*

Very rare passage migrant: nine records

The monotypic Melodious Warbler breeds throughout western and southern Europe and the Mediterranean edge of northwest Africa where it occurs in scrub and woodland margin as well as large gardens and orchards in suburban and rural areas. The species winters in the savannah belt north of the rainforests in west Africa.

1961	Nazeing	12th–13th August	
1964	Navestock	10th August	Female, ringed
1971	East Mersea	15th September	
1973	Romford	20th September	
1980	Benfleet Downs	24th September	
1981	West Thurrock	26th May	Trapped and ringed
1996	The Naze	19th May	
2001	The Naze	28th July	Trapped and ringed
2004	Fairlop CP	1st–2nd October	

Given that until relatively recently field separation of *Hippolais* warblers was considered exceptionally difficult because of uncertainties about identification criteria, all the pre-1980 records, except for the female trapped at Navestock, must be considered with some caution.

With a generally western distribution in Europe, it is not surprising that Essex records are so few, with the majority nationally occurring on the south coast and especially in the southwest. Despite spreading northwest as far as the Netherlands, Belgium and Germany in recent years, it has shown no signs of becoming more regular either nationally or in Essex. In fact, quite the opposite has occurred. In Essex there have been just three records in the last 21 years, compared with six in the previous 21, whilst nationally an average of 39 were recorded annually in the 1980s but only 27 in the 2000s (Fraser & Rogers 2004). Unlike Icterine Warbler, this species is generally uncommon nationally in spring, so the two May records are notable. Autumn records, which invariably involve first-winter birds dispersing northwards from their breeding grounds far outnumber those in spring (Cottridge & Vinicombe 1996).

Icterine/Melodious Warbler — *Hippolais icterina/H. polyglotta*

Ten records

1951	Colne Point	6th May
1956	Kirby Cross	3rd August
1958	Bradwell	14th September
1960	Bradwell	9th September
1969	North Fambridge	13th September
1976	The Naze	25th–26th September
	Bradwell	25th September
1977	The Naze	23rd August
1981	Bradwell	6th October
1984	Colne Point	19th August

In almost all cases, the observers considered that Icterine Warblers were involved.

Blackcap — *Sylvia atricapilla*

Common summer visitor and passage migrant. A few winter

The Blackcap is a highly arboreal species that has a mainly European distribution, although the species is found as far east as western Siberia and also in northwest Africa and the Atlantic islands. It breeds mainly in the temperate zones where it shows a preference for mostly mature but especially humid deciduous mixed woodland and riparian forests (European Atlas). European populations in general have been fairly stable but increases have occurred in Denmark, Scandinavia, the former Czechoslovakia and Britain and Ireland, where populations have doubled since 1945 (Population Trends), partly attributable to an increase in underbush due to human activity. Of the five recognised subspecies (Shirihai *et al.* 2001), the nominate race *atricapilla* occurs throughout Europe and southwest Siberia, south to the Balkans, Levant, Turkey, Greece, northern Italy and Pyrenees with *pauluccii* occurring in the central Mediterranean and *heineken* in Iberia, Madeira/Canaries, Morocco/Algeria. Northern and eastern populations are wholly migratory, generally wintering to the south of the breeding range as far as sub-Saharan Africa.

Christy described the Blackcap as "A fairly common summer migrant", whilst Glegg considered the species to be a "Common summer resident ... on the whole somewhat more common than the Garden Warbler, although the relative numbers of the species vary locally". Both Hudson & Pyman and Cox gave similar descriptions of its status, although the latter in particular noted the species' increasing occurrence during winter.

The *EBR*s made little mention of breeding records until the 1980s. Countywide, the various Atlas surveys confirmed that the Blackcap was the third most common warbler after Whitethroat (95%) and Willow Warbler (89.5%). There was little obvious change in distribution

Atlas	Survey Area	% of 10km squares or tetrads in which bred/probably bred	possibly bred or present
First National 10km	Essex	89.5	5.3
Second National 10km	Essex	89.5	8.8
First London Tetrad	Met. Essex	43.0	8.5
Second London Tetrad	Met. Essex	81.5	11.0
Essex Tetrad	Essex	61.5	23.0

Summary of results of Atlas surveys for Blackcaps

between the two National Atlas surveys, although in Metropolitan Essex there was an increase throughout the area between the two London surveys, even allowing for greater observer coverage. Breeding pairs can be found in relatively small urban parks and gardens provided there is sufficient cover; conifers, however, appear to be avoided. The Essex Atlas survey located Blackcaps in 84.5% of all tetrads and in 98.2% of 10km squares and absent only from the square that included the southern Dengie and eastern Foulness where suitable habitat is almost non-existent. The Blackcap's distribution was also sparse in the more industrialised areas along the Thames and in coastal areas.

Since at least the 1950s there has been a consistent country-wide population increase, making the Blackcap the most successful of our warblers in recent decades. Only the newly colonising Cetti's Warbler has shown comparable growth (Population Trends), with the CBC/BBS (England) Index for Blackcap for the period 1977–2002 increasing by 119% and the BBS (England) Index increasing by 22% from 1994–2003. The CBC Local Index for Essex and surrounding counties has increased markedly since 1981, although the local BBS Index suggests a slower rate of increase in recent years.

Fewer Blackcaps migrate across the Sahara than do other British breeding warblers, which may explain why the species has been largely unaffected by the Sahel droughts. The reasons for the marked population increase remain unclear. Continuing range expansion into some suburban areas has occurred since the Essex Atlas, particularly in the southwest, and it is now possible that, with the current serious decline in Willow Warbler numbers, the Blackcap may have become the second most widespread warbler in Essex.

Cox detailed average breeding densities on woodland CBC plots in Essex of 31 pairs per km^2 and on farmland, three pairs per km^2. Since 1980, average breeding densities in woodland have been 55 pairs per km^2 (range 28-83) and on farmland, nine pairs per km^2, which although based on a small sample, suggests that not only has the breeding range expanded but population densities have increased as well.

With the presence of over-wintering individuals now commonplace, first arrivals are impossible to pinpoint. Hudson & Pyman noted that most arrived in April/May, whilst Cox considered late April as the peak arrival date. Analysis of double-figure counts of assumed migrants, of which there are very few, do not indicate a clear spring peak. Apart from an exceptional count of 50 at Abberton on 5th April 2002, the highest counts of assumed migrants have been: 20 at The Naze, 24th April 2002; 15 at Bradwell, 29th March 1998; and 12 at Bradwell, 11th May 1975.

Nationally, the main autumn passage of British individuals starts in late August, although local dispersal may occur before then; British birds head southeast within the country and then head south or southwest (BWP). In Essex, numbers peak in late September with small numbers of migrants regularly recorded to the end of October and often arriving at the same time as influxes of thrushes and drift migrants; many Blackcaps occurring during October are likely to be of Continental origin (Langlow 1976).

Surprisingly, there has been just one three-figure count of presumed migrants: 100+ at Pitsea on 10th September 1988 (with 80 on 17th), of which 46 were ringed. Indeed, it is only at Pitsea and The Naze that counts of 50+ have been made with the other highest counts being: Pitsea, 70 on 19th September 1982, 65 trapped on 12th September 1992 and 60 on 20th September 1986; The Naze, 60, 26th September 1999.

Passage is certainly not restricted to the coast. An estimated 300 passed through the Roding Valley in combined influxes of 2nd–3rd and 23rd–24th August 1980 and in a garden at Stock 3,116 were ringed between 1962

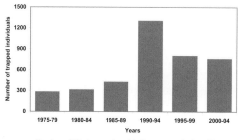

Number of Blackcaps ringed in five-year periods at Pitsea
from 1975-2004 (Data courtesy B. Manton)

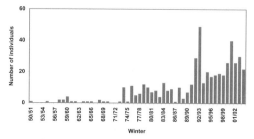

Annual winter totals (December-February) of Blackcaps
from 1950/51-2003/04

and 1988 (Hurrell 1989), whilst up to 45, on 10th September 1993 and 18th September 1998 at Abberton, and 30–35 in August and September 2002 at Newport are all more than comparable with peak counts from the coast and only hint at the numbers that pass through the interior of the county largely unnoticed.

Wintering in Essex is a relatively recent phenomenon. Experimental studies have shown that the Blackcap is characterised by definite genetic control of annual processes such as migration, breeding and moult. These processes are subject to considerable genetic variation and some, such as migration, may be subject to quite

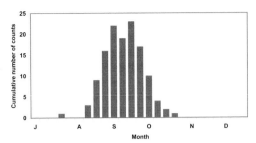

Seasonal occurrence of counts of 10+ assumed migrant Blackcaps during autumn from 1971-2004

rapid adaptation should environmental changes occur (Berthold 1994). This may explain the notable change in status of the species as a winter visitor as, since 1965, a central European sub-population has developed a new migratory direction to the west-northwest to novel wintering areas in Britain and Ireland (Berthold *et al.* 1992). Simms (1985) noted that high winter numbers tended to follow heavy autumn passage movements, which correlated with change in the migration pattern of Continental birds.

Whilst most of our wintering birds may be central European in origin (Migration Atlas), Dennis (1992b) considered it likely that some British-bred birds wintered on a regular basis in Essex; this may well explain the presence of birds singing on territory as early as late February. However, to date there have been no national winter ringing recoveries of British-bred individuals.

Historically, Glegg considered notable records during November; the species was considered annual in that month at Lexden. Hudson & Pyman and Cox noted 14 winter reports between 1956 and 1969. However, between 1970 and 1978 there were 28 including 12 in the severe winter of 1978/79, many of which visited garden bird-tables (Leach 1981). The subsequent increase has been dramatic. Dennis (1992b) noted that many of the records involved pairs suggesting that this indicated some territorial bonding during winter, although in general more males than females are noted (nationally, the ratio is 60:40). Many of the records have come from well-vegetated gardens, particularly those with well-stocked bird-tables or berry-bearing bushes. Whether the species is actually more common in gardens than elsewhere is unclear as observer coverage in such habitat is probably far greater than in any other habitat in winter. However, the great variety of food available in gardens must prove attractive to the species as it probably ensures a greater survival rate.

	Jan	Feb	Mar	Apr	May	Jun	Jul	Aug	Sep	Oct	Nov	Dec
Essex		1		1	9	3	2	5	3	1		
South England		1		3	10	4	12	4	10	1		
Germany										1		
The Netherlands									1			
Belgium						1			3			
France				1					1			1
Spain		1	1							1		
Portugal	1						1				1	
Morocco	1	2	2	2						2	1	1
Algeria	1	1	3								1	1
Totals	*4*	*6*	*6*	*7*	*20*	*8*	*14*	*9*	*18*	*6*	*3*	*3*

Month and location of recovery of Blackcaps ringed in Essex

Many of the earlier wintering records came from the south and southwest of Essex, although during the 1990s, with the marked upturn in records, reports have come from many parts of the county.

Recoveries of Essex-ringed Blackcaps illustrate the species' movement through France and Iberia to wintering areas in southern Spain and northwest Africa, although the increased incidence in late autumn and early spring of recoveries suggests that they may still have been on migration to/from areas south of the Sahara when controlled in Morocco and Algeria. In addition, foreign-ringed birds from Austria, the Netherlands, Belgium (two) and Portugal have been recovered in Essex. The Austrian record of one ringed at Salzburg on 26th September 1971 and controlled at Pitsea on 10th October 1971 perhaps involved an individual that subsequently wintered somewhere in Britain.

The Blackcap is clearly prospering in today's environment and, apart from possible negative factors affecting the species in its winter quarters, the Blackcap's future in Essex appears secure. The increasing trend towards more of our breeding population wintering north of the Sahara should lead to increased winter survival, and thus still higher populations (Second National Atlas), although possibly at the expense of the Garden Warbler (q.v.).

Sponsored by Martin Henry

Garden Warbler

Sylvia borin

A fairly common summer resident and passage migrant

The Garden Warbler breeds throughout much of Europe, being absent principally from much of Portugal and southern Spain, Italy and much of Greece. It has a Palearctic distribution, which spreads as far east as western Siberia (European Atlas). In western Europe the species is represented by the nominate race *borin* with *woodwardi* occurring to the east (Shirihai *et al.* 2001). Its typical habitat is deciduous woodland and scrub, where it prefers a fairly open canopy combined with fairly dense ground cover for nesting (European Atlas). The species is common throughout much of England, Wales and southern Scotland, although it is most abundant in Wales and southern England south of a line between the Mersey and Humber rivers. The Garden Warbler winters in west and east Africa, south to South Africa.

All of the early writers described the Garden Warbler as either common or fairly common. Christy considered it to breed throughout Essex, albeit sparingly, with Glegg adding that it was somewhat less numerous than the Blackcap. Unfortunately, the Garden Warbler was not mentioned in the Systematic List of the *EBR* until 1979

Atlas	Survey Area	% of 10km squares or tetrads in which	
		bred/probably bred	possibly bred or present
First National 10km	Essex	84.2	8.8
Second National 10km	Essex	84.2	8.8
First London Tetrad	Met. Essex	27.5	3.5
Second London Tetrad	Met. Essex	47.0	14.0
Essex Tetrad	Essex	35.0	13.9

Summary of results of Atlas surveys for Garden Warblers

so longer-term trends are difficult to assess. Cox, however, believed that a decline had taken place over the previous 20–30 years. Garden Warblers, like Whitethroats, seemed to have been affected by the Sahel droughts with sharp declines noted in the mid-1970s, the low point being reached around 1975–76. However, the Garden Warbler recovered more quickly than the Whitethroat, possibly because the species wintered further south than the Sahel region, so their problem was crossing the drought region rather than surviving within it (Population Trends).

Little change was evident between the two National Atlases but the London Atlas surveys suggested a range expansion in Metropolitan Essex, although to what extent this was influenced by improved coverage is unclear. The Essex Atlas survey located the Garden Warbler in 48.9% of tetrads compared with 84.5% for Blackcap. Across Essex its distribution is far patchier than that of the Blackcap with notable gaps in the northwest and in the southeast where suitable nesting habitat is probably limited. The Garden Warbler has one advantage over the Blackcap in that it nests in young conifer plantations as well as in typical Blackcap nesting habitats such as open deciduous woodland with secondary growth, patches of tall shrubs, scrubby areas and hedgerows. Hudson & Pyman noted that Garden Warblers will sometimes, like Blackcaps, breed in town parks and large gardens but on the whole its English name is inappropriate as it is a woodland, not a garden, bird and is somewhat intolerant of disturbance. The local CBC Index showed a general increase from 1980, including an exceptional year in 1998, although more recent BBS data have detected a decline. The national CBC/BBS (England) Index for 1977–2002 showed a 22% increase, although BBS (England) indices for the period 1994–2003 suggested a 21% decline.

Cox detailed breeding densities averaging 13 pairs per km² in woodland and two pairs per km² in farmland. Since 1980, breeding densities have averaged eight pairs per km² in woodland (range 5.2–12.3) and four pairs per km² on farmland (range 0.2-9.3). The former figure, however, does not include an exceptional density of 95 pairs per km² from Marks Hall, Coggeshall, where the combination of conifers and deciduous woodland clearly provides optimal breeding habitat with up to 13 breeding pairs recorded in 10.2 hectares.

The first Garden Warblers begin to arrive

Seasonal occurrence of Garden Warblers at coastal sites from 1971-2004

around the second or third week of April, with numbers peaking in mid-May, coinciding with arrivals in the rest of the country (BWP). Along the coast, only small numbers are normally noted in spring. Counts of ten at Bradwell/ Dengie on 11th May 1975, six along Benfleet Downs on 11th May 1980 and five at The Naze on 15th May 1995 are exceptional with all other counts being of 1–2. The earliest record involved one at The Naze on 3rd April 1983, whilst there was one at Mountnessing on 6th April 1975.

Return migration through Essex normally begins in late July, although there was one at Bradwell on 6th July and two on 13th July 1987. Migration peaks during mid-September, although numbers are never large, there being

472

just six double-figure counts since 1979, the largest being 20 at The Naze on 16th and 17th September 1982 and 15 at Nazeing GP on 14th August 1996. In addition, there were ten at: The Naze, 16th September 1989 and 6th September 1998; Bradwell, 7th September 1982; Wakering Stairs, 10th September 1995. Numbers in 1982 were the largest yet reported with around 40 recorded (the record of at least 15 at Willingale in the third week of October 1982 is now considered unsatisfactory). Essex has missed out on the large arrivals that other counties have experienced during easterly drift conditions, although odd birds usually arrive along the coast with other Scandinavian migrants during periods of easterly winds, suggesting that the origin of a proportion of migrants lies in Scandinavia. The count from Nazeing GP mentioned above suggests that small numbers pass through inland Essex at this time: more recently there were seven at Newport on 20th August and five on 10th September 2002.

Most Garden Warblers have departed by the middle of October, although occasional stragglers are reported to the end of the month. There have been three November records: Dagenham Chase, 2nd in 1998; The Naze, 11th in 1967; Hanningfield, 24th November–1st December in 1982.

Most Garden Warblers head south to southwest in autumn and pass through France and Iberia. Of the 16 recoveries of Essex-ringed individuals, five have occurred abroad with single recoveries from Germany (May), Belgium (May), France (August), Morocco (April) and Switzerland (August). The Swiss recovery involved a locally bred individual that was ringed at Stanford Rivers on 5th July 1979 and found dead at Leistal, Baselland, on 15th August 1979, and which was the first example from the BTO ringing scheme (Cox); it indicates that not all Garden Warblers head south or southwest. One ringed at Nevendon in August 1964 was at least six years old when found dead at Portsmouth, Hampshire, in May 1970.

Although it would appear that there is sufficient suitable habitat for the Garden Warbler in Essex, there are factors operating outside the county that have caused historic declines, and these will continue to be a primary influence in the future. The continuing success of the Blackcap may pose a threat to the Garden Warbler: Blackcaps arrive much earlier in spring and establish territories that are not then colonised by Garden Warblers (Second National Atlas).

Barred Warbler   *Sylvia nisoria*

Scarce passage migrant: 54 records

The Barred Warbler breeds across much of central and eastern Europe and western Siberia from northern Italy and Germany eastward across the Urals to Mongolia. Birds move southeast out of Europe to winter in a relatively small area of east Africa (*BWP*). The nominate race *nisoria* occurs in the west of the species' range with *merzbacheri* occurring in the central Palearctic. The species is a regular autumn passage migrant to the east coast of Britain that averaged 158 records annually during the 1990s (Fraser & Rogers 2004) but is exceptionally rare in spring.

This large, chunky warbler was first recorded in Essex as recently as 1961, when a juvenile was at The Naze on 10th September. Since then, it has been recorded in 28 years, with the most in one year being five in 1996.

Barred Warblers have been recorded with increasing frequency in Britain over the last 20 years, probably due to increased observer coverage, although there has been a slight westerly shift in its breeding range.

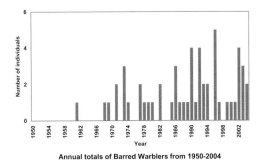

Annual totals of Barred Warblers from 1950-2004

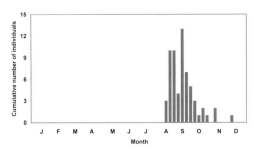

Seasonal occurrence of Barred Warblers from 1950-2004

All the Essex records bar one have fallen in the period 18th August–9th November with most occurring from late August–mid September. Quite why it is so regular in autumn is difficult to explain, although it is quite possible that it is a simple case of pre-migratory dispersal rather than reverse migration as it is only inexperienced first-winter birds that occur. The lack of spring records may be explained by the fact that Barred Warblers' northward-bound migration from east Africa is on a north–south bearing; hence any overshooting birds are unlikely to be on a route that takes them to our shores (cf. Collared Flycatcher).

The only record outside the main migration period was one at South Woodham Ferrers from 4th–6th December 1992, which was at the time only the second British record from that month. It was obviously sick and was eventually killed by a Cat.

Nearly 60% of the records have come from the extreme northeast, with the county's most favoured site being The Naze with 23 records (43%), whilst there have been seven (13%) at Holland Haven. The only other sites that have recorded more than one individual are: Bradwell (five); Foulness (three); and Holliwell Point (two). Records of singles have come from a further 11 sites around the coast including singles at East Tilbury from 6th–9th November 1994 and Barking Bay on 11th–13th September 1996. There have been three inland records of singles: trapped and ringed at Abberton, 22nd August 1971; Buckhurst Hill, 31st August 1986; and Sewardstone Marsh, 1st October 2003.

Lesser Whitethroat *Sylvia curruca*

Common summer resident and passage migrant

The Lesser Whitethroat has a vast and almost continuous range from Britain in the west to the Yakutsk region of eastern Siberia, east Mongolia and the Tian Shan in China in the east. In Europe the species is absent from the Iberian peninsula and the southwestern half of France and also Italy. The Lesser Whitethroat complex presents the most difficult taxonomic problems within the *Sylvia* genus with Shirihai *et al.* (2001) suggesting that the five races form a superspecies consisting of four allospecies: *curruca* occurs across the Western Palearctic, parts of the Middle East and much of Siberia; *halimodendri* from the lower Volga east to western Mongolia; *minula* from the southwest Caspian region east to western China; and two other races occur in central Asia. The last two named races have occurred as late autumn migrants in Britain (e.g. Money 2000). Lesser Whitethroats are generally found in scrubby areas, parkland and farmland with mature trees and in Britain occur principally in south and eastern England and parts of eastern Scotland (Second National Atlas). The species has a southeasterly autumn migration route that takes it through the eastern Mediterranean and then on into northeastern Africa, principally to Ethiopia and Sudan (European Atlas) for winter; the same route is used in reverse in spring.

The status of the species appears to have altered very little over the last 150 years or so, although periodic fluctuations seem to occur. Christy described the Lesser Whitethroat as "A fairly common summer visitor … though it is at all times less abundant than the Common Whitethroat", although at Epping in 1831 Doubleday considered that it was, "… equally common with the larger one and much more destructive to fruit in gardens". Glegg described the species similarly but felt that it was "… considerably less numerous than the Whitethroat". A pair of Lesser Whitethroats was observed assisting a Dunnock to rear a Cuckoo at Felsted in July 1913.

Long-term trends since 1950 are difficult to assess, although there appears to have been an ongoing decline since the late 1970s with ringing sites at both Stock and Pitsea recording much reduced numbers after 1977, which appears to have been an exceptional year for the species. The variability of numbers may be due to the natural variations in the scale of spring arrivals at the edge of the species' breeding range (Population Trends). Lesser Whitethroats, unlike most other migrants, migrate southeast in autumn to their winter quarters and are therefore not influenced by the droughts in the Sahel, although northeast Africa has also experienced substantial rainfall deficits since the mid-1970s. Apparent recent declines appear to be linked to a reduction in productivity.

Being so common, little attention was given to the species in *EBR*s until the 1980s, although 1955 was considered an "… exceptional year for this species" and in 1962 the species was considered to be increasing in parts of Essex. Both Hudson & Pyman and Cox described the Lesser Whitethroat in a similar vein to earlier writers. However, Cox observed that the national CBC Index had declined to just

Atlas	Survey Area	% of 10km squares or tetrads in which	
		bred/probably bred	possibly bred or present
First National 10km	Essex	91.2	7.0
Second National 10km	Essex	86.0	14.0
First London Tetrad	Met. Essex	21.0	7.5
Second London Tetrad	Met. Essex	68.0	14.0
Essex Tetrad	Essex	44.6	8.4

Summary of results of Atlas surveys for Lesser Whitethroat

50% of the 1966 figure, but that long-term trends were difficult to assess as, despite apparent significant habitat loss in Essex over the previous 30 years, ringing data had suggested a recent increase.

There was only a marginal change in range between the two National Atlas surveys, but in Metropolitan Essex there was

Location	Habitat	Period	Lesser Whitethroat	Whitethroat	Ratio LW:W
Romford	Dairy-farm/Sewage-farm	1954-66	733	11	66.64:1
Layer Breton	Scrub adjacent Abberton	1951-60	1073	303	3.54:1
		1961-70	669	836	0.80:1
		1971-80	92	564	0.16:1
Stock	Large garden	1963-70	450	168	2.68:1
		1971-80	179	417	0.43:1
		1981-88	175	132	1.33:1
Ongar/Epping	Mixed woodland/Sewage-farm	1971-80	600	438	1.37:1
Pitsea/Basildon	Mainly scrubland	1976-80	725	791	0.92:1
		1981-90	358	354	1.01:1
		1991-00	456	809	0.56:1
Bradwell	Coastal Observatory	2002-04	48	186	0.26:1

Cumulative ringing totals of Lesser Whitethroats and Whitethroats at various sites from 1951-2000
data courtesy of Cox, Hurrell (1989) and Chris Harris

an apparently marked range expansion between the two London Atlases. Cox had previously described the Lesser Whitethroat as the "… least widespread of the *Sylvia* warblers in Metropolitan Essex" with breeding confirmed in just 21% of tetrads during the First London Atlas survey but by the time of the Second London Atlas, the number had more than trebled to 68%, making the species more widespread than the Garden Warbler. Although greater observer coverage must have accounted for some of the increase, it appears that the Lesser Whitethroat expanded its range in south and southwest Essex during the 1970s and 1980s. The Essex Atlas survey recorded the Lesser Whitethroat in 53% of tetrads, with the northeast and southwest being particularly favoured and the fewest in the extensively farmed areas of the southeast and parts of the north. Essex farmland CBC sites have shown an average density of 2.1 pairs per km^2 (range 1.2–4.0). Levels of abundance in west Essex are amongst the highest in the country (Second National Atlas).

Since the end of the Essex Atlas survey, there have been signs of continuing declines at regularly monitored sites since about 1995. The local CBC/BBS data have shown marked fluctuations since 1980, although overall the indices have changed little since the mid-1990s. The CBC/BBS (England) Index for the period 1977–2002 showed a 33% decline with a 39% decline in the BBS (England) Index between 1994–2003.

The first arrivals in spring usually occur around mid-April, with numbers peaking around mid-May. Glegg referred to a Lesser Whitethroat at an unnamed site on 1st April 1912; otherwise the earliest arrivals have been at Bradwell on 3rd April 1979, Sewardstone on 5th April 1988 and Hornchurch CP on 5th April 2001. The largest numbers are normally recorded from the main coastal watchpoints, although double-figure counts are less than annual, with the highest being: 20 at Pitsea, 3rd and 17th May 1986; 16 at The Naze, 9th May 1998; and 14 at East Tilbury, 3rd May 1992.

Autumn passage commences during late July and peaks around late August/early September, with the major-ity having departed by the end of September. Lesser Whitethroats become surprisingly skulking when on migration but, nonetheless, double-figure counts are recorded regularly from many coastal watchpoints, although typically numbers vary considerably from year to year. A recent increase in double-figure counts may perhaps be attributed to greater observer coverage at The Naze where many of the highest counts now occur. There, the highest counts have been: 110, 12th August 2001; 100, 6th September 1998; 90, 29th August 1999; 82, 1st September 2002; and 80, 1st September 1996. Elsewhere, the only other count in excess of 50 was 60 on Foulness on 11th September 1976. At Bradwell, the highest day count was 25 on 29th August 1993. Passage during autumn 2002 was the heaviest on record. Some influxes have coincided with the arrival of Scandinavian drift migrants and suggest a Continental origin for some of the Lesser Whitethroats present in autumn.

Not surprisingly, given its southeasterly migration route, the species moves through inland Essex in quite substantial numbers. The largest passage was noted during August 1980 when separate falls on the nights of the 2nd–3rd and 23rd–24th in the Roding valley totalled

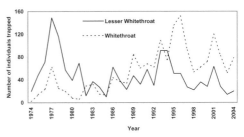

Annual totals of Lesser Whitethroats and Whitethroats ringed at Pitsea from 1974-2004 (Data courtesy B. Manton)

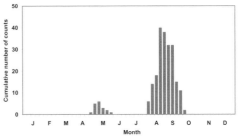

Seasonal occurrence of counts of 10+ Lesser Whitethroats from 1971-2004

some 200 birds (Cox), whilst at least 150 were estimated to be present on 30th at Hanningfield. Subsequent reports have involved lower numbers but double-figure counts are regularly noted from well-watched inland sites.

Small numbers of Lesser Whitethroats are recorded into October. Exceptionally, birds have been recorded in November and December. In November, singles have occurred at: The Naze, 10th in 1982; St. Osyth, 21st in 1981; Heybridge GP, 22nd in 1994; North Fambridge, 24th–10th December in 1954; The Naze, 26th in 2002; Dagenham Chase, 30th November–21st December in 1993. Another was at Dagenham Chase from 6th–9th December 1990. In 2004, there was one at Chafford Hundred from 4th December into 2005. The 1993 and 2004 records involved typical individuals of the nominate race *curruca*; the others were not racially identified.

Ringing recoveries of Lesser Whitethroats ringed in Essex confirm the species' migration route through the eastern Mediterranean. Northern Italy is thought to be a main stopping-over area for refuelling before they continue south (Migration Atlas). In addition, there are recoveries from Essex of birds ringed in Belgium and Germany. One ringed at Stock on 5th July 1969 was found dead at Ilminster, Somerset, in May 1970, on the western edge of the species' range in Britain.

	Jan	Feb	Mar	Apr	May	Jun	Jul	Aug	Sep	Oct	Nov	Dec
Essex				1	2	5	7	2	3			
North England					1							
South England					4	3	2	1	2			
Belgium				1					1	1		
Austria									1			
Italy								1	5			1
Greece										1		
Cyprus					2							
Egypt										1		
Totals	0	0	0	2	9	8	9	4	12	3	0	1

Month and location of recovery of Lesser Whitethroats ringed in Essex

Lesser Whitethroats are more likely to be influenced by climatic conditions in their winter quarters or along their migration routes than by any events on their breeding grounds (Population Trends). Undoubtedly the species has lost habitat over the last 30 years, particularly with the removal of many hedgerows, but their requirements are such that there should always be suitable areas within Essex; the increase in planting of hedgerows and community woodlands and creation of parklands will hopefully increase habitat availability.

Sponsored by Russell Neave

Asian Desert Warbler

Sylvia nana

Vagrant: one record

The monotypic Asian Desert Warbler breeds in steppe-desert areas of southeast Russia to northwest of the Caspian Sea then through Kazakhstan and into central Asia and winters in northeast Africa, the Arabian peninsula and northwest India.

1975	Frinton-on-Sea	20th–21st November

There have been just ten national records of this small *Sylvia* warbler, the last in 2000 (BBRC 2001); the Frinton bird was the third. Apart from two spring records, all have occurred between mid-October and early January and probably involved individuals that reverse migrated from their breeding areas.

This individual favoured an 180m stretch of seawall, where it moved about amongst vegetation and grasses growing between the concrete blocks (Harris 1976).

(Common) Whitethroat

Sylvia communis

Common summer resident and passage migrant

The Whitethroat has an extensive breeding range that stretches from Ireland in the west to central Siberia in the east and the Arctic Circle in Norway in the north to Morocco in the south. (European Atlas) Three of the four rather subtle subspecies breed in Europe, with *communis* the most widespread occurring in Britain and much of Europe, whilst *volgensis* occurs in eastern Europe and across to western Siberia and *icterops* in Turkey, then east to western Turkmenistan (Shirihai *et al.* 2001). It is generally a lowland species, breeding in open scrub and farmland, generally avoiding dense scrub, mature woodland and urban habitats. In Britain, it is widespread although absent from the highest ground and is most abundant in eastern England (Second National Atlas). Whitethroats from Britain winter principally across northern tropical Africa as far north as the southern edge of the Sahara desert.

Christy, who gave the species the local names 'Haychat' or 'Hayjack,' described the Whitethroat as "A very common summer visitor", whilst Glegg noted: "The Whitethroat is a very common summer resident. It is easily the commonest of the warblers, which visit Essex, being found … even … in exposed positions on the edge of saltings. The commonness of the species is due to the fact that it is a hedgerow bird and in a highly cultivated county like Essex, it finds suitable habitat in all directions". Hudson & Pyman considered that it was "Probably … still the most numerous and widely distributed of warblers in Essex, though recent grubbing out of hedgerows and loss of waste ground has brought about some reduction". However, and as noted by Cox, they could not have anticipated the widespread "non-arrival" of the species in the spring of 1969, not only nationally but across Europe as far as 15° E (Berthold 1973) which was attributed to the long drought in the Sahel region of Africa (Winstanley *et al.* 1974). In 1968, the species was recorded in 60% of all tetrads in Metropolitan Essex (First London Atlas) but this would have been considerably lower if surveyed a year later as some 77% of the previous year's breeding stock failed to reappear (First National Atlas). At Bishop's Stortford SF, there were three pairs in 1969, compared to 20–30 in previous years, whilst just four pairs were found in the whole of Danbury/Little Baddow and at Hainault Forest CP just 8–10 pairs compared with about 20 in 1968. In 1970, numbers were considered to be almost back to normal in some areas but with no improvement in others. Thus in the Writtle, Roxwell and Highwood area there were just 11 pairs in 1970 compared to 25 in 'normal' years and around North Weald numbers were only 30% of pre-1969 levels. Overall, the First National Atlas survey recorded the species in every 10km square, with breeding in most.

Atlas	Survey Area	% of 10km squares or tetrads in which	
		bred/probably bred	possibly bred or present
First National 10km	Essex	98.2	1.8
Second National 10km	Essex	96.5	3.5
First London Tetrad	Met. Essex	51.5	8.5
Second London Tetrad	Met. Essex	91.5	3.5
Essex Tetrad	Essex	88.8	5.5

Summary of results of Atlas surveys for Whitethroats

Cox considered that despite some recovery, numbers in the early 1980s were still well below those prior to 1969. A further crash occurred after the winter of 1983/84 with populations again much reduced following a further drought in the Sahel. Since then, however, helped by an improvement in rainfall in the wintering areas, numbers have in general continued to increase such that by 1999, the local CBC Index had doubled since 1980: the population is, however, still considered to be about half the level it was prior to 1969 (Population Trends). The CBC/BBS (England) Index for 1977–2002 suggested a 40% increase.

Despite another national decline in 1991, the Essex Atlas survey found the Whitethroat in 94.3% of tetrads, with breeding in most, still representing the most widespread of all warblers in Essex. The only gaps apparent in the species' distribution were in some built-up areas and in areas of intensive farming lacking suitable habitat such as in the northwest and parts of Dengie and Wallasea Island for instance. In Metropolitan Essex, the number of occupied tetrads increased between the two London Atlases particularly in the Thames-side area and, although this increase is undoubtedly in part due to increased observer coverage, it is possible that increased planting and environmen-tal improvements in these areas encouraged the species to expand into more suburban habitat as populations increased. The most recent BBS (England) Index has shown a 13% increase over the period 1994–2003.

Typical habitat in Essex is low-lying thickly vegetated areas such as river valleys, waste ground, thicker hedgerows, woodland edges, scrub, roadside verges and heathland. The latter habitat is now scarce in Essex but where it does occur, for example in the Roman River Valley, breeding densities can be high, although areas of pure Gorse and Heather are usually avoided (Goodey 1986). Cox noted that CBC sites from 1969 showed a mean density of five pairs per km²,

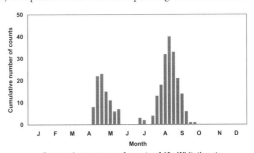

Seasonal occurrence of counts of 10+ Whitethroats
from 1971-2004

compared with 14 pairs per km² up to 1968 for farmland and woodland combined. A 1964 census at Chalkney Wood in 25.5ha of young conifers with mature, deciduous trees found 28 territories, an exceptional density. Since 1980, mean densities in woodland have been 9.2 pairs per km² (range 4.4–14.8) and on farmland 16.7 pairs per km² (range 9.7–31.0).

The Whitethroat arrives in spring around the second week of April, usually slightly earlier than the Lesser Whitethroat, with passage peaking around mid-May. There are two March records, singles on 29th at Ingatestone in 1959 and 31st at Leigh/Two Tree Island in 1963. Numbers of migrants reported from coastal locations in spring (and autumn) are in general not as great as Lesser Whitethroats; this may be due to the species' migration route which takes them southwest in autumn and northeast in spring. Double-figure counts in spring were irregular prior to the 1990s but have become annual presumably as populations have recovered and observer coverage has increased; passage in spring 2004 was particularly strong. Although many are reported from the usual coastal watch sites such as Bradwell or The Naze, where there were 86 on 23rd April 2000, it is along Thames-side that many of the largest counts have occurred with 102 at East Tilbury on 3rd May 1992, 69 at Creekmouth, Barking, on 21st May and 67 at Hole Haven on 9th May in both 1996 and 2004: a southwesterly bias to such reports confirms the species' arrival from a southwesterly direction.

Return migration becomes apparent again in late July but numbers reported generally do not match those of the Lesser Whitethroat. Numbers peak around the second half of August with few remaining beyond the end of September. On the coast, counts have increased over the past decade, probably due to a combination of greater observer coverage and increasing populations; at The Naze differentiating between migrants and local birds is becoming increasingly difficult earlier in the autumn. Cox stated that coastal falls had "... been on a small scale over the last decade, with no published record involving more than 20 ...", with a fall of 25 at Foulness on 14th September 1986 considered notable in that year's *EBR*. However, since then counts of up to 40 have become regular and there were 61 on Two Tree Island on 7th August 1998; also seven counts of 50+ at The Naze in August/September 2002 with a maximum of 70 on both 24th August and 10th September. There were also 50+ inland at Newport on 24th August of the latter year and 70 again at The Naze on 15th August 2004.

Unfortunately, there are no published records of pre-1969 migration counts with which to compare current data, although Glegg mentioned 30 killed at the Kentish Knock Lightship on the night of 14th–15th May 1909.

Inland passage has been noted in recent years with a cumulative total of 120 in the Roding Valley in August 1980, combining separate influxes on 2nd–3rd and 23rd–24th, the most to be reported to date. Interestingly, this was at a time of generally low population levels.

After the end of September, it is usual for a very few stragglers to remain in Essex but the species is rare beyond mid-October. There have been just three November records, the latest being one at Leigh/Two Tree Island on 10th in 1913, whilst there were singles at Hadleigh on 9th in 1954 and at The Naze on 9th in 2001. There have been three winter records, the first described by Christy: "I have ... a fresh specimen having been found by the gardener on a heap of coals in an outhouse ... at Great Baddow on or about Dec. 22nd, 1886, after a heavy snowstorm". The other records involved a male that was present at Bishop's Stortford SF from 21st January until the end of February 1975, during which time it was trapped and ringed, and one at Lakeside, Thurrock, on 6th December 2004.

	Jan	Feb	Mar	Apr	May	Jun	Jul	Aug	Sep	Oct	Nov	Dec
Essex					5	1	8	4	2			
South England			1	2	6	4	3	2	1			
France					1				1			
Spain	1						1		1			
Portugal									3	3	1	
Totals	*1*	*0*	*1*	*3*	*11*	*5*	*12*	*6*	*8*	*3*	*1*	*0*

Month and location of recovery of Whitethroats ringed in Essex

Recoveries of Essex-ringed birds confirm the species' southwesterly route to its wintering grounds. The concentration of records in Spain and Portugal suggests that many Whitethroats fly southwest to those areas direct and largely overfly much of France. One trapped at Epping on 3rd June 1968 had been ringed 19 days earlier on the Isle of May, Fife, Scotland, and provides a good illustration of how in this case an overshooting spring migrant may redirect itself back to typical breeding areas. No foreign-ringed Whitethroats have been recovered in Essex.

Large-scale losses of hedgerows, scrub and similar habitats have undoubtedly affected Whitethroat numbers in Essex and it is to be hoped that the increase in the planting of hedgerows and woodlands and the move towards more environmentally friendly farming will assure the species' future. However, past experience has shown that it is major climatic events outside the county that ultimately influence Whitethroat numbers.

Dartford Warbler   *Sylvia undata*

Scarce but increasing passage migrant and winter visitor: around 40 individuals, 31 since 1989. Bred in 1948

Amber List

The Dartford Warbler breeds from northwest Africa northwards to southern England and west from Portugal to southern Italy. Most are resident in their breeding grounds, although the species is partially migratory and some individuals reach north Africa. The nominate race *undata* occurs throughout much of the species' range with *dartfordiensis* in Britain and northwest France and *toni* in northwest Africa. The English population increased markedly during the 1990s and totalled well over 2,000 pairs in 2002 (RBBP 2004). It is almost entirely confined

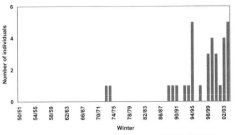

Annual totals of Dartford Warblers from 1950/51-2003/04

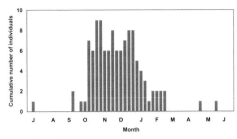

Seasonal occurrence of Dartford Warblers from 1837-2004

to the southern heathlands of Devon, Hampshire, Dorset and Surrey, although a small but expanding population now exists on the Suffolk coast (Piotrowski 2003). Being on the extreme northwest edge of the species' range, populations in England are severely affected by cold winters.

The first documented Essex record involved one shot at South Shoebury on 7th November 1837; the specimen remains in Southend-on-Sea Museum (Accession No. N81.261). Whilst Christy considered that "… a careful search of our furze-covered commons might reveal the bird …", there were just three more 19th century records, the last in 1880. The first 20th century occurrence involved a pair with one newly fledged young at Frinton-on-Sea on 13th July 1948; it was assumed breeding took place locally and it remains the only instance of breeding in Essex (Burton 1949). However, records from Colne Point in 1994 of a singing male in spring followed by two different birds in autumn are perhaps suggestive of breeding nearby, although there was no evidence to confirm this.

There were just two more records prior to 1989 since when the species has increased markedly, coincident with the expansion of the species' breeding range in England. This expansion has no doubt been assisted by the recent run of very mild winters. The majority of Essex records relate to migrant/wintering individuals but there have been two singing males: at Walthamstow, 12th–28th February 1989 and Colne Point, 3rd May 1994. There was a female at Colne Point on 23rd May 1993. In addition to records already mentioned, the only one involving more than a singleton was two at Colne Point during October and November 2000. Since 1989, all but six records have come from the coast, the exceptions being: Epping, trapped and ringed, 23rd September 1973; Walthamstow, 12th–28th May 1993; Fairlop CP, 20th October 1994; Walthamstow Marsh, 12th December 1996–5th January 1997; Dagenham Chase, juvenile, 4th October–5th November 1999; and Pages Wood, Upminster, 21st October–3rd November 2002.

Numbers peak in autumn and early winter but decline sharply after mid-January; are they already returning to breeding/natal areas?

The marked increase in numbers seen in recent years perhaps holds out hope of the species becoming established in Essex in small numbers, although there have been no singing males for nearly a decade. With so little Gorse heathland left in Essex, perhaps it will utilise its apparently preferred habitat in the county, Shrubby Sea Blite?

Subalpine Warbler   *Sylvia cantillans*

Very rare passage migrant: 11 records

The Subalpine Warbler breeds throughout the Mediterranean from Morocco and Iberia in the west to western Turkey and northwest Libya in the east where it inhabits dry, warm and mostly evergreen Mediterranean shrubland. Four subspecies are recognised (Shirihai *et al.* 2001): the nominate race *cantillans* occurs mainly in coastal and Continental Europe; *moltoni* is found on the western Mediterranean islands; *albistriata* is in southeast Europe; and *inornata* occurs in northwest Africa. The majority winter in the Sahel region of tropical Africa.

1971	Billericay	27th April	Male, dead by road
	Fingringhoe Wick	11th July	Male
1989	Lawford	17th April	Male, dead by road
	Holland-on-Sea	18th April	Male
1993	The Naze	14th August–2nd September	Male
1994	Walthamstow Marshes	15th May	Male

1995	Priory Park,		
	Southend-on-Sea	29th September	Male
1999	Colne Point	16th May	Male
2001	Fingringhoe Wick	12th–13th May	Male
2004	Abberton	6th May	Singing male

Up to the end of 2004, there were 525 British records, about 420 of which have been since 1980 (BBRC 2005). Although populations appear stable, the increase may not entirely be due to increased observer coverage but may indicate as yet undetected population increases (Shirihai *et al.* 2001). Nationally, the majority occur between mid-April and June, with a smaller peak in autumn, from mid-August to early November. Most spring records probably involve overshooting nominate race individuals. However, it is possible that late spring records may involve the more contrastingly marked eastern race *albistriata* as birds with characteristics of this race have been noted in Britain with some regularity, whilst *moltoni* has reached Britain and the Netherlands at least once.

The fact that all county records have involved males perhaps suggests that females are being overlooked.

Sponsored in memory of Tariq Watson

Greenish Warbler   *Phylloscopus trochiloides*

Vagrant: two records

The Greenish Warbler breeds from the Baltic east to western Siberia, the Himalayas and central Asia. It inhabits many forest types, but in northeast Europe prefers old, spruce-dominated forests. The taxonomy of the group is complex with six subspecies generally recognised, three of which have occurred in Britain: *viridanus*, which breeds in northeast Europe east to the Yenisey and southeast to Kashmir; *plumbeitarsus* (Two-barred Greenish), which occurs in eastern Asia; and *nitidus* (Green Warbler) from Turkey across to Afghanistan. The northeast European race winters in India and southeast Asia.

1983	Bradwell	1st–2nd June	Singing male
2004	The Naze	12th September	1st-winter

There had been 409 British records of *viridanus* to the end of 2004 (BBRC 2005), all but 12 having occurred since 1958; three were *plumbeitarsus* with just one *nitidus* bird. The increase in records of *viridanus* is probably linked to the slow westward spread of the European breeding range since at least the mid-19th century. The southwest European breeding range limit fluctuates, suggesting that the westward expansion may be driven by climatic trends (European Atlas).

Whilst typically an autumn vagrant, range expansion has led to a number of spring records of singing male *viridanus*, presumably overshooting migrants, the Bradwell individual being one of 29 nationally to the end of 2004; it appeared after a night of heavy thunderstorms and, despite singing on and off until noon on 1st, was rarely seen (Wagstaff 1984). The 2004 individual was extremely elusive (Rhymes 2006), but was a long overdue second record of a species regular in Norfolk in most autumns.

Arctic Warbler   *Phylloscopus borealis*

Vagrant: one record

Arctic Warblers breed from northern Scandinavia east through arctic Siberia and on to Alaska. The nominate race *borealis* occurs throughout the species' European range.

2004	The Naze	5th–7th October

This was a species that seemed to be overdue in making an appearance in Essex; its finding was down to a fortuitous last look after an otherwise unrewarding visit to The Naze (Bond 2006). It was found during a westerly airflow and had presumably arrived further north in Britain earlier in the month and had coasted southwards. A total of 268 had been recorded nationally to the end of 2004 (BBRC 2005).

Pallas's (Leaf) Warbler

Phylloscopus proregulus

Rare passage migrant – 36 records involving 39 individuals, all since 1960

The Pallas's Warbler breeds from southern central Siberia, east to the Sea of Okhotsk and south to the Himalayas and borders of Afghanistan with the nominate race *proregulus* occurring over much of the species' range; most winter in southern China, India and Indochina. Changes in weather patterns, habitat change on breeding grounds and perhaps greater observer coverage has resulted in a considerable increase in the number of British records since the 1960s with 1,474 recorded to the end of 2002 and the most in any one year being 171 in 1997 (Fraser & Rogers 2004).

1960	The Naze	16th October	
1985	Mile End, Colchester	8th November	
1987	Holland Haven	28th October	
	Holliwell Point	1st November	Two
	Holland Haven	25th November	
1988	Coate Outfall, Dengie	17th October	One, perhaps two
1990	Gunners Park	11th November	
1994	The Naze	14th October	
	Deal Hall, Dengie	16th–17th October	
	Holland Haven	20th–23rd October	
	Bradwell	3rd November	
	Foulness	5th November	
	The Naze	6th November	
	Harwich	13th November	Two
1995	The Naze	5th November	
	Foulness	5th November	
1996	The Naze	17th October	
	Holland Haven	23rd–24th October	
	Holland-on-Sea	24th–25th October	
	The Naze	24th–25th October	
		12th–13th November	
1997	Coney Hall, Dengie	19th October	
	Deal Hall, Dengie	19th October	
	Bridgewick, Dengie	19th October	
	Gunners Park	21st October	
1999	The Naze	16th October	
		22nd October	
		23rd October	
		25th October	
2000	The Naze	15th October	
2003	Deal Hall, Dengie	14th October	
	The Naze	18th October	
		5th November	
2004	Bradwell	20th October	Two
		with one until 31st October	
	The Naze	22nd October	
	Harwich	30th October	

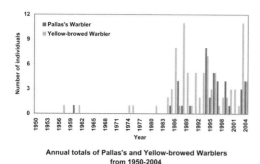

Annual totals of Pallas's and Yellow-browed Warblers
from 1950-2004

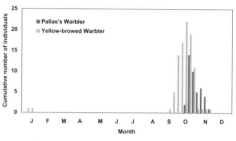

Seasonal occurrence of Pallas's and Yellow-browed
Warblers from 1950-2004

For many birders, this is *the* Siberian vagrant, the fleeting glimpse of the lemon-yellow rump enough to make the heart of even the most hardened twitcher race. Whilst numbers of this species have increased in a similar vein to Yellow-browed Warblers, rarely do influxes of the two species coincide.

The first Essex record was only the fifth British occurrence (Clarke *et al.* 1961), whilst the second remains the county's only inland bird.

As with Yellow-browed Warbler, the northeast coast is particularly favoured. However, there is a slightly different pattern of occurrence, the reason for which is unclear, with the proportion reported in the northeast almost identical to that for Yellow-browed Warblers (64%), but 28% coming from Dengie, as opposed to just 8% of Yellow-browed Warblers.

In Essex, one Pallas's Warbler has been recorded for every 2–3 Yellow-browed Warblers; in Suffolk similar numbers of each are reported (Piotrowski 2003).

Sponsored in memory of Tariq Watson

Yellow-browed Warbler   *Phylloscopus inornatus*

Scarce passage migrant – a minimum of 90 individuals

The monotypic Yellow-browed Warbler breeds right across Siberia from the northern Urals east to the Sea of Okhotsk and south to the northern Sayan Mountains. It winters from central Nepal and Bangladesh east to southeast China, Hainan and Taiwan, south to the Malay peninsula. Whilst numbers fluctuate annually, the species has increased markedly in recent years; this trend is probably attributable to a combination of greater observer coverage, an increase in easterly winds during late autumn over the last 30 years and more difficult to determine causes such as population cycles, habitat change and even a genetic change in part of the population which has altered migration strategies. Over 8,200 had been reported nationally to the end of 2002, with 739 in 1988 the largest number in any one year (Fraser & Rogers 2004).

The first Essex record was an individual at North Fambridge on 20th October 1957, which arrived at the same time as several others along the east coast. With just four further records until 1984, Essex missed out on the increase first noted nationally in the early 1970s. However, since 1984 it has been an annual visitor with the most in any year being 11 in 1988 and 2003. Whilst the majority of records have involved singles, there were four at Holland Haven on 27th September 1986. In addition there were three at The Naze on 3rd October 1988, 15th October 1993 and 18th October 2003; two on Foulness on 13th October 1985, The Naze on 18th October 1989, 9th October 1994, 13th–15th October 1996, 15th October 2000, 2nd and 19th and 22nd October 2003 and Holland Haven on 12th October 1991.

Numbers generally peak in mid/late October. The earliest was at Holliwell Point on 16th–17th September 1989, whilst the latest was at The Naze on 25th November 2002. Although arrivals undoubtedly occur during calm anticyclonic conditions, light southwesterlies also produce arrivals, which may involve birds that have made landfall further up the east coast and then coasted southwards. At The Naze, many are not found until mid-morning; either they are diurnal migrants arriving from some distance or some do not start to migrate until daybreak and originate from much closer.

There are two winter records, both in January 2004, following the large influx the previous autumn: Basildon on 11th and Fairlop CP on 15th and 18th. There are a further ten inland records, 50% of which occurred in Metropolitan Essex: Abberton, 10th October 1986 and 14th October 1995; Eastwood SF, 22nd October 1989; Stock, individuals on 27th September 1981 and 24th September 1984 were both found in mist-nets and subsequently ringed; Essex

Filter Beds, 28th October 2001; Hainault Forest CP, 21st September 1996; Dagnam Park, 9th October 1994; New Barns Lake, Buckhurst Hill, 27th–28th October 1990 and 19th–23rd September 1991.

On the coast, Yellow-browed Warblers have been reported from 14 sites, from Harwich in the northeast to Pitsea in the south. There is a considerable bias to the northeast with 63% of all records coming from there (The Naze 40, Holland Haven/Holland-on-Sea 11, Harwich five, and singles at Frinton-on-Sea and Colne Point). Only seven (8%) have occurred on Dengie and six (7%) on Foulness, with three at Gunners Park and singles at North Fambridge, Wakering Stairs, Little Wakering, and Pitsea.

The majority of those found at The Naze have been located in Sycamores with those in and around the spinney near an area known as the Cricket Pitch and around Walton Hall Farm pond the most favoured.

A record of one at The Naze on 16th March 1961 is no longer considered acceptable.

Sponsored in memory of Tariq Watson

Hume's (Leaf) Warbler *Phylloscopus humei*

Vagrant: one record

Hume's Warblers breed in the montane areas of south-central Asia and winter mainly in the Indian subcontinent. The nominate race *humei* occurs as a vagrant in Europe.

2004	Fairlop CP	11th January–25th April	Male

Another remarkable inland find, although it followed an unprecedented arrival of 22 in Britain during autumn 2003 which coincided with a bumper arrival of Pallas's and Yellow-browed Warblers (BBRC 2004). This individual was quite vocal and remained faithful to the same general area during its long stay; it was singing on the last but one day of its residence (Bell 2006). In all, there had been 82 records nationally to the end of 2004 (BBRC 2005).

Sponsored by Jim Martin and Old Parkonians Cricket Club

Radde's Warbler *Phylloscopus schwarzii*

Vagrant: one record

The monotypic Radde's Warbler breeds from west-central Siberia eastwards in a narrow band to the Pacific and winters in southeast Asia. The species' typical habitat is open forests, glades, clearings and other open habitats, avoiding dense forest (*BWP*).

2000	Fairlop CP	1st–2nd October

A total of 258 had been recorded in Britain to the end of 2004 (BBRC 2005). This is another exceptional inland record and recalls the 1999 Fishers Green Paddyfield Warbler. This individual occurred at a time of an exceptional influx of 31 nationally (BBRC 2001) and was a long overdue addition to the county list, although it was far from obliging (Bell 2001).

Dusky Warbler *Phylloscopus fuscatus*

Vagrant: four records

The Dusky Warbler breeds over much of Siberia, south to the eastern Himalayas. Unlike other *Phylloscopus* warblers (except Radde's) it is not typically arboreal, being found more in shrubby areas and thickets (*BWP*). The nominate race *fuscatus* occurs across most of the species' range. Dusky Warblers winter in the northern Indian subcontinent, south China and southeast Asia.

1987	The Naze	22nd October
1992	The Naze	10th–12th October

1999	The Naze	22nd October
2001	The Naze	14th October

The Dusky Warbler is an increasingly regular vagrant to Britain with 295 records to the end of 2004 (BBRC 2005), the majority since 1980. The first Essex record occurred in one of the larger influxes into Britain. Numbers generally peak around late October and early November, but individuals have been recorded as early as the end of September and recent examples of wintering have occurred, including two in Suffolk. In Britain, Dusky Warblers tend to occur on average slightly later than Radde's Warblers.

Given the species' skulking nature and the large expanse of thick vegetation at The Naze, it is not surprising that every one was initially located by its distinctive, repeated *tak* call; more have probably occurred than the record suggests.

[Bonelli's Warbler sp.] *Phylloscopus bonelli/P. orientalis*

Vagrant: one record

Western Bonelli's Warbler *P. bonelli* breeds through much of central and southern Europe, whilst Eastern Bonelli's Warbler *P. orientalis* breeds in the former Yugoslavia, Greece and Turkey. Both species typically inhabit warm, light and dry woodlands containing glades and clearings together with a range of undergrowth (European Atlas) and winter immediately south of the Sahara with *bonelli* as a rule in the west and *orientalis* in the east.

1988	The Naze	2nd October

In 1997, the two subspecies of Bonelli's Warbler were given specific status by the BOURC (*British Birds* 90: 70). However, the species are extremely similar, the most important field character for separating them being the diagnostic call-note of *P. orientalis*. There had been 70 British records of *P. bonelli* to the end of 2004 but only four of *P. orientalis* (BBRC 2005), making the latter the rarest *Phylloscopus* on the British List. In addition, there are 139 records of individuals accepted as either *P. bonelli* or *P. orientalis*.

Unfortunately, the Essex bird was not heard to call and so specific status could not be confirmed. Although there was a Western Bonelli's Warbler at Reculver, Kent, the same day and the Essex individual was considered to be of this form, it nonetheless arrived in Essex the same day as five Yellow-browed Warblers. In addition, there were records of an Isabelline Wheatear on the Isles of Scilly and Black-headed Bunting on Bardsey, Caernarvonshire; these species have east or southeasterly origins, similar to *P. orientalis*.

Wood Warbler *Phylloscopus sibilatrix*

Irregular and rare summer resident that last bred in 1991. Uncommon passage migrant   Amber List

The monotypic Wood Warbler breeds throughout much of central and northern Europe into Russia as far east as western Siberia where it is a bird of the forest interior, inhabiting mature deciduous or mixed stands. In Britain it is a bird of the west and north where it particularly favours Sessile Oak and Beech woods. Nationally, there were decreases in the east and west but gains in the north of its range between the two National Atlases, but between 1994 and 2003 the BBS has detected a sharp decline, the UK Index falling by 68%. Wood Warblers winter in equatorial Africa.

Christy considered the Wood Warbler to be "A summer visitor, though very local, and not common". He only knew of breeding records from Epping Forest and Saffron Walden. At the former, the species was described as "... common ... but only locally distributed" during the 1830s, whilst it was still breeding there in the 1880s, when it was considered "... local, rather than rare, generally frequenting tall trees". At Saffron Walden during the 1840s, the Wood Warbler was "not uncommon ...". Glegg confirmed that the Wood Warbler was confined to just two localities, at neither was it numerous: Epping Forest and in

Atlas	Survey Area	% of 10km squares or tetrads in which	
		bred/probably bred	possibly bred or present
First National 10km	Essex	15.8	5.3
Second National 10km	Essex	5.3	19.3
First London Tetrad	Met. Essex	2.5	3.0
Second London Tetrad	Met. Essex	3.5	5.5
Essex Tetrad	Essex	1.4	1.5

Summary of results of Atlas surveys for Wood Warblers

the woods between Warley and Thorndon CP where 7–8 were singing on 19th May 1919, although he felt that generally the species was not as numerous, as he had unsuccessfully searched the area himself. Wood Warblers may have bred around Felsted in the second half of the 19th century. According to Hudson & Pyman, immediately after WWII, the only regular breeding locality was Epping Forest where no more than four pairs were found, except for a quite exceptional 24 singing males in 1943. Irregular breeding records also came from the Ingatestone and Margaretting area up until 1948 and around Warley there were five singing males in 1948.

The distinctive trilling song of the Wood Warbler is unlikely to be overlooked but confirming breeding is more difficult with just 16 records since 1950: between Brentwood and Shenfield, 1950; Stifford, 1952; Woodham Walter Common, 1964 (note incorrect date of 1954 given by Hudson & Pyman); Epping Forest, 1967 and 1982; Sewardstonebury, 1967; Blakes Wood, Little Baddow, 1972; Mill Green, 1973 (unsuccessfully), 1974 and 1984 (2–3 broods from three pairs) and 1990; Hainault Forest CP, 1979, 1982, 1983, 1990 and 1991. Almost all the breeding records have come from fairly open deciduous woodlands, mainly of Oak and Beech with high closed canopies and little or no scrub layer.

Wood Warblers are polygamous (a male attended two nests 200m apart in Hainault Forest CP in 1991). Numerous singing males may also be recorded in suitable territory. However, singing may only last for a short time and so some breeding pairs are likely to be missed. Most records of singing males continue to come from the Epping Forest and Hainault Forest CP areas of southwest Essex, Thorndon CP, Danbury and the Mill Green/Ingatestone areas of central Essex, a distribution

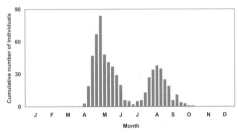

Seasonal occurrence of Wood Warblers from 1950-2004 (excluding breeding pairs)

that is confirmed by the Essex Atlas. Intermittent records of singing males have also come from Weeleyhall Wood and the woods around Colchester. Wood Warblers show very low site tenacity and change their breeding areas from year to year, a characteristic which perhaps explains the apparent inexplicable population fluctuations at its few sites in Essex. In the Bialowieza National Park, Poland, where breeding densities are extremely high, numbers varied by 18-fold over 19 years of observation. Likewise, apparent surpluses of males in particular years are not unusual (Migration Atlas).

Notwithstanding the Wood Warbler's variable population size, there has been a general decline in the breeding population since the 1980s, perhaps linked to the national decline identified by the BBS since 1994. Cox estimated a breeding population of 1–5 pairs, whilst the more recent Essex Atlas suggested fewer than ten pairs annually. Currently, the Wood Warbler has been lost as a breeding species. Local extinctions have been blamed upon tree felling and growth of the shrub layer, so habitat change may be a local factor working on the population.

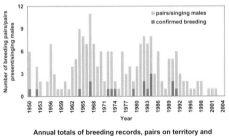

Annual totals of breeding records, pairs on territory and singing male Wood Warblers from known breeding areas from 1950-2004

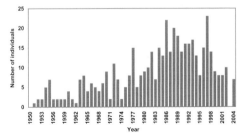

Annual totals of Wood Warblers from 1950-2004 (excluding breeding pairs)

Many records of spring migrants involve males singing on territory for a few days usually in inland woodlands, although a few are reported from coastal localities. Total numbers generally increased up until the mid-1990s, since when there has been a decline; indeed for the first time in the EBS's history, there were no Wood Warbler records in 2003. The first individuals start to arrive during April with the earliest at The Hythe on 9th April 1955, numbers peaking during the first two weeks of May.

Autumn migration is one of the earliest of any warbler with individuals occurring from mid-July and numbers peaking during August; total counts have increased with greater observer coverage, although more recently there has been a decline. More are recorded on the coast at this time of year, although regular inland passage has been noted at several well-watched inland sites. The earliest autumn individuals were on 11th July at Maldon Wick in 1992 and Thorndon CP in 1967. The latest individuals were at The Naze until 19th October 1976 (from 2nd) and Bedfords Park on 12th October 2000.

In autumn, individuals usually occur singly although two birds have been reported together on occasions. There is just one record of three birds, at Langdon Hills on 27th September 1986, part of a large fall of warblers following the passage of a severe rainstorm (Les Steward pers. comm.).

Chiffchaff   *Phylloscopus collybita*

The Chiffchaff breeds from the Canary Islands, northwest Africa and Portugal throughout Europe and most of northern Asia to the Kolyma River, almost the entire boreal and temperate forest areas in the north of its range, whilst in the south it reaches the Black Sea and parts of the Mediterranean coast and to the southeast, the northern limit of the steppe/semi-desert belt east to central Siberia and the central Asian mountains. Six races are recognised (Migration Atlas). Most western populations winter south of their breeding areas in the Mediterranean region and in sub-Saharan Africa north of the rainforests.

(Common) Chiffchaff   *P. c. collybita*

Abundant summer resident and passage migrant. Uncommon winter visitor

The nominate race breeds over most of west and central Europe as far north as southern Sweden and Denmark. Central and western European birds breed in deciduous and coniferous forests that possess an open canopy, some tall trees and a luxuriant, lofty herb or bush layer (European Atlas). The race is widespread throughout Britain and Ireland, although scarce in Scotland (Second National Atlas). Many British Chiffchaffs winter in Senegal, although small but increasing numbers have wintered in Britain since the 1940s (Dennis 1992b).

The breeding population of Chiffchaffs in Essex appears to have fluctuated histori-cally. Christy described the species as "... by no means common and decidedly local ...", although he considered the Chiffchaff to be common in the Paglesham district, Harwich,

Atlas	Survey Area	% of 10km squares or tetrads in which	
		bred/probably bred	possibly bred or present
First National 10km	Essex	96.5	3.5
Second National 10km	Essex	87.7	10.5
First London Tetrad	Met. Essex	43.0	9.0
Second London Tetrad	Met. Essex	61.0	11.0
Essex Tetrad	Essex	54.8	12.9

Summary of results of Atlas surveys for Chiffchaffs

Wrabness, Colchester district, Danbury, Writtle and Blackmore. By Glegg's time the species was "... a common summer resident throughout ..."; the Chiffchaff increased nationally during the 19th century (Historical Atlas). Hudson & Pyman referred to the Chiffchaff as "... fairly common ..." but indicated that there was "... some evidence of a decrease over the last few years ...", whilst Cox considered the species to be a "Common summer resident..." Fieldwork for the First National Atlas recorded probable or definite breeding in every Essex 10km square, a situation that remained virtually unchanged during the Second National Atlas survey, when the Chiffchaff was absent from just TQ99, which lacks suitable habitat for arbo-real warblers. The First London Atlas confirmed the Chiffchaff's presence in just 52% of Metropolitan Essex tetrads, 10.5% less than the Willow Warbler, although the Second London Atlas suggested an increase, most noticeable in southern Essex.

Countywide, the Essex Atlas survey located the Chiffchaff in 67.7% of tetrads (Willow Warbler 89.5%), its gen-eral absence from Dengie and Foulness areas, as well as large parts of the Thames corridor, reflecting lack of suitable breeding habitat. Elsewhere, its distribution was very patchy, unlike Glegg's description of the species breeding "... evenly throughout the county". In the northwest, the species was particularly thinly distributed. Since the comple-tion of the Essex Atlas survey, there appears to have been a continuation of the species' range expansion, which, like that of the Blackcap, appears to be linked to wintering numbers. The local CBC Index increased significantly from 1981, as has the National Index, which has seen a 129% increase in the CBC/BBS (England) Index from 1977–2002 and a 46% increase in the BBS (England) Index for the period 1994–2003; the local BBS Index has increased by a similar amount.

Cox noted mean densities on CBC plots of 21 pairs per km^2 (range 4–50) for woodland, less than half that for Willow Warbler and only one pair per km^2 for farmland, though examples could be found where Chiffchaffs out-numbered Willow Warblers. Data since 1981 suggest densities on woodland CBC plots averaging 29 pairs per km^2 (range 22–35), although this does not include a very high density of 91 pairs per km^2 at Marks Hall, Coggeshall, whilst on farmland the average density was around three pairs per km^2 (range 1–5).

The Chiffchaff is a very common passage migrant right across Essex. Christy noted, "Of all our spring migrants, it is the earliest to arrive, being sometimes heard by the middle of March" the earliest was singing in Colchester on 5th March 1878. Glegg considered March arrival dates common, but gave the earliest as one at Felsted on 19th February 1920, which presumably involved a wintering individual. With the increase in wintering numbers it has become impossible to differentiate between wintering birds and arrivals of spring migrants. However, double-figure counts of assumed migrants peak in late March/early April, the highest being 26 at The Naze on 16th April 2004 with 25 at Bradwell on 28th March 2004, 30th March and 4th April 1994, although 30 'Willowchiffs' on Foulness on 6th May 1978 were thought to be mainly Chiffchaffs.

Glegg considered that most Chiffchaffs had left Essex by the end of September, somewhat earlier than today when many double-figure counts of migrants occur in late September and early October. Autumn passage of British birds generally occurs over the last 20 days of September, peaking towards the end of the month (*BWP*) with Continental birds arriving from mid-October as either displaced migrants or winter arrivals (Riddiford & Findley 1981). Autumn coastal falls generally rarely exceed 20–30. By far the largest count was 100 along the Dengie coast on 3rd October 1993, whilst there were 70 at The Naze on 6th October 2004, 57 on Foulness on 3rd October 2004 and 50 at The Naze on 1st October 1994. Passage is discernible inland; indeed in Hainault Forest CP numbers have, at times, matched or bettered those on the coast with peaks of 50 on 19th September 1992, 13th August 1995, 3rd September 1995 and 10th September 2000 and 60

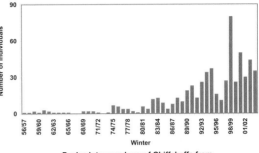

Peak winter numbers of Chiffchaffs from 1956/57-2003/04

on 10th September 1995 and 1st September 2001. Elsewhere, there were 55 at Newport on 8th September 2004 with 40 there on 10th September 2002 and 11th and 15th September 2003. Numbers invariably peak inland at least one month earlier than those on the coast.

Christy knew of no winter records, whilst Glegg referred to just one. Between 1958 and 1966, Hudson & Pyman were aware of 16 records between December and February. The 1970s saw 27 records, which included several *Phylloscopus* warblers, which were almost certainly Chiffchaffs. Numbers continued to increase through the 1980s with a maximum of 11 in any one winter, although it was noted that fewer were present during severe weather. Most records involved single birds and no more than two were reported together. The increase accelerated through the 1990s, culminating in a peak of 80 in the winter of 1998/99 including 20–30 in the Fishers Green area. The majority have tended to occur along the Lea Valley and Thames-side, although reports are now countywide. As with Blackcaps, the fact that Chiffchaffs are turning up with increasing regularity suggests a marked change in behaviour of a proportion of the population.

Even during winter, Chiffchaffs are entirely insectivorous, which makes successful wintering seem remarkable. However, water plays a very important part in the winter habitat of the species and it is thought likely that it is here that the species takes advantage of the considerable insect life that can be present even in severe weather. In Metropolitan Essex most are found in areas of Sallow, often around standing water with reed beds, sewage farms and refuse tips (Dennis 1992b). These sites also tend to have a microclimate of their own which may make them slightly warmer than surrounding areas. This factor may enable Chiffchaffs to survive the harsh weather that can cause mortality in the wintering population (Winter Atlas). In the most favoured areas, small groups of birds may be found. There were seven at: Essex Filter Beds, December 1994; Beckton SF, 1997/98; Walthamstow, late 1998; and Wat Tyler CP, February 1999. Most other winter records are of single birds. The origin of these wintering birds is not at all clear, as there have been no recoveries in Britain of chicks ringed in the nest, although wintering birds undoubtedly have an origin from across northern Europe (Migration Atlas). The recovery of one in Belgium in April, a few days after it was originally trapped on Foulness on 22nd April 1990, perhaps hints at a Continental origin, assuming this was indeed heading back to breeding grounds after wintering in Britain. British breeding birds probably winter in Essex, but the proportion is probably small (Migration Atlas). All the ringing recoveries of birds ringed in Essex and found abroad, except for the Belgian recovery mentioned above, have been along the main migration route through France and Iberia, whilst there is a single recovery from Senegal. National winter ringing recoveries provide evidence that some local birds remain for winter and may indeed remain loyal to the site over successive winters: one ringed at Pitsea on 21st December 1991 and retrapped there on 19th December 1992 is a good illustration of this. One ringed at Pitsea on 31st December 1991 was presumably heading further north to breed when retrapped at Sheringham on 2nd April 1992.

There have been three records of Chiffchaffs (or Willow Warbler/ Chiffchaff hybrids?) with songs that were intermediate between Chiffchaff and Willow Warbler: one at Maldon on 6th April 1988 was reported to be a possible hybrid; one at Chigborough

	Jan	Feb	Mar	Apr	May	Jun	Jul	Aug	Sep	Oct	Nov	Dec
Essex							1		1			1
South England			1	6	1	1		1	6	1		
Belgium				1								
France	1											
Spain			1							1	1	
Senegal											1	
Totals	*1*	*0*	*2*	*7*	*1*	*1*	*1*	*1*	*7*	*2*	*2*	*1*

Month and location of recovery of Chiffchaffs ringed in Essex

Lakes in the late 1980s looked like a Chiffchaff but after initially singing typically then broke into a full Willow Warbler repertoire; and one at High Beech on 3rd May 2003 included sections of Chiffchaff song within the normal Willow Warbler song. When encountering an oddly singing Chiffchaff, it should be borne in mind that the recently split Iberian Chiffchaff *P. brehmii* (Clement & Helbig 1998) is a potential vagrant to Essex.

The Chiffchaff appears to be thriving at present and is likely to remain a common summer visitor for the foreseeable future. Global warming, which until now has produced a run of increasingly mild winters, may have encouraged Chiffchaffs to winter nearer to their breeding areas, resulting in improved survival and breeding success.

Scandinavian Chiffchaff   *P. c. abietinus*

Common passage migrant and possible winter visitor

The Scandinavian Chiffchaff is found in Norway and Sweden (except the south), east to the Urals, and in the Caucasus, Transcaucasia and northern Iran (*BWP*).

Subspecific field identification of Chiffchaffs is not straightforward, with autumn migrants in particular showing a bewildering range of plumage tones, whilst the presence of intergrades undoubtedly makes subspecific identification extremely difficult. However, birds passing through Essex undoubtedly include Scandinavian Chiffchaffs, which pass through Britain on their southwesterly migration route to Iberia and beyond (Migration Atlas).

[Siberian Chiffchaff]   *P. c. tristis*

Rare passage migrant: 15 records of individuals showing characteristics of *tristis*

The Siberian Chiffchaff is generally found to the east of *abietinus* from the Pechora basin and Urals eastward and in northeast Iran to Kopet-Dag (*BWP*). The individuals listed below showed characteristics of *tristis*.

1987	Chelmsford	12th–17th January	
1988	The Naze	12th October	
1990	Dagenham Chase	January–5th March	
1990	Walthamstow Marsh	26th October	Singing male
1991	Dagenham Chase	3rd January	
1991/92	Dagenham Chase	8th November–23rd March	
1993	Dagenham Chase	1st January–29th February	
1995	Bradwell	19th October	
2000	Bradwell	10th December	Trapped and ringed
2001	Bradwell Power Station	17th January	
	Dagenham Chase	27th–29th November	
2002	Newport SF	28th March–7th April	Singing male
	The Naze	1st November	
2003	Ardleigh	13th November	
2004	Walthamstow Marsh	17th October	

This race is not on the British List, and although 'classic' grey-brown individuals are distinctive, it should be borne in mind that some northern *abeitinus* can be similarly grey-brown (Dean & Svensson 2005). Nationally, there has been a marked increase in records in recent years, coinciding with the increasing occurrence of other Siberian *Phylloscopus* warblers.

Willow Warbler

Phylloscopus trochilus

Very common summer resident and passage migrant

Amber List

The Willow Warbler is one of the commonest breeding birds through much of its range which stretches from western Europe, east through Siberia to the Chukotsky peninsula between the July 10° and 22° C isotherms. It is found in all kinds of habitat provided that scrub is present. In Europe it does not breed in Iceland and is rare or absent as a breeding bird south of 45° North (European Atlas). The nominate race *trochilus* breeds throughout the middle latitudes of western Europe north to southern Sweden and east to southern Poland and northern Romania, intergrading with *acredula* in Scandinavia and Ukraine eastwards (Beaman & Madge 1998). It is entirely migratory and spends the winter in Africa south of the Sahara. In Britain, the Willow Warbler is widespread and the common-est summer visitor (Second National Atlas), although serious declines have been noted in southern Britain since the early 1990s with more northerly populations affected by the late 1990s (Migration Atlas).

The Willow Warbler has always been a familiar feature of Essex summers with Christy describing the species as "A very common sum-mer visitor ... It breeds I believe abundantly throughout the county" and Glegg noting that it was "... a very common summer resident,

Atlas	Survey Area	% of 10km squares or tetrads in which	
		bred/probably bred	possibly bred or present
First National 10km	Essex	98.2	1.8
Second National 10km	Essex	93.0	7.0
First London Tetrad	Met. Essex	52.5	10.0
Second London Tetrad	Met. Essex	85.5	8.0
Essex Tetrad	Essex	84.7	4.8

Summary of results of Atlas surveys for Willow Warblers

increasing, and the most numerous of the leaf-warblers". Hudson & Pyman's description was almost identical, a "Common summer resident ... the most numerous of the *Phylloscopus* warblers in Essex", a point further emphasised by Cox. Both National Atlases found the Willow Warbler present in all 10km squares across the county with breeding in most, whilst the Essex Atlas survey located the species in every 10km square and in 89.5% of tetrads, being absent only from heavily built up areas, Colne Point, the southern Dengie and Canvey Island areas. The two London Atlases pointed to a slight increase in southern Essex, although greater observer coverage undoubtedly played a part in this trend; Willow Warblers were present in 91.5% of Metropolitan Essex during the Second Survey compared with 72% for Chiffchaff, as may be expected of a species able to exploit a wider variety of breeding habitats.

For the 20 years or so preceding the late 1980s, Willow Warbler populations had been relatively stable; indeed the species was one of the few passerines to have shown only limited fluctuations and obvious long-term trends. High site tenacity and saturation of available habitat perhaps contribute to this stability (Nilsson 1986). The species winters further south of the Sahel than many migrants and during this period appeared to have largely avoided the effects of the drought there. However, both national and local CBC/BBS data have revealed a strong decline since the late 1980s with a 53% decline in the national CBC/BBS Index between 1977 and 2002 and a 37% decline in the BBS (England) Index over the period 1994–2003. The decline in southern Britain (and probably the Netherlands) has probably resulted from increased adult mortality (Peach *et al.* 1995).

Although the Willow Warbler is more catholic in its choice of breeding habitat than the Chiffchaff, the species tends to avoid mature woodland with closed canopy, preferring younger woods, woodland edges and scrub; it also utilises mature hedgerows and young conifer plantations. Cox mentioned mean CBC densities of 49 pairs per km^2 (range 9–107) in woodland and five pairs per km^2 in farmland. CBC data since 1980 have suggested densities of 52 pairs per km^2 in woodland (range 29–91) and 13 pairs per km^2 in farmland (range 6–35).

Always known as a common spring and autumn migrant, numbers have undergone a notable decline in the last few years and, whilst there is little historical data available with which to compare, it seems now to be a much less numerous coastal migrant than previously; data from inland sites are inconclusive. This appears to tie in with the recorded fall in breeding numbers.

The Willow Warbler is one of the earlier summer migrants. Numbers in spring have naturally always tended to be lower than in autumn, but falls of 150 on May 8th 1965 and 100 on May 11th 1975 at Bradwell are excep-tional. Subsequently, numbers at individual sites have never exceeded 50, with 10-20 more usual, although these have been fewer in recent years. The first arrivals usually occur during the last week of March with the earliest being on Foulness on 1st March 1969; the main arrival is during the first two weeks of May.

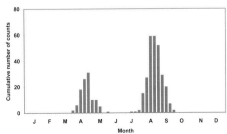

Seasonal occurrence of counts of 10+ Willow Warblers from 1971-2004

In autumn, numbers vary from year to year but tend to be higher (and peak earlier) than Chiffchaff, with counts of 50 or so regular every few years prior to the 1990s, especially at Bradwell, which historically has been the species' favoured coastal site. From time to time, larger falls have taken place, mostly during late August. There was "a spectacular passage" at The Naze in late August 1963, "hundreds being present on 28th", "several hundred" on Foulness in late August 1980 (when 150 were noted inland at Hanningfield on 30th), 100 at Bradwell and 110 on Foulness on 26th August 1984, 100 at Bradwell and 200 on Foulness on 18th August 1985 and 100 in Belfairs Park on 12th August 1986. Since that date, numbers have only exceeded 50 on seven occasions, with 110 at The Naze on 7th August 2002 by far the highest. Inland numbers are generally smaller, although there have been a number of counts of around 50. Few Willow Warblers are recorded in Essex beyond the end of September. Aside from obvious winter records, the latest individual was at Sewardstone Marsh on 8th November 2003, whilst an adult was trapped and ringed at Holliwell Point on 5th November 1989.

Not surprisingly for a bird which winters in sub-Saharan Africa, there have been only seven records during winter: Southminster, 31st January 1954; South Weald CP, 9th December 1958; Chadwell Heath, 19th December 1983; Hanningfield, 9th December 1984; Stanway, 28th December 1992–February 1993; Hanningfield, 20th December 1999; and Chafford Hundred, singing, 6th December 2004.

	Jan	Feb	Mar	Apr	May	Jun	Jul	Aug	Sep	Oct	Nov	Dec
Essex				4	2	3	3	1				
Scotland					2	1	2					
North England					2		1					
South England				2	5	1	2	4	2			
Denmark					1							
Switzerland				1								
France			1		1							
Spain			1	1				2	1	1		
Portugal										1		
Totals	*0*	*0*	*2*	*8*	*13*	*5*	*8*	*7*	*3*	*2*	*0*	*0*

Month and location of recovery of Willow Warblers ringed in Essex

During autumn, most British Willow Warblers migrate on a southeasterly bearing through Britain before turning south or southwest on departure from England with many recoveries through southwest France, northern Spain and western Iberia.

Recoveries of Willow Warblers ringed in Essex mainly during autumn in northern Britain and Scotland during subsequent breeding seasons confirm the southeasterly passage through the county. A mix of British and Continental Willow Warblers occurs in autumn, and to a lesser extent spring, probably as a result of adverse winds deflecting them from their intended migration routes (Migration Atlas) with Continental drift migrants probably involved in autumn. The recovery at Valois, Switzerland, in April 1975 was unusually far to the east and may have involved a Fennoscandian individual that in a previous autumn had passed through Essex.

Until the late 1960s, Willow Warblers considered to be of the northern race *acredula* were trapped almost annually and always during spring, but there have been no convincing records since 1969. National ringing recoveries suggest that small numbers are probably annual along the east coast but subspecific identification is very difficult with much overlap in the appearance of the two races.

Despite recent declines, the Willow Warbler remains a common summer visitor to Essex. The cause of the decline remains unclear. The fact that it has catholic breeding habitats suggests that the problem may lie in its wintering quarters. Whether the trend is just a short-term fluctuation or something more severe remains to be seen: it would not be the first time that the population of an apparently abundant species has declined dramatically.

Goldcrest   *Regulus regulus*

Common resident, passage migrant and winter visitor

Amber List

The Goldcrest is the smallest European passerine and is typically associated with boreal and temperate forests, especially Spruce and Fir. The species' range extends across most of north and central Europe and into Asia, with separate populations in east and west China. The nominate race *regulus* occurs over much of mainland Europe (European Atlas). It is one of the most widespread birds in Britain, being absent or scarce only in generally treeless areas such as the Northern Isles, Outer Hebrides and the Fens around The Wash (Second National Atlas). More northerly populations in Scandinavia and the Baltic move south in winter, augmenting resident populations in Britain, Ireland and the Low Countries (European Atlas).

The earliest reference to the Goldcrest comes from Upminster prior to 1738. Christy considered the species to be a "... resident throughout the county, though not common" and noted breeding at Saffron Walden, around Sudbury, in Epping Forest and in Colchester

Atlas	Survey Area	% of 10km squares or tetrads in which	
		bred/probably bred	possibly bred or present
First National 10km	Essex	75.4	7.0
Second National 10km	Essex	64.9	14.0
First London Tetrad	Met. Essex	17.0	4.0
Second London Tetrad	Met. Essex	37.5	10.0
Essex Tetrad	Essex	21.2	12.7

Summary of results of Atlas surveys for Goldcrests

and Paglesham districts. Glegg described the Goldcrest as "... a resident, breeding in limited numbers throughout the county." Little change in status was apparent over the next four decades with Hudson & Pyman considering the species a scarce and patchily distributed resident that was "... nesting in limited numbers in suitable localities throughout the county". Cox confirmed the Goldcrest's strong preference for conifers and thought that the species may have increased since WWII, as there had been a considerable increase in conifer planting. In general, however, broad-leaved woodland predominates in Essex and Goldcrests are therefore found at relatively low densities. Cox referred to woodland CBC plots showing densities averaging just four pairs per km^2; more recent CBC data are insufficient to produce meaningful densities.

The Goldcrest is one of the most abundant breeding passerines in British woods, occurring in 85% of them, although it is less likely to be found in those under 10ha (Fuller 1982). In coniferous woodland, it can form 30–60% of the total bird community. In areas of forest or plantation, Goldcrests prefer to forage in European Larch, Pine, Spruce and Sycamore and tend to avoid Oak, Japanese Larch, Birch, Beech, Alder and Ash (Peck 1989).

The First National Atlas survey located the species in 82.4% of 10km squares in Essex, being absent chiefly from coastal habitat or in highly developed areas, particularly along Thames-side. After recovering from the population crash following the severe winter of 1962/63, populations remained high from the early 1970s into the early 1980s. However, the prolonged cold during the winter of 1985/86, perhaps the most severe since 1946/47, caused populations to crash. Over the period 1977–2002, the English population was estimated to have declined by 29%, although the BBS (England) recorded a 51% increase over the period 1994–2003. Following a decline during the 1990s, the local CBC/BBS Indices have recently increased in line with the trend nationally.

It is possible that many of the conifer plantations that initially benefited the Goldcrest are now over-mature or have been removed in favour of broad-leaved woodland. However, good numbers may still be found in parks and large gardens and churchyards where Yews seem particularly attractive to the species. Indeed, CBC data may be unrepresentative as the survey has relatively poor coverage of conifer plantations. The Second National Atlas found the Goldcrest in a similar number of 10km squares to the first, although there had been an apparent change in distribution in the south of the county. The Essex Atlas survey located the Goldcrest in 93% of 10km squares and in 33.9% of tetrads, being scarcest in the southeast, along Thames-side and in much of the Tendring peninsula. Since the mid-1990s, the run of mild winters appears to have benefited the species and breeding numbers seem to have increased, contrary to the CBC trends.

Movements of Goldcrests through Essex are regularly recorded. Counts vary significantly from year to year, probably as a result of prevailing weather conditions (Migration Atlas) with substantial falls in some years following strong northeasterly airflows and an almost complete absence in others. Numbers tend to peak around mid- to late October. One of Christy's correspondents noted that migratory individuals arrive "... on the Essex coast in vast flocks and singly about the 10th of October; I have had them fly aboard when off the Sunk Lightship, so tame that they would hop all over one, apparently looking for water to drink". Glegg detailed the Goldcrest's migratory movements: migration started as early as mid-August and contin-

ued into the first week of December with significant movements at the Light[ship]s off the Essex coasts, although none were, quantified.

Today, autumn passage is most obvious along the coast, although strong passage may be discernible inland. For instance, there were 200–300 at Hanningfield during October 1980 and 110 at Hainault Forest CP on 15th October 2000 where regular coverage has shown that numbers comparable with the best coast sites can move through inland locations on a regular basis. Indeed, since the early 1990s, numbers inland have often exceeded those on the coast.

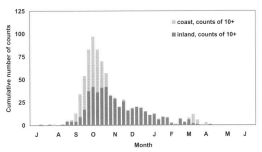

Seasonal occurrence of counts of 10+ Goldcrests from 1971-2004

The largest documented fall occurred in October 1975, with 400 on Foulness on 11th, "hundreds" at The Naze on both 18th and 23rd and 150–200 through Colne Point during the month, plus smaller but above-average counts all around the coast: a substantial fall also occurred at Sandwich Bay and Dungeness, Kent, around 11th October. Another substantial influx, which was also recorded in Suffolk (Piotrowski 2003), occurred in October 1988 with numbers peaking at 300 at Bradwell on 17th. Inland, wintering numbers were considered higher than normal. A large influx in October 1990 was perhaps only marginally smaller than that in 1975 with over 500 noted in the first two hours of daylight on Foulness and 145 in the Shoebury area on 23rd October. Unfortunately, no reports were received from The Naze or Holland Haven at the time, but very few were noted at Bradwell.

During winter, numbers nationally may be augmented by as many as one million Continental birds (*BWP*). However, the number of immigrants occurring in Essex and the number of local birds that move out in winter are unknown and whether the overall winter population varies significantly from the summer population is difficult to assess. Although the Goldcrest appears to be widespread across Essex during winter, when most birds spend their time with loose flocks of tits and Treecreepers, few reports of any significant concsentrations have occurred. Maximum gatherings have been: 46 at Woodham Walter Common, 7th January 1984; 45 in Wintry Wood, Epping, 18th December 1988; 42 at Hanningfield, 9th February 1997; and 50 wintering in Hainault Forest CP, 2000/01.

Spring passage is generally light and in some years barely detectable. However, an exceptional influx occurred in 1958, when at its peak on 20th April, numbers into three figures passed through The Naze and "scores" were present at Bradwell; 60 were at Bradwell on 29th March 1998.

From the remarkably little data available (Migration Atlas), it seems that many British Goldcrests spend winter on or near their breeding grounds. Some, especially immatures, will disperse considerable distances, mainly south or southeast through Britain. There are a number of movements of Goldcrests between northeast England and Essex, one from the Isle of Man and another ringed at Copeland Down, Ireland, on 28th September 1997 was recovered 20 days later at South Fambridge. During autumn, there is an influx of Continental birds from Fennoscandia and the Baltic region, although rather surprisingly there have been just two recoveries of foreign-ringed birds in Essex: a Goldcrest ringed in Finland was recovered during October 1975 at the time of a large influx, and a first-year male ringed at Kragery, Telemark, Norway, on 28th September 2003 was controlled at The Naze on 21st October 2003.

Although survey data appear contradictory, the Goldcrest seems to be holding its own or even increasing across the county. Significant areas of mixed woodland are being planted in both rural and suburban areas and this, together with the run of very mild winters suggest that for the foreseeable future the Goldcrest's future in Essex is secure.

Firecrest   *Regulus ignicapilla*

Uncommon passage migrant and winter visitor: breeds occasionally   **Amber List**

The Firecrest is a Western Palearctic species that breeds principally in central Europe as far north as Denmark, Poland and western Russia and through Iberia and the Mediterranean as far as Turkey, with outposts in Asia Minor. The nominate race *ignicapilla* occurs across much of the species' range with *balearicus* breeding in the Balearic Islands, Tunisia, Algeria and part of Morocco. Throughout the 20th century there has been a slow, sporadic northwesterly breeding range extension (Migration Atlas) with the first British breeding record occurring in 1962. Currently, 100–120 breeding pairs are reported annually (RBBP 2004). In Britain, Firecrests breed in various types of woodland and are therefore unlikely to be limited by habitat availability (Second National Atlas).

The first documented Essex record involved one trapped by a bird-catcher at Epping on 26th November 1878, which apparently ended up in the British Museum. Apart from five taken at the Galloper Lightship in November 1888, there were just six more recorded to the end of 1956. Since then, Firecrests have been recorded in every year except 1963 and 1965.

The first summer record, one at Bradwell on 11th June 1962, perhaps involved a late spring migrant. It was not until the 1970s, however, that the first suggestions of breeding occurred. In 1971, one was ringed and photographed at Coopersale in suitable habitat on 12th June, having been heard singing during the previous week. Three singing males in Hainault Forest CP and another male at Thorndon CP followed a large influx in spring

Atlas	Survey Area	% of 10km squares or tetrads in which	
		bred/probably bred	possibly bred or present
First National 10km	Essex	0.0	1.8
Second National 10km	Essex	5.3	8.8
First London Tetrad	Met. Essex	0.0	1.0
Second London Tetrad	Met. Essex	1.0	5.0
Essex Tetrad	Essex	0.2	1.1

Summary of results of Atlas surveys for Firecrests

1975. Both sites had singing males present the following year. Breeding was finally confirmed in 1980 when one pair raised young at Harlow Woods, this success being repeated in 1982. By this time, increasing numbers of singing males were being reported and breeding has subsequently been confirmed in an area of Oak and Holly woodland at Hainault Forest CP in 1987, in Havering CP in 1994 (although the male was paired with a Goldcrest) and Copped Hall Warren in 2001. Although typical Firecrest breeding habitat in England is Norway Spruce (Batten 1973), most Essex territories have been in mixed and deciduous woodlands where an understorey of Holly appears important (Essex Atlas).

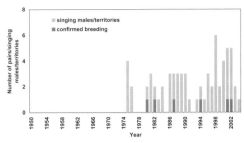

Annual totals of breeding Firecrests from 1950-2004

As Firecrests are extremely unobtrusive and some observers do not hear their high-pitched calls, it is not surprising that confirmed breeding records are so rare. Despite the fact that a high proportion of single males remains unmated (Second National Atlas), breeding may be annual and, given the amount of suitable habitat within Essex, they are most certainly overlooked. However, perhaps only 1–3 pairs breed annually in Essex, despite the higher numbers of singing males. As the species continues to expand its range in northwest Europe, a very slow consolidation of the breeding range is likely.

Migrant numbers have continued to increase over the last few decades. In general and prior to the 1990s, more were noted during spring than autumn: large autumn influxes since 1990 have meant that the trend has been reversed. The largest influxes were in the autumns of 2003, 2002 and 1996 when there were totals of 184, 113 and 93 respectively. In 2003, numbers peaked around 15th–19th October with 36 on 18th at The Naze and 12 at Deal Hall on 15th. In 2002, the peak was around 11th–13th October with 32 at The Naze on 12th. In 1996, the majority occurred around 21st September with 22 in the vicinity of The Naze, 16 between Bradwell and Holliwell Point and ten on Foulness. The only other significant site counts have all come from The Naze: 20 on 22nd October 1999; 17 on 12th October 2004; and ten on 22nd October 2000.

Migrants tend to start arriving at the end of February/early March and peak in early April with occasional individuals occurring until early June. Returning Firecrests begin to appear in late August, although a particularly early individual was at Bradwell on 5th August 1990. Numbers peak from mid to late October, with the largest numbers generally occurring after east/southeasterly winds. Late migrants continue to appear until mid-November.

Wintering Firecrests have been noted since the mid-1970s; until the late 1990s, 1–5 were usually present at a wide range of localities. From the late 1990s, wintering numbers increased to around 5–10 annually with in early 1997 perhaps as many as nine present, including three in the Friday Wood area; there were ten in 1998/99, ten in 2001/02, 15–20 in 2002/03 and 25 in 2003/04 including up to ten around the Warley and Weald CPs area.

Whilst migrants are most regularly recorded on the coast, many turn up at inland sites throughout Essex with no particular preference to any location, although many occur in broad-leaved woodland; there are very few records from the northwest. On the coast, the most regular site is The Naze where, apart from 1977, Firecrests have been recorded annually since 1970.

Nationally, there have been just 29 recoveries of Firecrests of which two involve Essex: one ringed on Foulness on 2nd April 1995 was retrapped near Mablethorpe, Lincolnshire, on 2nd May 1995; one ringed at Landguard Point, Suffolk, on 5th May 1985 was retrapped the next day at Little Waltham.

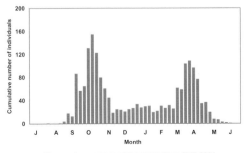

Seasonal occurrence of Firecrests from 1949-2004

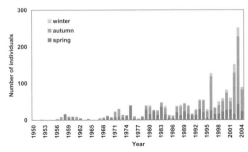

Annual totals of Firecrests from 1950-2004

Spotted Flycatcher

Muscicapa striata

Much declined summer resident and passage migrant

Red List

The Spotted Flycatcher's breeding range covers almost the whole of Europe and stretches from Morocco and the Atlantic coast east to beyond Lake Baikal. Over half of its range lies in Europe with strongholds in Russia, Finland, Belarus and Sweden (European Atlas); the nominate race *striata* occurs over much of Europe. The species can be found in almost any habitat containing trees such as woodlands, parks, farmyard copses, human settlements and mountain forests. In Britain, although widespread, there has been an almost continuous decline measured by the CBC since 1961, a decline that apparently accelerated in the 1980s (Marchant & Balmer 1994). This has mirrored an overall decline in northern and central European populations. Spotted Flycatchers are long-distance migrants that winter in the southern half of Africa.

To Christy, the Spotted Flycatcher was a "… common summer visitor …". The fact that he says little more about the species is a fair indication that the species was truly common as other well-known and common species were given equal short shrift in his species' summaries. If

Atlas	Survey Area	% of 10km squares or tetrads in which bred/probably bred	possibly bred or present
First National 10km	Essex	93.0	5.3
Second National 10km	Essex	87.7	10.5
First London Tetrad	Met. Essex	40.5	11.0
Second London Tetrad	Met. Essex	65.0	9.0
Essex Tetrad	Essex	45.1	13.5

Summary of results of Atlas surveys for Spotted Flycatchers

Glegg's description is true of its status, it appears that a decline had taken place since Christy's time "The Spotted Flycatcher is a fairly common summer resident, evenly distributed throughout the county, although it ranks as one of our less numerous summer visitors". Hudson & Pyman described the species similarly just over 30 years later "A not uncommon summer-resident … [that] cannot be called a numerous species". The species nonetheless remained widespread at this time and was still apparently relatively numerous: there were 15 pairs in Chelmsford and district in 1950, including four pairs in the town centre, although it was considered an exceptional year, whilst in 1968, 21 pairs bred in the Lea Valley between Waltham Abbey and Fishers Green, a distance of just 3km.

Prior to 1970, the Spotted Flycatcher was sufficiently common to be mentioned in the Systematic Lists of just six *EBRs*, with breeding numbers mentioned in just two. The *EBR* 1974 was the first to suggest that the species was declining, although Cox noted a few years later "… a slight recent decrease … has been suggested by several observers". Initially, signs of a decline were noticed primarily in woodland areas with numbers apparently remaining stable in other habitats, which in

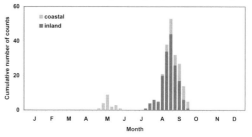

Seasonal occurrence of counts of 5+ Spotted Flycatchers from 1971-2004

Essex typically included wooded streams, lake sides, orchards, churchyards, public parks and large gardens. For example, in 1983 a total of 45–55 pairs was located in the parishes of Ingatestone and Fryerning, almost all of them in large gardens with numbers remaining stable until at least the early 1990s (Essex Atlas).

By the time of the Essex Atlas survey, the Spotted Flycatcher was still fairly widespread, being found in 58.6% of tetrads with confirmed breeding in 45.1%. The species was absent only from the largely treeless areas along the coastal strip, the industrial areas of the southern Lea Valley and the arable northwest. Survey work for the two London Atlases suggested a slight increase until the early 1990s, but increased observer coverage was probably a significant factor in this trend, whilst little change was evident between the two National Atlases, with the species being found in almost every 10km square and breeding in most of these.

During the 1990s, however, *EBRs* have detailed what by the end of the Essex Atlas survey had become a rapid decline; local CBC data confirmed the collapse in numbers.

Regular monitoring at Hainault Forest CP, a predominantly woodland site, appeared to show a trend typical of the rest of Essex. Whilst it has maintained a good breeding population longer than in many woodlands (perhaps due to continued woodland management), numbers have declined, markedly since the early 1990s. Across the county, breeding was reported from just 20 sites in 2004, involving less than 40 pairs.

The situation in Essex mirrors the national trend. The CBC/BBS (England) for the period 1977–2002 fell by 81% with the more recent BBS (England) recording a 38% decline from 1994–2003. Decreases in annual survival rates of birds in their first year are most likely to have driven the decline (Freeman & Crick 2003) and are probably caused by factors outside Britain, either on their migration routes or in their wintering grounds. Nationally, the steeper decline in woodland has also been noted, although the CBC does not survey suburban and rural garden habitats.

Cox mentioned CBC densities on woodland plots that averaged 19 pairs per km^2, although this included an unusually high density of 14 territories in 21.5ha in Hainault Forest CP in 1976. More recently, Spotted Flycatchers have become so rare on CBC/BBS sites that it is not possible to calculate meaningful densities.

The Spotted Flycatcher is one of the latest summer migrants to arrive back in the county; indeed it spends perhaps only one third of the year in its breeding area. Most return from mid-May to early June, although late April records are not unusual. The earliest involved one at Billericay on 31st March 1957, whilst others were at Fingringhoe Wick on 4th April 1970 and Foulness on 9th April 1983 (two). Larger numbers were recorded on the Essex coast in spring than during autumn, this perhaps being due to the generally more easterly migration route used in spring than in autumn (*BWP*). The few spring double-figure counts have all been coastal: ten at Bradwell, 11th May 1975; ten at Bradwell, 30th May 1976; 12 at Bradwell, 20th–21st May 1978; 15 on Foulness, 17th May 1987; 20 at Holland Haven, 9th May 1988; ten at Hockley Woods, 14th May 1988; 12 at Holland Haven, 19th May 1990; ten at The Naze, 13th May 1992; and 15 at Bradwell, 16th May 1993.

Return passage through Essex begins in early August and is usually more pronounced inland than on the coast with the majority of double-figure counts occurring inland, although it is possible that some individuals are locally bred. The largest single count was 40 at Havering on 20th August 1967, with the largest coastal count at this season being 27 at Gunners Park, Shoebury, on 12th September 1995. Other counts in excess of 20 have been: 25 near Cheshunt, but in Essex, 26th August 1973; 25 at Havering, 4th September 1978; 37 at Dagnam Park, 30th August 1979; 25 at Belfairs Park, 22nd August 1985; 25 at Belfairs Park, late August 1986; 25 at Hainault Forest CP, 3rd September 1988; 23 at Havering, 23rd August 1993; and 21 at Hockley, 13th September 1995. Migrant numbers have declined in line with the fall in the breeding population, the higher number of large counts during the 1980s and 1990s almost certainly being due to increased observer coverage.

Peak counts from inland and the coast occur at different times; inland most are in late August/early September with those on the coast around mid- to late September. The distribution suggests that different populations of birds may be involved in inland and coastal records. Indeed, national ringing recoveries suggest that those occurring inland are probably British-bred birds and those on the coast drift migrants from the very large Scandinavian populations (*BWP*); Spotted Flycatchers are often recorded in association with typical drift migrants such as Pied Flycatchers.

Small numbers of Spotted Flycatchers are recorded into October, although records beyond mid-October are rare. There have, however, been two November records: Fingringhoe Wick on 7th in 1974, and Mountnessing on 3rd in 1968. Cox rejected a record of one at The Hythe on 22nd November 1970.

Most Spotted Flycatchers follow a south or southwesterly heading on migration that takes them through France and Iberia during August to October and into north Africa from October, with returns through north Africa and the Mediterranean during mid-April and the end of May. Recoveries of Essex-ringed Spotted Flycatchers in Spain (one), Portugal (two) and Morocco (two) broadly follow this pattern, although one found dead in Portugal in January 1986 was unusually far north for the time of year. The sole recovery of a foreign bird, ringed near Zaragoza, Spain, on 12th May 1984 and retrapped at Little Waltham on 7th July 1984, illustrates the typically late passage through Europe. Four individuals that were retrapped in the same summering areas in subsequent years suggest strong site fidelity.

The Spotted Flycatcher population has declined significantly over the last 25 years and particularly since the mid-1990s, such that numbers are but a small fraction of those even 20 years ago. Despite being a Red List species, there seems little in the way of positive management that could be carried out to assist the species, given that the main causes for the declines are considered to be outside the breeding range. That said, more positive woodland management and a reduction in the use of insecticides might go a small way to help the species.

Sponsored by Margaret Mitchell in memory of Jean Patterson

Red-breasted Flycatcher   *Ficedula parva*

Very rare passage migrant: 27 records involving at least 29 individuals

The monotypic Red-breasted Flycatcher breeds in the boreal taiga and temperate zones from Sweden, eastern Germany and Croatia, east to the southern Caspian and almost to the Urals (Migration Atlas). The species' preferred habitat is mature forest and is a long-distance migrant that winters principally in India and Pakistan.

1959	Foulness	30th August	Juvenile
1961	Dengie coast	1st October	

1965	Parkeston	14th November	Female or immature
1966	Howe Outfall, Dengie	18th September	
	Frinton-on-Sea	20th September	
1968	Wanstead Park	4th September	
1969	Little Oakley	21st April	
1972	East Mersea	14th August	Female or immature
1973	Upminster	30th August	
1976	Walton	13th November	
1980	Bradwell	15th September	
		21st September	
1981	Foulness	18th October	
1984	The Naze	6th–8th October	Three, possibly four
1986	Holland Haven	19th October	
1987	Bradwell	6th September	Female or immature
1988	Holliwell Point	13th October	Female or immature
1989	Holland Haven	2nd October	
	Maplin Flats	30th September	On P.S. *Waverley*
	Holliwell Point	27th October	One, perhaps two
1990	The Naze	15th September	
		10th October	
1992	Foulness	27th September	Trapped and ringed
1998	Foulness	4th October	
	The Naze	10th October	
2003	The Naze	22nd October	Female or immature
2004	The Naze	9th October	Immature

It is likely that all autumn individuals were immatures; all, bar the multiple arrival in 1984, have been one-day records. The species averaged 87 records per annum nationally during the 1990s, a significant reduction from 115 per annum in the 1980s, although this has increased to 107 per annum during the 2000s (Fraser & Rogers 2004). Both nationally and in Essex, records have increased during the last three decades, probably due to greater observer coverage, although the species has spread westward in the last 50 years into Norway and Sweden.

Spring records are decidedly scarce in Britain, averaging slightly fewer than six per annum (Fraser Rogers 2004), so the single county record is not atypical.

Autumn records may simply relate to first-winter individuals dispersing from their breeding grounds. However, it is possible that they are true reverse migrants, originally from further east and indeed they often appear with recognised eastern vagrants during anticyclonic weather. A few of the latter individuals may be of the recently split eastern species Taiga Flycatcher *F. albicilla*, which is very similar to the European species, although its call and song are very different (Cederroth *et al.* 1999); there are currently two accepted British records, but it can probably be assumed that if it does occur it is likely to be from October onwards. All individuals should be observed very carefully in future.

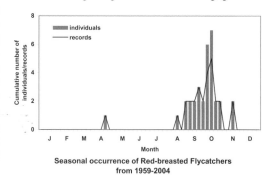

Seasonal occurrence of Red-breasted Flycatchers
from 1959-2004

Collared Flycatcher   *Ficedula albicollis*

Vagrant: one record

The monotypic Collared Flycatcher breeds across central Europe from eastern France and southern Germany and through eastern Europe into southwestern Russia where, as a cavity-nesting species, it is found in most forest types, preferring deciduous woodland. The species winters mainly in central and east Africa (European Atlas).

| 1979 | Frinton-on-Sea | 6th June | Male |

This was the 10th British record of a species that, despite the relative proximity of its breeding range, is only a very rare vagrant to Britain with 27 records to the end of 2004 (BBRC 2005). Its rarity is probably due to its north-south migration route; any overshooting individuals or reverse migrants are unlikely to orientate towards Britain as their range is well to the east (Cottridge & Vinicombe 1996).

There were two records nationally in 1979, the first year in which more than one was recorded.

A previously accepted record of a male at North Fambridge from 21st–23rd September 1962 is now considered inadequately documented (BBRC 2000).

It has been suggested that Collared Flycatchers (and White-backed Woodpeckers) may have occurred in Britain prior to the introduction of woodland management techniques over 2,000 years ago (Tomiatojc 2000).

Pied Flycatcher   *Ficedula hypoleuca*

Rare spring but fairly common autumn passage migrant

The Pied Flycatcher breeds from northwest Africa across Europe to central Siberia where it occurs in most forest habitat containing suitable cavity nesting sites. It is commonest in Fennoscandia, the Baltic States, Russia and Belarus (European Atlas). The nominate race *hypoleuca* occurs over much of Europe, although *iberiae* is found in parts of northern and central Iberia and *sibirica* breeds east of the Urals. In Britain, the species is typical of hilly areas with high rainfall where Sessile Oak is the dominant woodland tree (*BWP*) and is therefore found mainly in the forested upland areas of western Britain. It is commonest in Wales, western England (from Devon north to Cumbria, with some gaps) and parts of southwest Scotland. It is a very rare breeder in southeastern England (Second National Atlas). Pied Flycatchers probably winter in tropical Africa from Guinea, the Ivory Coast and Ghana south to the Equator.

The Pied Flycatcher's status has changed very little over the last 150 years or so. There is no conclusive proof that the species has ever nested in Essex, although there are several rather vague references. Christy noted that Harting in his book *Our Summer Migrants* (1889) suggested that the species was known to have nested in Essex but this was not mentioned in his *Handbook of Birds* (1882). Although he did not allude to any further breeding records, Glegg mentioned a report of a male and female at Great Waltham on 22nd June 1912 but gave no further information. Cox referred to "… a pair seen in woodland at Little Baddow, sometime in the mid-1960s". The only recent observation relates to a male seen entering a nest box at Colchester between 10th and 21st May 1988, which was joined by a female on 14th–15th. The male was behaving aggressively at the nest box on 21st but on 22nd House Sparrows had taken possession of the box.

All previous authors considered the Pied Flycatcher to be in general an uncommon and irregular double passage migrant. Christy detailed observations in at least 13 years (with further records noted just inside Suffolk) from the first at Wrabness on 16th May 1822. Glegg added further records that almost doubled the total. Interestingly, he considered that more were seen in spring than autumn (albeit based on just a few records), a trend quite opposite to that today. Over the last 50 years, the Pied Flycatcher's status has remained unaltered, with generally higher numbers in autumn than spring, although annual totals vary considerably.

Hudson & Pyman noted that no more than three individuals had been seen in any one spring; probably as a result of increased observer coverage numbers have increased slightly over the last 30 years. However, nine in any one year (1984 and 1985) is the largest spring total to date. All spring records have involved single birds except for two at: Langham, 4th June 1967 (males); on a fishing boat off Clacton-on-Sea, 18th April 1973 (males); Great Holland, 30th April 1973 (male and female); Fingringhoe Wick, 3rd May 1973 (females); and Gunners Park, Shoebury, 9th May 2000 (males).

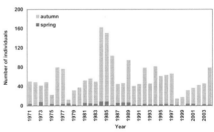

Annual totals of Pied Flycatchers from 1971-2004

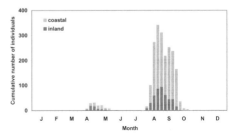

Seasonal occurrence of Pied Flycatchers from 1971-2004

The earliest Pied Flycatcher arrival was in Harts Wood, Brentwood, on 9th April 1994, and there was one at Hainault Forest CP on 12th April 1969. Peak numbers usually occur within a week or so of the first arrivals and then tail off thereafter. Since 1950 there have been just five June records, one being the two males at Langham in 1967 mentioned above. The others were all singles at: The Naze, 3rd June 1975; St Osyth, 3rd June 1997; Hatfield Peverel, 6th June 1994 (female); and a boat off the Maplin Sands, 7th June 1982. Although it is possible that these June records involved birds still heading north, they could conceivably be females that failed to breed and were already moving south (*BWP*).

The proportion of inland records is far greater in spring than autumn. Few occur on the coast in spring suggesting that most Pied Flycatchers move directly to their breeding grounds. The very low spring totals are probably also due to the northerly migration route being much farther east than that in autumn (*BWP*).

The earliest returning autumn passage bird was a male at Colchester on 19th July 1993. However, it is not until mid-August that the main passage begins. Numbers tend to peak around late August/early September with records regular throughout September but tailing off very quickly in October with extremely few noted after the middle of the month. There appear to be two autumn peaks about three weeks apart; the former probably involves the arrival of British birds, the latter of Scandinavian origin. One at The Naze on 29th October 1999 is the latest county record, whilst there were singles on 22nd October at The Naze in 1987 and on Foulness in 1979.

Numbers vary considerably from year to year. The largest influxes have occurred when large anticyclones, usually centred on the Baltic area, produce ideal conditions for drift migration of Scandinavian birds onto the Essex coast. Such falls appear, however, to be geographically very isolated. Thus the Great Fall of 1965 that occurred in Suffolk and involved "some tens of thousands" (Piotrowski 2003) was barely noticed in Essex and likewise not all of the falls detailed below coincided with large numbers in adjacent counties. In 1956, the total of 100 birds between 2nd and 4th September included 40–50 at Bradwell on 2nd and at least 30 on The Naze on 3rd with "… a number on the roadside between Walton and Dedham". In the region of 130–150 were noted between 1st and 3rd September 1961 including 60–70 on Foulness on 2nd and 35 at The Naze on 3rd. The highest annual total, in excess of 150 birds in 1984, was the result of two influxes, the first around the 12th August, which included 26 on Foulness, and the other around 26th when there were some 40 individuals on Foulness. Nearly as many occurred in 1985, when a similar double arrival resulted in 60 on Foulness on 18th August and at least 35 at The Naze on 27th. The reason for the decline in numbers during the 1990s is unclear, although it is possible that changing weather patterns have resulted in the formation of fewer classic anticyclonic systems. However, numbers increased again during the early 2000s.

Inland, small numbers generally occur annually in autumn, although they do not necessarily occur at the same time as falls on the coast. This is possibly because inland records usually involve British breeding birds that tend to move southeast and then southwest in autumn (*BWP*) and those on the coast are typically Scandinavian birds. By far the largest inland count was 20 at Billericay on 21st August 1966. Other inland counts of five or more have come from: Langdon Woods, ten, 21st August 1974; Havering, eight, 11th September 1965; Havering, six, 21st August 1966; and East Donyland, six, 12th August 1976. Totals of 51 in 1966 and 49 in 1978 are the largest inland influxes.

Both Continental drift migrants and British-bred birds pass through Essex, there being two recoveries of foreign-ringed Pied Flycatchers, one ringed on Helgoland, Germany, on 4th September 1969 that was found dead at Brightlingsea eight days later and another ringed in the Netherlands on 17th August 1968 was controlled at White Roding just five days later. There is also a handful of recoveries of Pied Flycatchers ringed in northern England.

Although Essex is of apparently marginal conservation significance for the Pied Flycatcher, it is interesting to note that the Netherlands was colonised from the east during the 19th century, the species taking advantage of significant afforestation of the lowlands (Lundberg & Alatalo 1993).

Bearded Tit   *Panurus biarmicus*

Uncommon resident, passage migrant and winter visitor   **Amber List**

The Bearded Tit ranges through the central and western Palearctic between the 17° and 32° C July isotherms. In the west of its range it is patchily distributed through Europe. The nominate race *biarmicus* is found throughout western Europe and the Balkans. The species' distribution reflects that of *Phragmites* reedbeds, on which it largely depends, and in particular large reed marshes. In general, the European population is increasing despite an overall reduction in wetlands, perhaps helped by the run of mild winters since 1987 (European Atlas). Bearded Tits are irruptive and some populations partially migratory which may lead to colonisation as the species utilises the same habitat in summer and winter.

Christy considered that the Bearded Tit once bred commonly in Essex. However, with few exceptions the evidence presented, including the earliest reference to the species during the 1730s, involved either winter records or were undated. The sole breeding report referred to a nest found on the Essex side of the Stour in April 1868. Three of the five young birds in the nest were removed from it, hand-reared and exhibited at the Crystal Palace the following February, when they were almost ten months old. Several seen in a reed bed at Tollesbury in September 1858 may have been locally bred. Winter records came from Barking Creek (pre-1829), where the species was sufficiently well known to have acquired the local name 'Reed Pheasant', Dagenham (1830s) and Colchester, whilst several other records did not mention specific sites. Glegg knew of no other breeding records, although the shooting tenant at Bowers Gifford Marsh noted birds in the winters of 1902 and 1910–14. At the time, the species was considered sedentary and Glegg considered this to be fair evidence of breeding in that area. Unbeknown to Glegg, however, seven were observed on Cattawade Marshes during 1913; breeding was confirmed there around 1917 with birds persisting until 1927 (Ticehurst 1932).

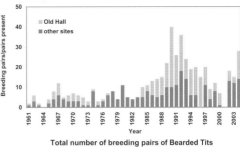

Total number of breeding pairs of Bearded Tits from 1961-2004
Note: no 2001 data due to FMD epidemic

Although Hudson & Pyman recorded that it was not until 1959 that the Bearded Tit was reported again from Essex, unpublished private correspondence between Pyman and Glegg (Pyman 1947) stated that "… Major Holman … a most reliable bird-watcher saw a party of Bearded Tits on several occasions on a fleet in the South Woodham marshes … during the cold spell last winter". The severe winter of 1946/47 almost wiped out the British population and it took many years to recover.

However, by the autumn of 1959, the Suffolk population was increasing steadily and the first of a series of irruptive movements was noted at Minsmere, Suffolk (Axell 1966). During the winter of 1959/60, around 60 were observed in Essex, although 40–50 of these were on Cattawade Marsh. A further irruption occurred in the autumn of 1960 involving perhaps 50 individuals at a wide scattering of sites, including several along the Lea Valley. At the same time, the Dutch population in the newly created polders was increasing significantly and immigration from these probably increased the number occurring in Essex. The species has been recorded annually since 1959.

In 1961 breeding was suspected at Old Hall and confirmed in 1962 when two of the 3–5 pairs present bred successfully. This remained the only Essex colony until 1968 when breeding was also noted at one, possibly two, coastal sites in north Essex. Since then, a number of colonies have occurred in coastal reed beds from St Osyth around to Thames-side, although most have only been used for a very few years. Breeding probably occurs at the main sites annually, although occasional access restrictions at some and variable numbers from year to year mean that confirmation has been intermittent.

The total of Bearded Tits nesting in Essex is generally small. The peak of around 40 pairs in 1990 was boosted by an exceptional count of 30 pairs at Old Hall, well above the average from there at the time; there were 36–40 pairs in 1992, 18–19 at Old Hall. It

Atlas	Survey Area	% of 10km squares or tetrads in which	
		bred/probably bred	possibly bred or present
First National 10km	Essex	5.3	
Second National 10km	Essex	8.8	1.8
First London Tetrad	Met. Essex	0.0	0.0
Second London Tetrad	Met. Essex	1.5	0.5
Essex Tetrad	Essex	1.3	0.5

Summary of results of Atlas surveys for Bearded Tits

is possible that some of the early 1990s counts from Old Hall were overestimates; a change in survey methods of this notoriously difficult species resulted in lower counts thereafter (Hawkins 1995). That said, the decline at Old Hall is genuine and the reasons for it remain obscure (Chris Tyas pers. comm.), although there was a significant improvement in 2004 when 14 pairs bred. The 1992 national survey produced a British population of some 374 pairs at 44 sites in nine counties. The 36–40 pairs in Essex represented around 10% of the British population with Old Hall holding almost 5% and Fobbing 3% of the national total. These two sites were among just 12 across Britain holding ten or more pairs (Campbell *et al.* 1996). The Essex Atlas survey recorded Bearded Tits in 19 tetrads with breeding probable or confirmed in 14, although only 4–5 sites were used in any one year. The 2002 survey found just 19–20 pairs in Essex, with only five pairs at Old Hall, currently just 1% of the British population; however, in 2004 nearly 3% of the British population bred there. A total of 92 was ringed at Wat Tyler CP during summer 1999; presumably the majority bred locally.

In winter, Bearded Tits range widely, although generally remaining faithful to their breeding habitat and rarely being found away from *Phragmites* reed beds, however small. Since 1959 Bearded Tits have occurred at many sites across Essex, although the majority have been along the coast. Abberton and Hanningfield have regularly been visited, as have sewage farms. Usually counts are small, rarely exceeding 20 individuals, but sometimes larger gatherings have been noted during autumn and through winter. Counts of 50 or more have come from: Old Hall, 50 on 22nd October 1986, 60 on 15th November 1990 and the county record of 75 on 17th October 1997; Rainham, 50 during February 1973, January 1974 and 6th December 1986; and Pitsea Marsh, 50+ during December 1982. Counts of around 40 have also been noted at Heybridge GP and Bradwell.

Site	Year first bred	Peaks		Trend since 1990
		Year	Pairs	
Old Hall	1962	1990	30	Decline until 2003 but 14 pairs in 2004
		1992	18-19	
Langenhoe & Fingringhoe Ranges	1970	2002	5	Intermittent breeding
		1989	5	
Wat Tyler CP	1973	1994	8-10	Decline, although numbers variable
		1998	8-10	
Bradwell	1974	1978	5	Extinct 1994
		1980-82	3	
Stanford Warren	1978	2004	6	Intermittent breeding
		1982	5	
Fobbing	1990	1992	10-12	Apparent decline
		1993 & 97	7	

Principal Bearded Tit colonies from 1962-2004

There is no apparent correlation between the number of birds recorded in winter and the numbers of breeding pairs in the subsequent summer. Indeed, there have been occasions when high winter counts have been followed by lower than average breeding numbers.

Despite the relatively small number of Bearded Tits occurring in the county, there have been 20 recoveries of birds ringed in Essex, four within the county, 15 in southern England and one, ringed on 20th January 1974 at Rainham, recovered near Dusseldorf, Germany, on 22nd April 1974. In addition to nearby counties, Bearded Tits ringed in Avon and Warwickshire have been controlled in Essex.

The principal threat to Bearded Tits is habitat loss either by drainage or natural succession (Batten *et al.* 1990). In Essex, however, the largest single threat is rising sea-levels. Inundation by sea-

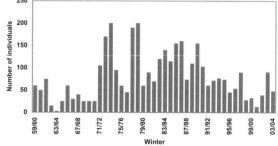

Annual autumn/winter (Sep-Feb) totals of Bearded Tits from 1959/60-2003/04

water or even leaching of seawater through coastal defences would quickly destroy the reed beds. Only the creation of large inland reed beds is likely to guarantee the long-term survival of the Bearded Tit as an Essex breeding species. It is not clear why, until recently, the Old Hall population was in decline, although a similar trend was noted in some other counties. However, the very latest available Essex data show an upturn, which is in line with the trend nationally, with 505–554 pairs in 2002 (RBBP 2004) representing a significant increase since the 1992 survey.

Sponsored by Peter Dwyer

Long-tailed Tit   *Aegithalos caudatus*

The Long-tailed Tit is a widespread species that shows considerable variation in plumage: 19 races are recognised (Harrap & Quinn 1996). The species breeds from Portugal to Ussuriland and south to Iran and central China, occurring throughout Europe apart from Iceland, northern Fennoscandia, the Balearics, Sardinia and Crete. Long-tailed Tits are generally found in dense woodland habitats, although in western Europe the species is partial to non-woodland sites such as areas of thorny scrub and hedgerows (European Atlas). It has recently become commoner in populated areas where the species inhabits shrubberies, parks, cemeteries and large gardens. Most Long-tailed Tits are sedentary but periodically northern populations may make irregular, sometimes large-scale irruptions to the west (Harrap & Quinn 1996).

Long-tailed Tit   *A. c. rosaceus*

Common resident and rare passage migrant mainly in autumn

British birds belong to the race *rosaceus*, which is very similar to some of the west European races e.g. *anemoricus* and *europaeus*. The species is widespread throughout Britain, although populations generally thin out northwards (Second National Atlas).

The Long-tailed Tit has always been a familiar Essex species. Christy considered it to be a common resident and noted several local names that made reference to its nest building, for example 'Bottle-tit' and 'Oven-builder', although the origin of the bizarre 'Long-tom-capon-bones' is obscure. Glegg considered that Long-tailed Tits were the third most common of the tits, after Blue and Great Tits.

Hudson & Pyman described the Long-tailed Tit as a "… fairly common resident …" that was particularly well represented in the wooded areas of central and west Essex. Being almost entirely insectivorous means that Long-tailed Tits are particularly susceptible to severe weather and upwards of 80% may perish in the severest winters (Second National Atlas); those of 1916/17, 1946/47 and 1962/63 decimated local populations. However, although nesting densities are generally low, fledging success is usually very high; this factor, combined with clutch sizes of 7–12 eggs, ensures that populations recover rapidly. Cox suggested that on farmland Long-tailed Tits were probably less common than before WWII due to large-scale removal of hedgerows with breeding pairs found on just two Essex CBC farmland plots. In woodland, densities reached eight pairs per km^2, which Cox considered high following a decade without any severe winters. Overall densities reached 0.7 pairs per km^2 across the 17 plots analysed. More recent survey data point to far higher densities, which perhaps reflect the prolonged run of winters without severe weather. Woodland plots have averaged 13 pairs per km^2 (range 4.2–25) and those on farmland 3.7 pairs per km^2 (range 1.6–7.4), with overall densities averaging eight pairs per km^2.

The Essex Atlas survey revealed that the Long-tailed Tit was generally widespread with the notable exception of much of Thames-side, the southeast and parts of the northeast. Here, the lack of trees in heavily built-up or intensively farmed areas was presumably the reason for its absence. In all, Long-tailed Tits were reported from 73% of tetrads, with breeding confirmed in 69%.

Atlas	Survey Area	% of 10km squares or tetrads in which	
		bred/probably bred	possibly bred or present
First National 10km	Essex	94.7	1.8
Second National 10km	Essex	93.0	5.3
First London Tetrad	Met. Essex	25.5	9.5
Second London Tetrad	Met. Essex	74.0	8.0
Essex Tetrad	Essex	69.0	4.0

Summary of results of Atlas surveys for Long-tailed Tits

The increase in Essex over the last 25 years mirrors the trend nationally, with the CBC/BBS (England) Index having increased by 38% over the period 1977–2002. However, there has been a marginal (3%) decline in the BBS (England) Index during 1994–2003.

A considerable range expansion in Metropolitan Essex between the two London Atlas periods may have been in part due to greater observer coverage, although the species has been able to adapt and spread into suburban habitats; the reported increased use of bird-feeders has probably helped. During the 1990s, increasing numbers were recorded breeding along parts of the coast where the species was formerly scarce. Thus, at The Naze, following an increase in year-round occurrence, breeding occurred in 1994 and has probably done so annually since. This may have been possible because the run of mild winters allowed the species to spread into what was otherwise sub-optimal habitat.

Outside the breeding season individuals of the British race rarely disperse further than a few kilometres from their breeding areas (Winter Atlas); the most distant movement of an Essex-ringed Long-tailed Tit to date is 147km, from Mucking to Burlingham, Norfolk. Of 13 Long-tailed Tits ringed in southern England and controlled in Essex, the furthest movement was 159km from Southam, Warwickshire, to Belfairs Park.

The origin of small flocks of Long-tailed Tits moving along the coast has always been a matter of debate and the increase in numbers breeding in coastal areas over the last decade has made it even more difficult to differentiate locals from potential immigrants. That some Long-tailed Tits arrive from the Continent has been suggested by occasional birds seen flying in off the sea. In 1960, one arrived off the sea at The Naze on 8th November and eight were seen flying high to the northwest on 23rd October, whilst a "flock" flew in high off the sea on 7th October 1965. Three flocks totalling some 60 birds flew north across the Blackwater from Bradwell on 29th September 1975. On 21st October 2001, an influx of around 50 Long-tailed Tits to The Naze saw three trapped that had previously been ringed together near Antwerpen, Belgium, just 11 days previously, the first foreign-ringed birds to be recovered in Britain. These are likely to have been of the race *europaeus*, which are very difficult to differentiate from the British race in the field.

During winter, Long-tailed Tits will form large loose flocks often in association with other tits, Treecreepers, Goldcrests and warblers. These flocks tend to vary in size from year to year with little apparent correlation with the severity of the winter. A number of three-figure flocks have been recorded: Asheldham, 100, 23rd January 1977; Epping Forest, 100, November 1983; Piercing Hill, Epping, 80% of a mixed flock of 200 tits, 9th February 1984; Hainault Forest CP, 100, 27th September 1992; Fishers Green, 150, 5th November 1995.

Spring migration has rarely been noted in Essex and, if it was not for observations of four flying out to sea at Clacton-on-Sea on 20th March 1974 and individuals on the shingle spit at Colne Point on 27th March 1990 and 25th March 1991, it would have gone entirely unrecorded in *EBRs*; the similarity of the dates is notable.

	Jan	Feb	Mar	Apr	May	Jun	Jul	Aug	Sep	Oct	Nov	Dec
Essex	7	5	8	7	1	1	1	1	1	1	6	2
South England	1	1	2	2					1		1	1
Totals	*8*	*6*	*10*	*9*	*1*	*1*	*1*	*1*	*2*	*2*	*7*	*3*

Month and location of recovery of Long-tailed Tits ringed in Essex

The Long-tailed Tit has, following a run of very mild winters, increased steadily since the mid-1990s and has begun to colonise new areas. It is increasingly making use of gardens for feeding, foraging and nesting which should allow the species to continue to prosper.

Northern Long-tailed Tit   *A. c. caudatus*

Vagrant: five records of six birds

The distinct, white-headed Northern Long-tailed Tit is found from Fennoscandia and northeast Europe from Poland, east through Siberia to Kamchatka and south through eastern Asia and China. The race is prone to irregular, sometimes large-scale irruptions westward, rarely as far as western Europe.

1912	Bradfield	22nd March	Two
1975	Bradwell	2nd December	Trapped and ringed
1978	Fingringhoe Wick	23rd March	
1988	Pattiswick	18th December	
2004	Hampden Wood, Warley	23rd–29th February	

Whilst it is likely that most of these records involved genuine *caudatus*, it should be borne in mind that some white-headed birds are no more than mutant forms thrown up by local populations; in Germany white-headed birds occur at low frequency and may therefore do so within the British race as well (Perrins 1979).

The 2004 record followed the arrival of several in Suffolk and Sussex; small numbers also occurred in the Netherlands. The 1912 record involved two birds watched for ten minutes at a range of 10m with powerful binoculars; Glegg did not accept the record simply because a specimen was not obtained. The late Tariq Watson observed an apparent *caudatus* at Little Clacton on 27th January 1982; unfortunately the record was never submitted (*per* Simon Cox).

Sponsored by Liz Fuller

Blue Tit   *Cyanistes caeruleus*

Abundant resident and scarce passage migrant

The Blue Tit's breeding range extends over the entire Western Palearctic between 35° and 65° N, from the Canary Islands and north Africa to central Fennoscandia and southeast to the Caucasus and northern Iraq. Fifteen races are recognised, with the nominate race *caeruleus* occurring over much of Contin ental Europe and *obscurus* in Britain, Ireland and the Channel Isles and western France where it intergrades with *caeruleus*. Primarily adapted to mature Oak forests, the species inhabits a great variety of deciduous, evergreen and mixed woodlands including parks, orchards and gardens (European Atlas). In Britain, the Blue Tit is almost ubiquitous in England, Ireland and Wales, whilst in Scotland it is absent only from the most mountainous areas and some of the offshore islands. Its abundance is generally greatest south of a line from the Tees to the Mersey (Second National Atlas). Western and south European populations are generally sedentary, whilst northern and central ones undertake fairly regular southerly, movements.

After the Robin, this is probably the most familiar bird in Essex, and from the rather scant evidence provided by previous authors, it seems always to have been so. Christy described the Blue Tit as "A very abundant resident" but provided no other data, whilst Glegg regarded it as "… an abundant resident throughout the county … the most numerous of the … titmice … that occur in Essex". Apart from noting that in 1913 Blue Tits robbed two Lesser Spotted Woodpecker nests in Epping Forest (very unusual behaviour the like of which appears to have never been reported elsewhere [*BWP*]), he provided no further information. Hudson & Pyman and Cox all described the Blue Tit as an abundant resident.

The species was recorded in every 10km square in both National Atlas surveys, and the two London Atlases confirmed increases along Thames-side, which were considered to have been due to improved observer coverage rather than a genuine range expansion. However, it is possible

Atlas	Survey Area	% of 10km squares or tetrads in which	
		bred/probably bred	possibly bred or present
First National 10km	Essex	100.0	0.0
Second National 10km	Essex	100.0	0.0
First London Tetrad	Met. Essex	64.0	12.0
Second London Tetrad	Met. Essex	99.5	0.5
Essex Tetrad	Essex	95.0	1.0

Summary of results of Atlas surveys for Blue Tits

that the provision of nest boxes has assisted this spread; nesting densities in urban areas can match those in woodlands, although reproductive rates are fairly low (Cowie & Hinsley 1987). It is also possible that the provision of food in winter by householders may have enhanced winter survival in these areas (Perrins 1979).

The Essex Atlas survey recorded breeding in 96% of tetrads with the most notable absence being around the Crouch and Roach. Since completion of the Essex Atlas survey in 1994, *EBRs* have generally reported a stable situation. The local CBC/BBS Indices have shown a steady increase, whilst, nationally, both the CBC/BBS (England) Index for the period 1977–2002 and the BBS (England) for 1994–2003 rose 10%.

Blue Tits are abundant in mature woodlands comprising Oak and Beech but can be found almost anywhere where there are either suitable trees for nest-holes or where nest boxes are provided. More unusually single pairs have bred in holes in an active Sand Martin colony some 12m above the water at Stanway GP in 1990 and 1994 and a pair nested in a life-belt holder on the west reservoir bank at Hanningfield in 2003. Cox reported densities in Weeleyhall Wood of 301 pairs per km^2, although roughly half used nest boxes. Other Essex CBC woodland plots averaged around 96 pairs per km^2 (range 33-140) with farmland plots averaging 13 pairs per km^2. More recent CBC data suggest average densities on woodland plots of 124 pairs per km^2 (range 63–197) and on farmland of 23 pairs per km^2 (range 7–34).

Once the breeding season is over, Blue Tits range widely and can be found in a variety of habitats from the late summer through to spring. Reed beds seem to be particularly favoured, but woodland habitat is also widely used and it is here that Blue Tits will join other tits, Treecreepers, warblers and woodpeckers to form mixed feeding flocks. The largest flocks tend to occur in the late summer and early autumn when large numbers of juveniles boost flock sizes with several flocks of 100+ reported. Severe weather can cause high mortality, although it is food availability rather than temperature that influences survival (Population Trends).

Wandering occurs widely outside the breeding season. Small parties may be noted at coastal sites heading purposefully in one general direction and on several occasions birds have been seen arriving off the sea or reported from fishing boats offshore. In most autumns, flocks usually numbering in the region of 10–30, but occasionally more, can be seen in almost any habitat along the coast, with small flocks almost 'bouncing' their way along open shingle ridges or thick stands of *Sueda*. Some of these apparent migrants may suddenly spiral up high into the sky, only apparently to lose their confidence and plunge back to the safety of the nearest cover. Interestingly the numbers reported from the Essex coast seem to be slightly higher than those noted on the north Norfolk coast (Taylor *et al.* 1999).

The origin of most birds is probably local: of 650 Blue Tits ringed in Essex that were subsequently recaptured elsewhere, 608 had remained in Essex with the rest being controlled in southern England. The longest movement involved one ringed at Pitsea on 1st July 1979 and found dead near Birmingham on 12th June 1982, a distance of 210km. There have been very few national recoveries of foreign-ringed Blue Tits, although it is quite likely that small numbers of the larger, brighter-plumaged Continental race arrive along the east coast annually; field separation of the races is, however, almost impossible because of an overlap in the brightness of plumages of the races. A Norwegian-ringed bird was trapped at Landguard Point, Suffolk, on 17th October 1994 (Piotrowski 2003). The extent of these migrations is very difficult to judge as local movements undoubtedly mask it. Numbers, however, probably vary significantly from year to year. A substantial arrival of tits from the Continent, primarily Blue and Great, occurred along the Essex coast in late 1957. First noted in mid-September, numbers slowly increased through autumn with flocks of up to 50 at Bradwell throughout October and peaking at 70 on 8th December. A number of birds ringed in other counties during winter were later reported from abroad. Inland localities also reported a general increase in numbers with a maximum of 60 at Romford SF on 26th October. This influx, which was noted across Britain and northwest Europe, was attributed to high numbers surviving the mild winter of 1956/57; the irruption was a response to high numbers before food shortages occurred (Cramp *et al.* 1960). One ringed near Settle, North Yorkshire, on 23rd January 1958 was found at Kirby-le-Soken on 20th April 1958; perhaps it was attempting to return to the Continent? Other counts of 50+ at coastal sites have been 65 at The Naze on 30th October 2002, and 60 at Bradwell on 29th September 1974. The highest numbers appear to move along the coast from mid-September to the end of October.

Overall the Blue Tit is coping remarkably well with the modern environment despite the multitude of different pressures exerted upon it. Undoubtedly its ability to exploit the urban environment and the trend towards milder winters since the mid-1980s have helped the species to prosper and there is no reason to think that it will do otherwise in the future.

Great Tit

Parus major

Abundant resident and scarce passage migrant

The Great Tit has the largest geographical distribution of any of the European tits; it extends throughout the Palearctic from Portugal and Ireland to Kamchatka and the western Kuril Islands and into the Oriental zoogeographical regions of the Indian subcontinent, southeast Asia, Japan, Malaysia and Indonesia. The species has a complex taxonomy: 33 races are recognised (Harrap & Quinn 1996). British birds belong to the race *newtonii*, whilst those in much of Continental Europe are of the nominate form *major*: those in southeast England are intergrades between the races (Harrap & Quinn 1996). It is one of the most abundant species in Europe and occurs virtually anywhere where there are trees. Great Tits are found throughout Britain, apart from the most exposed areas of the north and west, being most abundant in the south and Midlands of England (Second National Atlas). The species is gener-ally sedentary in Britain and Ireland as well as much of Europe, although birds will irrupt west when the seed crops fail and no other alternative foods are available (European Atlas).

Christy simply stated that the Great Tit was "A common resident" and that the species seemed to be more common in winter than summer. Glegg added little to this, noting that the "... Great Tit ... is an abundant resident throughout the county, and after the Blue Tit the most common of the group". The change from "common" to "abundant" suggests an increase but whether this was genuine is now impossible to confirm: it may have simply been down to a choice of words. Likewise, Hudson & Pyman described the Great Tit as a "... common resident" and Cox "... very common resident".

The two National Atlas surveys found Great Tits in every 10km square in Essex, whilst the two London Atlas surveys suggested an increase in Metropolitan Essex along Thames-side where, as with the Blue Tit, observer coverage and the species' adaptability may have been factors in the range expansion. The Essex Atlas survey recorded the species as breeding/probably breeding in 93.6% of tetrads, only marginally fewer than the Blue Tit. Breeding numbers vary nationally from year to year (Second National Atlas) depending on the size of the Beech mast crop. Fluctuations also occur in areas with little Beech, suggesting that the failure of other seed-bearing crops, Hornbeam being the most likely in Essex, may also influence county populations (Essex Atlas). Local CBC data for the period since 1981 illustrate this variability from year to year, although the overall trend suggests a steady increase during the 1990s: the national

BBS (England) Index has shown a similar trend, with an 18% increase over the period 1994–2003.

In most areas, Great Tits are usually outnum-bered by Blue Tits. Cox noted mean densities of 64 pairs per km^2 (range 30–103) in woodland CBC plots and seven pairs per km^2 (range 1–19) on

Atlas	Survey Area	% of 10km squares or tetrads in which	
		bred/probably bred	possibly bred or present
First National 10km	Essex	100.0	0.0
Second National 10km	Essex	100.0	0.0
First London Tetrad	Met. Essex	62.5	10.5
Second London Tetrad	Met. Essex	99.0	0.5
Essex Tetrad	Essex	93.0	0.6

Summary of results of Atlas surveys for Great Tits

farmland; the provision of nest boxes in Weeleyhall Wood did not increase the density of Great Tits in comparison with similar sites where data were available, although several pairs did use them. More recent data suggest average densities in woodland of 76 pairs per km^2 (range 52–100) and in farmland 12 pairs per km^2 (range 3–17). The larger size of Great Tits may mean that the species is able to exploit fewer potential breeding localities than the somewhat smaller Blue Tit. Nevertheless Great Tits are opportunistic like Blue Tits and nests have been found in a wide variety of locations. The most unusual, however, was described in the *Chelmsford Chronicle* of 6th June 1884 "In a hole one inch in diameter on one of the buffers of railway carriage No.79, the property of the Great Eastern Railway Company, which makes daily excursions between Thorpe and Clacton-on-Sea [eight km], a Tomtit has made its nest, laid its eggs, and is at the present sitting upon them ... The buffer ... is often in violent concussion with other carriages. Notwithstanding this fact, the bird is always to be found on its nest".

Great Tits are extremely sedentary and most coastal influxes and movements may involve *major*, rather than the local *newtonii*. However, the two races are very similar, *major* being separated from *newtonii* by its shorter and narrower bill (Harrap & Quinn 1996) and it is only through national ringing recoveries that we know that there is a very small influx from the Continent in some years. Over 90% of Great Tits ringed in Essex have been re-trapped in the county. Of the remainder, 7% were found in southern counties, with the furthest national recovery being one that was ringed at Colchester on 14th February 1965 and recovered at Formby, Lancashire, on 12th May 1965.

Glegg knew of several records of Great Tits at the lightships off the Essex coast. Although he considered that the Continental race *major* had not been conclusively identified in Essex, he thought it likely that one on the Galloper Lightship on 13th October 1883, five on the Kentish Knock Lightship on 26th November 1903 and a few on the Longsands Lightship from 21st–24th October 1910 were probably of this race.

Following a report of one flying in from the south at Colne Point on 23rd March 1957, there was a substantial influx of tits into eastern England from the Continent. Although not as numerous as the Blue Tit at the time, numbers at The Naze and Bradwell were well above the normal level from early October onwards, with a maximum of at least 25 noted at Bradwell on 5th October. Two ringing recoveries supported the idea that many of these were probably of Continental origin; one ringed at East Tilbury on 30th November 1957 was recovered in France on 12th March 1958, and another ringed at Colchester on 10th January 1958 was recovered in France on 19th April 1958. On 3rd April 1958, three flew in from the sea at considerable height at Foulness, whilst in 1959 a Great Tit ringed as a nestling in the Netherlands was found on the Sunk Lightship (16km off The Naze) on 28th September.

In 1974, a flock of 30 Great Tits was at Bradwell on 29th September with 20–25 present throughout October. A Great Tit ringed at Epping on 30th November 1975 was subsequently recovered in Lithuania on 25th October 1977. This represents one of very few recoveries east of Denmark of a British-ringed Great Tit and suggests that some migrants may originate from much further east than expected. In 1978 up to 35 were at Bradwell during October, whilst "several" were seen from a fishing boat 9.6km off Clacton-on-Sea on 8th October 1982. The only record in the last 20 years perhaps attributable to genuine migrants involved one showing characteristics of one of the eastern races at Bradwell on 3rd December 2000. The decline in recent records may be due to a reduction in westward irruptions through Europe that may be due to greater provision of food at bird tables (van Balen & Hage 1989). Whether these movements provide a true indication of the extent of migration through Essex is unclear; the species is not uncommon in the coastal strip and local populations may mask regular movements.

Like the Blue Tit, the Great Tit has adapted well to the modern environment and its future in the county seems assured at the present time.

	Jan	Feb	Mar	Apr	May	Jun	Jul	Aug	Sep	Oct	Nov	Dec
Essex	27	17	20	42	50	30	15	7	16	6	12	14
North England					1							
South England	1	1	3	2		2		1	1	2	6	1
France			1	1								
Lithuania										1		
Totals	28	18	24	45	51	32	15	8	17	9	18	15

Month and location of recovery of Great Tits ringed in Essex

Crested Tit   *Lophophanes cristatus*

Vagrant: three 19th century records

The Crested Tit is endemic to the Western Palearctic where it is found in Scotland and over much of Continental Europe north to Scandinavia and Russia. Five subspecies are recognised with *scoticus* occurring in Scotland, *cristatus* in Scandinavia eastward and *mitratus* in central Europe. In northern Europe the species is typical of pine forests but habitat choice becomes more catholic further south. Crested Tits are in general extremely sedentary.

undated	Audley End Park	Undated	Many years prior to 1890
1829	Ashdon	Undated	Two shot
1844	Saffron Walden	Undated	Shot

There were a handful of records of Crested Tits across southern England during the 19th century, mainly prior to 1850 (Witherby *et al.* 1938–41) which were probably of the Scandinavian or central European races. Glegg and thus subsequent authors rejected the records. However, two of the three Suffolk records were shown to have been of the Scandinavian race and all three are accepted as genuine (Piotrowski 2003). There seems no reason for rejecting the Essex records so they are accepted at face value.

Coal Tit   *Periparus ater*

The Coal Tit's distribution covers the greater part of Europe, the mountains of northwest Africa and much of northern central Asia as far as the Pacific, including Asia Minor, Iran, the Himalayas, China and Taiwan. In the Palearctic, the species is widely distributed in boreal, temperate, Mediterranean and montane zones as far as 65° N. Twenty subspecies are recognised across the vast range, of which about 30% occur in Europe. Over much of its range the Coal Tit is closely associated with coniferous forests, particularly mature ones, especially of Norway Spruce (European Atlas). European populations are prone to marked annual fluctuations in breeding numbers which, when there is an imbalance between numbers and food supply, may lead to large scale irruptions (van Gasteren *et al.* 1992).

Coal Tit *P. a. britannicus*

Common resident and scarce passage migrant

The race *britannicus* is endemic to Britain and is generally sedentary and, whilst it may use conifer forests typical of other races, it will also breed in pure broad-leaved woodland. The Coal Tit is generally widespread and abundant throughout (Second National Atlas).

Christy considered the Coal Tit to be "A resident, though somewhat local and uncommon". He added little further information, apart from noting the species was common in the Colchester district, Danbury, Ilford and Upminster "… pretty common…" in Paglesham district, not common at Orsett and rare around Chignal. Glegg described the Coal Tit as "… a resident throughout the county, but somewhat local … It is certainly the least common of our titmice", suggesting that the species was even rarer than the Marsh Tit. Glegg suggested that the general lack of conifers throughout Essex was the reason for its scarcity. Coal Tits were, however, regarded as common in Epping Forest where it had used nest boxes. Around Felsted it was thought to be not common and declining.

Following WWI and the establishment of the Forestry Commission, considerable numbers of conifers were planted, a trend that accelerated after WWII; wherever conifers were planted the Coal Tit increased (Historical Atlas). Hudson & Pyman did not refer to population trends, simply noting that the Coal Tit was most common in

Atlas	Survey Area	% of 10km squares or tetrads in which	
		bred/probably bred	possibly bred or present
First National 10km	Essex	84.2	12.3
Second National 10km	Essex	64.9	17.5
First London Tetrad	Met. Essex	26.5	12.5
Second London Tetrad	Met. Essex	46.5	8.0
Essex Tetrad	Essex	33.4	14.7

Summary of results of Atlas surveys for Coal Tits

conifer plantations around the county. Cox, however, considered that the increase in coniferous woodlands was probably the reason for the species' recent expansion, perhaps aided by the long sequence of relatively mild winters since 1962/63. A further factor has perhaps been the post-war boom in gardening and the consequent increase in conifers in gardens (Essex Atlas). Unfortunately, virtually no breeding data were published in *EBRs* prior to 1982, the sole comment made in 1979 noting "… there is some evidence of a marked increase".

Between the two National Atlas surveys, there was a slight range contraction witnessed mainly in the east of Essex, perhaps because isolated conifer plantations had matured and had been harvested in the intervening years: Coal Tits were absent from much of Dengie. There was a range increase in the years between the two London Atlases, although it seems likely that this may have been due to greater observer coverage. The Essex Atlas survey found Coal Tits in 87.7% of 10km squares, the main absences being from coastal squares, and in 48.1% of all tetrads. The largest concentrations were in the wooded areas of the southwest, Hainault Forest CP, Thorndon CP, Ongar Park Wood and Epping Forest, although greater observer coverage may account for the apparent concentration in Metropolitan Essex. The species was least common in areas adjacent to the coast and estuaries as well as in intensively farmed areas inland. Away from woodlands, Coal Tits were found breeding in parks, gardens and cemeteries. Given their similar habitat requirements, it is not surprising that the Goldcrest's distribution is broadly similar to that of Coal Tit.

Since the early 1990s, *EBRs* have reported minor fluctuations in populations at several sites but the overall trend appears to be stable, a situation mirrored by the recent local BBS data. The local CBC Index, however, detected a sharp decline in the second half of the 1990s, the reasons for which are unclear. Nationally, the CBC/BBS (England) Index for the period 1977–2002 confirmed a 7% decline but the more recent BBS (England) Index suggested a 9% increase from 1994–2003. Generally, national populations are considered stable.

Woodland surveys prior to 1980 revealed mean densities of around 25 pairs per km². In places where conifers were well represented at this time, it was considered "plentiful" and "common". More recent CBC data have suggested a mean woodland density of around 18 pairs per km² (range 4–45).

Although generally sedentary, *britannicus* Coal Tits occasionally occur at coastal sites principally in autumn, although in general movements are small and usually local in nature. They will often join roving tit flocks during winter. Food shortages in their preferred woodland habitat may, however, cause Coal Tits to travel further. Of 29 recoveries of Essex-ringed Coal Tits, only three have been recorded outside the county.

Overall it seems that Coal Tit numbers are relatively stable and the species may be spreading into new habitat. Although many large commercial conifer plantations have matured and are being felled, conifers are being planted in new housing developments, which should replace recent losses. The Coal Tit's future in Essex thus appears to be secure.

Continental Coal Tit

P. a. ater

Rare migrant but subject to periodic influxes; recorded in at least 11 years

The Continental Coal Tit breeds across Continental Europe and Asia, east to Sakhalin Island, Siberia, and south to France across to northeast China. Some northern and eastern populations regularly move south in autumn and winter.

1952	St Osyth	31st October	One
1957	Coincident with the huge influx of tits from the Continent, four Coal Tits were at The Naze on 27th September, 2–3 on 28th October and one on 2nd November; although not specifically identified, they were probably of the race *ater*		
1960	One trapped and ringed on 24th April at Bradwell was found ten days later on a light-ship off the Dutch coast: the skin was preserved and deposited at the Natural History Museum		
1969	A Coal Tit, presumed to be *ater*, landed on a boat 4km off The Naze on 10th October		
1974	Bradwell	29th September	One trapped and ringed
1982	Fingringhoe Wick	17th–24th February	One
[1989	Holland Haven	10th November	One: race unknown]
[1990	Bradwell	18th March	One: race unknown]
1993	Foulness	12th September	One
	In addition, two probable migrants were reported from East Tilbury on 15th September		
[1994	West Mersea	19th January	One: race unknown
	Bradwell	6th April	One: race unknown]
1996	Unprecedented influx during 19th–22nd September with around 44 involved, including eight at Holland Haven on 19th and five on Foulness on 21st with inland records from Abberton on 15th September and Hanningfield on 13th October		
2002	Bradwell	24th March	One
		7th April	One
2003	Deal Hall, Dengie	17th October	One
	The Naze	18th October	Two
		24th October	Six
2004	Bradwell	24th March	One
		4th April	One
		11th April	One

When seed crops are poor, large-scale irruptions of northern and eastern populations occur and many of the large Essex influxes have coincided with large numbers moving along the coast of the Low Countries. The number of spring records from Bradwell are of note.

Willow Tit

Poecile montanus

Scarce and declining resident

Red List

The Willow Tit has an extensive range across the Palearctic and into the Oriental region, from Great Britain in the west to Anadyr on the Pacific coast in the east, in a belt generally between 50° and 63° N. In Europe, the species has a wide distribution generally within the temperate middle and upper middle latitudes. Its main habitat component is the presence of decaying tree stumps into which it can excavate a nest hole (European Atlas). In Britain, the species has a broadly similar distribution to the Marsh Tit, although some significant differences exist (Second National Atlas). The race occurring in Britain, *kleinschmidti*, is endemic and generally very sedentary. Two races occur on the Continent, the northern race *borealis*, which is partially migratory, and *rhenanus* of western Europe, which tends to be sedentary. The Willow Tit is generally a bird of damper habitat than Marsh Tit and usually inhabits smaller areas of woodland, such as farmland spinneys, more regularly than Marsh Tit.

Willow Tits were first described in Britain in 1897 but it was not until the winter of 1911/12 that the species was recorded in Essex, when several were seen in the Felsted district. A nest was found in the same area in 1912 with a second at "Saling" in 1913; Glegg knew of no others.

During the 1930s the species was outnumbered 3:1 in southern Essex by the Marsh Tit (Warren unpublished). Hudson & Pyman considered the Willow Tit to be "Resident, rather scarce ...", being widely but thinly distributed and chiefly confined to woodland and common land, often in damp situations. Cox described an apparent increase during the 1960s and 1970s at the same time as the Marsh Tit declined (q.v.). The increase suggested by the ringing totals accorded with the national trend at the time. However, it is not possible to be sure whether this apparent change in respective populations reflected improved identification, changed trapping methods, a decline in Marsh Tits or an increase in Willow Tits, or a combination of these (First National Atlas). The fact that Willow Tits are more likely to be recorded in habitat other than just woodland may also bias the numbers of each caught. Nonetheless observations suggested that the Willow Tit was going through a phase of increase. Thus, the *EBR* 1970 noted "There is growing evidence to suggest that in many areas, particularly in the northern half of the County, the Willow Tit has become the dominant species", whilst the *EBR* 1972 reported "... the Willow Tit is now as

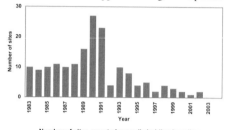

Number of sites reported annually holding breeding Willow Tits from 1983-2004

common as the Marsh and probably outnumbers it in some areas, particularly the NE". In 1970, the Willow Tit was reported from 26 localities and Marsh Tit just three.

The apparent increase did not last for long, however, and by 1979 the first concerns were noted in the *EBR* regarding an apparent decline; nationally numbers peaked around 1975 (Population Trends). By the end of the 1980s, the decline had even begun to affect sites that historically had been the species' strongholds. At Hainault Forest CP the population fell from around 4–5 pairs in the mid-1980s to nil by 1993.

The Willow Tit population in Hertfordshire followed a very similar trend, although there is no evidence to suggest that the patterns were no more than coincidental (Population Trends). Overall, the Essex Atlas survey revealed the species' presence in 19.5% of tetrads with confirmed breeding in 10.2% (Marsh Tit, 21.8% and 14.2%). The Willow Tit's distribution was very similar to the Marsh Tit's with the highest numbers occurring in the west and north-central Essex and few in the south, east and northeast. The two National Atlases suggested a contraction in range from the east, although the two London Atlases confirmed that, despite a shift in distribution, the overall range appeared stable.

During the 1990s the population collapsed, with few confirmed breeding records. By the beginning of the 21st century, the species was almost extinct with only two sightings in both 2003 and 2004, although more concentrated observer coverage may well reveal that a small breeding population still survives in a small area of Essex within a 10–15km radius of Thaxted, with most recent observations coming from Hatfield Forest/Takeley area and West Wood, Great Sampford. In all probability the species is overlooked as Willow Tits are very secretive. Interestingly, the highest number of sites at which the species was noted during the breeding season were 27 in 1990, one of the early years of the Essex Atlas survey, which suggests that intensive survey work may reveal that the species is still present at a very low density.

Nationally, the CBC/BBS Index (England) for the period 1977–2002 fell by 82% and the more recent BBS (England) Index for the period

Atlas	Survey Area	% of 10km squares or tetrads in which	
		bred/probably bred	possibly bred or present
First National 10km	Essex	63.2	8.8
Second National 10km	Essex	38.6	14.0
First London Tetrad	Met. Essex	15.5	7.5
Second London Tetrad	Met. Essex	14.5	12.5
Essex Tetrad	Essex	10.2	9.3

Summary of results of Atlas surveys for Willow Tits

declined by 62%. Reasons for the decline are unclear. It has been suggested that increased competition from other tits may be a factor (Second National Atlas). The increase in numbers of Great Spotted Woodpeckers and Grey Squirrels may be at least partly responsible, too; the young are readily accessible in their nests low down in rotten and soft wood stumps (Taylor *et al.* 1999). Other possible causes include agricultural intensification and the drainage of small damp areas (Second National Atlas).

Cox stated that CBC data from three sites (Hainault Forest CP, Parndon and Weeleyhall Wood) revealed average breeding densities of three pairs per km². More recently, the species has become so rare that no useful data on breeding densities are available.

Wintering and breeding distributions are similar as Willow Tits are very sedentary with adult pairs often remaining on site throughout winter, although some do wander locally, probably first-winter birds. Ringing totals from Romford SF during the late 1970s suggested that Willow Tits wandered more than Marsh Tits: for example, nine Willow Tits and only four Marsh Tits were ringed in 1977, although this may simply reflect the relative size of nearby populations. Of the four Essex ringing recoveries, the furthest distance travelled was just 16km from Ware, Hertfordshire, to Copped Hall, Epping. Singles at Rainham in March 1986 and on 14th May 2000 and two at Bradwell on 26th October 1975 may have just wandered from local populations, or were they longer-distance migrants?

A full survey of likely breeding areas is required to establish the species' true current status and establish the typical habitat in these areas. However, until the causes of the catastrophic decline are known, there is probably very little that can be done to halt or reverse the current trend.

Marsh Tit *Poecile palustris*

Uncommon resident Red List

The Marsh Tit has a disjunct world distribution with the eastern Palearctic range separated from the western by 2,000km. The species' western range covers most of Europe, its range tending to be marginally more southerly than Willow Tit (Perrins 1979). There are five subspecies in Europe: two occur in Britain, *dresseri* from central England through western France to the Massif Central and the nominate race *palustris*, which occurs in northern England and Scotland. Three other races occur in Europe. Marsh Tits are hole nesters that prefer deciduous woodland, particularly those dominated by Beech (Beech mast is a major winter food source) and Oak (for caterpillars in the breeding season). They are sometimes associated with damp areas but can equally well be found in drier habitat. In Britain, the Marsh Tit is distributed somewhat patchily over England and Wales as well as the south-easternmost corner of Scotland.

The early status of Marsh and Willow Tits is clouded by the fact that the Willow Tit was not recognised as a separate species until 1897 (Kleinschmidt 1898). Thus Christy's reference to the "Marsh Tit" being a "… very common resident in most parts of the county" applied to

Atlas	Survey Area	% of 10km squares or tetrads in which	
		bred/probably bred	possibly bred or present
First National 10km	Essex	78.9	8.8
Second National 10km	Essex	47.4	21.1
First London Tetrad	Met. Essex	21.5	8.5
Second London Tetrad	Met. Essex	21.5	3.0
Essex Tetrad	Essex	14.2	7.6

Summary of results of Atlas surveys for Marsh Tits

both species. What is clear, however, from his description is that the abundance of both species was far greater than that today. Glegg commenting specifically on the Marsh Tit noted that the species "… is a fairly common resident throughout the county. It is distinctly more numerous than the Coal-Tit, although it is an uncommon species as compared with the Great Tit".

A survey in south Essex in 1936–37 found that Marsh Tits outnumbered Willow Tits by a ratio of at least 3:1 (Warren unpublished). Little further was written about the species' status for another 30 years. However, in the mid-1960s, Hudson & Pyman considered that the species was still a "Locally common resident … well-distributed in Essex; it is more numerous than the Willow and Coal Tit but less so than the Blue and Great Tits". Marsh Tits were most common in the wooded belt that extended from Epping Forest across to Danbury. That the species remained relatively common until the 1980s is suggested by the fact that in only two years prior to 1983 was the Marsh Tit mentioned in the Systematic List of the *EBRs*. However, this contrasted markedly with the almost annual occurrence of Willow Tit in the Systematic List, a situation that was probably due to the imbalance of recording effort given to the two species, the much rarer Willow Tit receiving the attention, whilst the more common Marsh Tit was largely ignored.

Following signs of an increase during the 1960s, the Marsh Tit has subsequently declined with losses first noted in parts of central and southwest Essex, including at Danbury, a former stronghold, and some coastal regions (Cox). Historic ringing totals from two areas of south/southwest Essex bear out the trend.

That the Willow Tit increased as the Marsh Tit declined may be no more than coincidence. The ongoing decline has mirrored the national trend, which has revealed a steady decline since the 1960s (Population Trends): a 34% reduction in the CBC/BBS Index (England) occurred between 1977 and 2002. A contraction in range was evident between the two London Atlases with the number of occupied tetrads declining from 30% to 24.5%. As observer coverage was undoubtedly greater during the Second London Atlas survey period, the decline appears to have been significant. Likewise, the number of occupied 10km squares fell from 87.7% to 68.5% between the two National Atlas surveys. The Essex Atlas sur vey located Marsh Tits in 21.8% of tetrads with breeding confirmed in 14.2%: very few were noted in the south, east and far northwest. The species' distribution was remarkably similar to that of the Willow Tit. The ongoing decline appears to be due to low annual survival rates (G. M. Sinwardena unpublished) which have perhaps been caused by a number of factors, such as increasing woodland isolation, loss of woodland under-storey due to grazing and a reduction in dead wood (Vanhinsbergh *et al.* 2003, Perrins 2003).

Since the end of the Essex Atlas survey in 1994, the contraction in range has continued across many areas with the rate of decline appearing to increase during the 1990s. Thus at Hainault Forest CP the population dropped rapidly after 1995. However, there were signs in the late 1990s that some populations may have at least stabilised and possibly increased, although these hopes seem to have been dashed in the early 2000s; variable observer coverage may be a factor. Almost all breeding records now come from the west of Essex with very few east of a line drawn north-south between Halstead and Chelmsford. Recently up to eight pairs have been found in Epping Forest (1999), five in Chesterford Park (1998), four in Chalkney Wood (2004), three in 2004 in Garnetts Wood and Newport area (where a count of 12 on 3rd September 2004 presumably involved family par-ties) and two at: Hatfield Forest, Barnston and Newport in 2003; Ongar Park Wood and Belchamp Walter in 2000; and Latton Park and Parndon Wood in 1999. A record in the *EBR* 1998 of breeding at Hockley Woods is erroneous (Steve Arlow pers. comm.).

Marsh Tits are at their most common in deciduous woodlands and during 1975–80, CBC data from Hainault Forest CP, Parndon and Weeleyhall Wood revealed a mean density of 11 pairs per km^2 (cf. Willow Tit). More recently, the species has become so scarce in Essex that it has not occurred on CBC/BBS sites, except in The Mores Wood, near Brentwood, where there was just one pair during the 1990s.

The Marsh Tit is remarkably sedentary. Birds apparently pair for life and seldom wander outside their territories even in hard weather. They may occasionally attach themselves to a feeding flock passing through their territory but will drop out of it as the flock passes across the territorial boundary (Perrins 1979). Of the four ringing recoveries involving Essex, the furthest movement was just 12km, from Langdon Hills to Hadleigh. Undoubtedly some do wander further, as Marsh Tits appear to be more widespread during winter than in the breeding season. A juvenile that was ringed at Bradwell and stayed in the area for over a month had presumably wandered from a nearby population; the movement is nonetheless unusual.

Although a number of suggestions have been made for the Marsh Tit's decline, the actual causes are unclear. In Essex, pressure from grazing by deer in woodland has undoubtedly reduced woodland undergrowth and the appar-ent overzealous desire to tidy away deadwood may have reduced the number of nest sites. Has the success of the Blue and Great Tit in adapting and using artificial feeding given them a distinct survival advantage over Marsh (and Willow) Tits, which simply cannot compete (Radford 2003)? The Marsh Tit's future in Essex remains uncertain.

Stock*					
	1962-66	1967-71	1972-76	1977-81	1982-86
Marsh Tit	31	53	17	1	0
Willow Tit	4	29	55	36	19

Ongar/Epping**		
	1971-80	* large garden
Marsh Tit	90	** mixed woodland/sewage farm
Willow Tit	303	

Cumulative ringing totals of Marsh and Willow Tits in two areas of southern Essex, adapted from Hurrell (1989) and Cox

Nuthatch

Sitta europaea

Locally common and sedentary resident

The Nuthatch occurs in Continental middle latitudes of the Palearctic from Morocco and Portugal east through Russia to Japan and Kamchatka and then south and west to China, southeast Asia into India and the Himalayas (European Atlas). In Britain, the species is represented by the race *caesia*, which is also found across much of Continental Europe, whilst the nominate race *europaea* occurs across northern Europe; although largely sedentary *europaea* shows slight irruptive tendencies. Nuthatches are found throughout England and Wales with the greatest abundance occurring south and west of a line drawn from the Mersey to the Thames (Second National Atlas). Nuthatches are birds of old woodland, parkland and extensive gardens where there are sufficient numbers of large trees for feeding and nest holes. They are strictly territorial and monogamous, their first autumn/winter territory usually becoming their breeding territory in which they then remain (Enoksson 1990). This highly sedentary behaviour is a requirement for a good knowledge of their territories, which in turn enables a pair to find and hoard food. Food hoarding is vital for their survival through winter (Enoksson 1990).

Christy described the Nuthatch as "A fairly-common resident throughout the county, especially in Skreens, Audley End, Thorndon, Hylands, Danbury and other parks, where the numerous ancient trees afford suitable nesting sites". He also noted its presence around Sudbury, Buckhurst Hill, Stanway and Harwich. Glegg's summary of the species' status was similar with almost all records coming from the old parks, namely Gosfield, Easton, Birch and Lawford, as well as in Epping and Hatfield Forests. In Epping Forest it was considered local, its headquarters being around the High Beech area.

Hudson & Pyman considered the Nuthatch to be local and scarce, noting that it favoured old parkland and woodland lacking secondary growth. The rapid growth of Birch over many areas of Essex probably reduced the amount of suitable habitat during the 20th century. For these sedentary birds, fragmentation of the British woodland landscape and the resultant small size of many ancient woods surrounded by predominantly open farming landscapes, has had a marked effect; many seemingly suitable small woodlands are unoccupied (Second National Atlas). This goes some way to explain the species' rather patchy distribution both nationally and in Essex.

Despite this, the overall trend across Essex since WWII appears to have been one of colonisation and population increase. Nationally, the CBC/BBS (England) Index for the period 1977–2002 increased by 86% with the BBS (England) Index for 1994–2003 increasing by 37%. The local CBC Index has, however, shown a slow decline, which has also been suggested by anecdotal evidence from some well-watched sites across Essex since the early 1990s, although this may have been due to reduced observer coverage following the end of the Essex Atlas survey period in 1994. Local BBS Indices have, since the mid-1990s, been relatively stable.

The first *EBR* in 1949 suggested that declines had been noted from some areas, with increases in others. By 1951, Nuthatches were apparently extending their range, at least in mid-Essex and had probably increased in the Colchester area too. Reports during the rest of

Atlas	Survey Area	% of 10km squares or tetrads in which	
		bred/probably bred	possibly bred or present
First National 10km	Essex	45.6	8.8
Second National 10km	Essex	56.1	19.3
First London Tetrad	Met. Essex	12.5	4.5
Second London Tetrad	Met. Essex	30.0	4.0
Essex Tetrad	Essex	14.5	4.8

Summary of results of Atlas surveys for Nuthatches

the 1950s were inconclusive but suggestive of a steady increase. During the 1960s, a decline appears to have taken place, although the species was first recorded from Hainault in 1962. The *EBR* 1968 noted that the Nuthatch was "Apparently even scarcer than it was formerly", whilst the *EBR* 1969 stated that the species was "… very thin on the ground" outside Metropolitan Essex. The trend through the 1970s was unclear but, during the 1980s, numbers certainly increased again with a new 'colony' of 2–3 pairs established at Chalkney Wood, away from the main population centres, in 1984. In addition, there were substantial increases at several sites: Hainault Forest, three pairs in 1969 to 15 by 1990; Thorndon CP, 3–4 pairs in 1974 to 18 in 1987; Writtle Forest area, about five pairs in 1971 to 10–15 in 1982; and Hatfield Forest, 1–2 pairs in 1960 to seven in 1982.

Surveys for the two National and two London Atlases revealed a range expansion, particularly in northern Metropolitan Essex. It has been suggested that the Nuthatch has benefited from the range expansion of the Great Spotted Woodpecker, the Nuthatch following once the woodpecker has carved out the nest holes (Second London Atlas).

The Essex Atlas survey revealed the Nuthatch to be present in 19.3% of all tetrads, with confirmed breeding in 14.5%. The population was concentrated in the southwest and at sites such as Hatfield Forest, Belfairs Park and the woodlands of the Danbury Ridge, with a general absence in the northeast and along the coast. By the end of the 1990s a significant decline appears to have occurred at Hainault Forest where, following a rapid rise and fall in breeding numbers between 1986 and 1992, rather than levelling out at early-1980s densities, the population has shown continued signs of decline (the late Mike Dennis pers. comm.). At sites in or around the Roman River, Nuthatches appear to have almost completely disappeared since the beginning of the 21st century. Elsewhere, however, trends have been less clear, with some populations stable, some showing slight increases and others decreasing. At Little Baddow, for example, numbers peaked in the early 1990s but appear to have declined during the mid-1990s, yet at Danbury Park, only a short distance away, numbers appear to have remained stable. In recent years, *EBRs* have confirmed that Weald CP, with seven pairs, and Ongar Park Wood, with five, have the largest populations away from Epping Forest, although the species is undoubtedly under-recorded elsewhere.

The pattern of increase and decline seems to be fairly typical of the Nuthatch and may be related to autumn food supplies (e.g. Enoksson 1990) but there are no detailed records from sites to corroborate this hypothesis, nor sufficient information about Beech or Hornbeam mast crops. However, it is known that in areas with Beech (e.g. Epping Forest) the mast crop is an important food source for Nuthatches and the size of this crop is closely correlated to the population level of the birds the following year (Enoksson & Nilsson 1983, Nilsson 1987). Such a close link to such a variable winter food supply suggests vulnerability of small, fragmented Nuthatch populations to extinction. Perhaps the rapid population decreases seen at Lexden from 15+ pairs in 1961 to none in 1965 and more recently at Hainault are examples of this.

Despite the range expansion, the fragmented nature of the species' habitat means that the county population is small. Cox estimated that there might only be between 250 and 300 pairs (0.23% of the British population), over 50% of which were thought to be in the Epping Forest area. The Epping Forest population of 150–200 pairs was extrapolated from sample densities in various CBC plots. In 1990, the *EBR* noted 14 pairs in Wintry Wood, a density of 7–8 pairs per km^2, whilst in 1999 50 random point counts across 1,100 hectares of woodland in Epping Forest produced an estimate of 140–150 pairs for the whole Forest at a density of 12.5 pairs per km^2 (J. R. Dagley unpublished data). Within the limits of the comparison of these different methods, this suggests a stable, if patchily distributed, population in Epping Forest of 150–200 pairs during the last 20 years. At Parndon Wood CBC site, densities averaged around 23 pairs per km^2 during the 1980s whilst in The Mores Wood, near Brentwood, the density equated to slightly fewer than four pairs per km^2. At the time of the Essex Atlas survey the total Essex population probably stood at 300 to 350 pairs, although apparent declines since then suggest that today the population is nearer the lower end of this estimate.

Nuthatches are extremely sedentary; of all ringed Nuthatches ringed nationally that have been reported subsequently, 95% were recovered within 15km of the ringing locality, with many within 1km. There have, however, been several records during the 1990s that suggest a degree of wandering from natal areas. These included two records from Bradwell, the first records for Dengie, on 1st July 1991 and 21st June 1992, respectively. More remarkable was one ringed at Shifnal, Shropshire, on 9th August 1985 and found dead nearly 12 years later on 19th May 1997 at Bradwell Power Station. The distance of 246km travelled is by far the furthest of any Nuthatch recovered in Britain. It is also the oldest British-ringed Nuthatch to have been reported to the BTO. Coincidentally, the next longest movement of 87km involved one first ringed at Reedham, near Great Yarmouth, Norfolk, on 26th September 1987, re-trapped there on 20th February 1988 and subsequently recovered at Colchester on 14th April 1990.

It is not clear yet how to interpret the most recent data from the Nuthatch's Essex strongholds. Monitoring work is planned which should help understand the apparent trends. Elsewhere in Essex, and supported by the national figures, there is still reason to be optimistic about the future of this species and its habitat. However, to understand better the dynamics of the county population, many more reports are needed from the fringes of its range and from isolated, smaller woodland and parkland sites.

(Eurasian) Treecreeper — *Certhia familiaris*

Common resident

The Treecreeper is distributed across the Palearctic from Ireland to the Caucasus, Himalayas, Siberia and Tian Shen, reaching Korea and Japan. Treecreepers breed in most European countries, generally between the 14°–24°C July isotherms. In Britain, the species is generally widespread, although absent mainly from highlands, open moorland and extensive areas of commercially managed forestry (Second National Atlas). It is typical of lowland deciduous woodlands in Britain, a role taken by the Short-toed Treecreeper *C. brachydactyla* on the Continent, where the Treecreeper is more typical of upland coniferous forests. The Treecreeper is a tree bark specialist, nesting, feeding and roosting there and usually only resorting to very short flights between trees. Its specialist adaptations make it one of the most sedentary of birds (Flegg 1973). The British and Central European race *britannica* is generally sedentary, although subject to small-scale dispersal outside the breeding season. Northern populations of the nominate race *familiaris* head southwest in autumn but normally stay within Scandinavia (European Atlas).

Both Christy and Glegg described the Treecreeper as a common resident, found in suitable habitat throughout Essex. Glegg and Hudson & Pyman commented on the species' inconspicuous nature, which was probably the reason for the rather brief and vague summaries given by all the previous authors. Likewise, the Treecreeper was not mentioned in the Systematic List of the *EBR* until 1974 and it was not until 1979 that any reference to breeding numbers or distribution was made. Even during the last two decades this unobtrusive behaviour appears to have affected reporting, and population estimates from sites appear to vary markedly from year to year.

Like the Nuthatch, the Treecreeper's distribution is determined largely by the distribution of suitable woodland. The two National Atlases confirmed a generally westerly distribution in Essex, with apparent declines in the east between the two survey periods. The Essex Atlas survey located the Treecreeper in 35.9% of all tetrads, with breeding in 27.8%. It is thus more widespread than the Nuthatch, being more able to use conifers regularly and adapt to plantations and smaller woodlands. Particularly when popula-

Atlas	Survey Area	% of 10km squares or tetrads in which	
		bred/probably bred	possibly bred or present
First National 10km	Essex	84.2	10.5
Second National 10km	Essex	71.9	15.8
First London Tetrad	Met. Essex	21.0	9.5
Second London Tetrad	Met. Essex	50.0	4.0
Essex Tetrad	Essex	27.8	8.1

Summary of results of Atlas surveys for Treecreepers

tion levels are high, Treecreepers will hold territory in other habitats that include mature trees such as farmland spinneys and tree lines, parks, churchyards and large gardens (Population Trends). The species' stronghold remains in the more wooded southwest of the county, and it is absent from some squares in the south and southeast, although it breeds at several locations on Dengie and in the northeast. The two London Atlas surveys revealed a notable range expansion that is unlikely to be due to increased observer coverage alone and may be related to improved winter survival following a run of mild winters.

From CBC survey data, Cox produced an extrapolated estimate of 13–30 pairs per km^2. The lower figure was the average from all the survey data, which included plots from 1964 in which none were recorded after the severe winter of 1962/63. The higher figure was taken from other CBC plots as an estimate of a likely upper limit to the average density. CBC data since 1980 suggest average densities from woodland to be around 12 pairs per km^2 (range 6–17), whilst on farmland fewer than one pair per km^2 (range 0–1.4). Until recently, the main counts from Epping Forest came from Wintry Wood, near Epping, where an average of 15 pairs was noted through the late 1980s, increasing to 20 pairs in 1990. This provides a relatively low density estimate in the range of 8–10 pairs per km^2. In 1999, a census in Epping Forest using 50 random point counts across 1,100ha of woodland, produced a density estimate of 13 pairs per km^2 (J. R. Dagley unpublished data) which is similar to other Essex data, although it is possible that as the survey was conducted at the end of April and early May, the peak of Treecreeper activity was missed. For Epping Forest as a whole, a density of 13 pairs per km^2 approximates to a population of 156 pairs, the largest concentration of Treecreepers in Essex.

It seems, therefore, that the Essex population as a whole has remained generally stable, although increases may have occurred in the Metropolitan area, whereas the local BBS has identified a decline since 1999. Nationally, the pattern has been of fluctuation with no overall long-term trend with the BBS (England) Index for 1994–2003 declining by just 2%; local trends have also been fairly dynamic.

In winter, when Treecreepers associate with tit flocks, the species can be at its most conspicuous. In the 1960s, ringers at Colchester used to catch (by dazzling) significant numbers of Treecreepers at night roosting on *Wellingtonia* trunks in the grounds of an elderly persons' home near Distillery Pond (Simon Cox pers. comm.). Otherwise there have been no other noteworthy winter records or reports of winter roosts. The species is badly affected by cold winters, particularly when there are extended periods of glazed frost or freezing rain (Harrap & Quinn 1996). After the winter of 1962/63, none could be found on Essex CBC plots during 1964 (Essex Atlas); populations generally contract back to the favoured woodland habitat when levels are low (Population Trends).

Albinos have been noted on two occasions: Larkswood, Chingford, 25th January–20th February 1986; and Weald CP during 1996/97, last seen on 31st March 1997.

As the British race is very sedentary, records at coastal sites are very rare and could conceivably involve the nominate northern race or even the very similar Short-toed Treecreeper. One possible migrant, not ascribed to a species, was at Holliwell Point on 15th April 1974, whilst two individuals appeared in the Observatory thicket at Bradwell on 31st October 1982, the first in 30 years of regular recording. At least one appeared to show characteristics of Short-toed Treecreeper but could not be identified with certainty. Treecreepers were not recorded at Bradwell again until 1993 when individuals were seen on 10th March and 1st August. One was at Holland Haven on 20th July 1991 and another was trapped and ringed there on 23rd August 1998; the two races are very difficult to separate, even in the hand, although it is most likely that the latter was *britannica*.

There are just eight ringing recoveries affecting Essex and all involved individuals that had travelled less than 15km, four having travelled less than 5km. One trapped as an adult near Little Burstead on 2nd March 1969 was at least seven years old when retrapped at the same site on 30th March 1975.

At present the Essex population appears to be stable and perhaps increasing, helped by the relatively mild winters of recent years. Against a background of a steadily increasing national population, well-protected sites in its areas of highest populations and with the promise of new community forests in many areas, there seems to be a favourable long-term outlook for this species in Essex. Abroad, the provision of nest boxes has markedly increased population densities (*BWP*), something that has yet to be attempted on any great scale in this country.

Short-toed Treecreeper   *Certhia brachydactyla*

Vagrant: one record

The Short-toed Treecreeper is found throughout central and southwest Europe, Italy and the Balkan countries as well as Turkey and northern-most Africa. The nominate race *brachydactyla* occurs throughout much of Continental Europe, with *megarhyncha* being found in western Europe.

1975	Epping Forest	26th May

Although considered extremely sedentary, it has been postulated that in recently occupied breeding areas along the edge of its breeding range in, for instance, western Netherlands, Denmark and Poland, the species might be a partial winter migrant (European Atlas). This could possibly explain why all but four of the 21 British records to the end of 2003 (BBRC 2004) have been from Kent. However, its extreme similarity to Common Treecreeper must act against more regular identification.

This was just the sixth British record and one of very few historic records accepted by BBRC before field identification criteria were determined. It was identified by, amongst other more subtle field characters, its distinctive Coal Tit-like call. At least one of two treecreepers at Bradwell on 31st October 1982 was considered to show characteristics of Short-toed Treecreeper.

(Eurasian) Penduline Tit   *Remiz pendulinus*

Vagrant: three records of five birds

The Penduline Tit is a southern Palearctic species breeding from Finland, Sweden, Portugal, Spain and Iran across to northeast China. The species' typical habitat is wetland with a mosaic of reeds, bulrushes and other rank vegetation with patches of bushes and small trees (Harrap & Quinn 1996). The nominate race *pendulinus* is principally restricted to Europe west of the Don/Volga watershed and winters in south and southwest Europe; south European populations are largely resident (European Atlas).

1982	North Ockendon	during June	
1997	Cudmore Grove CP	30th October–5th November	Female/1st-winter
2004	Rainham	29th December	Three adults

The 1982 occurrence was the fifth British record, whilst 1997 was the best year on record nationally with 22 reported. Multiple occurrences are not unusual. The first British record was not until 1966, since when the species has become far more regular with a total of 183, mostly autumnal occurrences, to the end of 2004 (BBRC 2005); a considerable range expansion has occurred on the Continent since the 1950s and the species is a strong candidate to colonise this side of the Channel (European Atlas). Although the Netherlands, which was colonised in 1981, may be a likely source of vagrants, two Swedish individuals have been recovered in Britain and one ringed at Icklesham, Sussex, in October 1988 was subsequently recovered in Sweden in May 1989.

(Eurasian) Golden Oriole   *Oriolus oriolus*

Scarce passage migrant and summer visitor — has bred unsuccessfully on three occasions   Amber List

The Golden Oriole inhabits the Palearctic region east as far as the Altai Mountains and India: the nominate race *oriolus* occurs throughout Europe, where its distribution generally matches that of Oak, occurring in open woodland with a light understorey and adjacent small water bodies. Numerous physiological and behavioural characteristics indicate that it is an exotic, a bird of tropical woodland origin (European Atlas). In Britain, the Golden Oriole is largely confined to the East Anglian fen basin, where it nests almost exclusively in hybrid Black Poplar plantations: a nucleus of around 30–40 breeding pairs across ten 10km squares (Second National Atlas, Dagley 1994) declined, however, to just 4–8 pairs in 2002 (RBBP 2004). The Golden Oriole winters primarily in eastern Africa and south as far as South Africa and exhibits a tendency to migrate further west in spring than in autumn.

Christy noted that the Golden Oriole was "A rare and accidental summer visitor, though a good many specimens have been shot in the county. It seems very probable that it would on more than one occasion have bred with us, had it not been molested ...". The exotic coloration of the species clearly fascinated the Victorian hunter-naturalist, some 13 of the 16 19th century records subsequently accepted by Glegg involving birds that had been shot. The earliest documented Essex record involved one shot by a gamekeeper at Lawford Hall, Manningtree, on 10th May 1830. It was not, however, only the hunter-naturalists who were interested by the species, Christy himself devoting more text to it than most others in his book. He considered that there were no satisfactory Essex breeding records, although it was suggested that breeding occurred on more than one occasion at Warley Place, whilst a pair was said to have bred in a conifer near Saffron Walden in 1841. A pair frequented a garden at Leyton for several days in 1850; the female was shot on 25th May and found on dissection to contain two fully developed eggs. On 16th June 1874, a pair was shot in the rectory garden at Bradwell.

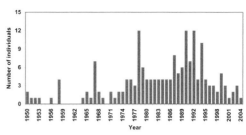

Annual totals of assumed migrant Golden Orioles (i.e. those observed on no more than three days at any one site) from 1950-2004

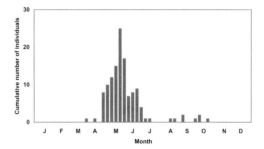

Seasonal occurrence of Golden Orioles from 1950-2004

The Golden Oriole was observed consistently enough in the 19th century to be considered an Essex breeding bird worthy of conservation. In a lengthy response to the EFC's petition of 1895 to the County Council seeking enhanced protection for certain nesting birds, the chairman of the Council's Wild Birds Protection Committee, Mr Champion B. Russell, informed the Club that amongst other birds that his Committee would shortly be seeking to protect were "such rare, useful and easily distinguished birds as owls, reed pheasant [Bearded Tit] and the golden oriole" (Cole 1895).

Glegg was only able to add two further records, noting "It would seem that the visits of the Golden Oriole to the county are becoming more infrequent". Of the 18 records he considered acceptable, all fell in the period 25th April–16th June.

Hudson & Pyman described the Golden Oriole as an "Irregular non-breeding summer visitor", a description that fitted the national picture of a rare bird in decline at that time (Sharrock 1974, First National Atlas).

In the late 1960s, what was perhaps the same male made protracted stays on Foulness from 1967–69, being paired with a female on 13th May 1967 but otherwise on its own. From the 1970s, Golden Orioles began to be recorded with increasing regularity in Essex. Whilst this may have been in part due to increased observer coverage, this does not appear to have been the sole reason; it was probably no more than coincidence that the increase occurred at the time of the expansion of the Poplar plantation populations in East Anglia as the respective populations may have had different origins (see below). The increase saw individuals and pairs making increasingly protracted stays in suitable habitat at several sites across Essex. In 1978, a considerable increase in spring records resulted in the first breeding attempt when a pair nested at Tillingham. Unfortunately, although a nest with young was located, it was thought that they did not fledge. Territories were held at three further sites that year with birds present at one of these, a site in the Tendring Hundred, for the following two years as well. During the early 1980s, Golden Orioles were present at two sites in central Essex during mid-June but breeding was never proven. By the late 1980s, sites in the Tendring Hundred had become favoured with many tantalising accounts of birds behaving territorially at a number of woods during the middle of the breeding season. In 1989 a breeding attempt was confirmed at one of the most favoured woodlands in this area, in which two singing males were present that year. The nest was in a Sweet Chestnut at a height of 15m, close to the average recorded in studies of this species (Dagley 1994, Bijlsma 1995). It was situated in a typical location in the outer canopy towards the end of a main branch. However, the pair was disturbed by Jays and Grey Squirrels (Reg Arthur pers. comm.) and the nest later abandoned, possibly as a result of continuing interference or predation.

In 1991, breeding probably occurred at one site in the northeast and possibly in central Essex, too. In the national survey, coordinated by the Golden Oriole Group in 1994, singing males were heard at a record six sites in the northeast. However, no further breeding attempts were uncovered even with a repeated national survey in 1995 and by 1997 there were no reports from the most favoured woodlands including the 1989 breeding site, which was surveyed specifically by experienced observers. In 1999, a pair was present in central Essex from 18th–23rd July, whilst in 2002 a pair was found in woodland near Thorpe-le-Soken on 29th June, although there was no evidence that they had bred. The decline in apparently territorial birds has mirrored the declines seen in the main Fenland population. Bad weather in the late 1990s at critical times probably affected rearing and fledging success and probably increased the predation risk (RBBP 2001).

Almost all of the more recent Essex breeding attempts have been in ancient coppiced woodlands of Sweet Chestnut, Hornbeam and Oak, not in Poplar plantations typical of the Fenland population. This may suggest that, despite the increases in Essex occurring at the same time as those in the Fens, Essex Golden Orioles have a different origin (Essex Atlas). In countries on the limit of its European breeding range, the species tends to be very specific in its habitat requirements, almost exclusively favouring commercial Poplar cultivars on damp or wet soils near open water or rivers (Second National Atlas, Bijlsma 1995). Even when a Poplar plantation adjoins a larger broad-leaved woodland area, Golden Orioles will invariably use the plantation for nesting and carrying out the majority of their foraging (Dagley 1994, Bijlsma 1995). Across the wider Continent, however, the species is much more catholic in its choice of nest sites, which range from parks, gardens and orchards through to coniferous woodland. The most frequently used trees for nesting and feeding are Oaks, with Alders and Poplars also much frequented. In the Netherlands, close to the edge of the breeding range, preference is shown towards Poplar plantations, whereas in core areas of population, such as in France, Oaks and Chestnuts are preferred: breeding attempts in Essex may therefore involve French rather than Dutch birds.

The Golden Oriole is a relatively late migrant with most records falling in May and usually involving singing males at one site for a day. They are followed ten days or so later by the more unobtrusive females (Dagley 1994). The earliest arrival involved one on Foulness on 11th April 1990; the record of male at Fingringhoe Wick on 29th March 1973 must, on current knowledge, be considered suspect. Passage peaks around the end of May, although there appears to be a secondary peak in June: perhaps the two peaks suggest the arrival of individuals from different (French and Dutch) areas?

Autumn passage is rarely observed, the first Essex record not occurring until 1958 when a male was at North Fambridge on 9th September. Since then there have been just five more: Fingringhoe Wick, a male, 22nd August 1971; Hanningfield, one, 16th August 1980; Dagenham Chase, a male, 24th September 1992; The Naze, one, 4th September 1996; and Coney Hall, Dengie, one, 19th October 1997, the latest county record. A record of a male and female/immature in Epping Forest on 3rd October 1976 must be considered suspect in the light of current knowledge.

The total number of records varies considerably from year to year. Records of assumed migrants are split fairly evenly between coastal and inland sites and, although no inland site has been particularly favoured, many have come from well-wooded areas with the majority involving singing males for one day only. On the coast, almost 40% of the records have come from Foulness and 20% from Dengie and, although most involve single birds, there were three (a male and two females) at Linford on 6th May 1967 and two at: The Naze, 18th May 1965 and 24th May 1998; Foulness, 13th May 1967 (although the male of the pair stayed until mid-June), 23rd–26th April 1986 and 30th–31st May 1992; Hadleigh, 25th April 1975; Belfairs, 27th May 1985, as well as the previously mentioned October 1976 record in Epping Forest.

There seems to be no shortage of habitat for the Golden Oriole in Essex; pairs can breed in very small plantations with access to relatively few trees (Dagley 1994). It is unclear why in this century no nest sites have been found in the garden locations apparently so regularly used in the 19th century, and Poplar too seems to be underused (or perhaps simply under-recorded because of lack of access). However, the rarity of the bird and its high rate of breeding failures make it difficult for the species to expand its range.

Although global climate change has raised the average yearly temperature, the wet summers of recent years have been unfavourable to breeding success. Nest predation (e.g. by Jays) may also be a limiting factor for Golden Orioles in the majority of woodlands. Poplar plantations may be favoured because of the lack of winter resident species, including predators, and the high proportion of summer migrants: the 'tundra effect' (Dagley 1994). Whatever the problems, the Golden Oriole has remained an exceptionally rare Essex breeding bird for at least 150 years. Given a run of drier summers, higher average annual temperatures and promotion of new woodlands, there is still a good chance that it may maintain its precarious foothold and yet become a bright symbol of the changing climate.

Isabelline Shrike

Lanius isabellinus

Vagrant: one record

The Isabelline Shrike breeds from Iran east to Mongolia and winters in south and southwest Asia. Three races are recognised, of which two — *isabellinus* and *phoenicuroides* — have occurred as vagrants in Europe (Worfolk 2000). In the species' eastern Palearctic range it inhabits rather dry steppes or semi-deserts (Lefranc & Worfolk 1997).

1988	Sandbeach, Dengie	23rd–28th October	1st-winter

This individual was initially seen flying below the observers as they cycled along the seawall (O'Dowd 1989); it was not subspecifically identified. A total of 66 had been recorded nationally to the end of 2004 (BBRC 2005), the majority since the mid-1970s and it is now an almost annual vagrant. The increase in occurrence has probably been due to greater observer coverage. This was the 23rd British record on a typical date and in the best year for this species when seven occurred. It had presumably reverse migrated from its breeding grounds.

Red-backed Shrike

Lanius collurio

Uncommon, principally autumn passage migrant: bred until 1981

Red List

The Red-backed Shrike is a Palearctic species breeding throughout Europe except for Britain and Ireland, northern Fennoscandia, northern Russia, much of central/southern Iberia and most of the Mediterranean Islands. The nominate race *collurio* occurs over much of the species' range. A severe decline has occurred at the northern and western limits of the Red-backed Shrike's range across northwest Europe over the last 50 years and particularly in the last 20–30. This decline saw populations collapse in Sweden, the Netherlands and Belgium; there have been recent signs of a small recovery in most of these countries. A general decline over the species' range, however, continues (Migration Atlas). In Britain, the rapid decline to extinction as a breeding bird has been well documented. Still common around 1900, by 1940 there were signs of a range contraction. By 1960, there were only about 253 pairs left and in 1971 just 80–90. In 1989, the Red-backed Shrike was lost as a regular breeding species, although sporadic breeding has occurred since. Possibly the decline was climatically induced (Bibby 1973) with cooler, wetter summers reducing insect prey, hence its particular effect in the Atlantic climate belt. However, deterioration and destruction of farmland habitat (Hustings & Bekhuis 1993) and droughts in the Kalahari (Bruderer & Bruderer 1993, Herremans 1993) may have also had a negative influence. Red-backed Shrikes winter principally in the tropics and southern Africa across to the Persian Gulf and northwest India.

Even as early as 1890, Christy had observed that Red-backed Shrike numbers were prone to varying markedly from year to year. He commented that "... it appears to be decreasing with us", although added little to support

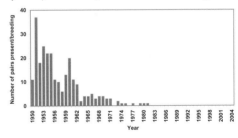

Annual number of pairs of Red-backed Shrikes from 1950-2004

his statement. This accords with a general decline noted across the country from about the mid-19th century (Historical Atlas). Even by Glegg's time, however, there were no signs of a serious decline but he, too, noted the considerable annual variation in numbers. For instance, there were 14 nests around Felsted School in 1911 but only 3–4 in the next five years.

From the 1940s, the decline appeared to accelerate, although there were still 17 pairs around Epping Forest in 1945. The subsequent decline was rapid. By the time of a countywide survey in 1951, which was considered a very good year for the species, there were just 37 pairs and eight single birds spread widely across Essex. Of the 37 pairs, eight were in Chelmsford and 11 in Colchester districts. By 1965–66, just 6–7 pairs remained, the population centred on the remnant heathland around Danbury and Colchester. The species last bred at: Rochford in 1961 (five pairs); Great Chesterford, Epping Forest, Brentwood and Havering in 1962; Sewardstone and Grays probably in 1964; and Highwood, near Blackmore, in 1967. At Danbury the last pair bred in 1969, when at the fifth attempt a pair successfully raised young. By 1973, there were just two pairs and an odd male around Colchester. Odd pairs bred here, albeit less than annually, until 1981 when the species was last recorded breeding in Essex, on

Layer Breton Heath eight years before the species' last stand in Suffolk. There have been no further records of likely breeding attempts.

The Red-backed Shrike is well known as the 'Butcher-bird', its habit of impaling prey on thorns for later consumption being described by one of Christy's correspondents in the 1880s: "It is very common in Essex ... I have seen the old bird kill as many as five field-mice in one day. They lift the mouse up on their beaks and hitch it on to a thorn and then pull it down with all their weight and strength. I think they are put on thorns for the convenience of eating at the time, as they seldom finish any animal".

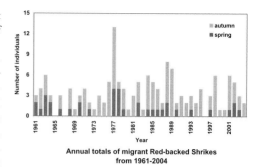

Annual totals of migrant Red-backed Shrikes
from 1961-2004

Numbers of migrants have remained fairly constant over the last 50 years, although fewer were recorded in the 1990s; nationally, annual occurrences have fallen from an average of 255 per annum from 1986–89 to 200 from 2000–02 (Fraser & Rogers 2004).

The first generally arrive in late April, the earliest being at Creeksea on 23rd April 1963 and a female at Stambridge on 23rd April 1978. Spring migrants are less than annual and rarely number more than two. Arrivals peak during May.

During the last 25 years there have been just four mid-summer records of single birds away from breeding areas: The Naze, 24th June 1977; a male at Heybridge GP, 8th July 1987; a male at Woodford, 5th July 1994; and a male at Old Hall, 23rd June 2002.

Autumn passage commences in early July and peaks in mid-September. Some individuals have made extended stays, the longest being a juvenile at Holland Haven from 27th August–20th September 1995. The latest county record involved a juvenile trapped and ringed at Wanstead SF on 1st November 1980, whilst singles were present at Wat Tyler CP on 28th October 2001 and St Lawrence Bay on 24th October 1976.

Migrants have been recorded all around the coast, although the northeast is particularly favoured and individuals have been recorded at The Naze in 14 years since 1980. Occasional migrants turn up well inland with 16 since 1980, including an immature killed by a car at Clavering in the extreme northwest on 16th September 1989.

Although there have been no ringing recoveries in Essex, it is likely that migrants are from both Fennoscandian and north/east European populations displaced here by easterly winds.

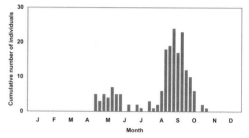

Seasonal occurrence of migrant Red-backed Shrikes
from 1961-2004

Lesser Grey Shrike *Lanius minor*

Vagrant: two records

The Lesser Grey Shrike breeds across southern Europe east to southern Russia where it is typical of the steppe. Two races are recognised: *minor* in the western part of the range and *turanicus* in the east (Lefranc & Worfolk 1997). The species is a long-distance migrant that winters in southern Africa.

1989	Great Wakering	17th–27th August	Male
1990	Old Hall/Salcott	26th June–5th July	Male

The MoD allowed special access for the hundreds of birders to view the 1989 individual (Prentice 1990). Whilst there had been 170 British records to the end of 2004 (BBRC 2005), the species has shown signs of becoming less frequent in recent years, mirroring a worrying decline on the Continent that began after WWI, but has accelerated since the 1960s (European Atlas). Nationally, most records occur between mid-May and the end of July and peak in late May/early June; presumably these are overshooting northward-bound migrants. Smaller numbers occur between mid-August and mid-November, either involving birds dispersing from their breeding grounds or, perhaps, reverse migrants.

Great Grey Shrike

Lanius excubitor

Scarce passage migrant and winter visitor

The Great Grey Shrike is a Holarctic species comprising some nine races and having a wide breeding range lying mainly in the taiga belt, which extends over the northern parts of the American continent and Eurasia. In the latter region, it is absent from Iceland and the British Isles in the west and from the Kamchatka peninsula in the east. The species reaches its southwest limit in the Old World in France (Lefranc & Worfolk 1997). The nominate race *excubitor* occurs over most of Europe. The species is a partial migrant with northern populations vacating their breeding areas in winter. The species declined over much of western Europe during the 20th century.

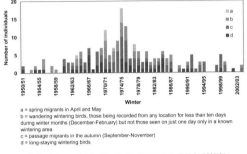

a = spring migrants in April and May
b = wandering wintering birds, those being recorded from any location for less than ten days during winter months (December-February) but not those seen on just one day only in a known wintering area
c = passage migrants in the autumn (September-November)
d = long-staying wintering birds

Estimated annual totals of Great Grey Shrikes from 1950/51-2003/04

Christy went into great detail in respect of the species' status in Essex. He considered that the Great Grey Shrike was at one time more common and described it as "An occasional visitor met with ... in most years from autumn to spring, and very exceptionally in summer". In all, he detailed records in at least 23 years from the first, at "Wendon" in 1827, to the last in 1890; almost all were shot. It would appear to have been relatively common in some districts, for example around Colchester it was apparently shot most years, whilst in the 1830s around Saffron Walden "... generally two or three are killed every season, during the winter". Five in 1889 appears to be the most recorded in any one year, whilst one that was found dead after flying against telegraph wires at Colchester in 1888 was an early example of such an unnatural death.

Although the Great Grey Shrike has never been proved to breed in Britain (European Atlas), Christy described a nest belonging to a "grey slate-coloured bird" taken near Audley End "... many years ago". The eggs were taken to Walden Museum for comparison, where in the opinion of the very respected naturalist Joseph Clarke they were considered to belong to the Great Grey Shrike, but he could not persuade the boy who collected the nest to part with it.

Glegg described the species as "... a very scarce winter visitor ... recorded almost annually". He added a further ten or so records, noting that, of the 38 dated occurrences, 20 fell between October and December and 18 between January and March and that occasionally individuals would remain in some areas for several months. It is difficult to discern a particular trend during the first half of the 20th century; it appears that numbers remained fairly stable.

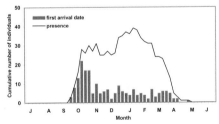

Seasonal occurrence of Great Grey Shrikes from 1950-2004 by a) first arrival date and b) weekly presence

Numbers of wintering Great Grey Shrikes are notoriously difficult to estimate as they probably wander over huge areas (Fraser & Ryan 1995), a problem alluded to by Cox. Hudson & Pyman suggested that there were never more than six individuals each "winter" and "... usually only two or three..." including migrants. Up until 1967, only eight birds had been known to make extended stays in Essex. However, a genuine increase occurred from the mid-1960s (Cox) with an average of seven for the winters 1967/68–1981/82, with just one in 1967/68 but two exceptional influxes of 18 in 1974/75 and 13 in the following winter. Since 1975/76, however, numbers have declined with six being the highest recent count and the average number reported being fewer than three. By the 1990s, the species was becoming particularly scarce with none reported in several winters. The graph of occurrence has been produced using similar methods to those employed by Fraser & Ryan (1995). Nationally, the number occurring annually has declined from an average of 131 from 1986–89 to 89 during 2000–02 (Fraser & Rogers 2004).

It is noticeable that the decline seems to have occurred because of a reduction of long-staying individuals, since the number of autumn migrants has remained around the long-term average. Many autumn individuals are

Location	Years with consecutive winter records	Winters with records
Finchingfield	1953/54-1955/56	3
Lea Valley/ Epping Forest	1965/66-1966/67, 1975/76-1976/77, 1980/81-1981/82	21
Colne Estuary	1969/70-1970/71	13
Maldon/Mundon/Althorne	1974/75-1975/76	2
Thorndon CP	1977/78-1978/79	4
Hatfield Forest	1979/80-1980/81	3
Friday Wood/Roman River	1989/90-1990/91	6

Principal wintering sites of Great Grey Shrikes from 1950/51-2003/04

probably drift migrants. Is it possible that our wintering birds are from a different area to the autumn migrants? Or has increasing disturbance of lowland heaths and scrubby habitat favoured by the species simply meant that few now remain to winter? There does not appear to be a simple correlation between autumn and wintering numbers.

The earliest autumn arrivals were at The Naze on 24th September 1972 and Holland Haven from 24th–26th September 1986, whilst the only other September record came from The Naze on 26th in 1976. Numbers initially peak during October as migrants arrive, particularly along the coast, and then again during mid-winter once birds are on territory.

Cox considered that more were being reported during winter than prior to 1968 with only a small proportion known to make protracted stays in any one area. Winter territories are usually set up from late November, although apparently 'new' wintering birds have occurred regularly as late as January. Most stay on site until late February or early March.

Although regularly reported from the coast, the county's principal locations for both wintering and passage Great Grey Shrikes are the Lea Valley and Epping Forest. The species has been present during no fewer than 21 autumn/winters in these areas, within which Fishers Green, Waltham Abbey and Sewardstone, and the southern Forest area are particularly favoured.

Wintering individuals may return to the same area over a period of several winters. However, Great Grey Shrikes are known to have wintered in consecutive years in only seven areas in the county; given the large winter home ranges of the species, the true figure is probably much higher.

The most favoured coastal sites by far are Foulness, with records in 20 autumn/winters since 1950/51, and The Naze, in 11.

In some years there are signs of a spring movement, although the numbers involved are very small. The largest numbers reported followed the exceptional winters of 1970/71 and 1974/75. The latest spring record involved one at Chingford on 24th May 1916, whilst the only other May records came from Kelvedon/Feering on 12th May 1889 and Foulness on 7th May 1978.

Apart from two together on Foulness on 15th October 1961, all Essex records have involved single birds.

Southern Grey Shrike   *Lanius meridionalis*

The Southern Grey Shrike is rather patchily distributed over parts of north Africa, the Middle East, central Asia and the northern part of the Indian subcontinent; about 11 races are recognised. The nominate and predominantly resident race *meridionalis* occurs in France and Iberia and the migratory *pallidirostris* occurs across much of central and eastern Eurasia. Southern Grey Shrikes are typical of Mediterranean, desert and even tropical savannah areas.

Steppe Grey Shrike   *L. m. pallidirostris*

Vagrant: two records

Steppe Grey Shrike breeds from the Caspian Sea, Iran and Afghanistan east to Mongolia and China and winters in northeast Africa, parts of the Arabian peninsula, Iraq and Pakistan (Lefranc & Worfolk 1997). Although its English name suggests that the species is a denizen of the steppe, it is not a typical steppe species and the alternative name, Saxaul Grey Shrike, has been proposed (Svensson 2004). Some authorities consider this race to be a distinct species.

| 1994 | Great Wakering | 26th–30th October | 1st-winter |
| 1996 | Holland-on-Sea | 18th November–4th December | 1st-winter |

Southern Grey Shrike was split from Great Grey Shrike in 1997 by the BOURC (*Ibis* 139: 197–201). There were 18 British records, all of this race, to the end of 2004 (BBRC 2005) with 1994 being the best year on record with five occurrences. All except one arrived between mid-September and early December. The Holland-on-Sea individual exploited the local House Sparrow population as a wholesome source of protein.

Christy gave details of a Southern Grey Shrike, said to have been a male, shot at Dedham during the last week of October 1875. It was described as, "… 10 in. in length, and had the four central tail-feathers black, though one is slightly tipped with white". Christy, quite rightly, rejected the record as he felt that there was something suspicious about the fact that, despite it being at that time the first British record, no further details had been forthcoming.

Sponsored by Heatherlea Hotel, Scotland, in memory of Tariq Watson

Woodchat Shrike

Lanius senator

Very rare passage migrant: 16 records involving 18 individuals

The Woodchat Shrike breeds primarily in the Western Palearctic, from Portugal to the Caucasus and from Poland to north Africa, as well as in the Levant and from Turkey to Iran. Three races are recognised: the nominate *senator* in north Africa and Europe from Spain to western Turkey; *badius* from the western Mediterranean islands; and *niloticus* from eastern Turkey and the Levant east to Iran (Lefranc & Worfolk 1997). The species inhabits a wide range of habitats including maquis scrub, open ground, heathland, orchards and gardens. The Woodchat Shrike winters in Africa south of the Sahara but north of the Equator.

undated	Marks Tey	Undated	Male and female
about 1872	Highwoods, Colchester	Undated	
1880	Elmdon/Arkesden	27th August	Male and female
1952	Fordham	5th June	Adult
1959	Foulness	6th–7th June	Male
1960	Mucking	24th May	Male
1979	Foulness	16th June	
1990	Foulness	7th May	Adult
1991	Gunners Park	23rd–28th June	Female
	The Naze	30th June–1st July	Male
1992	Frinton-on-Sea	11th–13th June	Female
1993	Old Hall	5th June	Male
1994	Stanford Warren	13th–17th September	Juvenile
1995	Barking Creek	5th–7th July	Female
1996	Friday Wood/Roman River	27th April	Adult female
1997	Tollesbury Wick	6th July	

The first two records were listed by Christy and Glegg but not mentioned by Hudson & Pyman nor Cox. The 1880 pair remains in Saffron Walden Museum (Accession Nos NB199B and NB199C). Nationally, numbers have shown a long-term increase with an annual average of 12 from 1958–69 rising to 21 from 1990–99 (Fraser & Rogers 2004). This is despite declines during the 20th century, and particularly from the 1960s, in the north and west of its breeding range, suggesting that the increase in British records is probably due to greater observer coverage.

Those occurring in spring involve overshooting northward-bound adults and first-years. Late spring/early summer records may involve non-breeders or failed breeders, whilst those in autumn are predominantly juveniles dispersing from breeding grounds. Nationally, most occur between mid-April and early June with a smaller peak between mid-August and early October, broadly similar to the occurrence pattern in Essex.

The records have shown a wide geographical spread with only Foulness (three) recording more than one. All modern records, apart from 1952 and 1996, have come from the coast. The majority of the records have involved the nominate race. However, a recent national review of several records, in the light of a better understanding of the characteristics of the race *badius*, has seen three records of this race accepted onto the British List (BBRC 2004). The individual at The Naze in 1991 was photographed (*EBR* 1991) and, although it

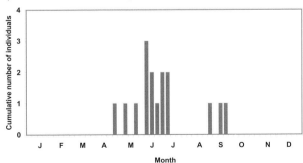

Seasonal occurrence of Woodchat Shrikes from 1880-2004

appears from the photographs that there were no white patches at the base of the primaries on the closed wing (a diagnostic feature of *badius*), they were apparently present (Tony Critcher *per* Adrian Kettle). This race has, therefore, not been recorded positively in the county.

Sponsored by Heatherlea Hotel, Scotland, in memory of Tariq Watson

(Eurasian) Jay   *Garrulus glandarius*

Common resident and scarce passage migrant, subject to periodic influxes

The Jay is ubiquitous throughout the Palearctic and much of the Oriental region. It occurs through most of Europe, although it is absent from Iceland, northern Scotland, the Balearics and above 68° N in Scandinavia (European Atlas). Perhaps 30–60 races exist, with nine in Europe alone; the race *rufitergum* occurs over most of Britain, the Netherlands and Belgium, with the very similar nominate race *glandarius* occurring over much of central and northern Europe. The species prefers mixed and broad-leaved woodlands, particularly those containing Oaks; acorns are its preferred winter food. In Britain Jays are generally widespread although largely absent from upland areas. Although largely sedentary, northern populations that breed in conifer forests are migratory and usually move southwest; in some years these movements appear almost irruptive (European Atlas).

Christy described the Jay as "A common resident, especially in thickly-wooded districts, in spite of incessant persecution". The Jay was, apart from the Magpie, probably the most victimised of all the corvids for its alleged stealing of other birds' eggs. Even the Epping naturalist Buxton

Atlas	Survey Area	% of 10km squares or tetrads in which	
		bred/probably bred	possibly bred or present
First National 10km	Essex	96.5	1.8
Second National 10km	Essex	80.7	14.0
First London Tetrad	Met. Essex	24.0	22.5
Second London Tetrad	Met. Essex	57.5	17.5
Essex Tetrad	Essex	49.1	18.8

Summary of results of Atlas surveys for Jays

(in Christy) noted: "No bird is a more inveterate destroyer of other birds than this. Eggs are to it an irresistible temptation". He made this comment in support of an edict ordering the destruction of the Jay in Epping Forest. The resulting shoots were a controversial aspect of Epping Forest's management and provoked outcries from the fledgling Essex Field Club (Cole 1885). One shoot on 17th April 1888 killed a total of 106 Jays with just 17 guns (Hanson 1992). Organised Jay shoots in Epping Forest continued on and off well into the second half of the 20th century (Essex Atlas). In the woods around Writtle Park, 95 were killed in just one month during 1878, whilst 46 were trapped with eggs at Little Baddow in 1887 and another 28 in 1889. Despite this slaughter, the Jay appears to have held its own in most districts, perhaps because its more secretive habits made it less vulnerable than the Magpie (Historical Atlas). The numbers culled annually in some areas must, however, have been sufficient to keep the population in a generally depressed state. It was, however, not just shot because it was a pest; its blue wing-covert feathers were highly valued for fishing flies as well as for the adornment of Victorian ladies (Historical Atlas). Both these fashions passed, and with the decline of gamekeepers during WWI persecution must have declined markedly in the early years of the 20th century. Glegg gave little detailed information on breeding numbers, simply stating that the Jay was "… a resident and a common breeder throughout the wooded parts of the county". Such a brief description suggests that the Jay had become sufficiently common to attract not much attention.

Hudson & Pyman and Cox described the species as a common resident, a situation unchanged at the time of the Essex Atlas survey and today. It seems, therefore, that the population has remained fairly stable since at least the 1950s and perhaps as far back as the 1920s. Nationally, populations have also been stable over the same period. Little change in range was evident between the two National Atlases; however, there was a 12% decline in the CBC/BBS between 1977 and 2002 and the BBS (England) Index fell by 20% between 1994 and 2003.

The Essex Atlas survey revealed the Jay to be widespread across Essex, even being found in the sparsely wooded regions of Dengie with fewest in urban areas and 'agricultural deserts'. Not surprisingly, the pattern of occurrence is similar to that of Oak woodlands upon which the Jay is dependent; it has been estimated that in an average winter a Jay may 'plant' 3,000 Oak acorns in its efforts to hide or store them for future retrieval.

Unfortunately, the Jay was only mentioned three times in the Systematic List of the *EBRs* from 1955–81 and so trends at particular sites are only available for the last two decades, and only from The Mores Wood, near Brentwood, and Hainault Forest CP are sufficient data available to pass comment. At The Mores Wood, the population remained at 1–2 pairs from 1981–98 (Gibbs 2000), whilst at Hainault Forest CP the population appears to have remained stable. In recent years, there has been a spread into Metropolitan Essex with a 140% increase in the number of occupied tetrads between the two London Atlases. Breeding was first confirmed at Rainham in 1995, Beckton in 1998 and Collier Row in 2001, and some consolidation was noted in urban areas around Romford, Canning Town and Essex Filter Beds. Jays remain absent from the most heavily built-up areas.

In wooded areas, Cox noted mean densities of 16 pairs per km^2. In addition, record cards submitted to the Game Conservancy confirmed its general abundance; 146 were destroyed on one Essex estate of eight km^2 during the 1977/78 season. CBC data since 1981 have suggested average densities in woodland of 15.6 pairs per km^2 (range 8.1-20) and 1.2 pairs per km^2 (range 0.5–1.9) on farmland.

Prior to the 1990s, passage movements in Essex were observed in just four years (1957, 1962, 1975 and 1983) but since then their incidence appears to have increased markedly. On 21st–22nd September 1957, at least 600 and possibly as many as 1,000 flew southwest over Ingatestone; over 1,000 were noted along the Kent coast at this time (Taylor *et al.* 1981). Cox considered that at least some of those involved were of the Continental race. In 1962, a total of 57 in two parties flew south-southeast over Nazeing on 16th November.

A remarkable influx occurred throughout England and Wales in mid-October 1983 with movements numbered in thousands in Norfolk, Devon and Cornwall. In Essex the numbers were far more modest. Along the coast in the region of 100–150 were reported, the largest counts coming from Colne Point, where there were 24 on 13th and 14 on 19th. Inland, 50 at Hainault Forest CP on 8th October and 30–40 at Havering on 9th October were well above average. It is difficult to ascertain the origin of these birds as the acorn crop failed in both Britain and on the Continent. There was much wandering by local birds with all those observed closely along Dengie considered to be of the British race, although many Jays observed in Norfolk were thought to be of the Continental race; none of the latter were identified with certainty in Essex.

The increase in influxes of Jays during the 1990s is interesting and mirrors the pattern seen in Norfolk (Taylor *et al.* 1999). Essex saw small autumn movements in 1993, 1994, 1996, 1999, 2000 and 2002. In 1998, on 4th October, 120 flew northwest over The Naze and 20 flew over Bradwell. Also on the 4th, there were at least 50 in Hainault Forest CP and 30–40 on Whitehall Plain, Epping Forest. In 1996, there were 13 at The Naze and ten at Bradwell on 1st October and 17 at Middlewick, Dengie, on 3rd. Once again there was an almost complete failure of the acorn crop locally and abroad and, whilst local wanderers may have been involved, it is notable that in Norfolk there was once again a substantial arrival from the Continent, including 131 through Holme on 9th (Taylor *et al.* 1999). Unusually for Essex, return spring passage in 1997 was marked, especially during May, the highest count being 27 at The Naze on 25th–26th (again mirrored in Norfolk). In 2002, a steady movement through Bradwell and The Naze during September and October saw peaks of 23 at Bradwell on 22nd September and 14 there on 29th, with 13 at The Naze on 7th October.

Quite why there should have been a greater incidence of Jay movements during the last decade remains unclear. Although greater observer awareness may be a factor, the marked increase suggests other factors may be at work. Is it possible that the changing weather patterns are making acorn crops more erratic? Recent BBS data have recorded a decline in the population; perhaps a proportion of the population has to move further to find sufficient food?

Of 58 recoveries of Essex-ringed Jays, over 80% were found within 10km of the ringing site and only two have been recovered outside Essex, including one ringed at Romford in January 1958 that was recovered in Surrey in March 1962 following the exceptional inland movement at that time. The longest movement involved one ringed at Pitsea on 5th September 1993 that was shot at Ipsden, Oxfordshire, 109km to the west. Nationally, only 5% of Jays have moved more than 40km, although this increased following the failure of the acorn crop in 1983/84. All Jays ringed in Essex, bar those below, were of the British race *rufitergum*. Continental, nominate race Jays are known to occur in Britain in varying but generally small numbers, although, surprisingly, there have been no foreign-ringed Jays recovered in Essex and just one foreign recovery of a British-ringed bird (Migration Atlas). There have been just three confirmed Essex records of the nominate race: one obtained at Layer Marney, 22nd November 1934; one at Colne Engaine, December 1935; and one trapped at Bradwell, 1st October 1975, when three arrived in a small fall. Glegg noticed that numbers tended to increase in Epping Forest during October, although the movement appeared to be more noticeable in some years than others.

Unlike the Magpie, the Jay does not form large, visible flocks and its secretiveness and relative scarcity in urban areas means that it is not likely to become a target for culling (Essex Atlas). In general, woodlands are now better protected and increasing areas of new woodland are being planted. Thus, the future for the species seems assured for the time being.

(Black-billed) Magpie   *Pica pica*

Common resident

The Magpie is confined to the northern hemisphere between 15° and 70° N, its range continuous through Europe and Asia and including western North America. There are five subspecies across Europe, the nominate race *pica* occurring from Ireland and northern France, west to northern Poland and most of Norway and Sweden. The Magpie is fairly evenly distributed through urban, suburban and rural landscapes. Since 1965 there have been increases in most European countries with urban densities increasing spectacularly in, amongst others, Britain and Ireland (European Atlas). In Britain it is found throughout England and Wales, although it is quite localised in Scotland. Magpies are remarkably sedentary (Birkhead 1991), although the recent and substantial colonisation of suburban and urban habitats appears contrary to this.

The Magpie was, during the latter half of the 19th century at least, an uncommon bird. Christy noted that it was "A scarce resident, except in a few localities, though formerly quite common. Its decrease is due chiefly to persecution by gamekeepers". He considered it more common in the Dengie Hundred than anywhere else in Essex. It was quite common around the woods of Danbury in 1883 and at Harwich was fairly common. Elsewhere, individual nesting attempts were considered rare enough to detail. At around the time of Christy's publication, the Wild Birds Protection Committee of Essex County Council recommended the Magpie as one of the birds within Metropolitan Essex for which the Council should apply to the Secretary of State for protection under the Wild Birds Protection Act 1880. In his account of the action, Cole (1895) recorded the rarity of the species around Epping Forest and added comments from Edward North Buxton, who at the time was trying to create a sanctuary for this and other birds in Epping Forest: "The Magpie is another bird full of wickedness; but it has got so scarce in this neighbourhood that I am glad to be able to do something to prevent its total extinction". Ironically, the very same commentator had noted a few years earlier: "This predatory foe to other birds is happily not common hereabouts". This attitude to the species seems almost to have been ingrained deep in the human psyche for as long as can be remembered, the almost illogical and extreme hatred shown for the species dogging it even today. Maybe it is the fact that the Magpie has, perhaps as far back as pagan times, been associated with evil (Greenoak 1981); even the *EBR 1988* made the comment "Is nowhere safe?"

By the 1920s, its status appeared to have changed very little with Glegg reporting that it had increased since the 1880s but that it was still a "... somewhat uncommon resident" spread throughout the county. It was still most

Atlas	Survey Area	% of 10km squares or tetrads in which	
		bred/probably bred	possibly bred or present
First National 10km	Essex	86.0	10.5
Second National 10km	Essex	98.2	1.8
First London Tetrad	Met. Essex	41.5	16.5
Second London Tetrad	Met. Essex	92.5	7.5
Essex Tetrad	Essex	93.2	3.1

Summary of results of Atlas surveys for Magpies

common in the Dengie Hundred and was rare in the southwest. Buxton (1923) recorded only three pairs within the vicinity of Waltham Abbey and none in Epping Forest itself. Its scarcity was sufficient for him to add "... they should be protected when they occur".

After WWI, gamekeeper activity declined and nationally the Magpie began to increase; Glegg noted a small increase in Essex around this time. Nationally, from around 1940 a spread into urban and suburban areas began (Second National Atlas), when numbers also increased. In Essex, the increases must have occurred at about this time as the *EBR 1953* was able to report that it was "... much increased and is now to be found over virtually the whole of the county; approaches abundance in certain areas such as the coast between the rivers Blackwater and Crouch and the mid-Essex farmlands", whilst the *EBR 1955* described a noticeable increase in the chalk uplands of the northwest. However, in the early 1960s populations began to fall markedly. The *EBR 1963* noted that at least in the eastern half of Essex "... it had suffered a dramatic decline in numbers during the past few years". In central Essex, 18 pairs in 1956 in the Writtle/Roxwell/Highwood area had fallen to eight in 1960 and just one by 1965. This decline coincided with the introduction of organochlorine pesticides (Second National Atlas). However, following the banning of these substances, numbers soon began to recover, the *EBR 1969* noting that "There is growing evidence that this species is now on the increase...". For instance, there were 11 pairs in the Writtle/Roxwell/Highwood area that year compared to one just four years earlier.

The Magpie was not mentioned in the *EBR* again until 1982 but Cox noted a steady increase in Essex since the 1960s, confirming that it was now a common species in both suburban and rural areas, with the Second National Atlas confirming a spread into northern Essex. From 1977–2002, the CBC/BBS (England) Index increased by 59%, whilst the local CBC Index increased at around the same rate; Birkhead (1991) suggested a growth rate of 6–12% per annum.

The Essex Atlas survey confirmed breeding in 93.2% of tetrads. Nationally the evidence suggests that the increase in Magpie numbers has levelled off, the BBS (England) Index being stable between 1994 and 2002. Although only anecdotal, the evidence from across Essex paints much the same picture; Birkhead (1991) predicted such stabilising of the population as a consequence of the limitations of territory size.

Magpies reach their greatest densities in the suburbs of the southwest, including the areas around Epping Forest. Randomised transect counts in 1999 in the central area of Epping Forest between Chingford and Loughton gave an estimated density of 52 birds per km^2, which included non-breeders, perhaps as many as 20 pairs per km^2 in some areas (J. R. Dagley unpublished data). This is far higher than the average of ten pairs per km^2 estimated for woodland (Gooch *et al.* 1991), although not as great as the 32 pairs per km^2 found in northern England (BWP). Cox noted densities in woodland of six pairs per km^2. CBC/BBS data since 1981 have produced average densities on farmland of three pairs per km^2 (range 0.5-6) and in woodland of seven pairs per km^2 (range 0.5-18).

In line with the rise in breeding numbers, an increase in the number and size of winter gatherings has been noted. Christy made no mention of any winter gatherings and, although Glegg commented on the phenomenon, he did not consider it a common one, the largest flock reported being "… a remarkable one…" of 50 in Boxted Woods on 8th February 1922. Hudson & Pyman described, "… some winter aggregates of up to 100 birds being reported from mid-Essex and Dengie Hundred". Organochlorine poisoning during the 1960s meant that winter numbers remained depressed until the early 1980s, since when there have been counts of 100+ from: Stour Wood, 75–100, at an autumn/winter roost in 1990; South Woodham Ferrers, 60–100, 3rd January 1982; Pitsea, 200+, January 1984 and 136, 6th January 1992; Dunton, 110, 15th February 1989; Berwick Ponds, 100+, December 1989 and 19th January 1991; Belfairs Park, 100, 21st January 1990 and 1st January 1991; Rainham, 150, 17th November 1990 and 100, 9th December 1995 and 8th January 2000; Woodford GC, 100+ roosting, January to March 1999; Chingford Football Club, 100+, January and February 1999 and 102+ roosting, 8th February 2000.

Magpies are extremely sedentary. Of 25 Essex-ringed Magpies subsequently recovered, 19 were reported within 10km of the ringing site and five from between ten and 99km; the most distant was found 100km away in Sussex. None of the previous authors provided any evidence of coastal movements and there have been no obvious records during the last two decades. However, although there has been no definite evidence to confirm passage, occasionally flocks of birds have been noted to head off in a northerly direction during autumn at The Naze, only to make a U-turn and dive back into cover as soon as the tideline is crossed; whether this suggests a 'migratory urge' is unclear.

The Magpie has become one of the birds most encountered by people going about their daily lives. This familiarity appears to have bred contempt. Many, perhaps the majority of people, see the Magpie as the principal reason for the decline in garden songbirds. This seems to be particularly acute in southwest and Metropolitan Essex where Magpie and human densities are at their greatest. So far no apparent correlation has been shown to exist between the increase in Magpie numbers and decline in songbird populations (Gooch *et al.* 1991, Thomson *et al.* 1998). The authors, however, do not rule out local effects and there is some evidence from work by the Game Conservancy on farmland in Leicestershire that corvids, including Magpies, have had a significant effect on populations of open-nesting birds such as Song Thrushes, Blackbirds, Chaffinches and Linnets (Stoate & Thomson 1999).

Culling remains widespread but patchy across Essex. However, it is unlikely that such control will amount to the consistent and effective level of population control exerted a century or so ago on a much smaller population of birds. The resourcefulness and adaptability of the Magpie should ensure that it remains a common bird within Essex well into the current millennium. It will be interesting to see whether the high population densities remain and if this in turn affects the species' territorial behaviour.

(Spotted) Nutcracker **Nucifraga caryocatactes**

Vagrant – prone to irruptions: 24 individuals including 16 in 1968

The Nutcracker is a widespread corvid that is found throughout the pine forests of Europe and Asia; eight subspecies are recognised (Madge & Burn 1994), the nominate thick-billed race *caryocatactes* occurring from Scandinavia and central Europe east to the Urals, and the slender-billed *macrorhynchos* breeding in the Siberian taiga from the Urals to the Pacific. The species is noted for its dependence on the Arolla Pine; periodic irruptions occur into western Europe whenever an abundant crop is followed by a poor one. Normally, the species rarely reaches Britain, but in 1968 it was thought that adverse weather conditions in Siberia,  combined with a huge high pressure weather system stationary over Europe in August contributed to the scale of influx (Hollyer 1970). A total of 316 occurred nationally in 1968; just 14 have been recorded since taking the national total to 400 to the end of 2003 (BBRC 2004).

about 1858	Ardleigh, Horkesley and Boxted	September	Three shot

1872	Tollesbury	September	Shot
1900	Bradwell	27th October	Shot
	Epping Forest	5th November	Shot
1951	Little Dunmow	2nd October	
1961	Holland-on-Sea	20th February	
1968	The Naze	23rd August–2nd September	Two
	Parkeston	23rd August	
	Brentwood	For three weeks before 14th September	One, probably two
	Brightlingsea	26th August	
	Dovercourt	27th August	
	East Mersea	27th August–3rd September	
	West Mersea	Before 2nd September	
	Little Oakley	5th–7th September	
	Dedham	7th September	
	Great Yeldham	10th September	
	Hadleigh	16th and 18th September	
	Harlow	3rd–4th October	
	Beaumont	15th November	
	Shenfield	8th December	
	Point Clear, St Osyth	24th December.	

Glegg dismissed a sight record of one at Maldon in November 1911, despite the observer being a well respected local naturalist and 1911 being the only year prior to 1968 that more than 1–2 were reported nationally. Even then there were only six, in Norfolk (two), Suffolk, Kent (two) and Buckinghamshire. Christy mentioned an old, cased specimen belonging to a gentleman at Boreham, although its origin was not known.

The 1968 irruption involved the slender-billed race and it is likely that the other records also involved this race. Most Nutcrackers in 1968 were recorded between Dover, Kent and The Wash, Norfolk, and it is therefore not surprising that only Norfolk, Suffolk and Kent recorded more than Essex (Hollyer 1970). Many of the individuals that made this 'death wandering' had probably succumbed by the end of the year and it was estimated that nationally there were only ten or so of the original invasion left by then (Hollyer 1970), so the St Osyth bird managed to survive longer than most. The bias to the northeast is notable.

(Red-billed) Chough   *Pyrrhocorax pyrrhocorax*

Vagrant: one 19th century record involving two birds   Amber List

The Chough occurs in western Britain and in isolated mainly mountainous areas of Europe, east through western Asia to central and northern China. In Britain, the species is typical of rocky coastline. Of five recognised races, the nominate *pyrrhocorax* occurs in Britain and Ireland and *erythopthalmus* over much of the rest of Europe. Choughs are generally sedentary.

1888	The Stour	2nd April	Seen from Landguard, Suffolk

"In a migration schedule received this morning … is the following entry: — 'April 2nd, 1888: Two Crows put in an appearance, 7.30 a. m.; larger than Jackdaws: they had red beaks and legs, and went north-west.'." (Christy). As the record was accepted by Piotrowski (2003) and the birds must have crossed Essex waters to get to Landguard Point, Suffolk, there seems no reason for the species not to be placed on the Essex List.

Records of 'Chough' from the West Tilbury and Stifford area around 1840 (Christy), probably involved Jackdaws, as Chough was a local name for the species.

One at Leigh/Two Tree Island between 23rd February and 13th March 1963, during and immediately following the period of extreme hard weather, was considered an escape from captivity.

(Eurasian) Jackdaw

Corvus monedula

Common resident, winter visitor and passage migrant

The Jackdaw breeds throughout Europe and the Western Palearctic from subarctic Finland to the Mediterranean, south to Morocco and Algeria and east to the Himalayas and western Siberia (European Atlas). The race *spermologus* occurs in Britain and Ireland and western Continental Europe and is generally the least migratory form. The east European race *soemmerringii* and the nominate race *monedula* that occurs in Fennoscandia are more migratory, moving south and west to avoid severe winter weather. The Jackdaw is generally widespread throughout Britain and Ireland, although it is noticeably absent from the high moorlands of northwest and west Scotland. Breeding densities are much lower in eastern England (and large urban areas) than in western England, Wales and the Borders (Second National Atlas).

Christy commented very little on the Jackdaw's status, merely noting that it was "An abundant resident, breeding chiefly in holes in large old trees in parks". Glegg considered that the species was "... a resident ... and, although not as abundant as the Rook, is a common breeder". Typical nesting places included spires and towers of churches (High Beech and Dedham), old and ruined castles (Hadleigh, Colchester and Castle Hedingham - being particularly abundant at the latter) as well as in old parks (Audley End, Weald CP and St Osyth Priory). Indeed, any suitable location providing a suitable nest hole was likely to be used, including the old chalk quarries at Purfleet and chimneys of houses. Whether its numbers had actually decreased since Christy's time is now impossible to ascertain, and the varying descriptions given by Christy ("... abundant...") and Glegg ("... common...") perhaps come down to no more than a choice of words.

Hudson & Pyman reaffirmed Glegg's status, noting that Jackdaws were common and widespread and probably only absent from the most built-up areas; the species was thought to be not as abundant as the Rook. Mature parkland was considered the species' preferred habit, the authors noting Danbury and Weald CP as favourite localities. The colony at the latter sites appears to have shown continuity of use since Glegg's time with numbers increasing recently to 50 pairs in 2003.

Cox noted a decline that began around the mid-1960s caused primarily by agricultural change but a loss of nesting sites may have also contributed. Despite the increase in dead Elms across the countryside caused by

Atlas	Survey Area	% of 10km squares or tetrads in which	
		bred/probably bred	possibly bred or present
First National 10km	Essex	98.2	1.8
Second National 10km	Essex	82.5	7.0
First London Tetrad	Met. Essex	25.5	19.5
Second London Tetrad	Met. Essex	31.0	31.5
Essex Tetrad	Essex	28.0	28.2

Summary of results of Atlas surveys for Jackdaws

Dutch Elm disease, the Jackdaw did not appear to benefit (Population Trends). A 50% decline in the number shot on East Anglian estates over 15 years was linked to a reduction in the area of ley grassland (Tapper 1981). The decline did not appear to halt until the 1990s, when the Essex Atlas showed that the Jackdaw remained widespread being found in 56.2% of tetrads, although populations were clustered around areas of suitable habitat. Small declines were apparent locally between the two National Atlas surveys, although increases were apparent in Metropolitan Essex between the two London Atlas survey periods: here the species appeared to have colonised the increasing number of quarries around the Thurrock area. In southwest Essex, anecdotal evidence points to a general increase in the area with populations at several sites doubling since the late 1980s. At Dagnam Park increases were ascribed to the greater willingness to use a wider variety of trees to nest in such as Oak, Ash and Field Maple. Increases have, however, occurred nationally in areas of agricultural intensification and it is possible that early ripening grain crops are aiding juvenile survival rates (Population Trends).

Nationally, Jackdaw numbers have increased through most of the 20th century (Second National Atlas) and recent BBS data suggest that this trend has continued with a 30% increase in the BBS (England) Index from 1994–2003. Quite why it is only recently that the Essex population has shown signs of an increase is unclear. Local CBC data since 1980 reveal average densities of around four pairs per km^2 in woodland and one pair per km^2 in farmland, although these figures can be misleading due to the species' habit of nesting in colonies.

Around Epping Forest, where reasonable numbers might be expected, Jackdaws are concentrated around the Victorian houses at the edge of the Forest (e.g. Chingford), where they utilise the chimneys, and in old trees in the parkland areas such as those at Warlies Park and Copped Hall. They will nest within old trees in the Forest but rarely in groups of more than 1–2 pairs, despite the abundance of old hollow trees. There is certainly nothing comparable to the 'galleries' of Jackdaws that can be observed in similar pasture woodland adjacent to Bristol, Avon. This seems to reflect the relative dearth of livestock and associated grassland feeding sites nearby. Recent notable increases at Weald CP may be due to the abundance of old trees and the increase in livestock (e.g. Horses and farmed deer) nearby.

Jackdaws remain well known for using church towers in Essex and elsewhere for nesting. Their habit of adding twigs to the nest annually means that if left undisturbed, some nest structures may grow to a metre in depth and spread out over an entire belfry floor.

Occasionally this opportunist will switch from feeding on grassland invertebrates and take advantage of local abundance of, for example caterpillars in foliage; a group of 60 was noted feeding in this way in two Oaks in Bury Wood, near Chingford, in June 1998.

Glegg devoted about one third of his species' account to describing observations on immigration, particularly during autumn: "There is an annual influx of immigrants to the east coast of England, including Essex, when large numbers of Jackdaw arrive from Central Europe, although outnumbered by Rooks". The principal autumn movement usually began around the middle of October, with a smaller movement from mid-February peaking in March. The timing of movements was much the same as today, with almost all recent significant coastal movements occurring in October and March. Comparison of Glegg's observations with those of today suggest that the Jackdaw may have been a more common migrant in his time: is it possible that, like other corvids, fewer Jackdaws now find it necessary to move west out of Scandinavia to find food as man now provides sufficient opportunities for formerly migrant populations to become year round residents?

Hudson & Pyman described "... small to moderate numbers of immigrants ... on the coast in autumn", small flocks occasionally being seen flying in off the sea, whilst Cox noted: "Diurnal immigration, usually of small proportion..." In recent years, more extensive coverage of coastal areas during migration periods has shown that the Jackdaw is a regular immigrant in small, but variable numbers with double-figure counts in autumn fairly regular. In 1994, 70 flew in off the sea at The Naze on 1st October and 85 flew west at Colne Point on 2nd November, whilst in 2001 a loose flock of 200 heading southwest at The Naze on 28th October presumably consisted of coasting birds. Numbers in March can sometimes be as large as the autumn movement with, in 1995, 26 flying north at The Naze on 12th March and 50+ high north over the Thames at East Tilbury on 12th March 1996.

British Jackdaws are generally sedentary and are therefore likely to winter locally. The extent to which immigrants contribute to the large mixed corvid wintering flocks has always been uncertain. What is, however, noticeable is that the overall size of flocks has declined markedly since the mid-1970s, although there have been signs of an increase during the late 1990s. The fact that local populations increased but winter flock sizes declined points to these gatherings perhaps including a fair proportion of immigrants.

The largest winter gatherings were reported during the 1960s. A winter roost of 25,000 Rooks and Jackdaws in equal proportions at Easton Lodge near Great Dunmow in 1960 and a pre-roost assembly of some 50,000 near Great Horkesley on 2nd January 1966 are far greater than any subsequent counts. During the 1970s, there were no published records of corvid flocks where the number of Jackdaws was thought to exceed 1,000 (Cox). However, in early 1982 up to 2,000 flew west at Ingatestone on 19th February and 2,000–3,000 were at Woodham Mortimer during January and February, whilst in 1983, 3,000 roosted at Ingatestone on 6th January. A count of 5,500 feeding on ploughed fields at Epping Upland on 18th November 1988 remains the largest count since the mid-1960s. Four-figure counts had, until the late 1990s, become particularly scarce but since then there have been several counts of 2,000+ from two well-known roost sites at St Osyth Priory and Holyfield Lake. At the former, the largest gatherings were 2,500 on 10th January 1998 and 2,000–2,500 on 3rd January 2000, whilst at Holyfield Lake up to 3,000 were present in early 2001 and during the 2002/03 winter. Other sites holding four-figure gatherings have been: Copped Hall, 1,300, 3rd February 1985 and 1,000, 28th August 1990; Fishers Green, 1,000, 26th October 1991; Waltham Abbey, 1,500, 26th January 1992; Mucking Tip, 1,400, 6th February 1999; Abberton, 1,750, 1st July 2000 and 2,000, 5th December 2004.

Of the 62 Jackdaws ringed in Essex and subsequently recovered, all bar five had moved less than 5km, confirming the species' sedentary nature. However, the recovery in winter of birds ringed as young in the Netherlands (two) and near Malmo, Sweden, confirms that, at least on occasions, a proportion of our wintering population originates from the east.

Glegg considered the Jackdaw beneficial "... as it does more good than harm". Unlike other crow species they are not perceived as 'villains' and, although still a pest species and subject to legal control, serious culling of numbers in future seems unlikely. Their future, however, is likely to be determined by changes to farmland habitat management, reform of the CAP and the after effects of both the BSE and FMD epidemics. Increasing awareness of the value of 'veteran trees', so often ideal for nesting sites, should be beneficial to the Jackdaw. Counter to this, however, are the renovation of the older building stock (Second National Atlas) and the apparent reluctance of many to accept Jackdaws nesting on their property.

Rook   *Corvus frugilegus*

Common resident, winter visitor and passage migrant

The Rook is a highly gregarious Palearctic corvid that is widely distributed across the temperate and boreal mid-latitudes of Europe and the boreal, steppe and desert zones of Asia Minor to the Yenisey River, northwest Altai and northwest Sinkiang. The nominate race *frugilegus* occurs across Europe (European Atlas). In Britain, Rooks are absent only from most of the uplands of Scotland, Wales, northern England and Ireland and the centres of large cities (Second National Atlas). The species builds conspicuous nests in the tops of tall trees and is therefore relatively easy to census. West European populations are largely resident and sedentary but may be augmented in winter by birds from north, east and central Europe (European Atlas).

To Christy, the Rook was a "… very abundant resident" but he presented no numerical data. Glegg described the Rook as "… one of the most abundant birds of the county, breeding, commonly, in all directions". He continued: "The characteristic rookeries are found all over the county; of a series counted in different localities, the smallest contained ten nests, and the largest a hundred and four, giving an average of about forty nests per rookery". A large rookery existed at 'Saling' in 1922, containing several hundred nests. Three heronries, at Wanstead, Boreham and St Osyth had attendant rookeries.

Apart from the Grey Heron, the Rook's breeding population has probably been surveyed more than any other common Essex breeding bird. The first survey was carried out in 1945, when 9,624 nests were found during sample counts in four areas, which, when extrapolated to the county as a whole, gave a population of around 22,300 pairs. In 1956, 20 members of the Bishop's Stortford Natural History Society carried out a survey, which covered the entire county and was considered to be reasonably complete (Darlington 1957). A total of 18,252 nests in 822 rookeries was found, around 60% in central west Essex and more particularly the upper reaches of the Stort, Roding, Chelmer and Pant. Overall, the breeding densities were around 4.7 pairs per km^2 with the lowest in the south of the county, south and west of Brentwood, around the coastal strip and in Metropolitan Essex. A sample repeated in 1957 suggested an 8% increase in that year.

Hudson & Pyman concluded that there were probably in the order of 20,000–22,000 breeding pairs of Rooks in Essex, averaging about 5.4 pairs per km^2; the English average at that time was around seven pairs per km^2. The next full survey in 1975 revealed a marked decline to 9,738 nests, around 2.4 pairs per km^2. Breeding densities across England also fell dramatically to just 3.9 pairs per km^2. Nesting densities in Tendring district from 2001–03 were around 5.0 pairs per km^2 (Mason & Macdonald 2004). Recent anecdotal evidence suggests that Rook numbers have been increasing during the 1990s with the number of rookeries of 100+ having increased during the last decade.

The Rook's range changed little between the two National Atlas surveys and both London Atlas surveys (there was, in fact, a small range increase), whilst the Essex Atlas survey revealed a range that appeared to be very similar to that during the 1950s, suggesting that breed-

Atlas	Survey Area	% of 10km squares or tetrads in which	
		bred/probably bred	possibly bred or present
First National 10km	Essex	93.0	3.5
Second National 10km	Essex	84.2	8.8
First London Tetrad	Met. Essex	19.0	14.0
Second London Tetrad	Met. Essex	16.5	28.5
Essex Tetrad	Essex	25.8	34.1

Summary of results of Atlas surveys for Rooks

ing densities had indeed declined over the previous 50 years. Although the decline of Elms, due to Dutch Elm disease, was suggested as a cause of the declines (65% of Rook nests in Essex in 1975 were in Elms), the species was in decline well before the disease had any serious impact (Tapper 1981). More likely is the fact that the Rook population is closely bound to agricultural practice. The declines seen during the 1960s coincided with the peak use of organochlorine seed dressings in cereal growing areas mainly in eastern England (Second National Atlas). This decline was illustrated by figures from the Writtle/Roxwell/Highwood area where the total number of nests from several rookeries fell from 494 in 1965 to 212 in 1968, 168 in 1972 and just 44 in 1981 (Cox). Additionally the shift away from spring to autumn sown crops may have adversely affected invertebrate availability during the breeding season (O'Connor & Shrubb 1986) and the loss of much grassland to arable crops would have reduced the amount of habitat suitable for foraging. In the Tendring District, the distribution of rookeries during 2001–03 was associated with the amount of grassland, a colony of 100 nests requiring some 122ha of grass within 1km (Mason & Macdonald 2004).

The largest-known Essex rookery was in Wanstead Park in 1898 with 430 nests on Rook Island. Other 19th century rookeries were probably larger but were never counted. The only other rookeries containing 300+ nests are: Hall Wood, North Fambridge, since at least the mid-1950s, with 321 nests in 1996 and 306 nests in 2000; and Beddall's Green, near Braintree, with 300+ nests in 1957. The number of rookeries containing 100+ nests generally declined in line with the fall in the breeding numbers but has begun to increase again as Rook numbers have begun to recover.

Although the Rook is known for nesting at the tops of trees, the majority deciduous, other less typical nesting locations have been used. Glegg mentioned one in a Willow bed at Dedham in 1899, whilst more recently five pairs nested on electricity pylons over a sub-station at Sandon in 1995; hedges have also been used on Dengie peninsula.

The Rook is the most conspicuous of the corvids during autumn immigration. Glegg referred to arrivals of immigrant Rooks at Harwich in 1879, 1880 and 1881 and at Foulness in 1903. Although he made no specific mention of the numbers involved, it was known at that time that large flocks of immigrant Rooks arrived on the east coast from mid-September to mid-November with a smaller return passage noted from mid-February to mid-May. Since 1950, small numbers have regularly been reported arriving off the sea during autumn. Only two movements of 100+ Rooks have been recorded: at The Naze in 1956, 13 flocks totalling around 500 birds arrived off the sea on 25th October in just one hour; in 1962, around 200 corvids, almost all of which were Rooks, flew southwest over Little Clacton on 2nd November. From the rather limited evidence available the number of immigrant Rooks appears to have declined, a fact that seems to accord with comments made in the European Atlas that suggested that winter immigration has become less predictable. Very few data exist relating to spring movements.

Most of the recoveries of Essex-ringed Rooks have been within the county, with few having travelled further than 10km from the ringing site. That some Rooks may still come from eastern Europe to winter in Essex, is suggested by one ringed

	Total nests	Total rookeries	Rookeries of >100 nests
1945	22,300*		
1956	18,252	822	25
1957	19700*		
1975	9,738	482	9

* extrapolated from sample counts

(National surveys in 1980 and 1986 provided insufficent data)

Summary of Rookery survey results carried out in Essex since 1945, adapted and updated from Cox

as a nestling near Moletai, Lithuania, on 19th May 1983 and found dead at Little Wakering on 29th December 1983. Other Rooks ringed in Finland, Germany and the Netherlands have also been recovered in Essex during winter.

Outside the breeding season, Rooks, often in association with Jackdaws, will form huge flocks particularly during winter. Huge roosts comprising of both species also occur. Flights to and from these roosts at dawn and dusk are a familiar sight in the Essex countryside with trails of birds sometimes kilometres long all heading for traditional roost locations. By far the largest gatherings were all recorded prior to the mid-1960s when populations were much higher than today and perhaps when greater numbers of immigrants boosted numbers further. Glegg mentioned a roost at Gosfield Park, which was alleged to have been used for centuries and to number "… as many as twenty thousand birds": it was suddenly deserted in November 1926 and not reoccupied by 1929. In 1952, an estimated 13,000 birds roosting at High Wood, Easton Lodge, contained both Rooks and Jackdaws in the ratio of 10:1. By 1960, this communal roost contained 25,000 birds. In the last 20 years, counts have been much smaller with four-figure counts generally uncommon. The largest count in the 1980s was 5,000–6,000 at Woodham Mortimer on 22nd–23rd November 1980, 90% of which were Rooks, whilst the largest in the 1990s was 5,500 at St Osyth Priory on 10th January 1998; there were 4,000–5,000 there on 3rd January 2000.

Like so many other farmland species, the Rook has not fared well in the intensively farmed landscape. Although there are recent signs of an increase, the Rook nonetheless appears to be far less common than it was 50 years ago. Only a significant shift in agricultural practice that results in a return to a mosaic of arable and pastoral farming is likely to return the Rook to its former population levels.

Carrion Crow   *Corvus corone*

Common resident, scarce winter visitor and passage migrant

The monotypic Carrion Crow is widespread across western Europe and eastern Asia, the two populations separated by the recently split Hooded Crow *C. cornix*. In the contact zones the species regularly hybridise (Madge & Burn 1994). In Britain, the Carrion Crow is widespread and common, being absent only from northwest Scotland, where it is replaced by the Hooded Crow. Carrion Crow has increased its numbers and range over the last 50 years. Although generally sedentary, some northern populations may move south and west in autumn.

Christy knew the species to be "A resident in various parts of the county, though local and nowhere abundant" and noted "It is rapidly becoming scarcer through persecution". As early as 1845, a decline was noted around Saffron Walden. During the period 1866–77, the species was, however, considered common at Shoebury, Orsett, Grays, Upminster and Harwich and not uncommon or fairly common around Thorndon and Warley, Finchingfield and for some kilometres around Felsted. Thirty years later, Glegg described it as "… a resident, and breeds freely in some parts of the county, but it is very unevenly distributed". Surprisingly, he considered its chief haunt to be the London district, especially the Lea Valley. Here during April and May 1922 some 19 nests were destroyed "... in the interests of the many wildfowl" which nested on the reservoirs.

Atlas	Survey Area	% of 10km squares or tetrads in which	
		bred/probably bred	possibly bred or present
First National 10km	Essex	89.5	8.8
Second National 10km	Essex	98.2	1.8
First London Tetrad	Met. Essex	54.5	18.5
Second London Tetrad	Met. Essex	95.0	5.0
Essex Tetrad	Essex	92.5	2.7

Summary of results of Atlas surveys for Carrion Crows

Inland, it was common south of Chelmsford, along the Thames Estuary and up the coast to the Blackwater but became less so along the Colne and Stour, the latter areas generally being those where the Hooded Crow was at that time more common in winter. In northern Essex, Carrion Crows appeared to have been rare, Glegg observing the species just once on his many visits to Saffron Walden. The species was very rare between Haverhill, Suffolk, in the north, Chelmsford in the south, Colchester in the east and Finchingfield in the west. At Felsted, Bishop's Stortford and Harlow it was occasional or uncommon.

With the progressive decline in gamekeeping after WWI and WWII, this corvid, perhaps the most persecuted of all crows, began to prosper such that by the mid-1960s it was considered by Hudson & Pyman to be a common resident "... it would be difficult to find an Essex parish without its breeding Carrion Crows". The increase seemed particularly rapid during the 1960s with, for example, the population in the Writtle/Roxwell/Highwood area increasing from 37 nests in 1962 to 92 in 1965.

The First National Atlas noted the species in every 10km square except TL72, which included Braintree, which interestingly is almost exactly in the centre of the area that Glegg noted it to be very rare some 40 years earlier; birds were present in TL72 during the Second National Atlas survey. Unlike the Jackdaw and Rook, there were few other squares in central and northwest Essex where breeding was not confirmed. The two London Atlas surveys confirmed some range expansion along the Thames, although this may have been due to increased observer coverage as the species was already thought to be widespread by the 1950s.

Although found in any habitat, from agricultural land to coastal salt marshes, urban areas support the largest populations of Carrion Crows with large resident populations occurring in parts of London, for example 300–500 are present at Rainham all year, although few breed on site, whilst 400–500 are resident in the Wanstead/Leyton Flats area; these high density populations exhibit a high frequency of albinism. CBC data since 1980 produce average breeding densities of six pairs per km^2 in woodland (range 3–10) and two pairs per km^2 in farmland (range 1–2).

The Essex Atlas survey found the Carrion Crow in 95.2% of all tetrads, with breeding confirmed in 92.5%: the species was common and widespread throughout.

The local CBC/BBS Indices for Essex and surrounding counties have confirmed the increase, the apparent rate perhaps accelerating in recent years; nationally the CBC/BBS (England) Index increased by 55% of the period 1977–2002 with an 18% rise in the BBS (England) Index from 1994–2003.

The Carrion Crow's adaptability has allowed the species to take advantage of any opportunities as they arise. Thus, six pairs bred in the Abberton Cormorant colony in 2000 and were seen to predate both chicks and young, whilst a Carrion Crow took a Starling in flight after a chase of 50m at Harold Wood in 1969.

With scant national evidence for immigration from the Continent, and the vast majority of British birds wintering close to their breeding ranges, the Carrion Crow's increasing abundance can be gauged by data from feeding assemblies and winter roosts. Prior to 1974 there were no three-figure counts, at least in modern times. In that year, 200 were present on Wanstead GC on 4th October, whilst 120 were at Walthamstow during December. Since 1985, three-figure counts have become annual with a steady increase in flock sizes apparent.

The seasonal occurrence of large flocks suggests that there is some evidence for post-breeding gatherings prior to a general dispersal in late summer, the flocks reforming as winter arrives. Many of these gatherings involve non-breeding birds (adults and immatures), although large counts at Rainham refuse tip, which have peaked at over 500 on a number of occasions (peak 600 on 10th June 1994), must also involve local breeding birds exploiting a readily available food source. The majority of the largest counts have come from southern Essex and particularly the southwest. Away from Metropolitan Essex, Hanningfield supported large roost numbers during the mid-1990s with a peak of 600 during January–March 1994. There were 500 at Belfairs Park on 9th October 1981.

On several occasions, mainly during September to November and again in March and April, small influxes have been noted at coastal localities with some small flocks apparently arriving in off the sea. The largest recorded movement occurred in October 1955 when 75 flew west into the estuary at Bradwell on 24th in just two hours and a total of about 50 passed north-northwest there on 25th with a smaller movement on 26th. More recently 27 arrived off the sea at Bradwell on 16th October 1998. Such movements have been attributed to light spring and autumn passage. However, the British population is considered largely non-migratory with some short-distance dispersal of young at the end of the breeding season and some local wandering by adults. No British-ringed birds have been recovered abroad, the median distance travelled for all birds recovered dead being just 3km (Migration Atlas). Those birds occurring on the coast are therefore probably no more than local birds making short-distance coasting movements, although it is possible that a few Carrion Crows from mainland Europe do occur in Britain from time to time.

Of the 14 recoveries of Carrion Crows ringed in Essex, only four have been recovered further than 10km from the ringing site; the longest movement involved one ringed as a nestling at Pitsea on 16th May 1981 that had its ring read at Swindon, Wiltshire, on 30th June 1981, 158km to the west, one of the longest movements of a British-ringed Carrion Crow.

The Carrion Crow has proved to be highly adaptable and well suited to the modern environment. Locally, the species has proved a challenge for conservation bodies as they may have a significant impact on rare breeding birds, but overall the species is unlikely to attract calls for population control, although it is still shot in moderate numbers. This and the lack of natural avian predators, such as the Goshawk, mean that Carrion Crow's future seems assured for the coming decade.

Hooded Crow   *Corvus cornix*

Formerly fairly common 19th century resident; now rare winter visitor

The monotypic Hooded Crow is generally found in eastern Europe, the Middle East and western Asia. In Europe the species breeds in northwest Scotland and Ireland and as far west as central Europe; a zone of hybridisation occurs across Scotland where the population meets that of Carrion Crow. In England, it is principally a passage migrant and winter visitor from Scandinavia and parts of eastern Europe, although numbers declined considerably during the 20th century.

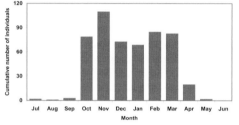

Seasonal occurrence of Hooded Crows
from 1950/51-2003/04

To Christy, the Hooded Crow was "A winter visitor common enough on and near the coast, but rather rare as a rule inland … It seems that formerly it bred in some numbers on our coast, but it certainly never does so now…" Breeding was noted, at least until the early 1860s, along the Blackwater Estuary, with nests being taken on Osea Island and from Ramsey Island, Paglesham and on Foulness where they bred on a 'haulm-wall' (a wall made of the stalks of peas, beans, etc.). During this colder period, breeding also took place in Suffolk (Piotrowski 2003) and in Norfolk in 1867 (Taylor *et al.* 1999). Around Saffron Walden about 1845 the species was "… common in winter" and there were, "… a great many [there] in 1854"; Christy himself had seen small flocks in the area. Ones and twos were also noted inland at: Epping Forest, where it was an occasional winter visitor; Lindsell; Sudbury, where it was also an occasional winter visitor; and Ongar Park Wood. On the coast, the main arrival was during October; at Shoebury in 1865 the first arrived on 28th after which they "… became plentiful on the saltings". The punt gunners on the Blackwater found them "… most daring and voracious in hard weather" and would "… seize wounded Plover and other birds before one's eyes".

Although Glegg described the Hooded Crow as a regular winter visitor, he observed: "… as such it is steadily decreasing". Only close to the coast did he consider the species common and then only in the north, from Mersea Island to the Stour, did he consider it truly common. Despite apparently being common on the south side of the Thames, it was considered rare along the northern shore. In its stronghold, large flocks were considered unusual, however, there were 30 on the Stour on 3rd December 1901 and 50 on 27th November 1917. These, together with the flocks noted below, are the largest gatherings to be reported in Essex, although larger numbers almost certainly occurred during the 19th century. Inland it was rare, particularly south of Chelmsford. In the Felsted district in

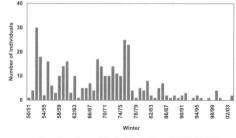

Annual numbers of Hooded Crows from 1950/51-2003/04

1918, the Hooded Crow was a regular but scarce winter migrant that had formerly been quite common. Glegg saw a number at Gosfield Park in 1927 where the species could still be seen on most days during winter. At Bishop's Stortford SF, up to 40 occurred during the 1920s. Such numbers were, however, exceptional inland by then.

By the time of Hudson & Pyman, the Hooded Crow was described as "… a very scarce, much decreased winter visitor and passage migrant", whilst Cox noted that the species was "… currently a scarce, but annual visitor…" Although numbers had declined during the period 1930–60, numbers seemed not to fall significantly throughout the 1960s and 1970s, although this may be simply due to increasing observer coverage. From the early 1980s, however, a marked decline occurred such that by the end of the century, the Hooded Crow had become a less than annual visitor to Essex. The last double-figure flock to be recorded in Essex was ten at East Tilbury on 14th February 1954 and the last time that more than two were reported from a single locality was in the winter of 1976/77, at a time of a significant influx, following a similar sized one the previous winter, when there were six around St Osyth during late November and early December.

This decline has been noted throughout England and has been attributed to the change in migratory behaviour of Scandinavian birds, with a greater proportion wintering further north due to climatic amelioration and perhaps also improved food availability in winter due to human activity (Migration Atlas).

The first Hooded Crows normally arrived in Essex during October and most departed by April. There have, however, been two September arrivals: Abberton, 28th in 1952, and East Tilbury, 23rd in 1979. There have been two May records: one at Maldon refuse tip on 5th in 1979, which may have been the same bird that frequented the Leigh/Two Tree Island area from July 1979 until April 1980; and one on 2nd at both Bradwell and Colne Point in 1991. In addition, there was one at Rayleigh on 13th July 1976. Clearly there was an autumn and spring passage through the county, presumably as birds headed/returned from wintering areas further west in southern England.

The majority of recent records have come from coastal localities with refuse tips favoured, although old-fashioned sewage farms used to be visited regularly.

(Common) Raven   *Corvus corax*

Vagrant: 14 records since 1909. Formerly fairly common: last bred in 1890

The Raven is the largest of all the passerines and is found throughout the Holarctic region where some ten races occur. The nominate race *corax* breeds from Britain and Ireland across northwest Eurasia and is largely sedentary in the south, although it has a tendency to make first autumn and winter dispersive movements (*BWP*).

The earliest written reference to a bird species involving Essex concerns the Raven (and White-tailed Eagle q.v.) and related to a passage from the Anglo-Saxon poem about the The Battle of Maldon in AD 991: "Now was riot raised, the Ravens wheeled, The eagle, eager for carrion, there was a cry on earth" (translation by Wilfrid Berridge).

Once a common bird throughout the whole of Britain, its sad decline and ultimate extinction in Essex was well documented by Christy and Glegg. Christy writing in 1890 stated that it was once a common bird, breeding throughout the county and that in his time there were still many 'Raven Trees', sites regularly occupied by nesting pairs for many years. The name Raven still occurs in a number of local place names. Christy pleaded for the protection of the last few pairs and considered extinction to be imminent: "In Essex, the species is already on the verge of extinction and it can hardly be expected that under any circumstances it can exist with us very many years longer".

Glegg, writing some 40 years later, set out a detailed chronology of the decline, which began inland where persecution was the greatest. He could not point to the start of the decline, although it bred fairly regularly along the coast until the 1850s by which time it was rare inland. It was not uncommon around Saffron Walden in 1815 and Sudbury around 1838 and was nesting annually at Audley End/Debden Hall, although by 1839 was rare. Nesting also occurred in the Wanstead Heronry in 1833 and 1834 and at Copt Hall, Epping in 1846. Ravens nested at Feering until 1840, with odd birds being seen for 25 years after and at Willingale in 1865, whilst a pair also nested in a large Oak that used to stand by the Chelmer at Broomfield Mills. The last inland breeding may have been at Thundersley, where two pairs bred from 1872–80. Glegg, however, noted that breeding might have continued at Pudsey Hall, Hockley "… until a few years ago", suggesting that breeding Ravens may have clung on in Essex until the early years of the 20th century. Only in Sussex did the species hold out longer in southern and eastern England.

On the coast, nests were noted at Ramsey in 1826, Great Wigborough about 1830 and birds were present at Southminster in 1832. There were winter congregations of 50–60 birds at Shoebury in the late 1820s and early 1830s, giving some idea of numbers still present on the coast. By the 1860s, Ravens were almost entirely restricted to the coast and even here numbers were falling. Two pairs nested 1.6km south of Steeple between 1862 and 1866 and in the latter year, three pairs nested at Shoebury. Between 1870 and 1890, nesting was only confirmed from 15 coastal sites: Stansgate Grove, Mayland; Brickhouse, Mundon Hall; Whitehouse, Mundon; Goldhanger Decoy; Northey Island; Jingle Hills; Osea Island; East Hall, Stannet's Grove and Church Hall, Paglesham; Latchingdon; East Mersea; Bradwell; near Tolleshunt D'Arcy; Lawford Hall (one pair from 1870-78); South Benfleet. The last three confirmed nests were all in 1890, singles being recorded from: Brick House, Mundon; Goldhanger Decoy; North Fambridge.

The Raven came under intense persecution during the 19th century due to its alleged attacks on lambs and sheep. Adults were shot, and nests and nesting trees regularly destroyed, 23 young being taken from the Osea Ravens in just seven years, whilst in the late 19th century, the use of poisons became more widespread with treated eggs being used at Canewdon and North Fambridge in 1888. As the Raven became rarer, the species became the target of collector-naturalists who ultimately sealed the fate of the Essex population.

Subsequently, the only records that probably involved 'resident' Essex Ravens were: one at North Fambridge until 1897, with one there in September 1901; one at Felsted in November 1891; and three on Wakering Marshes on 1st February 1909.

Records since 1909 are:

1958	East Mersea	20th August	One flew northeast
1963	Farnham pits	5th–7th May	Pair displaying
1975	Bradwell	13th June	One flew north
1976	The Naze	18th January	
1978	South Harlow	28th October	Two flew north
1982	Danbury	19th May	Two
1987	Colchester	14th October	Adult
	Great Dunmow	November and December	Adult
1992	Ardleigh	24th October	One flew west
1996	Wanstead Flats	On and off during year	
2003	Rainham	3rd–4th September	
2004	Ingrebourne Valley	23rd February	
	Wat Tyler CP	25th June	
	Walthamstow town	28th September	

The 1963 record may refer to escapes; at least one was known to have escaped in Hertfordshire a short time previously. The 1987 records probably both relate to one bird that was almost certainly an escape; it fed on kitchen scraps in gardens. The 1996 bird had a small, unmarked silver ring on its right leg. The escape possibility must also be considered likely for most of the remaining records, although with the Raven now breeding within just 10km of the LNHS recording boundary, the credentials of the 2003 and 2004 individuals are probably good.

(Common) Starling   *Sturnus vulgaris*

Abundant but declining resident, passage migrant and winter visitor   Red List

The Starling is a widespread Palearctic species found between 40° and 70° N. It has also been successfully introduced into North America, southernmost Africa, south Australia and New Zealand. In Europe, where the species principally occupies the temperate and boreal climatic zones, there are perhaps as many as ten subspecies, the nominate race *vulgaris* being widespread east to the Ural Mountains. Starlings are typically hole and cavity nesters that nowadays inhabit pastures, meadows and roadside verges; gardens and lawns provide attractive alternative feeding locations, enabling areas of densely populated human settlements to be colonised (European Atlas). In Britain, the species is absent only from the highland areas of northwest Scotland and reaches greatest abundance in central and southeast England (Second National Atlas). Declines have been noted in Britain and Europe since the 1950s and particularly since the 1980s. The British population is largely resident but is augmented in winter by immigrants from northeast Continental Europe.

Atlas	Survey Area	% of 10km squares or tetrads in which	
		bred/probably bred	possibly bred or present
First National 10km	Essex	100.0	0.0
Second National 10km	Essex	100.0	0.0
First London Tetrad	Met. Essex	79.0	5.0
Second London Tetrad	Met. Essex	100.0	0.0
Essex Tetrad	Essex	98.4	0.3

Summary of results of Atlas surveys for Starlings

Christy considered the Starling "An abundant resident ... [that] has become of late years very much commoner than formerly". The species apparently declined across Britain during the 18th century but this was followed by an increase from around 1830 with much of the lost ground regained by the end of the 19th century. Although reasons for the decline are unknown, it may have been a climatic one (Population Trends). In Essex during the 1830s, Starlings occurred "... in immense clouds on the marshes" near Southminster, were "... perhaps the most abundant bird ... after the House Sparrow" in the Epping Forest district and "... almost darkens the air on our meadows [at Sudbury] in winter". Thus, even at the time of the Starling's apparent lowest ebb nationally, it seems that the species was abundant in Essex. For Christy to have noticed a greater abundance during his lifetime suggests that a substantial increase in what were apparently already large numbers must have occurred. Such increases were probably a result of several factors: changes in agricultural practice; climatic change; the heavy persecution of raptors; the increasing urban environment that provided new nest sites, food sources and warmer winter temperatures than the open countryside that resulted in lower mortality (Elkins 1983).

Glegg regarded the Starling, as an abundant resident but gave no breeding data. He did, however, note: "... this bird may still be increasing..." Hudson & Pyman similarly regarded it as an abundant resident, passage migrant and winter visitor that was particularly numerous in urban and suburban habitats. Cox noted that the Starling was numerous at all seasons, especially in areas where buildings or trees provided suitable nesting cavities, although he conceded that Starlings rarely featured in census data and that there was no information available on Essex breeding densities or on any actual changes in abundance. In fact, only since the 1980s has such information been available and little direct reference and comparison of populations and trends is possible prior to then.

Nationally, Starlings continued to spread and expand until the 1960s, after which time numbers fell markedly. Like so many other species it was adversely affected by the use of persistent organochlorine insecticides. Following their ban, there was some recovery but this was relatively short-lived with declines again noted from the 1970s (O'Connor & Shrubb 1986). Unfortunately no comments were made on Essex breeding data in *EBRs* until the early 1990s.

The Starling was recorded in every 10km square in both National Atlas surveys, whilst the Essex Atlas survey located the species in 98.7% of tetrads with breeding confirmed in most of these, with Starlings absent only from parts of the arable prairies of Dengie, Wallasea Island and the south side of the Roach. There was an apparent increase in range in Metropolitan Essex between the two London Atlases.

Since 1981, the local CBC/BBS Indices have shown a significant decline, mirroring the national trend where the CBC/BBS (England) Index for 1977–2002 fell by 76% and the BBS (England) for 1994–2003 declined by 28%.

Cox made no reference to breeding densities. Since 1980, breeding densities on woodland sites have varied markedly from 0.9 to 212 pairs per km^2 (average 73), whilst on farmland the average densities were 8.1 pairs per km^2 (range 1.2-18.1). Long-term CBC sites, such as The Mores Wood, near Brentwood, have seen breeding numbers decline from around ten pairs in 1988 to 2–3 during the mid-1990s and 0–1 by the end of the decade, whilst at Hainault Forest CP 35 pairs in 1990, itself a reduction on previous years, had fallen to 12 by 1994.

Anecdotal evidence presented in recent *EBRs* suggests that breeding numbers have continued to decline across Essex in the early 21st century. Changes in farming practice appear to be affecting the Starling's foraging habits. Reduced spring ploughing, autumn sowing of crops and conversion of pasture to arable seem to all be factors at work in our region (Essex Atlas). A lack of suitable invertebrate food for chicks on intensively farmed land appears to be causing poor productivity (Mead 2000).

Glegg considered that Starling movements were "... of an exceptionally complex nature". In general, local birds are usually sedentary, although subject to some limited wandering, with immigrants arriving from Europe from October to swell the numbers wintering in Essex.

From as early as June, Starlings, particularly juveniles, form flocks that roam across the countryside and around the coast. At this time of year, reed bed roosts may form, albeit not of the scale seen during autumn and winter. These roosts tend to be used until the onset of severe weather during autumn/winter, when they are abandoned in favour of tree roosts. These roosts/flocks, whilst still relatively common, are smaller than 20–30 years ago. The origin/destination of 3,800 that flew south at Bradwell on 1st July 2001 is uncertain; westerly passage is noted in Norfolk from early June but it is unclear whether British or Continental Starlings are involved (Taylor *et al.* 1999).

Numbers arriving from northeast Europe have, in general, declined since Glegg's time as Continental populations have decreased over the last few decades. Thus, whilst large arrivals along the coast were almost annual from the 1950s–1970s, today they are rare and numbers are usually small.

Starlings are diurnal migrants, which in Essex at least do not begin to arrive until a few hours after sunrise, although movements may often carry on until dusk. Most flocks are small, usually in the region of 20–50 and many arrive low in off the sea, often in the company of larks and thrushes; many appear to continue inland rather than settle along the coast. Observations at Bradwell have shown that many Starlings arriving off the sea from the east headed north on arriving along the coast and then turned west and headed along the Blackwater. Glegg commented on the use of the Thames Valley as a migration route.

Around 10,000 arrived at Bradwell on 23rd October 1955, the largest single coastal movement, although 20,000 in fields at Colne Point on 23rd October 1990 and 10,000 along Dengie on 11th October 1982 may well have involved immigrants given the date of the counts. Other large arrivals have been: 5,100 west along the Crouch, 14th October 1984; 5,000 in off the sea at Hamford Water, 12th October 1980; 4,350 at Foulness, 12th October 1980; 4,000 at Colne Point, 17th October 1976; and 4,000 at Holliwell, 17th October 1982. Apart from a vague report of "thousands" moving at The Naze on 29th October 1992, there have been no significant influxes since the early 1990s except for 7,789 at Foulness on 15th October 2000. Some of these movements would seem to continue inland, small flocks regularly being reported flying west at the time of coastal movements, although 5,000 flying west-northwest over Rayne between 0930 and 1330 hrs on 24th October 1958 was exceptional. A total of 3,000 heading northwest early on 27th October 1956 and 2,000 heading in the same direction on 1st November 1959 along the Lea Valley may well have been immigrants, although by November large roost movements begin to become conspicuous.

In 1956, an exceptional movement occurred on 25th–26th November. Although the date is perhaps late enough to involve Starlings moving to/from roosts, the exceptional scale of the movement suggested a substantial arrival in the county, although no influxes were reported from the coast at the time. In northwest Essex, a late afternoon movement of some 200,000 birds passed over Coploe Hill, Strethall, in just 45 minutes on 26th, whilst on 25th 30,000 flew west at Fambridge and on occasions during November, 75,000 flew northeast over Chelmsford.

Some huge winter roosts were reported in Essex, many during the 1980s. Flight lines to these roosts are conspicuous on winter afternoons with birds sometimes flying some 20km back to their roost from daytime feeding sites (Winter Atlas). In 1953, an estimated 300,000 were at White Roding on 28th November with 100,000 at Boreham on 21st and 22nd. At least 500,000 and perhaps nearer 1 million roosted in Braxted Park or Chantry Wood, Wickham Bishops, between 1978 and 1982, whilst 400,000–500,000 roosted at Asheldham GP during 1983/84. The largest roost ever found in Essex was at Wrabness in Blakey Grove and grew from some 500,000 on 26th November 1975 to 2 million during 1980. Further counts revealed some 2.1 million on 8th November 1988 and a peak of 3 million in December 1988. Some 2 milliosn were present on 26th November 1989, but the roost could not be located the following year. A roost at Layer Marney in 1988 contained "hundreds of thousands if not a million".

Subsequently, there has been a significant decline in the number and size of roosts with just three six-figure counts since 1990: 500,000 on Skippers Island, late October 1990; 100,000 at Holland Haven, 20th October 1991; and 100,000 at Royal Terrace, Southend-on-Sea, 1st March 2000. Five-figure roost counts have become less than annual and, when they occur, these rarely hold more than 10,000, giving a very stark idea of the apparent scale of the decline of the Starling in Europe.

Most winter roosts have broken up by March. Little has been reported on the spring movement, although it is probably more extensive than the few records suggest.

The decline of the Starling would seem to have been caused by a number of factors linked to modern farming methods. Until there is a substantial overhaul of the CAP and hence modern farming methods, little progress will be made in reversing the

	Jan	Feb	Mar	Apr	May	Jun	Jul	Aug	Sep	Oct	Nov	Dec
Essex	143	91	128	213	259	200	88	45	34	42	40	48
North England	1	2	1									
South England	32	37	33	43	51	32	15	14	9	11	18	19
Wales		2										
Ireland	1										1	
Finland					2	1		1				
Norway				2			1					
Sweden					3	1			1			
Baltic States					2	5	5	2	2	1		
Russia	1		1	7	7	5	1	5	3	1		
Poland			2	7	5	1	2	2		2	1	
Denmark		1	2	1			2	3	1			
Germany	1	4	10	11	6	10	10	4	5	6	3	1
The Netherlands	4	8	12	4	11	7	2	5	2	1	2	3
Belgium						1	1		1	17	9	1
France	2	1			1	1	1		1		2	1
Totals	*185*	*146*	*191*	*293*	*348*	*265*	*125*	*79*	*55*	*81*	*76*	*73*

Month and location of recovery of Starlings ringed in Essex

negative trends seen over the last few decades. For now, the Starling remains common across the county but the future of what was once an extremely abundant Essex species must remain in doubt.

	Jan	Feb	Mar	Apr	May	Jun	Jul	Aug	Sep	Oct	Nov	Dec
Finland					1							
Sweden			1				1					
Baltic States					2	4	5	2				
Russia							1					
Denmark			1									
Germany				1		1						
The Netherlands					2		1		1	3	5	1
Belgium		1	1		1		1			3	3	1
Totals	*0*	*1*	*2*	*2*	*6*	*5*	*9*	*2*	*1*	*6*	*8*	*2*

Month of ringing and origin of Starlings ringed abroad and recovered in Essex

Large numbers of Starlings have been trapped in Essex resulting in a significant number of recoveries of Essex-ringed and foreign-ringed Starlings from northeast Europe. Nearly 70% of all Starlings ringed in Essex that have been reported subsequently were found within 10km of the ringing site, confirming the generally sedentary nature of British populations. Some locally bred Starlings do, however, make longer distance movements with several ringed as nestlings subsequently being recovered in the Low Countries, France and Spain. Migrants from northeast Europe usually start to arrive during October with as a rule Dutch birds arriving first, then German and Scandinavian birds from mid-October and finally Polish, Finnish and Russian Starlings from late October and November (Migration Atlas). The furthest movement involved one ringed at Abberton on 15th December 1956 and found dead near Kilemary, Russia, on 15th August 1960, some 3,021km to the east. One ringed at Clacton-on-Sea as an adult on 2nd January 1964 was at least seven years old when found dead at Kalinin, Russia, on 15th January 1971.

Sponsored in memory of Tariq Watson

Rose-coloured Starling (Rosy Starling) *Sturnus roseus*

Very rare passage migrant: 16 records

The monotypic Rose-coloured Starling occurs from Central Asia to west and southern Russia northwards. The species' typical habitat is steppe and dry grassland, where this mainly insectivorous species feeds on locusts and grasshoppers. Locust plagues perhaps trigger periodic irruptions of Rose-coloured Starlings beyond their normal range and into central and western Europe.

1856	Strethall	mid-September	Shot
about 1860	Sturmer Mere	Undated	Shot
about 1870	Maldon/Heybridge	Undated	Shot
1887	Kelvedon	August	Shot
1889	Heybridge	29th–30th December	
1906	Pitsea	autumn	Shot
1953	Great Chesterford	4th September	Killed by a car
1961/62	Southminster	30th September–10th January	
1992	Bradfield	9th–10th June	Adult
1994	Walthamstow	22nd June	Adult
1997	Stambourne	4th August	Adult
	The Naze	19th October	Juvenile
2000	Greenstead Estate, Colchester	17th–20th October	Juvenile
2002	St Lawrence Bay	16th–18th June	Adult
	Fryerns, Basildon	4th July	Adult
2003	Customs House, Canning Town	6th July	Adult

The 1961/62 individual was very pale and washed out and considered to have escaped from an aviary. However, the timing of the occurrence is typical and a wintering individual is not unprecedented.

Hudson & Pyman dismissed the 1860 record but gave no reasons; a relative of the respected naturalist Edward Fitch shot it. Glegg rejected the 1889 record; he dismissed many sight records. In addition, a record mentioned by Glegg involving one shot in Essex prior to 1856, but dismissed by Hudson & Pyman, may well have involved one shot at Heydon, Cambridgeshire, on 15th August 1830 (Yarrell 1845). Christy also made a vague reference to one at Havering.

There is a certain amount of confusion about the date and location of the 1870 record. Christy referred to one shot at Maldon but gave no date. He also mentioned one shot "Some twenty years ago", around 1870, in Heybridge. In addition, there is an adult in Chelmsford Museum (Accession No. D6256), labelled as taken at Maldon prior to 1881 that may refer to either the Maldon or Heybridge bird. The likelihood is, however, that they probably all refer to the same specimen.

Rose-coloured Starling was removed from the list of species considered by BBRC in 2001. An unprecedented national influx of 182 individuals in 2002 represented 28% of the sum total since 1958 and increased the total number of British records to 647 since 1958 (Fraser & Rogers 2004). Until recently, fewer irruptions have occurred due to the control of Locusts with insecticides, which often killed huge numbers of Rose-coloured Starlings as well. However, the 2002 influx was the largest invasion into Europe in living memory; 2000 and 2001 also saw significant influxes. Autumn records, which usually involve juveniles, probably involve individuals that have reverse migrated out of their breeding area.

House Sparrow   *Passer domesticus*

An abundant but currently declining resident   Red List

The House Sparrow is probably one of the world's most familiar birds. Its natural range covers Eurasia, northwest Africa and the Nile Valley, extending above the Arctic Circle in the west and up to 62° N in Siberia. It is absent from Siberia east of around 130° East, China, Japan and Indochina. The nominate race *domesticus* occurs throughout much of Europe and as far east as Mongolia and northern Manchuria, although *biblicus* occurs from Turkey and Cyprus through much of the Middle East. Introductions across the world have meant it is now probably the most widely distributed passerine, being absent only from much of tropical Africa and South America and western and northern Australia.

Throughout its range it lives in close association with man, breeding primarily in holes in inhabited houses or other artificial structures (European Atlas). It is widespread throughout Britain, being absent only from the high ground of the Scottish Highlands, and it reaches its greatest abundance in eastern England, where rainfall is generally low. Sparrows of the genus *Passer* show a preference for more arid environments (Second National Atlas). A significant decrease has occurred across western Europe since the 1970s. The House Sparrow is probably one of the most sedentary of wild birds (Migration Atlas).

During the 19th century, the House Sparrow was probably the most abundant of all breeding birds in Essex. Christy considered the species "An all-too-abundant resident everywhere". It was clearly not one of his or his correspondents' favourite birds and he went on "It is unquestionably a very injurious bird to the farmer, consuming a large amount of young green wheat when in the ear, and much fewer insects than some sentimentalists would have us believe. It also drives away Martins, by taking possession of their nests". Unfortunately he gave no details of breeding numbers or flock sizes.

The nocturnal pursuit of roosting House Sparrows for sparrow pie with batfowling nets was still a favourite pastime in the last few decades of the 19th century and the early 20th century. Smith (1996) noted that at Barns Farm, Springfield, 78 were caught on 3rd December 1881, with 79 being caught around Moulsham Lodge on 11th December 1882. Not only would this haul have filled a few pies, it would have also served to keep the considerable sparrow numbers in check.

Glegg observed that the "House Sparrow is an abundant resident, and apparently has been always very numerous as far back as records exist". In the churchwardens' accounts for the parish of Orsett, there was a series of entries between 1808 and 1835 that showed the efforts taken to reduce the House Sparrow's numbers. Local boys were encouraged to destroy the birds, being rewarded for the destruction of the birds or the eggs, the former at one halfpenny each: "1808, February 11. Paid for five dozen of birds, 2/6 ... 1829, April 4. Sparrow's eggs from 25th March 1837 to 3rd April 1829, £6.2s.4d." Once again no data on breeding numbers were provided, although Glegg did

Atlas	Survey Area	% of 10km squares or tetrads in which	
		bred/probably bred	possibly bred or present
First National 10km	Essex	100.0	0.0
Second National 10km	Essex	100.0	0.0
First London Tetrad	Met. Essex	82.5	5.0
Second London Tetrad	Met. Essex	100.0	0.0
Essex Tetrad	Essex	99.3	0.0

Summary of results of Atlas surveys for House Sparrows

note: "As the crops approach ripeness the Sparrows collect in the fields, until the assemblies reach large dimensions. It is on these occasions, more than at any other time, that the abundance of the Sparrow in the county can be estimated". It was considered to be one of the worst pests and "… every effort should be made to reduce its numbers".

Despite the apparently regular culls that occurred throughout the 19th and early 20th century, the House Sparrow could still be described by Hudson & Pyman as an abundant resident in the mid-1960s and "… one of the most numerous and familiar of Essex birds". Cox continued in much the same vein as previous writers, noting that "There are now few tracts of Essex countryside which bear no evidence of man's occupation, and even these frequently harbour a pair or two … but breeding densities are highest in towns and villages or around farm buildings".

Both National Atlases recorded the House Sparrow as breeding in every 10km square, whilst the Second London Atlas revealed a range identical to the First with breeding in every tetrad. Breeding was confirmed in 99.3% of all tetrads by the Essex Atlas survey.

Unfortunately, the House Sparrow was rarely mentioned in *EBRs* until 1988, its abundance and the lack of any obvious population changes resulting in little interest being shown in the species. This clearly makes it difficult to assess long-term population trends. Nationally, it was only after 1976 that the CBC monitored the species. Serious declines have, however, occurred since then across the country. From 1977–2002, the CBC/BBS (England) Index fell by 69% and the BBS (England) for 1994–2003 has declined by 11%. Local CBC data are insufficient to produce meaningful breeding densities. Across Essex, anecdotal evidence points to dramatic declines, although there are little data with which to quantify these. Declines appear to have been particularly marked since the early 1990s, although the *EBR* 1994 the first one to make any comment on House Sparrow populations, noted "This ubiquitous bird has been declining, probably since the mid-1980s…" Almost every *EBR* since has commented on the on-going decline.

It seems that declines are likely to have been driven by reductions in winter survival (Siriwardena *et al.* 1999) with declines in urban and rural environments having different causes, which may include a reduction in food supply due to a decline in spilt grain and tighter hygiene regulations, increased predation and poisoning by toxic additives in unleaded petrol (Crick *et al.* 2002). Increases in Sparrowhawk and Magpie numbers have been implicated in the decline but there is no evidence to support this other than at a very local level where a particular individual may come to specialise on sparrows. Small flocks of House Sparrows will abandon a regular garden feeding station for several months if the pressure from hunting Sparrowhawks becomes excessive (Simon Wood pers. obs.). Tawny Owls and Cats are major predators: one study (Churcher & Lawton 1987) showed that Cats were responsible for the loss of some 30% of House Sparrows.

The House Sparrow is an exceptionally adaptable bird. It is quick to take advantage of any opportunities that come its way even if the reason for its behaviour seems unclear. Thus in 1954, House Sparrows regularly flew 2km to the end of Southend Pier to forage for food, although there must have been an adequate supply on the waterfront. In 1984, House Sparrows were watched chasing and sometimes successfully snatching the soft belly feathers from other species, mainly Collared Doves but also Woodpigeons and a Rook, as they flew by. In the same year, one or more birds were observed catching and eating small fish fry from shallow water alongside a weir at Springfield on the Chelmer–Blackwater canal, whilst in 1998 a female was noted feeding a juvenile Great Tit on 27th May. Although typical denizens of buildings and other man-made structures, House Sparrows have been noted taking over House Martin nests, Sand Martin holes and have even been noted nesting in a Grey Heron nest (Hudson & Pyman).

Colour-ringing has shown that once an individual has bred, it will remain faithful to its breeding colony for life, with village and suburban sparrows making short movements of up to 2km to feed on ripening grain in autumn. Young birds make similar movements but disperse around neighbouring breeding colonies and do not necessarily return to their natal site (Migration Atlas). Autumn coastal movements along the east coast of Britain used to be a well-known occurrence particularly until the 1950s, although subsequently these have been far less obvious: these were probably coastal movements of British birds, given the lack of ringing evidence of movements from the Continent. Glegg described large flocks of sparrows, including House Sparrows, passing the lightships in the mouth of the Thames during September and October during the early years of the 20th century. However, apart from observations at Colne Point during the 1970s and 1980s, little has subsequently been published on coastal movements in Essex. The movements at Colne Point, Cox considered, took two distinct forms. Firstly, there were large westerly movements, often in association with Greenfinches. From soon after dawn, flocks could be observed flying low along the coastline, sometimes pausing to feed in vegetation or tideline debris. A similar phenomenon has been noted at other sites along the east coast of Britain. The second involved mixed flocks, often of House and Tree Sparrows, that appeared high overhead, circled and called repeatedly. This behaviour suggests an attempt at re-orientation by birds arriving on the coast, perhaps pointing to a Continental origin. However, nationally there have been only three recoveries abroad of British-ringed birds and none in Britain or Ireland of foreign-ringed House Sparrows (Migration Atlas).

At Colne Point, an estimated 7,500 moved west with finches during October 1976, including peaks of 1,100 on 9th and 10th, 2,350 on 13th and 1,300 on 16th. In 1983, more than 3,000 passed through during the week commencing 17th October, peaking at 2,000–2,500 on 19th. Smaller numbers were reported from The Naze, Bradwell and Foulness at this time. In recent years, numbers reported have generally been small and rarely reach double figures. Nonetheless recent observations from The Naze confirm that, despite the much-reduced numbers, the two types of movement are still readily discernible.

In winter, large communal roosts and feeding flocks may form. The House Sparrow's sedentary nature means that its distribution in winter remains much the same as in the breeding season (Winter Atlas). Late afternoons in winter will often find birds arriving close to large communal roosts where they continue their conversational twittering until after dark. Roosts of up to 5,000 individuals were reported during the 1950s. More recently the largest roosts have been in Romford town centre, where numbers peaked at 2,500 in the winter of 1991/92, and at Essex University where 2,000 were noted in January and February 1988. The last four-figure count came from Wickford in February 1996 (1,000), since when roost counts have only exceptionally exceeded 300 birds. Large feeding flocks were noted at Bradwell on 28th January 1961 when about 4,000 were disturbed from a 0.2ha field and there were 3,000–4,000 in a stubble field at The Naze during September 1962. Today, it is rare for such feeding flocks to number more than 200 individuals.

Between 1970 and 1993, ringers were actively discouraged from ringing a species considered largely sedentary and of little interest, so that for such a common bird relatively few House Sparrows have been ringed and recovered. Of over 380 House Sparrows ringed in Essex and subsequently reported, over 92% were within 9km of the ringing sites. Some have, however, travelled further having found their way to Suffolk, Norfolk and Kent, whilst one ringed at Bradwell on 28th May 1960 was found dead near Stoke-on-Trent, Staffordshire, on 24th April 1965. In addition, an individual ringed at Spurn Point, East Yorkshire, on 7th October 1967 was found dead at Holland-on-Sea on 18th July 1970.

That such a common species as the House Sparrow should decline so rapidly must be a lesson to us all. Good long-term records are essential in order to monitor a species, however familiar. The problems faced by the House Sparrow are typical of those facing many other farmland species, added to which urban populations appear to be struggling in the face of environmental pollution. The House Sparrow is still sufficiently common and adaptable that it is unlikely to decline to extinction. That said, the species' status will remain uncertain unless significant changes are made to the CAP and air pollution controls are tightened.

(Eurasian) Tree Sparrow *Passer montanus*

Scarce passage migrant and winter visitor. Probably now extinct as a breeding species following recent massive declines

Red List

The Tree Sparrow has an extensive range in the Palearctic and Oriental regions with introductions in North America, Australia and parts of the Far East (Summers-Smith 1988). The species breeds throughout much of Europe, where it is represented by the nominate race *montanus*. The race *transcaucasicus* occurs in the Caucasus and Bulgaria where it intergrades with *montanus* and has apparently expanded its range in southern Finland and in parts of the Mediterranean in the last 40 years or so (European Atlas). In Britain, where the Tree Sparrow is typically a lowland species occurring in areas with hedgerows and open woodland, it has declined significantly over the last 30 years. At the time of the Second National Atlas it was most abundant in the central counties of England and east Wales and scarce or absent from much of the south and southwest of England, west Wales and west and north Scotland (Second National Atlas). Tree Sparrows are generally sedentary, although a proportion of the British population shows a generally southerly dispersal in autumn and winter (Migration Atlas).

The Tree Sparrow has, since the early part of the 19th century, been prone to marked periodic fluctuations in population size. Such a pattern is often typical of a species at the western edge of its range, which the Tree Sparrow is in Britain, and there is evidence to suggest that numbers may depend on cyclic fluctuations or movements of birds from Europe or other areas of high density (Summers-Smith 1989). More recent declines may, however, be linked to the change to intensive farming methods over the last 40 years that have resulted in a loss of suitable breeding sites and a reduction in invertebrates due to increased herbicide use (Population Trends).

Christy considered that the Tree Sparrow was "A resident, breeding more or less sparingly in

Atlas	Survey Area	% of 10km squares or tetrads in which bred/probably bred	possibly bred or present
First National 10km	Essex	96.5	1.8
Second National 10km	Essex	73.7	14.0
First London Tetrad	Met. Essex	48.5	12.5
Second London Tetrad	Met. Essex	34.0	11.0
Essex Tetrad	Essex	24.4	13.9

Summary of results of Atlas surveys for Tree Sparrows

several parts of the county, I believe, though I have never found a nest. In winter its numbers are largely increased … and it is then fairly common in all, or most, parts of the county". Although he gives no absolute data, it appears that, apart from in a few areas of Essex, the Tree Sparrow was no more than a winter visitor. In the last quarter of the 19th century, breeding or a presence in the nesting season was noted at Paglesham where it apparently bred in "… considerable numbers…" at Ramsey where it was "… fairly common…", at Danbury where it was "… not common…" at Frating Abbey in 1875 and Dagenham in 1878.

An increase had clearly occurred by the 1920s with Glegg noting" If the older reports can be accepted it would appear to be an increasing nester". He described it as "… a not uncommon resident, although breeding somewhat locally". He went on to observe "Its distribution throughout the county during the summer is sufficiently general as not to necessitate description of nesting localities". He detailed nothing further regarding breeding numbers.

There seems to have been little significant change in numbers at least until the mid-1960s when Hudson & Pyman observed that Tree Sparrows were "Resident, locally common … A somewhat local species … of late years it has certainly increased in central Essex … and around Colchester". In the Writtle/Roxwell/Highwoods area, 400 nests in 1964 had increased to 900 in 1968.

The pattern of increase and decrease to this point in time should be seen against the national situation. After high population levels at the turn of the 20th century, much of Britain experienced a phase of decrease and range contraction. Then in the 1950s and early 1960s, populations began to increase and expand again with numbers reaching a plateau in the mid-1970s, after which a marked decline began (Population Trends).

Quite when the latest long-term decline began in Essex is unclear. However, Cox considered that the "… current impression is of a decline in the overall Essex population…" Figures from the Writtle/Roxwell/Highwood area revealed just how marked the decline was in some areas, the 900 nests in 1968 having, by the early 1980s, fallen to just a few dozen pairs: the removal of old pollarded Willows and diseased Elms, the destruction of old farm buildings and the reduction in haystacks were considered likely causes at the time. Whilst some of these may have been at least in part responsible, the causes of the decline appeared to be far more complex.

The First National Atlas survey confirmed breeding season records in all but one 10km square (TL74, bordering Suffolk) with breeding confirmed in almost all; there was a net loss from six 10km squares by the time of the Second National Atlas survey. In Metropolitan Essex there was a significant decline between the two London Atlas surveys. The Essex Atlas survey recorded the Tree Sparrow in 38.3% of tetrads, mainly in the north, west and central Essex with breeding confirmed in 24.4% of tetrads; it was then estimated that the population may have numbered well in excess of 1,000 pairs. However, just a few years after completion of the survey, these figures were considered optimistic given the marked rate of decline (Essex Atlas), the population having perhaps declined by as much as 90% in the 25 years to 1996. A flock of 250 at Boreham on 25th June 1990 that included many young birds suggests that this area was one of the last strongholds. By 1994 it had disappeared from m any breeding localities including at least a dozen tetrads in both central and Metropolitan Essex and all sites on Dengie. By the mid-1990s most breeding records were restricted to the southwest of the county, in the Metropolitan area or central/west Essex.

Although inconspicuous in the breeding season, thereby raising the possibility of an undetected pair or two in some underwatched part of the county, nesting has not been confirmed since 1999, when pairs were reported at three sites, two fewer than in the previous year. A single bird at Little Canfield on 15th June 2000 could have been part of a breeding pair.

	Period in October	Total	Peak	Peak date
1970	16th-18th	1,350	750	17th
1971	23rd	1,200	1,200	23rd
1973	17th-24th	1,500	600	20th
1974	11th-27th	2,700	600	21st
1975	4th-20th	2,300	1,650	18th
1976	1st-31st	11,400	2,500	10th
1977	1st-23rd	1,120	300	13th
1978	1st-21st	120	80	21st
1980	6th-25th	620	300	9th
1981	21st-23rd	350	150	23rd
1982	23rd-24th	450	400	23rd
1983	2nd-23rd	1,720	1,500	19th
1984	27th	100	100	27th
1985	21st-25th	8	4	21st/25th

NB: Observer coverage was variable in periods shown

**Weekly movements of Tree Sparrows at
Colne Point from 1970-1985**

Nationally, the CBC/BBS (England) recorded a 96% decline between 1977 and 2002, although more recent data from the BBS (England) suggest a 23% increase between 1994 and 2003. It should be borne in mind, however, that the population currently stands at just 3% of its level in the 1970s.

Although mainly nesting in tree holes and occasionally building typical weaver-type nests in thick hedgerows, Tree Sparrows in Essex have been observed utilising the nests of other species including Rooks and Magpies and holes excavated by Sand Martins. Haystacks, thatched roofs, cavities in bridges and jetties and even under the loose metal cap of a wooden telegraph pole are sites that have been used. Around 20–30 pairs used nest boxes in Saffron Walden during the 1970s.

In October 1833, flocks numbering hundreds settled on a ship bound for the Thames as she passed the Norfolk, Suffolk and Kent coasts (Yarrell 1871–85) and in November 1860 thousands boarded a vessel between the Dogger Bank and the Galloper Lightship (Christy). Glegg also referred to westerly passage from the Kentish Knock Lightship between 23rd September and 18th October 1903, at times in considerable numbers. Although the Tree Sparrow is resident in Britain, big passage movements used to occur along the south and southeast coasts in some autumns. There was a certain amount of randomness about these movements, but there was a tendency for large numbers to occur in groups of consecutive years which tended to occur at times of recovery of the British population (for example from 1958–62), and it is possible that these involved irruptions from the Continent (Summers-Smith 1989). The largest single day movement in Essex occurred on 8th October 1961, when approximately 3,000 flew west during the day over Foulness. Otherwise only small numbers were generally observed on migration during the 1950s and 1960s.

However, around the period that numbers were thought to have peaked nationally, observations at Colne Point revealed quite substantial movements, their character being not dissimilar to those of the House Sparrow (Cox). After 1985 these movements appeared to cease, except for occasional birds. Away from Colne Point, regular movements on a smaller scale were noted at Bradwell, where up to 1,200 were noted during November 1976 following the huge movement through Colne Point in October. Since the mid-1990s, it has been rare for more than 1–2 to be recorded from coastal locations; the last double-figure count from the coast was ten over The Naze on 28th September 2002. The number of

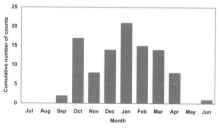

Seasonal occurrence of flocks/counts of 100+
Tree Sparrows from 1971-2004

records outside the breeding season in 2004 was higher than in the last 2–3 years and this, together with the fact that outside the county there have been signs of increase, may point to a change in fortune for the species.

The size and number of large wintering flocks have generally mirrored the size of the breeding population, with the largest flocks having occurred in the late 1960s and early 1970s, around the time that the breeding population reached its peak. At Romford SF there were 1,000 in late December 1961, 2,500 in February 1967 and 3,000 in December 1967, rising to 4,000 in January 1968. Elsewhere, there were 2,000 in Thorndon CP in January 1967, a maximum of 1,200 at Tollesbury in January 1971 and 1,500 roosted with Starlings at Roydon during February 1971. No four-figure flocks were recorded before 1961 or after 1971. Three-figure flocks were, however, regular from the 1950s to mid-1980s. Subsequently, they

have become scarce with the last three-figure flocks noted in Essex during the winter of 1989/90, with 200 at Great Braxted on 26th December 1989 and 105 at Fairlop CP on 20th January 1990. The above-average number of large flocks in 1979/80 suggests that either the species formed larger flocks during the period of severe weather or Essex received an influx from elsewhere.

With the rapid decline of the breeding population, double-figure counts quickly became rare with ten at Walthamstow in late November 2000 being the first since 16 at Margaret Roding on 4th February 1996 and ten at Rainham on 24th February 1996.

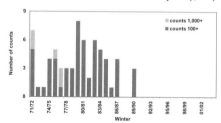

Annual totals of flocks of 100+ Tree Sparrows
from 1971/72-2003/04

A small spring passage used to occur throughout Essex, with some sites noting their largest counts of the year after the autumn influx. Of the eight three-figure counts in April, 300 at Barling on 3rd April 1981 and 200 north over Bradwell on 9th April 1981 and 250 at Ulting and 150 at Goldhanger on 3rd April 1984 are suggestive of influxes.

Of over 60 recoveries of Tree Sparrows ringed in Essex, around 50% moved less than 10km and over 95% less than 99km confirming the species' generally sedentary nature. However, single birds ringed at Toot Hill on 22nd May 1971 and recovered at Eure, France, on 24th January 1974 and Rainham on 31st January 1967 and recovered in Belgium on 19th June 1967 confirm an exodus of some local birds. In addition, two nestlings ringed in Belgium and recovered at Romford in winter (one subsequently recaptured at its birthplace) point to the arrival of immigrants at least in some years (Cox). All these movements were at the time of high population levels and may have been made in response to population pressures (Migration Atlas).

It is hard to be optimistic about the Tree Sparrow's future in Essex. It appears to be extinct as a breeding species and non-breeding season records continue to decline. Although large fluctuations in population appear to be a natural occurrence, modern farming methods have probably exacerbated the declines seen over the last three decades. Perhaps the only hope of a return lies in an irruption from the Continent; even there, however, numbers are much reduced.

Chaffinch

Fringilla coelebs

Abundant resident, passage migrant and winter visitor

The Chaffinch is a bird of the Western Palearctic where it occurs in boreal, temperate and Mediterranean zones. It is widely distributed in Europe, almost reaching the limit of trees in the north, whilst it reaches north Africa and Iran in the south as well as Siberia to the east and the Azores and Madeira in the west. Thirteen races are recognised (Clement *et al.* 1993) with the nominate race *coelebs* occurring throughout much of mainland Europe and as far east as western Siberia, and *gengleri* breeding in the British Isles. It is one

of the most familiar of European birds, breeding in all types of woody habitat from lowland to montane and sub-alpine zones and from extensive forests and woods to tall hedgerows, orchards, parks and gardens including those in some towns and cities. There was a northerly spread in Europe during the 20th century with 10–20% increases in many countries including Britain during the 1970s and 1980s (European Atlas). In Britain it is ubiquitous and is one of the commonest of all birds (Second National Atlas). Numbers are greatly increased during winter by immigrants from Fennoscandia, with British Chaffinches generally sedentary (Migration Atlas).

The earliest documented record involved a semi-albino at Havering in 1732 (Albin 1731-38).

In general, the Chaffinch appears to have always been an abundant resident (Christy, Glegg). However, Hudson & Pyman referred to a general decrease from around 1961, the first year that breeding numbers were referred to in the *EBR*s, a decline subsequently attributed to the use of organochlorine chemicals from which the Chaffinch, primarily a seed-eater, suffered particularly. In some areas, the declines were dramatic with 50 pairs in the Writtle/ Roxwell/Highwood area in 1962 falling to just 12 in 1963; the severe winter of 1962/63 may have also had an effect on population levels. With the banning of the toxic chemicals, a steady recovery followed; Cox described the Chaffinch as a common resident.

Both National Atlases confirmed breeding in every 10km square, whilst the two London Atlas surveys pointed to small increases in Metropolitan Essex, probably due to increased observer coverage. The Essex Atlas survey located Chaffinches

Atlas	Survey Area	% of 10km squares or tetrads in which	
		bred/probably bred	possibly bred or present
First National 10km	Essex	100.0	0.0
Second National 10km	Essex	100.0	0.0
First London Tetrad	Met. Essex	62.0	10.5
Second London Tetrad	Met. Essex	84.5	7.5
Essex Tetrad	Essex	83.8	3.8

Summary of results of Atlas surveys for Chaffinches

in 87.6% of tetrads with breeding confirmed in almost all. Although widespread, Chaffinches were absent from some treeless coastal areas and the most densely populated urban areas of the county.

Local CBC data revealed a relatively stable population from 1981–92, since when there has been a marked increase; the local BBS Index has increased similarly. Nationally, the CBC/BBS (England) Index for the period 1977–2002 increased by 27%, whilst more recently the BBS (England) Index for the period 1994–2003 has increased by 13%.

Cox described mean densities on Essex CBC plots of 15 pairs per km^2 (range 2–39) on farmland and 68 pairs per km^2 (range 44–103) in woodland. However, a separate survey of Hatfield Forest in 1976 revealed just 15 pairs per km^2. Since 1981, mean densities on farmland have been 26 pairs per km^2 (range 4–46) and 64 pairs per km^2 (range 39–101) in woodland.

Around 90% of British Chaffinches move no further than 5km from the natal site and the rest, almost entirely first-year birds, less than 50km (Newton 1972). The British winter population is roughly doubled by the immigration of Continental birds, mostly of Scandinavian origin.

Diurnal migration on an apparently large scale used to be a feature of autumn, both along the Essex coast and inland. On the coast, arrivals generally occurred from between northeast and southeast, although some appeared to arrive from almost due south. Movements on the whole do not occur when the other common finches are moving. Chaffinches' strategy for crossing the North Sea or English Channel appears to depend on wind direction (Elkins 1988), although unlike Bramblings, which migrate at night directly across the North Sea, they migrate on a narrow front through Denmark, northwest Germany, the Netherlands, Belgium and northeast France. The main passage occurs during the early hours of daylight. Very considerable numbers have been reported passing ships offshore and over The Naze, Bradwell, Foulness and other coastal sites.

Glegg noted "… great influxes of this species from east to west have been recorded at the lights off the Essex coast in the autumn". Unfortunately, the numbers involved in the largest movements along the coast since the 1950s have almost without exception not been estimated. Thus, at least 1,000 that arrived from the east and northeast at The

Naze on 19th October 1958, "several thousand" passing a boat off Clacton-on-Sea between 8th and 10th October 1974 and an estimated 1,000 that passed south at The Naze between the 13th and 15th December 1983 are the only direct references to four-figure counts.

From the evidence available, it seems that the scale of immigration has declined since the 1970s, although this trend does not appear to have been observed outside Essex. Certainly, since the 1980s numbers appear to have been much reduced, despite increased observer coverage, and most arrivals are small; indeed it is rare these days for more than 300 to be recorded in a single day's movement at individual coastal sites.

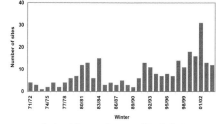

Number of sites recording counts of 50+ Chaffinches from 1971/72-2003/04

During the 1950s, there were regular autumn counts of several hundred Chaffinches from the then well-watched northwest of Essex. Passage in this area appeared to adopt flight lines in either a west or southerly direction with the Cam Valley and the western flank of Coploe Hill, Strethall, forming the southern flight line and the Strethall escarpment the westerly one. Some substantial counts were also observed along the Lea Valley where the general direction of migration was northwest. A total of 5,000–10,000 passed over on 27th October 1956 and 5,000 on 1st November 1959. Visible migration of Chaffinches is possible to observe at almost any inland location, although the numbers recorded are generally small, with recent observations of 100–300 on passage over Newport and Navestock being particularly notable.

Despite the apparent decline in the scale of immigration, wintering numbers appear to have been largely unaffected, the number and size of flocks having not altered significantly since the 1950s. Indeed, since the late 1990s numbers appear to have increased overall. Typically flocks range in size up to 200 and exceptionally more. The largest winter flocks reported in Essex involved some 600–1,000 at The Hythe in January–February 1960 that fed on the seeds of Sea Aster on the old sludge lagoons and at least 2,000 at High Beech on 2nd February 1991 that fed on Beech/Hornbeam mast. These large winter flocks often include other finches, especially Bramblings and buntings.

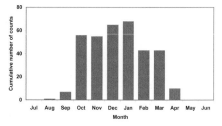

Seasonal occurrence of counts of 50+ Chaffinches from 1971-2004

Chaffinches can be fairly mobile within their wintering area, although they do not move around as much as Bramblings.

Occasionally, mid-winter cold-weather movements have occurred, with birds moving generally west to southwest through the county.

Spring passage in March and April, although generally low-key, can occasionally be more extensive than the autumn movement and was quite exceptional in the early 1980s. At Hanningfield, there were 750 on 1st April 1980 and 2,000 on 1st April 1981. Also in 1981, an estimated 5,000 were present along the roadsides between Latchingdon and Bradwell from 15th–18th March.

The number of three-figure counts varies markedly from year to year; the early 1980s saw a particularly large number of sites recording flocks of 50 or more, with strong spring passage coinciding with the peak years.

Over 60% of the Essex-ringed Chaffinches subsequently reported have remained within the county, suggesting that they were of the sedentary race *gengleri*. Of the remainder, most are likely to have been nominate *coelebs* with recoveries from Scandinavia and along the Chaffinch's migration route through northern central Europe. One recovered in Ireland probably resulted from a hard-weather movement to the west. The furthest movement involving a Chaffinch ringed in Essex was from Colchester to near Oulu, Finland, a distance of 1,957km. A number of foreign-ringed Chaffinches have also been recovered in Essex from both typical breeding areas and migration routes.

	Jan	Feb	Mar	Apr	May	Jun	Jul	Aug	Sep	Oct	Nov	Dec
Essex	16	17	12	20	17	14	6	4	1	1	2	
South England	3	3	1	1	1	1				1	1	1
Ireland			1									
Finland							1					
Norway					2							
Sweden					1	3	1	1				
Denmark			1	2	1			1				
Germany	1		1	3						1		1
The Netherlands				1		1				2	1	
Belgium	1		1							13	3	1
France										1		
Totals	*21*	*20*	*17*	*30*	*22*	*18*	*8*	*4*	*1*	*19*	*7*	*3*

Month and location of recovery of Chaffinches ringed in Essex

544

A male resembling one of the African races *africana/spodiogenys* was near Fingringhoe village on 9th–24th April 1994 and 1st–15th January 1995. It was, however, not accepted by BBRC as the first British record of this race on the grounds that there were several "important" anomalies in the plumage typical of those two races, and an unusually marked aberrant nominate *coelebs* or *gengleri* was the most likely identity of the individual. However, the distribution and seasonal occurrence of the 15 European reports attributed to *africana/spodiogenys* lend support to the possibility that they refer to birds that have travelled unaided from Africa (Oreel 2004).

There is every reason to be optimistic for the future of the Chaffinch in Essex. It has adapted well to the modern environment and readily uses garden feeding stations. Apparent climate changes over the last two decades have resulted in a run of exceptionally mild winters which appear to have increased survival rates.

Brambling *Fringilla montifringilla*

Fairly common passage migrant and winter visitor in variable numbers

The monotypic Brambling is distributed extensively from Scandinavia across northern Eurasia to the Pacific. Although inhabiting a wide range of habitats, the species favours Birch woodland in Fennoscandia. It is the northern ecological counterpart of the Chaffinch and is perhaps the most migratory of all European finches—and the only one that entirely vacates its breeding quarters in winter (Newton 1985). It is highly mobile during and between winters and will only concentrate in areas of abundance of its principal food, Beech mast. Numbers in Britain and elsewhere, therefore, vary considerably from year to year depending on the availability of Beech mast both here and abroad. Britain generally receives only a very small proportion of birds wintering in Europe. A few pairs breed in northern Scotland each year.

Christy described the Brambling as "A somewhat irregular and usually rather uncommon winter visitant, though sometimes appearing in considerable numbers, especially during severe weather". However, apart from one of the first documented Essex records at Epping around 1st October 1840 (the species was occasional around Sudbury prior to 1838), which referred to a "large flock" and "large flocks feeding on beech-nuts" at Epping on a later date, Christy made no reference to numbers. Glegg described the Brambling in a similar vein, "… a regular winter resident, but very irregular in its numbers", the only counts he detailed being 30 at Dagenham on 22nd February 1920 and "hundreds" at the Kentish Knock Lightship on 9th October 1887. He believed that its occurrence in Epping Forest was influenced by the amount of Beech mast. Hudson & Pyman and Cox described the Brambling similarly, suggesting that its status had changed very little since Christy's time. However, it is clear that numbers have in general declined since the 1970s.

Although the Brambling has never bred in Essex, it is not unusual for males on spring migration in April and sometimes May to set up temporary territories and sing for a day or so. There have been two June occurrences: in Epping Forest from 12th–25th in 1932 (*London Naturalist* 1932: 97), and a male at Weeleyhall Wood on 28th in 1985.

Although Bramblings have been recorded in Essex in every month apart from July, they are rare before September or after early May.

Autumn passage usually begins during early October, although in recent years increasing numbers have been reported in September. A total of 36, which flew in off the sea at The Naze on 30th September 1979, remains by far the largest count for that month. There have been four records in August involving seven birds, presumably all exceptionally early migrants: one at Thundersley on 16th in 1965; two at Chelmsford on 31st in 1978; three at Shoebury on 28th in 1986; a female at Deal Hall, Dengie, on 15th August in 2004.

Generally numbers reported on passage, which peak in October, are small. Unlike the Chaffinch, the Brambling is mainly a night migrant and therefore few are normally reported from coastal localities unless caught up in adverse weather conditions that cause

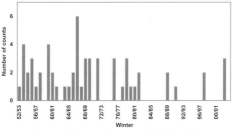

Number of sites recording counts of 100+ Bramblings from 1952/53-2003/04

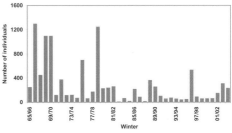

Peak annual monthly counts of Bramblings from 1965/66-2003/04

an abrupt halt to movements. There have been just nine three-figure counts during October, four from coastal watchpoints and two of these within two days of each other. A large arrival occurred around the Saffron Walden area on 25th October 1953 when more than 100 were discovered feeding amongst the refuse in the centre of the town, whilst on the same day a mixed flock of 150 Bramblings and Chaffinches was observed along the Takeley–Dunmow Road. Unfortunately, there were no observations from the coast at the time. In 1957, approximately 100 were at Audley End during the third week of October. Around 150 migrated northwest over Fobbing on 16th October 1960, whilst in 1966 there were 300 at Epping Long Green on 20th October and a similar number at Mistley during October (and November). During October 1988 there were 230 at Foulness on 16th with at least 100 at Holliwell Point on 18th–19th, whilst 120 passed over The Naze on 8th October 2002. The latter arrivals were influenced by anticyclonic drift conditions. The 1988 arrival front appeared to be very narrow as numbers at Bradwell and elsewhere remained unexceptional.

The general decline in numbers wintering in Essex in recent years has meant that, through much of the 1990s and into the 2000s, most peak monthly counts have occurred during the autumn migration period.

Numbers tend to decline during November and December, but thereafter a significant increase is often detectable; this is probably linked to ongoing movement from the Continent as a result of weather conditions and the availability of Beech mast. Bramblings' winter distribution is largely dictated by the availability of Beech mast, and they will wander all over Europe looking for it. Since good crops are irregular, Bramblings will seldom spend successive winters in the same place. Thus numbers reported in Britain vary markedly from year to year, with perhaps as few as 50,000 nationally in poor years and two million in good years (Winter Atlas).

Peak counts during winter have been: 800 at Rainham, 3rd and 25th February 1969 and 620 on 26th January 1979; 750 at Romford SF, 18th–19th February 1967; 500 on Foulness, January 1963; and 400–500 at East Tilbury, January 1968. In addition, there have been a further six counts of 300 during winter. There have been no counts in excess of 250 since 1979.

The status of those birds occurring in the county from March onwards is unclear. Many are probably wintering birds, but it is likely that from the end of March there is an increasing number of returning migrants involved. The largest flock to occur in Essex, 1,000 at Rainham on 16th March 1969, built up steadily to the peak from 30th January when there were 400, with 800 present on 3rd and 25th February and 23rd March. Whilst it is possible that the build-up in numbers was due to local flocks gathering in an area of good feeding, some of the increase may have been due to passage birds. Other large flocks noted during March have been 450 at Rainham on 14th in 1970 and 500 at Mucking/East Tilbury on 8th in 1970. Reasonable numbers can remain until well into April, although there is a rapid decline towards the end of the month. Totals of 130 in Epping Forest on 9th in 1970, 118 at Hanningfield on 7th in 1981 and 150 in Epping Forest on 1st in 2003 are the highest April counts. In

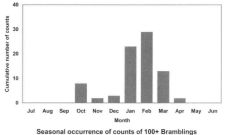

Seasonal occurrence of counts of 100+ Bramblings from 1971-2004

1981, when an above-average passage of Chaffinches occurred, relatively large numbers of Bramblings lingered in Essex later than usual.

Although some individuals may utilise garden feeding stations in winter, it is during spring migration that they are used more readily and Bramblings will often remain at these well into April before moving on.

Many of the largest flocks have occurred along Thames-side, between East Tilbury and Rainham where the refuse tips have proved attractive, but other big flocks have occurred across a wide variety of habitats, there being no clear preference for Beech/Hornbeam woods, at least in Essex.

If the number of three-figure flocks can be taken as a guide to overall abundance, the Brambling steadily became a less common visitor to Essex through the second half of the 20th century. This decline is perhaps linked to the series of very mild winters experienced in Europe since the mid-1980s. If the climate continues to warm, it is likely that Beech mast will become available further north than at present, reducing the need to make longer journeys to feed (Migration Atlas) and thus reducing the number arriving in Britain and Ireland.

There have been eight recoveries of Bramblings ringed in Essex, including three in Belgium and one in France in subsequent winters, which illustrate the species' wandering nature. However, one ringed at Saffron Walden in February 1950 was recaptured at the same location two years later, an example of site fidelity.

Sponsored by Julie Maynard

(European) Serin
Serinus serinus

Very rare passage migrant: 14 records, almost annual since 1996
Amber List

The monotypic Serin breeds across much of mainland Europe, east to the Black Sea, as well as north Africa and Turkey, with northern populations wintering around the Mediterranean.

1976	Linford	6th May	Male
1987	Holland Haven	1st September	Female or immature
1988	Wivenhoe	3rd–7th April	Female
1991	Roydon GP	6th January	Male
1993	Fingringhoe village	1st–3rd April	Male
1996	Braintree	5th April	Male
1997	Broxted	30th April	Male
1998	The Naze	24th May	Male
2000	Colne Point	23rd April	Female
2001	Gunners Park	20th–31st March	Immature male
2002	East Tilbury	11th–12th May	Immature female
2003	Rainham	3rd August	Male
2004	Gunners Park	17th April	Male
	Chingford	27th April	Male

Fourteen records is a surprisingly meagre total given that nationally during the 1990s an average of 68 was reported annually (Fraser & Rogers 2004); there had been 31 Suffolk records to the end of 2004 (*Suffolk Bird Report 2004*). The Serin has spread throughout Europe from the shores of the Mediterranean in the last 180 years and has bred in southern counties of England on and off since 1967. Most occur during spring, peaking between mid-April and June, so four of the Essex records are relatively early. The winter record, whilst not unique, is unusual.

(European) Greenfinch
Carduelis chloris

Abundant resident, passage migrant and winter visitor

The Greenfinch breeds over much of the Western Palearctic in boreal, temperate, steppe and Mediterranean zones, its range extending from 70° N in Scandinavia and 62° N in Russia, south to northwest Africa and to the northern Sinai, and from Ireland east to the western Urals and through the Caucasus to northern Iran; there is an isolated population in Russian Turkestan (European Atlas). The nominate race *chloris* occurs over much of northern Europe and in the British Isles. Originally a bird of forest edge and open bushy areas, it now breeds throughout cultivated landscapes wherever there are tall bushes for nesting. In Britain, it breeds in most areas apart from the high treeless parts of central Wales and northwest Scotland and the Shetland Islands. Over the last 40 years it has become much less abundant in farmland and more numerous in towns and villages (Second National Atlas). Birds from northern areas move south and southwest to winter mostly within or to the south of the range (Clement *et al.* 1993).

To both Christy and Glegg the Greenfinch was an abundant resident, the latter observing that the species was "… evenly distributed throughout the county". Hudson & Pyman described the Greenfinch as a common resident and passage migrant, although they commented "It is doubtful … whether it is quite as numerous as formerly in some areas". Cox also considered the Greenfinch a common resident and passage migrant that nested throughout Essex in all areas except those totally devoid of trees. Its successful occupation of suburbia was illustrated by the fact that breeding was confirmed in 97.5% of Metropolitan Essex tetrads during the Second London Atlas survey, with a presence in a further 1.5%, making it the most widespread finch in the region.

Greenfinches were reported breeding in all but one 10km square during the Second National Atlas survey, a very similar distribution to that revealed by the First, whilst the Essex Atlas survey recorded the species in 96% of tetrads and breeding

Atlas	Survey Area	% of 10km squares or tetrads in which	
		bred/probably bred	possibly bred or present
First National 10km	Essex	100.0	0.0
Second National 10km	Essex	98.2	1.8
First London Tetrad	Met. Essex	73.0	12.0
Second London Tetrad	Met. Essex	97.5	1.5
Essex Tetrad	Essex	95.3	0.9

Summary of results of Atlas surveys for Greenfinches

confirmed in most. The areas from which the Greenfinch was absent were almost entirely open coastal localities lacking suitable cover for nesting or in the most built-up areas of Metropolitan Essex.

Nationally, CBC farmland studies revealed low populations during the early 1960s, probably as a result of the use of organochlorine chemicals, combined with the effect of the 1962/63 winter. Numbers recovered rapidly from the mid-1960s but a decline set in from the mid-1970s until the mid-1980s, since when there has been a steady recovery. The CBC/BBS (England) Index for the period 1977–2002 increased by 25%, whilst the more recent BBS (England) Index for 1994–2003 increased by 23%. Local CBC/BBS data for the period 1981–99 have shown a steady decline, which is contrary to the national trend although there has been a subsequent increase.

	Period in October	Total	Peak	Peak date
1974	11th-27th	1,600	250	21st
1975	4th-18th	710	230	15th
1976	2nd-24th	3,000	830	16th
1977	2nd-13th	555	175	11th
1978	1st-31st	400	140	20th
1979	6th-11th	75+	55	11th
1980	6th-12th	820	350	9th
1981	21st-25th	1,800	900	21st
1982	23rd-31st	350+	200	23rd
1983	2nd-23rd	2,925	1,000+	19th
1984	15th-27th	130	50+	15th
1985	5th-21st	300	250	11th
1986	5th-24th	810	350	24th

NB: Observer coverage was variable in periods shown

Weekly movements of Greenfinches at Colne Point from 1974-86

Cox mentioned that CBC plots showed a mean density of 14 pairs per km^2 (range 3–37) in farmland and 33 pairs per km^2 in woodland, although in the latter there was considerable variation from site to site with a complete absence from several to a maximum density equivalent to 102 pairs per km^2 in Hainault Forest CP. CBC data since 1981 suggest average densities in farmland of seven pairs per km^2 (range 2–10) and in woodland 30 pairs per km^2 (range 8–57). Christy observed around 12 nests in a thick thorn hedge bordering an orchard some 60–70m long.

In autumn, coasting movements of Greenfinches are of regular occurrence, although the size of these movements has apparently declined since the early 1980s. Christy made no reference to passage movements but Glegg described small movements at the lightships off the Essex coast, although he was unsure of their origin. Hudson & Pyman described visible migration on a small scale, 300 per hour coasting southwest over Holland-on-Sea during the morning of 25th October 1959 being the largest movement. Cox, however, detailed significant westerly movements at Colne Point from the mid-1970s to mid-1980s. These movements generally occurred between late September and early November, with a peak in the third week of October. Southerly movements noted at Landguard Point, Suffolk, provide further indication of the magnitude of passage past the Essex coast. For instance, 10,500 headed south between 27th September and 26th November 1981 and around 14,625 during October 1983 (Piotrowski 2003). Large autumn movements away from Colne Point are generally uncommon, even at sites as close as Bradwell.

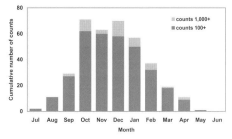

Seasonal occurrence of Greenfinches from 1970-2004

Although inland movements are less obvious, 1,100 were present at Good Easter on 27th September 1991, and in the Boreham area there were 1,000 during September 1990, 2,500 in November 1990 and 1,500 during October 1992.

Since Glegg's time there has been much conjecture about the size of the Essex wintering population. Glegg could not, on the evidence available to him, assess whether it was more common in winter than at other times of year. Hudson & Pyman were more equivocal and considered that there was no difference in the size of summer and winter populations. Cox made no comment on the matter; indeed given the abundance of the species it is virtually impossible to assess any differences. Almost all of the four-figure counts of Greenfinch have, however, occurred during winter.

Many of the largest winter counts have come from the coast, where Greenfinches feed on wild flower seeds and particularly Sea Aster along the seawalls, on salt marshes and along the tideline. Following a below-average westerly passage, numbers at Bradwell built up to impressive levels in the winter of 1975/76. After a count of 1,000 in November, numbers grew rapidly to 3,500 in December and 4,500 on 1st January, although this reduced to just 500 by the 11th. Elsewhere there were 2,500–3,000 on Foulness on 6th January 1985 and 2,800 along the entire north Blackwater on 11th November 1984.

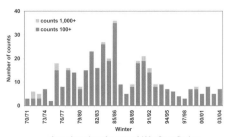

Annual number of counts of 100+ Greenfinches from 1970/71-2003/04

Spring passage has never been particularly evident on the coast and, if it were not for the activities of ringers at inland sites, the considerable numbers moving through Essex at this time would never have been realised. For example, a total of 2,000 was ringed in just one garden in Epping between March and May 1982 with 1,200 ringed there between February and April 1983. Elsewhere, 500 were ringed in a garden at Willingale between February and April 1982 and more than 5,000 were ringed in a Boreham garden between 1988 and 1993.

Numbers of Greenfinches passing through or wintering in Essex have declined in the last decade or so. During autumn migration, there have been few significant counts since 1994, 300 at Tollesbury Wick on 12th September 1999 being the highest and three-figure counts having generally declined. Likewise during winter, apart from 1,000 with Chaffinches at East Tilbury on 19th December 1999, the last four-figure count was around 1,000 at Boreham in January and February 1991. The decline in large flocks mirrors the decline revealed by the local CBC Index.

Large numbers of Greenfinches have been ringed in Essex and over 2,200 have subsequently been recovered, just over 60% in Essex and most of the remainder across southern England, confirming the relatively sedentary behaviour of the species.

	Jan	Feb	Mar	Apr	May	Jun	Jul	Aug	Sep	Oct	Nov	Dec
Essex	113	144	217	224	227	155	131	59	18	16	31	53
North England	3				1	1		1				
South England	101	126	155	133	61	26	35	14	9	9	49	89
Wales		1	2									
The Netherlands		1	1	1								
Belgium	1					1					1	
France/Channel Is.	11	2		1				1				2
Totals	*229*	*274*	*375*	*359*	*290*	*182*	*166*	*75*	*27*	*25*	*81*	*144*

Month and location of recovery of Greenfinches ringed in Essex

In addition to the general southwesterly movement of Greenfinches through southern England outside the breeding season, small numbers periodically cross the English Channel, probably as a result of high breeding densities or local food shortages (Migration Atlas). Movements to the Channel Islands are not uncommon and this is confirmed by the recovery of three Greenfinches ringed in the Channels Islands during winter and controlled in Essex during spring. Two Belgian-ringed birds have also been recovered in Essex. National ringing recoveries have confirmed that most immigrants are of Norwegian origin (Migration Atlas); to date there have been no Norwegian Greenfinches recovered in Essex, although it is likely that small numbers winter in the county.

Since the mid-1970s Greenfinches have increasingly exploited Oil-seed Rape, a very common crop in Essex, although this has perhaps been more than offset by a decline in available winter food due to modern farming methods (Population Trends). As natural foods decline during winter and spring, Greenfinches make increasing use of garden feeding stations. Here they take a wide variety of foods but seem to prefer Peanuts and Sunflower seeds. This source of food may have gone some way to counter the reduction in food availability due to modern farming techniques. Despite this, the local Greenfinch population appears to be in decline, in contrast to the national trend. Estimating the overall extent of the decline is difficult because of the lack of CBC data from urban and suburban areas. However, the BTO Garden Birdwatch Survey has shown remarkably constant trends since the mid-1990s. Despite the apparent declines, the Greenfinch remains an abundant species across Essex and should remain so for the foreseeable future.

Sponsored by Graham Ekins

(European) Goldfinch   *Carduelis carduelis*

Very common summer visitor and passage migrant. Small numbers winter

The Goldfinch has a Palearctic distribution from Portugal east to around 96° E from the boreal margins south through the temperate and Mediterranean zones into the steppe and desert fringes, from southern Fennoscandia south to northern Africa, the Caucasus, Nile Valley and Himalayas (Migration Atlas). The nominate race *carduelis* occurs throughout northern mainland Europe and east to the Urals, with the very similar *britannica* breeding in Britain, Ireland and the Netherlands; several other races occur around the Mediterranean. Originally a bird of sunny forest edge and open woodland, the Goldfinch now breeds throughout the cultivated landscape of Europe, often nesting in trees, in orchards, towns and villages (European Atlas). More than any other finch species, it specialises on seeds of the daisy family on which its numbers and distribution largely depend (Newton 1972), although it becomes more widely distributed in winter. The Goldfinch, which is commonest on low ground, is widespread across Britain, being absent only from mountains and moorland, especially in northwest Scotland and the Northern and Western Isles (Second National Atlas). Birds breeding in northwest Europe move south and west during autumn, wintering in large numbers in Iberia.

To Christy, the Goldfinch was "A resident … though local, not abundant and to some extent migratory". He went on "… it is to be feared that its numbers in the county are decreasing". The Goldfinch was a very popular cage-bird in the 19th century and some of Christy's correspondents referred to them being "… often … caught by the birdcatchers on Wanstead Flats" and that a bird-stuffer "… used to take a good many on the common…", possibly at Nazeing. Just how many were taken by trappers is unknown but the problem was particularly bad in the more built-up areas of Essex, particularly on the edge of Metropolitan Essex. By the 1870s, numbers had fallen so low nationally that it was included in the Wild Bird Protection Acts of 1880 and 1881, although it was not until the Amendment Act of 1894 that the widespread collection of Goldfinches began to lessen (Historical Atlas). At the same time and probably as a result of it, the fashion for captive birds in the parlour began to wane and, by the turn of the century, large increases in Goldfinch numbers were being noted across the country. A long period of agricultural recession, which may have encouraged an abundance of thistles, one of the Goldfinch's major food sources, may have also helped populations to recover (Population Trends).

In Essex, it seems that the recovery was relatively gradual as Glegg described only a slow increase, mainly in the north of the county. He considered the species to be no more than "… a somewhat uncommon and unevenly dis-tributed resident". It was thinly distributed south of a line between Walton and Bishop's Stortford but far better represented north of this line, becoming not uncommon in some areas.

Atlas	Survey Area	% of 10km squares or tetrads in which	
		bred/probably bred	possibly bred or present
First National 10km	Essex	100.0	0.0
Second National 10km	Essex	100.0	0.0
First London Tetrad	Met. Essex	61.0	12.5
Second London Tetrad	Met. Essex	88.5	9.5
Essex Tetrad	Essex	84.2	3.8

Summary of results of Atlas surveys for Goldfinches

Numbers continued to increase over the next 40 years with Hudson & Pyman reporting that the Goldfinch was a common resident and passage migrant. It was quite common in rural country but also bred in smaller numbers in many suburban areas. Cox reported that its numbers appeared to have been maintained, with nesting typically occurring in orchards, parks and gardens and also open countryside.

Both National Atlases found the Goldfinch breeding in every 10km square in Essex. Some minor range expansion was evident in Metropolitan Essex between the two London Atlas surveys, although this may have in part been due to increased observer coverage. Across Essex as a whole, the Goldfinch was reported from 88% of tetrads during the Essex Atlas survey, with breeding confirmed in most. The main gaps in the distribution appeared to have been in mainly rural areas, suggesting a shift away from arable farmland, where wild seed production had been severely depressed by herbicides, to parks and gardens with adequate food supplies. In fact, the Essex Atlas survey may have caught the Goldfinch at the start of a steady decline that has perhaps been in progress since the early 1990s. Annual counts from very few well-monitored sites have pointed to declines and the local CBC/BBS indices suggest that, despite recovering after a sharp decline during the mid-1980s, numbers once again reduced significantly around the mid-1990s but have subsequently recovered. Nationally, the CBC/BBS (England) Index for the period 1977–2002 fell by 19% but more recently the BBS (England) for 1994–2003 increased by 16%.

Cox reported breeding densities on farmland CBC plots of four pairs per km^2, though since 1981 average densities have been closer to three pairs per km^2 (range 2–3).

Many British and Irish Goldfinches winter in Britain and Ireland (Winter Atlas), with some remaining close to their breeding areas and others undertaking predominantly southerly movements. Others move south-southwest through western France to winter in Iberia (Migration Atlas).

Although Christy referred to the Goldfinch as being "… to some extent migratory", he made little further reference other than to arrivals in Essex around 10th October. Glegg observed "During the winter the Goldfinch is much more noticeable than in summer, although there is no evidence of immigration … movements can be observed in the autumn".

By the late summer and early autumn, small flocks of Goldfinches are noticeable, with regular movements along the coast and inland that peak strongly during October. On the coast, the largest numbers occur during early mornings when winds are light to moderate and have a westerly element (Cox). These movements were most noticeable north of the Colne Estuary and Cox detailed typical day totals of 1,000–1,600. Radar studies over the Suffolk coast have revealed much 'unseen' finch migration in varying wind conditions at this time of year (Newton 1972) and it is therefore likely that even greater numbers were involved

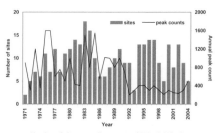

Number of sites recording counts of 100+ Goldfinches and annual peak count from 1971-2004

(Cox). In addition to the typical southerly coasting movements, small flocks are periodically noted flying in off the sea. Most likely, these are coasting birds of the race *britannica*, but it is possible that some birds from Europe arrive here occasionally. However, the nominate race is not on the British List and, although a Tayside Ringing Group study of Goldfinches strongly suggested that winter flocks consisted of both *britannica* and *carduelis*, no recoveries have confirmed this yet (Robertson 1997).

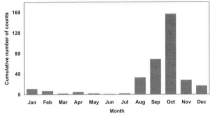

Seasonal occurrence of counts of 100+ Goldfinches
from 1971-2004

Although the number of counts of 100+ have not changed significantly, peak flock sizes have been much reduced since the early 1990s, a fact that may be linked to declines seen through the 1990s.

Goldfinch numbers are noticeably lower across Essex during winter and in some areas they may be completely absent. In severe weather, the species will make cold-weather movements to escape the conditions (Newton 1972). In the severe winter of 1962/63, Goldfinches were almost entirely absent from Essex with, for example, none reported from Bradwell from 13th January–30th March. During winter, the species will supplement its usual diet with seeds of Alder and Birch and will often form mixed feeding flocks, particularly with Siskins and until recently Lesser Redpolls. A flock of 600 feeding in Alders at Waltham Abbey in January and February 1977 is by far the largest winter gathering. Otherwise, there were 200 at Tollesbury Wick on 18th December 1991 and at Writtle from 6th–12th December 1993.

A small spring passage is evident. This lasts from March through into May and peaks in April, although there were no references in *EBRs* until 1973. Three-figure counts at this time are relatively uncommon, although there were 400 at Bradwell in late March 1975 and "several hundred" moved through Colne Point on 7th May 1983. In 1975 there were 150 at Hann ingfield on 17th April and 150 at Bradwell on 19th April. Although the spring movement is mainly coastal, and most noticeable around the Colne Estuary, small but increased numbers at many inland sites at this time suggest an arrival on a broad front.

	Period	Total	Peak	Peak date
1974	11th-27th	7,500	1,350	20th Oct
1975	21st Sep-18th Oct	4,800	1,600	4th Oct
1976	October	7,500	1,600	8th Oct
1977	2nd-23rd Oct	3,700	1,060	23rd Oct
1978	1st Oct-4th Nov	2,230	753	20th Oct
1980	6th-12th Oct	2,580	1,000	9th Oct
1981	21st-25th Oct	1,100	250	24th-25th Oct
1982	13th-23rd Oct	330	230	23rd Oct
1983	2nd-22nd Oct	4,030	1,500	18th Oct
1984	1st-21st Oct	3,500	n/a	
1985	5th-11th Oct	2,600	1,550	11th Oct
1986	23rd-24th Oct	1,050	550	24th Oct
1987	11th-15th Oct	1,100	1,018	11th Oct

NB: Observer coverage was variable in periods shown

**Westerly autumn movements of Goldfinches
at Colne Point from 1971-1987**

Ringing recoveries have confirmed that, whilst some local breeders remain through winter in Essex, they are joined by Goldfinches from further north, whilst a proportion of the population heads south or southwest through western France and into Iberia. One ringed at Kirby-le-Soken on 23rd August 1964 and recovered in Morocco on 14th November 1965 is one of only three recoveries of British-ringed Goldfinches in Africa. A first-year Goldfinch, ringed on 30th September 1982 at Leigh/Two Tree Island, was found dead eight years later near Norwich, Norfolk; this is the oldest British-ringed Goldfinch to have been reported to the BTO. In addition, there is one recovery of a foreign-ringed Goldfinch in Essex: a bird ringed at Hondarribia, Spain, on 16th April 1985 was found dead at Great Chesterford on 13th May 1987.

It is unclear why the Goldfinch should have declined locally during the 1990s, whilst on a national level it increased. The obsessive desire to tidy every possible area of town and country, together with the increased use of herbicides, has undoubtedly meant reductions in the species' favourite food plant. However, these factors have been in play for many years, so perhaps other pressures are affecting populations. Goldfinches are increasingly making use of garden feeding stations, with the 2001/02 Garden Bird Feeding Survey noting the species using feeders in 72% of gardens surveyed nationally (Glue 2002). This adaptability and the fact that the Goldfinch remains relatively widespread and common across Essex should ensure that the species remains so in years to come.

	Jan	Feb	Mar	Apr	May	Jun	Jul	Aug	Sep	Oct	Nov	Dec
Essex	1	2	2	3	12	3	3	3	1	3	1	1
South England		1	1	1	6	1	2	1	1			
Belgium	1	1		2	1					4		
France	2	2			1						4	1
Spain	1	1	1	3	3					3	11	3
Portugal			1									
Morocco											1	
Totals	5	7	5	9	23	4	5	4	2	10	17	5

Month and location of recovery of Goldfinches ringed in Essex

(Eurasian) Siskin

Carduelis spinus

Common winter visitor and passage migrant

The monotypic Siskin breeds in the coniferous forests of the boreal and temperate zones, from Britain and Ireland across to Sakhalin Island in the far east. In the north, its European range just reaches 70° N and to the south it extends to the central European mountains, the Pyrenees, Balkans and Lesser Caucasus. Although the Siskin will breed in any conifer type, it prefers Spruce-dominated forests. It has increased in Europe since the late 1960s (European Atlas). In Britain, it has increased during the last 30 years and, although it is mainly a bird of the Spruce forests of the north and west, it has colonised the increasing number of matured post-WWII plantations wherever they occur in England with particular concentrations in the New Forest, Dorset, the Peak District, Lake District and Pennines (Second National Atlas). Northern populations move south and southwest to winter within or south of the breeding range; periodic irruptive movements occur at times of food shortages (Clement *et al.* 1993).

Although conifer plantations have existed in Essex for 200 years or so, particularly around the Audley End estate near Saffron Walden, there have been no confirmed Essex breeding records, despite the increase in conifer acreage during the latter half of the 20th century. Neither Christy nor Glegg provided even a shred of evidence to "… even suggest nesting" and the latest departure date that Hudson & Pyman could provide was 29th April. However, with the increase in the Norfolk/Suffolk Brecklands' population, where by the late 1980s it was considered to be common (Piotrowski 2003), Essex records during June and July have increased; young birds can be out in force by the middle of June.

There have, however, been a number of recent June records that suggest breeding might have taken place in Essex. In 1991 small numbers were present all year at Great Braxted and breeding was considered possible, whilst a pair was present there during the breeding season in 2002. In 1991 a male was present at Belfairs Park on 11th and 26th June, with two birds present on 6th July, whilst in 1994 a male was present at Ramsey on 14th and 26th June, 1–2 were present in late May and early June at Havering CP and a pair summered in Hainault Forest CP. The remaining June records have all involved single birds recorded on just one date.

Outside the breeding season, the Siskin appears to have always been a passage migrant

Atlas	Survey Area	% of 10km squares or tetrads in which	
		bred/probably bred	possibly bred or present
First National 10km	Essex	1.8	3.5
Second National 10km	Essex	1.8	10.5
First London Tetrad	Met. Essex	1.0	0.5
Second London Tetrad	Met. Essex	1.0	3.0
Essex Tetrad	Essex	0.2	1.4

Summary of results of Atlas surveys for Siskins

and winter visitor in variable numbers, although the species was less common during Christy and Gleggs' times. Christy considered the Siskin to be a winter visitor, but one of his correspondents noted that it was common during migration at Harwich, the only coastal site mentioned by Christy. Glegg also regarded the species as primarily a winter visitor, although he quoted records from October through to 29th April. These he considered extreme dates, noting that their stay was generally much shorter, usually arriving much later and leaving by the middle of March. Hudson & Pyman also made scant reference to migrants and indeed prior to the late 1960s there were few reports. Even by the early 1980s the largest flocks rarely exceeded 20, and a total of 45 flying in off the sea at Foulness on 26th October 1975 was considered unusual. Since the mid-1980s, however, annual numbers of migrants have increased, although totals vary considerably from year to year.

The autumn movement begins as early as August, although an exceptional influx occurred in July 1991 with 30 at Belfairs Park on 15th and 40 the next day, an arrival noted in many other parts of southern England. Numbers generally peak in October when small groups can often be observed moving through with Chaffinches and, when they were more common, Lesser Redpolls. Coastal movements have been most obvious in the northeast, but are also regularly observed at Bradwell and Foulness. The largest autumn influx occurred from 22nd–24th September 1996 and involved around 1,430, many (but not all) moving through coastal sites. The largest counts were all from the northeast: 200 passed over Holland Haven on 21st and 250 on 22nd; 100 over The Naze on 22nd and 24th; and 135 passed through Bradwell on 22nd. Inland, there were 100 at Weald CP on 22nd and 100 at Thorndon CP on 24th. The only other three-figure autumn counts have come from: Oliver's Orchard, Colchester, 250 in November 1985; Marks Hall, Coggeshall, 100 on 28th November 1993; Waltham Abbey, 100 on 15th October 1994; Weald CP, 200 in November 1997; and The Naze, 158 on 23rd September 2001.

Numbers tend to increase significantly during December as the wintering population builds up to a peak in January. During winter, Siskins will feed on Alders and Birch, often in association with other finches (Clement *et al.* 1993). Christy referred to "... flocks of over hundred in the Park" at Saffron Walden around the 1830s but it was not until 1965 that three-figure flocks were reported again, when there were up to 350 at Fishers Green from January to March. In fact, the large stands of Alder in the Fishers Green/Waltham Abbey area have held substantial wintering flocks since the mid-1960s, although 1982 was the last time more than 300 were recorded; the largest recent three-figure count was 150 at Cornmill Meadows on 15th January and 12th February 2003 with 200 at Seventy Acres Lake on 5th January 2000. The largest counts were 350 from January–March 1965, 400 during January and February 1973 and 350 in January 1982. Away from this area, sites regularly holding three-figure flocks during winter have been few. In 1976 there were 200 on 18th January and 300 during early February at Belfairs Park, with 201 being ringed between 1st January and 11th April, and 270 in Weald CP on 10th January 2000, 200 of these still present on 14th February. A total of 200 was in Epping Forest during February–April 1982 and around Coleman's in January 1997. Counts of 150 have also come from: Epping Forest, 14th February and 20th March 1976; Beeleigh, 8th and 22nd February 1995; Weald

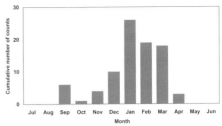

Seasonal occurrence of counts of 100+ Siskins from 1971-2004

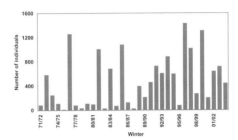

Peak monthly counts of Siskins from 1971/72-2003/04

CP, February 1997; and Wanstead, late December 1997. Smaller numbers are reported widely from across Essex, although the species' preference for Alders means that river valleys, gravel-pits and other damp areas are favoured.

By the end of February, spring passage is evident from a build-up of numbers at inland sites and small flocks moving north along the coast. It is at this time of year that Siskins are most evident in gardens, where they will visit both peanut and seed feeders and also fat balls, a relatively recent phenomenon, first noted in Essex in 1971 (Spencer & Gush 1973). The largest numbers occur inland where in some years wintering flocks peak in March. An exceptional influx during February–March 1976 saw 300 at Mill Green/Beggar's Hill from early March–April, 200 at Ongar Park Wood on 26th March and 300 at Thorndon CP on 7th March, with counts of 100+ at three other inland sites. Away from Waltham Abbey/Fishers Green, spring counts of 100+ have occurred at: Backwarden NR, Danbury, 100 on 7th March 1989; and Marks Hall, Coggeshall, 240 on 29th March 1991.

The majority of spring migrants (and wintering birds) have left the county by mid-April but there are usually a few stragglers into May. Exceptionally there were 40 at Weald CP on 15th May 1992 and 50 in the Waltham Abbey area until early May 1993.

Recoveries of Siskins ringed in Essex suggest that birds from Scotland may make up a fair proportion of the wintering population, although recoveries of birds ringed in Wales and southern England point to a cosmopolitan mix. These are joined by Continental Siskins that begin to arrive along the east coast from mid-September with many entering the country from the southeast via Belgium and the Netherlands, although some take a direct route across the North Sea from Scandinavia (Migration Atlas). The recovery at Pape, Latvia, on 16th October 1987 of a Siskin ringed at Old Heath, Colchester, on 11th January 1986 is one of the more easterly recoveries of any British-ringed Siskins. Remarkably, it was present at Chipping Camden, Gloucestershire, from 18th–27th March 1989 (its ring was read in the field). One ringed at Colchester on 15th January 1966 and found dead in

Guipuzcoa, Spain, on 25th February 1969 points to some Siskins perhaps heading further south to winter, although it may have been an immigrant that simply changed its wintering location in a subsequent year. Four foreign-ringed Siskins have also been recovered in Essex from Germany, Belgium (two) and the Channel Islands.

	Jan	Feb	Mar	Apr	May	Jun	Jul	Aug	Sep	Oct	Nov	Dec
Essex			1	1								
Scotland	1		2	4	3							
North England		1		1								1
South England	1		7	2								
Sweden								1				
Baltic States										1		
Germany			1									
The Netherlands		1		1								
Belgium	1									1	2	
Spain		1										
Totals	*3*	*3*	*11*	*9*	*3*	*0*	*0*	*1*	*1*	*3*	*0*	*1*

Month and location of recovery of Siskins ringed in Essex

Many of the conifer plantations in Essex are now mature and at their most attractive to Siskins. As the plantations mature, it is likely that many will be clear-felled; these are likely to be replanted with broad-leaved species, which would be to the detriment of the Siskin.

(Common) Linnet   *Carduelis cannabina*

Common resident, summer visitor and passage migrant with small numbers wintering   Red List

The Linnet is widely distributed throughout most of the Palearctic, much of central Siberia and central Asia and patchily in the Near East and northwest Africa with the nominate race *cannabina* occurring across much of Europe. It is a semi-colonial nester and occupies a variety of open habitats containing shrubs or young plantations, including overgrown heathland, woodland edges, forest clearings and fragmented farmland. It breeds in suburban habits, having increased since the 1960s (European Atlas). It was a common species in the early 20th century when farming was of relatively low intensity. However, numbers declined drastically by more than 50% between 1970 and 1990 in Finland, Britain and the Netherlands and by 20–50% in the same period over much of central and northwest Europe. In Britain, the declines have been attributed to changing farming practices (Population Trends). The Linnet remains widespread throughout Britain, being very local only in the Highlands of Scotland and the Inner Hebrides. It reaches its greatest abundance in east and southern England and around the coastline (Second National Atlas). Linnets rely largely on a diet of seeds, even when feeding their young (Migration Atlas). Northern European populations move south and southwest to winter mostly within the breeding range.

Both Christy and Glegg considered the Linnet an abundant resident, the former noting "… especially in the vicinity of commons and uncultivated grounds, the more so if near the coast". At Shoebury during the 1860s it was considered that "Next to the lark there is hardly any bird so common on this coast … They nest here in great numbers", whilst as a migrant immense numbers were occasionally reported arriving along the coast. Large numbers were taken by the bird-catchers on Wanstead Flats.

Atlas	Survey Area	% of 10km squares or tetrads in which bred/probably bred	possibly bred or present
First National 10km	Essex	100.0	0.0
Second National 10km	Essex	94.7	5.3
First London Tetrad	Met. Essex	55.0	17.0
Second London Tetrad	Met. Essex	87.5	9.0
Essex Tetrad	Essex	89.5	1.8

Summary of results of Atlas surveys for Linnets

Glegg made no specific comment on breeding numbers but did note that "The Linnet is harmless, but it is considered that a check should be kept on its numbers where it has increased very rapidly". This reference to apparent increases in Essex during the first three decades of the 20th century mirrors increases nationally at this time.

Hudson & Pyman described the Linnet as numerous and widely distributed and absent only from the built-up areas and even present around the coast, where other finches were absent, whilst Cox noted that the species was a numerous breeding bird in coastal Essex where nests were commonly constructed in the extensive areas of Annual/Shrubby Seablite; more unusually, up to 150 pairs nested in Sea Purslane along Dengie during the 1970s, although this habit was abandoned by the end of the decade probably due to the increased tidal flooding of the salt marshes. Another favourite habitat along the coast is in isolated clumps of Gorse that somehow prosper, whilst all other vegetation taller than the surrounding grass fails. Inland, it was considered widespread, especially in areas of scrub and heathland, although it tended to avoid built-up areas.

Little change in distribution was revealed by the two National Atlas surveys with Linnets present in every 10km square across Essex, although breeding was confirmed in every 10km square in the First, but not in three (5.3%) during the latter. The Second London Atlas survey pointed to an increase in southern Essex; this may have been due to increased observer coverage, although it may represent birds taking advantage of temporary habitat on vacant land. Overall, the Linnet was generally less widespread than both Goldfinch and Greenfinch in Metropolitan Essex, being absent particularly from the built-up areas, habitats that other finches have managed to exploit more successfully.

Unfortunately, it was not until the mid-1980s that breeding numbers were mentioned in *EBRs*. The Essex Atlas survey was undertaken when the serious population declines

	Period in October	Total	Peak	Peak date
1974	October	12,000	1,750	20th
1975	4th-21st	4,710	1,500	15th
1976	2nd-23rd	18,000	5,800	8th
1977	1st-23rd	7,245	2,185	10th
1978	1st-21st	5,885	2,075	20th
1979	6th-11th	830	500	11th
1980	6th-11th	4,750	2,500	9th
1981	21st-25th	2,750	750	21st
1982	n/a	n/a	830	23rd
1983	17th-20th	7,250	2,850	17th
1984	1st-21st	5,000	500	21st
1985	5th-25th	4,400	1,800	11th
1986	19th-24th	2,000	1,050	23rd
1987	n/a	n/a	3,666	11th

NB: Observer coverage was variable in periods shown

**Autumnal movements of Linnets
at Colne Point from 1974-1987**

observed across Britain were well underway. Nonetheless, the Linnet remained widespread and was found in 91% of all tetrads, with breeding confirmed in almost all.

Nationally, the Linnet has declined significantly since the early 1980s. The CBC/BBS (England) Index for the period 1977–2002 showed a relatively stable population until about the very late 1970s (Population Trends), since when there was a sharp decline, resulting in an overall reduction in the Index during that period of 54%. More recent BBS (England) data suggest a slight decline of 9% from 1994–2003. Local CBC/BBS data have revealed a similar trend.

The Linnet takes little invertebrate food compared to other Palearctic finches, depending heavily on the seeds of the cabbage and dock families (*BWP*). The species' decline has been attributed to the effect of diet on its breeding productivity with nest failure occurring during the egg period (Siriwardena 2000); in other words, the adults had insufficient food to raise young successfully. A reduction in the quality of hedgerows and the increased exposure of nests to predators have also been suggested as causing low productivity.

Since completion of the Essex Atlas survey, anecdotal evidence from several well-monitored sites across Essex suggests that numbers may have stabilised and perhaps increased slightly in some areas. It is therefore possible that more recently the species has fared slightly better as a result of a general switch in its diet to a preponderance of Oil-seed Rape in areas where the crop cover is extensive (Moorcroft *et al.* 1997).

Cox noted that Essex farmland CBC plots showed a mean density of 13 pairs per km² (range 6–37). CBC data since 1981 suggest a mean farmland density of just five pairs per km² (range 3–9), although with the declines since the early 1980s current densities have probably fallen from this level.

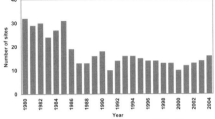

Annual number of sites recording counts of 100+ Linnets from 1980-2004

Prior to the population declines, large gatherings occurred in late summer and early autumn and communal roosts developed (Cox). At Navestock, a flock of 800 on 6th August 1972 had built up to 1,500 on 9th September. At a roost in Flag Creek, St Osyth, along a short stretch of *Phragmites*-filled borrow dyke bordered by scattered clumps of Willow and Bramble, 2,830 were ringed in the nine autumns 1977–85; four-figure numbers probably used the roost each year (Cox).

Linnets, like Greenfinches and Goldfinches, regularly undertake coasting movements during autumn. These movements are rarely noticed before early August and peak in October. Unlike the two aforementioned finches, however, small numbers continue to move during December. Glegg noted "I am of the opinion that there is a marked decrease in the numbers of the species during winter. The birds appear to decrease about the middle of October, an increase being noticeable about the end of March." Many of the largest passage movements were reported from the northeast coast and particularly from Colne Point, where passage was west into the estuary (Cox) with some impressive counts logged during the 1970s and 1980s. Such movements usually occur at the same time as those of Greenfinches and Goldfinches, although not exclusively, and in general tended not to be weather related. Away from Colne Point, four-figure movements are rare, and examples include: 1,000 on Foulness on 28th September 1980 and 1,000 on 6th October 1984; 1,000 at The Naze on 7th September 1986; 1,842 at Holland Haven on 11th October 1987; 1,443 at Wakering Stairs, also on 11th October 1987; and 1,000 at Rainham during October 1986 and October 1987, 1,250 on 1st October 1989 and 1,200 on 29th September 1990 and 20th October 1990. It is interesting to compare these movements with the situation in other nearby

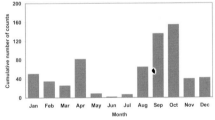

Seasonal occurrence of counts of 100+ Linnets from 1971-2004

counties. In Norfolk (Taylor *et al.* 1999) the autumn movement is on a smaller scale to that in Essex; conversely a substantial spring passage occurs there, which dwarfs the spring movement in Essex and is also larger than the autumn movement. In Suffolk, numbers at both seasons are generally on a par with Essex, whilst in Hampshire (Clarke & Eyre 1993) autumn numbers are fewer than in Essex but greater than those in Norfolk with spring passage comparable to the Essex movements. Numbers recorded on migration since the early 1990s have generally been lower than before, although there are some signs that numbers may be increasing in the 21st century.

Numbers present in Essex during winter are generally small and, when flocks occur these are invariably in coastal and/or estuarine habitats. Given the significant amount of setaside habitat across the country, it is perhaps surprising that Linnets have not taken to this habitat in Essex at this season, as appears to be the case in Norfolk (Taylor *et al.* 1999). During the severe weather of 1978/79 a quite exceptional count of 2,500 was made around Hamford Water. There have only been three other four-figure winter counts: 1,000 with other finches at Kirby-le-Soken on 30th December 1951; 1,500 at Romford SF on 21st January 1967; and 1,000 at Rainham on 7th December 1983. It should, however, be borne in mind that Linnets can be surprisingly difficult to locate at this time as the entire population from an area may congregate into just 1–2 flocks (Winter Atlas).

	Jan	Feb	Mar	Apr	May	Jun	Jul	Aug	Sep	Oct	Nov	Dec
Essex	3	3	2	3	14	10	5	6	4			3
South England	1	3	3	2	2	6		1				
The Netherlands				1				1				
Belgium		2								1		
France	2	1	1							9	2	3
Spain	3	1	1	2						1	6	2
Morocco											1	
Totals	9	10	7	8	16	16	5	8	4	11	9	8

Month and location of recovery of Linnets ringed in Essex

As at other times of the year, the number of wintering Linnets have declined over the last two decades with, in recent years, counts of more than 300 particularly rare. It is possible that the reduction in availability of seed-rich stubbles has altered the movement patterns of Linnets and caused increases in the number of birds emigrating during winter in recent years (Migration Atlas).

Spring passage was relatively poorly documented prior to 1980 (Cox); indeed there is no reference in the *EBR* until 1972 but, since then, a regular but variable passage has been noticeable both along the coast and inland. Three-figure counts are regular, albeit that numbers appear to have declined in recent years. On the coast, the largest movements have been recorded around the mouth of the Blackwater and Colne Estuaries at Bradwell and Colne Point, respectively. At this time of year the movement at Bradwell and along Dengie is to the north; at Colne Point during autumn it is to the west. By far the largest day-count was 900 passing Bradwell on 29th April 1986. Otherwise, large counts have been: 500 at Colne Point on 11th April 1979; 500 at Foulness on 16th April 1983; 430 north at Bradwell on 20th April 1996; 420 at Bradwell on 9th April 2000 and 400 there on 27th April 1995. Additionally, a total of 1,000 moved through Bradwell between 7th and 11th April 1981, with 1,000 at Colne Point during the last week of April 1991. Linnets have been noted both arriving off the sea, (e.g. 230 arriving at Foulness in three hours on 12th April 1981) and also heading out to sea (e.g. small flocks heading offshore at Holliwell Point on 12th April 1992), suggesting that both departures and arrivals occur at this time. Some quite large flocks also build up inland during spring and, although many of these probably represent wintering birds, many flocks peak in size during March and April, suggesting an influx at this time. These flocks rarely number more than 200, but at Fairlop CP in 1984 a flock increased from 100 in early April to 500 on 23rd.

A proportion of British breeding birds moves south in winter, reaching the Low Countries and France by August and then heading broadly south through France and Spain, with some crossing into north Africa to winter. Recoveries of birds ringed in Essex are typical of the national situation. The recovery in Morocco on 2nd November 1975 of a Linnet ringed at St Osyth on 21st September 1975 is one of very few recoveries in that country. One ringed near Linford on 22nd July 1972 was recovered in Zuid, Netherlands, on 18th April 1973 and again on 22nd August 1974, suggesting that some local Linnets disperse to other breeding areas on the near-Continent. Additionally, there have been two recoveries of foreign-ringed Linnets from Spain and Belgium.

The Linnet's future in Essex will be very much tied to agricultural land-use methods. Its absolute dependence on weed seeds means that without a major change in modern farming techniques, there will continue to be a lack of food for the species. Areas of permanent setaside may provide some small relief in particular areas but a wholesale change to the Common Agricultural Policy will be required to assist any recovery. Unlike its congeners, the Greenfinch, Goldfinch and Siskin, the Linnet has not adapted to life in urban areas. Thus, although still relatively widespread and fairly common, the outlook for the species must remain uncertain.

Sponsored by Alex Johnson

Twite   *Carduelis flavirostris*

Declining and now locally scarce winter visitor and passage migrant   **Red List**

The Twite is one of a very few passerines that occurs in Britain in internationally important numbers (Batten *et al.* 1990). It has an unusual world distribution, being split into two centres, one in northwest Europe (where it is the sole representative of the Tibetan fauna) and the other, the ancestral one, more than 2,500km away through the Caucasus to central and east Asia (European Atlas). This disjunct distribution probably came about as the result of range expansion during the last glaciation (18,000–20,000 years ago) when the population radiated out from central Asia and inhabited the widespread steppe-like tundra. With subsequent climate warming, Twites in Europe followed the tundra north and became isolated. Most of the European population occurs in Norway (100,000–500,000 pairs). The British population of 5,000–15,000 pairs is associated with treeless areas, mainly moorlands in the Highlands and northern England and crofts close to the north and west seaboards of Scotland (Second National Atlas). Recent significant declines have occurred in northwest Scotland and to a lesser extent

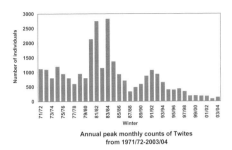

Annual peak monthly counts of Twites
from 1971/72-2003/04

in Lancashire, Cheshire and Derbyshire, although there has been a southeasterly range expansion in southeast Scotland and a new Welsh population founded (European Atlas). British breeding birds belong to the race *pipilans*, whilst those from Scandinavia and northwest Russia belong to the nominate race *flavirostris*. Whilst Scottish populations are generally sedentary, those from northern England disperse southeast to winter in coastal habitats, particularly salt marshes, between Lincolnshire and north Kent (*BWP*). Scandinavian birds move south to winter around the southern North Sea.

Christy described the species as "… a common winter visitor to the sea-coast. It often abounds on the saltings around Maldon and elsewhere, going in small flocks". During the early 19th century, Twites were "… plentiful in the month of October on Pewit Island and on the mainland of Essex near it in flocks of ten and twenty together, and towards evening we noticed flocks of about one hundred …". One of Christy's observers commented that prior to 1876 in "… some winters they rise from the saltings in tens of thousands". Twites were also considered very common at Harwich prior to 1890. Inland, Twites were occasional visitors to Epping Forest, around Sudbury where "… it frequently appears in small flocks in the winter" and Danbury, where it was considered common during winter and taken by the bird-catchers.

The Twite's status in Glegg's time is less clear, Glegg himself observing "The status of the Twite is obscure". If correct, it appeared to point to a decline in numbers in Essex since the end of the 19th century. E. A. Fitch, a well-known observer, first noted the species on the Northey saltings in November 1890 only following the publication of Christy's book,

	No. of years with counts of 100+						Population around 1980	Current population
	1950s	1960s	1970s	1980s	1990s	2000s		
Hamford Water	1	8	9	7	6	0	2,000	20
Colne	0	2	7	5	1	0	1,000	10
Dengie	8	8	9	5	1	0	2,000	20
Blackwater	1	6	9	10	5	0	600	50
Crouch/Roach	1	4	4	5	1	0	1,000	20
Foulness	0	3	8	5	1	0	500	20
Leigh/Two Tree Is.	1	1	8	7	1	0	500	10

Annual occurrence and estimated regional maxima of Twites based on BoEE (Cox) and current data

whilst W. B. Nichols in 25 years of observations noted the Twite just once, in March 1907. Added to this, Glegg, a very experienced field ornithologist with experience of Twites, failed to find it in more than seven winters of steadily working the Essex coast. With this limited evidence to hand, Glegg concluded that the Twite was no more than an irregular passage migrant. So what are we to conclude today? Did Glegg, and therefore presumably all of his contemporaries, overlook the Twite (Cox)? It seems hard to believe. Perhaps numbers were particularly low during the early 20th century. Unfortunately we have no further data, even from adjacent counties, although Stevenson (1866–90) considered the Twite only an occasional visitor to Norfolk, and Riviere (1930) described the species as an irregular passage migrant and winter visitor there.

Whatever its earlier status, by the mid-1960s Hudson & Pyman observed that "… regular post-war observations have shown it to occur annually in numbers …", adding that "… there is no reason to suppose that this has not always been the case". Numbers wintering in Essex peaked around the early 1980s, since when there has been a dramatic decline. The reasons for the reduction are unclear but it is possible that there has been a significant decline in the Pennines' breeding populations which winters in the county; this explanation is supported by evidence of marked declines since the mid-1970s on two Pennines CBC plots (Migration Atlas). However, it may be possible, despite the lack of ringing evidence, that at least part of the massive Norwegian population does periodically winter in East Anglia; this would explain counts in the tens of thousands in The Wash, Norfolk, during the 1970s and 1980s and the huge Essex totals at around the same time (Taylor *et al.* 1999, Migration Atlas); counts in Suffolk were also higher in this period than currently (Piotrowski 2003).

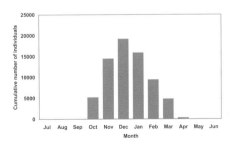

Seasonal occurrence of Twites from 1971-2004

The earliest Twites usually appear along the coast in late September. However, an exceptionally early individual was at Tollesbury on 22nd August 1982, whilst singles were in Hamford Water on 1st September 1978 and at Abberton on 7th September 1993; 12 were at Holland Haven on 12th September 2001. Numbers rise steadily to a mid-winter peak in most years, although in some years numbers may dip after October before peaking again in December/ January, suggesting ongoing passage through the county. Indeed, during October some coasting movement has been evident with small numbers regularly passing west with Linnets and Goldfinches at Colne Point. Likewise, small inland movements have been noted at many sites throughout Essex during autumn. The most significant included: a daily passage over Coploe Hill, Strethall, from 15th–20th November 1955, peaking at 12 on 16th; at least 18 through Hanningfield on 2nd November 1986 during a strong finch passage; and eight at KGV on 16th October 1994.

Coastal marshes are the species' favoured habitat, where they may form either single-species flocks or mixed flocks with other *Carduelis* finches and feed typically on the seeds of glassworts, Sea Lavender, Annual Seablite and Sea Aster, whilst coastal stubbles and weedy fields may also be used. Because of their habit of forming large mixed flocks, Twites can be particularly difficult to count. In addition, studies in Norfolk have revealed that daily movements of up to 10km are regular, with some moving as far as 25km (Migration Atlas). However, based on data collected during the BoEE, Blindell (1977) arrived at an Essex population of approximately 5,000 spread around the coast.

Cox set out regional maxima, based on the BoEE figures, complemented by subsequent observations. The peaks did not all occur together but a wintering population figure of 4,000–5,000 was similar to Blindell's. Today, numbers are significantly lower at perhaps just 2% of those 20 years ago.

The largest individual counts have come from the largest areas of salt marsh in Hamford Water: 2,000 on 18th December 1983; 1,515 on 13th December 1981; and 1,000 on 20th December 1980. There were also 1,000 at Bradwell on 29th October 1978. The last is a particularly early date for such large numbers and presumably involved a proportion of migrants. The Hamford Water counts were reached by totalling counts of all Twites observed on WeBS count days and illustrates the fact that there are probably far more Twites in a particular area than casual observation suggests.

In the Colne Estuary there was a peak of 400 at Fingringhoe Wick on 27th October 1969. Along the Blackwater, the most favoured area has been around Tollesbury Wick/Old Hall where there were 650 on 7th November 1982 and 600 in January 1972. In addition, there were 600 at Goldhanger on 14th November 1965. On Foulness and the Crouch/Roach, numbers have tended to be lower, with the highest count being 450 on 15th November 1981, although observer coverage must be a factor in these less regularly watched areas. A total of 400 was on Canvey Island on 6th November 1980.

Although most Twites are recorded along the coast during winter, there have been a number of unusual inland records. In Belfairs Park, during the winter of 1975/76 and several subsequent winters, up to 50 regularly fed with Siskins and Lesser Redpolls beneath Birches, presumably on the trees' seed (Smart 1978), whilst up to 120 (on 6th January 1991) fed on the nearby golf course. Up to 50 fed with Goldfinches and Lesser Redpolls beneath Birches at Berechurch during the winter of 1984/85, whilst from early 1989 until early 1991 small flocks fed on Colchester Recreation Ground, peaking at 88 on 28th February 1991. Football pitches and school playing fields have also held small numbers.

Unusually, there was an inland roost at Donyland Wood from 1972/73–1984/85, which held up to 100 Twites. The direction of arrival of birds at the roost pointed to these being individuals that spent the day feeding on the sludge lagoons at The Hythe, where counts of 100+ were regular from the mid-1960s to mid-1980s, peaking at 300 during 1972/73. Whilst not strictly inland, Rainham used to hold small numbers during winter, and in the early 1980s numbers increased, peaking at 200 on 27th February 1975.

By February, numbers of Twites decline significantly and most have left the county by mid-March, although small numbers linger into April. However, 95 at Southend-on-Sea on 8th April 1975 with 40 still there on 17th, and 100 at Leigh/Two Tree Island on 1st April 1977 with 50 there on 1st April 1986 are notable. A small passage is usually evident during March and April with small numbers arriving at sites at which they have not occurred during winter. Although almost all have left Essex by mid-April, there have been three May records: five at The Naze on 23rd in 1960; Bradwell on 4th in 1995; and Leigh/Two Tree Island on 3rd in 1978.

A number of ringing recoveries (and 11 sightings of colour-ringed birds in 2004) have confirmed the presence of Pennine-bred birds in Essex: one ringed at Blackmoorfoot, Huddersfield, West Yorkshire, on 25th July 1976 was controlled at The Hythe on 4th February 1979 and again on 1st January 1980, indicating a degree of site fidelity between winters. Several other recoveries link Essex to Belgium and the Netherlands and presumably refer to nomadic wanderings of British breeders.

Sponsored by Liz Leeder

Lesser Redpoll   *Carduelis cabaret*

Much declined and now scarce resident, passage migrant and winter visitor   Amber List

The monotypic Lesser Redpoll's breeding range encompasses Britain and Ireland and countries bordering the North Sea from France to southern Norway and central Europe (European Atlas). Populations winter in Britain and Continental Europe south to the Alps. The species' range has changed dramatically over the last 150 years. In the mid-1800s it was restricted to northern Britain, Ireland and the Alps but by 1910 it had increased in lowland Britain. A subsequent decline was soon followed by a marked expansion from the 1950s with populations crossing the North Sea to northern and central Europe. Although still spreading in Europe, significant reductions have occurred in Britain, the Netherlands and Belgium since the early 1980s. Lesser Redpoll was split from Common Redpoll *C. flammea* by the BOURC in 2000 (Knox *et al.* 2001).

Christy described the Lesser Redpoll as "... best known as a winter visitor, though individuals certainly sometimes remain and breed with us", although he added that "It appears not to be so common ... as formerly". He gave just four breeding records: Saffron Walden, 1879; Chesterford Park; Chelmsford, 1869; Orsett, probably in 1887. A fifth record, of annual breeding "... among the shrubby sea-blite on the east side of Osey Island" seems unlikely on current knowledge. Glegg considered the Lesser Redpoll to be "...

Atlas	Survey Area	% of 10km squares or tetrads in which	
		bred/probably bred	possibly bred or present
First National 10km	Essex	54.4	24.6
Second National 10km	Essex	49.1	17.5
First London Tetrad	Met. Essex	12.5	8.0
Second London Tetrad	Met. Essex	26.5	22.0
Essex Tetrad	Essex	15.1	13.8

Summary of results of Atlas surveys for Lesser Redpolls

chiefly a winter resident, but also a sparing breeder" with wintering birds arriving in November and leaving in March, though he noted "... the duration of the period appears to vary", a situation which remains to the present day. Glegg added a further nine breeding records, giving a total of 13 between 1879 and 1918, including eight in Epping Forest.

Hudson & Pyman added just a few more nesting records up to 1958, with "a pair or two" at Saffron Walden in 1953, at Shenfield/Hutton from 1954–58 and "(apparently) in Thorndon Park" in 1958. However, by 1963 an increase had begun, with breeding occurring or suspected in Epping Forest (20–25 pairs), Ongar Park Wood and Felsted (three pairs each), and 1–2 pairs at 3–4 other locations.

Numbers continued to increase through the 1970s. The First National Atlas survey confirmed breeding or probable breeding in 54.4% of 10km squares. Numbers continued to increase after the end of the survey (1972) with a substantial colonisation of much of Essex by the mid-1970s, which included the coastal fringe, although strongholds were in Epping Forest, Mill Green/Blackmore, Tiptree and the Colne Valley. At that time it was sufficiently common for only peak numbers to be reported in the *EBRs*.

The increase from the 1950s was thought to have coincided with the increased planting of conifers, whilst it is also likely that the rapid increase in Birch woodland following the wartime fellings of 1939–45, which reached a peak in the 1960s and 1970s, provided increased seed production which the Lesser Redpoll exploited (Second National Atlas). At their peak, however, pairs were also noted nesting in Birch thickets, old orchards and large gardens, and a pair even managed to raise young from a nest in a *Buddleia* on Ingatestone railway station (Essex Atlas).

The first signs of a decline, at least in some localities, were noted as early as 1978, but it remained a relatively common breeder. The Second National Atlas survey found the Lesser Redpoll in slightly fewer 10km squares than the First, whilst the Second London Atlas survey pointed to an increase, although this was almost certainly due to greater observer coverage. The Essex Atlas survey located the Lesser Redpoll in 28.9% of tetrads, with confirmed breeding in 15.1%. Geographically, most records came from the wooded corridor running southwest to northeast across Essex, with few in the northwest or the coastal belt from the Blackwater around to the Thames.

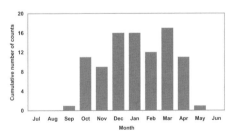

Seasonal occurrence counts of 100+ Lesser Redpolls from 1960-2004

This apparently healthy situation was perhaps deceptive, however, with the long running Hainault Forest CP CBC studies showing what was described as "a more pessimistic, and probably more accurate picture" (Essex Atlas), with steady or perhaps slowly declining numbers until the mid-1980s, followed by a steep fall, so that a peak of 25 pairs at Hainault Forest CP in 1978 had slumped to two by 1994.

The subsequent decline of the Lesser Redpoll as a breeding bird has been dramatic, with a 97% fall in the CBC/BBS (England) Index from 1977–02 and a 51% reduction in the BBS (England) Index from 1994–2003;

the sample size has become so small locally that BBS data do not produce meaningful results. Although now on the Amber List of Birds of Conservation Concern, a move to the Red List looks overdue. In Essex, since the end of the Essex Atlas survey the decline appears to have continued unchecked such that by 2001–02 there were no confirmed Essex breeding records, although in 2003 single pairs bred at Furze Hill, Mistley and Ongar Park Wood.

	No. of counts of 100+				
	1960s	1970s	1980s	1990s	2000s
Belfairs Park	1	5	2	0	0
Little Baddow	0	4	0	0	0
Mill Green	1	3	0	0	0
Thorndon CP	1	4	2	1	0
Hainault Forest CP	0	4	3	3	0
Epping	5	2	1	0	0
Other sites	2	6	4	3	0
Totals	10	28	12	7	0

**Location of flocks of
100+ Lesser Redpolls from 1961/62-2003/04**

The local CBC Indices for the period 1981–99 have shown what is effectively a 100% decline.

In Essex at least, this appears to mark a return to its former status prior to 1960, although the national trend involving a species typically considered almost exclusively British is of deep concern. Reduced Birch seed production due to a decline in the proportion of Birch in woodlands as a result of woodland succession over the last 30 years is perhaps one reason for the reduction, coupled with agricultural intensification over the last 20 years that has seen significant losses of hedgerows and farmland trees (Second National Atlas). There have been long-term declines in productivity and evidence of falling survival rates (Siriwardena *et al.* 1998).

Lesser Redpolls have long been known as passage migrants, with Christy reporting the species as common on migration at Harwich, whilst it was noted that birds were "... caught near Upminster in large quantities in autumn and fetch 2d. each in London". Glegg made scant reference to migrants, except to state that wintering birds appeared in numbers in November. Likewise, Hudson & Pyman referred only to numbers being augmented in winter. However, since the 1950s, *EBRs* have detailed small movements along the coast in spring and autumn. It was not until the mid-1970s, at the time of peak breeding numbers, that any significant movements occurred during autumn, and day totals of up to 50 became regular. Daily westerly movements, often in the company of other *Carduelis* finches, involving three-figure totals were noted at: Bradwell, 100 on 19th October 1975 and 10th October 1977; Colne Point, 120 on 10th October 1977; and Leigh/Two Tree Island, 100 on 14th October 1981. Flocks were often noted arriving off the sea. Occasionally, large numbers were reported inland at this time: of 450 in Thorndon CP on 7th–8th October 1967, 200 were ringed, with two being recovered in Belgium on 24th October 1967.

Although it is clearly difficult to distinguish between passage and wintering flocks, there is clearly an increase in large gatherings during December indicating either fresh arrivals from outside Essex or possibly consolidation of smaller flocks. Typically for an irruptive species, winter numbers fluctuate widely from year to year, linked with both breeding success and food abundance. The largest winter gatherings have invariably occurred in stands of Alder and Birch where they often feed in association with other *Carduelis* finches, particularly Siskins. In Essex, the prevalence of large flocks showed an increase from the late 1960s linked to increasing breeding numbers, with a subsequent decline from the peak during the 1970s, as might be expected given the dramatic recent decline in breeding numbers nationally. That most of these have, until recently, been of relatively local origin seems borne out by the very low frequency of Mealy Redpolls in the flocks, which was not the case in the most recent arrival during the winter of 1995/96 (q.v.).

Small numbers of migrant Lesser Redpolls were generally reported along the coast in spring. However, some of the largest wintering flocks actually increased in size during March, suggesting that there was occasionally a strong inland passage. Thus, at Thorndon CP in 1976, a flock of 500 in January that declined to 200 by March, increased again to 500 on 4th April, whilst in 1980, 175 in February had increased to 250+ in early March and 600 by the 30th. The 1976 and 1980 peaks remain the largest gatherings reported. In addition, and perhaps as a prelude to the largest winter influx seen in Essex, during the 1975/76 winter, an exceptional westerly movement involving some 250 occurred at Bradwell from 1st–14th June 1975.

More recently, numbers have been very much reduced but small movements continue to be reported from coastal localities during both spring and autumn.

Over the years, the geographical distribution of large wintering flocks has changed. Historically, Epping Forest was the most favoured site, but no three-figure gatherings have been reported since 1984. Likewise, no counts of

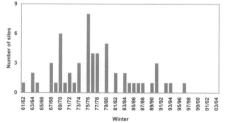

**Number of sites recording flocks of 100+ Lesser Redpolls
from 1961/62-2003/04**

100+ have occurred at Belfairs Park since 1982. More recently, Hainault Forest CP has been the most favoured locality for large flocks, with Thorndon CP also consistently recording large flocks. This may be due to the changing local availability of Birch and/or Alder seed. Records from later in the winter clearly show a more random distribution than during December, perhaps as flocks consolidate in areas where shrinking food supplies are still available.

Many of the peak counts occurred during the 1970s, principally in the winter of 1975/76.

Previously, large numbers were also found outside the period October–April. The winter of 1975/76 saw one of the largest invasions of Lesser Redpolls into Essex

	Jan	Feb	Mar	Apr	May	Jun	Jul	Aug	Sep	Oct	Nov	Dec
Essex	1	1	1	1	1	1				1		
Scotland	1						1	1				
North England				1								
South England	1		4	1	2	2	1			4		
The Netherlands			1									
Belgium		1			1	1				2	1	
France												1
Totals	3	2	6	4	4	3	2	1	0	7	1	1

Month and location of recovery of Lesser Redpolls ringed in Essex

and it is probable that in addition to the June 1975 movement at Bradwell mentioned above, 140 in Hainault Forest CP on 3rd May 1976 was in some way linked to this. In September 1976, 300 were noted in Ongar Park Wood.

Cox mentioned that ringing recoveries confirmed that breeders from northern Britain wintered in Essex and that, in addition, there were some autumn departures to the near-Continent; this mirrors the national situation (Winter Atlas).

It seems with hindsight that the high breeding numbers of the late 1960s/1970s were a response to certain specific conditions both within Essex and elsewhere, and were probably therefore locally at least quite random and perhaps typical of a species that exhibits irruptive behaviour. The Lesser Redpoll continues to be an Essex breeding species (just) and passage migrant in greatly reduced numbers and seems likely to continue to be so. The presence of substantial flocks in winter and early spring is clearly heavily geared to certain favoured sites and is likely to continue in invasion years, provided the species can find feeding conditions to its liking. For this to happen, it is clear that substantial stands of seeding Birch or Alders are required and any conservation measures probably need to be most closely linked to improving these conditions.

Sponsored by Anthony and Patricia Harbott in memory of Arthur and Kathleen Tingey

Common Redpoll   *Carduelis flammea*

Uncommon winter visitor and passage migrant: subject to occasional influxes

The Common Redpoll has a circumpolar distribution, breeding throughout the low-arctic. The nominate race *flammea* breeds in Europe in northern Scandinavia, whilst the race *islandica* occurs in Iceland and *rostrata* breeds in Greenland (Knox *et al.* 2001). The nominate race typically moves southeast from its nearest northern European breeding grounds (*BWP*), so occurrences in southwest Europe are generally irregular.

Christy referred to the Common Redpoll—or Mealy Redpoll, as it is probably better known—as an irregular and uncommon winter visitor. The earliest reference to the species in Essex was in 1836 when two were shot at Colchester on an unknown date and one was killed near Saffron Walden in May. Other records came from: Saffron Walden during 1845; Colchester in spring 1862; Canvey Island on 8th December 1881; Danbury, a few with Lesser Redpolls during winter in the late 19th century; and the Epping Forest area, many trapped prior to 1885. In Epping Forest it "… only appears at long intervals, and, like the Crossbills, in considerable numbers, probably in quest of food". Glegg added just one further record of more than a dozen caught in a garden at Chingford in November 1913.

Hudson & Pyman wondered whether the decline in shooting and trapping might have been the cause of the reduction in records; historically most were probably identified after they were shot and it is only recently that with increased observer awareness and superior modern optics that records have increased again. Many, but not all, associate with Lesser Redpolls.

Numbers are generally small. Prior to the exceptional influx in 1995/96, 27 in Epping Forest on 18th January 1972 (Cox) was the largest single flock to be recorded in Essex. There were some 280 during the winter of 1995/96, most in mixed flocks with Lesser and a few Arctic Redpolls. Observers considered that Mealys were in

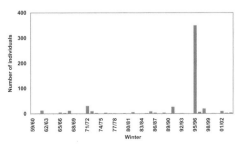

Annual totals of Mealy Redpolls from 1959/60-2003/04

the majority at each locality. At Thorndon CP, the peak count was 200, of which at least 120 were considered to be Mealy Redpolls, whilst mixed flocks at Hainault Forest CP and Havering both peaked at 100. A mixed flock of 30 was at Marks Hall, Coggeshall, with odd Mealy Redpolls at other localities including a fishing boat off the northeast coast. Male and female Mealy-type Redpolls were subsequently present at Hainault Forest CP early in the breeding season.

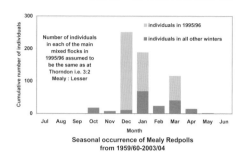

Seasonal occurrence of Mealy Redpolls
from 1959/60-2003/04

Peak numbers of Mealy Redpolls in Essex broadly occur at the same time as Lesser Redpolls. However, numbers invariably peak in January with a second smaller peak in March.

The earliest autumn record involved two at The Naze on 14th October 1972, whilst the latest was at Harlow on 5th May 1979. However, a pair and two males showing characteristics of Mealy Redpoll summered at Hanningfield in 1972.

The recovery of a Mealy Redpoll, ringed in Belfairs Park on 21st February 1976, at Nurmes, Finland, 2,143km to the northeast on 13th April 1979, is one of very few national recoveries; some probably reach Britain in most years, although the last large-scale influx was in 1910 (Migration Atlas).

Arctic Redpoll   *Carduelis hornemanni*

Very rare winter visitor: seven records involving up to ten individuals

The Arctic Redpoll has a circumpolar subarctic and high-arctic distribution where it breeds in Alpine Willow and perhaps also Birch woods (European Atlas). The nominate race *hornemanni*, or Hornemann's Redpoll, breeds in northern Greenland and adjacent Canadian arctic islands, whilst the subspecies *exilipes*, or Coue's Arctic Redpoll, breeds across northern Eurasia, Alaska and the remainder of northern Canada. Although Arctic Redpolls winter within or near to their breeding range, longer distance movements do sometimes occur when the species will migrate south with Common Redpolls.

1976	Brentwood	4th April	
1990	Mill Creek, Tollesbury	16th–17th December	
1991	Hockley Woods	10th–16th March	
1995	Hainault Forest CP	26th December	
1995/96	Thorndon CP	17th December–17th February	Up to four
1996	Chingford Plain	1st February	
	Hainault Forest CP	30th March	

Although there had been 821 British records of this winter visitor to the end of 2004 (BBRC 2005), over 450 of these occurred in an unprecedented influx during the winter of 1995/96 (Riddington *et al.* 2000). Normally the species is recorded from the Northern Isles and Scottish east coast but this influx was sufficiently widespread to reach many areas of southern England with up to seven occurring in Essex. The four at Thorndon CP were discovered by observers checking through a large flock of redpolls, following news of the apparent influx of Arctic Redpolls elsewhere (Bond 1997). It gave many observers the opportunity to study the plumage characteristics at close range for the first time (Votier *et al.* 2000). The 1976 record, which presumably involved a migrant rather than a wintering individual, occurred following the previous large redpoll influx and was the first to be accepted by BBRC on field identification alone. The majority of national records have been of Coue's Arctic Redpoll, and all the Essex records are considered to belong to this race.

Two-barred Crossbill   *Loxia leucoptera*

Vagrant: two 19th century records

The Two-barred Crossbill is a Holarctic species that occurs in the boreal coniferous forests of the Northern Hemisphere. In the Old World, where the species is represented by the race *bifasciata*, it breeds in northern European Russia and Siberia with occasional breeding in northern Fennoscandia. In years in which its principal food crop of Larch cones is poor, many thousands irrupt into western Europe from late summer.

| about 1846 | Epping Forest | Undated | Immature, shot |
| 1866 | Dedham | July | Immature male, shot |

The 1846 record, whilst without a description, occurred at around the time of a national influx during the winter of 1845/46. The 1866 individual was described in Christy as "… a male in immature plumage. The lower bars on the wings were much more distinct than the upper ones, which consisted of just a few white feathers…" It should, however, be borne in mind that "wing-barred" Common Crossbills may occur very rarely (Clement *et al.* 1993). This individual was shot out of a flock of 6–8 crossbills, which was also been seen across the Stour in Suffolk (Christy). This record was listed as 1886 in Cox (Green 2006)

A total of 225 Two-barred Crossbills had been recorded in Britain to the end of 2004 (BBRC 2005), principally between mid-July and mid-September. Essex missed out on the most recent large-scale national influx when 23 occurred in 1990.

(Common) Crossbill   *Loxia curvirostra*

Irregular visitor in variable numbers: has bred sporadically, last in 1998

The Crossbill breeds throughout the coniferous forests of the northern Hemisphere, from Eurasia right across to the North American continent, with the nominate race *curvirostra* breeding through much of its Eurasian range. It has spread south in Europe in the 20th century by taking advantage of the increase in conifer plantations. Crossbills are widespread but local across Britain, being completely dependent on conifer woods where the species feeds on the cones of Larch and Spruce; when these fail widely, huge numbers irrupt across the whole of Europe in search of food. Birds finding areas of good cone crops may settle and even breed for a few years well outside their normal range.

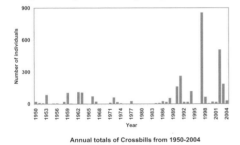

Annual totals of Crossbills from 1950-2004

Seasonal occurrence of Crossbills from 1950-2004

In Essex, the first documented record dates from 1826 (Green 2002) when a pair nested, but subsequently deserted, near The Aviary at Audley End, whilst another pair was shot before completing a nest in an apple tree in the middle of Saffron Walden around the same time. The presence of individuals in conifers near Saffron Walden during the winter of 1835 may point towards breeding in the area at this time although, apart from seeing young birds being fed and an empty, unused nest, Christy's correspondent produced no firm evidence. A nest and eggs were taken from a tall fir tree at Theydon Garnon in spring 1839 and a pair "nested in some firs at the Bower, close by Epping Railway Station" prior to 1885; breeding may have taken place in Birdbrook parish in 1838. Glegg added just one further record, two nests being found at Bradfield in April 1910.

Since 1950, breeding has been suspected on very few occasions and remarkably has been confirmed beyond doubt just once. The presence of juveniles being fed by adults cannot be taken as evidence of breeding, as it is not unknown for family parties to stay together even after considerable journeys (Clement *et al.* 1993). The presence of flocks of ten near Distillery Pond, Colchester, during 1959/60, 9–11 at Langford Reservoir in 1962/63 and about 25 at Widford GC in 1963/64 are, however, worthy of mention given that breeding may occur as early as late December/early January, although it was not suggested at each locality. On 7th June 1986, a pair with four juveniles was at a site near Colchester and, although breeding was not proven, the gamekeeper reported that Crossbills had bred there for at least ten years. In 1990, a singing male was present at Hanningfield on 27th December and was followed by

Atlas	Survey Area	% of 10km squares or tetrads in which	
		bred/probably bred	possibly bred or present
First National 10km	Essex	0.0	1.8
Second National 10km	Essex	1.8	5.3
First London Tetrad	Met. Essex	0.0	0.0
Second London Tetrad	Met. Essex	1.5	2.5
Essex Tetrad	Essex	0.4	0.8

Summary of results of Atlas surveys for Crossbills

occasional sightings through winter, and a family party was reported from 14th April 1991. In 1991, 14 were present at Marks Hall, Coggeshall, from 10th–27th March, seven at Rawreth on 6th April and 14 at Thorndon CP on 20th April. These were all unusually early for irrupting

Year	Main Influx	Peak monthly count	Peak site counts			No .of sites with counts 20+
			Site	No.	Date	
1959	July	50	Havering	50	18th July	2
1962	July	63	Havering	27	21st July	2
1990	September	83	Hanningfield	26	12th June	1
1991	June	132	Bradwell Brook	40	2nd June	3
1994	May	61	Friday Wood	39	19th May	2
1997	June	626	Marks Hall	250	29th June	8
2002	August	399	Clacton-on-Sea	100	27th August	8

Summary of principal Crossbill influxes from 1950-2004

birds so probably involved birds making local movements. In 1994, at least 20 were at Thorndon CP from 25th February–11th May with at least three pairs initially, including two singing males, and nesting behaviour was noted. In 1998, one pair raised two young at Havering CP, the only definite modern breeding record, whilst breeding was suspected at Rowney Wood, Debden, and Ongar Park Wood.

Between 1835 and 1839, the number of Crossbills in Essex appears to have been greater than at any time until 1997, although during the 19th century irruptions the species was only recorded from around Saffron Walden and in 1838/39 only around Epping Forest; this, however, probably reflected observer coverage. Around Saffron Walden during the 1835/36 influx, the species was said to "abound", whilst in Epping Forest in 1838/39 "About the middle of July we were visited by hundreds of Crossbills, but at that time the plumage was so bad they were not worth preserving. Many of them were nestlings." Crossbills were also recorded in varying, but usually small numbers in 1833, 1840–41, 1862, 1881, 1890–91, 1894–95, 1898, 1902, 1909–11, 1913 and 1927.

In the last 50 years, irruptions involving more than 100 Crossbills have occurred on seven occasions with the largest, in 1997, probably being the most substantial since the early 19th century; irruptions have become more regular since 1990. Other large counts during the period 28th–30th June 1997 were 150 at Thorndon CP, 50 at Coney Hall, Dengie, and 32 at Kelvedon Hatch. The flocks dispersed rapidly, presumably due to a lack of food and habitat and only 30 were present at Marks Hall, Coggeshall, the following week.

Other counts of more than 30 have come from: The Naze, 51 on 27th August 2002; Marks Hall, Coggeshall, 45 on 31st August 2002; Thorndon CP, 40 on 30th August 2002; Great Braxted, 41 on 27th August 2002; Alresford, 30–40 on 8th July 1953; Havering, 35 on 9th July 1966; Margaretting, 32 on 3rd August 1963; Hainault Forest CP, 32 on 13th August 2002; and Epping Forest, 31 on 5th June 1991.

Irrupting birds generally start to arrive in June and peak in July and, although the timing varies from year to year, the largest numbers occur between May and September. Typically, there is a second arrival in October–November, which usually involves fewer birds. Small numbers of coasting birds may be recorded in autumn from migration watchpoints during years of higher numbers.

Sponsored by Heatherlea Hotel, Scotland, in memory of Tariq Watson

Parrot Crossbill *Loxia pytyopsittacus*

Vagrant: one 19th century record involving three individuals Amber List

The monotypic Parrot Crossbill is found principally in the mature coniferous woods of the boreal zone throughout Norway, Sweden, Finland and European Russia and in smaller numbers in the Baltic States and Denmark. Recent studies of the crossbills in parts of Scotland have shown that in some areas many of the crossbills are Parrot Crossbills (Summers & Piertney 2003). Like other crossbills, the species is irruptive if its food source, principally the Scots Pine, fails.

1862	Near Colchester	21st February	Male and two females shot

These birds, which occurred during a large influx into Britain, were somewhat larger than Swedish specimens of Parrot Crossbills that they were compared with (*Zoologist* 1862: 8032-8033), so the identification appears sound (Catley & Hursthouse 1985). They remain in Yorkshire Museum, York. A record of three at Lambourne on 20th September 1861 is now considered unacceptable.

Christy detailed two further records: a pair shot in Saffron Walden in 1823 and one taken in Epping Forest in the autumn of 1835. Neither winter was noted for an influx of Parrot Crossbills (Newton 1972), although 1835 saw many Common Crossbills present and thus, without further details, must be considered unproven. A record of a pair with four juveniles at Fingringhoe Wick on 5th June 1988, which showed characteristics consistent with this species, was never submitted to the BBRC (*EBR* 1988).

Apart from the recently discovered Scottish population, the Parrot Crossbill is a generally rare irruptive vagrant to Britain with 486 records to the end of 1999 (BBRC 2000), although more than 100 occurred in the winter of 1982/83 and 264 in 1990/91. Breeding occurred in Norfolk in 1983 and in Suffolk in 1984 and 1985. Irruptions typically occur later than Common Crossbill.

Trumpeter Finch   *Bucanetes githagineus*

Vagrant: one record

The Trumpeter Finch breeds from the Canary Islands, east across the Sahara, from where the species has spread north into southern Spain since the 1960s, to the Middle East and on to Afghanistan, Pakistan and India. The race *zedlitzi* occurs in Spain and northern Africa. Whilst generally resident, it is known to be erratically nomadic and dispersive (European Atlas).

1985	Foulness	21st September

The species is an extremely rare vagrant to Britain, with just seven records up to 1999 (BBRC 2000) and the first in 1971, with all but two having occurred between late May and early June. This was the fifth (Wright 1986).

Common Rosefinch   *Carpodacus erythrinus*

Very rare summer visitor and passage migrant: 16 records   Amber List

The Common Rosefinch has a very large breeding range extending from Fennoscandia and central Europe, east through Russia to the Pacific where it occurs typically in woody or bushy habitats. The nominate race *erythrinus* occurs throughout much of its European range. Significant expansion west into Europe has occurred since 1900, a trend that seems to be continuing (Wallace 1999). European populations are thought to winter in Iran and north and central India. Breeding has occurred in Britain intermittently since 1982, although from a peak of 20 possible breeding pairs in 1992 numbers had declined to just one in 2001. Such changes in population are typical of a species on the absolute western limit of its breeding range.

1981	Fingringhoe Wick	10th September	Immature
1986	The Naze	14th September	Immature
1989	Benfleet Creek	12th–13th September	Female/immature
1992	Abberton	9th August	Female/immature
	Foulness	6th September	Immature, ringed
	The Naze	18th–19th September	Immature
1993	The Naze	28th May	Immature male, singing
1994	Hainault Forest CP	2nd September	Immature
	Old Hall	7th–11th November	Immature
1995	Bradwell	20th August	Female/Immature
1996	The Naze	4th September	Immature
1999	St Osyth	19th June	Singing male
	The Naze	28th September	Immature
2001	The Naze	21st October	Immature
	The Naze	27th October	Immature
2004	Foulness	11th September	Immature

With the range expansion on the Continent, the recent increase in Essex records is to be expected. Nationally, 1992 was by far the best year on record with 244 recorded. The 1990s saw an average of 149 recorded annually in Britain (Fraser & Rogers 2004). Over the last decade, more have occurred in spring than autumn, a reverse of the trend prior to the mid-1980s. It is a late spring migrant with numbers peaking nationally during May and June and in autumn during September and October, a pattern mirrored in Essex.

Although not unprecedented, the November record is late. Do the late October/early November records involve Common Rosefinches from more easterly populations? The timing of the records is typical of the arrival of Siberian vagrants.

With the continued expansion on the Continent and the considerable amount of scrubby habitat along our coast, the first Essex breeding record may not be too many years away. The Naze, with nearly 44% of Essex records, would seem to be an ideal locality.

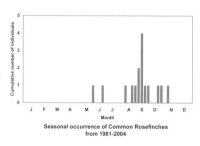

Seasonal occurrence of Common Rosefinches from 1981-2004

Bullfinch   *Pyrrhula pyrrhula*

The Bullfinch breeds in forests and other woody habitats right across the Palearctic region, occurring in boreal, temperate and montane areas. In western Europe the species occurs commonly in broad-leaved woodland and scrub and in bushy town parks and gardens and also orchards (European Atlas). The northern and eastern European races, mainly *pyrrhula* and *europea*, are partially migratory and irruptive whilst the British race *pileata* is non-migratory (Migration Atlas).

(Common) Bullfinch   *P. p. pileata*

Fairly common but decreasing resident   Red List

The Bullfinch is widespread throughout Britain, being absent only from north and west Scotland (Second National Atlas). Despite its bright colourings, it is a decidedly inconspicuous species. Declines have been noted nationally over the last 30 years following a period of unusual abundance, although Continental populations appear to be stable (European Atlas).

Christy described the Bullfinch as "… a fairly common resident … which is often very destructive to the buds of fruit trees. I believe it has become commoner of late years". The Bullfinch probably declined in the 19th century due to the cage-bird trade. However, it was not just trapped for its plumage but also for its song; Bullfinches are very good mimics. The Wild Bird Protection Acts of the 1880s and 1890s helped reverse the declines (Historical Atlas). The increase apparently continued into the early 20th century with Glegg describing the species as "… a not uncommon resident". He highlighted its destructive nature and considered that "… its destruction is advised in all fruit-growing districts".

The increase appears to have continued and accelerated during the 1950s. Bullfinches are a significant prey item for the Sparrowhawk and it is possible that the very low numbers of the raptor allowed the species to feed further from cover, thus making food more readily available; it is also possible that changing garden habitats provided new plant foods in abundance (Winter Atlas). Hudson & Pyman described a definite increase that affected all parts of Essex, despite the species being removed from the list of species protected by law in 1952.

The Bullfinch was not mentioned in any *EBRs* from 1961–84 but annually from 1988. Being common, it was generally overlooked and only since the 1990s have any regular counts been made.

The two National and London Atlases suggested little change in range between the two survey periods, the slight expansion along the urban fringe of southwest Essex noted in the latter probably being due to increased observer coverage. At the time of the Essex Atlas survey, the Bullfinch remained widespread throughout Essex, being recorded in 80.3% of tetrads with breeding confirmed in 57.6%. Bullfinches were absent from innermost Metropolitan Essex and the main conurbations as well as in coastal areas, notably Dengie and north and east of Rochford.

Atlas	Survey Area	% of 10km squares or tetrads in which bred/probably bred	possibly bred or present
First National 10km	Essex	98.2	0.0
Second National 10km	Essex	94.7	1.8
First London Tetrad	Met. Essex	39.0	21.0
Second London Tetrad	Met. Essex	70.0	13.0
Essex Tetrad	Essex	57.6	22.7

Summary of results of Atlas surveys for Bullfinches

National CBC data showed an increase during the 1960s and 1970s, with a sharp fall since (Population Trends). The CBC/BBS (England) Index for the period 1977–2002 declined by 58%, whilst from 1994–2003 the BBS (England) Index fell by 18%. Local CBC/BBS Indices have shown a similar trend. Anecdotal evidence suggests that the Bullfinch may still be declining across Essex. The reasons for this remain unclear (Siriwadena *et al.* 1999, 2000) but agricultural intensification may have played a part with the loss and over-management of hedges and the clearance of agricultural 'wasteland', where the species obtains weed seeds, perhaps the most significant. The increase in Sparrowhawk numbers has also been cited as a factor since it has increased as the Bullfinch has decreased, but the patterns of increase/decrease do not coincide (Second National Atlas).

Birds inhabiting purely woodland locations appeared to have fared little better than those in farmland habitats. In Hainault Forest CP, for instance, 20 pairs in 1986 had fallen to nine in 2000.

Prior to 1980, CBC plots showed average breeding densities in woodland of ten pairs per km^2 and two pairs per km^2 on farmland, although the latter included several negative surveys. Despite the falls, CBC data since 1980 have suggested higher densities in woodland of 16 pairs per km^2 (range 9–22) and on farmland of three pairs per km^2 (range 1–9); even on these sites, however, there was a general decline through the 1990s.

Small gatherings of Bullfinches may occur outside the breeding season. Birds are known to remain for some weeks within a short distance of a good food source before suddenly moving on to a new site. Since Bullfinches do not appear to be territorial, it means that a single orchard or thicket may be in range of dozens, or even hundreds, which travel independently to such sites (Winter Atlas). Consequently in the period of high populations they became a major pest on fruit farms and large numbers were shot. A total of 300–400 was said to have been shot on one north Essex farm alone in 1956, a fact deplored by the EBS: "This slaughter could not have taken place had not the Home Secretary persisted in legalising the shooting of this species ... despite the representations made to him by the County Council with the full support of the Society". Even during the 1970s, up to 750 were destroyed annually on a 100ha fruit farm in central Essex in an attempt to reduce damage to pear and plum buds in the late winter, at a time when control was being energetically pursued in other areas (Cox). Bullfinches can eat up to 45 buds per minute, although trees can lose up to 50% of their buds without affecting fruit production (Winter Atlas). Despite this apparently considerable toll, Bullfinch populations did not appear to be affected overall, although locally the effect must have been telling on population levels.

While such large numbers were regularly destroyed, gatherings of more than 20 were rare, 40 at Stansted SF on 25th–26th December 1961 being the largest to be reported in Essex. Recently, counts have only been made with any regularity in Hainault Forest CP where, during November and December 1989, there was an apparent influx with numbers peaking at 50+; at the same time it was, "... more widespread than usual" in Dagnam Park. Counts have in general declined with the fall in breeding numbers.

Of the Bullfinches ringed in Essex that have been recovered, more than 75% have remained within 10km of the ringing site. However, although considered sedentary, four Bullfinches ringed in Essex have moved more than 100km: one to Norfolk and three to Hampshire. The most distant of these was found dead at New Milton, Hampshire, on 14th September 1998, 203km from Foulness where it was ringed on 14th March 1998.

The Bullfinch still appears to be declining, although the species remains widespread across Essex. However, without a considerable change in management of the countryside the Bullfinch's future must remain uncertain. Many hedges that have not been grubbed out are nonetheless worthless in conservation terms because they are cut back and flailed to such an extent that they are no more than stunted low level, thin plantings: Bullfinches are partial to the large thick hedges that were once a common sight across the country. Only when such habitat is recreated in sufficient quantity and suitable food sources provided is a reverse in numbers likely to occur.

Northern Bullfinch   *P. p. pyrrhula*

Vagrant: up to 50 in the winter of 2004/05

Northern Bullfinches occur across northern Europe from Scandinavia and the White Sea, east through Russia to northern Mongolia and in the south through much of central Europe and into the Balkans.

Until 2004 there had been no definite Essex records of Northern Bullfinches, although it is interesting to note that at the time of the large flock at Stansted SF mentioned earlier, 16 were at The Naze and several were on the saltings in Hamford Water on 17th November 1961.

Following reports of an unprecedented invasion of Northern Bullfinches in the Northern Isles during October 2004, it soon became apparent that reasonable numbers of what were considered to be Northern Bullfinches were drifting south along the east coast. The first claimed Essex record came from Rainham on 27th October; the next were in mid-November at Thorndon CP, where it soon became clear that there was a small flock present, which peaked at 12 on 12th December. The flocks generally fed high in Birch trees. Records also came from nearby Warley CP where there was a maximum of ten on 20th December. Up to 23 were also present throughout Epping Forest, whilst Bullfinches considered to be of the northern race were also recorded at: Weald CP (one); Fryerning (one); The Mores Wood, near Brentwood; Hainault Forest CP; Fairlop CP; and Seventy Acres Lake (four).

'Continental' Bullfinch

P. p. europea

Vagrant: one record

This race is found from northwest Spain and the Pyrenees east through France to Belgium, the Netherlands, western Germany and Denmark.

There has been just one foreign-ringed Bullfinch recovered in Britain: ringed in the Netherlands, it was subsequently found in Essex (Migration Atlas).

Hawfinch

Coccothraustes coccothraustes

Uncommon and declining local resident and rare passage migrant

Amber List

The Hawfinch is the second largest Palearctic finch. The species' huge conical beak allows it to break open the hard fruits of certain deciduous trees, which ultimately determine its distribution. It breeds patchily across the Palearctic from the southern boreal, through temperate and Mediterranean zones into the fringes of steppe and desert, provided that suitable large seeds are available. Hawfinches occur from Great Britain (except Ireland) east to Japan but are absent from much of north and east Spain, southern Italy and Sicily, and are extremely localised in Great Britain and Fennoscandia beyond 60° N. The nominate race *coccothraustes* occurs across Europe. Anecdotal evidence points to an increase in west and central Europe since 1985/86, although in Britain there has been a decline. Northernmost populations are migratory and head generally southwest.

There is an intriguing 17th century reference to the Hawfinch in Epping Forest area that suggests that Hawfinches were "… as common as are pigeons in Guildhall Yard" (Mountford 1957). Did it breed there at this early date? In fact, it seems generally accepted that the Hawfinch was first confirmed breeding in Britain in the Epping Forest area during the 1830s, which, excepting the single breeding record of Gull-billed Tern, is a unique claim for an Essex breeding species. There are earlier records from Kent in 1828 and Tooting Common in 1833 but these appear never to have been generally accepted, and an 1829 claim of a nest found in an Elm hedge somewhere in Essex seems to have been unsubstantiated. Recently, however, Piotrowksi (2003) mentioned an 1830 breeding record from Bury St Edmunds, Suffolk.

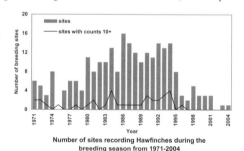

Number of sites recording Hawfinches during the breeding season from 1971-2004

One of the earliest detailed observations of the Hawfinch was made by Mr J. Gurney-Barclay who noted "This species came first under my notice about the winter of 1825, when a fine cock bird fell dead on the gravel walk before the gardener—from what cause was not ascertained; but it was not until 1837 that I was aware of their being resident and rather numerous in the neighbourhood … In the winter season and especially during severe weather, these birds were frequently seen in the neighbourhood of the forest in large flocks from fifty to a hundred or more, feeding on the seeds of hornbeam, to which they appear particularly partial … I am inclined to think that their shy habits, together with their being a very local species, has led to their having remained so long comparatively unobserved" (Christy). In 1831, Henry Doubleday noted: "The Grosbeak, I believe, breeds in our extensive forest every year" and in 1832 he found the first nest "I am happy in being able to send one rarity, viz. two eggs of the Hawfinch which till this spring I never saw". He described how they were particularly common in the winter of 1835/36 feeding on an abundant crop of Hornbeam seeds. Peas were also a favourite food. Doubleday published his observations in Jardine's *Magazine of Zoology* in 1837.

Following severe frosts in the springs of 1837–40, Hornbeam seed became scarce; so did the Hawfinch. However, spring 1842 was warm and a large seed crop resulted the following winter and hundreds of Hawfinches were noted with many nests the following

Atlas	Survey Area	% of 10km squares or tetrads in which	
		bred/probably bred	possibly bred or present
First National 10km	Essex	26.3	15.8
Second National 10km	Essex	17.5	22.8
First London Tetrad	Met. Essex	4.0	3.0
Second London Tetrad	Met. Essex	11.5	10.0
Essex Tetrad	Essex	4.5	2.9

Summary of results of Atlas surveys for Hawfinches

year. It was scarce again around the end of the 1840s. In later years, Henry Doubleday believed that numbers were augmented by arrivals from the Continent, particularly during 1865/66. Prior to 1881, flocks of 200–300 had been seen in Epping Forest.

Whilst Epping Forest was clearly the species' stronghold in the 19th century, Hawfinches were also noted around Colchester in the winter of 1881 when they were much more common than usual in the Saffron Walden area, whilst breeding was reported from Coggeshall (1857), Audley End (1858), Alresford (1871), Danbury Park (1877) and Colchester (1871–81). Comments from observers suggested that it was becoming more common and widespread at this time.

Had the Hawfinch merely been overlooked as suggested by Barclay and Doubleday or was it in fact a recent arrival? Naturalists during the 17th and 18th centuries generally regarded it as just a winter visitor, although in Norfolk, Browne (1605–82) wrote that the species was "chiefly seen in the summer time about cherrie time". Edwards (1743–51) described it as "... not a native of England", whilst Gilbert White referred to it as "... an occasional wanderer" and that "... birds of this sort are rarely seen in England and only in winter". In Norfolk, historical evidence of large-scale winter influxes exists for the period 1823–90.

The weight of the evidence points to the fact that it was not until the early 19th century that Hawfinches began to breed in any numbers in England or Essex. Indeed, it seems remarkable that if Hawfinches were breeding before then that they had never been seen and no nests found, despite the early naturalists' ability to find other secretive species such as Crossbill. The Hawfinch is on the southwest edge of its range in Britain, which means that the population is prone to fluctuations, so perhaps the species was at a low ebb at the time of the earliest naturalists and only increased during the 19th century. The periodic influxes observed in

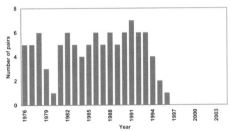

Annual number of breeding pairs of Hawfinches in Hainault Forest CP from 1976-2004

Norfolk may also point to the boosting of local populations by what may be irruptions from the Continent; to date, however, there is no evidence to back this assertion.

Nationally, a range expansion occurred from its stronghold in the southeast of England from around 1836 and continued into the early 20th century. Expansion then slowed, with southwest England and Wales colonised in the 1950s and 1960s. The reason for the expansion, which also saw a spread across Essex, was perhaps due to the combination of a number of factors. The increase in the acreage of Cherry orchards provided an additional source of food into the early winter (Historical Atlas), whilst the trees themselves may have provided more nesting sites; in some areas increases followed plagues of Oak moth caterpillars (Ticehurst 1909). In addition, the increasing urbanisation and creation of large gardens increased the amount of habitat suited to Hawfinches and hunting pressure may have been reduced after the Bird Acts of the 1880s (Historical Atlas).

By Glegg's time, the Hawfinch was an "... irregular resident and a local breeder, and almost certainly a winter visitor, although there is no evidence that any reach the county from abroad". By the 1920s, it was felt by several observers that the Hawfinch was declining and, although Glegg acknowledged that numbers in the Forest appeared to vary considerably from year to year, the species was particularly uncommon in Epping Forest during the period 1922–27.

Away from Epping Forest, Glegg considered the Hawfinch a very local species,

	Year of first count of 10+	No. of years with counts of 10+ of 10+	Last year in in which 10+ recorded	Peak counts
Danbury/ Little Baddow	1968	8	1996	38 Jan/Feb 1994
Chalkney Wood	1965	2	1980	18 11th April 1965
Thorndon CP	1975	2	1993	16 28th September 1975
Hatfield Forest	1957	4	1994	17 10th February 1990
Epping Forest	1963	3	1973	62 2nd September 1963
Dagnam Park	1983	12	1994	50 23rd February 1986

Principal sites with flocks of 10+ Hawfinches, 1950-2004. Other sites recording 20+ include Hockley Woods (25-30 in Feb 1952); Harlow (20 from Jan-Mar 1971); Harold Hill (25 on 2 January 1984).

with breeding confirmed in the early 20th century at: Harwich "… increasingly"; Mistley in 1902; Yeldham and Gosfield, in four years from 1897–1913; "Saling"; Great Waltham; and Lexden, annually. In addition, there were intermittent records from other parts of Essex, although mostly during winter.

Despite far greater observer coverage over the last 50 years, we still know very little about Hawfinch populations. Its extremely secretive nature makes assessment of population trends very difficult and the species is not indexed on CBC plots because it occurs on too few (Population Trends). Nor are the year-to-year variations in the size of winter flocks a reliable guide to population change as local distribution is dictated largely by food availability, depending on the distribution of the favoured tree species and the quantity of food crop available at the time.

In Essex at least, since the 1950s it appears from anecdotal evidence that the population declined slowly until the early 1990s, since when there has been a dramatic fall. The *EBR* 1951 noted that the Hawfinch was "still well represented in Epping Forest … although it may have decreased, whilst a few pairs are concentrated in the Terling area, where it has increased, and in a wooded locality in the Rochford Hundred. Elsewhere scattered pairs are to be found in most well-wooded districts, notably in the Brentwood area. It is rare in North Essex and is unknown in the east of the county except as a vagrant in winter", whilst in the *EBR* 1954 "Breeding season reports of this species are declining and all instances should be reported in future years". At Terling, there were 17 pairs in 1952, far more than the usual 3–4. Away from the well-wooded districts pairs were noted at Widdington (1953 and 1955), Mistley (1956 and 1961), Saffron Walden (1957), Parndon (1966 and 1969), Kirby-le-Soken (1968) and South Hanningfield (1968).

Hudson & Pyman considered the Hawfinch a "Somewhat uncommon resident" and summarised the species' status as "widely distributed in the wooded belt of central and southwest Essex and probably in the west and around Colchester also; but it is very local in Tendring and Rochford Hundreds, and absent from Dengie Hundred. Though never common, there are concentrations at Earls Colne [Chalkney Woods], Terling, Danbury/Little Baddow,

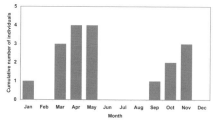

Seasonal occurrence of Hawfinches along the northeast coast, Dengie and Foulness/Wakering/Shoebury area from 1950-2004

Thundersley and in Hatfield and Epping Forests". Ten pairs reported in the Danbury area in 1965 was the largest count from any area at this time, no estimate having ever been made of the population in its stronghold of Epping Forest even to this day.

Over the next 15 years, Hawfinch numbers appeared to remain fairly stable and called for no comment in the *EBR*. Cox described it as an uncommon resident. The Two National Atlas surveys revealed a decline that was most notable in south and central areas of the county; nationally, similar falls were observed. Although, the Second London Atlas survey recorded a range expansion since the First, increased observer coverage was a significant factor as anecdotal evidence from *EBRs* suggested declining numbers, whilst the LNHS Woodland Bird survey of 1985–87 (Palmer 1988) pointed to falls in the LNHS recording area since the First London Atlas.

The Essex Atlas survey found Hawfinches in 7.4% of all tetrads with confirmed breeding in just 4.5%, predominantly in the wooded belt running southwest to northeast in Essex. The species' range appeared to have changed little since the 1960s.

Although a slight decline had occurred since the late 1960s, there was a more obvious fall in breeding numbers from the late 1980s, a trend that accelerated markedly from 1995. It should, however, be borne in mind that the Essex Atlas survey came to an end in 1994; increased observer coverage over the period 1988–94 may have masked a marked decline that only became apparent from 1995. Away from the main wooded areas, the small isolated pockets of Hawfinches apparently disappeared and previously favoured sites across Essex appear to have been steadily abandoned. For example Chalkney Wood and Dagnam Park all lost breeding Hawfinches during the mid-1990s, whilst Ongar Park Wood, which held 12 pairs in 1988, has more recently held only the odd pair. The Danbury/Little Baddow population also seems to have disappeared, although reduced observer coverage may be a factor. In Epping Forest, the number of breeding season records declined markedly from around the mid-1990s with only occasional sightings by the turn of the century. At Hainault Forest CP with the most complete set of records for the last 25 years or so, the trend has been the same. By 2002, no breeding season reports were received, although a small breeding colony appears to have survived at Braxted Park; six birds were observed in February 2003 with a juvenile in August and two pairs probably bred in 2004.

Nationally, Hawfinch numbers may have declined by around 40% between 1985 and 1999 (Langston *et al.* 2002). A number of potential causes for the species' decline have been suggested: storm damage to broad-leaved woodland during 1987; loss of orchards; and predation, particularly by crows and Grey Squirrels. The relative importance of each of these factors is unknown.

During winter, the distribution of the Hawfinch broadly corresponds with its breeding range in Essex. Small flocks form from late summer with the largest generally recorded between January and March with a distinct peak in February. The location of such gatherings is almost entirely dependent on the distribution of Hornbeam and Cherry, and the numbers present in Essex appear to vary considerably from year to year, probably depending primarily on the size of the Hornbeam crop. Since the beginning of the 20th century, there has been just one three-figure count during winter, a flock of 200 in Epping Forest on 28th February 1942 (*LBR* 7: 2). The only subsequent flocks of 50+ were in Epping Forest on 2nd September 1963 where a roost peaked at 62 and 50+ in a feeding flock in Dagnam Park on 23rd February 1986. Few sites have recorded flocks of 10+ and these have declined rapidly during the 1990s.

Outside Essex, there is historical evidence for large-scale irruptions of Hawfinches into Norfolk (Taylor *et al.* 1999), whilst more recently arrivals on the east coast, north to the Shetland Islands and on the Isles of Scilly suggest that there are some arrivals and departures during spring/autumn. The origin of the few Hawfinches that have occurred on the Essex coast is unclear and there are no ringing recoveries. Most of the records have come from the northeast coast but a few have been recorded from Dengie and Foulness/Thames. All bar one have fallen in the periods March–May or September–November and nearly 60% have occurred during spring migration. All the records have involved single birds except for three at Wakering Stairs on 28th November 1993, two ringed at Holland-on-Sea on 24th January 1962, and two in the Observatory thicket at Bradwell on 14th April 1966.

The reasons for the Hawfinch's decline remain unclear because of a dearth of knowledge concerning its status, population size and trends as well as conservation requirements (Langston *et al.* 2002). The RSPB has taken steps to increase our understanding of the Hawfinch's needs but this will take time. In the meantime it appears that, without any specific conservation measures being available, the Hawfinch may be heading for extinction as an Essex breeding species within the next 5–10 years if the current trend continues. Whether this is simply a return to its status prior to the 19th century is a matter for conjecture.

Sponsored in memory of Tariq Watson

Lapland Bunting (Lapland Longspur)   *Calcarius lapponicus*

Uncommon winter visitor and passage migrant in variable numbers

The Lapland Bunting is a northern Holarctic species breeding in arctic and subarctic areas above the tree line, where it is one of the commonest passerines. The species' range extends from the mountains of Norway, east through Siberia and into northern Canada and parts of Greenland. The nominate race *lapponicus* occurs from northern Norway to eastern Siberia with the race *subcalcaratus* breeding from Greenland to northern Canada. Breeding occurred in Scotland in four years between 1974 and 1981 with 11 pairs in 1979, but since 1981 only odd birds have summered. In the Western Palearctic, Lapland Buntings winter around the shores of the southern North Sea and from eastern Hungary and southern Russia east into central Asia. The relatively small numbers wintering in Britain principally occur along the east coast from southern Scotland southwards.

It was not until the mid-18th century that it was realised that small numbers of Lapland Buntings were occurring in autumn and winter along the east coast of Britain, although it is possible that prior to then it had simply been overlooked; appreciable numbers were not recorded until 1890. The first Essex record came from inland, a male being caught near "Waltham, Essex" in 1872; whether this refers to Little or Great Waltham or Waltham Abbey is

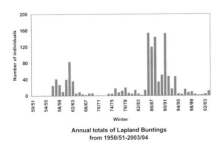

Annual totals of Lapland Buntings
from 1950/51-2003/04

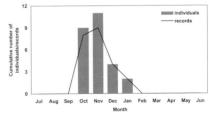

Seasonal occurrence of inland Lapland Buntings
from 1950-2004

unclear. The next documented record was not until 1953, when one was at Walthamstow on 19th March, although Hudson & Pyman considered the record to be unsubstantiated and did not recognise it; the record is treated similarly here. The next accepted record, at The Naze on 4th October 1956, coincided with a significant influx into western Europe involving birds suspected to originate from Greenland (Williamson & Davis 1956); *subcalcaratus* is, however, not on the British List (BOU 1992).

Since then it has become an almost annual passage migrant and winter visitor, although prone to marked variations in numbers, with the highest numbers present from 1956/57–1962/63 (when there was a maximum of 83 in the winter of 1962/63) and from 1985/86–1990/91, when numbers peaked at 154 in 1985/86 and 151 in 1990/91. The influxes of the 1950s and 1960s were noticed almost entirely on Foulness, with maximum counts of: 40 in 1957/58; 25 in 1958/59; 20 in 1959/60; 40 in 1960/61; 70 in 1961/62; and 30 in 1962/63. A rapid decline followed with none recorded there at all during the late 1970s, although access restrictions may have been a factor. As numbers increased in the mid-1980s, counts rose to 25 in 1985/86 and 40 in 1990/91, but only odd birds have been reported since.

During the 1980s and 1990s by far the most favoured site was Holland Haven where birds were very easy to observe as they fed just inside the seawall, apparently on the seeds of Sea Purslane and other low saltwater tolerant plants. Numbers here peaked at around 70 on 27th November 1985, with 50 in 1986/87 and 40 in 1987/88. Here, too, numbers fell away rapidly, although habitat change and disturbance brought about by sea defence works undoubtedly contributed to this. In 1985/86 there was also a flock that peaked at 45 at Old Hall, where there had previously been very few records, as well as 20 at Barling. In 1986/87 there were 30 at East Tilbury with 40 there the following winter when 22 were at Rolls Farm, Tollesbury. There were 23 on Dengie during 1988/89, whilst in 1990/91 a flock of around 60 was at East Mersea. Very few other sites have recorded more than ten individuals: Leigh/Two Tree Island, 10–12 on 21st–26th October 1961; and South Woodham Ferrers, 14 on 17th January 1988. Records have occurred all around the coast from Hamford Water to Rainham, where up to three have been reported.

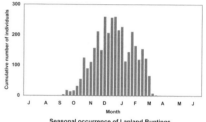

Seasonal occurrence of Lapland Buntings
from 1970/71-2003/04

Recently, numbers have once again declined, as they have done nationally, although the reasons for the dramatic peaks and troughs in wintering numbers are unclear.

There have been 23 inland records involving 26 birds, all involving singles unless stated otherwise: Fairlop CP, eight records; Walthamstow, 26th January 1979, 13th–14th November 1989; KGV, 5th November 1990 and 8th October 2002; Hanningfield, two, 2nd November and one, 17th November 1986; Dagenham Chase, 3rd November 1988 and two, 4th November 1996; Waltham Abbey, 22nd December 1989; Fishers Green, 9th December 1990 and 31st October 2004; Dagnam Park, two, 17th October 1993; Hainault Forest CP, 30th October 1993; Latton Common, Harlow, a female, 23rd October 1973; and Abberton, 29th October 1978. There was clearly a late autumn inland passage at times of high populations.

Typically, the first autumn arrivals occur in late September. However, the earliest for the county were three at Bradwell on 2nd September 1956 and, more recently, two were at East Tilbury on 18th September 1993. These early autumn birds invariably occur at coastal migration watch-points and seldom linger suggesting that they are on passage.

The main arrival of wintering birds occurs from late October with numbers building through November and remaining constant until February, after which there is a fairly rapid decline as birds begin returning north. No obvious spring migration has been noted, there being just two April records: Foulness, two on 2nd in 1961; and Holland Haven, one on 7th in 1988.

Snow Bunting   *Plectrophenax nivalis*

Locally common winter visitor and passage migrant   Amber List

No other land bird has a more northerly breeding distribution than the Snow Bunting. It inhabits sparsely vegetated tundra on the fringes of the Arctic Ocean, Alaska, northern Canada, Greenland, Iceland and the mountains of Scotland and Scandinavia where mid-summer temperatures rarely exceed 10°C. The nominate race *nivalis* occurs through western Alaska to Canada, Greenland and Europe with *insulae* occurring in Iceland. Most Snow Buntings move south in

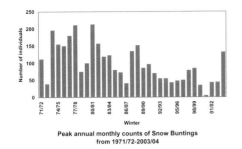

Peak annual monthly counts of Snow Buntings
from 1971/72-2003/04

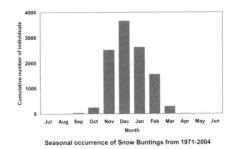

Seasonal occurrence of Snow Buntings from 1971-2004

winter, although movements are complex and tend to be much later in autumn than other migrants. Most of those wintering in Europe are found around North Sea coasts in low country with sparse and low vegetation (European Atlas). Icelandic birds make up around 70–85% of the British wintering population.

The status of the Snow Bunting in Essex has changed very little over the last 150 years or so, its distribution linked to its favoured winter habitat of sandy shorelines or the lower levels of salt marshes (Winter Atlas). Thus, northeast Essex from Harwich south to East Mersea, where it favours the shell and shingle banks, was and remains the stronghold of the wintering population.

To Christy, the Snow Bunting was "… a winter visitant … it usually occurs on the coast during severe winters in greater or less numbers, but individuals have occasionally been shot … inland". The first documented Essex record involved one shot on New England Island on 29th November 1830. On the coast the species was noted at Walton and Dovercourt, where large flocks were said to occur and also Harwich, Maldon and "Shoebury". In 1888, one of Christy's correspondents observed "I saw the first, which was very tame … on Sept. 24th, just before a gale, but they generally arrive in flocks of hundreds about a month or six weeks later". Inland records occurred at "Bardfield", "Dunmow", Halstead and Epping.

Glegg described the Snow Bunting as "… a not infrequent but irregular winter visitor to the county … The numbers have varied very much from year to year, most being recorded during severe winters". Surprisingly, he was not able to add many records after 1890 (cf. Twite); of the seven records, four came from Bradfield between 1903 and 1922 and only one record, of "… a good many…" along the Blackwater in January 1894, hinted at anything other than very small numbers. A decline therefore seems to have taken place in the preceding 30 years or so.

Over the next 30 years, numbers appeared to have increased again, Hudson & Pyman noting that the Snow Bunting was "… a not uncommon winter-visitor to tidal shores". Certainly there was a significant increase in numbers during the 1960s: from 1949–59 a total of just six flocks of 50+ occurred, but from 1960–66, 20 such flocks were noted. For the period 1958/59–1962/63, it was probably more common than at any time subsequently (Cox). Some of the largest flocks ever reported in Essex were observed around this time: 250 on Foulness in January 1960; 250 at The Naze during the winter of 1961/62; and 400 on Horsey Island duing December 1961. Only two flocks have subsequently reached these proportions: 200 in Hamford Water in December 1966 and 200 on Dengie in November 1967. There have been a further 12 three-figure counts: seven from Hamford Water, the biggest being 180 on 25th January 1960 on Horsey Island; two from Foulness; and single three-figure counts from Bradwell, Dengie and along the Blackwater. Surprisingly, given the regularity with which Snow Buntings have occurred at Colne Point, the highest count recorded from there is 90, on both 10th December 1950 and 3rd February 1988.

Following the exceptional numbers of the late 1950s/early 1960s, numbers remained relatively stable over the next 15 years, although typically subject to marked annual variations. Such fluctuations may be the result of climatic factors and it is typical of the species to appear in unusually high numbers for a number of years, followed by a marked decline over a similar period (Winter Atlas). Higher winter temperatures may encourage greater numbers of Snow Buntings to remain nearer their breeding area and hence reduce wintering populations further south. What is interesting, however, is that in Essex at least there appears to be a clear pattern of high and low

	Years with counts of			Peak counts	
	10+	50+	100+		
Dovercourt/Harwich	9	1	0	50	6th November 1965
Hamford/Naze	28	13	9	400	17th December 1961
St Osyth/Colne Point	38	15	0	90	10/12/50 & 3/2/88
Mersea	13	0	0	50	3rd January 1959
Blackwater	24	4	1	114	15th December 1962
Bradwell/Dengie	32	13	3	200	4th November 1967
Foulness	17	4	3	250	January 1960

Summary of principal sites for Snow Buntings from 1950/51-2003/04

573

wintering populations every 5–7 years or so. Such a cyclical pattern of abundance suggests that other factors aside from climatic ones are at work; perhaps like other species Snow Bunting numbers are affected by the abundance of Lemmings from year to year.

Numbers have fallen slightly since 1980 despite a significant increase in observers, which suggests that in real terms a decline has occurred. Numbers recorded in Essex during the winter of 2000/01 were the lowest yet

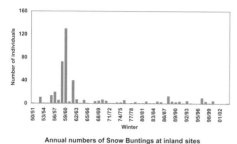

Annual numbers of Snow Buntings at inland sites from 1950/51-2003/04

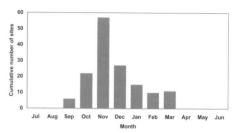

Seasonal numbers of inland sites recording Snow Buntings from 1950-2004

recorded in an *EBR*, with no double-figure flocks reported for the first time. However, the winter of 2003/04 saw an increase in numbers with 40–60 at Bradwell, Old Hall and East Mersea, probably the same individuals being involved at each site.

The first autumn Snow Buntings are usually recorded towards the end of September, with the earliest arrival involving two at Colne Point on 7th in 1952 with 12 at The Naze on 19th in 1989. Numbers build to a peak in December and January but decline quickly during February as birds head north back to their breeding areas.

By mid-March very few are left in Essex. There have been 13 April records, all of 1–2 birds, except for three at Colne Point on 2nd in 1988 and 12 on 5th in 1986. There is one May record, from Colne Point on 4th in 1984. There are two June records: a male at The Naze on 26th in 1993; and one at Old Hall from 23rd–30th in 1995. Whether these were early/late migrants or even summering individuals is unclear.

The northeast of Essex has been and remains the species' stronghold but regular wintering flocks occur along parts of the Blackwater Estuary, Dengie and the Foulness/Wakering/Shoebury area. Further into the Thames Estuary, numbers tend to be small, although periodically moderately sized flocks have occurred, the largest being 50 at East Tilbury during November 1961 and 30 on Canvey Island in December 1997.

Inland, the Snow Bunting is almost annual, although numbers are generally small. However, during the period of unusual abundance in the late 1950s/early 1960s exceptional numbers were noted at Abberton, particularly in 1958/59 and 1959/60. In 1958/59, 70 were present from 16th November–4th January, declining to 35 by 22nd February and last seen on 13th March, whilst in 1959/60 there were up to 120 during January and February, with the last two on 18th March. Smaller peaks were noted in 1952/53 (11), 1955/56 (13), 1956/57 (18) and 1961/62 (35). Subsequently, numbers have remained in single figures with six in 1969/70 the highest. Elsewhere, smaller numbers have been reported from most of the other main reservoirs. Double-figure totals away from Abberton have occurred only once, at Hanningfield where there were 11 on 26th November 1961. A record of 12 at Fairlop CP on 1st December 1987 (*EBR* 1987), should have read "1 or 2" (Green 2004b).

November is the peak time for inland reports when coastal records are relatively low, suggesting that Snow Buntings are arriving overland from the west as well as from the east at this time. In addition to reports from the main reservoirs, there have been a small number from sites across the county, all single birds except for two at Elsenham on 23rd November 1962.

One ringed at Foulness on 1st November 1961 and recovered at Le Zoute, Belgium, on 21st November 1961 indicates some onward migration through Essex; several similar movements have occurred nationally. One ringed on Cairn Gorm, Highland, on 25th March 1990 and trapped at Shoeburyness on 17th March 1991 raises the possibility that some of our wintering population may originate from the Scottish breeding population, which is generally considered to undertake only local movements (European Atlas); so this individual is more likely to have been heading further north when trapped on Cairn Gorm. Trapping at Felixstowe Ferry, Suffolk, during February 1997 found that 90 were of the race *insulae*, 12 of the nominate race *nivalis* and 12 were indeterminate (Odin 1997); the composition of flocks in Essex is likely to be very similar.

Numbers of Snow Buntings wintering in Essex are largely influenced by factors operating far outside the county's boundaries. At present there is sufficient habitat for the species along the Essex coast. Despite increasing sea levels, the ever-changing nature of sand, shell and shingle banks and the recharging of beaches using dredgings from the shipping channels should ensure sufficient habitat in the immediate future. If global warming causes warmer winters, the Snow Bunting's breeding and wintering range may move north and so reduce numbers visiting Essex.

Sponsored by Anthony and Patricia Harbott in memory of Authur and Kathleen Tingey

Pine Bunting   *Emberiza leucocephalos*

Vagrant: one record

The nominate race of Pine Bunting, *leucocephalos*, breeds across a large part of Siberia from the western slopes of the Urals to the Pacific, including Sakhalin Island and the Kuril Islands (Occhiato 2003a). It winters mostly in Afghanistan, Pakistan, northwest India, Nepal and northern China. Recently small numbers have been found wintering in Israel (Shirihai 1996) and, remarkably, in Italy (Occhiato 2003).

1992	Dagenham Chase	12th February–17th March	1st-winter male

This was the 21st of a total of 43 British records to the end of 2004 (BBRC 2005) and the tenth away from the Northern Isles. Numbers occurring in Britain peak around October to early November, so this individual presumably arrived the previous autumn and wintered; conceivably very small numbers winter annually in Britain. This individual spent much of its time feeding in horse paddocks with Yellowhammers but left too soon to attain full adult plumage or sing (Barrett 1993).

Yellowhammer   *Emberiza citrinella*

Common but declining resident; scarce passage migrant   Red List

The Yellowhammer has a trans-Palearctic distribution, being found in temperate, boreal and mountainous regions. The breeding range of the nominate race *citrinella* covers most of Europe, including England, with the race *caliginosa* occurring in Scotland, Wales and Ireland (European Atlas). It is the commonest and most widespread bunting in the Western Palearctic (*BWP*), although in central and northwest Europe the species has declined during the 20th century. It is widespread across Britain where it has traditionally been considered a bird of farmland, although it is absent or occurs at generally low densities on the higher ground of England, Wales and Scotland. Significant declines have occurred in Britain since the 1970s. The Yellowhammer is sedentary in Britain and Ireland but a partial short-distance migrant in large parts of its range, with northernmost breeding sites vacated entirely in winter (European Atlas).

Originally a bird of woodland edge and scrub, the species would have benefited greatly from woodland clearance and the conversion to farm-

Atlas	Survey Area	% of 10km squares or tetrads in which	
		bred/probably bred	possibly bred or present
First National 10km	Essex	98.2	1.8
Second National 10km	Essex	94.7	3.5
First London Tetrad	Met. Essex	44.5	11.5
Second London Tetrad	Met. Essex	72.5	5.5
Essex Tetrad	Essex	77.0	9.1

Summary of results of Atlas surveys for Yellowhammers

ing (Harrison 1988) so it was probably common and widespread by Roman times when wheat growing was the mainstay of farming in Essex. Enclosure of fields by hedgerows during the 19th century would have made the Essex countryside almost perfect Yellowhammer habitat. By 1800 there were 80,000ha under Wheat in Essex (Corke 1984). Nationally, the Yellowhammer was one of the commonest birds throughout Britain and Ireland during the 19th century (Historical Atlas). Christy described the species as "An abundant resident", but mentioned little else regarding its status. He noted a pair nesting on the grassy bank of New Street, Chelmsford, by the railway arch in 1877 where "… many scores of people passed daily within four feet": this remains the only reported breeding from an urban area. Perhaps the ready availability of food in the form of horse fodder/droppings was the reason for such a choice; did the Yellowhammer nest regularly in urban areas at this time? Glegg noted "… an abundant resident throughout the county … that is especially numerous on the chalk uplands in the northwest of the county". Like Christy, and perhaps because it was so abundant, he added little further information.

The first half of the 20th century saw little change in the Yellowhammer's national range and distribution (Historical Atlas). Hudson & Pyman noted that the Yellowhammer "… was very common (even abundant) until 1960–61, when a considerable decline became apparent". This decline has been attributed to the use of organochlorines as seed dressings since the Yellowhammer is a seed-eating bird. Additionally, the severe winter of 1962/63 may have exacerbated the

575

declines that were noted countrywide (Population Trends). In Essex, by way of example, 38 pairs in the Writtle/Roxwell/Highwoods area in 1964 were "... little more than half ..." the number of pairs in 1962.

Hudson & Pyman suggested a partial recovery was underway by 1964, although this was very patchy. Unfortunately, the Yellowhammer was not mentioned in *EBRs* from 1967–74, so the speed of recovery was not recorded. However, Cox noted an increase on an 85ha farmland CBC at Little Waltham from 11 pairs in 1966 to 24 in 1971.

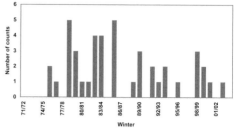

Annual totals of counts of 100+ Yellowhammers
from 1971/72-2003/04

What seems clear is that the Yellowhammer has never recovered its pre-1950 population levels, a time when there was far more scrub and hedgerow across Essex (Parslow 1973, Cox). In the breeding season, Yellowhammers are strongly associated with hedgerows and their density in farmland is closely correlated with areas of cultivated crops, hedgerow availability and altitude (Migration Atlas).

The First National Atlas survey reported breeding from almost every 10km square in Essex, a situation that had apparently remained unchanged by the time of the Second National Atlas, although anecdotal evidence suggested that a serious decline was underway by the mid-1980s. The Second London Atlas suggested little change from the First, despite increased observer coverage; a general retreat from suburban areas had been in progress since around 1900 (Homes 1957).

The Essex Atlas survey confirmed breeding in 77% with birds present in a further 9.1%. Yellowhammers were still widespread across Essex but with absences from the main urban areas in the county, particularly those along the Thames and in the southwest and also from the most exposed parts of the coast.

Local CBC/BBS data have shown a significant decline since 1981 with the national CBC/BBS (England) Index falling by 53% between 1997 and 2002 and the BBS (England) Index falling by 17% between 1994 and 2003.

Cox noted that on farmland CBC plots Yellowhammers bred at a mean density of 18 pairs per km^2 (range 8–31). CBC data since 1980 produced mean densities on farmland of 13 pairs per km^2 and six pairs per km^2 in woodland. Yellowhammers will breed along the edges of woods and young conifer plantations but not within them.

Since the Essex Atlas survey, *EBRs* have continued to report declines, for example a "... 50% decline..." being noted at Boreham in the eight years to 1998. However, it seems that Yellowhammer numbers may have stabilised and even increased slightly in recent years, at least at some sites, from a low point reached around 1998. Thus at Hainault Forest CP, where numbers declined by 70% over 20 years to 5–6 pairs in 1993 and just one in 1995, there was an increase to some ten pairs in 2001. A further three sites have reported increases in recent years: Ingrebourne Valley; Alresford CBC; and Great Notley.

The declines apparent during the 1950s and 1960s may have been caused by the loss of hedgerows, urbanisation and increased use of pesticides. More recently, the dramatic declines have probably been caused by the switch from spring to autumn sowing of Wheat, which has had a severe impact on winter survival through the loss of the Yellowhammer's most important winter-feeding habitat, stubble fields (Historical Atlas). A reduction in weed densities may have also reduced feeding opportunities at other times of year.

Outside the breeding season, Yellowhammers make local movements to new feeding areas with stubble fields favoured, although other agricultural land and salt marshes are used (Migration Atlas). These movements may result in the formation of large flocks where food is plentiful and these are often mixed and contain finches and sparrows. The general pattern of decline in the breeding population has not apparently been matched by a decline in the number of three-figure wintering flocks, their occurrence being rather random, although the largest number of counts were noted in the cold winters of 1978/79 and 1985/86, perhaps suggesting that flock sizes increased in response to cold weather and a reduction in food supplies.

The largest flock reported from Essex was 500 at Twinstead on 20th January 1983. Other counts of 200+ have come from: Old Hall, 270 on 30th December 1975; Fryerning, 250 on 7th February 1980; Rainham, 250 on 25th January 1982; Hanningfield, 250+ on 7th

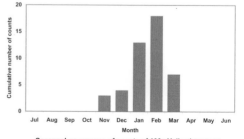

Seasonal occurrence of counts of 100+ Yellowhammers
from 1971-2004

January 1983; Old Hall, 211 on 7th January 1986; East Mersea, 200 on 1st November 1988; Holliwell Point, 300+ on 25th February 1990; Little Bromley, 200 on 31st March 1996; West Bergholt, 200 on 27th March 2000; and Great Notley, 310 on 19th January 2001. Most large flocks have been reported during January (30%) and February (41%) with all falling in the period November to March.

Although not reported in recent years, a small-scale passage was sometimes evident along the Essex coast at times when other passerines were moving in large numbers (Cox). In 1955 three flew in off the sea at The Naze with Chaffinches on 30th October. On 27th October 1957 a southwesterly coasting movement at Holland Haven included up to 100, whilst at the same locality in 1959 Yellowhammers were moving through at around 50 per hour on 25th October. Also in 1959 a northwesterly passage was noted along the Lea Valley in early November. Remarkably, 1959 was the last year in which any movements were reported in the *EBR*. In recent years, despite greater observer coverage at coastal sites, Yellowhammers have very rarely been observed making obvious passage movements.

Of 19 Yellowhammers ringed in Essex and subsequently recovered, 17 had remained within the county with 14 having moved no more than 10km. The furthest movement involved one ringed at Bradwell on 31st March 1961 and found dead at Spalding, Lincolnshire, on 21st April 1963. Nationally, 95% of all recoveries are within 25km of the ringing site (Migration Atlas). Small numbers of Continental birds are known to pass down the east coast (Taylor *et al.* 1999, Piotrowski 2003).

The Yellowhammer's marked decline over the last 20 years or so has resulted from a combination of factors caused by modern farming methods, which have largely been influenced by the CAP, the reform of which will be fundamental to turning around the species' decline. The RSPB is leading the way in testing wildlife-friendly farming methods, as well as addressing issues of global warming, GM crops and organic farming which hoped by 2006 to have secured at least 25% of CAP subsidies for supporting wildlife friendly farming (Jameson 2000). Unfortunately this did not materialise. In the meantime, feeding stations may be a stop-gap measure. There have been signs of a slight reversal of fortune in recent years; it is to be hoped that this trend continues.

Sponsored by Martin Henry

Cirl Bunting   *Emberiza cirlus*

Vagrant: 16 records involving 22 individuals—bred in 1910 and 1913   **Red List**

The Cirl Bunting is a southwestern Palearctic species, with a breeding range broadly south of a line running south-southeast from south Wales through Strasbourg, southwest Hungary and northeast Bulgaria and into northwest Turkey, including northwest Africa and the larger Mediterranean islands (European Atlas). The species is typical of lightly forested and other similar semi-open habitats (Byers *et al.* 1995). The nominate race *cirlus* occurs over much of its range. In the northwest of its range, the species has declined dramatically over the last 30–40 years. The British population has, however, after 50 years of severe decline, begun to slowly increase again thanks to local conservation measures, although the 697 territories in 2003 were restricted to Devon (Wotton *et al.* 2004).

Glegg detailed two nesting records, both from Felsted in 1910 and 1913, where nests with 3–4 eggs were found. As Christy detailed just four records, two being somewhat vague, it appeared that the Cirl Bunting had colonised at least this area since his time; Felsted School had an active naturalists' club and it therefore seems unlikely that the species had been overlooked before then. These breeding records coincided with the species' maximum recorded breeding range in Britain, following a period of significant expansion. Between 1900 and 1939, Cirl Buntings bred in some 39 counties and it is possible that there were as many as 10,000 pairs in Britain (Evans 1997).

Apart from the breeding records, the species has been no more than a vagrant to Essex and all other records are detailed below. They include a previously unpublished record of one shot in Essex in 1888 and now in the Liverpool Museum (Accession No. T11681). It should be noted that whilst Hudson & Pyman cited 15 records, involving 22 birds in 12 years between 1946 and 1966 (repeated by Cox), these totals do not agree with the nine records involving 13 individuals published in the *EBR*s and no other records have been located in other publications.

1854	Latchingdon	Undated	Shot
about 1885	Thaxted	Undated	Shot
1888	Essex	Undated	Shot

1910	Wrabness	4th June	Male
1946	North Fambridge	28th June	Two males
1952	Great Totham	24th July	Male and female
1953	Strethall	18th January	Two males
1954	Stansted	28th January	Two males
1955	Strethall	14th April	Male
1957	Bridgemarsh Island	29th December	Male
1960	Takeley	11th December	Male
1961	Potter Street, Harlow	5th April	Male
1963	The Naze	3rd November	Male
1978	North Ockendon	7th May–10th July	Male

Two females may have also been present with the male at Bridgemarsh Island in 1957. In addition, Christy mentioned one "believed" to have been a Cirl Bunting at Middleton about 1832 and another undated (but perhaps during the 1880s) occurrence involving one heard near Saffron Walden. Neither record can be considered satisfactory.

The 1978 individual held three different territories but was apparently never paired.

Ortolan Bunting   *Emberiza hortulana*

Very rare passage migrant: 24 records involving 24 individuals

The monotypic Ortolan Bunting has a generally western Palearctic distribution and occurs throughout mainland Europe, although it is absent from coastal western Europe and larger Mediterranean islands. The species typically inhabits open, relatively dry and sunny areas with shrubs and sparse trees (Byers *et al.* 1995). Ortolan Buntings are long-distance migrants wintering in sub-Saharan Africa. The population over much of western Europe has been declining since the 1950s and perhaps more rapidly since the 1980s, the cause probably being modern farming practices.

1908	Plaistow	6th May	Male
1957	The Naze	6th October	1st-winter
1958	Weald CP	17th May	Male
1973	Hanningfield	1st May	Male
1977	Bradwell	1st May	Male
	Foulness	24th September	Immature male
	Bradwell	17th October	Female
1979	Two Tree Island	29th October	Female
1981	The Naze	7th May	
1983	Leez	29th August	Female or immature
1984	Heybridge GP	3rd May	
1985	Goldhanger	5th October	Female
1986	Pitsea	20th August	Probably male
1992	Stanford-le-Hope	26th September	Male
1996	KGV	3rd September	Probably 1st-year
1997	Bradwell	14th May	
	The Naze	24th August	Adult female
2000	White City, Foulness	20th August	Juvenile
2001	The Naze	22nd September	1st-winter
2003	Cob Fields, Sewardstone	3rd September	Immature
		28th September–1st October	Two immatures
		29th September	Three immatures
		4th October	Immature
2004	St Osyth	12th September	Immature

There is a wide geographic spread of records, with eight (33%) having come from inland locations, although this includes the exceptional series of records from Sewardstone in 2003, which was not just the only multiple occurrence involving four individuals, but also the only occasion that Ortolan Buntings have remained for more than a day. After an upsurge of records between the 1970s and mid-1980s, the species became rare during the 1990s, although there appears to have been an upturn during the 2000s; numbers recorded nationally are apparently increasing (Fraser & Rogers 2004), despite continuing declines on the Continent.

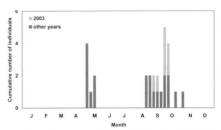

Seasonal occurrence of Ortolan Buntings from 1908-2004

Seven of the records have fallen in May with the remainder occurring in autumn. Spring records probably involve Scandinavian drift migrants, whilst those in autumn may involve either Scandinavian migrants or perhaps dispersing individuals from further south (Cottridge & Vinicombe 1996). Nationally, spring records used to outnumber autumn ones but this pattern has now reversed (Fraser & Rogers 2000), with numbers peaking in September; annual totals averaged around 71 per annum during the 1990s (Fraser & Rogers 2002).

Rustic Bunting   *Emberiza rustica*

Vagrant: one record

The Rustic Bunting breeds across the entire European and Asian boreal zone (European Atlas) where the species inhabits the margins between damp Spruce, Pine or Birch forests (Byers *et al.* 1995). European populations are of the nominate race *rustica*. The species winters in eastern China, Korea and Japan.

1966	Bradwell	18th September	Female

The Rustic Bunting is an annual vagrant to Britain with 445 records to the end of 2004 (BBRC 2005), although only small numbers reach the southeast and East Anglia. Nationally, there has been a significant increase in records in the last decade, despite apparent declines in the Finnish population, following significant increases in Fennoscandian populations that began at the end of the 19th century and that largely stabilised during the mid-20th century (European Atlas). Another county record seems long overdue. Nationally, autumn occurrences span the period late August to mid-November and peak in October, whilst small numbers are recorded in spring. A few have wintered.

Little Bunting   *Emberiza pusilla*

Vagrant: six records

The monotypic Little Bunting breeds in the subarctic and boreal zones of Scandinavia east to the Pacific where it inhabits the moist open taiga with undergrowth of Dwarf Birch and Willow as well as more open tundra habitat (Byers *et al.* 1995). The species winters in Nepal and northwest India, east to southern China and southeast Asia.

1892	Southchurch/Shoeburyness	September	Female, caught
1965	The Naze	5th October	
1987	East Mersea	25th October	
1989	Holland Haven	12th October	1st-winter, ringed
1994	Pitsea	29th October	
1995	Roman River Valley	13th March–14th April	

As with the Rustic Bunting, there has been a marked increase in records in recent years, linked to a westward range expansion in Fennoscandia during the late 20th century. However, it is far more common than the Rustic Bunting and was removed from the BBRC List in 1993 when there had been over 620 records. Nationally, the species averaged 29 records annually during the 1990s (Fraser & Rogers 2004), most occurring along the east coast. It is typically an autumn migrant with records peaking around early October. However, there has been an increasing trend towards winter and spring records, presumably involving the previous autumn's arrivals.

Yellow-breasted Bunting   *Emberiza aureola*

Vagrant: one record

The Yellow-breasted Bunting breeds widely across Russia and Siberia to Kamchatka and southern northeast China and northeast Hokkaido, Japan. There is a small but declining population in central Finland. The nominate race *aureola* occurs from Kamtchatka west. The species winters locally from eastern Nepal through the Himalayan foothills to northeast India and widely in southeast Asia.

2002	Colne Point	5th September	1st-winter

A total of 227 Yellow-breasted Buntings had occurred in Britain to the end of 2004 (BBRC 2005), with 66% on the Shetland Islands. The Essex record was, however, not unexpected as the species has occurred almost annually in recent years: there are four records from Norfolk and singles from Suffolk and Kent (Taylor *et al.* 1999, Piotrowski 2003, BBRC 2005).

Reed Bunting   *Emberiza schoeniclus*

Common but declined resident, passage migrant and winter visitor   Red List

The Reed Bunting has an extensive Palearctic distribution, where it occurs as several distinctive subspecies; nine of the 20 or so recognised races occur in Europe. One of the most widely distributed buntings, it ranges from western Europe east to Japan and Sakhalin Island, and from the subarctic to the warm continental zone of central Asia. The nominate race *schoeniclus* occurs over much of northern Europe. Reed Buntings inhabit dense low vegetation types, usually near still or running water. Marked declines have occurred across Britain and northwest Europe since around 1970 (European Atlas). In Britain, the species is fairly widespread although absent from most areas of high ground (Second National Atlas). Northernmost populations are migratory.

Historically, prior to the large-scale drainage of the marshy areas of Essex, there was probably a significantly greater amount of suitable habitat for the Reed Bunting than today, although some of the destruction would have been offset by the construction of reservoirs and gravel-pits that have subsequently flooded (Historical Atlas).

It appears that the Reed Bunting's status altered very little from the 19th century until the 1980s. Christy said very little about its status, other than noting that it was "A fairly-common resident throughout the county, especially in those parts which are more or less marshy". Glegg likewise described it as "... a common resident breeding freely throughout the county wherever suitable nesting quarters may be found along the rivers, in the vicinity of ponds, lakes and reservoirs, and along the reed-fringed fleets of the marshes of the coast".

Hudson & Pymans' description of the Reed Bunting's status was very similar, however. They noted "... a few pairs nest in dry situations such as are typical of the Yellowhammer". This behaviour, first noted in the 1950s in Essex, was part of a general move into drier habitats across the country, which was perhaps a response to intraspecific competition caused by the reduction in wetlands, as well as a reduction in interspecific competition resulting from the decline of the Yellowhammer (First National Atlas). It is also possible that high Reed Bunting populations simply spilled into sub-optimal habitat. In Essex, Reed Buntings were found breeding in uncultivated fields, young conifer plantations and more recently in Oil-seed Rape fields where in some areas during the Essex Atlas survey at least one pair could be found in every field.

Atlas	Survey Area	% of 10km squares or tetrads in which bred/probably bred	possibly bred or present
First National 10km	Essex	98.2	1.8
Second National 10km	Essex	94.7	3.5
First London Tetrad	Met. Essex	45.0	9.5
Second London Tetrad	Met. Essex	56.5	15.5
Essex Tetrad	Essex	44.0	14.5

Summary of results of Atlas surveys for Reed Buntings

Up until the early 1980s the Reed Bunting was still a common resident (Cox). The First and Second National Atlas surveys recorded Reed Buntings breeding in almost every 10km square with only a very marginal change in distribution between the two. Comparison of the two London Atlases pointed to a decline in northern Metropolitan Essex and an increase in the south with, overall, a move away from farmland and into suburban areas. The Essex Atlas survey located Reed Buntings in 58.5% of all tetrads with breeding confirmed in 44% and, although widespread, the species was at its commonest along the coast and major river valleys, being absent only from urban areas. It was also absent from large areas of farmland across Essex.

From around the late 1970s, anecdotal evidence and data from local CBCs confirmed that a decline in breeding numbers had begun. From 1981–99 the local CBC Index fell by some 60%, with CBC/BBS (England) Indices falling 52% between 1977 and 2002. Much of the decline occurred during the late 1970s to early 1980s, with a smaller 5% fall being noted in the BBS (England) Indices from 1994–2003.

Within Essex, this pattern of general decline appears to be less clear with anecdotal evidence suggesting falls in some areas, stability in others and small gains elsewhere; recent local BBS data point to a relatively stable position overall since the mid-1990s. At Langenhoe, 26 pairs in 1982 had increased to 86 in 1988, with 63 in 1992, 68 in 1995 but just 38 in 2003. At Old Hall, numbers during the 1990s and early 2000s appear to have remained fairly constant at around 60–70 pairs. Few other sites have been surveyed for a sufficient period to pass comment; there were 71 territories across Rainham in 2003. Reed Buntings are known to be sensitive to cold winters with extensive snow cover (Second National Atlas) and it is likely that, in the 1970s and 1980s at least, cold winters were responsible for some of the short-term reductions in numbers. However, the species is frequently double-brooded and recovery is often quite rapid.

Reed Bunting declines on farmland after the mid-1970s coincided with an increase in the use of herbicides for weed control (O'Connor & Shrubb 1986) and, though the species shows a strong association with Oil-seed Rape, this is not available during winter. A lack of food during winter may therefore be the cause and circumstantial corroborative evidence has come from the BTO's Garden Bird Survey, which showed a major and continuing increase in winter use of gardens for feeding during the 1980s.

Annual number of sites with counts of 50+ Reed Buntings from 1971/72-2002/03

Cox noted that the WBS showed an average of three pairs per km but that along the Stort (part Essex and Hertfordshire) densities of up to ten pairs per km occurred. Since 1980, densities of up to three pairs per km have been noted along the Chelmer and Roding, whilst on a handful of farmland CBC plots densities have averaged 1–2 pairs per km^2.

After the breeding season, sizeable roosts used to build up in coastal borrow dykes. By far the largest was some 1,500 at Sales Point, Dengie, on 22nd October 1976 (Cox). This built up from 300 during August with 800 in September. After October, numbers declined to 800 in November and 250 in December. An estimated 400+ roosted in reeds bordering a lake in Thorndon CP on 21st October 1967.

In winter, large concentrations used to form in association with finches and sparrows on agricultural land or on coastal marshes where seeds (or spilt grain) occurred (Cox). A total of 320 was present along the Crouch on 12th January 1982, whilst there were 225 during February and 230 in March 1986 at Old Hall. The largest flocks of Reed Buntings tend to occur in mid-winter. The number of large flocks reported outside the breeding season have fallen in line with that in the breeding population.

Small numbers are recorded regularly on diurnal passage in autumn. Remarkably *EBRs* did not detail any movements until 2000. Christy had commented that the Reed Bunting was "… to some extent migratory". The full extent of such movements is therefore unclear and requires further data. Although these movements probably involve some local birds, national ringing recoveries have shown that a very small number of Scandinavian and even smaller numbers of Finnish Reed Buntings winter in Britain with

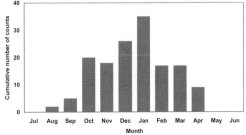

Seasonal occurrence of counts of 50+ Reed Buntings from 1971-2004

greater numbers moving down the east coast to winter in France and perhaps the Low Countries (Migration Atlas). Movements in recent years have often coincided with arrivals of other Fennoscandian migrants such as Chaffinches and Redwings.

In spring there is little national evidence for return migration to Scandinavia (Migration Atlas). However, in Essex at least at the time of high populations a conspicuous inland movement occurred from around the end of February to early April. This movement was particularly noticeable around the main reservoirs and almost entirely involved males (Cox). The highest count was 350 at Hanningfield on 1st April 1980. The trapping of Reed Buntings at winter roosts in central and southern England revealed sex ratios markedly biased in favour of males (Migration Atlas). Very few are now reported.

There have been four ringing recoveries linking Essex with the Continent, three from Belgium and one from Norway. The Norwegian bird was ringed as a juvenile at Fiskumvannet, Buskerud, on 23rd August 1983 and found dead at Loughton on 30th January 1984, a movement of 1,082km southwest. Of a further 90 Essex-ringed Reed Buntings that were subsequently reported, 85 had remained within 100km of the ringing site. Of the remainder, the longest movement involved one ringed at Abberton on 29th August 1985 and recovered at Winchester, Hampshire, 170km to the west-southwest on 7th March 1986. There have been far fewer Reed Buntings ringed during the 1990s and no recent recoveries of note. Small numbers of Reed Buntings will make movements to milder areas outside the breeding season (Migration Atlas).

Although the Reed Bunting has declined generally over the last 20 years or so, it has remained common and appears to be holding its own at many of the principal wetland sites in Essex. Breeding in drier areas seems largely to have been abandoned during the same period. Although the exact reasons for the declines remain unclear, it seems that, like many other birds, it is suffering due to reductions in winter seed availability caused by agricultural change.

Black-headed Bunting   *Emberiza melanocephala*

Vagrant: three records

The monotypic Black-headed Bunting breeds from Italy across into the Balkans and east to Iran, as well as around the Black Sea and Caspian Sea. It occurs in open areas with scattered trees, scrub and hedges (Byers *et al.* 1995) and winters in western and central India.

1979	West Mersea	7th May	Male
1986	Colne Point	5th–9th June	Male
1998	Two Tree Island	13th May	Singing male

Up to the end of 2004 there had been 175 British records (BBRC 2005), many of which were males. The species typically occurs as an overshooting spring migrant during May and June but may appear right through to October. Large numbers used to be imported into Britain and early records must be tainted with the escape possibility. However, it is now generally accepted that most individuals, and particularly spring vagrants, are genuine as there has been no decline in the number of occurrences since imports were banned in 1984 (Evans 1994).

Corn Bunting   *Emberiza calandra*

Locally common but much declined resident   Red List

This, the largest European bunting, is distributed from the Canary Islands in the west to 83° E in central Asia and from north-central Europe south to north Africa and southeast to Iran and Iraq. The nominate race *calandra* occurs throughout much of Europe, although the race *clanceyi* occurs in western Ireland and western Scotland. In the north of its range it is generally confined to farmland where it prefers cereals and hay meadows in many areas. Alarming declines have been noted across much of its range, including Britain since the 1950s (European Atlas), where the species has a patchy distribution in eastern England and Scotland (Second National Atlas). Although mainly sedentary, some east European populations are migratory, and central European ones are partially so (European Atlas).

From Christy's description of the Corn Bunting as "… local and not abundant" and the comments of several of his correspondents, it appeared that the Corn Bunting might have declined during the latter part of the 19th century. In 1929 Glegg described the species as a "… local resident, with a peculiarly restricted distribution". He added "It would appear that the species is decreasing". It was at this time largely restricted to the coast, Glegg noting "It might have been better to have said that it is found in Essex in the immediate vicinity of salt water for its thin line of distribution extends for some distance inland along each of the estuaries". Thus, he was aware of the Corn Bunting's presence as far up the Thames as Pitsea, the Crouch to Burnham, the Blackwater to Lawlings Creek, the Colne to Fingringhoe Wick and the Stour to Manningtree. Even in these areas, Glegg considered that the species was not common, although on Foulness, and perhaps between Walton and Harwich "… it approached commonness". Only in one inland locality did Corn Buntings

Atlas	Survey Area	% of 10km squares or tetrads in which bred/probably bred	possibly bred or present
First National 10km	Essex	93.0	1.8
Second National 10km	Essex	73.7	12.3
First London Tetrad	Met. Essex	11.5	3.0
Second London Tetrad	Met. Essex	18.0	8.0
Essex Tetrad	Essex	27.3	4.4

Summary of results of Atlas surveys for Corn Buntings

approach the abundance seen near to the coast, in the far northwest on the chalk uplands between Chrishall and Strethall. It is interesting to observe that Ticehurst (1909) noted that, apart from coastal areas, Corn Buntings were only found on the chalk in inland Kent. Elsewhere inland the species was scarce. The decline observed by Christy and Glegg mirrored the national trend, perhaps caused by the long-term agricultural depression that saw a 42% reduction in the total cereal acreage in Britain between 1875 and 1938 (Donald *et al.* 1994).

Around 1940, the national population stabilised (Historical Atlas), whilst Hudson & Pyman noted "… it increased considerably during the 1940s and 1950s". During this period, the populations that had been restricted to the vicinity of the estuaries spread up along the river valleys and then into the intervening areas to become thinly populous over most agricultural land. However, its stronghold remained along the coast and estuaries, particularly in the Dengie and Rochford Hundreds.

From around 1960 there appeared to be a reduction in breeding density, although the range seemed unaffected and the species remained widespread and locally common (Hudson & Pyman). The declines appeared to have been short-lived in most areas and were perhaps linked to the use of organochlorines as seed dressings. The subsequent 20 years or so saw a period of apparent stability in numbers. A summary of the Corn Bunting's status during 1980–82 (*EBR* 1982) confirmed that the species remained widespread but patchily distributed throughout Essex. In the northwest, the species was described as numerous, whilst in the north and northeast it was scarce between the Stour and The Naze but more numerous further south, especially in the St Osyth area. It was also common around the Colne Estuary and the north Blackwater as well as inland at Abberton. Dengie was considered the Corn Bunting's stronghold; there it was common along the south Blackwater and north Crouch, although here it was only found within a few kilometres of the coast. In central Essex the Corn Bunting was relatively common in a triangle that ran from Writtle south to Blackmore and across to Mountnessing. In the south and southeast it was widespread, especially along the Thames and Crouch and in Metropolitan Essex.

Nationally, the species began to become more scarce again during the early 1980s (Second National Atlas), the ensuing decline having been severe: an 88% reduction in the CBC/BBS (England) Index occurred between 1977 and 2002 with a 33% reduction in the BBS (England) from 1994–2003. However, even as late as 1990 the *EBR* commented "So far there is little evidence … of the steep decline that has taken place nationally during the last decade…". Indeed, it was not until the *EBR* 1994 that there was any suggestion that numbers were falling in Essex. However, comparison of the two National Atlases suggests that the range of the Corn Bunting in Essex was already contracting during 1988–92, the Second National Atlas survey noting that the species had disappeared from nine 10km squares that it was breeding in during 1968–72. Increases occurred in Metropolitan Essex between the two London Atlas surveys, particularly in the south; improved observer coverage may have been a factor, however.

The Essex Atlas survey located the Corn Bunting in 31.7% of all tetrads, with breeding confirmed in 27.3%. The species' stronghold remained around the coast on farmland adjacent to the main estuaries with Dengie particularly favoured. Some inland areas still held good numbers but many populations were by now isolated.

By the turn of the 21st century, the range appears to have contracted back to the original coastal strongholds but with a remnant inland population surviving in the northwest.

Cox noted that Essex farmland CBC plots averaged four pairs per km², the highest density being 17 territories in 97ha at Maldon in 1972.

Mason & Macdonald (2000b) carried out a detailed study of Corn Buntings over a five-year period in the Tendring District from 1994–98. A total of 278 singing males was located in 247km² of predominantly intensively cultivated arable farmland. This represented some 2–3% of the UK population. Mean densities on individual study plots within the Tendring District ranged from 8–15 territories per km², amongst the highest in northwest Europe, although there was evidence of a continuing decline over the study period. They concluded that food availability in winter, especially loss of winter stubble, was an important factor.

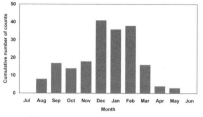

Seasonal occurrence of counts of 100+ Corn Buntings from 1971-2004

BBO carried out a survey of Dengie in 2003; in all 165 territories were located, almost all within 3km of the coast/river on large arable fields with hedgerows; the only limiting factor appeared to be song posts.

During winter, large flocks of Corn Buntings may form. Given the extremely sedentary nature of the species, the size and number of these flocks probably give a very good overall indication of the health of the breeding population (Cox). However, counts at a particular site should not be taken as an indication of the health of a population in a particular area as birds often occupy sites for several years then switch slowly to another locality. At Bradwell for example, where some of the largest counts have been made at a roost on the saltings near St Peter's Chapel since 1953, numbers peaked at 450–500 in 1955 only to fall away to 40–50 during the mid-1960s. By 1969 the peak had reached 400 but then declined to 200 in 1973 and remained at that level until the largest county site total of 650 was reported in September 1982; since then the site maxima have varied from 250 in 1992 to 100 in 1997. At no time was there evidence of rises and falls in the population in the immediate area but there was evidence of new roosts being utilised on Dengie. The number of flocks

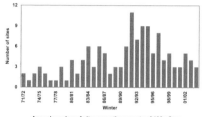

Annual number of sites reporting counts of 100+ Corn Buntings from 1971/72-2003/04

of 100+ reported annually declined since the mid-1990s, although greater interest in the species because of the range contraction may mean that more large flocks are now reported. Almost without exception, the largest flocks have been reported from the coastal strip where the Corn Bunting appears to have always been numerous. The largest counts have come from the Bradwell roost with counts in excess of 300 away from there coming from: Langenhoe, up to 350 in January and February 1995; Dengie, 340 on 26th August 1967; Crouch, 443 on 13th March 1994; South Woodham Ferrers, 495 going to roost on 12th February 1999 and 417 roosting on 26th February 1994; Foulness, 410 on 14th March 1976; and Rainham, 600 on 17th January 1987, with perhaps double the number present over the entire area. Three-figure counts have, however, been noted from many sites around the entire Essex coast, although only from the northwest have there been any large inland flocks, the most recent being 100 at Chrishall Grange on 16th April 1995. Large flocks become most numerous during the period December to February, building to a peak in February before declining rapidly during March. There is also a smaller peak during September.

British and Irish Corn Buntings appear to be largely resident (Migration Atlas). Occasionally Corn Buntings are noted passing through with other migrants along the Essex coast during autumn, although their origin is not known. There is some evidence, however, for some limited dispersal away from breeding areas in winter. One individual, recovered at Faversham, Kent, in January 1958 had been ringed 50km away the previous May at Abberton; this is the longest proven movement made by a British Corn Bunting.

The drastic fall in the population of Corn Buntings in Essex is part of a wider decline across Britain and Europe that appears, at least in this country, to be linked to the loss of winter stubbles and hence feeding. Mason & Macdonald (2000b) considered that the retention of winter stubbles on farmland destined for spring sowing could be highly beneficial to Corn Bunting populations and that initially it could be targeted at those areas with the densest breeding populations. Clearly this will require overhauling the CAP and the redirection of grants towards environmentally friendly farming, something that is finally beginning to happen. Although the Corn Bunting is unlikely to become extinct in Essex, it is equally unlikely that its numbers are ever going to return to the levels seen in the 1950s and 1960s without such measures being in place.

Sponsored by Martin Henry

Rose-breasted Grosbeak   *Pheuticus ludovicianus*

Vagrant: one record

The monotypic Rose-breasted Grosbeak breeds across southern Canada and the northeast of the USA where it breeds in wooded lowlands favouring edges between stands of tall trees and thickets (*BWP*). The species winters in Central America and northern South America.

1975/76	Leigh-on-Sea	20th December–4th January	Immature male

There have been 20 British records of this Nearctic vagrant, the last in 2001 (BBRC 2002). This was the second British record, the first from the east coast and the only December record, all others having occurred in the period late September to early November and mainly on the Isles of Scilly. All were immatures, many being males. This one fed at a garden bird table.

The autumn of 1975 was exceptional for American land birds and there was another European record that year, on Sark, Channel Islands, in September. This one may have arrived on the west coast earlier in the autumn and then moved east or possibly came ashore from a ship from North America as it sailed up the Thames Estuary. However, the species was also kept in captivity, so the escape possibility cannot be entirely ruled out (Cox).

Baltimore Oriole   *Icterus galbula*

Vagrant: one record

The monotypic Baltimore Oriole breeds in eastern Canada and the eastern United States west to a line from central Alberta to northeast Texas and winters south to northwest South America (*BWP*).

1992	Westcliff-on-Sea	1st February–24th March	1st-winter male

This individual may have been present in back gardens in Westcliff since 2nd December 1991.

There have been 22 British records, the last in the winter of 2003/04; this was the 18th and is the only east coast record. It is one of three that have wintered; in the USA small numbers use feeding stations to survive the winters as far north as New York (Jackson 1993).

A mounted specimen in the Chelmsford and Essex Museum (Accession No. D6267) has recently been accepted as the first British record by BOURC (Pennington *et al.* 2004) and involved one shot on the Shetland Islands on 26th September 1890.

APPENDIX 1
CATEGORY D SPECIES

White Pelican (Great White Pelican)   *Pelecanus onocrotalus*

Five records involving four individuals

The northern populations of the monotypic White Pelican breed from eastern Europe to western Mongolia and winter in northeast Africa and Iraq, east to northern India. (*HBW*).

1975	Hanningfield	16th July	
1996	Shoebury	6th December	
1999	Cattawade	26th April and 8th–22nd August	
	Manningtree	19th August,	Same as previous
2000	Fairlop CP	10th–12th November	

The 1999 individual was later reported from the Netherlands and Germany. A typical 'zoo' species, the White Pelican is usually considered an escape from captivity and some probably go unreported; vagrancy from their eastern European or Asian breeding grounds is, however, a possibility.

Greater Flamingo   *Phoenicopterus roseus*

Thirteen records of 15 individuals

The Greater Flamingo breeds in widely separated areas throughout southern Europe, central and southwest Asia, Africa and the Caribbean. The nominate race *roseus* occurs throughout most of its range. Christy mentioned one on the Essex coast in 1873 that was subsequently shot on the Isle of Sheppey, Kent, on 16th August. It was thought to have escaped from London Zoo on 16th July 1873. Glegg mentioned three further records of singles: shot at Bradwell, September 1909; near Tollesbury, May 1910; and shot off Bridgemarsh Island, 23rd September 1913. All these early records appear to have been poorly documented and failed to eliminate other flamingo species. All records since 1950 are:

1963 Stanford-le-Hope, a heavily oiled individual on 26th January, died the next day—probably an escape; *1964* Hanningfield, one of the New World races from 2nd–19th August and Havengore/Foulness, one from 18th October–15th November, "…a markedly pale bird"; *1970* Hanningfield, one on 4th September was considered an escape; *1972* Hanningfield, one on 13th February had escaped from Colchester Zoo; *1976* Hanningfield, three on 29th October; *1986* Paglesham, one on 4th October; *1994, intermittently into 1997* mainly East Tilbury (it was more regular at Cliffe, Kent) but also seen off Canvey, at Abberton and Old Hall—it associated with a Chilean Flamingo; *2003–2004* Colne/Blackwater 9th–15th December and into new year

The species almost certainly goes unrecorded because of its escape status: many flamingos are kept in captivity, although the majority in Britain appear to be either Chilean Flamingos *P. chilensis* or the Caribbean race *ruber* of Greater Flamingo. There has been much speculation about recent national occurrences; an extensive colour-ringing programme in Spain and The Camargue may yet provide the necessary evidence to add the species to the British List. However, none of the Essex records appear to have the credentials of a true wild vagrant.

Falcated Duck   *Anas falcata*

Two records

The monotypic Falcated Duck is found in southeast Siberia and Mongolia to Kuril Island and northern Japan and winters mainly in eastern Asia.

1994	Old Hall	16th January and 11th April	Male

2000	Connaught Water	26th August	Female

In 1993 the BOURC reviewed the species' status and concluded, "... whilst the possibility of escape cannot be excluded, neither can natural origin, although the latter seems unlikely" (*Ibis* 135: 493–499). The second record almost certainly involved an escape but the first had better credentials. Both times it was observed it was with Wigeon and may have departed with them; in the wild it often associates with that species (Madge & Burn 1988).

Baikal Teal   *Anas formosa*

Four records involving three individuals

The monotypic Baikal Teal breeds from east Siberia through to Kamchatka and winters mainly in east and southeast China and southern Japan. Since the middle of the 18th century, the species has commonly been kept in captivity (Eldridge & Harrop 1992).

1906	Marsh House Decoy, Dengie	1st January	Immature male, shot
1970	Abberton	28th–29th November	Male
1994	Old Hall	28th May–12th June	Male
	Holland Haven	16th–19th June	Same as previous

The 1906 individual was originally thought to be a hybrid but at a meeting of the BOC its true identity was confirmed (Glegg). At the time it was considered an escape. The mounted specimen is in Chelmsford Museum (Accession No. E9108).

The Baikal Teal was moved from Category D to A in 1980 (Wallace 1981) and then, following a review by the BOURC (*Ibis* 135: 495), back to D in 1993. Despite the generally held view that birds are of captive origin, a pattern of winter occurrences exists across Europe (Cottridge & Vinicombe 1996).

Booted Eagle   *Aquila pennatus*

One record

The monotypic Booted Eagle is found across the southern Palearctic and north Africa and winters south of sub-Saharan Africa and in southeast Asia and India.

2000	East Tilbury	8th April

This was a well-documented traveller, which all too briefly dropped into Essex, having also been seen across the Thames at Cliffe, Kent. All records were recently reviewed by the BOURC with the result that all were considered to be escapes.

Saker (Saker Falcon)   *Falco cherrug*

Eight records

The Saker is widespread from central Europe to western Russia and central Asia and north Africa. The nominate race *cherrug* occurs in Europe and Iran east to central Siberia.

1984–87	Pitsea		"Sid"
1991/92	Bridgemarsh Island/Crouch	28th November-19th April	
1996	Salcott	4th July	
2001	Holyfield Marsh	9th September	

2002	Dagenham	20th January
2003	Abberton	11th January
	Mundon/Tollesbury Wick	4th May
	Colne Point	1st October

Sakers are a favoured falconer's bird and are regularly used for scaring birds from rubbish-tips, airfields, etc.

Red-headed Bunting   *Emberiza bruniceps*

Five records

The monotypic Red-headed Bunting breeds in dry, relatively open country from Iran and Kazakhstan east to Mongolia and northwest China and winters in the Indian subcontinent. Large numbers were kept in captivity during the 1960s but far fewer are kept today (Evans 1994).

1958	The Naze	14th September	Male
1962	Colchester	29th April	Male
1964	Abberton	30th April and 5th May	Male
1993	The Naze	29th May–7th June	Male
2002	Lawford	21st–22nd May	Male

Despite the decline in numbers kept in captivity, the species continues to turn up with many occurring in the spring at the same time as records of its very close relative, the Black-headed Bunting, peak (Cottridge & Vinicombe 1996). Some must surely be vagrants?

Indigo Bunting   *Passerina cyanaea*

One record

The monotypic Indigo Bunting breeds in eastern Canada and adjacent parts of southern Canada and winters in southern Florida, West Indies and central America south into northern South America. Large numbers were imported from Mexico between 1966 and 1978 (Evans 1994) but, by the end of the 1980s, the species was a rare cage-bird in this country (Simpson 1990).

| 1973 | The Naze | 8th September | Male |

Although there is one accepted Category A record, this and another five currently languish in Category D. Such an early arrival date for a truly wild individual is unlikely so this is almost certainly an escape, although it might have arrived in western Europe in the previous year.

APPENDIX 2
CATEGORY E SPECIES

Please refer to the Systematic List for records involving escapes of species that are on the British List. Also included are details of a number of attempted 19th century introductions (Christy).

Greater Rhea   *Rhea americana*

One record

Eastern South America from Brazil southwards.

1992	A120 near Stansted	21st April	one

According to BBC Radio Essex, the police chased this individual along the road.

Red-winged Tinamou   *Rhynchotus rufescens*

Attempted 19th century introduction

Central South America.
  Christy noted that "An attempt has been made by Mr. John Bateman, of Brightlingsea, to introduce into Essex a new game bird, hailing from South America, where it is known to English colonists and Spanish-speaking sportsmen as the Perdix grande... In April, 1883, Mr. Bateman imported half-a-dozen, from which, owing to accidents, only eleven were reared. Additions were made, and eleven were turned out on the marshes; ... A few are still left in the neighbouring parishes, and these were increased in the spring of 1888 by eleven more birds which were turned out of Mr. Bateman's aviaries. ...". However, they soon died out.

Dalmatian Pelican   *Pelecanus crispus*

One record

Former Yugoslavia, discontinuously east to China and wintering from Greece, east to China.

1967	Shrub End GP	29th October–8th November

Presumably this was the same individual seen later in Kent and Cornwall. Dalmatian Pelicans were probably resident in southern England until the Neolithic/Bronze Age (Harrison 1988).

Sacred Ibis   *Threskiornis oethiopicus*

Two records

Africa south of the Sahara.

1912	Danbury	about 21st August	Shot
2000	Holland Haven	January	

The 1912 individual may have been the same as one that escaped from Woburn Abbey, Buckinghamshire. The specimen was presented to Chelmsford Museum where it remains to this day (Accession No. E8766). The 2000 individual may have been the same as one seen twice at Weybread, Suffolk (Piotrowski 2003).

African Spoonbill   *Platalea alba*

One record

East and central Africa south of the Sahara.

1988	Abberton	11th September	Pair; one had been ringed

Chilean Flamingo   *Phoenicopterus chilensis*

Up to 18 individuals since 1964

Central Peru southwards to the Andes to Tierra del Fuego and east to Brazil and Uruguay.

The total includes a long-staying individual that split its time between East Tilbury and Cliffe, Kent, from 1992–96, occasionally in the company of a Greater Flamingo. Most records occur during the second half of the year with very few during the winter.

Fulvous Whistling-duck   *Dendrocygna bicolour*

Two records

Southern USA southwards to north and eastern South America.

1991	Abberton	27th August	Two
2003	Abberton	26th April–1st May	Male

White-faced Whistling-duck   *Dendrocygna viduata*

Four records involving at least four birds

South America.

1996	Fishers Green	many dates	Two
1997	Fishers Green	many dates Feb-May	
	Walthamstow	21st April	
2002	Connaught Water	27th January	

White-backed Duck   *Thalassornis leuconotos*

One record

Central Africa and much of south and east Africa.

2002	Hooks Marsh	5th–6th October

Black Swan   *Cygnus atratus*

Very small feral population, probably not self-sustaining

Most of Australia, Tasmania and introduced to New Zealand.

Ornamental birds have been present in Britain since 1791 and have regularly escaped. The first Essex record involved one shot on Mersea Island on 10th June 1864, which was followed by four additional 19th century records (Christy, Glegg). The next documented records were in 1966, prior to which the species presumably went unrecorded, and the mid-1980s, since when a small population has established. Breeding first occurred in 1988, when a pair bred on the Colne at Colchester, although the nest was washed out. Subsequently, breeding has been noted on six occasions: Clockhouse Garden Ponds, 1998; Audley End, 2000 and 2003; Abberton, 2001, 2002 and possibly in 2004; and Hanningfield, 2001.

Overall, numbers increased steadily during the 1990s but have fallen during the 2000s. Most records involve 1–2 birds. However, there were nine at Hanningfield from August–October 2000 and six at Walthamstow during May 2003.

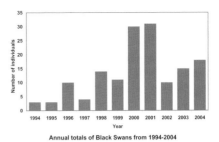

Annual totals of Black Swans from 1994-2004

Black-necked Swan   *Cygnus melanocorypha*

Four records involving 3–4 birds

Southern South America and the Falkland Islands.

1981	Abberton	29th October
1993	Nazeing GP	24th October
1998	KGV/Girling	8th May to at least 30th October
1999	KGV/Girling	19th July-30th October

Trumpeter Swan   *Cygnus buccinator*

Two records involving 2–3 birds

North Canada and northern North America.

1993	Weald CP	March	
1996	Weald CP	11th February	Two

Perhaps both records refer to wanderers from the same local collection?

Swan Goose   *Anser cygnoides*

Perhaps 4–5 residents

North central Asia.

Swan Geese, the domesticated variety of which are known as Chinese Geese, have been recorded annually since 1999 with the majority occurring on Walthamstow where there were four throughout 1999 and into early 2000; 2-3 have been resident in the general area since with 1–2 at three other sites.

Bar-headed Goose   *Anser indicus*

Very small feral population, probably not self-sustaining

Central Asia, mainly Mongolia and China.

The first documented Essex record was in 1985, one at Abberton on 30th January, although the species almost certainly occurred before then. Since then, the Bar-headed Goose has occurred annually with a small breeding colony of 1–4 pairs at Braxted Park from 1992–94 (but presumably present previously?) probably involving birds from the local collection with up to 18 on 29th June 1993 plus four Greylag hybrids.

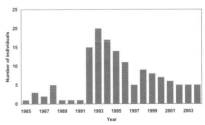

Annual totals of Bar-headed Geese from 1985-2004

Occasionally, these birds moved the short distance to Coleman's and possibly as far as Abberton, as 16 were noted at both sites during 1993. The only other breeding record came from Holyfield Lake, where one pair bred in 1999.

Away from Braxted Park/Coleman's and Abberton, most records have involved 1–2 birds, although there were nine at Walthamstow during November and December 1996. With the apparent demise of the Braxted Park colony, the number of individuals recorded annually have declined.

Snow Goose   *Anser caerulescens*

Scarce and wandering feral resident

Arctic North America, wintering in the southern states of the USA.

Glegg detailed three records: two at Leigh-on-Sea, 13th and 18th April 1911; two on marshes near Wickford, 11th May 1911; and one at Hatfield Broad Oak, 10th–14th January 1921. Although he considered the possibility of escapes, he seems to have accepted these records as genuine.

All records since 1950 have probably involved feral or escaped birds; many have been tame and long-staying individuals, usually at Abberton or in the Lea Valley. However, national records have increased markedly since 1979, corresponding to

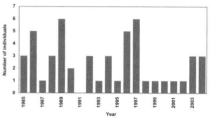

Annual totals of Snow Geese from 1985-2004

large population increases in North America (Scott 1995) and genuine vagrancy to Europe has been confirmed by the presence in the Netherlands in April 1980 of a flock of 18, one of which had been ringed near Churchill, Manitoba, Canada, in 1977 (Winter Atlas). A party of four that flew over Great Clacton on 16th April 1982 coincided with an apparent influx into East Anglia and Kent.

Six at South Woodham Ferrers on 23rd May 1997 is the largest flock recorded to date. Since the latter half of the 1990s, fewer have occurred.

Ross's Goose   *Anser rossii*

Two records

Arctic Canada in River Perry region and wintering mainly in Northern California.

1996	Abberton	November
2004	Holland Haven	9th February

Ross's Goose is a fairly close relative of the Snow Goose and, although regularly recorded in the feral state, it is a potential vagrant to Britain.

Emperor Goose   *Anser canagicus*

Small non-breeding feral population

Northeast Siberia and west Alaska, wintering mainly in the Aleutians and Alaska.

Historically, escaped Emperor Geese were poorly documented, with the first noted as recently as 1985 when singles were at Abberton on 30th January and Hamford Water on 15th December. Subsequently there have been records in 12 years with many coming from the Lea Valley where there appears to be a resident population of up to four birds. Most records have involved long-staying individuals. Ten on Horsey Island during 1994 were presumably part of the private collection there. Hybrid Emperor Geese x Barnacle Geese are noted occasionally.

Lesser Canada Goose

Branta hutchinsii

Escape

North America.

The only records involve presumed escapes of the smallest and darkest race *minima*, 'Cackling' Canada Goose, that was at Leez in October 1984 whilst it or another occurred on and off at Abberton from the late 1980s to the present day; five were reported from Hanningfield on 16th January 2004. Assumed vagrants of the races *hutchinsii*, *taverneri* and *minima* have all occurred recently in Scotland, Ireland and north Norfolk.

Hawaiian Goose

Branta sandivencis

One record

Hawaiian Islands.

1994	Braintree	12th June	Two

Blue-winged Goose

Cyanochen cyanopterus

One record

Ethiopia.

2002	Fishers Green	22nd December	

Ruddy Shelduck

Tadorna ferruginea

A regular visitor of uncertain origin

The world distribution of the monotypic Ruddy Shelduck is principally central Asian, but it stretches deep into southeast Europe where most of the population is found in the Black Sea region and in southeast Russia and Transcaucasia (European Atlas).

The species is common in captivity and the escape problem was realised as early as 1889 (Ogilvie 1892). Following a recent BOURC review, the species was retained in Category B of the British List, solely on account of an influx in 1892 (Harrop 2002), despite some fairly strong evidence that wild birds may now be occurring in Britain, albeit their origin remains uncertain (Vinicombe & Harrop 1999, Vinicombe 2004). Christy referred to one allegedly shot in the mouth of the Blackwater during the 1870s but the reference is vague. Glegg added three further records: Dedham, 14th March 1885 (rather vague); Wanstead Basin, one considered an escape, caught in 1891; Essex coast, three, two of which were shot, 1st January 1908.

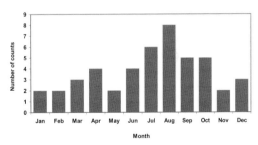

Seasonal occurrence of flocks of 3+ Ruddy Shelducks from 1966-2004

The next documented record was in 1966; the species has been recorded annually since 1980. Estimating annual numbers is difficult but in most years 1–3 have occurred. Around the late 1970s/early 1980s, however, 5–7 occurred annually and there were 5–10 during the first half of the 1990s.

It would seem that most, if not all, Essex records refer to escapes. However, many national records involve small flocks and a general absence of juveniles (Vinicombe & Harrop 1999): in Essex the prevalence of these flocks peaks in late summer at the time when influxes into western Europe might be expected (Vinicombe & Harrop 1999).

Four were at Abberton from 23rd August–3rd October 1973. In 1992, five were on Foulness on 16th September with four (part of the same flock?) at East Tilbury on 2nd October and possibly the same five in Hamford

Water from 11th–18th October. Four were at Walthamstow on 19th August 1982 and during July 1994, whilst five were there from 25th June–6th August 1995. One to two appeared to have been resident in the Lea Valley during the first half of the 1990s. Four flew south at Bradwell on 29th August 2004.

South African Shelduck   *Tadorna cana*

Over 20 records involving perhaps no more than 13 birds

Southernmost Africa.

South African or Cape Shelducks have occurred almost annually since the early 1990s. Many records since the mid-1990s occurred following the arrival of five at Maldon on 15th October 1995, which turned up at Walthamstow on 22nd October where perhaps three of the five were seen again on 22nd June 1996 with the other two back at Mundon on 15th November 1996.

Australian Shelduck   *Tadorna tadornoides*

Five records

Southwest and southeast Australia and Tasmania.

1955	Hanningfield	mid-June onwards	
1985	East Tilbury	1st week of October to mid-November at least	
1989	East Tilbury	30th September–17th November	
1997	Tollesbury Wick	21st December	
1998	Tollesbury Wick	21st December	Male

Ruddy-headed Goose   *Chloephaga rubidiceps*

One record

Southern South America and Falkland Islands.

2004	Holyfield/Cornmill Meadows	March–May

Muscovy Duck   *Cairina moschata*

Significantly under-unrecorded but probably breeds on isolated farm ponds and on lakes in country parks

Central America southwards to eastern Peru and north Uruguay.

Muscovy Ducks were first imported into England as early as 1550 (Kear 1990) and reared to produce eggs and meat. Some found their way into wildfowl collections and hybridised with other wildfowl. Records have only been documented in *EBRs* since 1999 and averaged around 3–4 annually; several appear to relate to a wandering pair. Eight in Bentley CP during 2000 is the largest documented single count.

Ringed Teal   *Callonetta leucophrys*

Fifteen records involving at least 12 birds

Central southern South America.

One to two have been recorded almost annually since 1994, including a male that appears to have been resident at Hanningfield from 2000–2004. Pairs have been noted on Connaught Water on 28th February 1997 and Abberton on 11th November 1998.

Wood Duck   *Aix sponsa*

Small feral population, probably not self-sustaining, although boosted by regular escapes

The monotypic Wood Duck is widespread through North America and winters in the southern part of its range. Although the species is commonly kept in captivity, the Wood Duck has, following declines during the early 20th century, recently increased significantly and is the most numerous breeding duck in eastern USA where there are perhaps one million birds (Madge & Burn 1988). All British records are considered to have involved escapes.

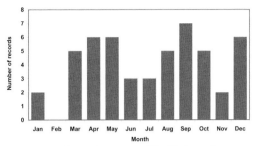

Seasonal occurrence of Wood Duck records
from 1971-2004

The earliest documented record came from Walthamstow during January 1960. Although breeding has been confirmed on just two occasions, at Hyde Lake, Ingatestone, in 1992 and at Coleman's in 2002, it seems possible that it has occurred more regularly. In recent years a small colony has existed around the Braxted Park/Coleman's area, probably deriving from the ornamental collection at the former locality and this may be the source of many records around the immediate area and as far away as Abberton where the Wood Duck is fairly regular.

Elsewhere, all but three of the records have occurred south of a line drawn between Abberton and Bishop's Stortford and usually number around 2–5 annually. Away from Braxted area, the pattern of occurrence of records shows peaks in the spring and autumn. The largest counts have come from the Braxted Park area where up to seven have been noted. Seven pinioned birds were released at Mill Green in 1992 and attracted two full-winged birds.

Chiloe Wigeon   *Anas sibilatrix*

Annual with records every year since 1991 and averaging 3–5 per annum

South America south of Central Argentina and Falkland Islands.

The most common feral duck recorded in Essex. The first documented record was in 1967 with one at Hanningfield on 3rd October. Records have been annual since 1991 all involving 1–2 birds, the majority on inland reservoirs and gravel-pits. Confusion may arise with American Wigeon. Although many are long-stayers, the pattern of occurrence shows peaks during the spring and autumn. Does the strong and instinctive urge to migrate mean more are successful at escaping at these times of year?

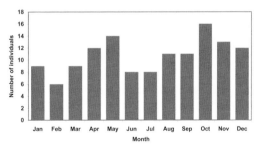

Seasonal occurrence of Chiloe Wigeons from 1967-2004

Speckled Teal   *Anas flavirostris*

Four records involving 3–4 birds

Widespread in western and southern South America.

1990	KGV	22nd July–21st September
1991	Hanningfield	15th August–22nd November
1992	Connaught Water	25th October
1993	Connaught Water	31st January

Cape Teal   *Anas capensis*

Eleven records involving at least 11 birds

Sudan and Ethiopia to Namibia and South Africa.

Cape Teals were first recorded in 1966 at Hanningfield, since when there have been records in eight years, the last in 1998. There were three at Hanningfield on 6th October 1978 and Abberton during September 1996. Other records have come from East Tilbury, Abberton, Walthamstow and Dagenham Chase.

Brown Teal   *Anas auklandica*

One record

New Zealand; rare and endangered.

2004	Wrabness	31st October

Yellow-billed Duck   *Anas undulata*

One record

Southern Sudan southwards to Cape Province.

1998	Margaretting	4th–11th January

Crested Duck   *Anas specularioides*

One record

Andes from southern Peru southwards and Falkland Islands.

1977	Hanningfield	17th April

White-cheeked Pintail   *Anas bahamensis*

One to three recorded annually

Caribbean and mainly central South America.

After Chiloe Wigeon, the White-cheeked Pintail is the commonest escaping duck. Following the first at Hanningfield on 19th September 1985, there have been records in most years since 1990, all involving singles except for two males on the Colne at Fingringhoe Wick on 27th November 1993 and a pair at Hanningfield on 8th August 1997. The pattern of occurrence shows far less of a spring/autumn bias than Chiloe Wigeon; nonetheless there are peaks at these times with very few reported during midsummer and none in June.

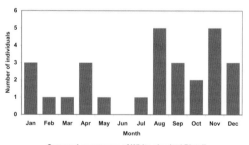

Seasonal occurrence of White-cheeked Pintail
from 1985-2004

Red-billed Duck   *Anas erythrorhyncha*

Eight records perhaps involving no more than 3–4 birds

Eastern and southern Africa.

After the first at St Osyth GP in 1973, all the remaining records have occurred since 1998 including six at Connaught Water, possibly all involving the same bird. The remaining records came from Paynes Lane GP and Basildon.

Silver Teal
Anas versicolor

Seven records involving at least six birds

Highlands of central Peru southwards including the Falkland Islands.
    Up to three have been resident on Connaught Water since 2001, with the only other records coming from there in 1988 and at Abberton in 1989 and 1996.

Hottentot Teal
Anas hottentota

Two records

Ethiopia to Cape Province and Madagascar.

1984	Hanningfield	29th March–30th April at least
2001	Warren Pond, Epping Forest	7th October

Cinnamon Teal
Anas cyanoptera

Three records

Western North America, Central America and mainly western and southern South America.

1982	Hanningfield	25th–26th April	Male
2001	Hornchurch CP	6th–29th July	Moulting male
2004	Valentines Park, Ilford	13th October	Male

Although many are kept in captivity, the Cinnamon Teal is a potential vagrant.

Red Shoveler
Anas platalea

Ten records involving at least seven birds

Southern South America from central Chile to Tierra del Fuego.
    All but one of the records have come from the Lea Valley/Epping Forest area. There were two males at KGV on 30th August 1990 and a pair on Connaught Water in 1997; all other records have been of singles.

Australian Shoveler
Anas rhynchotis

Nine records

Southwest and southeast Australia, Tasmania and New Zealand.
    All the records have occurred since 1992 with records coming from seven localities; only at Hanningfield and Walthamstow has the species occurred more than once.

Rosybill
Netta peposaca

Two records

Central South America.

2003	KGV	30th May	Two
2004	Mill Green	15th May	

Pink-eared Duck   *Malacorhynchus membranaceus*

One record

Southwest and southeast Australia.

1994	KGV	10th–16th December, also Highams Park and	
	Connaught Water.		

New Zealand Scaup   *Aythya novaeseelandia*

Fifteen records perhaps involving no more than 2–3 birds

New Zealand.

Apart from a male on KGV on 16th March 1997, all records have come from Connaught Water with a male in 1992 and 1993 and 1–2 there from 1997–2004. Single hybrids were also present in 2000 and 2002.

Barrow's Goldeneye   *Bucephala islandica*

One record

Western North America with smaller populations in Iceland and eastern Canada.

1979	Abberton	18th April–31st May	Male

The BOURC considered this to have been an escape. There had been just one accepted British record to the end of 2004.

Hooded Merganser   *Mergus cucullatus*

One 'clipped' pair plus one other record

South Central Canada to southeast USA.

Apart from a pair with clipped wings at Copped Hall from 2001–2003, the only other record involved a female/immature at Vange Marshes from 2nd–18th August 2002. Another potential vagrant?

White-headed Duck   *Oxyura leucocephala*

Six records perhaps involving no more than three birds

Southwest Mediterranean basin to extreme northwest China, mainly in southern, former USSR

1995	Abberton	2nd January–4th November	Young male
1996	Abberton	18th and 21st February,	
		20th March and 11th May	
	Hanningfield	1st, 7th, 15th and 28th January	
1999	Walthamstow	11th September and	
		29th December	Ring on right leg
	Abberton	17th September–27th October	Adult female
2003	Abberton	25th September–7th October	

The origin of White-headed Ducks occurring in Britain has been a matter of some controversy for several years. Although migratory, the species is very popular with aviculturalists but has declined significantly in the wild during the 20th century, although in Spain the population has responded positively to conservation measures. With the increasing numbers of Ruddy Ducks recorded wintering in Iberia (q.v.), it is possible that White-headed Ducks may get 'picked-up' by the Ruddy Duck flocks and head back north with them.

American Black Vulture   *Coragyps atratus*

One record

Extreme southern USA, central and South America.

> 2001   Leigh-on-Sea   20th–21st December

Harris's Hawk   *Parabuteo unicinctus*

Nine records

Southernmost USA south through much of South America.

Harris's Hawks are common falconers' birds and consequently the most regular escaping raptor. From the first in 1994 there have been records in a further four years with apparent clusters of records perhaps suggesting the wanderings of one individual.

Red-tailed Hawk   *Buteo jamaicensis*

Seven records involving eight birds

North and Central America and the Caribbean.

Another common falconers' bird which, from the first in 1990, has been recorded in a further four years. There were two together over Hanningfield on 1st March 2001.

Crested Caracara   *Polyborus plancus*

One record

Southernmost North America southwards throughout Central and South America.

> 2003   Bradwell   26th October

This individual wandered around East Anglia.

Lanner Falcon   *Falco biarmicus*

Five records involving six birds.

Africa, Asia Minor and Southeast Europe.

1991	West Thurrock	15th November	Wearing jesses
1992	Fingringhoe Wick	15th February	Two wearing jesses
	Bradwell	26th July	
1998	Colne Point	28th January	Wearing jesses
2002	Langenhoe	6th May	

The increasing number of hybrids bred in captivity by falconers and then escape are making identification of larger falcons very difficult.

Falcon sp.   *Falco sp.*

Nine records involving at least seven birds

Falcons of debatable identity have been recorded occasionally, some wearing jesses. Many appear to be falconers' crosses, usually of Saker or Lanner with another large falcon. A large immature Gyr-type knocked a Brent Goose out of the sky at Holliwell Point on 28th October 1993.

Red Grouse   *Lagopus lagopus*

Attempted 19th century introduction?

Northern Britain and Ireland to Scandinavia across Russia and Siberia to Alaska and northern Canada.

Glegg summarised three records: Little Tey, one shot, May 1864; Ulting Hall, one shot, about September 1887 (note Christy incorrectly stated 1878); and Ramsden Hall, Billericay, a pair in the summer of 1927. Whether these related to attempted introductions in to Essex is not known, although it seems unlikely. Releases were made in Suffolk on the Breckland heaths in the mid-1800s and the population at Elveden was estimated at 350 in 1908. Four were also released at Butley Abbey in 1886, but soon disappeared (Piotrowski 2003). Red Grouse were also introduced at Sandringham, Norfolk, in the 1870s. Presumably the British race *scoticus* was involved in the introductions.

Northern Bobwhite   *Colinus virginianus*

Attempted 19th (and 20th?) century introduction

Southern Canada and USA to the mountains of Columbia, Ecuador and Peru.

Christy recorded that "This is an introduction from America which has never been able to establish itself. Dr Bree records one met with near Birch about June 5th, 1878." He did not elaborate on where an introduction attempt was made or how many birds were involved.

More recently, there were three 1980s records: Sandbeach Outfall, Dengie, one, 12th October 1982; Foulness, two, 1st April and one, 5th May 1984.

Chukar   *Alectoris chukar*

Introduced during the 1970s

Greece, Asia Minor to China.

Chukars began to be released in Britain during the early 1970s, although when this first occurred in Essex is unclear. Cox noted that "It is known that this partridge had been released in parts of Essex e.g. Tollesbury and the Ingatestone area, during the last decade. It is rumoured also that the Rock Partridge *A. graeca* has been released recently in south Essex, but this has yet to be confirmed."

Little interest was shown in the species, probably because of its similarity to the Red-legged Partridge and the fact that it hybridised with that species. However, following an identification paper by Wright (1986), observers began to take note and Chukars were recorded widely across Essex, although most were in the Foulness area where over 1,100 were released in 1986; a similar number were released at Dovercourt the same autumn. Nowhere was breeding confirmed, although pure and mixed pairs were observed. In fact, nationally the annual release of around 800,000 hand-reared Red-legged Partridges involved mainly various generation hybrids with Chukars (Winter Atlas). Hence, most Red-legged Partridges at this time probably included Chukar genes.

These hybrids were not a success as they exhibited very poor breeding success and in 1992, the licence permitting the release of Chukars or hybrids was withdrawn. Surprisingly, Chukars have continued to be recorded with five being noted at South Woodham Ferrers on 2nd October 1999 and three at Black Notley in early 2004; either someone is releasing Chukars illegally or the species is breeding in the wild.

Golden Pheasant   *Chrysolophus pictus*

Six records

Central China.

Golden Pheasants are popular cage birds and have been imported since the 18th century; feral populations occur in several areas in Britain, the most important being in the Brecks of Suffolk/Norfolk.

1970s	Hartley Woods, Little Clacton		Male
1974	Eastwood Rise	8th April	Female
1992	Weald CP	24th May	Male
1998	Alresford Creek	5th November	
1999	Colchester	25th January	
	Coopersale Common	24th–25th March	Male
2003	Copped Hall estate	3rd May	Male

The Colchester bird was seen running through heavy traffic. Cox noted: "… a few isolated individuals are known to have existed 'in the wild' for limited periods in recent years." The Hartley Woods' bird survived for several years during the early 1970s.

Silver Pheasant   *Lophura nycthemera*

One record

Southeast Asia.

1986	Ashingdon/Canewdon	late September	Two

Reeve's Pheasant   *Syrmaticus reevesii*

Three records

North and central China.

1999	Tollesbury Wick	11th May	Male
2003	East Mersea	23rd July	
2004	Fingringhoe	30th November	Female

Indian Peafowl   *Pavo cristatus*

Five records

India and Sri Lanka.

1983–86	Lincoln Is. Wanstead Park	From the back of a shop in Lee Bridge Road!	
1989	Hockley	1st April	
1991	Thundersley	23rd July	Male
2004	Braxted	22nd May	
	Hanningfield	4th and 17th December	

Peacocks are regularly kept in the grounds of stately homes.

Helmeted Guineafowl   *Numida meleagris*

Two records involving three birds

Africa, mainly south of the Sahara.

| 2001 | Galleywood | 17th July | Two |
| 2004 | Ingatestone | 22nd May | |

This is an increasingly common farmyard bird.

Crowned Crane sp.   *Balearica regulorum/pavonina*

One record involving two birds

Sub-Saharan Africa.

| 1981 | Abberton | November | Two |

Demoiselle Crane   *Anthropoides virgo*

Six records involving two birds

Black Sea, east to Mongolia and northwest China, wintering in India and sub-Saharan Africa.

1970	Hanningfield	18th October and 15th November
1993	Coleman's	8th–10th October at least
	Silver End GP	26th October to 18th November at least
	Fingringhoe, Frinton	5th December
	and Landermere	

The 1993 individual originally turned up at Spurn, Humberside, and many Essex birders headed north in anticipation of it being a wild bird. Alas, it was not and to add insult to injury, it followed everyone home!

Sarus Crane   *Grus antigone*

Three records involving two birds

North India and Nepal, Cambodia and Laos and northern Australia.

1966	Hanningfield	1st May
1968-72	Abberton	Escaped from Colchester Zoo
1969	St Osyth	Same as previous

Purple Gallinule (Purple Swamphen)   *Porphyrio porphyrio*

One 19th century record

The Purple Gallinule is widespread, occurring in southern Europe and Asia and in Africa, Australasia and the west Pacific islands.

Generally the species is sedentary. Four races are found in the Western Palearctic, which are sometimes considered to represent three separate species.

| 1878 | Dedham | 30th October | Female, shot |

Many Purple Gallinules were imported into Britain especially in the second half of the 19th century with 60 released at Woburn, Bedfordshire, in 1897 (Taylor *et al.* 1999). Small numbers remain in captivity to this day. All British records are thought to relate to escapes.

The Dedham individual was seen by Dr Charles Bree in the flesh, preserved by Ambrose the Colchester taxidermist and retained by Mr Dunnet, who shot it: the race involved was not mentioned, although the specimen was described as 'Green-backed Gallinule', which suggests *madagascariensis*, *poliocephalus*, *caspius* or *siestanicus*.

Spur-winged Plover   *Vanellus spinosus*

Three records

Middle East, central and east Africa.

1974	Hanningfield	early November	Escaped from a private wildlife collection near Basildon
1988	Thurrock	17th December	Probably one of two that escaped from Crystal Palace
1989	Barking Creek	14th July	

Masked Lapwing   *Vanellus miles*

One record

Eastern Australia and New Guinea.

1998	Bradwell	17th April

Silver Gull   *Larus novaehollandiae*

One record

Australia and southwest Pacific Islands.

2002	Holland Haven	mid-June	Adult

African Collared Dove   *Streptopelia roseogrisea*

Five records

Central Africa just south of the Sahara.

1906	Stanway	June–August
1987	Upminster Railway Station	25th July
1991	Hullbridge	July
1993	Fishers Green	27th September and 7th October
2003	Priory Park, Southend	14th January

The widespread domesticated form, which is sometimes referred to as '*S. risoria*' of which most of the above records are thought to relate, is also known as Barbary Dove.

Laughing Dove   *Streptopelia senegalensis*

Four records

Much of Africa, Asia Minor and India and parts of the Middle East.

1984	The Naze	25th January

1987	Canewdon	18th November
1988	Wickford	May–July
1993	West Horndon	18th June

The Wickford individual was continually in song and often accompanied Turtle Doves.

Diamond Dove *Geopelia cuneata*

Four records

North and Central Australia.

1988	East Mersea	2nd August
1991	East Tilbury	2nd April
1997	Holland Haven	4th–5th October
2001	Southend-on-Sea	9th June

Sulphur-crested Cockatoo *Cacatua galerita*

Four records

Northern and eastern Australia and Papua New Guinea.

1991	Holland Haven	25th August
1995	Southend-on-Sea	4th October
1997	Thorndon CP	15th March
2000	Foulness	23rd–24th April

Cockatiel *Nymphus hollandicus*

Common escape with usually 1–2 but occasionally up to eight annually

Australia.

The Cockatiel is one of the most abundant cage birds and it is therefore not surprising that it is one of the commonest parrots to be recorded in Essex. Undoubtedly, the species was poorly documented prior to the mid-1980s, the only record being one at Colne Point on 13th June 1974. Like other escapes, there is a bias towards spring and autumn records with an August/September peak particularly noticeable. If monthly variations in observer coverage were a factor in these apparent trends, surely an October peak would be more likely?

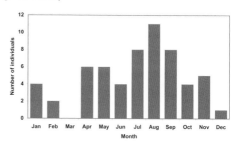

Seasonal occurrence of Cockatiels from 1974-2004

One at Abberton in the autumn of 1986 started rumours of a rare cuckoo, whilst another at Bradwell on 9th September 1992 was in pursuit of a Budgerigar!

Red-flanked Lorikeet *Charmosyna placentis*

One record

Eastern Indonesia, New Guinea and the North Solomons.

1997	Gunners Park	27th August

Eastern Rosella

Platycerus eximius

One record

Southeast Australia and Tasmania.

> 1993   Distillery Pond, Colchester   8th May

Crimson Rosella

Platycerus elegans

Seven records

Southeast Australia.

  Records have occurred at a total of seven sites in 1991 (3), 1993, 1995 (2) and 1997/98, although all except one have been in the east of the county.

Red-rumped Parrot

Psephotus haematonotus

One record

Southeast Australia.

> 1994   Dagenham Chase   11th July

Budgerigar

Melopsittacus undulatus

Regular escape

Australia.

  Budgies are probably the most commonly kept cage bird and consequently more escapes are recorded than any other species. However, documentation has been woefully poor and it is only since 1999 that the *EBR* has referred to the species, since when there have been 1–4 records annually.

  The late Rosemary Upton established a free-flying collection of Budgerigars at her house in Margaretting during the 1950s, which survived into the 1990s. The flock built up to 350–400 and individuals wandered up to a mile away (Upton 1983).

Senegal Parrot

Poicephalus senegalus

Two records

Western Africa.

> 1998   Holland Haven   27th April
> 1999   Leigh-on-Sea   4th November

Red-headed Lovebird

Agapornis pullarius

Three records

Central Africa.

> 1994   South Woodham Ferrers   July for about a week
> 1995   Chelmsford   26th June–23rd July
> 1996   Horsey Island   11th May had been present for several weeks and was
>   recorded at Holland Haven on one occasion

Peach-faced Lovebird

Agapornis roseicollis

Five records of at least eight individuals

Western southern Africa.

1990	Boreham	17th–21st August	Adult
1996	Heybridge Basin	August	"free-flying family"
1998	Laindon	18th July	Two
2000	Southend	6th August	
2003	Barking Park	29th May	

A pair bred in Dunbar, Lothian, in 2002.

Lovebird sp.

Agapornis sp.

1994	Eastwood SF	15th January

African Grey Parrot

Psicattus erithacus

Six records

Western Africa.

1987	Leigh-on-Sea	11th June
1990	Rainham	2nd June
1994	Southend-on-Sea	23rd October
1998	Clacton-on-Sea	27th August
2001	East Ham	6th November
2003	The Naze	January–April

Alexandrine Parakeet

Psittacula eupatria

Ten records involving 5–6 birds

India and southeast Asia.

Since the first in 1989, the species has occurred in a further six years. All except three of the records have come from the Ilford/Dagenham area and in particular around Parsloes Park. This species is similar in appearance to Ring-necked Parakeet.

Blossom-headed Parakeet

Psittacula roseate

One record

Assam, Burma to Indochina.

2000	KGV	20th July

Monk Parakeet

Myiopsitta monachus

Three records probably involving two birds

Central South America.

606

1999	Upminster, Stubbers Lakes	July–August at least	Territorial—nest constructed
	Corbets Tey	17th–22nd August	Nest
2002	The Naze	14th–27th July	

Small colonies exist in Hertfordshire and Wiltshire (Ogilvie 2004).

Scarlet-fronted Parakeet   *Aratinga wagleri*

One record

Venezuela, Columbia, Ecuador and Peru.

| 1989/90 | Dagenham Chase | November–February |

Mitred Parakeet   *Aratinga mitrata*

One record

Central Peru and Bolivia and northwest Argentina.

| 2004 | Holyfield Lake | 1st–9th September |

Nanday Parakeet   *Nandayus nenday*

Two records involving three birds

Southeast Bolivia, southwest Brazil, central Paraguay and northern Argentina.

| 1987 | Wakering refuse-tip | 18th July | |
| 2000 | Fairlop CP | 21st October | Two |

Burrowing Parakeet   *Cyanoliseus patagonus*

One record

Chile and Argentina.

| 1987/88 | Rose Inn, Wakering | 19th December–summer 1988 |

The bird survived the winter, being fed in the grounds of Eton House School, and was apparently recaptured during the summer.

Eagle Owl (Eurasian Eagle Owl)   *Bubo bubo*

Seven escapes: uncorroborated 19th century record

The Eagle Owl is found throughout Eurasia and northern Africa and is largely sedentary.

1982	Leigh-on-Sea	27th July	
	Little Wakering	5th August	
1986	Pitsea	April	Taken into care
1987/88	Pitsea/Gode Park /Hornchurch	17th November	

1988	East Tilbury	27th November	Wearing jesses
2000	Stebbing	17th March-16th April.	
2003	Valentines Park, Ilford	29th March	

The 2000 individual, which reputedly escaped from the Brentwood area, courted stardom briefly with appeals as to its whereabouts broadcast on BBC Radio Essex. Prey items included the unfortunate inhabitants of a local farmyard pond.

Glegg considered that there was "… no evidence even to suggest that this species has occurred in Essex", although Christy mentioned that Mr Hope had, "… seen it on the borders of Essex in May or October". Nationally, all recent records are considered to have involved escapes, although recent investigations suggest that there may be as many as 40 pairs across the country. The species is not on the British List.

Rock Eagle Owl   *Bubo bengalensis*

One record

Indian subcontinent.

1987	Canvey Island	24th–29th April	Recaptured on latter date

Red-whiskered Bulbul   *Pycnotus jocusus*

One record

Central Asia.

1995	Thorndon CP	May

Red-vented Bulbul   *Pycnotus caffer*

One record

Sri Lanka, India, Pakistan and Burma.

1989	Bradwell	25th August

Mongolian Lark   *Melanocorypha mongolica*

One record

Central Asia.

1999	Horndon	2nd March	Killed by a cat

Spotted Laughingthrush   *Garrulax ocellatus*

One record

Himalayas.

1999	Stanway	31st October–31st December

Remarkably, this individual was reported again around a year later.

Red-tailed Laughingthrush

Garrulax milnei

One record

Burma and southeast Asia.

1990	Chingford	5th April

Silver-eared Mesia

Leiothrix argentauris

One record

Himalayas and northeast India.

1989	Chelmsford	26th December	Male eating Holly berries in a garden

Red-billed Leiothrix

Leiothrix lutea

One record involving two birds

Himalayas and northeast India.

2002	West Mersea	1st September-2nd September	Two

Rufous Sibia

Heterophasia capistrata

One record

Himalayas.

1981	Old Heath, Colchester	19th December	Caught in a mist-net

Vinous-throated Parrotbill

Paradoxornis webbianus

One record

Eastern Asia.

1995	East Tilbury	30th April

Sunbird sp.

Nectarina sp.

One record

1988	The Naze	26th July

In 1987 an unidentified individual was at Landguard Point, Suffolk, on 26th–27th May and at Havergate Island, Suffolk, on 31st May (Piotrowski 2003).

Blue Magpie

Urocissa erythrorhyncha

One record

Eastern and southeast Asia.

1988	Walton and The Naze	13th and 29th June

Indian Treepie

Dendrocitta vagabunda

One record

India and eastwards over lowlands southeast Asia.

1973	Braintree	February	Picked up dead

Hill Mynah

Gracula religiosa

Two records

Parts of India and southeast Asia to China.

1985	Hullbridge	27th March
2004	Mersea Island	April and May

Common Mynah

Acridotheres tristis

Three records probably involving the same bird

India, Nepal and southeast Asia.

1990	Shoebury	late February	Feeding on bird tables
	Wakering SF	18th March	with Starlings
	Gunners Park	2nd April	

Greater Blue-eared Glossy Starling

Lamprotornis chalybaeus

One record

Africa.

2001	The Naze	22nd-30th June

Glossy Starling sp.

Lamprotornis sp.

One record

Africa.

1989	Hanningfield	15th May

Sudan Golden Sparrow

Passer luteus

Nine records

Central Africa south of the Sahara.

Although the species was recorded almost annually from 1989-93, there have only been records in two years since. None have occurred in the west of the county with all bar two being on the coast.

Masked Weaver

Ploceus intermedius

One record

Eastern and Central Africa.

1994	Colne Point	2nd–3rd June

Village Weaver   *Ploceus cucullatus*

Twelve records

Central and southern Africa.

   Most records occurred in the period 1987–1991 with others in 1974 and 1997. A pair built a nest in a Sycamore overhanging a garden in Romford in 1987; nest-building was also noted at Holland Haven in 1987 and Colne Point in 1989. The 1997 individual was occasionally reported as a Black-headed Weaver *P. melanocephalus*.

Red-billed Quelea   *Quelea quelea*

Four records

Central Africa.

1991	The Naze	2nd August–27th September	
	Bradwell	15th August	
1992	Braxted village	July–1st September	
1998	The Naze	22nd October	

Yellow-crowned Bishop   *Euplectes afer*

Three records

Central and Southern Africa.

1990	Old Hall	20th–25th October	Male
2000	The Naze	17th August	Male
	Cudmore Grove CP	23rd August	

Red-crowned Bishop   *Euplectes hordeacea*

One record

Central and southern Africa.

2004	The Naze	25th April	Male

Red Bishop   *Euplectes orix*

Two records

South Angola to Namibia, Botswana, Mozambique and north Cape Province.

2001	East Tilbury	29th July–16th November	Female
2004	Cudmore Grove CP	18th June	

Black-winged Bishop   *Euplectes hordeaceus*

Two records

Central and western Africa.

1998	Bradwell	6th–11th August
2001	Gunners Park	23rd August

Zanzibar Red Bishop   *Euplectes nigroventris*

Two records

East Africa.

1999	Eastwood SF	30th October–1st November	Male
2001	Haven Point, Wakering	21st July	

Orange Bishop   *Euplectes franciscanus*

One record

East Africa.

1987	East Tilbury	23rd September-24th November	Singing male

Orange-cheeked Waxbill   *Estrilda melpoda*

Four records involving six birds

Central and western Africa.

1998	Barking Bay	18th October	Pair
2000	Gunners Park	4th October	
2002	Gunners Park	1st September	Two
2003	East Tilbury	16th August	

Common Waxbill   *Estrilda astrild*

Seven records

Central and southern Africa.

Records have occurred in six years since the first in 1986. Geographically, the records show a wide spread, although most have occurred in the west of the county.

Zebra Waxbill   *Amandava subflava*

One record

Africa.

2002	Tillingham	23rd March

Zebra Finch   *Taeniopygia guttata*

Fourteen records involving 15 birds

Indonesia to Australia.

Most records occurred from the mid-1980s to mid-1990s with just two since 1996. Unsuccessful breeding occurred at Doddinghurst in 1991.

White-rumped Munia

Lonchura striata

One record

India and Nepal to southeast Asia to China and Taiwan.

1989	Shoebury Coastguards	28th August

White-capped Munia

Lonchura ferruginosa

One record

India and southeast Asia.

1985	Mountnessing	throughout August

Cut-Throat

Amadina fasciata

Two records

Northern and eastern Africa, south to Mozambique.

1988	Gunners Park	7th August	
1997	Dagenham Corridor	16th–18th May	Female

Shaft-tailed Wydah

Vidua regia

One record

Southern Africa.

1997	Brentwood	16th April

Pin-tailed Wydah

Vidua macroura

One record

Senegal to Ethiopia and Cape Province.

2004	Ingrebourne Valley	22nd September

Atlantic Canary

Serinus canaria

Three records

Canary Islands, Azores and Madeira Islands.

1985	Leigh-on-Sea	21st October
2001	Cudmore Grove CP	15th July
2002	East Tilbury	29th September

Yellow-fronted Canary

Serinus mozambicus

Nine records

Africa south of the Sahara.

Records have occurred in seven years since the first in 1986 with occurring mainly in the east of the county and just one in Metropolitan Essex; all occurred between June and December.

Chinese (Japanese) Grosbeak

Euphona personata

One records

Japan and China.

2000	The Naze	13th May

Black-tailed Hawfinch

Coccothraustes migratorius

One record

North Korea and East China.

2001	Marden Ash	19th August–28th December

APPENDIX 3
UNSUBSTANTIATED RECORDS AND
OTHER RECORDS OF INTEREST

Shearwater sp.   *Puffinus sp.*

Christy referred to two records of "Dusky Shearwaters, *Puffinus obscurus*", found at Sampford (sic) around 6th September 1878 and at Seward's End on 17th September 1884. He considered both were probably Manx Shearwaters. They are, however, published here for the record: the taxonomy of the *Puffinus* shearwaters has always been confusing but 'Dusky Shearwater' has been an alternative name for Little Shearwater *Puffinus assimilis*.

Wilson's Petrel   *Oceanites oceanicus*

One uncorroborated record

The Wilson's Petrel breeds in the Southern Hemisphere but visits the north Atlantic from June to October.

Christy (1903) referred to a petrel bought at the sale of Mr Doubleday's collection that was considered to be of this species. It may have been the bird taken near Epping in November 1840 and identified as a Leach's Storm-petrel. Glegg felt the chain of evidence to be incomplete. The specimen was placed in Chelmsford and Essex Museum but does not now exist.

Harlequin Duck   *Histrionicus histrionicus*

One uncorroborated record

The monotypic Harlequin Duck breeds on the Arctic tundra by fast-flowing streams. In Europe the species occurs only in Iceland where it is sedentary (European Atlas).

Glegg noted that "Mr J. H. Owen records that three, a drake and two females, were seen more than once on the Chelmer during February during 1919. The male was shot by the Rev. H. G. Vincent but not preserved." Glegg, in accepting the record, concluded that it depended entirely on the identification as so few were held in captivity. Owen was satisfied with the identification and Vincent regularly went duck shooting in northern Scotland, the Orkney Islands and the Shetland Islands. Hudson & Pyman rejected the record outright "… surely a case of mistaken identity."

Swallow-tailed Kite   *Elanoides forficatus*

One record, originally ascribed to Essex but actually a Suffolk specimen

Swallow-tailed Kites breed in the southern-most USA, Central and South America.

Glegg described how "A Swallow-tailed Kite, catalogued as having been shot in Essex about 1860 by Mr Travers, formed part of the collection of the late Sir Vauncey Harpur Crewe, Bart., which was sold at Steven's Rooms on 23rd February 1926. The purchase was made by Mr E. T. Clarke, Cheltenham, who sold it to the Essex Museum, at Stratford." Glegg subsequently dealt with the record in the *Essex Naturalist* 21: 269 where he concluded that, "… the history of this Essex specimen is so obscure that no other course is open but to label it as of doubtful origin." Subsequently, Glegg (1929) noted that it "… has come to my notice that the specimen in the Essex Museum at Stratford was shot by Mr. O.W. Travers near Mildenhall, Suffolk, between 1830 and 1840." Glegg's information came from a Mr W. R. Butterfield. It remains in the EFC collection, Accession No. 15988.

Black-shouldered Kite   *Elanus caeruleus*

Possible vagrant? One record

The Black-shouldered Kite is typically Afro-tropical and Indo-Malayan but is also found in southwest Europe and northern Africa. The nominate race *caeruleus* occurs in Europe. The species is usually sedentary but some migratory and irruptive movements occur.

1956	Bradwell	4th March

On 4th March 1956, "… an unfamiliar raptor flew N. past the trap thicket … and was described by the observers (Foott and Griffiths) as follows: size as Black-headed Gull, in full sunlight plumage appeared white all over save for conspicuous black patches on wings close to body, wings sharply arched, flight rapid. Also seen (independently) by W. Linnett, who afterwards described the bird as a white hawk with long, falcon-like wings, longish tail and black 'shoulders'" (*EBR* 1956). The conclusion was that the bird was a Black-winged Kite, as it was then known. Prior to the date of observation, the weather had been abnormally warm for the time of year and an anticyclone had been centred to the northeast of the Azores with a ridge of high pressure extending over the Iberian peninsular where the species occurred. The record was referred to the editors of British Birds (the BBRC came into existence in 1958), who considered the details insufficient to constitute the first British record. It is, however, a quite exceptional claim by respected observers and requires documenting here.

Golden Eagle   *Aquila chrysaetos*

Two 19th century records of uncertain status: one recent escape

The Golden Eagle breeds from Europe to Siberia and Japan, north Africa, Canada and West USA, with the nearest breeding populations in northern-most England and Scotland.

The great difficulty in assessing any Essex Golden Eagle records is that immature White-tailed Eagles used to be called Golden Eagles; most records are therefore likely to have involved that species. Christy detailed two records:

1858	Claverham Bury Farm, Nazeing	15th November	Immature shot
1887	Easton Park	9th March	

The observer of the latter individual was well acquainted with Golden Eagles. In addition, in the late 19th century "Mr Hope says it is, 'seen passing up the coast and off the main'." Unidentified eagles were also killed in a wood at Great Totham in 1684 and around 1831. Glegg highlighted the identification problem and referred to the 1858 and 1887 records, noting "… it cannot be said that the evidence is complete in either case." He also referred to one in Maldon Museum, alleged to have been taken at Tollesbury, but again he considered its history incomplete.

A Golden Eagle at West Horndon from 31st May–early June 1989 had escaped from nearby and was recaptured a few days later.

Gyr Falcon   *Falco rusticolus*

Five uncorroborated 19th century records

The monotypic Gyr Falcon is a Holarctic species that in Europe breeds in Iceland, Norway, northwest Sweden, north Finland and north Russia.

In 1665, Lord Petre lost a Gyr Falcon and an advertisement offering a reward was placed in The Newes of 9th November 1665 "Lost on the 28th October last, betwixt Stock and Billerica, in Essex, a white Goshawk … Whoever shall deliver the said hawk safe in to the house of … Lord Petre, at Thorndon, in Essex, or to Mr Andrews, at the 'White Horse' in Drury Lane, shall beside his charges defraied, have 40s. for a reward". White Goshawk was a common name for a Gyr Falcon.

Christy detailed three records, although Glegg considered the evidence for each incomplete. One was apparently shot close to Coggeshall in 1855, whilst one was present around Paglesham in February 1888 and one was shot there in mid-November 1888. Glegg felt that "The most likely occurrence was one trapped at Hatfield Broad Oak in December 1891". However, the authorities of the day could not decide whether it was a Peregrine or a Gyr Falcon. He added that a pair was seen around Southend in December 1888, one being shot. The grouping of records in 1888 is of note. Neither Hudson & Pyman nor Cox mentioned the species.

Macqueen's Bustard   *Chlamydotis macqueenii*

One apparently fraudulent 19th century record

Macqueen's Bustard is found in the Sinai Peninsula and east Turkey, through to Mongolia, and migrates to the Persian Gulf and Pakistan for the winter.

Christy noted "At a sale held at Argyll Street Auction Rooms, London, in 1871, Lot 689 was described as " A Macqueen's Bustard shot at Harwich in 1823, and preserved by Hall of Finsbury Square".". Gurney in the *Zoologist* (34:4763) showed that the bird was not shot in England, the information having come from a Catalogue that contained other "… gross mis-statements".

Short-billed Dowitcher   *Limnodroma griseus*

One or two uncorroborated 19th century records

The Short-billed Dowitcher breeds across northern North America and winters in southern North America, Central America and northern South America.

In Southend Museum there is a specimen (Accession No. N75.92) which is alleged to have been shot and stuffed by Christopher Parsons and, although no dates are specified, it would have been around the 1830s–40s. The specimen is a first-winter bird. Although Parsons was very parochial in his ways, he was known to have travelled and may have purchased specimens for his collection. However, the record remains unsubstantiated.

Far less satisfactory was a reference made by Christy to one at Harwich on 15th April 1882 where G. P. Hope "… walked to within five yards of it, and it then flew away"; Glegg rejected it.

Brünnich's Guillemot   *Uria lomvia*

One uncorroborated 19th century record

Brünnich's Guillemot is an Arctic species wintering south to central Norway, which is a rare vagrant to Britain.

Christy referred to a specimen in Canon Babington's collection that the Canon had purchased at the sale of the Sudbury Museum. It formed part of a case of twelve "British Aquatic Birds, Lot 230". Although Christy considered that there was, "… considerable reason for presuming that it was obtained near the mouth of the Orwell [Suffolk] or Stour, whence so many of the aquatic birds in that museum came…" he considered that the lack of direct evidence meant that the species should not be admitted to the Essex List.

Great Auk   *Alca impennis*

No known Essex record but specimen formerly kept at Brentwood

The Great Auk was an Arctic species that has been extinct since 1844.

Although there are no known Essex records, a specimen that originally belonged to a Mr Hoy passed into the possession of Mr J. F. Lescher of Boyle's Court Brentwood, at the time one of just 22 remaining specimens. It was in Lescher's possession around 1890.

Sooty Tern   *Onychoprion fuscata*

One uncorroborated record

Sooty Terns are found throughout the Tropics.

According to Christy one was allegedly shot near Colchester in the winter of 1880/81 and preserved but the specimen was lost. Both he and Glegg accepted the record because of the reputation of Dr Bree who documented it; Hudson & Pyman quite rightly rejected it.

Passenger Pigeon   *Ectopistes migratorius*

One vagrant or possible 19th century escape?

Formerly super-abundant resident of North America that was shot to extinction by hunters in the early 20th century.

Passenger Pigeons were imported from America from the 1830s (Evans 1994) and it is likely that one shot just inside Hertfordshire at Melbourne in July 1844 was from this source, although neither the legs nor plumage exhibited any signs of confinement. Christy accepted the record as, although the Passenger Pigeon was shot 400 yards west of the boundary, "… the bird, probably, had crossed that boundary before being shot, and could easily have recrossed it in less than half a minutes flight…".

The Passenger Pigeon is not on the British List, although it is possible that with such a large population, some early 18th century records may have involved genuine vagrants.

Hawk Owl (Northern Hawk Owl)   *Surnia ulula*

Three presumed fraudulent records

The Hawk Owl is largely resident in the northern forests of Eurasia and the Nearctic.

Three were allegedly taken around Essex in February 1913: Colchester, male on 28th; near Chelmsford, male shot on 18th and a female on 28th. They found their way into Sir Vauncey Harpur Crewe's collection and were sold at Steven's Auction Rooms on 23rd February 1926 (Glegg). They were not, however, recorded at the time and Hudson & Pyman, quite rightly, suspected fraud. The individual shot on 23rd February is now in the Booth Museum, Brighton (Accession No. 207259). Unscrupulous dealers duped the unsuspecting Crewe on more than one occasion.

Black Woodpecker   *Dryocopus martius*

One record

Southern, central and Eastern Europe eastward to Kamchatka and Japan.

| 1847 | Audley End | 5th June |

Despite many claims nationally, some of which appear to have a strong case for being vagrants, none are accepted as such (Fitter 1959, 1992) although, as the species expands its range on the Continent, a genuine record seems likely in the near future. A total of seven or eight was released in Suffolk in 1897.

Purple Martin   *Progne subis*

Two uncorroborated records

The Purple Martin is widespread throughout North America and winters in South America.

Christy referred to two records, although he accepted neither. The first was reported flying around the barrack exercising ground at Colchester on about 26th September 1878, following a "… strong prevalence of westerly winds for the last month". A Captain Dugmore, who had lived in Canada and knew the species well, saw it. Around 1870, one was allegedly shot along the Stour, and although preserved, the specimen's whereabouts was never known.

The first accepted records of Purple Martins to be recorded in the Western Palearctic occurred in 2004 on the Outer Hebrides and Azores.

American Robin   *Turdus migratorius*

One uncorroborated record

The American Robin is widespread throughout North America and winters in the southern USA and Central America.

Harting (1901) referred to one recorded near Southend in the winter of 1894/95, which Glegg assumed to be an escape. Frustratingly, Harting gave no reference for the record. There were 22 British records to the end of 2004, all in late autumn/winter (BBRC 2005).

2005 RECORDS

For full details, readers should refer to the *Essex Bird Report 2005* published by the Essex Birdwatching Society.

Whooper Swan	18 over Wivenhoe on 28th November
Brent Goose	One of the best breeding seasons since the 1980s saw significant numbers of juveniles arriving during late 2005
Green-winged Teal	Singles at East Tilbury on 12th March and Old Hall on 3rd–23rd April
Red-crested Pochard	Three pairs bred at Hanningfield with 21 present by the autumn
Ferruginous Duck	The Heybridge GP individual reappeared on Chigborough Lakes GP on 15th–16th January, whilst a different male was at Abberton from 23rd February–23rd March.
Lesser Scaup	The first-winter male stayed at Abberton until 15th January
Purple Heron	One at Fobbing on 2nd May
White Stork	Possibly four birds recorded during the year
Spoonbill	One at Holland Haven on 12th–13th May
Black Kite	Three sightings of one bird on Dengie from mid-September
Buzzard	A detailed survey located 28 breeding pairs (*per* A. Thompson)
Rough-legged Buzzard	Singles at Chingford on 19th March and The Naze on 4th April
Hobby	13 at Fishers Green on 5th June
Stone Curlew	One at Holland Haven on 17th August
Black-winged Stilt	Four at Old Hall on 11th May, the largest flock since 1968 with two returning on 31st May
Collared Pratincole	One at Rainham from 2nd–5th July, the first record for 47 years!
Kentish Plover	East Tilbury 5th–11th September
Sociable Plover	First-winter at Rainham from 4th–20th December
Pectoral Sandpiper	One at Holland Haven on 1st May is only the second spring record with three further records in the autumn
White-rumped Sandpiper	Juvenile at East Tilbury from 23rd–27th October
Long-billed Dowitcher	One at Old Hall from 25th September–11th November
Marsh Sandpiper	One at Holland Haven on 28th July
Lesser Yellowlegs	One at Holland Haven from 11th–13th October
Great Skua	One at Hanningfield on 30th December
Mediterranean Gull	A new county record of 104 on Southend Seafront on 25th July
Sabine's Gull	Two in the autumn
Ring-billed Gull	"Rossi" returned for the 7th winter on 22nd August, whilst two others occurred during March

Caspian Gull	"Caspar" returned for the 9th winter on 30th October, whilst up to 12 at just two Thames-side locations lend support to its status as a scarce late autumn/early winter passage migrant
White-winged Black Tern	Singles at Abberton on 21st–28th August and East Tilbury on 10th September
Roseate Tern	Two adults at East Tilbury on 10th–11th September, with another on 11th
Arctic Tern	One at West Thurrock on 6th November
Guillemot	One at Abberton on 16th January
Ring-necked Parakeet	Twelve at Hornchurch during the year; a pair bred at Corbets Tey
Hoopoe	Three in spring/summer
Shorelark	One remained at Abberton until 29th March and perhaps the same returning bird reappeared on 22nd November
Waxwing	Although recorded at few other sites, two significant flocks built up early in the year, one of them, the largest to ever be recorded in Essex. There were up to 117 on 20th January in the Basildon/Pitsea area, whilst a flock in the Chafford. Hundred area peaked at 260 on 12th April
Dartford Warbler	With another 13 records during the year, the first breeding record for 50+ years must be due?
Yellow-browed Warbler	Influx during October involved perhaps nine birds
Nuthatch	A rare record from Bradwell on 15th April
Short-toed Treecreeper	One at Bradwell on 6th–10th April, only the 5th away from Kent
Penduline Tit	One at Rainham on 9th October and up to seven (nationally, a record count) from 18th–28th December
Hooded Crow	One at Wat Tyler CP on 9th November
Tree Sparrow	Numbers picked up during the year with ten at Great Horkesley during February and several small flocks during the spring and autumn.
Siskin	A huge movement in mid-September produced counts of 400 at Holland Haven on 12th September and 500 at The Naze on 11th with 400 there on 17th
Hawfinch	After marked declines in recent years, a national influx saw several records away from traditional breeding areas during December

SCIENTIFIC NAMES OF ORGANISMS MENTIONED IN THE TEXT

ANIMALS

Common Name	Scientific Name	Common Name	Scientific Name
Arctic Fox	*Alopex lagopus*	Lesser Sandeel	*Ammodytes marinus*
Badger	*Meles meles*	Lugworm	*Arenicola marina*
Baltic Tellin	*Macoma balthica*	Migrant Hawker	*Aeshna mixta*
Bluebottle Fly	*Calliphora vomitoria*	Mink	*Mustela vison*
Bank Vole	*Clethrionomys glareolus*	Muntjac Deer	*Muntiacus reevesi*
Blue Mussel	*Mytilus edulis*	Otter	*Lutra lutra*
Brown Rat	*Rattus norvegicus*	Painted Lady	*Cynthia cardui*
Brown Trout	*Salmo trutta*	Periwinkle	*Littorina littorea*
Carp	*Cyprinus* species	Pig	*Sus scrofa*
Cat (Domestic)	*Felix domesticus*	Plum-reed Aphid	*Hyalopterus pruni*
Cockles	*Cerastoderma edule*	Pygmy Shrew	*Sorex minutus*
Common Darter	*Sympetrum striolatum*	Rabbit	*Oryctolagus cuniculus*
Common Shrew	*Sorex araneus*	Rainbow Trout	*Oncorhynchus mykiss*
Cow	*Bos taurus*	Roach	*Rutilus rutilus*
Dainty Damselfly	*Coenagrion scitulum*	Rudd	*Scardinius erythrophthalmus*
Dog	*Canis familiaris*	Sandeel	*Ammodytes* and related species
Eel	*Anguilla anguilla*		
Fallow Deer	*Dama dama*		
Field Vole	*Microtus agretis*	Sheep	*Ovis aries*
Fisher's Estuarine Moth	*Gortyna borelii lunata*	Silver Y Moth	*Autographa gamma*
Fox	*Vulpes vulpes*	Slipper Limpet	*Crepidula fornicala*
Garfish	*Belone belone*	Soft Clams	*Mya arenaria*
Grass Snake	*Natrix natrix*	Stickleback	*Gasterostreus* species
Grey Squirrel	*Sciurus carolinensis*	Stoat	*Mustela erminea*
Herring	*Clupea harengus*	Summer Chaffer	*Amphimallon solstitialis*
Horse	*Equus cabalus*	Turkey	*Meleagris galloparvo*
Harvest Mouse	*Micromys minutus*	Water Vole	*Arvicola terrestris*
House Mouse	*Mus domesticus*	Weasel	*Mustela nivalis*
Laver Spire Shell	*Hydrobia ulvae*	Wood Ant	*Formica rufa*
Lemming	*Myopus* and *Lemmus* species	Wood Mouse	*Apodemus sylvaticus*
		Zebra Mussel	*Driessena polymorpha*

PLANTS

Common Name	Scientific Name	Common Name	Scientific Name
Alder	*Alnus glutinosa*	Butterfly Bush	*Buddleia davidii*
Annual Seablite	*Sueda maratima*	Cabbage	*Brassica* species
Apple	*Malus domestica*	Cherry	*Prunus* species
Arolla Pine	*Pinus cembra*	Clover	*Trifolium* species
Ash	*Fraxinus excelsior*	Common Cord-grass	*Spartina anglica*
Barley	*Hordeum distichon*	Common or Stinging Nettle	*Urtica dioica*
Beech	*Fagus sylvatica*	Common Reed	*Phragmites australis*
Birch	*Betula pendula*	Common Saltmarsh Grass	*Puccinellia maratima*
Black Poplar hybrid	*Populus x canadensis*	Dock	*Rumex* species
Blackthorn	*Prunus spinosa*	Dwarf Birch	*Betula nana*
Bracken	*Pteridium aquilinum*	Dwarf Eelgrass	*Zostera noltii*
Bramble	*Rubus* species	Dwarf Willow	*Salix herbacea*

Eelgrass	*Zostera marina*	Plum	*Prunus* species
Elm	*Ulmus* species	Poplar	*Populus* species
European Larch	*Larix deciduas*	Red Goosefoot	*Chenopodium rubrum*
Fennel Pondweed	*Potamogeton pectinatus*	Rowan	*Sorbus acuparia*
Field Maple	*Acer camestre*	Rhubarb	*Rheum rhaponticum*
Glasswort	*Salicornia* species	Samphire	*Inula crithmoides*
Gorse	*Ulex europaeus*	Scots Pine	*Pinus sylvestris*
Great Reedmace/Bulrush	*Typha latifolia*	Sea Aster	*Aster tripolium*
Hawthorn	*Crataegus monogyna*	Sea Club-rush	*Scirpus maritimus*
Heather	*Calluna vulgaris*	Sea Couch	*Elytrigia atherica*
Hog's Fennel	*Peucedanum officinale*	Sea-heath	*Frankenia laevis*
Holly	*Ilex aquifolium*	Sessile Oak	*Quercus petraea*
Hornbeam	*Carpinus betulus*	Sea Purslane	*Atriplex portulacoides*
Japanese Larch	*Larix kaempferi*	Shrubby Seablite	*Sueda vera*
Larch	*Larix* species	Small Cord-grass	*Spartina maritime*
Laurel	*Prunus* species	Smooth Cord-grass	*Spartina alterniflora*
Lesser Bulrush	*Typha angustifolia*	Spruce	*Picea* species
Linseed	*Linum usitatissimum*	Stonecrop	*Sedum* species
Marsh Mallow	*Althaea officinalis*	Sunflower	*Helianthus annuus*
Meadowsweet	*Filipendula ulmaria*	Sweet Chestnut	*Castanea sativa*
Mountain Avens	*Dryas octopetala*	Sycamore	*Acer* species
Nettle	*Urtica* species	Water Cress	*Nastertium nasturtium*
Norway Spruce	*Picea abies*		*aquaticum*
Oak	*Quercus* species	Wellingtonia	*Sequoia giganteum*
Oil-seed Rape	*Brassica napus* var. *oleifera*	Wheat/Corn	*Triticum* species
Pea	*Pisum sativum*	Wild Garlic	*Allium ursinum*
Peanut	*Arachus hypogaea.*	Willow	*Salix* species
Pear	*Pyrus* species	Willowherb	*Epilobium* species
Pine	*Pinus* species	Yew	*Taxus baccata*

BIBLIOGRAPHY

Standard References

The standard references with their abbreviations are as follows:

BBRC (year)   Annual report of the British Birds Rarities Committee (BBRC) published in *British Birds*.

BWP   Cramp, S. (ed.) 1977–94. *Handbook of the Birds of Europe, the Middle East and North Africa: the birds of the Western Palearctic.* 9 Vols. Oxford University Press, Oxford.

Christy   Christy, R. M. 1890. *The birds of Essex.* Essex Field Club. Durant, Chelmsford.

Cox   Cox, S. 1984. *A new guide to the birds of Essex.* Essex Birdwatching and Preservation Society.

Essex Atlas   Dennis, M. K. 1996. *Tetrad Atlas of the Breeding Birds of Essex.* Essex Birdwatching Society.

European Atlas   Hagemeijier, E. J. M. & Blair, M. J. (eds.) 1997. *The EBCC Atlas of European Birds: Their distribution and Abundance.* Poyser, London.

First London Atlas   Montier, D. 1977. *Atlas of breeding birds of the London area.* London.

First National Atlas   Sharrock, J. T. R. 1976. *The Atlas of Breeding Birds in Britain and Ireland.* Poyser, Calton.

Glegg   Glegg, W. E. 1929. *A history of the birds of Essex.* London.

HBW   del Hoyo, J., Elliott, A. & Christie, D. 1992. *Handbook of the Birds of the World.* 9 Vols. Lynx Edicions, Barcelona.

Historical Atlas   Holloway, S. 1996. *The historical atlas of breeding birds in Britain and Ireland: 1875–1900.* Poyser, Calton.

Hudson & Pyman   Hudson, R. & Pyman, G. A. 1968. *A Guide to the Birds of Essex.* Essex Birdwatching and Preservation Society.

Population Trends   Marchant, J. H., Hudson, R., Carter, S. P. & Whittington, P. 1990. *Population trends in British breeding birds.* BTO, Tring.

RBBP (year)   Annual report of the Rare Birds Breeding Panel (RBBP) published in *British Birds*.

Second London Atlas   Hewlett, J. (ed.) 2002. *The breeding birds of the London area.* LNHS, London.

Second National Atlas   Gibbons, D. W., Reid, J. B. & Chapman, R. A. 1993. *The New Atlas of Breeding Birds in Britain and Ireland; 1988–91.* Poyser, London.

Other references

Adcock, M. 1993. The Foulness Hailstorm. *Essex Bird Report 1992*: 150–151.

Aebischer, N. J., Browne, S. J. & Calladine, J. R. 2001. An update on population trends, breeding ecology and migration of British Turtle Doves. In *Status, Management and conservation of the Species Alectoris, Black Francolin, Thrush, Quail and Turtle Dove in the Mediterranean region*, pp 20–32. Game Fund Service, Ministry of Interior, Nicosia.

Albin, E. 1731–38. *A natural history of birds.* London.

Alexander, H. G. 1914. A report on the Land-Rail Inquiry. *British Birds* 8: 86.

Alexander, W. B. & Lack, D. 1944. Change in status of British breeding birds. *British Birds* 38: 62–69.

Allport, G. O'Brian, M. & Cadbury, C. J. 1986. Survey of Redshank and other breeding birds on saltmarshes in Britain 1985. *RSPB Report to NCC.*

Alström, P. & Mild, K. 2003. *Pipits and Wagtails.* Christopher Helm, London.

Anon. 1958. Pacific Black Brant. *Essex Bird Report 1957*: 12.

Arlow, S. 2004. The status of the Mediterranean Gull in the Southend area. Essex Bird Report 2003: 145–156.

Armitage, M. J. S., Rehfisch, M. M. & Wernham, C.V. 1997. (Published 2005). Abstract from Research Report No 193. *The 1997 Breeding Sawbill Survey.*

Atkins, C. 1990. Black-eared Wheatear at Jaywick 26th May 1989 – A new bird for Essex. *Essex Bird Report 1989*: 111–112.

Atkinson, Rev. J. C. 1871. *British Birds' eggs and nests popularly described*. 8 Vols. Warne and Routledge, London.

Attenborough, D. 1998. *Life of Birds*. BBC Books, London.

Axell, H. E. 1966. Eruptions of Bearded Tits during 1959–65. *British Birds* 59: 513–543.

Babington, C. 1884–86. *Catalogue of the birds of Suffolk*. John van Voorst, London.

Bannerman, D. A. & Lodge, G. E. 1959. *The Birds of the British Isles*, Vol. 8. Oliver & Boyd, Edinburgh.

Barnes, J. A. G. 1952. The status of the Lesser Black-backed Gull. *British Birds* 45: 3–17.

Barrett, J. & Barrett, C. F. 1985 Divers in the Moray Firth, Scotland. *Scottish Birds* 13: 149–154.

Barrett, K. 1990. Great Snipe at Dagenham Chase 1st–2nd June 1989. *Essex Bird Report 1989*: 109–111.

Barrett, K. 1993. Pine Bunting at Dagenham Chase A First for Essex 12th February to 17th March 1992. *Essex Bird Report 1992*: 135–136.

Barrett, K. 1998. The status of the Marsh Warbler in Essex. *Essex Bird Report 1997*: 159–166.

Barton, B. A. B. 1958. Note on Desert Wheatear in Essex. *British Birds* 51: 275–276.

Batten, L. A. 1973. The colonisation of England by the Firecrest. *British Birds* 66: 159–166.

Batten, L. A., Bibby, C. J., Clement, P., Elliot, G. D. & Porter, R. F. 1990. *Red Data Birds in Britain*. Poyser, London.

Batty, C., Lowe, T. & Millington, R. 2003. Branta goose gallery: winter 2002/2003. *Birding World* 16: 108–113.

Baxter, E. V. & Rintoul, L. J. 1953. *The Birds of Scotland*. Oliver & Boyd.

Bayes, K. & Henderson, A. 1988. Nightingales and coppiced woodland. *RSPB Conservation Review 2*: 47–49.

Beaman, M. & Madge, S. 1998. *The Handbook of Bird Identification*. Christopher Helm, London.

Belik, V. P. 2005. The Sociable Lapwing in Eurasia; what does the future hold? *British Birds* 98: 475–485.

Bell, A. 2001. Radde's Warbler at Fairlop 1st–2nd October 2000, The first Essex record. *Essex Bird Report 2000*: 141–142.

Bell, A. 2006. Hume's Yellow-browed Warbler at Fairlop 11th January to 25th April 2004 The First Essex Record. *Essex Bird Report 2004*: 147.

Bell, B. D., Catchpole, C. K. & Corbett, K. J. 1968. Problems of censusing Reed Buntings, Sedge Warblers and Reed Warblers. *Bird Study* 15: 16–21.

Bellamy, P. E., Hinsley, S. A. & Newton, I. 1996. Factors influencing bird species numbers in small woods in southeast England. *Journal of Applied Ecology* 33: 249–262.

Benton, E. 1988. *The Dragonflies of Essex*. Essex Field Club, London.

Berthold, P. 1973. On the marked decline of the Whitethroat *Sylvia communis* and other species of song-birds in western Europe. *Journal of Ornithology* 114: 348–360.

Berthold, P. 1994. Microevolution of migratory behaviour in a bird species, the Blackcap *Sylvia atricapilla*: 1993 Witherby Lecture. *Bird Study* 42: 89–100.

Berthold, P., Helbig, A. J., Mohr, G. & Querner, U. 1992. Rapid microevolution of migratory behaviour in a wild bird species. *Nature* 360: 668–669.

Bibby, C. J. 1973. The Red-backed Shrike: a vanishing British species. *British Birds* 63: 185–205, 225–239.

Bibby, C. J. 1981. Wintering Bitterns in Britain. *British Birds* 74: 10–16.

Bibby, C. J. & Green, R. E. 1981. Autumn migration strategies of Reed and Sedge Warblers. *Ornis Scandinavica* 12: 1–12.

Bijlsma, R. G. 1995 Wielewalen Oriolus en Populieren Populus spec. Beneden Zeeniveau. *Limosa* 68: 21–28.

Bircham, P. M. M. 1989. *The Birds of Cambridgeshire*. Cambridge University Press, Cambridge.

Birkhead, T. R. 1991. *The Magpies*. Poyser, London.

Birks, J. 1990. Feral Mink and nature conservation. *British Wildlife* 1: 313–323.

Blaker, G. B. 1934. *The Barn Owl in England and Wales*. RSPB, London.

Blindell, R. M. 1975. The status of the Little Tern *Sterna albifrons* in Essex. 1950–74. *Essex Bird Report 1974*: 69–75.

Blindell, R. M. 1977. Internal Report to the Institute of Terrestrial Ecology (abridged version). *Essex Bird Report 1976*: 71–102.

Bond, G. 1992. The birds of Hanningfield Reservoir — an update for the Nineties. *Essex Bird Report 1991*: 122–131.

Bond, G. 1997. Arctic Redpolls in Thorndon Park in winter 1995/96. *Essex Bird Report 1996*: 119–124.

Bond, G. 2001. An influx of Storm Petrels into Essex in October 2000. *Essex Bird Report 2000*: 159–160.

Bond, G. 2006. Arctic Warbler at The Naze 5th–7th October 2004 The First Essex Record. *Essex Bird Report 2004*: 146.

Boorman, L. & Ranwell, D. S. 1977. *Ecology of Maplin Sands*. Institute of Terrestrial Ecology, Norwich.

Bourne, Dr W. R. P. 2003. Fred Stubbs, Egrets, Brewes and climatic change. *British Birds* 96: 332–339.

Boyd, H. 1954. The 'wreck' of Leach's Petrels in the autumn of 1952. *British Birds* 47: 137–163.

Boyd, H. 1959. Movements of marked sea and diving ducks in Europe. *Wildfowl Trust Annual Report* 10: 59–70.

Bradshaw, C. 1999. Rarities Committee Announcements. *British Birds* 92: 113–114.

Branson, N. J. B. A. & Minton, C. D. T. 1976. Moult, measurements and migration of the Grey Plover. *Bird Study* 23: 257–266.

Bree, C. R. 1863. *History of the birds of Europe, not observed in the British Isles.* Groombridge and Sons, London.

Bregnballe, T., Engstrom, H., Knief, W., van Eerden, M. R., Rijn, S. V., Kieckbusch, J. J. & Eskildsen, J. 2003. Development of the breeding population of Great Cormorants *Phalacrocorax carbo sinensis* in The Netherlands, Germany, Denmark, and Sweden during the 1990s. *Vogelwelt* 124, Suppl.: 15–26.

Briggs, K. B. 1984. The breeding ecology of coastal and inland Oystercatchers in north Lancashire. *Bird Study* 31: 141–147.

Brown, A. F. 1993. The Status of the Golden Plover *Pluvialis apricaria* in the South Pennines. *Bird Study* 40: 196–202.

Browne, Sir T. 1605–82. *Extracts from the writings of Sir Thomas Browne relating to the natural history and architecture of Norfolk in the seventeenth century.*

Bruderer, B. & Bruderer, H. 1993. Distribution and habitat preferences of Red-backed Shrikes *Lanius collurio* in southern Africa. *Ostrich* 64: 141–147.

Bryant, D. M. 1975. Breeding biology of House Martins *Delichon urbica* in relation to aerial insects abundance. *Ibis* 117: 180–216.

Buckingham, D. L., Evans, A. D., Morris, A. J., Orsman, C. J. & Yaxley, R. 1999. Use of set-aside land in winter by declining farmland bird species in the UK. *Bird Study* 46: 157–169.

Burd, F. H. 1992. Erosion and Vegetation change on the salt marshes of Essex and North Kent between 1973 and 1988. Nature Conservancy Council, Peterborough (*Research and Survey in Nature Conservation* No. 42).

Burns, D. W. 1993. Oriental Pratincole: new to the Western Palearctic. *British Birds* 86: 115–120.

Burton, R. E. 1949. Dartford Warbler breeding in Essex. *British Birds* 42: 246.

Burton, J. F. 1972. The Yellow Wagtail in London. *London Bird Report 1971*: 30–32. London Natural History Society.

Buxton, E. N. 1885. *Epping Forest.* 1st Edition. Edward Stanford, London.

Buxton, E. N. 1923. *Epping Forest.* 9th Edition. Edward Stanford, London.

Byers, C., Olsson, U. & Curson, J. 1995. *Buntings and Sparrows. A guide to the buntings and North American sparrows.* Pica Press, Mountfield.

Campbell, B. 1960. The Mute Swan census in England and Wales. 1955–56. *Bird Study* 7: 208–223.

Campbell, L., Cayford, J. & Pearson, D. 1996. Bearded Tits in Britain and Ireland. *British Birds* 89: 335–346.

Campbell, L. H. 1977. Local variations in the proportion of adult males in flocks of Goldeneye wintering in the Firth of Forth. *Wildfowl* 28: 77–80.

Camphuysen, C. J. & Leopold, M. F. *1994 Atlas of seabirds in the southern North Sea.* IBN research Report 94/6, NIOZ-Report 1994–8, IBN-DLO and NZG, Texel.

Carss, D. N. & Ekins, G. R. 2002. Further European integration: Mixed sub-species colonies of Great Cormorants *Phalacrocorax carbo* in Britain: Colony establishment, diet, and implications for fisheries management. *Ardea* 90 (1): 23–41.

Catley, G. P. & Hursthouse, D. 1985. Parrot Crossbills in Britain. *British Birds* 78: 482–505.

Cederroth, C., Johansson, C. & Svensson, L. 1999. Taiga Flycatcher in Sweden: the first record in western Europe. *Birding World* 12: 460–468.

Chandler, R. 2003. Rose-ringed Parakeets — how long have they been around? *British Birds* 96: 406–408.

Chandler, R. J. 1981. Influxes into Britain and Ireland of Red-necked Grebes and other waterbirds during winter 1978/79. *British Birds* 74: 55–81.

Chapman, A. H. 1999. *The Hobby.* Arlequin Press, Chelmsford.

Charleton, W. 1668. *Onomasticon Ziocon.*

Charman, K. 1977. The seasonal pattern of food utilisation by *Branta b. bernicla* on the coast of southeast England. pp 64–76 in *Technical Meeting on Western Palearctic Migratory Bird Management.* The Wildfowl Trust, Slimbridge.

Childrey, J. 1662. *Britannica Baconica.*

Christy, R. M. 1903. *The Victorian History of the County of Essex, Aves* pp 232–253.

Churcher, P. B. & Lawton, J. H. 1987. Predation by domestic cats in an English village. *Journal of Zoology* 212: 439–455.

Clark, J. M. & Eyre, J. A. (eds.) 1993. *Birds of Hampshire.* Hampshire Ornithological Society.

Clarke, F. & McNeil, D. A. C. 1980. Cliff-nesting colonies of House Martin *Delichon urbica* in Great Britain. *Ibis* 122: 27–42.

Clarke, R & Hewitson, G. 1993. Diets of Hen Harriers and Merlins roosting at Roydon Common. *Norfolk Bird Report 1992*: 439–443. Norfolk & Norwich Naturalists' Society.

Clarke, R. B., Coath, M., Johns, R. J. & Jones, D. B. D. 1961. Pallas's Warbler in Essex. *British Birds* 54: 73–74.

Clement, P. & Hathway, R. 2000. *Thrushes.* Christopher Helm, London.

Clement, P. & Helbig, A. J. 1998. Taxonomy and identification of chiffchaffs in the Western Palearctic. *British Birds* 91: 361–376.

Clement, P., Harris, A. & Davis, J. 1993. *Finches and Sparrows.* Christopher Helm, London.

Clements, J. F. 2000. *Birds of the World: A Checklist.* Pica, Sussex.

Clements, R. 2001. The Hobby in Britain. *British Birds* 94: 402–408.

Clements, R. 2002 .The Common Buzzard in Britain. *British Birds* 95: 377–383.

Clifton, J. 1992. Least Tern at Colne Point EWT Reserve — 29th June–1st July 1991. *Essex Bird Report 1991*: 120–121.

Cole, W. R. 1895. The Protection of Wild Birds in Essex. *Essex Naturalist* 9: 42–51. Essex Field Club.

Cook, T., O'Dowd, B. & Durdin, C. 1994. Breeding Redshanks on Essex salt marshes in 1993. *Essex Bird Report 1993*: 125–148.

Cooper, N. J., Skrzypczak, T. & Burd, F. 2000. Erosion of the salt marshes of Essex between 1988 and 1998. *Report to the Environment Agency.*

Corke, D. 1984. *The Nature of Essex.* Barracuda Books, Buckingham.

Cottridge, D. & Vinicombe, K. 1996. *Rare Birds in Britain and Ireland.* Collins, London.

Cowie, R. J. & Hinsley, S. A. 1987. Breeding success of Blue Tits and Great Tits in suburban gardens. *Ardea* 75: 81–90.

Cox, S. 1976. Some observations on the Black-headed Gull in Essex based on ringing data. *Essex Bird Report 1975*: 67–77.

Cox, S. 1983. Mute Swan Survey. *Essex Bird Report 1982*: 91–92.

Cox, S. 1993. Swallow x House Martin hybrid 21st August 1992. *Essex Bird Report 1992*: 136–137.

Cox, S. & Inskipp, T. 1978. Male Citrine Wagtail feeding young wagtails in Essex. *British Birds* 71: 209–213.

Cramp, S. & Gooders, J. 1967. The return of the House Martin. *London Bird Report 1966*: 93–98. London Natural History Society.

Cramp, S., Pettet, A. & Sharrock, J. T. R. 1960. The irruption of tits in autumn 1957. *British Birds* 53: 49–77, 99–117, 176–192.

Cranswick, P. A., Kirby, J. S. & Waters, R. J. 1992. *The Wetland Bird Survey 1991/92: Wildfowl and Wader counts.* WWT/BTO, Slimbridge.

Cranswick, P. A., Musgrove, A. J. & Pollitt, M.S. 1997. *The wetland bird survey 1995/96: Wildfowl and wader counts.* BTO/WWT/RSPB/JNCC, Slimbridge.

Cranswick, P. A., Pollitt, A., Musgrove, A. & Hughes, R. 1999. *The wetland bird survey 1997/98: Wildfowl and wader counts.* BTO/WWT/RSPB/JNCC. Slimbridge.

Cranswick, P. A., Waters, R. J., Evans, J. & Pollitt, M. S. 1995. *The Wetlands Bird Survey 1993/94: Wildfowl and Wader counts.* BTO/WWT/RSPB/JNCC, Slimbridge

Crick, H., Banks, A. & Coombes, R. 2003. Findings of the National Peregrine Survey 2002. *BTO News* 248: 8–9.

Crick, H. Q. P. 1993. Trends in breeding success of Merlin (*Falco columbarius*) in Britain from 1937–1989. In: Nicholls, M. K. & Clarke, R. (eds.) *Biology and Conservation of Small Falcons.* Hawk and Owl Trust, London: 30–38.

Crick, H. Q. P., Robinson, R. A., Appleton, G. F., Clark, N. A. & Rickard, A. D. (eds.) 2002. Investigation into the causes of the decline of starlings and house sparrows in Great Britain. *Research Report 290.* BTO, Thetford.

Dagley, J. R. 1994. Golden Orioles in East Anglia and their conservation. *British Birds* 87: 201–219.

Dale, S. 1730. *The history and antiquities of Harwich and Dovercourt.* Davis and Green, London.

Dally, A. J. A. 2000. Peregrine – A new breeding species for Essex. *Essex Bird Report 1998*: 167.

Dally, A. J. A. 2001. Stonechats in Essex. *Birding World* 14: 305–306.

Daneilsen, F., Skov, H. & Durinck, J. 1993. Estimates of the wintering populations of Red-throated Diver *Gavia stellata* and Black-throated Diver *Gavia arctica* in north-west Europe. *Proc. Nord. Congr. Ornithol. 7th* (1990): 18–24.

Daniel, Rev. W. B. 1801. *Rural Sports.* Bunny and Gold, London.

Dare, P. J. 1966. The breeding and wintering population of the Oystercatcher (*Haematopus ostralegus*)

in the British Isles. *Fisheries Invest. London*, Ser. II, 25 (5): 1–69.

Dark, S. T. E. 1936. *The Little Owl*. School Nature Study 31: 59.

Darlington, A. 1957. The status of the Rook as a nesting species in Essex. *Essex Bird Report 1956*: 51–53.

Davenport, D. L. 1982. Influxes into Britain of Hen Harriers, Long-eared Owls and Short-eared Owls in winter 1978/79. *British Birds* 75: 309–316.

Davidson, N. C., Laffoley, D. d'A., Doody, J. P., Way, L. S., Gordon, J., Key, R., Drake, C. M., Pienkowski, M. W., Mitchell, R. & Duff, K. L. 1991. *Nature Conservation and Estuaries in Great Britain*. Nature Conservancy Council, Peterborough.

Davidson, N. C. & Rothwell, P. (eds.) 1993. Disturbance of waterfowl on estuaries. *Wader Study Group Bulletin 68 Special Issue*. RSPB/WSG.

Davidson, N. C. & Wilson, J. R. 1992. The migration system of European-wintering Knot *Calidris canuta islandica*. *Wader Study Group Bulletin 64 Supplement*: 39–51.

Davies, C. 2002. The European Bird Report. *British Birds* 95: 174–188.

Davies, D. 1992. Bridled Tern at West Thurrock — A first for Essex — 2nd June 1991. *Essex Bird Report 1991*: 118.

Davies, P. 1965. Some comments on the problems of separating Reed and Marsh Warblers — a series of letters. *British Birds* 58: 181–188.

Dean A.R. & Svensson, L. 2005. 'Siberian Chiffchaff' revisited. *British Birds* 98, 8: 396–410.

Defoe, D. 1724. *Tour through the whole island of Great Britain*. Vol. 1. D. Strahan, London.

Delaney, S., Greenwood, J. J. D. & Kirby, J. 1992. *Mute Swan National Survey 1990*. Unpublished report to JNCC.

Dennis, M. K. 1986. Wintering birds in the London area. Part one: Owls. *London Bird Report 50*: 140–150. London Natural History Society.

Dennis, M. K. 1989. Pipits in Essex. *Essex Bird Report 1988*: 101–117.

Dennis, M. K. 1990. The Kingfisher. *Essex Bird Report 1989*: 122–125.

Dennis, M. K. 1991. Breeding birds in Essex 1990. *Essex Bird Report 1990*: 18–28.

Dennis, M. K. 1992a. Water Pipits at Rainham Marsh. *Essex Bird Report 1991*: 141–145.

Dennis, M. K. 1992b. Wintering Blackcaps and Chiffchaffs in the London area. *London Bird Report 1992*: 145–152. London Natural History Society.

Dennis, M. K.. 1994. Changes in breeding birds in Metropolitan Essex between 1968/72 and 1988/92. *London Bird Report 1993*: 145–158. London Natural History Society.

Dennis, M. K. 1998. Large Gulls in Essex. *Essex Bird Report 1997*: 167–176.

Dent, M. 2001. Woodcock survey of Epping Forest 2000. *Essex Bird Report 2000*: 161–163.

Dickens, C. 1877. *Dictionary of the Thames*. 8 Vols. London.

Dittberner, H. & Dittberner, W. 1987. Zur Brutbiologie der Löffelente (*Anas clypeata*). *Vogelwelt* 108: 81–98.

Dobinson, H. M. & Richards, A. J. 1964. The effects of the severe winter of 1962/63 on birds in Britain. *British Birds* 57: 373–434.

Donald, P. F., Wilson, D. W. & Shepherd, M. 1994. The decline of the Corn Bunting. *British Birds* 87: 106–132.

Donovan, E. 1799–1819. *Natural History of Birds*. London.

Doody, J. P., Johnston, C. & Smith, B. (eds.) 1993. *Directory of the North Sea Coastal Margin*. JNCC, Peterborough.

Doubleday, H. 1836. *A nomenclature of British birds*. Wesley and Davis, London.

Dowsett, R. J., Backhurst, G. C. & Oatley, T. B. 1988. Afrotropical ringing recoveries of Palearctic migrants 1. Passerines (Turdidae to Oriolidae). *Tauraco* 1: 29–63.

Dubois, P. J. 2001. Les formes nicheuses de la Bergeronnette printanière *Motacilla flava* en France. *Ornithos* 8: 44–73.

Durinck, J., Skov, H. & Andell, P. 1993. Seabird distribution and numbers in selected offshore parts of the Baltic Sea, winter 1992. *Ornis Svecica* 3: 11–26.

Dymond, J. N., Fraser, P. & Gantlett, S. 1989. *Rare birds in Britain and Ireland*. Poyser, Calton.

Eagle Clarke, W. 1912. *Studies in Bird Migration*. Gurney and Jackson, London.

Ebbinge, B. S. 1989. A multifactorial explanation for variation in breeding performance of Brent Geese. *Ibis* 131: 196–204.

Ebbinge, B. S. 1991. The impact of hunting on mortality rates and spatial distribution of geese wintering in the Western Palearctic. *Ardea* 79: 197–209.

Ebbinge, B. S. & St Joseph, A. K. M. 1992. Population limitation in Arctic-breeding geese. The Brent Goose colour-ringing scheme 93–104.

Edwards, G. 1743–51. *A Natural History of Uncommon Birds*. London

Ekins, G. R. 1984. Notes on an apparent Wigeon/ American Wigeon hybrid. *Essex Bird Report 1983*: 84–85

Ekins, G. R. 1995. The Abberton Reservoir Cormorant colony. *Essex Bird Report 1994*: 153–167.

Ekins, G. R. 1998. Essex Ringing Report 1997. *Essex Bird Report 1997*: 119–130.

Ekins, G. R. 2000. Spotted Redshanks at Abberton Reservoir in autumn 1998. *Essex Bird Report 1998*: 168–173.

Ekins, G. R. 2002. The Passage of Honey Buzzards through Essex in Autumn 2000. *Essex Bird Report 2000*: 144–158.

Ekins, G. R. & Steward, L. 1994. Analysis of the Food of Long-eared Owls. *Essex Bird Report 1993*: 149–155.

Eldridge, M. & Harrop, A. 1992. Identification and status of Baikal Teal. *Birding World* 5: 417–423.

Elkins, N. 1983. *Weather and bird behaviour*. Poyser, Calton.

Elkins, N. 1988. *Weather and bird behaviour*. 2nd Edition. Poyser, Calton.

Elkins, N. & Yesou, P. 1998. Sabine's Gulls in western France and southern Britain. *British Birds* 91: 386–397.

Enoksson, B. 1990. Autumn territories and population regulation in the Nuthatch *Sitta europaea*: an experimental study. *Journal of Animal Ecology* 59: 1047–1062.

Ennokson, B. & Nilsson, S. G. 1983. Territory size and population density in relation to food supply in the Nuthatch *Sitta europaea*. *Journal of Animal Ecology* 52: 927–935.

Evans, A. 1997. Cirl Buntings in Britain. *British Birds* 90: 267–281.

Evans, L. G. R. 1994. *Rare birds in Britain*. Privately published.

Felstead, G. 1961. The Nesting of the Collared Dove in Essex. *Essex Bird Report 1960*: 54–55.

Ferguson-Lees, J. & Christie, D. A. 2001. *Helm Identification Guides: Raptors of the World*. Christopher Helm, London.

Fisher, J. 1953. The Collared Turtle Dove in Europe. *British Birds* 46: 153–181.

Fisher, J. 1966. *The Shell Bird Book*. Ebury Press & Michael Joseph, Norwich.

Fitter, R. S. R. 1959. The status of the Great Black Woodpecker in the British Isles. *Bulletin BOC* 70: 79–87, 102–108, 109–113.

Fitter, R. S. R. 1992. From the Archives. The Black Woodpecker, a lost British bird. *Birding World* 5: 75–77.

Fiuczynski, D. & Nethersole-Thompson, D. 1980. Hobby studies in England and Germany. *British Birds* 73: 275–295.

Flegg, J. J. M. 1973. A study of Treecreepers. *Bird Study* 21: 287–302.

Forsman, D. 1995. The Stiffkey harrier. *Birding World* 8: 420–421.

Forsyth, L. 2005. *Island of Wildlife*. Essex Wildlife Trust.

Fox, A. D. 1988. Breeding status of the Gadwall in Britain and Ireland. *British Birds* 81: 51–66

Fox, A. D. 1991. History of the Pochard breeding in Britain. *British Birds* 84: 83–98.

Fraser, P. & Ryan, J. 1995. The status of the Great Grey Shrike in Britain and Ireland. *British Birds* 88: 478–485.

Fraser, P. A., Lansdown, P. G., & Rogers, M. J. 1997. Report on Scarce Migrant Birds in Britain in 1995. British Birds 90: 413–439.

Fraser, P. A., Lansdown, P. G., & Rogers, M. J. 2000. Report on Scarce Migrant Birds in Britain in 1998. *British Birds* 93: 588–641.

Fraser, P. A. & Rogers, M. J. 2002. Report on scarce migrants in Britain in 2000. *British Birds* 95: 606–630.

Fraser, P. A. & Rogers, M. J. 2004. Report on scarce migrants in Britain in 2002 Part 1. *British Birds* 97: 647–664.

Fraser, P. A. & Rogers, M. J. 2005. Report on scarce migrants in Britain in 2002 Part 2. *British Birds* 98: 73–88.

Freeman, S. N. & Crick, H. Q. P. 2003. The decline of the Spotted Flycatcher *Muscicapa striata* in the UK: an integrated population model. *Ibis* 145: 400–412.

Frith, M. & Gedge, D. 2001. The Black Redstart in urban Britain – a conservation conundrum? *British Wildlife* 11: 381–388.

Fuller, R. J. 1982. *Bird Habitats in Britain*. Poyser, Calton.

Fuller, R. J. & Lloyd, D. 1981. The Distribution and Habitats of Wintering Golden Plovers in Britain, 1977–78. *Bird Study* 28: 169–185.

Fuller, R. J., Baker, J. K., Morgan, R. A., Scroggs R. & Wright, M. 1985. Breeding populations of the Hobby *Falco subbuteo* on farmland in the southern Midlands of England. *Ibis* 127: 510–516.

Fuller, R. J., Gregory, R. D., Gibbons, D. W., Marchant, J. H., Wilson, J. D., Baillie, S. R. & Carter, N. 1995. Population declines and range contractions among lowland farmland birds in Britain. *Conservation Biology* 9: 1425–1441.

Fuller, R. J., Noble, D. G., Smith, K. W. & Vanhinsbergh, D. 2005. Recent declines in populations of woodland birds in Britain: a review of possible causes. *British Birds* 98: 116–143.

Fuller, R. J. & Youngman, R. E. 1979. The Utilisation of Farmland by Golden Plovers wintering in Southern England. *Bird Study* 26: 37–46.

Fuller, T. 1662. *History of the Worthies of England.*

Furness, R. W. 1987. *The Skuas.* Poyser, Calton.

Gantlett, S. & Millington, R. 2000. Honey Buzzards in September 2000. *Birding World* 13: 363–365.

Garner, M. & Quinn, D. 1997. Identification of Yellow-legged Gulls in Britain. *British Birds* 90: 25–62.

Garner, M., Quinn, D. & Glover, B. 1997. Identification of Yellow-legged Gulls in Britain. *British Birds* 90: 369–383.

Gibbs, G. 1993. Wildfowl and waders of the Blackwater Estuary. *Essex Bird Report 1992*: 138–148.

Gibbs, G. 2000. A survey of breeding birds in the Mores Wood from 1981–1998. *Essex Bird Report 1998*: 159–166.

Gibson, C. 2003. *The Essex Coast — its wildlife and conservation.* English Nature, Colchester.

Gibson, C. 2005. Wildlife and Conservation review of the year 2004. *Essex Naturalist* 22: 15–25. Essex Field Club.

Gilbert, G. 2002. The status and habitats of Spotted Crakes *Porzana porzana* in Britain in 1999. *Bird Study* 49: 79–86.

Gilbert, G., Gibbons, D. W. & Evans, J. 1998. *Bird Monitoring Methods.* RSPB, Sandy.

Giles, N. 1992. *Wildlife after gravel.* Game Conservancy Ltd., Fordingbridge.

Gillings, S. & Fuller, R. J. 2001. Habitat selection by Skylarks *Alauda arvensis* wintering in Britain in Britain in 1997/98. *Bird Study* 48: 293–307.

Glegg, W. 1927. On the authenticity of a specimen of American Swallow-tailed Kite recently added to the Essex Museum, Stratford. *Essex Naturalist* 21: 269. Essex Field Club.

Glegg, W. 1929. Various notes on the birds of Essex. *Essex Naturalist* 23: 19. Essex Field Club.

Glover, R. 1979. Roosting movements on Essex estuaries. *Essex Bird Report 1978*: 70–92.

Glue, D. E. 1994. The Black Redstart: Rise and fall. *Birdwatch* 29: 4–7.

Glue, D. E. 2000. Conserving Britain's trio of woodpeckers. *BTO News* 228: 22–24.

Glue, D. E. 2002. Kites and Parakeets add colour to midwinter bird tables. *BTO News* 242: 6–7.

Glue, D. E. & Boswell, T. 1994. Comparative nesting ecology of the three British breeding woodpeckers. *British Birds* 87: 253–269.

Gooch, S., Baillie, S. R. & Birkhead, T. R. 1991. Magpie *Pica pica* and songbird populations. Retrospective investigation of trends in population density and breeding success. *Journal of Applied Ecology* 28: 1068–1086.

Goodey, A. 1986. *A History of the Birds of the Roman River Valley. Nature in North East Essex.* CNHS, Colchester.

Goodey, A. 2001. The Woodlark in Essex. *Essex Bird Report 1999*: 141–153.

Grant P. J. & the Rarities Committee. 1982. Removal of species from Rarities Committee list. *British Birds* 75: 338.

Green, N. 2000. Obituary Geoffrey A. Pyman 1920–1999. *Essex Bird Report 1998*: 3–4.

Green, N. 2002. American Bittern *Botaurus lentiginosus*: an historic first for Essex. *Essex Naturalist* 19: 23–42. Essex Field Club.

Green, N. 2003. Avifauna update: Essex's 1908 Spotted Eagle, setting the record straight. *Essex Birding* 103: 34–35.

Green, N. 2004a. Immature White-tailed Eagle at Alresford, Essex: December 1868. *Essex Birding* 105: 29–30.

Green, N. 2004b. Missing London Bird Report data. *Essex Bird Report 2003*: 136–144.

Green, N. 2005. Yellow-billed Diver in Chelmsford Museum — the earliest record for Scotland and fourth for Britain. *Scottish Birds* 25: 59–61.

Green, N. 2006. 1866 Two-barred Crossbill at Dedham, Essex. *Essex Birding* 108: 24.

Green, P. 1995. Bonaparte's Gull at Hadleigh marshes, 27th August. The first Essex Record. *Essex Bird Report 1994*: 123.

Green, R. E. & Cadbury, C. J. 1987. Breeding waders of Lowland Wet Grasslands. *RSPB Conservation Review* 1: 10–13.

Greenoak, F. 1981. *All the Birds of the Air.* Penguin. London.

Greensmith, J. T. & Tucker, E. V. 1965. Salt marsh erosion in Essex. *Nature* 206: 606–607.

Gregory, R. D., Wilkinson, N. I., Noble, D. G., Robinson, J. A., Brown, A. F., Hughes, J., Procter, D., Gibbons, D. W. & Galbraith, C. A. 2002. The population status of birds in the United Kingdom, Channel Islands and Isle of Man: an analysis of conservation concern 2002–2007. *British Birds* 95: 410–448.

Grimmett, R., Inskipp, C. & Inskipp, T. 1998. *Birds of the Indian Subcontinent.* Christopher Helm, London.

Grussu, M. & Biondi, M. 2004. Record numbers of wintering Richard's Pipits in the Western Palearctic. *British Birds* 97: 192–197.

Hanson, M. W. 1992. *Epping Forest*. Essex Field Club, London.

Harrandine, J. 1985. Duck shooting in the United Kingdom. *Wildfowl* 36: 81–94.

Harrap, S. & Quinn, D. 1996. *Tits, Nuthatches and Treecreepers*. Christopher Helm, London.

Harris, A. 2004. Lesser Scaup at Seventy Acres Lake area 23rd–25th March 2003 The first Essex record. *Essex Bird Report 2003*: 130–131.

Harris, P. 1976. Desert Warbler at Frinton-on-Sea. *Essex Bird Report 1975*: 60–61.

Harris, S. 2001. Changes to Wetland Bird Survey areas and Essex recording boundaries. *Essex Bird Report 2000*: 18–19.

Harrison, C. 1988. *The history of the Birds of Britain*. Collins, London.

Harrison, J. G. 1979. A new overland migration route of *Branta bernicla bernicla* on the coast of south-east England in autumn. *Proceedings of the First Technical Meeting on Western Palearctic Migratory Bird Management* 60–63.

Harrison, J. G. & Grant, P. J. 1976. *The Thames Transformed*. London.

Harrison, J. M. 1953. *The Birds of Kent*. Witherby, London.

Harrison, T. H. & Hollom, P. A. D. 1932. The Great Crested Grebe enquiry, 1931. *British Birds* 26: 62–92, 102–131, 142–155, 174–195.

Harrop, A. 1992. The status of Red-crested Pochard. *Birding World* 4: 171–175

Harrop, A. 2002. The Ruddy Shelduck in Britain. *British Birds* 95: 123–128.

Harting, J. E. 1872. *A Handbook of British Birds*. 1st Edition. Van Voorst, London.

Harting, J. E. 1901. *A Handbook of British Birds*. 2nd Edition. Nimmo, London.

Hawkins, I. 1995. The Birdlife of Old Hall Marsh, an update. *Essex Bird Report 1994*: 126–152.

Hayman, P., Marchant, J. & Prater, T. 1986. *Shorebirds*. Croom Helm, London.

Hengveld, R. & van den Bosch, F. 1991. The expansion velocity of the Collared Dove *Streptopelia decaocto* population in Europe. *Ardea* 79: 67–72.

Herremans, M. 1993. Seasonal dynamics in the sub-Kalahari bird communities with emphasis on migrants. *Proc. VIII Pan-African Ornithological Congress* 555–564.

Heubeck, M. 2002. The decline of the Shetland's Kittiwake population. *British Birds* 95: 118–122.

Hibbert-Ware, A. 1922. Notes on gizzard contents of birds collected by Miller Christy. *Essex Naturalist* 20: 142–150. Essex Field Club.

Hibbert-Ware, A. 1938. Report of the Little Owl Food Inquiry 1936–37. *British Birds* 31: 62–187, 205–229, 249–264.

Hill, D. 1988. Population dynamics of the Avocet (*Recurvirostra avosetta*) breeding in Britain. *Journal of Animal Ecology* 57: 669–683.

Hirschfield, E., Roselaar, C. S. & Shirihai, H. 2000. Identification, taxonomy and distribution of Greater and Lesser Sand Plovers. *British Birds* 93: 162–189.

Hobbs, M. 2003. Searching souls. *Birdwatch* 134: 27–30.

Hollinshed, R. 1587. *The Chronicles of England, Scotland and Wales*. 3 Vols. London.

Hollyer, J. N. 1970. The invasion of Nutcrackers in autumn 1968. *British Birds* 63: 353–373.

Homes, R. C. (ed.) 1957. 1st edition. *The Birds of the London Area since 1900*. Rupert Hart-Davis, London.

Hoodless, A. 1995. Studies of West Palearctic birds. 195. Eurasian Woodcock *Scolopax rusticola*. *British Birds* 88: 578–592.

Howard, N. S. & Carroll, J. P. 2001. Driven game shooting on farms in Essex, UK: Implications of land management and conservation. *Game and Wildlife Science* 18: 157–169.

Hudgell, S. & Smith, J. T. 1974. The birds of Hanningfield Reservoir. *Essex Bird Report 1973*: 63–78.

Hudson, R. 1972. Collared Doves in Britain and Ireland during 1965–70. *British Birds* 65: 139–155.

Hudson, R. 1974. Feral Parakeets near London. *British Birds* 67: 33.

Hudson, W. H. 1898. *Birds in London*. Longmans, Green & Co., London.

Hughes, B., Bruce, J., Ekins, G. & Newson, S. 2000. Movements and distribution of inland Cormorants breeding in Great Britain. *Research Report 360*. English Nature, Peterborough.

Hughes, B., Underhill, M. & Delaney, S. 1998. Ruddy Duck breeding in the UK in 1994. *British Birds* 91: 336–353.

Hughes, S. W. M., Bacon, P. & Flegg, J. J. M. 1979. The 1975 census of the Great Crested Grebe in Britain. *Bird Study* 26: 213–226.

Hurrell, Sir A. 1989. 26 years garden ringing. *Essex Bird Report 1988*: 118–123.

Hustings, F. & Bekhuis, J. 1993. Red-backed Shrikes in present-day Netherlands: remnants of a glorious past. *Vogeljaar* 41: 2–17.

Hutchinson, B. & Neath, C. D. 1978. Little Gulls in Britain and Ireland. *British Birds* 71: 563–582.

Inglis, I. R., Isaacson, A. J., Theale, R. J. P. & Westwood, N. J. 1990. The effects of changing agricultural practices upon Woodpigeon numbers. *Ibis* 132: 262–272.

Jameson, C. 2000. Farming and Wildlife. *Birds* Spring 2000 pp 37–48 RSPB.

Jarry, G. 1994. Turtle Dove *Streptopelia turtur*. In Birds in Europe: their conservation status, pp 320–321. *Conservation Series No. 3*. Birdlife International, Cambridge.

Jarry. G. 1995. Tourterelle des bois *Streptopelia turtur*. In *Nouvel Atlas des Oiseaux nicheurs de France 1985–1989*, pp 380–383. Société Ornithologique de France, Paris.

Jennings, A. R., Soulsby, E. J. L. & Wainwright, C. B. 1961. An outbreak of disease in Mute Swans at an Essex Reservoir. *Bird Study* 8: 19–24.

Jesse, E. 1844. *Scenes and Tales of Country Life*.

Johnson, I. G. 1970. The Water Pipit as a winter visitor to the British Isles. *Bird Study* 17: 297–319.

Jonsson, L. 1998. Baltic Lesser Black-backed Gull *Larus fuscus fuscus* — moult, ageing and identification. *Birding World* 11: 295–317.

Jourdain, Rev. F. C. R. 1918. On the breeding of the Honey Buzzard in Essex. *Essex Naturalist* 18: 238–240. Essex Field Club.

Kane, A. 1993. Greater Sand Plover at East Tilbury. A first for Essex — 10th–14th August 1992. *Essex Bird Report 1992*: 132–133.

Kear, J. 1990. *Man and wildfowl*. Poyser, Calton.

Kelsey, M. G., Green, G. H., Garnett, M. C. & Hayman, P. V. 1989. Marsh Warblers in Britain. *British Birds* 82: 239–256.

Kettle, A. 2006. Lesser Scaup at Abberton Reservoir 11th December to 2005 The Second Essex record. *Essex Bird Report 2004*: 144.

King, J. 1999. Ruddy Duck hybrid in Turkey. *Birding World* 12: 260.

Kirby, J. S. & Lack, P. C. 1993. Spatial Dynamics of Wintering Lapwings and Golden Plovers in Britain and Ireland, 1982/83 to 1983/84. *Bird Study* 40: 38–50.

Kirby, J. S., Salmon, D. G., Atkinson-Willes, G. L. & Cranswick, P. A. 1995. Index numbers for waterbird populations, III. Long-term trends in the abundance of wintering wildfowl in Great Britain, 1966/67–1991/92. *Journal of Applied Ecology* 32: 536–551.

Kirby, J. S., Waters, R. J. & Prys-Jones, R. P. 1990. Wildfowl and Wader Counts 1989–1990. *The Results of the National Wildfowl Counts and Birds of Estuaries Enquiry in the United Kingdom*. Wildfowl and Wetlands Trust, Slimbridge.

Kleinschmidt, O. 1898. *Weitere Notizen über Sumpfmeisen. Orn. Monatsber* 6: 33–36.

Knox, A. G. 1988. Taxonomy of the Rock/Water Pipit superspecies *Anthus petrosus*, *spinoletta* and *rubescens*. *British Birds* 81: 206–211.

Knox, A. G. 2001. The Bufflehead in Britain. *British Birds* 94: 61–73.

Knox, A. G., Helbig, A. J., Parkin, D. T. & Sangster, G. 2001. The taxonomic status of Lesser Redpoll. *British Birds* 94: 260–267.

Kramer, D. 1995. Inland spring passage of Arctic Terns in southern Britain. *British Birds* 88: 211–217.

Kuhnen, K. 1975. Bestandsentwicklung, Verbreitung, Biotop und Siedlungsditche der Uferscwalbe (*Riparia riparia*) 1966–73 am Niederrhein. *Charadrius*. 11: 1–24.

Lambrecht, K. 1917. Die Ausbildung und Geschichte der europäischen Vogelwelt. *Aquila* 24: 191–221.

Lane, S. J. & Miyabayashi, Y. 1997. Status and distribution of Pacific Brent Geese (*Branta bernicla nigricans*) wintering in Japan. *Wildfowl* 48: 108–117.

Langlow, D. R. 1976. Weights of Blackcaps on migration. *Ringing and Migration* 1: 78–91.

Langston, Dr R., Gregory, Dr R. & Adams, R. 2002. The Status of the Hawfinch in the UK. *British Birds* 95: 166–173.

Lansdown, A. 2004. A trio of Red-rumped Swallows at Ardleigh 2nd May 2003. *Essex Bird Report 2003*: 135.

Larkin, P. & Mercer, D. 2004. Canvasback in Kent: new to Britain. *British Birds* 97: 139–143.

Laursen, K. 1989. Estimates of sea duck wintering populations of the Western Palearctic. *Danish Review of Game Biology* 13: 1–22.

Laursen, K., Pihl, S. & Komdeur, J. 1992. New figures of sea duck wintering populations in the Western Palearctic. *IRWB Seaduck Bulletin* 1: 6–8.

Laver, H. 1898. The Mammals, Fishes and Reptiles of Essex. *Essex Field Club Special Memoirs No. 3*.

Lawton, N. 2000. An unprecedented movement of Swallows and House Martins. *Norfolk Bird Report, 1999*: 282–283. Norfolk & Norwich Naturalists' Society.

Leach, I. H. 1981. Wintering Blackcaps in Britain and Ireland. *Bird Study* 28: 5–14.

Lefranc, N. & Wolfolk, T. 1997. *Shrikes*. Pica Press, Robertsbridge.

Legge, W. V. 1880. *History of the birds of Ceylon*. Privately published.

Lever, C. 1977. *The Naturalised Animals of the World.* Hutchinson.

Lever, C. 1987. *The Naturalised Birds of the World.* Longman, London.

Lewis, C. 2000. *Birds of the Foulness area: a report for the millennium.* Privately published.

Lilford, Lord. 1885–1897. *Coloured Figures of the Birds of the British Isles.*

Linsell, S. E. 1969. Pre-dusk and nocturnal behaviour of Goldeneye, with notes on population composition. *Wildfowl* 20: 75–77.

Little, B. & Furness, R. W. 1985. Long-distance moult migration by British Goosanders *Mergus merganser. Ringing and Migration* 6: 77–82.

Lloyd, C., Tasker, M. L. & Partridge, K. 1991. *The status of Seabirds in Britain and Ireland.* Poyser, London.

Lock, L. & Cook, K. 1998. The Little Egret in Britain: a successful colonist. *British Birds* 91: 273–280.

Lockwood, W. B. 1993. *The Oxford Dictionary of British Bird Names.* Oxford University Press, Oxford.

Lorand, S & Atkin, K. 1989. *The Birds of Lincolnshire & Humberside.* Leading Edge, North Yorkshire.

Love, R. A. 1997. The analysis of Barn Owl pellets from the Dengie Hundred, Essex. *Essex Bird Report 1996*: 125–131.

Luff, R. 1993. *Colchester Archaeological Trust Report 12;* Animal bones from excavations in Colchester, 1971–85. Colchester Archaeological Trust Ltd., Colchester.

Lundberg, A. & Alatalo, R. V. 1993. *The Pied Flycatcher.* Poyser, London

Mackenzie-Grieve, C. 1979. Terek Sandpiper at Old Hall Marshes, Tollesbury, May 29th 1978, *Essex Bird Report 1978*: 61–62.

Madge, S. & Burn, H. 1988. *Wildfowl, an Identification Guide.* Christopher Helm, London.

Madge, S. & Burn, H. 1994. *Crows and Jays.* Christopher Helm, London.

Madsen, J. 1991. Western Palearctic Geese: Status and Trends of Goose Populations in the Western Palearctic in the 1980s. *Ardea* 79: 113–122.

Mairs, D. 2004. The charlatans who tried to stuff history. *Birdwatch* 141: 6–7.

Marchant, J. H. & Balmer, D. 1994. Common Bird Census: 1992–93 index report. *BTO News* 193: 11–14.

Marchant, J. H., Freeman, S. N., Crick, H. Q. P. & Beaven, L. P. 2004. The BTO Heronries Census of England and Wales 1928–2000: new indices

and a comparison of analytical methods. *Ibis* 146: 323–334.

Mason, C. F. 1998. Habits of the Song Thrush *Turdus philomelos* in a largely arable landscape. *J. Zool. Lond.* 244: 89–93.

Mason, C. F. 2000. Thrushes now largely restricted to the built environment in eastern England. *Diversity and distributions* 6: 189–194.

Mason, C. F. 2001. Woodland area, species turnover and the conservation of bird assemblages in lowland England. *Biodiversity and Conservation* 10: 495–510.

Mason, C. F. 2003. Some correlates of density in an urban Blackbird *Turdus merula* population. *Bird Study* 50: 185–188.

Mason, C. F. & Macdonald, S. M. 1999a. Habitat use by Lapwings and Golden Plovers in a largely arable landscape. *Bird Study* 46: 89–99.

Mason, C. F. & Macdonald, S. M. 1999b. Estuarine feeding by Lapwings *Vanellus vanellus* and Golden Plovers *Pluvialis apricaria. Wildfowl* 50: 205–207.

Mason, C. F. & Macdonald, S. M. 1999c. Winter bird numbers and land-use preferences in an arable landscape in eastern England. *Bird Conservation International* 9: 119–127.

Mason, C. F. & Macdonald, S. M. 2000a. Influence of landscape and land-use on the distribution of breeding birds in farmland in eastern England. *J. Zool. Lond.* 251: 339–348.

Mason, C. F. & Macdonald, S. M. 2000b. Corn Buntings *Miliaria calandra* populations, landscape and land-use in an arable district of eastern England. *Bird Conservation International* 10: 169–186.

Mason, C. F. & Macdonald, S. M. 2000c. Numbers of wintering waterbirds on rivers in eastern England. *Wildfowl* 51: 215–219.

Mason, C. F. & Macdonald, S. M. 2004. Distribution of foraging Rooks *Corvus frugilegus* and rookeries in a landscape in eastern England dominated by winter cereals. *Folia. Zool.* 53 (2): 179–188.

Mayhew, P. W. The daily energy intake of European Wigeon in winter. *Ornis Scandinavica* 19: 217–223.

Mead, C. J. 1978. Tern mortality in West Africa and shown by British and Dutch ringing recoveries. *Ibis* 120: 110.

Mead, C. J. 1984. Sand Martins slump. *BTO News* 133: 1.

Mead, C. J. 2000. *The state of the nation's birds.* Whittet Books, Stowmarket.

Meadows, B. S. 1961. The Gull roosts of the Lea Valley Reservoirs. *London Bird Report 60*: 55–60. London Natural History Society.

Meadows, B. S. 1972a. Heron numbers since the severe winter of 1962/63. *Essex Bird Report 1971*: 63–69.

Meadows, B. S. 1972b. The recovery of the Kingfisher in London after the 1962/63 hard winter. *London Bird Report 36*: 60–65. London Natural History Society.

Merrett, C. 1666. *Pina Rerum Natularium Britannicarum*.

Messanger, D. 2001. Adult Little Gulls summering in Britain, 1975–97. *British Birds* 94: 310–314.

Metcalfe, N. B. & Furness, R. W. 1985. Survival, winter population stability and site fidelity in Turnstone *Arenaria interpres*. *Bird Study* 32: 207–214.

Middleton, A. D. 1965. *Game records and census in Great Britain*. International Union of Game Biologists.

Middleton, J. 1986. Wing-lengths and weights of Wheatears *Oenanthe oenanthe* caught on the northwest coast of Norfolk. The Northwest Norfolk Ringing Group Annual Report 1996: 38–48.

Mikkola, H. 1983. *Owls of Europe*. Poyser, Calton.

Miller, J. 1977. Sociable Plover at Hanningfield Reservoir. *Essex Bird Report 1976*: 62–63.

Miller, J. 1994. Pallid Harrier at Holliwell Point. The first record for Essex. *Essex Bird Report 1993*: 122.

Milne, B. S. 1959.Variation in a population of Yellow Wagtails. *British Birds* 52: 281–295.

Mitchell, I. P., Newton, S. F., Ratcliffe, N. & Dunn, T. E. 2004. *Seabird Populations of Britain and Ireland: Results of the Seabird 2000 Census (1998–2002)*. Poyser, London.

Møller, A. P. 1983. Breeding habitat selection in the Swallow *Hirundo rustica*. *Bird Study* 30: 134–142.

Møller, A. P. 1989. Population dynamics of a declining Swallow *Hirundo rustica* population. *Journal of Animal Ecology* 58: 1051–1063.

Money, D. 2000. The Desert Lesser Whitethroat on Teesside. *Birding World* 13: 451–453.

Montagu, Col. G. 1831. *Ornithological Dictionary of Birds*. 2nd edition. Hurst, London.

Mooij, J. H. 1997. The status of the White-fronted Goose (*Anser a. albifrons*) in the Western Palearctic. *Die Vogelwarte* 39:61–81.

Moon, H. J. 1926. Early bird marking records. *British Birds* 20: 158.

Moorcroft, D., Bradbury, R. B. & Wilson, J. D. 1997. The diet of nestling Linnets *Carduelis cannabina* before and after agricultural intensification. In *The 1997 Brighton Crop Protection Conference — Weeds* pp 923–928. British Crop Protection Council, Farnham.

Morant, P. 1768. *The history and antiquities of the county of Essex*. T. Osborne, Essex.

Moreau, R. E. 1951. The British status of the Quail and some problems of its biology. *British Birds* 44: 257–276.

Morgan, R. A. & Glue, D. E. 1977. Breeding, mortality and movements of Kingfishers. *Bird Study* 24: 15–24.

Morrison, D. 2002. Black-necked Grebe: the first successful breeding in Essex. *Essex Bird Report 2001*: 144–145.

Mountford, G. 1957. *The Hawfinch*. Collins, London.

Mullarney, K., Svennson, L., Zetterström, D. & Grant, P. 1999. *Collins Bird Guide*. HarperCollins, London.

Munster, O. A. G. 1989. The wintering of Green Sandpipers in the sewage farm of Munster. *Vogelwelt* 110: 130–142.

Murton, R. K. & Ridpath, M. G. 1962. The autumn movements of the Woodpigeon. *Bird Study* 9: 7–41.

Musgrove, A. J. 2002. The non-breeding status of the Little Egret in Britain. *British Birds* 95: 62–80.

Musgrove, A., Langston, R., Baker, H. & Ward, R. (eds.) 2003. *Estuarine Waterbirds at Low Tide: the WeBS Low Tide Counts 1992/93 to 1998/99*. WSG/BTO/WWT/RSPB/JNCC.

Nau, B. S. 1961. Sand Martin colonies in the London area. *London Bird Report 25*: 69–81. London Natural History Society.

Naylor, K. 1996. *A Reference to the Rare Birds of Britain*. Vol. 1. Privately published, Nottingham.

Neave, R. 2003. Terek Sandpiper at Heybridge GP, Maldon 25th–29th August 2002 The third Essex record. *Essex Bird Report 2002*: 139–140.

Nehls, G., Kempf, N. & Theil, M. 1992. Bestand und Verteilung mausernder Brandenten (*Tadorna tadorna*) im deutschen Wattenmeer. *Vogelwarte* 36: 221–232.

Nelson, B. 1978. *The Gannet*. Poyser, Berkhamsted.

Newson, S., Ekins, G., Hughes, B., Russell, I. & Sellers. R. 2005. Separation of North Atlantic and Continental Cormorants. *Birding World* 18: 107–111.

Newton, I. 1972. *Finches*. Collins, London.

Newton, I. 1979. *Population Ecology of Raptors*. Poyser, Berkhamsted.

Newton, I. 1985. *Finches*. 2nd Edition. Collins, London.

Newton, I. 1986. *The Sparrowhawk*. Poyser, Calton.

Newton, I. & Haas, M. B. 1984. The return of the Sparrowhawk. *British Birds* 77: 47–70.

Newton, I. & Haas, M. B. 1988. Pollutants in Merlin eggs and their effects on breeding. *British Birds* 74: 258–269.

Nicholson, E. M. 1951. *Birds and Men*. Collins, London.

Nightingale, B. & Allsopp, K. 1994. Invasion of Red-footed Falcons in spring 1992. *British Birds* 87: 223–231.

Nightingale, B. & Sharrock, J. T. R. 1982. Seabirds inland in Britain in late April 1981. *British Birds* 75: 558–566.

Nilsson, S. G. 1986. Different patterns of population fluctuations in the Wood Warbler Phylloscopus sibilatrix and the Willow Warbler *Phylloscopus trochilus*. *Vår Fågelvärld*, Suppl. 11: 161–164.

Nilsson, S. G. 1987. Limitation and regulation of population density in the Nuthatch *Sitta europaea* (Aves) breeding in natural cavities. *Journal of Animal Ecology* 56: 921–937.

Nisbet, I. C. T. 1956. Records of Wood Sandpipers in Britain in the autumn of 1952. *British Birds* 49: 49–62.

Norden, J. 1594. *Speculi Britanniae Pars: an Historical and Chorographical Description of the County of Essex*. Royal Historical Society, London.

O'Connor, R. J. & Shrubb, M. 1986. *Farming and birds*. Cambridge University Press, Cambridge.

O'Dowd, B. 1989. Isabelline Shrike at Bradwell. *Essex Bird Report 1989*: 98–99.

Occhiato, D. 2003a. Identification of Pine Bunting. *Dutch Birding* 25: 1–16.

Occhiato, D. 2003b. Pine Bunting in Italy: its status and distribution. *Dutch Birding* 25: 32–39.

Odin, N. 1997. Snow Buntings at Felixstowe Ferry — early 1997. *The Harrier* 111: 7–9. Suffolk Ornithological Group.

Ogilvie, F. M. 1892. On the recent occurrence in the British Islands of the Ruddy Sheldrake. *Zoologist* 16: 392–398.

Ogilvie, M. A. 1981. The Mute Swan in Britain, 1978. *Bird Study* 28: 87–106.

Ogilvie, M. A. 1987. Movements of Tufted Duck ringed in Britain: a preliminary assessment. *Wildfowl* 38: 28–36.

Ogilvie, M. A. 2004. Non-native birds breeding in the UK in 2002. *British Birds* 97: 633–637.

Ogilvie, M. A. & St Joseph, A. K. M. 1976. Dark-bellied Brent Geese in Britain and Europe. *British Birds* 69: 422–439.

Olney, P. J. S. 1963. The food and feeding habits of Tufted Duck, *Aythya fuligula*. *Ibis* 105: 55–62.

Olsen, K. M. & Larsen, H. 2004. *Gulls of Europe, Asia and North America*. Christopher Helm, London.

Oreel, G, J. 2004. Origin of presumed African Chaffinch on Maasvlakte in April 2003. *Dutch Birding* 26: 47–48.

Owen, M., Atkinson-Willes, G. L. & Salmon, D. G. 1986. *Wildfowl in Great Britain*. 2nd Edition. Cambridge University Press, Cambridge.

Pain, D. J. & Pienkowski, M. W. (eds.) 1997. *Farming and birds in Europe: the Common Agricultural Policy and its implications for bird conservation*. Academic Press, London.

Palin, Rev. W. 1872. *More about Stifford and its neighbourhood*. Private.

Palmer, P. 2000. *Firsts for Britain and Ireland 1600–1999*. Arlequin Press, Chelmsford.

Parr, R. 1993. Nest Predation and numbers of Golden Plovers *Pluvialis apricaria* and other moorland waders. *Bird Study* 40: 223–231.

Parr, S. 1972. *Birds of Surrey*. Batsford, London.

Parrinder, E. D. 1989. Little Ringed Plovers *Charadrius dubius* in Britain in 1984. *Bird Study* 36: 147–153.

Parrinder, E. R. & Parrinder, E. D. 1969. Little Ringed Plovers in Britain in 1963–1967. *British Birds* 62: 219–223.

Parrinder, E. R. & Parrinder, E. D. 1975. Little Ringed Plovers in Britain in 1968–1973. *British Birds* 68: 359–368.

Parslow, J. L. F. 1973. *Breeding Birds of Britain and Ireland*. Poyser, Berkhamsted.

Patterson, I. J. 1982. *The Shelduck*. Cambridge University Press, Cambridge.

Paulson, R. 1926. *The Botanical Investigation of Essex*. Southeast Union of Scientific Societies.

Payn, W. H. 1962. *The Birds of Suffolk*. 1st Edition. Barrie & Rockliff, London.

Payn, W. H. 1978. *The Birds of Suffolk*. 2nd Edition. Ancient House, Ipswich.

Peach, W. J., Baillie, S. & Underhill, L. 1991. Survival of British Sedge Warblers *Acrocephalus schoenobaenus* in relation to west African rainfall. *Ibis* 133: 300–305.

Peach, W. J., Crick, H. Q. P. & Marchant, J. H. 1995. The demography of the decline in the British Willow Warbler population. *Journal of Applied Statistics* 22: 905–922.

Peach, W. J., Robinson, R. R. & Murray, K. A. 2004. Demographic and environmental causes of the decline of rural Song Thrushes *Turdus philomelos* in lowland Britain. *Ibis* (Suppl.2): 50–59.

Pease, R. M. & Sutherby, J. C. 1991. Circus summer. *Essex Bird Report 1990*: 137–139.

Peck, K. M. 1989. Tree species preferences shown by foraging birds in forest plantations in northern England. *Biological Conservation* 48: 41–57.

Pennant, T. 1777. *British Zoology: Genera of Birds*. 4 Vols. Chichester and London.

Pennington, M., Harvey, P., Osborn, K., Ellis, P., Heubeck, M. & Okill, D. 2004. *The Birds of Shetland*. Christopher Helm, London.

Pepper, N. 1996. Hermit Thrush at Chipping Ongar 28th October–3rd November 1995, the first Essex and fifth British record. *Essex Bird Report 1995*: 114–115.

Percival, S. M. 1990. Recent trends in Barn and Tawny Owl populations in Britain. *BTO Research Report No. 57*. BTO, Tring.

Perrins, C. 1971. Age of first breeding and adult survival rates in the Swift. *Bird Study* 18: 61–70.

Perrins, C. 1979. *British Tits*. Collins, London.

Perrins, C. 2003. The status of Marsh and Willow Tits in the UK. *British Birds* 96: 418–426.

Peterson, R., Mountford, G. & Hollom, P. A. D. 1954. *Field Guide to the Birds of Britain and Europe*. Collins, London.

Pienkowski, M. W. & Evans, P. R. 1982. Breeding behaviour, productivity and survival of colonial and non-colonial Shelducks *Tadorna tadorna*. *Ornis. Scandinavica* 13: 101–116.

Piotrowski, S. 2003. *The birds of Suffolk*. Christopher Helm, London.

Pollitt, M., Cranswick, P., Musgrove, A., Hall, C., Hearn, R., Robinson, J. & Holloway, S. 2000. *The Wetland Bird Survey 1998–99: Wildfowl and Wader counts*. BTO/WWT/RSPB/JNCC. Slimbridge.

Pollitt, M., Hall, C., Holloway, S., Hearn, R., Marshall, P., Musgrove, A. J., Robinson, J. & Cranswick, P. A. 2003. *The Wetland Bird Survey 2000–01: Wildfowl and wader counts*. BTO/WWT/RSPB/JNCC. Slimbridge.

Potts, G. R. 1981. Fewer Woodpigeons? *Game Conservancy Annual Review* 12: 83–87.

Poulsen, J. G. & Sotherton, N. W. 1993. Skylarks on farmland: A species in decline. In *Game Conservancy Review of 1992*.

Prater, A. J. 1972. The wader populations of the Essex coast. *Essex Bird Report 1971*: 52–60.

Prater, A. J. 1973. The wintering population of Ruffs in Britain and Ireland. *Bird Study* 20: 245–250.

Prater, A. J. 1981. *Estuary Birds of Britain and Ireland*. Poyser, London.

Prater, A. J. 1989. Ringed Plover *Charadrius hiaticula* breeding population of the United Kingdom in 1984. *Bird Study* 36: 154–159.

Prater, A. J., Marchant, J. H. & Vuorinen, J. 1977. Guide to the identification and ageing of Holarctic Waders. *BTO Guide No 17*: 168.

Prentice, I. 1990. Lesser Grey Shrike at Wakering Stairs 17th–19th August 1989 — A new bird for Essex. *Essex Bird Report 1989*: 113–114.

Prestt, I. & Mills, D. H. 1966. A census of the Great Crested Grebe in Britain, 1965. *Bird Study* 13: 163–203.

Prince, P. & Clarke, R. 1993. The Hobby's breeding range in Britain — What factors have allowed it to expand? *British Wildlife* 4: 341–346.

Pyman, G. A. 1938a. Private correspondence with W. E. Glegg 24th February 1938.

Pyman, G. A. 1938b. Private correspondence with W. E. Glegg 24th March 1938.

Pyman, G. A. 1938c. Private correspondence with W. E. Glegg 11th April 1938.

Pyman, G. A. 1938d. Private correspondence with A. R. Thompson 24th May 1938.

Pyman, G. A. 1938e. Private correspondence with Mr Hortin 30th May 1938.

Pyman, G. A. 1947. Private correspondence with W. E. Glegg 25th November 1947.

Pyman, G. A. 1948. Private correspondence with A. R. V. Marshall 2nd November 1948.

Pyman, G. A. 1953. Swallow and House Martin Autumn migration Inquiry 1952. *Essex Bird Report 1952*: 41–43.

Pyman, G. A. 1956. Hanningfield Reservoir — notes on the flooding of the reservoir and its effect on the ornithology. *Essex Bird Report 1955*: 50–51.

Pyman, G. A. 1959. The Status of the Red-crested Pochard in the British Isles. *British Birds* 52: 42–55.

Pyman, G. A. 1967. The Stone Curlew in Essex. *Essex Bird Report 1966*: 51–53.

Pyman, G. A. 1980. A. E. Holman NDP An Appreciation. *Essex Bird Report 1979*: 95.

Pyman, G. A. & Spencer, R. 1954. Bird-Watching in Essex. (leaflet). *Occasional Publications No. 21*. Royal Society for the Protection of Birds. Claridge, Lewis & Jordan Ltd., London.

Pyman, G. A. & Wainwright, C. B. 1952. The breeding of the Gull-billed Tern in Essex. *British Birds 1952*: 337–338.

Rackham, O. 1986. Animals & Plants. Extinctions and new Arrivals. *The History of the Countryside*. Dent, London.

Rackham, O. 1989. *The Last Forest: The Story of Hatfield Forest*. Phoenix, London.

Radford, D. 2003. Food for thought? *BTO News* 2003: 22.

Ransdale, N. 2006a. American Golden Plover at Old Hall Marshes RSPB 24th July to 4th August The First Essex Record. *Essex Bird Report 2004*: 142.

Ransdale, N. 2006b. Squacco Heron at Abberton Reservoir 5th June 2004 The First Essex record. *Essex Bird Report 2004*: 143.

Raven, M. & Noble, D. 2003. Common bird population changes — 1994–2002. *BTO News* 249: 8–9.

Raven, P. 1986. Changes in the breeding bird population of a small clay river following flood alleviation works. *Bird Study* 33: 24–35.

Ravenscroft, N. O. M. & Beardall, C. H. 2003. The importance of freshwater flows over estuarine mudflats for wintering waders and wildfowl. *Biological Conservation* 113: 89–97.

Ray, J. 1678. *Ornithology of Francis Willoughby*.

Ray, J. 1686. *Historia plantarum*.

Reaney, P. H. 1969. The Place-Names of Essex. Cambridge University Press, Cambridge.

Rebecca, G. W. & Bainbridge, I. P. 1998. The breeding status of the Merlin *Falco columbarius* in Britain in 1993–94. *Bird Study* 45: 172–187.

Rehfisch, M. M. 2002. Climate change and coastal waders. *BTO News* 240: 8–9.

Rehfisch, M. M., Austin, G. E., Armitage, M., Atkinson, P., Holloway, S. J., Musgrove, A. J. & Pollitt, M. S. 2003. Numbers of wintering waterbirds in Great Britain and the Isle of Man (1994/95–1998/99): II. Coastal waders (Charadrii). *Biological Conservation* 112: 329–341.

Rehfisch, M. M., Austin, G. E., Holloway, S. J., Allan, J. R. & O'Connell, M. 2002. An approach to the assessment of change in the numbers of Canada *Branta canadensis* and Greylag Geese *Anser anser* in Southern Britain. *Bird Study* 49: 50–59.

Rhymes, D. 1989. Broad-billed Sandpiper at Old Hall Marshes 22nd May 1988. *Essex Bird Report 1988*: 95–96.

Rhymes, D. 2006. Greenish Warbler at The Naze 12th September 2004 The Second Essex Record. *Essex Bird Report 2004*: 146.

Riddiford, N. 1983. Recent declines of Grasshopper Warblers *Locustella naevia* at British bird observatories. *Bird Study* 30: 143–148.

Riddiford, N. & Findley, P. 1981. *Seasonal movements of summer migrants*. Tring.

Riddington, R., Votier, S. C. & Steele, J. 2000. The Influx of redpolls into western Europe, 1995/96. *British Birds* 93: 59–67.

Riviere, B. B. 1930. *A History of the Birds of Norfolk*. H. F. & G. Witherby, London.

Roberts, S., Lewis, J. & Williams, I. 1999. Breeding European Honey Buzzards in Britain. *British Birds* 92: 326–345.

Robertson, D. G. 1997. The structure of a Goldfinch (*Carduelis carduelis*) flock in winter. *Tay Ringing Group Report 1996–97*: 4–7.

Robinson, J. A. 1999. Migration and morphometrics of the Red-breasted Merganser *Mergus serrator* in northern Eurasia and the implications for conservation of this species in Britain and Ireland. *Wildfowl* 50: 139–148.

Robinson, R. A., Green, R. E., Baillie, S. R., Peach, W. J. & Thompson, D. L. 2004. Demographic mechanisms of the population decline of Song Thrushes *Turdus philomelos*. *Journal of Animal Ecology* 73: 670–682.

Rose, P. M. 1995. *Western Palearctic and South-West Asia Waterfowl Census 1994*. Publication 35. International Waterfowl & Wetlands Research Bureau, Slimbridge.

Rossiter, N. 2000. The Honey Buzzard Movement in Britain in Autumn 2000. http:/www.nrossiter.supanet.com/hb/hbsept2000.htm

Rowlands, A. 1999. Marsh Harriers breeding on Sheppey, Kent. *Kent Bird Report 1997*: 137–142. Kent Ornithological Society.

Rowlands, A. 2003. A 'Black-headed Wagtail' in Essex in 1999 — a suspected *feldegg* intergrade. *British Birds* 96: 291–296.

RSPB. 1995. *Species Action Plan 0421* Corncrake *Crex crex* a Red Data Bird. Sandy, UK: Royal Society for the Protection of Birds.

Rudge, P. 1970. The birds of Foulness. *British Birds* 63: 49–66.

Ruggles-Brise, A. W. 1933. Shooting reminiscences in Essex and elsewhere: a few hints on shooting and gamekeeping. *Essex Chronicle*, Chelmsford.

Rusanen, P. 1993. Waterfowl migration in western Estonia. *Linnut* 28: 7–10 (in Finnish with English summary).

St Joseph, A. K. M. 1979. *Proceedings of the First Technical Meeting on Western Palearctic Migratory Bird Management*. 132–145. The development of inland feeding by *Branta bernicla bernicla* in south-eastern England.

Sage, B. L. 1959. *A History of the Birds of Hertfordshire*. Barrie & Rockliffe, London.

Sangster, G., Collinson, M., Helbig, A. J., Knox, A. G., Parkin, D. T. & Prater, A. 2001. The taxonomic status of Green-winged Teal *Anas carolinensis*. *British Birds* 94: 218–226.

Sangster, G., Collinson, M., Helbig, A. J., Knox, A. G. & Parkin, D. T. 2002. The specific status of Balearic and Yelkouan Shearwaters. *British Birds* 95: 636–639.

Saward, J. 1991. Seawatching in the Outer Thames. *Essex Bird Report 1990*: 123–132.

Scott, D. A. & Rose, P. M. 1996. *Atlas of Anatidae Populations in Africa and western Russia*. Special Publication 41. Wetlands International, Wageningen, The Netherlands.

Scott, M. 1995. The status and identification of Snow Goose and Ross's Goose. *Birding World* 8: 56–63.

Scott, R. E. 1978. Rough-legged Buzzards in Britain in the winter of 1966/67. *British Birds* 61: 449–465.

Seebohm, H. 1883–85. *A History of British Birds*. 4 Vols. Porter, London.

Sellers, R. M., Ekins, G. R., Hughes, B. & Kirby, J. S. 1997. Population development of inland breeding Cormorants in Great Britain. *Ricerche di Biologia della Selvaggina* 26 (suppl. 1): 11–21.

Sharrock, J. T. R. 1973. *The natural history of Cape Clear Island*. Poyser, Berkhamsted.

Sharrock, J. T. R. 1974. *Scarce Migrant Birds in Britain and Ireland*. Poyser, Berkhamsted.

Shawyer, C. R. 1988. The Barn Owl in Essex. *Essex Bird Report 1987*: 98–102.

Shepherd, E. F. 1836. Letter to Mr Heysham 19th January 1836.

Sheppard, Rev. R. & Whitear, Rev. W. 1824–25. A Catalogue of Norfolk and Suffolk birds, with remarks. *Trans. Linn. Soc.* 15: 1–62.

Shirihai, H., Gargallo, G., Helbig, A. J., Harris, A. & Cottridge, D. 2001. *Sylvia Warblers*. Christopher Helm, London.

Shrubb, M. & Lack, P. C. 1991. The Distribution of Lapwings *V. vanellus* in England and Wales. *Bird Study* 37: 30–35.

Simms, E. 1971. *Woodland Birds*. Collins, London.

Simms, E. 1978. *British Thrushes*. Collins, London.

Simms, E. 1985. *Finches*. Collins, London.

Simms, E. 1992. *British Larks, Pipits and Wagtails*. HarperCollins, London.

Siriwardena, G. M., Baillie, S. R. & Wilson, J. D. 1998. Variation in the survival rates of British farmland passerines with respect to their population trends. *Bird Study* 45: 276–292.

Siriwardena, G. M., Baillie, S. R., Crick, H. Q. P. & Wilson, J. D. 2000. The importance of variation in the breeding performance of seed-eating birds for their population trends on farmland. *Journal of Applied Ecology* 37: 1–22.

Siriwardena, G. M., Baillie, S. R. & Wilson, J. D. 1999. Temporal variation in the annual survival rates of six granivorous birds with contrasting population trends. *Ibis* 141: 621–636.

Smart, J. H. 1978. Twites wintering in woodland. *British Birds* 71: 86.

Smith, A. J. M. 1975. Studies of breeding Sandwich Terns. *British Birds* 68: 142–156.

Smith, B., Wood, S. D. & Cox, S. 1999. Red-throated Thrush in Essex: New to Britain and Ireland. *British Birds* 92: 40–46.

Smith, G. 1980. The winter food of Long-eared Owls (*Asio otus*) at an Essex roost site. *Essex Bird Report 1979*: 80–82.

Smith, G. 1981. Observations on the Short-eared Owl along the R. Crouch. *Essex Bird Report 1980*: 74–77.

Smith, G. 1996. The Wildlife of a Victorian Farm. *Essex Birding* 90: 9–11.

Smith, G. 2005. Mandarins in Essex. *Essex Field Club Newsletter* 48: 14–15. Essex Field Club.

Smith, G. 2006. A History of Bradwell Bird Observatory 1954–2003. *Essex Bird Report 2004*: 148–181.

Smith, J. 1979. Spotted Sandpiper at Hanningfield Reservoir, Essex, 3rd to 14th September 1978. *Essex Bird Report 1979*: 62–63.

Smith, J. 1992. Bridled Tern at Hanningfield Reservoir — 2nd June 1991. *Essex Bird Report 1991*: 119.

Smith, K. W. 1997. Nest site selection of the Great Spotted Woodpecker *Dendrocopus major* in two oak woods in southern England and its implications for woodland management. *Biological Conservation* 80: 283–288.

Smith, K. W., Dee, C. W., Fearnside, J. D., Fletcher, E. W. & Smith, R. N. 1993. *The Breeding Birds of Hertfordshire*. Hertfordshire Natural History Society.

Snow, B. K. & Snow, D. K. 1984. Long-term defence of fruit by Mistle Thrush *Turdus viscivorus*. *Ibis* 126: 39–49.

Snow, D. W. 1958. *A study of Blackbirds*. George Allen & Unwin, London.

Sotherton, N. W. 1998. Land use changes and the decline of farmland wildlife: An appraisal of the set-aside approach. *Biological Conservation* 83: 259–268.

Southern, H. N. 1954. Tawny Owls and their prey. *British Birds* 96: 384–410.

Spencer, R. & Gush, G. H. 1973. Siskins feeding in gardens. *British Birds* 66: 91–99.

Stevenson, H. 1866–90. *The birds of Norfolk*. John van Voorst and Gurney and Jackson, London.

Steward, L. 1989. Broad-billed Sandpiper at East Tilbury 22nd May 1988. *Essex Bird Report 1988*: 96–97.

Stoate, C. & Thomson, D. L. 1999. Predation and songbird populations in *Proceedings of the BOU Farmland Bird Conference 1999, Ibis supplement*.

Stone, B. H., Sears, J., Cranswick, P. A., Gregory, R. D., Gibbons, D. W., Rehfisch, M. M., Aebischer, N. J. & Reid, J. B. 1997, Population estimates of birds in Britain and in the United Kingdom. *British Birds* 90: 1–22.

Summers, R. W. & Piertney, S. B. 2003. The Scottish Crossbill — what we know and what we don't. *British Birds* 96: 100–111.

Summers-Smith, J. D. 1988. *The Sparrows*. Poyser, Calton.

Summers-Smith, J. D. 1989. A history of the status of the Tree Sparrow *Passer montanus* in the British Isles. *Bird Study* 38: 23–31.

Sutherby, J. 1998. Surf Scoter at Bradwell-on-Sea The First Essex Record. *Essex Bird Report 1997*: 133.

Sutherland, W. J. & Allport, G. 1991. The distribution and ecology of naturalized Egyptian Geese *Alopochen aegyptiacus* in Britain. *Bird Study* 38: 128–134.

Svensson, L. 1988a. Field identification of black-headed Yellow Wagtails. *British Birds* 81: 77–78.

Svensson, L. 1988b. Field identification of black-headed Yellow Wagtails. *British Birds* 81: 655–656.

Svensson, L. 2004. One steppe beyond. *Birdwatch* 146: 34–38.

Tabor, R. 2004. Observations on the Song Thrush *Turdus philomelos* Brehm at Shadwell Wood SSSI. *Essex Naturalist* 21: 121–125.

Tapper, S. 1981. The effects of farming and Dutch elm disease on corvids. *Game Conservancy Annual Review* 12: 98–101.

Tasker, H. 1868. Egyptian Goose. *The Field* 30: 64.

Tatner, P. 1978. A review of House Martins *Delichon urbica* in parts of south Manchester, 1975. *Naturalist* 103: 59–68.

Taylor, B. & van Perlo, B. 1998. *A guide to the Rails, Crakes, Gallinules and Coots of the World*. Pica Press, London.

Taylor, D. W., Davenport, D. L. & Flegg, J. J. M. 1981. *The Birds of Kent*. Kent Ornithological Society, Meopham.

Taylor, K. 1984. The influence of watercourse management on Moorhen breeding biology. *British Birds* 77: 141–148.

Taylor, M., Seago, M., Allard, P. & Dorling, D. 1999. *The Birds of Norfolk*. Christopher Helm, London.

Thom, V. M. 1986. *Birds in Scotland*. Poyser, Calton.

Thompson, A. 1996. *Aspects of Abberton Reservoir*. Essex Wildlife Trust.

Thompson, A. 2003. Pallid Swift at Cudmore Grove CP 18th October 2001 The first Essex Record. *Essex Bird Report 2001*: 142–143.

Thompson, P. 1930. A short history of the Essex Field Club. *Essex Field Club Special Memoirs Vol. VII*. Essex Field Club.

Thomson, D. L., Green, R. E., Gregory, R. D. & Baillie, S. R. 1998. The widespread declines of songbirds in rural Britain do not correlate with the spread of their avian predators. *Proceedings of the Royal Society of London, Series B* 265: 2057–2062.

Ticehurst, C. B. 1932. *A history of the birds of Suffolk*. Gurney and Jackson, London.

Ticehurst, C. B. 1957. *The Mute Swan in England*. Cleaver-Hume, London.

Ticehurst, N. F. 1909. *A History of the Birds of Kent*. Witherby, London.

Todd, C. 1985. Field descriptions: Cream-coloured Courser. *Essex Bird Report 1984*: 76–77.

Tomiatojc, L. 2000. Did White-backed Woodpeckers ever breed in Britain? *British Birds* 93: 453–456.

Toms, M. 1999. Could climate change bring the Barn Owl back from the brink? *BTO News* 223: 10–12.

Toms, M. P. & Clark, J. A. 1998. Bird ringing in Britain and Ireland in 1996. *Ringing & Migration* 19: 95–168.

Toms, M. P. & Clark, J. A. 1999. Bird ringing in Britain and Ireland in 1997. *Ringing & Migration*.

Toms, M. P., Crick, H. Q. P. & Shawyer, C. R. 2000. *Project Barn Owl Final Report*. BTO Research Report 197/ HOT Research Report 98/1. British Trust for Ornithology/Hawk & Owl Trust, Thetford.

Tucker, G. M., Davies, S. M. & Fuller, R. J. (eds.) 1994. *The Ecology and Conservation of Lapwings Vanellus vanellus*. JNCC, Peterborough, UK.

Tucker, G. M. & Heath, M. F. 1994. *Birds in Europe; their conservation status*. Conservation Series no 3. Birdlife International, Cambridge.

Turner, A. & Rose, C. 1989. *A Handbook to the Swallows and Martins of the World*. Christopher Helm, London.

Turner, A. K. 1982. Counts of aerial-feeding birds in relation to pollution levels. *Bird Study* 29: 221–226.

Underhill, L. G. 1995. The relationship between breeding and non-breeding localities of waders: the Curlew Sandpiper *Calidris feruginea* as an extreme example. *Ostrich* 66: 41–45.

Underhill, M. C., Gittings, T., Callaghan, D. A., Kirby, J. S., Hughes, B. & Delaney, S. 1998. Pre-breeding status and distribution of the Common Scoter *Melanitta nigra* in Britain and Ireland in 1995. *Bird Study* 45: 146–156.

Upton, R. 1983. *A dip into my diary*. Billericay.

Urquhart, D. 2000. Birding at Cudmore Grove Country Park. *Essex Birding* 97: 34–41.

Urquhart, E. 2002. *Stonechats.* Christopher Helm, London.

van Balen, J. H. & Hage, F. 1989. The effect of environmental factors on tit movements. *Ornis Scandinavica* 20: 99–104.

van den Berg, A. B. 2004. WP Reports. *Dutch Birding* 26: 56–68.

van den Berg, A. B., Lambeck, R. H. D. & Mullarney, K. 1984. The occurrence of the 'Black Brant' in Europe. *British Birds* 77: 458–465.

van den Berg, M. & Oreel, G. J. 1985. Field Identification and status of black-headed Yellow Wagtails in Western Europe. *British Birds* 78: 176–183.

van Gasteren, H., Mostert, K., Groot, H. & van Ruiten, L. 1992. The irruption of the Coal Tit Paris ater in the autumn of 1989 in The Netherlands and NW-Europe. *Limosa* 65: 57–66.

van Rhijn, J. G. 1991. *The Ruff.* Poyser, London.

Vanhinsbergh, D., Fuller, R. J. & Noble, D. G. 2003. An analysis of changes in the populations of British woodland birds and a review of possible causes. *BTO Research Report 245.* British Trust for Ornithology, Thetford, Norfolk.

Vaughan, R. 1980. *Plovers.* Lavenham.

Vernon, J. D. R. 1963. Icelandic Black-tailed Godwits in the British Isles. *British Birds* 56: 233–237.

Vickery, J. & Sutherland, W. J. 1996. Changing perceptions of the Dark-bellied Brent Goose. *British Wildlife* 7: 341–347.

Village, A. 1990. *The Kestrel.* Poyser, London.

Vinicombe, K. 1982. Breeding and population fluctuations of the Little Grebe. *British Birds* 75: 204–218.

Vinicombe, K. E. 2003. A disgrace to everybody involved. *Birdwatch* 132: 15.

Vinicombe, K. E. 2004. Ruddy Shelduck — a tick in waiting? *Birdwatch* 141: 42–45.

Vinicombe, K. E. & Chandler, R. J. 1982. Movements of Ruddy Duck during the hard winter of 1978/79. *British Birds* 75: 1–11.

Vinicombe, K. E. & Harrop, H. 1999. Ruddy Shelducks in Britain and Ireland, 1986–94. *British Birds* 92: 225–255.

Voous, K. H. 1960. *Atlas of European Birds.* Nelson, London.

Voslamber, B. 1994. De ontwikkeling van de broedvogelaantallen van de Lepelaar (Platalea leucorodia) in Nederland in de periode 1961–93. *Limosa* 67: 89–94.

Votier, S. C., Steele, J., Shaw, K. D. & Stoddart, A. M. 2000. Arctic Redpoll *Carduelis hornemanni* exili-pes: an identification review based on the 1995/96 influx. *British Birds* 93: 68–84.

Wagstaff, D. 1984. Greenish Warbler: Bradwell. *Essex Bird Report 1983*: 77.

Wainwright, C. B. 1957. How to make and use a duck trap. *Wildfowl Trust Annual Report 8*: 44–47.

Walker, D. 2001. Apparent Continental Stonechats in England. *Birding World* 14: 156–158.

Wallace, D. I. M. 1981. Baikal Teal: new to Britain and Ireland. *British Birds* 74: 321–326.

Wallace, D. I. M. 1999. History of the Common Rosefinch in Britain and Ireland, 1869–1996. *British Birds* 92: 445–471.

Wallace, D. I. M., Bradshaw, C. & Rogers, M. J. 2006. A review of The 1950–57 British rarities. *British Birds* 99: 460–464.

Wanless, S., Frederiksen, M. Harris, M. P. & Freeman, S. N. 2006. Survival of Gannets *Morus bassanus* in Britain and Ireland, 1959–2002. *Bird Study* 53: 79–85.

Waters, R. J. & Cranswick, P. A. 1993. *The wetland bird survey 1992/93: Wildfowl and wader counts.* BTO/WWT/RSPB/JNCC, Slimbridge.

Waters, R. J., Cranswick, P. A., Musgrove, A. J. & Pollitt, M. S. 1998. *The wetland bird survey 1996/97: Wildfowl and wader counts.* BTO/WWT/RSPB/JNCC. Slimbridge.

Wetlands International. 1999. *Report on the Conservation Status of Migratory Waterbirds in the Agreement Area. Report to the Secretariat of the Agreement on the Conservation of African-Eurasian Migratory Waterbirds.*

Westell, W. P. 1903. Ring-Ouzel near London. *Zoologist* 454.

White-Robinson, R. 1984. The ecology of Canada Geese (*Branta canadensis*) in Nottinghamshire and their importance in relation to agriculture. PhD Thesis, University of Nottingham.

Whitfield, C. D. & Whitfield, K. M. 1998. Naumann's Thrush at South Woodford; The second for Essex and Britain. Essex Bird Report 1997: 137–138.

Williamson, K. 1975. Birds and climatic change. *Bird Study* 22: 143–164.

Williamson, K. & Davis, P. 1956. The autumn 1953 invasion of Lapland Buntings and its source. *British Birds* 49: 6–25

Wilson, A. 2000. Boom and bust — mixed news from the 1999 Nightingale survey. *BTO News* 227: 6–7.

Wilson, A. M. & Vickery, J. 2003. Wet grassland waders in decline. *BTO News* 247: 12–13.

Wilson, A. M., Vickery, J. A. & Browne, S. J. 2001. Numbers and distribution of Northern Lapwing

Vanellus vanellus breeding in England and Wales in 1998. *Bird Study* 48: 2–17.

Wilson, J. R., Czazkowski, M. A. & Pienkowski, M. W. 1980. The migration through Europe and wintering in western Africa of Curlew Sandpipers. *Wildfowl* 31: 107–122.

Wimpress, D. 1999. A founder member reminisces: Gwen Foott talks to the Editor. *Essex Birding* 94: 21–22.

Wimpress, D. 2001. Adding to the Tally: The Editor in conversation with Stan Hudgell. *Essex Birding* 97: 7–8.

Winkler, H. Christie, D. A. & Nurney, D. 1995. *Woodpeckers.* Pica Press, Bexhill-on-Sea.

Winstanley, D., Spencer, R. & Williamson, K. 1974. Where have all the Whitethroats gone? *Bird Study* 21: 1–14.

Witherby, H. F. (ed.) 1920. *The Popular Handbook of British Birds.* Witherby & Co., London.

Witherby, H. F., Jourdain, F. C. R., Ticehurst, N. F. & Tucker, B. W. 1938–41. *The Handbook of British Birds.* 5 Vols. Witherby, London.

Wood, S. D. 1996. Rare birds in Essex: an update. *Essex Bird Report 1995*: 115–150.

Wood, S. D. 1998. Waxwings in Essex. The invasion of early 1996. *Essex Bird Report 1996*: 132–134.

Worfolk, T. 2000. The identification of Red-backed, Isabelline and Brown Shrikes. *Dutch Birding* 2000: 22: 323–362.

Wotton, S., Rylands, K., Grice, P., Smallshire, D. & Gregory, R. 2004. The status of the Cirl Bunting in Britain and the Channel Islands on 2003. *British Birds* 97: 376–384.

Wright, G. 1986. Chukars in Essex. *Essex Bird Report 1985*: 91–94.

Wright, M. T. 2001. *Survey of Breeding Raptors and Owls in Suffolk 1995–1998.* Suffolk Ornithological Group, Ipswich.

Yarrell, W. 1845. *A History of British Birds.* 2nd Edition. 3 Vols. Van Voorst, London.

Yarrell, W. 1871–85. *A History of British Birds.* 4th Edition. 3 Vols. London

GAZETTEER

Abberton Reservoir	TL 98 17	Bicknacre	TL 78 02
Abbotts Hall Farm NR EWT	TL 96 14	Billericay	TQ 67 94
Abridge	TQ 46 96	Birch	TL 94 19
Aldham	TL 92 25	Birch Lake	TL 94 20
Alexandra Lake, Wanstead Flats	TQ 40 86	Birchanger	TL 50 22
Alresford	TM 06 21	Birdbrook	TL 70 41
Althorne	TQ 91 99	Bishops Stortford, Hertfordshire	TL 48 21
Ardleigh	TM 05 29	Bittern Watchpoint, Lea Valley	TL 37 03
Ardleigh Reservoir	TM 03 28	Black Notley	TL 76 20
Arkesdon	TL 48 34	Blackmore	TL 60 01
Ashdon	TL 58 42	Blake's Wood, near Danbury	TL 77 06
Asheldham Bridge	TQ 96 01	Blue House Farm EWT, North Fambridge	TQ 80 97
Ashingdon	TQ 86 92	Boarded Barns Farm, Ongar CBC	TL 56 05
Aubrey Buxton NR, near Stansted	TL 52 26	Bocking	TL 76 24
Audley End	TL 52 37	Boreham GP	TL 74 10
Aveley	TQ 56 80	Borley	TL 84 42
Aveley Landfill	TQ 55 81	Bournes Green, Southend-on-Sea	TQ 91 86
Backwarden, Danbury	TL 78 03	Boxted	TM 0032
Banbury Reservoir, Lea Valley	TQ 36 91	Bradfield	TM 14 30
Bardfield	TL 67 30	Bradwell Bird Observatory (BBO)	TM 03 08
Barking	TQ 45 84	Bradwell-on-Sea	TM 00 06
Barking Bay/Marsh	TQ 45 81	Braintree	TL 76 23
Barking Park, Barking	TQ 44 85	Brandy Hole	TQ 82 95
Barling Marsh	TM 93 90	Braxted Park	TL 85 15
Barton Hall Creek, R. Roach	TQ 91 90	Brent Hall, Lawns Farm, near Finchingfield	TL 67 33
Bathside Bay, Dovercourt	TM 25 32	Bretons, Hornchurch	TL 51 84
Battlesbridge	TQ 78 94	Brickhouse Farm, Peldon	TL 99 16
Beachet Wood	TL 49 00	Bridgemarsh Island, Crouch Estuary	TQ 89 96
Beauchamp Roding	TL 58 10	Bridgewick Farm, Dengie	TR 02 00
Beaumont	TM 17 25	Brightlingsea	TM 08 17
Beazley End	TL 74 30	Brookes Reserve EWT, near Greenstead Green	TL 81 26
Beckton	TQ 44 81	Broomfield, Chelmsford	TL 70 10
Beckton SW	TQ 45 82	Broxted	TL 58 27
Becontree, Dagenham	TQ 47 85	Buckhurst Hill	TQ 41 93
Beddalls Green, near Braintree	TL 74 21	Bully Pt NR, Stratford	TQ 37 83
Bedfords Park EWT, Havering-atte-Bower	TQ 51 92	Bulphan Fen	TQ 64 86
Beeleigh	TL 84 07	Bumpstead	TL 67 41
Belchamp Otten, near Sudbury	TL 80 41	Bures	TL 90 34
Belchamp Walter, near Sudbury	TL 81 40	Burnham-on-Crouch	TQ 94 96
Belfairs Wood NR, Hadleigh	TQ 82 86	Burstead	TQ 67 92
Belhus Wood CP, Havering	TQ 57 82	Canewdon	TQ 90 94
Bendysh Wood	TL 61 40	Canning Town	TQ 40 81
Benfleet	TQ 77 86	Canvey Island, Thames Estuary	TQ 81 82
Benfleet Creek, Canvey Island	TQ 78 85	Carrolls Farm, Sewardstone	TQ 38 96
Berechurch, Colchester	TL 99 21	Cattawade Marsh/Splodge	TM 09 32
Berwick Ponds, Rainham	TQ 54 83	Chafford Hundred, Thurrock	TQ 60 79
		Chalkney Wood	TL 87 27

Chantry Wood, Wickham Bishops	TL 84 13	Cripplegate, Southminster	TL 96 00
Chesterford	TL 51 41	Crowsheath Wood, near Hanningfield Reservoir	TQ 72 96
Chigborough Lakes	TL 87 08	Cudmore Grove CP, Mersea Island	TM 06 14
Chignal Smealey	TL 66 11	Curry Farm, Bradwell	TM 99 05
Chignall St James	TL 66 09	Dagenham	TQ 50 84
Chigwell	TQ 44 93	Dagenham Chase	TQ 51 85
Childerditch	TQ 61 89	Dagenham Corridor	TQ 49 87
Chingford	TQ 38 94	Dagnam Park, Harold Hill	TQ 55 93
Chingford Marsh, Lea Valley	TQ 36 92	Danbury	TL 78 05
Chingford Plain, Epping Forest	TQ 39 95	Danbury Common	TL 78 04
Chipping Ongar	TL 56 03	Deal Hall, Dengie	TR 01 97
Chrishall	TL 44 39	Debden	TL 55 33
Cindery Island, Brightlingsea Creek	TM 09 16	Debden Green	TQ 43 98
City of London Cemetery, Wanstead	TQ 42 86	Decoy Point, Heybridge Basin	TL 89 06
Clacton-on-Sea	TM 17 15	Dedham	TM 05 33
Clavering	TL 47 31	Distillery Pond, Colchester	TM 01 23
Clayhall, near Wix	TQ 42 90	Dobbs Weir, Nazeing	TL 38 08
Coalhouse Fort, East Tilbury	TQ 69 76	Doddinghurst	TQ 59 98
Coate Outfall, Dengie	TR 03 99	Donyland Wood	TM 01 22
Cobmarsh Island, near West Mersea	TM 00 12	Dovercourt	TM 25 31
Cockaynes Wood, near Alresford	TM 05 21	Dovers Corner GP, Hornchurch CP	TQ 52 83
Coggeshall	TL 85 22	Downham, near Wickford	TQ 72 95
Colchester	TL 99 25	Dunmow	TL 62 21
Cold Norton	TL 84 00	Dunton	TQ 66 88
Coleman's Farm	TL 83 15	Earls Colne	TL 85 28
Coleman's Reservoir	TL 83 15	East Donyland	TL 03 21
Collier Row, Romford	TQ 49 91	East Ham	TQ 43 83
Colliers Reach, R. Blackwater	TL 07 88	East India Dock	TQ 63 75
Colne Pt	TM 10 12	East Mersea	TM 04 74
Connaught Water, Epping Forest	TQ 40 95	East Tilbury	TQ 68 77
Cooksmill Green, Writtle	TL 63 06	Easters, The (see Good & High Easter)	
Coopers Creek, Blackwater Estuary	TL 90 05	Easton Lodge, near Dunmow	TL 59 23
Coopersale	TL 47 02	Eastwood, near Southend-on-Sea	TQ 84 88
Copford SW, near Stanway	TL 93 24	Elmdon	TL 46 39
Copped Hall Estate, Epping Forest	TL 43 01	Elmstead	TM 06 25
Copped Hall Warren, Epping Forest	TQ 43 00	Elsenham Hall, near Stansted Mountfitchett	TL 54 25
Copperas Bay, Stour Estuary	TM 19 32	Epping	TL 46 02
Copperas Wood	TM 20 31	Epping Forest	TQ 42 98
Copt Hall, Tollesbury	TL 98 14	Essex Filter Beds	TQ 36 86
Corbets Tey	TQ 56 85	Essex Regiment Way GC, Colchester	TL 96 24
Cornmill Meadows, Lea Valley	TL 38 01	Fairlop	TQ 45 85
Corringham	TQ 70 83	Fairstead, near Terling	TL 77 17
Coryton	TQ 74 82	Farnham, near Bishops Stortford	TL 47 24
Cranham Marsh, Upminster	TQ 57 87	Felsted	TL 67 20
Crays Hill, Wickford	TQ 71 92	Finchingfield	TL 68 32
Creekmouth, near Beckton	TQ 45 81	Fingringhoe	TM 02 20
Creeksea, near Burnham-on-Crouch	TQ 93 96	Fingringhoe Mill	TM 03 20
Cressing, near Braintree	TL 78 20	Fingringhoe Wick NR EWT	TM 09 19

Fishers Green, Lea Valley	TL 37 03	Great Holland Pits NR	TM 20 19
Flag Creek, St Osyth	TM 10 16	Great Horkesley	TL 97 30
Fleet Head, Wakering	TR 94 89	Great Leighs	TL 73 38
Fobbing	TQ 71 83	Great Maplestead	TL 80 34
Fordham	TL 92 28	Great Notley	TL 74 21
Fordham Heath	TL 94 26	Great Oakley	TM 19 27
Fordstreet	TL 92 26	Great Parndon, Harlow	TL 43 08
Forest Gate	TQ 40 85	Great Sampford	TL 65 36
Foulness Pt	TM 04 95	Great Totham	TL 86 12
Frating	TM 09 23	Great Wakering	TR 94 87
Friday Lake, Lea Valley	TL 37 03	Great Waltham	TL 69 13
Friday Wood	TL 98 21	Great Wigborough	TL 96 15
Frinton-on-Sea	TM 23 19	Great Yeldham	TL 76 38
Fryerning, near Ingatestone	TL 63 00	Greensted Green	YQ 52 03
Fryerns, Basildon	TQ 72 89	Gunners Park, Shoebury	TR 93 84
Fullbridge, Chelmer	TL 85 07	Hackney Marsh	TQ 36 86
Fuller Street, River Ter	TL 73 15	Hadleigh	TQ 81 87
Galleyhill Wood, near Waltham Abbey	TL 39 03	Hadleigh Castle CP	TQ 80 86
Galleywood, near Chelmsford	TL 05 18	Hadleigh Downs	TQ 80 86
Gallows Corner, Danbury	TQ 53 90	Hainault Forest CP	TQ 47 93
Gallows Green, near Stanway	TL 92 26	Hall Marsh Scrape, Lea Valley	TL 37 01
Garnetts Wood, Great Dunmow	TL 63 18	Halstead	TL 81 30
Geedon Saltings, Colne Estuary	TM 04 18	Hamford Water	TM 22 25
Gestingthorpe	TL 81 38	Hampton Barns, R. Roach	TQ 90 91
Gidea Park, Romford	TQ 52 29	Handley Green Farm, Margaretting	TL 65 01
Gilwell Park, Roxwell	TQ 39 97	Hanningfield Reservoir	TQ 73 97
Girling Reservoir, Lea Valley	TQ 36 94	Hargreave's Scout Camp, Little Heath	TQ 46 89
Glebe Outfall, Dengie	TM 03 06	Harlow	TQ 45 10
Gloucester Park, Basildon	TQ 70 89	Harold Wood SW	TQ 56 91
Gobions Pit, near East Tilbury	TQ 68 97	Harrow Lodge Park, Hornchurch	TQ 53 86
Goldhanger	TL 98 08	Harwich	TM 25 30
Good Easter	TL 62 12	Hatfield Broad Oak	TL 54 16
Gosbeck's Farm, Colchester	TL 97 22	Hatfield Forest	TL 54 19
Gosfield	TL 78 29	Hatfield Heath	TL 52 15
Gosfield Lake	TL 78 29	Hatfield Peverel	TL 78 11
Grange Waters Complex	TQ 38 85	Haven Point, Wakering Stairs	TQ 97 87
Grays	TQ 61 77	Havengore Island, Foulness Group	TQ 97 88
Great Baddow, Chelmsford	TL 72 05	Havering CP	TQ 50 93
Great Braxted	TL 86 14	Havering-atte-Bower	TQ 51 93
Great Bromley	TM 08 26	Hawkwell	TQ 84 92
Great Chesterford	TL 50 42	Hayes Hill Farm, Lea Valley	TL 38 03
Great Cob Island, Blackwater Estuary	TL 98 10	Hazeleigh Wood	TL 83 04
Great Cob Island, Tollesbury Fleet	TL 99 12	Heckfordbridge	TL 94 21
Great Dunmow	TL 62 22	Hedge End Island, Hamford Water	TM 24 24
Great Edney Wood, near Margaretting	TL 66 03	Hempstead Wood	TL 65 38
Great Hallingbury	TL 51 19	Henny Street	TL 88 38
Great Henny	TL 86 37	Heybridge Basin	TL 87 07
Great Holland	TM 21 19	Heybridge GP	TL 86 06

High Beach	TQ 40 97	Langenhoe	TM 00 18
High Easter	TQ 62 14	Langenhoe/Fingringhoe Ranges	TM 04 17
High Ongar	TL 56 03	Langford, near Maldon	TL 83 08
High Roding	TL 60 17	Langham	TM 03 33
Highams Park, London E4	TQ 38 91	Langley, near Clavering	TL 43 34
Highwood, Mill Green	TL 63 04	Larkswood, Chingford	TQ 38 92
Hockley	TQ 84 92	Latchingdon	TL 88 00
Hockley Woods	TQ 83 91	Latton Common, Harlow	TL 46 08
Hole Haven, Canvey Island	TQ 76 82	Lawford, near Manningtree	TM 09 31
Holland Haven	TM 21 17	Lawling Creek, Blackwater Estuary	TL 91 04
Holland-on-Sea	TM 20 16	Layer Breton	TL 94 18
Hollingsons Mead, River Stort	TL 47 12	Layer Marney	TL 92 17
Holliwell Pt, Dengie	TR 02 96	Layer-de-la-Haye	TL 96 20
Hollow Pond, Leyton Flats	TQ 39 89	Lea Valley Reservoirs: see Banbury, Girling, King	
Holyfield Hall Farm, Lea Valley	TL 38 03	George V (KGV), Lockwood & Walthamstow	
Holyfield Marsh, Lea Valley	TL 38 03	Leabridge, Leyton	TQ 35 86
Hooks Marsh, Lea Valley	TL 37 01	Leez Reservoir	TL 20 18
Hornchurch	TQ 53 86	Leigh Marsh	TQ 83 85
Hornchurch CP	TQ 53 82	Leigh-on-Sea	TQ 84 86
Horndon-on-the-Hill	TQ 66 83	Lexden	TL 97 25
Horsey Island, Hamford Water	TM 23 24	Leyton Flats	TL 39 86
Horsey Wade, Hamford Water	TM 23 23	Leyton Marsh	TQ 37 85
Howe Outfall, Dengie	TM 02 02	Limbourne Creek, Blackwater Estuary	TL 87 05
Howlands Marsh NR, St Osyth	TM 11 16	Lingwood Common	TL 77 06
Hullbridge	TQ 81 94	Lippitts Hill, Epping Forest	TQ 39 96
Hunsdon Meads	TL 41 10	Liston	TL 85 44
Hutton	TQ 63 95	Little Baddow	TQ 78 07
Hydemarsh, Crouch Estuary	TQ 87 97	Little Baddow Heath	TL 77 07
Hylands Park, Chelmsford	TQ 68 04	Little Chesterford	TL 51 41
Ilford	TQ 44 86	Little Clacton	TM 16 18
Iltney Farm, Mundon	TL 88 04	Little Dunmow	TL 65 21
Ingatestone	TQ 64 99	Little Hallingbury	TL 50 17
Ingatestone SW	TQ 66 98	Little Heath	TQ 46 88
Ingrebourne Valley	TQ 53 84	Little Oakley	TM 21 29
Iron Latch NR EWT, Eight Ash Green	TL 95 26	Little Sampford	TL 65 33
Jaywick	TM 15 13	Little Wakering	TQ 93 88
Kelvedon	TL 86 18	Little Waltham	TL 70 12
Kelvedon Hatch	TQ 57 99	Littlebury	TL 51 39
King George V Reservoir (KGV), Lea Valley	TQ 37 95	Littlebury Green	TL 48 38
Kirby Cross	TM 21 20	Lockwood Reservoir, Lea Valley	TQ 35 90
Kirby-le-Soken	TM 22 22	Lofts Farm GP, Heybridge	TL 86 06
Laindon	TQ 68 89	Long Hills North, Epping Forest	TQ 40 96
Lamarsh	TL 89 35	Long Running, Epping Forest	TQ 43 99
Lambourne, near Abridge	TQ 47 96	Long Wood, Langdon Hills	TQ 67 86
Landermere	TM 19 23	Loughton	TQ 42 96
Landguard Point, Suffolk	TM 28 31	Maldon	TL 85 06
Landwick, Dengie	TL 99 00	Manningtree	TM 10 31
Langdon Hills NR EWT	TQ 68 87	Manuden	TL 49 26

Maplin Bank	TQ 98 83	Ongar	TL 56 03
Mardyke Valley	TQ 56 79	Ongar Park Wood	TL 50 02
Margaretting	TL 67 01	Oozedam, Coryton	TQ 73 83
Margaretting Tye, near Margaretting	TL 68 01	Orplands (managed retreat), Bradwell	TL 98 06
Marks Tey	TL 91 23	Orsett, Thurrock	TQ 64 81
Markshall Wood, Coggeshall	TL 83 26	Osea Island, Blackwater Estuary	TL 91 06
Marsh Farm, South Woodham Ferrers	TQ 81 96	Oxenham Farm, Great Wakering	TQ 96 88
Marsh House Decoy, Dengie	TM 01 04	Pages Wood, Upminster	TQ 55 91
Marshhouse, Dengie	TM 03 04	Paglesham	TQ 92 93
Matching Green	TL 55 10	Paglesham Lagoon	TQ 92 90
Mayesbrook Park, Dagenham	TQ 46 84	Parkeston	TM 22 32
Mayland	TL 92 02	Parndon, near Harlow	TL 44 06
Maylands GC	TQ 56 92	Parsloes Creek, Dagenham	TQ 47 84
Mersea Island	TM 03 14	Passingford Bridge	TQ 51 97
Mersea Strood	TM 01 15	Paynes Lane GP, Nazeing, Lea Valley	TQ 38 05
Middleton	TL 87 39	Peldon	TL 99 17
Middlewick Farm, Dengie	TR 01 98	Pete Tye Common	TM 00 18
Mill Green	TL 64 01	Pewet Island, Blackwater Estuary	TL 99 08
Mistley	TM 12 32	Pewit Island, Hamford Water	TM 23 26
Mollands GP, South Ockendon	TQ 59 82	Piercing Hill, Epping Forest	TQ 44 99
Monkhams Hall	TQ 40 92	Pitsea	TQ 74 88
Mount Bures	TL 90 32	Pitsea Marsh	TQ 74 87
Mountnessing	TQ 63 97	Plaistow	TQ 40 82
Moverons, near Brightlingsea	TM 06 18	Pod's Wood, Tiptree	TL 90 17
Mucking	TQ 68 81	Point Clear, St Osyth	TM 09 14
Mucking Creek, R. Thames	TQ 69 80	Pole Hill, Chingford, Epping Forest	TQ 38 95
Mundon	TL 87 02	Potton Island, Foulness Group	TQ 95 91
Navestock	TQ 53 97	Prior's Wood, near Takeley	TL 56 21
Nayland	TL 97 34	Priory Park, Southend	TQ 87 87
Naze, The	TM 26 24	Purfleet Chalk Pits	TQ 56 78
Nazeing GP, Lea Valley	TL 38 07	Purfleet-on-Thames	TQ 56 78
Nazeing, Lea Valley	TL 41 06	Pyefleet Channel, Mersea Island	TM 04 16
Nazeingbury	TL 38 06	Pyrgo Park, Havering	TQ 52 93
Netherhall GP, Lea Valley	TL 39 08	Quendon	TL 51 29
New England Island, Foulness Group	TQ 97 89	Rainham	TQ 52 82
Newney Green, near Roxwell	TL 65 07	Rainham GP	TQ 54 82
Newport	TL 52 33	Rainham Marshes NR RSPB	TQ 52 80
Norsey Wood, Billericay	TQ 68 95	Ramsden Heath	TQ 71 95
North Fambridge	TQ 86 97	Ramsey Island, Blackwater Estuary	TL 94 05
North Ockendon	TQ 58 94	Ramsey, near Harwich	TM 21 30
North Weald	TL 49 03	Rat Island, Colne Estuary	TM 05 17
North Woolwich	TQ 80 43	Rawreth	TQ 78 93
Northey Island, Blackwater Estuary	TL 88 06	Ray Sands, Dengie Coast	TM 04 00
Norton Heath	TL 52 33	Rayleigh	TQ 80 90
Norton Mandeville	TL 58 04	Rayne	TL 73 23
Oakley Marshes, Hamford Water	TM 23 28	Redward Outfall, Crouch Estuary	TQ 98 96
Old Hall Marshes NR RSPB	TL 98 11	Reeveshall Marsh, Mersea Island	TM 04 16
Olivers Orchard, Colchester	TL 96 21	Rettendon	TQ 76 98

Rickling Green	TL 65 25	South House Farm, Maldon	TL 86 05
Ridley Hall, near Fuller Street	TL 75 15	South Ockendon	TQ 58 81
Rivenhall End	TL 84 16	South Park, Ilford	TQ 45 86
Rochford	TQ 87 90	South Shoebury	TQ 92 84
Rock Farm, Colchester	TM 01 22	South Weald	TQ 57 93
Roding Valley NR	TQ 42 95	South Woodford	TQ 40 90
Rolls Farm, Tollesbury	TL 95 08	South Woodham Ferrers	TQ 80 97
Roman River Valley	TL 96 20	Southchurch Park, Southend-on-Sea	TQ 89 45
Rowhedge	TM 02 22	Southend Pier	TQ 88 84
Rowney Wood, Debden	TL 57 33	Southend-on-Sea	TQ 87 86
Roxwell	TL 64 08	Southey Creek, Blackwater Estuary	TQ 88 05
Royal Albert Docks, R. Thames	TQ 43 90	Southminster	TQ 95 99
Roydon	TL 40 10	Spitalfields	TQ 37 84
Runwell	TQ 74 94	Springfield, Chelmsford	TL 72 07
Russell Green GPs, near Chelmsford	TQ 12 75	Stambourne, near Steeple Bumpstead	TL 72 38
Saffron Walden	TL 54 23	Stambridge	TQ 89 91
St Lawrence, Dengie	TL 95 06	Stanford Rivers, near Chipping Ongar	TL 53 00
St Osyth	TM 12 15	Stanford Warren	TQ 68 81
Salcott	TL 94 13	Stanford-le-Hope	TQ 68 82
Sales Point, Dengie	TM 03 08	Stansted Airport Lagoons	TL 55 22
Saling, near Braintree	TL 70 25	Stansted Mountfitchett	TL 51 25
Sandbeach, Dengie	TR 02 05	Stanway GP	TL 94 23
Sandon GP, Great Baddow	TL 74 05	Stanway Green	TL 95 23
Sawbridgeworth Marsh	T L 48 14	Stapleford Tawney	TQ 50 99
Sawyer's Hall, Brentwood	TQ 59 94	Star Lane Pits, Wakering	TQ 93 87
Seven Kings	TQ 45 88	Stebbing	TL 66 24
Seventy Acres Lake, Lea Valley	TL 37 03	Steeple, Dengie	TL 93 03
Sewards End, Saffron Walden	TL 57 38	Stickling Green, Clavering	TL 47 32
Sewardstone	TQ 38 98	Stock	TQ 68 98
Sewardstonebury	TQ 39 95	Stone Marsh, The Naze	TM 15 26
Shadwell Wood, near Ashdon NR EWT	TL 57 41	Stone Point, Mersea Island	TM 07 15
Sheering	TL 50 13	Stone Point, The Naze	TM 24 25
Shell Haven, Coryton	TQ 74 81	Stour Reserve	TM 19 31
Shenfield	TQ 60 94	Stow Creek, North Fambridge	TQ 84 96
Shoebury	TQ 93 84	Stratford	TQ 38 84
Shoeburyness	TQ 93 83	Strawberry Hill Pond, Epping Forest	TQ 42 97
Shopland, near Southend-on-Sea	TQ 89 18	Strethall	TL 48 39
Shotgate Thickets, near Wickford	TQ 76 93	Stubbers OPC, Corbets Tey	TQ 57 84
Sible Hedingham	TL 77 34	Sturmer Mere, near Haverhill	TL 69 43
Silver End	TL 81 20	Sudbury, Suffolk	TL 87 41
Silvertown	TQ 40 79	Takeley	TL 56 21
Skipper's Island, Hamford Water	TM 21 24	Tendring	TM 14 24
Skreens Park	TL 62 07	Terling	TL 77 15
Slough House Farm, near Heybridge	TL 87 09	Thames Barrier	TQ 41 79
Snaresbrook, Waltham Forest	TQ 39 89	Thaxted	TL 61 31
South Benfleet	TQ 78 86	The Hythe, Colchester	TM 01 24
South Green	TM 04 20	The Mores Wood, near Brentwood	TQ 56 96
South Hanningfield	TL 74 97	The Naze at Walton	TM 26 24

The Strood, Mersea Island	TM 01 15	Watts Wood, Purfleet	TQ 56 78
The Warren (see Stanford Warren)		Weald CP, near South Weald	TQ 57 94
Theydon Bois, Epping	TQ 44 98	Weeley	TM 14 22
Theydon Garnon, near Theydon Bois	TQ 47 99	Weeleyhall Wood	TM 15 21
Thorley Wash, Stort Valley	TL 48 18	Wendens Ambo	TL 51 36
Thorndon CP (North)	TQ 60 91	Wennington	TQ 54 81
Thorndon CP (South)	TQ 62 90	West Bergholt	TL 95 27
Thorpe Bay	TQ 91 85	West Ham	TQ 40 83
Thorpe-le-Soken	TM 18 22	West Hanningfield	TQ 73 99
Thorrington	TM 09 20	West Mersea	TM 00 12
Thundersley	TQ 79 88	West Thurrock	TQ 58 77
Tilbury	TQ 63 76	West Tilbury	TQ 66 77
Tilbury Power Station	TQ 66 75	West Wick, near Burnham-on-Crouch	TQ 97 98
Tillingham	TL 99 03	West Wood EWT, Great Sampford	TL 62 33
Tillingham GP	TL 99 03	Westcliff-on-Sea	TQ 86 86
Tiptree	TL 89 16	Whipps Cross	TQ 38 88
Tollesbury	TL 95 10	White Colne	TL 87 30
Tollesbury Wick NR EWT	TM 04 19	White Notley	TL 78 18
Tolleshunt D'Arcy	TL 93 12	White Roding	TL 56 13
Tolleshunt Knights	TL 91 14	Whiteash Green, near Halstead	TL 79 30
Tolleshunt Major	TL 90 11	Wicken Bonhunt	TL 49 33
Toot Hill	TL 51 02	Wickford	TQ 75 93
Twinstead	TL 86 36	Wickham Bishops	TL 83 12
Two Tree Island, Leigh-on-Sea	TQ 82 85	Widford	TL 69 05
Tylers Common, Upminster	TQ 56 90	Wigborough Bay, Abberton Reservoir	TL 96 16
Ulting	TL 80 08	William Girling Reservoir, Lea Valley	TQ 36 94
University of Essex, Colchester	TM 02 23	Willingale	TL 59 07
Upminster	TQ 56 87	Wimbish	TL 59 36
Valentines Park, Ilford	TQ 43 87	Wintry Wood, Epping Forest	TL 47 03
Vange Marsh	TQ 72 85	Witham	TL 81 15
Virley Channel, R. Blackwater	TL 95 13	Wivenhoe	TM 03 21
Wake Arms Pond, Epping Forest	TQ 42 98	Wix	TM 15 03
Wake Valley, Epping Forest	TQ 41 98	Wixoe	TL 71 42
Wakering Boatyard	TQ 94 88	Woodford	TQ 40 91
Wakering Stairs	TQ 97 87	Woodford Green	TQ 41 92
Wallasea Island, Crouch/Roach Estuaries	TQ 96 93	Woodham Mortimer	TL 96 16
Waltham Abbey	TL 38 00	Woodham Walter	TL 80 06
Walthamstow Reservoirs, Lea Valley	TQ 35 89	Woodrolfe Creek, Blackwater Estuary	TL 97 10
Walton-on-The-Naze	TM 25 21	Woolwich	TQ 43 79
Wanstead Flats, Epping Forest	TQ 40 86	Wormingford, Colchester	TL 93 31
Wanstead Park	TQ 41 87	Wrabness	TM 17 31
Warley	TQ 59 92	Writtle	TL 67 06
Warley Place NR	TQ 58 90	Writtle Forest	TL 65 03
Warren Pond, Epping Forest	TQ 39 94	Writtle Park	TL 65 03
Wat Tyler CP, Pitsea	TQ 73 86	Yardley Hill, Epping Forest	TQ 38 95

INDEX

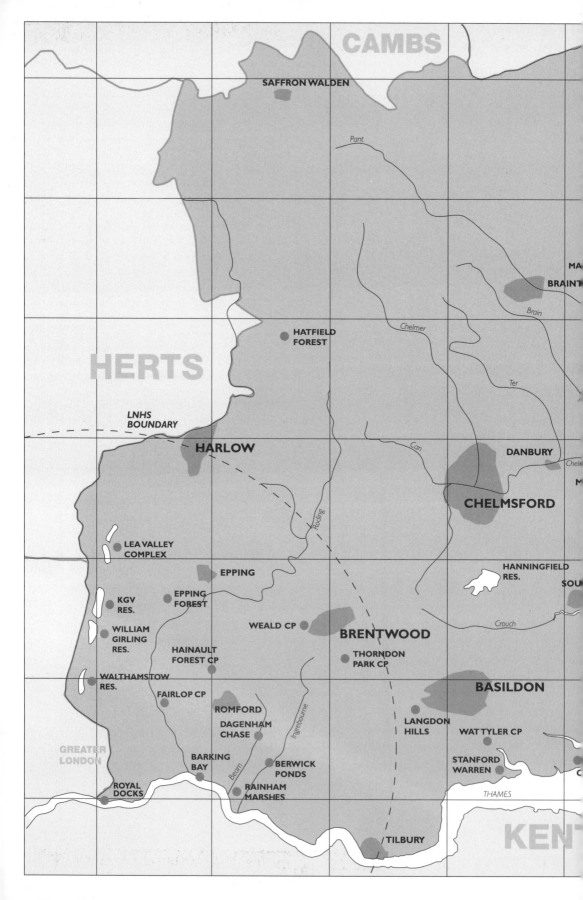